A TREATISE
ON THE
MATHEMATICAL THEORY
OF
ELASTICITY

A TREATISE
ON THE
MATHEMATICAL THEORY
OF
ELASTICITY

BY

A. E. H. LOVE, M.A., D.Sc., F.R.S.
HONORARY FOREIGN MEMBER OF THE ACCADEMIA DEI LINCEI
FORMERLY FELLOW OF ST JOHN'S COLLEGE, CAMBRIDGE
FELLOW OF QUEEN'S COLLEGE, OXFORD
SEDLEIAN PROFESSOR OF NATURAL PHILOSOPHY
IN THE UNIVERSITY OF OXFORD

FOURTH EDITION

NEW YORK
DOVER PUBLICATIONS
1944

First Edition 1892, 1893
Second Edition 1906
Third Edition 1920
Fourth Edition 1927

First American Printing 1944
By special arrangement with the
Cambridge University Press and The Macmillan Co.

Library of Congress Catalog Card Number: 45-7269

Manufactured in the United States of America

Dover Publications, Inc.
180 Varick Street
New York 14, N. Y.

PREFACE

THIS book is the fourth edition of one with the same title originally published in two volumes. When a second edition was called for, the book was almost entirely re-written, but, for subsequent editions, no such extensive revision has seemed to be necessary. In the intervals between editions new researches are made, or the Author may become acquainted with some that appeared before the last edition, but were unknown to him at the time of writing it. It happened, for example, that much of the literature published just before, and during, the years 1914–1918 was not available for the third edition. It is desirable to incorporate some account of, or reference to, such researches. Thus the book tends to expand, but efforts have been made to keep it within moderate bounds. It is hoped, however, still to present a fair picture of the subject in its various aspects, as a mathematical theory, having important relations to general physics, and valuable applications to engineering.

The present edition differs from its predecessors by additions and revisions. The most important additions are (i) a discussion of the theory of a rectangular plate, clamped at the edges, and bent by pressure applied to one face; (ii) a discussion of the theory of the resistance of a plate to pressure, when it is so thin that the extension of the middle plane, due to deformation of that plane into a curved surface, cannot be neglected; (iii) an account of the process by which stress-strain relations are deduced from the molecular theory of a crystalline solid. The last of these appears as an expansion of Note B. The reason for adopting this course is not that the subject appears to the Author to be unimportant, but that the theory developed in the text is essentially macroscopic, and a structure theory, though desirable, would disturb the logical development. No account has been given of the approximate methods that figure so largely in some recent books, e.g. those of J. Prescott and of Timoschenko and Lessels, both of which appeared too late for citation at the appropriate places in the text. The most important revision concerns the theory of the equilibrium of a sphere. It has been found to be possible to simplify very considerably the easier parts of that theory, and thus to lead, by comparatively elementary methods, to the most important geophysical applications of the subject. This revision necessitated a re-numeration of the relevant Articles (171–180), and another slight revision entailed a similar change in Articles 92 and 93, but, with these exceptions, the numeration is the same as that in the third edition, where new Articles or Chapters were marked with the letters "A" or "B." New Articles, which are additions, not revisions, in the present edition, are marked with letters beginning at "C," thus "335C." A few Articles have been re-written without comment, and a few misprints and other errors in the third edition have been corrected. The Author avails himself of this opportunity to express his grateful thanks to correspondents who have sent him such corrections.

A. E. H. LOVE

OXFORD

October, 1926

CONTENTS

Historical Introduction

Chapter I. Analysis of strain

CHAPTER III. THE ELASTICITY OF SOLID BODIES

CHAPTER IV. THE RELATION BETWEEN THE MATHEMATICAL THEORY OF ELASTICITY AND TECHNICAL MECHANICS

CHAPTER V. THE EQUILIBRIUM OF ISOTROPIC ELASTIC SOLIDS

Chapter IX. Two-dimensional elastic systems

Appendix to Chapters VIII and IX. Volterra's Theory of Dislocations

Chapter X. Theory of the integration of the equations of equilibrium of an isotropic elastic solid body

CHAPTER XI. THE EQUILIBRIUM OF AN ELASTIC SPHERE AND RELATED PROBLEMS

CHAPTER XII. VIBRATIONS OF SPHERES AND CYLINDERS

CHAPTER XIII. THE PROPAGATION OF WAVES IN ELASTIC SOLID MEDIA

CHAPTER XVI. THE BENDING OF A BEAM LOADED UNIFORMLY ALONG ITS LENGTH

CHAPTER XVII. THE THEORY OF CONTINUOUS BEAMS

CHAPTER XVIII. GENERAL THEORY OF THE BENDING AND TWISTING OF THIN RODS

CHAPTER XIX. PROBLEMS CONCERNING THE EQUILIBRIUM OF THIN RODS

CHAPTER XX. VIBRATIONS OF RODS. PROBLEMS OF DYNAMICAL RESISTANCE

CHAPTER XXI. SMALL DEFORMATION OF NATURALLY CURVED RODS

CHAPTER XXII. THE STRETCHING AND BENDING OF PLATES

CHAPTER XXIII. INEXTENSIONAL DEFORMATION OF CURVED PLATES OR SHELLS

CHAPTER XXIV. GENERAL THEORY OF THIN PLATES AND SHELLS

CHAPTER XXIVA. EQUILIBRIUM OF THIN PLATES AND SHELLS

EQUILIBRIUM OF THIN SHELLS

CYLINDRICAL SHELL

SPHERICAL SHELL

CONICAL SHELL

NOTES

INDEX

HISTORICAL INTRODUCTION

THE Mathematical Theory of Elasticity is occupied with an attempt to reduce to calculation the state of strain, or relative displacement, within a solid body which is subject to the action of an equilibrating system of forces, or is in a state of slight internal relative motion, and with endeavours to obtain results which shall be practically important in applications to architecture, engineering, and all other useful arts in which the material of construction is solid. Its history should embrace that of the progress of our experimental knowledge of the behaviour of strained bodies, so far as it has been embodied in the mathematical theory, of the development of our conceptions in regard to the physical principles necessary to form a foundation for theory, of the growth of that branch of mathematical analysis in which the process of the calculations consists, and of the gradual acquisition of practical rules by the interpretation of analytical results. In a theory ideally worked out, the progress which we should be able to trace would be, in other particulars, one from less to more, but we may say that, in regard to the assumed physical principles, progress consists in passing from more to less. Alike in the experimental knowledge obtained, and in the analytical methods and results, nothing that has once been discovered ever loses its value or has to be discarded; but the physical principles come to be reduced to fewer and more general ones, so that the theory is brought more into accord with that of other branches of physics, the same general principles being ultimately requisite and sufficient to serve as a basis for them all. And although, in the case of Elasticity, we find frequent retrogressions on the part of the experimentalist, and errors on the part of the mathematician, chiefly in adopting hypotheses not clearly established or already discredited, in pushing to extremes methods merely approximate, in hasty generalizations, and in misunderstandings of physical principles, yet we observe a continuous progress in all the respects mentioned when we survey the history of the science from the initial enquiries of Galileo to the conclusive investigations of Saint-Venant and Lord Kelvin.

The first mathematician to consider the nature of the resistance of solids to rupture was Galileo[1]. Although he treated solids as inelastic, not being in possession of any law connecting the displacements produced with the forces producing them, or of any physical hypothesis capable of yielding such a law, yet his enquiries gave the direction which was subsequently followed by many investigators. He endeavoured to determine the resistance of a beam, one end of which is built into a wall, when the tendency to break it arises from

[1] Galileo Galilei, *Discorsi e Dimostrazioni matematiche*, Leiden, 1638.

its own or an applied weight; and he concluded that the beam tends to turn about an axis perpendicular to its length, and in the plane of the wall. This problem, and, in particular, the determination of this axis, is known as Galileo's problem.

In the history of the theory started by the question of Galileo, undoubtedly the two great landmarks are the discovery of Hooke's Law in 1660, and the formulation of the general equations by Navier in 1821. Hooke's Law provided the necessary experimental foundation for the theory. When the general equations had been obtained, all questions of the small strain of elastic bodies were reduced to a matter of mathematical calculation.

In England and in France, in the latter half of the 17th century, Hooke and Mariotte occupied themselves with the experimental discovery of what we now term stress-strain relations. Hooke[2] gave in 1678 the famous law of proportionality of stress and strain which bears his name, in the words "*Ut tensio sic vis*; that is, the Power of any spring is in the same proportion with the Tension thereof." By "spring" Hooke means, as he proceeds to explain, any "springy body," and by "tension" what we should now call "extension," or, more generally, "strain." This law he discovered in 1660, but did not publish until 1676, and then only under the form of an anagram, *ceiiinosssttuu*. This law forms the basis of the mathematical theory of Elasticity, and we shall hereafter consider its generalization, and its range of validity in the light of modern experimental research. Hooke does not appear to have made any application of it to the consideration of Galileo's problem. This application was made by Mariotte[3], who in 1680 enunciated the same law independently. He remarked that the resistance of a beam to flexure arises from the extension and contraction of its parts, some of its longitudinal filaments being extended, and others contracted. He assumed that half are extended, and half contracted. His theory led him to assign the position of the axis, required in the solution of Galileo's problem, at one-half the height of the section above the base.

In the interval between the discovery of Hooke's Law and that of the general differential equations of Elasticity by Navier, the attention of those mathematicians who occupied themselves with our science was chiefly directed to the solution and extension of Galileo's problem, and the related theories of the vibrations of bars and plates, and the stability of columns. The first investigation of any importance is that of the elastic line or *elastica* by James Bernoulli[4] in 1705, in which the resistance of a bent rod is assumed to arise from the extension and contraction of its longitudinal filaments, and the

[2] Robert Hooke, *De Potentia restitutiva*, London, 1678.

[3] E. Mariotte, *Traité du mouvement des eaux*, Paris, 1686.

[4] Bernoulli's memoir is entitled, 'Véritable hypothèse de la résistance des solides, avec la demonstration de la courbure des corps qui font ressort,' and will be found in his collected works, t. 2, Geneva, 1744.

equation of the curve assumed by the axis is formed. This equation practically involves the result that the resistance to bending is a couple proportional to the curvature of the rod when bent, a result which was assumed by Euler in his later treatment of the problems of the *elastica*, and of the vibrations of thin rods. As soon as the notion of a flexural couple proportional to the curvature was established it could be noted that the work done in bending a rod is proportional to the square of the curvature. Daniel Bernoulli[5] suggested to Euler that the differential equation of the *elastica* could be found by making the integral of the square of the curvature taken along the rod a minimum; and Euler[6], acting on this suggestion, was able to obtain the differential equation of the curve and to classify the various forms of it. One form is a curve of sines of small amplitude, and Euler pointed out[7] that in this case the line of thrust coincides with the unstrained axis of the rod, so that the rod, if of sufficient length and vertical when unstrained, may be bent by a weight attached to its upper end. Further investigations[8] led him to assign the least length of a column in order that it may bend under its own or an applied weight. Lagrange[9] followed and used his theory to determine the strongest form of column. These two writers found a certain length which a column must attain to be bent by its own or an applied weight, and they concluded that for shorter lengths it will be simply compressed, while for greater lengths it will be bent. These researches are the earliest in the region of *elastic stability*.

In Euler's work on the *elastica* the rod is thought of as a line of particles which resists bending. The theory of the flexure of beams of finite section was considered by Coulomb[10]. This author took account of the equation of equilibrium obtained by resolving horizontally the forces which act upon the part of the beam cut off by one of its normal sections, as well as of the equation of moments. He was thus enabled to obtain the true position of the "neutral line," or axis of equilibrium, and he also made a correct calculation of the moment of the elastic forces. His theory of beams is the most exact of those which proceed on the assumption that the stress in a bent beam arises wholly from the extension and contraction of its longitudinal filaments, and is deduced mathematically from this assumption and Hooke's Law. Coulomb was also the first to consider the resistance of thin fibres to torsion[11], and it is his account of the matter to which Saint-Venant refers

[5] See the 26th letter of Daniel Bernoulli to Euler (October, 1742) in Fuss, *Correspondance mathématique et physique*, t. 2, St Petersburg, 1843.

[6] See the *Additamentum* 'De curvis elasticis' in the *Methodus inveniendi lineas curvas maximi minimive proprietate gaudentes*, Lausanne, 1744.

[7] *Berlin, Histoire de l'Académie*, t. 13 (1757).

[8] *Acta Acad. Petropolitanæ* of 1778, *Pars prior*, pp. 121—193.

[9] *Miscellanea Taurinensia*, t. 5 (1773).

[10] 'Essai sur une application des règles *de Maximis et Minimis* à quelques Problèmes de Statique, relatifs à l'Architecture,' *Mém....par divers savans*, 1776.

[11] *Histoire de l'Académie* for 1784, pp. 229—269, Paris, 1787.

under the name *l'ancienne théorie*, but his formula for this resistance was not deduced from any elastic theory. The formula makes the torsional rigidity of a fibre proportional to the moment of inertia of the normal section about the axis of the fibre. Another matter to which Coulomb was the first to pay attention was the kind of strain we now call *shear*, though he considered it in connexion with rupture only. His opinion appears to have been that rupture[12] takes place when the shear of the material is greater than a certain limit. The shear considered is a permanent set, not an elastic strain.

Except Coulomb's, the most important work of the period for the general mathematical theory is the physical discussion of elasticity by Thomas Young. This naturalist (to adopt Lord Kelvin's name for students of natural science) besides defining his modulus of elasticity, was the first to consider shear as an elastic strain[13]. He called it "detrusion," and noticed that the elastic resistance of a body to shear, and its resistance to extension or contraction, are in general different; but he did not introduce a distinct modulus of rigidity to express resistance to shear. He defined "the modulus of elasticity of a substance[14]" as "a column of the same substance capable of producing a pressure on its base which is to the weight causing a certain degree of compression, as the length of the substance is to the diminution of its length." What we now call "Young's modulus" is the weight of this column per unit of area of its base. This introduction of a definite physical concept, associated with the coefficient of elasticity which descends, as it were from a clear sky, on the reader of mathematical memoirs, marks an epoch in the history of the science.

Side by side with the statical developments of Galileo's enquiry there were discussions of the vibrations of solid bodies. Euler[6] and Daniel Bernoulli[15] obtained the differential equation of the lateral vibrations of bars by variation of the function by which they had previously expressed the work done in bending[16]. They determined the forms of the functions which we should now call the "normal functions," and the equation which we should now call the "period equation," in the six cases of terminal conditions which arise according

[12] See the introduction to the memoir first quoted, *Mém....par divers savans*, 1776.

[13] *A Course of Lectures on Natural Philosophy and the Mechanical Arts*, London, 1807, Lecture XIII. It is in Kelland's later edition (1845) on pp. 105 *et seq.*

[14] *Loc. cit.* (footnote 13). The definition was given in Section IX of Vol. 2 of the first edition, and omitted in Kelland's edition, but it is reproduced in the *Miscellaneous Works of Dr Young.*

[15] 'De vibrationibus...laminarum elasticarum...,' and 'De sonis multifariis quos laminae elasticae...edunt...' published in *Commentarii Academiæ Scientiarum Imperialis Petropolitanæ*, t. 13 (1751). The reader must be cautioned that in writings of the 18th century a "lamina" means a straight rod or curved bar, supposed to be cut from a thin plate or cylindrical shell by two normal sections near together. This usage lingers in many books.

[16] The form of the energy-function and the notion of obtaining the differential equation by varying it are due to D. Bernoulli. The process was carried out by Euler, and the normal functions and the period equations were determined by him.

as the ends are free, clamped or simply supported. Chladni[17] investigated these modes of vibration experimentally, and also the longitudinal and torsional vibrations of bars.

The success of theories of thin rods, founded on special hypotheses, appears to have given rise to hopes that a theory might be developed in the same way for plates and shells, so that the modes of vibration of a bell might be deduced from its form and the manner in which it is supported. The first to attack this problem was Euler. He had already proposed a theory of the resistance of a curved bar to bending, in which the change of curvature played the same part as the curvature does in the theory of a naturally straight bar[18]. In a note "De Sono Campanarum[19]" he proposed to regard a bell as divided into thin annuli, each of which behaves as a curved bar. This method leaves out of account the change of curvature in sections through the axis of the bell. James Bernoulli[20] (the younger) followed. He assumed the shell to consist of a kind of double sheet of curved bars, the bars in one sheet being at right angles to those in the other. Reducing the shell to a plane plate he found an equation of vibration which we now know to be incorrect.

James Bernoulli's attempt appears to have been made with the view of discovering a theoretical basis for the experimental results of Chladni concerning the nodal figures of vibrating plates[21]. These results were still unexplained when in 1809 the French *Institut* proposed as a subject for a prize the investigation of the tones of a vibrating plate. After several attempts the prize was adjudged in 1815 to Mdlle Sophie Germain, and her work was published in 1821[22]. She assumed that the sum of the principal curvatures of the plate when bent would play the same part in the theory of plates as the curvature of the elastic central-line in the theory of rods, and she proposed to regard the work done in bending as proportional to the integral of the square of the sum of the principal curvatures taken over the surface. From this assumption and the principle of virtual work she deduced the equation of flexural vibration in the form now generally admitted. Later investigations have shown that the formula assumed for the work done in bending was incorrect.

During the first period in the history of our science (1638—1820), while these various investigations of special problems were being made, there was a cause at work which was to lead to wide generalizations. This cause was

[17] E. F. F. Chladni, *Die Akustik*, Leipzig, 1802. The author gives an account of the history of his own experimental researches with the dates of first publication.

[18] In the *Methodus inveniendi*... p. 274. See also his later writing 'Genuina principia... de statu æquilibrii et motu corporum...,' *Nov. Comm. Acad. Petropolitanæ*, t. 15 (1771).

[19] *Nov. Comm. Acad. Petropolitanæ*, t. 10 (1766).

[20] 'Essai théorique sur les vibrations des plaques élastiques...,' *Nov. Acta Petropolitanæ*, t. 5 (1789).

[21] First published at Leipzig in 1787. See *Die Akustik*, p. vii.

[22] *Recherches sur la théorie des surfaces élastiques*. Paris, 1821.

physical speculation concerning the constitution of bodies. In the eighteenth century the Newtonian conception of material bodies, as made up of small parts which act upon each other by means of central forces, displaced the Cartesian conception of a *plenum* pervaded by "vortices." Newton regarded his "molecules" as possessed of finite sizes and definite shapes[23], but his successors gradually simplified them into *material points*. The most definite speculation of this kind is that of Boscovich[24], for whom the material points were nothing but persistent centres of force. To this order of ideas belong Laplace's theory of capillarity[25] and Poisson's first investigation of the equilibrium of an "elastic surface[26]," but for a long time no attempt seems to have been made to obtain general equations of motion and equilibrium of elastic solid bodies. At the end of the year 1820 the fruit of all the ingenuity expended on elastic problems might be summed up as—an inadequate theory of flexure, an erroneous theory of torsion, an unproved theory of the vibrations of bars and plates, and the definition of Young's modulus. But such an estimate would give a very wrong impression of the value of the older researches. The recognition of the distinction between shear and extension was a preliminary to a general theory of strain; the recognition of forces across the elements of a section of a beam, producing a resultant, was a step towards a theory of stress; the use of differential equations for the deflexion of a bent beam and the vibrations of bars and plates, was a foreshadowing of the employment of differential equations of displacement; the Newtonian conception of the constitution of bodies, combined with Hooke's Law, offered means for the formation of such equations; and the generalization of the principle of virtual work in the *Mécanique Analytique* threw open a broad path to discovery in this as in every other branch of mathematical physics. Physical Science had emerged from its incipient stages with definite methods of hypothesis and induction and of observation and deduction, with the clear aim to discover the laws by which phenomena are connected with each other, and with a fund of analytical processes of investigation. This was the hour for the production of general theories, and the men were not wanting.

Navier[27] was the first to investigate the general equations of equilibrium and vibration of elastic solids. He set out from the Newtonian conception of the constitution of bodies, and assumed that the elastic reactions arise from variations in the intermolecular forces which result from changes in the molecular configuration. He regarded the molecules as material points, and assumed that the force between two molecules, whose distance is slightly increased, is proportional to the product of the increment of the distance and some function

[23] See, in particular, Newton, *Optiks*, 2nd Edition, London, 1717, the 31st Query.

[24] R. J. Boscovich, *Theoria Philosphiæ Naturalis redacta ad unicam legem virium in natura existentium*, Venice, 1743.

[25] *Mécanique Céleste*, *Supplément au* 10e *Livre*, Paris, 1806.

[26] *Paris*, *Mém. de l'Institut*, 1814.

[27] *Paris*, *Mém. Acad. Sciences*, t. 7 (1827). The memoir was read in May, 1821.

of the initial distance. His method consists in forming an expression for the component in any direction of all the forces that act upon a displaced molecule, and thence the equations of motion of the molecule. The equations are thus obtained in terms of the displacements of the molecule. The material is assumed to be isotropic, and the equations of equilibrium and vibration contain a single constant of the same nature as Young's modulus. Navier next formed an expression for the work done in a small relative displacement by all the forces which act upon a molecule; this he described as the sum of the moments (in the sense of the *Mécanique Analytique*) of the forces exerted by all the other molecules on a particular molecule. He deduced, by an application of the Calculus of Variations, not only the differential equations previously obtained, but also the boundary conditions that hold at the surface of the body. This memoir is very important as the first general investigation of its kind, but its arguments have not met with general acceptance. Objection has been raised against Navier's expression for the force between two "molecules," and to his method of simplifying the expressions for the forces acting on a single "molecule." These expressions involve triple summations, which Navier replaced by integrations, and the validity of this procedure has been disputed[28].

In the same year, 1821, in which Navier's memoir was read to the Academy the study of elasticity received a powerful impulse from an unexpected quarter. Fresnel announced his conclusion that the observed facts in regard to the interference of polarised light could be explained only by the hypothesis of transverse vibrations[29]. He showed how a medium consisting of "molecules" connected by central forces might be expected to execute such vibrations and to transmit waves of the required type. Before the time of Young and Fresnel such examples of transverse waves as were known—waves on water, transverse vibrations of strings, bars, membranes and plates—were in no case examples of waves transmitted *through* a medium; and neither the supporters nor the opponents of the undulatory theory of light appear to have conceived of light waves otherwise than as "longitudinal" waves of condensation and rarefaction,

[28] For criticisms of Navier's memoir and an account of the discussions to which it gave rise, see Todhunter and Pearson, *History of the Theory of Elasticity*, vol. 1, Cambridge, 1886, pp. 139, 221, 277: and cf. the account given by H. Burkhardt in his Report on 'Entwickelungen nach oscillirenden Functionen' published in the *Jahresbericht der Deutschen Mathematiker-Vereinigung*, Bd. 10, Heft 2, Lieferung 3 (1903). It may not be superfluous to remark that the conception of molecules as material points at rest in a state of stable equilibrium under their mutual forces of attraction and repulsion, and held in slightly displaced positions by external forces, is quite different from the conception of molecules with which modern Thermodynamics has made us familiar. The "molecular" theories of Navier, Poisson and Cauchy have no very intimate relation to modern notions about molecules. See, however, Note B at the end of this book.

[29] See E. Verdet, *Œuvres complètes d'Augustin Fresnel*, t. 1, Paris, 1866, p. lxxxvi, also pp. 629 *et seq*. Verdet points out that Fresnel arrived at his hypothesis of transverse vibrations in 1816 (*loc. cit.*, pp. LV, 385, 394). Thomas Young in his Article 'Chromatics' (*Encycl. Brit. Supplement*, 1817) regarded the luminous vibrations as having relatively feeble transverse components.

of the type rendered familiar by the transmission of sound. The theory of elasticity, and, in particular, the problem of the transmission of waves through an elastic medium, now attracted the attention of two mathematicians of the highest order: Cauchy[30] and Poisson[31]—the former a discriminating supporter, the latter a sceptical critic of Fresnel's ideas. In the future the developments of the theory of elasticity were to be closely associated with the question of the propagation of light, and these developments arose in great part from the labours of these two savants.

By the Autumn of 1822 Cauchy[32] had discovered most of the elements of the pure theory of elasticity. He had introduced the notion of stress at a point determined by the tractions per unit of area across all plane elements through the point. For this purpose he had generalized the notion of hydrostatic pressure, and he had shown that the stress is expressible by means of six component stresses, and also by means of three purely normal tractions across a certain triad of planes which cut each other at right angles—the "principal planes of stress." He had shown also how the differential coefficients of the three components of displacement can be used to estimate the extension of every linear element of the material, and had expressed the state of strain near a point in terms of six components of strain, and also in terms of the extensions of a certain triad of lines which are at right angles to each other—the "principal axes of strain." He had determined the equations of motion (or equilibrium) by which the stress-components are connected with the forces that are distributed through the volume and with the kinetic reactions. By means of relations between stress-components and strain-components, he had eliminated the stress-components from the equations of motion and equilibrium, and had arrived at equations in terms of the displacements. In the later published version of this investigation Cauchy obtained his stress-strain relations for isotropic materials by means of two assumptions, viz.: (1) that the relations in question are linear, (2) that the principal planes of stress are normal to the principal axes of strain. The experimental basis on which these assumptions can be made to rest is the same as that on which Hooke's Law rests, but Cauchy did not refer to it. The equations obtained are those which are now admitted for isotropic solid bodies. The methods used in these

[30] Cauchy's studies in Elasticity were first prompted by his being a member of the Commission appointed to report upon a memoir by Navier on elastic plates which was presented to the Paris Academy in August, 1820.

[31] We have noted that Poisson had already written on elastic plates in 1814.

[32] Cauchy's memoir was communicated to the Paris Academy in September, 1822, but it was not published. An abstract was inserted in the *Bulletin des Sciences ă la Société philomathique*, 1823, and the contents of the memoir were given in later publications, viz. in two Articles in the volume for 1827 of Cauchy's *Exercices de mathématique* and an Article in the volume for 1828. The titles of these Articles are (i) 'De la pression ou tension dans un corps solide,' (ii) 'sur la condensation et la dilatation des corps solides,' (iii) 'Sur les équations qui expriment les conditions d'équilibre ou les lois de mouvement intérieur d'un corps solide.' The last of these contains the correct equations of Elasticity.

investigations are quite different from those of Navier's memoir. In particular, no use is made of the hypothesis of material points and central forces. The resulting equations differ from Navier's in one important respect, viz.: Navier's equations contain a single constant to express the elastic behaviour of a body, while Cauchy's contain two such constants.

At a later date Cauchy extended his theory to the case of crystalline bodies, and he then made use of the hypothesis of material points between which there are forces of attraction or repulsion. The force between a pair of points was taken to act in the line joining the points, and to be a function of the distance between them; and the assemblage of points was taken to be homogeneous in the sense that, if A, B, C are any three of the points, there is a point D of the assemblage which is situated so that the line CD is equal and parallel to AB, and the sense from C to D is the same as the sense from A to B. It was assumed further that when the system is displaced the relative displacement of two of the material points, which are within each other's ranges of activity, is small compared with the distance between them. In the first memoir[33] in which Cauchy made use of this hypothesis he formed an expression for the forces that act upon a single material point in the system, and deduced differential equations of motion and equilibrium. In the case of isotropy, the equations contained two constants. In the second memoir[34] expressions were formed for the tractions across any plane drawn in the body. If the initial state is one of zero stress, and the material is isotropic, the stress is expressed in terms of the strain by means of a single constant, and one of the constants of the preceding memoir must vanish. The equations are then identical with those of Navier. In like manner, in the general case of æolotropy, Cauchy found 21 independent constants. Of these 15 are true "elastic constants," and the remaining 6 express the initial stress and vanish identically if the initial state is one of zero stress. These matters were not fully explained by Cauchy. Clausius[35], however, has shown that this is the meaning of his work. Clausius criticized the restrictive conditions which Cauchy imposed upon the arrangement of his material points, but he argued that these conditions are not necessary for the deduction of Cauchy's equations.

The first memoir by Poisson[36] relating to the same subject was read before the Paris Academy in April, 1828. The memoir is very remarkable for its

33 *Exercices de mathématique*, 1828, 'Sur l'équilibre et le mouvement d'un système de points matériels sollicités par des forces d'attraction ou de répulsion mutuelle.' This memoir follows immediately after that last quoted and immediately precedes that next quoted.

34 *Exercices de mathématique*, 1828, 'De la pression ou tension dans un système de points matériels.'

35 'Ueber die Veränderungen, welche in den bisher gebräuchlichen Formeln für das Gleichgewicht und die Bewegung elastischer fester Körper durch neuere Beobachtungen nothwendig geworden sind,' *Ann. Phys. Chem.* (*Poggendorff*), Bd. 76 (1849).

36 'Mémoire sur l'équilibre et le mouvement des corps élastiques,' *Paris, Mém. de l'Acad.*, t. 8 (1829).

numerous applications of the general theory to special problems. In his investigation of the general equations Poisson, like Cauchy, first obtains the equations of equilibrium in terms of stress-components, and then estimates the traction across any plane resulting from the "intermolecular" forces. The expressions for the stresses in terms of the strains involve summations with respect to all the "molecules," situated within the region of "molecular" activity of a given one. Poisson decides against replacing all the summations by integrations, but he assumes that this can be done for the summations with respect to angular space about the given "molecule," but not for the summations with respect to distance from this "molecule." The equations of equilibrium and motion of isotropic elastic solids which were thus obtained are identical with Navier's. The principle, on which summations may be replaced by integrations, has been explained as follows by Cauchy[33]:—The number of molecules in any volume, which contains a very large number of molecules, and whose dimensions are at the same time small compared with the radius of the sphere of sensible molecular activity, may be taken to be proportional to the volume. If, then, we make abstraction of the molecules in the immediate neighbourhood of the one considered, the actions of all the others, contained in any one of the small volumes referred to, will be equivalent to a force, acting in a line through the centroid of this volume, which will be proportional to the volume and to a function of the distance of the particular molecule from the centroid of the volume. The action of the remoter molecules is said to be "regular," and the action of the nearer ones, "irregular"; and thus Poisson assumed that the irregular action of the nearer molecules may be neglected, in comparison with the action of the remoter ones, which is regular. This assumption is the text upon which Stokes[37] afterwards founded his criticism of Poisson. As we have seen, Cauchy arrived at Poisson's results by the aid of a different assumption[38]. Clausius[35] held that both Poisson's and Cauchy's methods could be presented in unexceptionable forms.

The theory of elasticity established by Poisson and Cauchy on the then accepted basis of material points and central forces was applied by them and also by Lamé and Clapeyron[39] to numerous problems of vibrations and of

[37] 'On the Theories of the...Equilibrium and Motion of Elastic Solids,' *Cambridge Phil. Soc. Trans.*, vol. 8 (1845). Reprinted in Stokes's *Math. and Phys. Papers*, vol. 1, Cambridge, 1880, p. 75.

[38] In a later memoir presented to the Academy in 1829 and published in *J. de l'École polytechnique*, t. 13 (1831), Poisson adopted a method quite similar to that of Cauchy (footnote 34). Poisson extended his theory to æolotropic bodies in his 'Mémoire sur l'équilibre et le mouvement des corps cristallisées,' read to the Paris Academy in 1839 and published after his death in *Paris, Mém. de l'Acad.*, t. 18 (1842).

[39] 'Mémoire sur l'équilibre intérieur des corps solides homogènes,' *Paris, Mém...par divers savants*, t. 4 (1833). The memoir was published also in *J. f. Math.* (*Crelle*), Bd. 7 (1831); it had been presented to the Paris Academy, and the report on it by Poinsot and Navier is dated 1828. In regard to the general theory the method adopted was that of Navier.

statical elasticity, and thus means were provided for testing its consequences experimentally, but it was a long time before adequate experiments were made to test it. Poisson used it to investigate the propagation of waves through an isotropic elastic solid medium. He found two types of waves which, at great distances from the sources of disturbance, are practically "longitudinal" and "transverse," and it was a consequence of his theory that the ratio of the velocities of waves of the two types is $\sqrt{3} : 1$[40]. Cauchy[41] applied his equations to the question of the propagation of light in crystalline as well as in isotropic media. The theory was challenged first in its application to optics by Green[42], and afterwards on its statical side by Stokes[37]. Green was dissatisfied with the hypothesis on which the theory was based, and he sought a new foundation; Stokes's criticisms were directed rather against the process of deduction and some of the particular results.

The revolution which Green effected in the elements of the theory is comparable in importance with that produced by Navier's discovery of the general equations. Starting from what is now called the *Principle of the Conservation of Energy* he propounded a new method of obtaining these equations. He himself stated his principle and method in the following words:—

"In whatever way the elements of any material system may act upon each "other, if all the internal forces exerted be multiplied by the elements of their "respective directions, the total sum for any assigned portion of the mass will "always be the exact differential of some function. But this function being "known, we can immediately apply the general method given in the *Mécanique* "*Analytique*, and which appears to be more especially applicable to problems "that relate to the motions of systems composed of an immense number of "particles mutually acting upon each other. One of the advantages of this "method, of great importance, is that we are necessarily led by the mere "process of the calculation, and with little care on our part, to all the equations "and conditions which are *requisite* and *sufficient* for the complete solution of "any problem to which it may be applied."

The function here spoken of, with its sign changed, is the potential energy of the strained elastic body per unit of volume, expressed in terms of the components of strain; and the differential coefficients of the function, with respect to the components of strain, are the components of stress. Green supposed the function to be capable of being expanded in powers and products of the components of strain. He therefore arranged it as a sum of homogeneous

[40] See the addition, of date November 1828, to the memoir quoted in footnote 36. Cauchy recorded the same result in the *Exercices de mathématique*, 1830.

[41] *Exercices de mathématique*, 1830.

[42] 'On the laws of reflexion and refraction of light at the common surface of two non-crystallized media,' *Cambridge Phil. Soc. Trans.*, vol. 7 (1839). The date of the memoir is 1837. It is reprinted in *Mathematical Papers of the late George Green*, London, 1871, p. 245.

functions of these quantities of the first, second and higher degrees. Of these terms, the first must be absent, as the potential energy must be a true minimum when the body is unstrained; and, as the strains are all small, the second term alone will be of importance. From this principle Green deduced the equations of Elasticity, containing in the general case 21 constants. In the case of isotropy there are two constants, and the equations are the same as those of Cauchy's first memoir[32].

Lord Kelvin[43] has based the argument for the existence of Green's strain-energy-function on the First and Second Laws of Thermodynamics. From these laws he deduced the result that, when a solid body is strained without alteration of temperature, the components of stress are the differential coefficients of a function of the components of strain with respect to these components severally. The same result can be proved to hold when the strain is effected so quickly that no heat is gained or lost by any part of the body.

Poisson's theory leads to the conclusions that the resistance of a body to compression by pressure uniform all round it is two-thirds of the Young's modulus of the material, and that the resistance to shearing is two-fifths of the Young's modulus. He noted a result equivalent to the first of these[44], and the second is virtually contained in his theory of the torsional vibrations of a bar[45]. The observation that resistance to compression and resistance to shearing are the two fundamental kinds of elastic resistance in isotropic bodies was made by Stokes[46], and he introduced definitely the two principal moduluses of elasticity by which these resistances are expressed—the "modulus of compression" and the "rigidity," as they are now called. From Hooke's Law and from considerations of symmetry he concluded that pressure equal in all directions round a point is attended by a proportional compression without shear, and that shearing stress is attended by a corresponding proportional shearing strain. As an experimental basis for Hooke's Law he cited the fact that bodies admit of being thrown into states of isochronous vibration. By a method analogous to that of Cauchy's first memoir[32], but resting on the above-stated experimental basis, he deduced the equations with two constants which had been given by Cauchy and Green. Having regard to the varying degrees in which different classes of bodies—liquids, soft solids, hard solids—resist compression and distortion, he refused to accept the conclusion from Poisson's theory that the modulus of compression has to the rigidity the ratio 5 : 3. He pointed out that, if the ratio of these moduluses could be regarded

[43] Sir W. Thomson, *Quart. J. of Math.*, vol. 5 (1855), reprinted in *Phil. Mag.* (Ser. 5), vol. 5 (1878), and also in *Mathematical and Physical Papers by Sir William Thomson*, vol. 1, Cambridge, 1882, p. 291.

[44] *Annales de Chimie et de Physique*, t. 36 (1827).

[45] This theory is given in the memoir cited in footnote 36.

[46] See footnote 37. The distinction between the two kinds of elasticity had been noted by Poncelet, *Introduction à la Mécanique industrielle, physique et expérimentale*, Metz, 1839.

as infinite, the ratio of the velocities of "longitudinal" and "transverse" waves would also be infinite, and then, as Green had already shown, the application of the theory to optics would be facilitated.

The methods of Navier, of Poisson, and of Cauchy's later memoirs lead to equations of motion containing fewer constants than occur in the equations obtained by the methods of Green, of Stokes, and of Cauchy's first memoir. The importance of the discrepancy was first emphasized by Stokes. The questions in dispute are these—Is elastic æolotropy to be characterized by 21 constants or by 15, and is elastic isotropy to be characterized by two constants or one? The two theories are styled by Pearson[47] the "multi-constant" theory and the "rari-constant" theory respectively, and the controversy concerning them has lasted almost down to the present time. It is to be understood that the rari-constant equations can be included in the multi-constant ones by equating certain pairs of the coefficients, but that the rari-constant equations rest upon a particular hypothesis concerning the constitution of matter, while the adoption of multi-constancy has been held to imply denial of this hypothesis. Discrepancies between the results of the two theories can be submitted to the test of experiment, and it might be thought that the verdict would be final, but the difficulty of being certain that the tested material is isotropic has diminished the credit of many experimental investigations, and the tendency of the multi-constant elasticians to rely on experiments on such bodies as cork, jelly and india-rubber has weakened their arguments. Much of the discussion has turned upon the value of the ratio of lateral contraction to longitudinal extension of a bar under terminal tractive load. This ratio is often called "Poisson's ratio." Poisson[36] deduced from his theory the result that this ratio must be $\frac{1}{4}$. The experiments of Wertheim on glass and brass did not support this result, and Wertheim[48] proposed to take the ratio to be $\frac{1}{3}$—a value which has no theoretical foundation. The experimental evidence led Lamé in his treatise[49] to adopt the multi-constant equations, and after the publication of this book they were generally employed. Saint-Venant, though a firm believer in rari-constancy, expressed the results of his researches on torsion and flexure and on the distribution of elasticities round a point[50] in terms of the multi-constant theory. Kirchhoff[51] adopted the same theory in his investigations of thin rods and plates, and supported it by experiments on the torsion and flexure of steel bars[52]; and Clebsch in

[47] Todhunter and Pearson, *History of the Theory of Elasticity*, vol. 1, Cambridge, 1886, p. 496.

[48] *Annales de Chimie*, t. 23 (1848).

[49] *Leçons sur la théorie mathématique de l'élasticité des corps solides*, Paris, 1852.

[50] The memoir on torsion is in *Mém. des Savants étrangers*, t. 14 (1855), that on flexure is in *J. de Math.* (*Liouville*), (Sér. 2), t. 1 (1856), and that on the distribution of elasticities is in *J. de Math.* (*Liouville*), (Sér. 2), t. 8 (1863).

[51] *J. f. Math.* (*Crelle*), Bd. 40 (1850), and Bd. 56 (1859).

[52] *Ann. Phys. Chem.* (*Poggendorff*), Bd. 108 (1859).

his treatise[53] used the language of bi-constant isotropy. Kelvin and Tait[54] dismissed the controversy in a few words and adopted the views of Stokes. The best modern experiments support the conclusion that Poisson's ratio can differ sensibly from the value $\frac{1}{4}$ in materials which may without cavil be treated as isotropic and homogeneous. But perhaps the most striking experimental evidence is that which Voigt[55] has derived from his study of the elasticity of crystals. The absence of guarantees for the isotropy of the tested materials ceased to be a difficulty when he had the courage to undertake experiments on materials which have known kinds of æolotropy[56]. The point to be settled is, however, more remote. According to Green there exist, for a material of the most generally æolotropic character, 21 independent elastic constants. The molecular hypothesis, as worked out by Cauchy and supported by Saint-Venant, leads to 15 constants, so that, if the rari-constant theory is correct, there must be 6 independent relations among Green's 21 coefficients. These relations I call Cauchy's relations[57]. Now Voigt's experiments were made on the torsion and flexure of prisms of various crystals, for most of which Saint-Venant's formulæ for æolotropic rods hold good, for the others he supplied the required formulæ. In the cases of beryl and rocksalt only were Cauchy's relations even approximately verified; in the seven other kinds of crystals examined there were very considerable differences between the coefficients which these relations would require to be equal.

Independently of the experimental evidence the rari-constant theory has lost ground through the widening of our views concerning the constitution of matter. The hypothesis of material points and central forces does not now hold the field. This change in the tendency of physical speculation is due to many causes, among which the disagreement of the rari-constant theory of elasticity with the results of experiment holds a rather subordinate position. Of much greater importance have been the development of the atomic theory in Chemistry and of statistical molecular theories in Physics, the growth of the doctrine of energy, the discovery of electric radiation. It is now recognized that a theory of atoms must be part of a comprehensive theory, which must include also sub-atomic constituents of matter (electrons), and that the confidence which was once felt in the hypothesis of central forces between material points was premature. To determine the laws of the elasticity of solid bodies without knowing the nature of the atoms, we can only invoke the known laws of energy as was done by Green and Lord Kelvin; and we may

[53] *Theorie der Elasticität fester Körper*, Leipzig, 1862.

[54] Thomson and Tait, *Natural Philosophy*, 1st edition Oxford 1867, 2nd edition Cambridge 1879—1883.

[55] W. Voigt, *Ann. Phys. Chem.* (*Wiedemann*), Bde. 31, (1887), 34 and 35 (1888), 38 (1889).

[56] A certain assumption, first made by F. E. Neumann, is involved in the statement that the æolotropy of a crystal as regards elasticity is known from the crystallographic form.

[57] They appear to have been first stated explicitly by Saint-Venant in the memoir on torsion of 1855. (See footnote 50.)

place the theory on a firm basis if we appeal to experiment to support the statement that, within a certain range of strain, the strain-energy-function is a quadratic function of the components of strain, instead of relying, as Green did, upon an expansion of the function in series.

The problem of determining the state of stress and strain within a solid body which is subjected to given forces acting through its volume and to given tractions across its surface, or is held by surface tractions so that its surface is deformed into a prescribed figure, is reducible to the analytical problem of finding functions to represent the components of displacement. These functions must satisfy the differential equations of equilibrium at all points within the surface of the body and must also satisfy certain special conditions at this surface. The methods which have been devised for integrating the equations fall into two classes. In one class of methods a special solution is sought and the boundary conditions are satisfied by a solution in the form of a series, which may be infinite, of special solutions. The special solutions are generally expressible in terms of harmonic functions. This class of solutions may be regarded as constituting an extension of the methods of expansion in spherical harmonics and in trigonometrical series. In the other class of methods the quantities to be determined are expressed by definite integrals, the elements of the integrals representing the effects of *singularities* distributed over the surface or through the volume. This class of solutions constitutes an extension of the methods introduced by Green in the Theory of the Potential. At the time of the discovery of the general equations of Elasticity the method of series had already been applied to astronomical problems, to acoustical problems and to problems of the conduction of heat[58]; the method of singularities had not been invented[59]. The application of the method of series to problems of equilibrium of elastic solid bodies was initiated by Lamé and Clapeyron[39]. They considered the case of a body bounded by an unlimited plane to which pressure is applied according to an arbitrary law. Lamé[60] later considered the problem of a body bounded by a spherical surface and deformed by given surface tractions. The problem of the plane is essentially that of the transmission into a solid body of force applied locally to a small part of its surface. The problem of the sphere has been developed by Lord Kelvin[61], who sought to utilize it for the purpose of investigating the rigidity of the Earth[62], and by G. H. Darwin in connexion with other

[58] See Burkhardt, 'Entwickelungen nach oscillirenden Functionen,' *Jahresbericht der Deutschen Mathematiker-Vereinigung*, Bd. 10, Heft 2.

[59] It was invented by Green, *An Essay on the Application of Mathematical Analysis to the Theories of Electricity and Magnetism*, Nottingham, 1828. Reprinted in *Mathematical Papers of the late George Green*, London, 1871.

[60] *J. de Math.* (*Liouville*), t. 19 (1854).

[61] *Phil. Trans. Roy. Soc.*, vol. 153 (1863). See also *Math. and Phys. Papers*, vol. 3 (Cambridge, 1890), p. 351, and Kelvin and Tait, *Nat. Phil.*, Part II.

[62] *Brit. Assoc. Rep.* 1876, *Math. and Phys. Papers*, vol. 3, p. 312.

problems of cosmical physics[63]. The serial solutions employed are expressed in terms of spherical harmonics. Solutions of the equations in cylindrical coordinates can be expressed in terms of Bessel's functions[64], but, except for spheres and cylinders, the method of series has not been employed very successfully. The method of singularities was first applied to the theory of Elasticity by E. Betti[65], who set out from a certain reciprocal theorem of the type that is now familiar in many branches of mathematical physics. From this theorem he deduced incidentally a formula for determining the average strain of any type that is produced in a body by given forces. The method of singularities has been developed chiefly by the elasticians of the Italian school. It has proved more effective than the method of series in the solution of the problem of transmission of force. The fundamental particular solution which expresses the displacement due to force at a point in an indefinitely extended solid was given by Lord Kelvin[66]. It was found at a later date by J. Boussinesq[67] along with other particular solutions, which can, as a matter of fact, be derived by synthesis from it. Boussinesq's results led him to a solution of the problem of the plane, and to a theory of "local perturbations," according to which the effect of force applied in the neighbourhood of any point of a body falls off very rapidly as the distance from the point increases, and the application of an equilibrating system of forces to a small part of a body produces an effect which is negligible at a considerable distance from the part. To estimate the effect produced at a distance by forces applied near a point, it is not necessary to take into account the mode of application of the forces but only the statical resultant and moment. The direct method of integration founded upon Betti's reciprocal theorem was applied to the problem of the plane by V. Cerruti[68]. Some of the results were found independently by Hertz, and led in his hands to a theory of impact and a theory of hardness[69].

A different method for determining the state of stress in a body has been developed from a result noted by G. B. Airy[70]. He observed that, in the case of two dimensions, the equations of equilibrium of a body deformed by surface

[63] *Phil. Trans. Roy. Soc.*, vol. 170 (1879), and vol. 173 (1882). Reprinted in G. H. Darwin's *Scientific Papers*, vol. 2, Cambridge 1908, pp. 1, 459.

[64] L. Pochhammer, *J. f. Math.* (*Crelle*), Bd. 81 (1876), p. 33.

[65] *Il Nuovo Cimento* (Ser. 2), tt. 6—10 (1872 *et seq.*).

[66] Sir W. Thomson, *Cambridge and Dublin Math. J.*, 1848, reprinted in *Math. and Phys. Papers*, vol. 1, p. 97.

[67] For Boussinesq's earlier researches in regard to simple solutions, see *Paris, C. R.*, tt. 86—88 (1878—1879) and tt. 93—96 (1881—1883). A more complete account is given in his book, *Applications des potentiels à l'étude de l'équilibre et du mouvement des solides élastiques*, Paris, 1885.

[68] *Roma, Acc. Lincei, Mem. fis. mat.*, 1882.

[69] *J. f. Math.* (*Crelle*), Bd. 92 (1882), and *Verhandlungen des Vereins zur Beförderung des Gewerbefleisses*, Berlin, 1882. The memoirs are reprinted in *Ges. Werke von Heinrich Hertz*, Bd. 1, Leipzig, 1895, pp. 155 and 174.

[70] *Brit. Assoc. Rep.* 1862, and *Phil. Trans. Roy. Soc.*, vol. 153 (1863), p. 49.

tractions show that the stress-components can be expressed as partial differential coefficients of the second order of a single function. Maxwell[71] extended the result to three dimensions, in which case three such "stress-functions" are required. It appeared later that these functions are connected by a rather complicated system of differential equations[72]. The stress-components must in fact be connected with the strain-components by the stress-strain relations, and the strain-components are not independent; but the second differential coefficients of the strain-components with respect to the coordinates are connected by a system of linear equations, which are the conditions necessary to secure that the strain-components shall correspond with a displacement, in accordance with the ordinary formulæ connecting strain and displacement[73]. It is possible by taking account of these relations to obtain a complete system of equations which must be satisfied by stress-components, and thus the way is open for a direct determination of stress without the intermediate steps of forming and solving differential equations to determine the components of displacement[74]. In the case of two dimensions the resulting equations are of a simple character, and many interesting solutions can be obtained.

The theory of the free vibrations of solid bodies requires the integration of the equations of vibratory motion in accordance with prescribed boundary conditions of stress or displacement. Poisson[36] gave the solution of the problem of free radial vibrations of a solid sphere, and Clebsch[53] founded the general theory on the model of Poisson's solution. This theory included the extension of the notion of "principal coordinates" to systems with an infinite number of degrees of freedom, the introduction of the corresponding "normal functions," and the proof of those properties of these functions upon which the expansions of arbitrary functions depend. The discussions which had taken place before and during the time of Poisson concerning the vibrations of strings, bars, membranes and plates had prepared the way for Clebsch's generalizations. Before the publication of Clebsch's treatise a different theory had been propounded by Lamé[49]. Acquainted with Poisson's discovery of two types of waves, he concluded that the vibrations of any solid body must fall into two corresponding classes, and he investigated the vibrations of various bodies on this assumption. The fact that his solutions do not satisfy the conditions which hold at the boundaries of bodies free from surface traction is a sufficient disproof of his theory; but it was finally disposed of when all the modes of free vibration of a homogeneous isotropic sphere were determined, and it was proved that the classes into which they fall do not verify

[71] *Edinburgh Roy. Soc. Trans.*, vol. 26 (1870). Reprinted in Maxwell's *Scientific Papers*, vol. 2, p. 161.

[72] W. J. Ibbetson, *An Elementary Treatise on the Mathematical Theory of perfectly Elastic Solids*, London, 1887.

[73] Saint-Venant gave the identical relations between strain-components in his edition of Navier's *Résumé des Leçons sur l'application de la Mécanique*, Paris, 1864, 'Appendice 3.'

[74] J. H. Michell, *London Math. Soc. Proc.*, vol. 31 (1900), p. 100.

Lamé's supposition. The analysis of the general problem of the vibrations of a sphere was first completely given by P. Jaerisch[75], who showed that the solution could be expressed by means of spherical harmonics and certain functions of the distance from the centre of the sphere, which are practically Bessel's functions of order *integer* + $\frac{1}{2}$. This result was obtained independently by H. Lamb[76], who gave an account of the simpler modes of vibration and of the nature of the nodal division of the sphere which occurs when any normal vibration is executed. He also calculated the more important roots of the frequency equation. L. Pochhammer[77] has applied the method of normal functions to the vibrations of cylinders, and has found modes of vibration analogous to the known types of vibration of bars.

The problem of tracing, by means of the equations of vibratory motion, the propagation of waves through an elastic solid medium requires investigations of a different character from those concerned with normal modes of vibration. In the case of an isotropic medium Poisson[78] and Ostrogradsky[79] adopted methods which involve a synthesis of solutions of simple harmonic type, and obtained a solution expressing the displacement at any time in terms of the initial distribution of displacement and velocity. The investigation was afterwards conducted in a different fashion by Stokes[80], who showed that Poisson's two waves are waves of irrotational dilatation and waves of equivoluminal distortion, the latter involving rotation of the elements of the medium. Cauchy[41] and Green[81] discussed the propagation of plane waves through a crystalline medium, and obtained equations for the velocity of propagation in terms of the direction of the normal to the wave-front. In general the wave-surface has three sheets; when the medium is isotropic all the sheets are spheres, and two of them are coincident. Blanchet[82] extended Poisson's results to the case of a crystalline medium. Christoffel[83] discussed the advance through the medium of a surface of discontinuity. At any instant, the surface separates two portions of the medium in which the displacements are expressed by different formulæ; and Christoffel showed that the surface moves normally to itself with a velocity which is determined, at any point, by the direction of the normal of the surface, according to the same law as holds for plane waves propagated in that direction. Besides the waves of dilata-

[75] *J. f. Math.* (*Crelle*), Bd. 88 (1880).

[76] *London Math. Soc. Proc.*, vol. 13 (1882).

[77] *J. f. Math.* (*Crelle*), Bd. 81 (1876), p. 324.

[78] *Paris, Mém. de l'Acad.*, t. 10 (1831).

[79] *St Petersburg, Mém. de l'Acad.*, t. 1 (1831).

[80] 'On the Dynamical Theory of Diffraction,' *Cambridge Phil. Soc. Trans.*, vol. 9 (1849). Reprinted in Stokes's *Math. and Phys. Papers*, vol. 2 (Cambridge, 1883).

[81] *Cambridge Phil. Soc. Trans.*, vol. 7 (1839). Reprinted in Green's *Mathematical Papers*, p. 293.

[82] *J. de Math.* (*Liouville*), t. 5 (1840), t. 7 (1842).

[83] *Ann. di Mat.* (Ser. 2), t. 8 (1877). Reprinted in E. B. Christoffel, *Ges. math. Abhandlungen*, Bd. 2, p. 81, Leipzig 1910.

tion and distortion which can be propagated through an isotropic solid body Lord Rayleigh[84] has investigated a third type which can be propagated over the surface. The velocity of waves of this type is less than that of either of the other two.

Before the discovery of the general equations there existed theories of the torsion and flexure of beams starting from Galileo's enquiry aud a suggestion of Coulomb's. The problems thus proposed are among the most important for practical applications, as many problems that have to be dealt with by engineers can, at any rate for the purpose of a rough approximation, be reduced to questions of the resistance of beams. Cauchy was the first to attempt to apply the general equations to this class of problems, and his investigation of the torsion of a rectangular prism[85], though not correct, is historically important, as he recognized that the normal sections do not remain plane. His result had little influence on practice. The practical treatises of the earlier half of the last century contain a theory of torsion with a result that we have already attributed to Coulomb, viz., that the resistance to torsion is the product of an elastic constant, the amount of the twist, and the moment of inertia of the cross-section. Again, in regard to flexure, the practical treatises of the time followed the Bernoulli-Eulerian (really Coulomb's) theory, attributing the resistance to flexure entirely to extension and contraction of longitudinal filaments. To Saint-Venant belongs the credit of bringing the problems of the torsion and flexure of beams under the general theory. Seeing the difficulty of obtaining general solutions, the pressing need for practical purposes of some theory that could be applied to the strength of structures, and the improbability of the precise mode of application of the load to the parts of any apparatus being known, he was led to reflect on the methods used for the solution of special problems before the formulation of the general equations. These reflexions led him to the invention of the *semi-inverse* method of solution which bears his name. Some of the habitual assumptions, or some of the results commonly deduced from them, may be true, at least in a large majority of cases; and it may be possible by retaining some of these assumptions or results to simplify the equations, and thus to obtain solutions—not indeed such as satisfy arbitrary surface conditions, but such as satisfy practically important types of surface conditions.

The first problem to which Saint-Venant applied his method was that of the torsion of prisms, the theory of which he gave in the famous memoir on torsion of 1855[50]. For this application he assumed the state of strain to consist of a simple twist about the axis of the prism, such as is implied in Coulomb's theory, combined with the kind of strain that is implied by a longitudinal displacement variable over the cross-section of the prism. The effect of the latter displacement is manifested in a distortion of the sections

[84] *London Math. Soc. Proc.*, vol. 17 (1887), or *Scientific Papers*, vol. 2, Cambridge, 1900, p. 441.
[85] *Exercices de mathématique*, 4me Année, 1829.

into curved surfaces. He showed that a state of strain having this character can be maintained in the prism by forces applied at its ends only, and that the forces which must be applied to the ends are statically equivalent to a couple about the axis of the prism. The magnitude of the couple can be expressed as the product of the twist, the rigidity of the material, the square of the area of the cross-section and a numerical factor which depends upon the shape of the cross-section. For a large class of sections this numerical factor is very nearly proportional to the ratio of the area of the section to the square of its radius of gyration about the axis of the prism. Subsequent investigations have shown that the analysis of the problem is identical with that of two distinct problems in hydrodynamics, viz., the flow of viscous liquid in a narrow pipe of the same form as the prism[86], and the motion produced in frictionless liquid filling a vessel of the same form as the prism when the vessel is rotated about its axis[87]. These hydrodynamical analogies have resulted in a considerable simplification of the analysis of the problem.

The old theories of flexure involved two contradictory assumptions: (1) that the strain consists of extensions and contractions of longitudinal filaments, (2) that the stress consists of tension in the extended filaments (on the side remote from the centre of curvature) and pressure along the contracted filaments (on the side nearer the centre of curvature). If the stress is correctly given by the second assumption there must be lateral contractions accompanying the longitudinal extensions and also lateral extensions accompanying the longitudinal contractions. Again, the resultant of the tractions across any normal section of the bent beam, as given by the old theories, vanishes, and these tractions are statically equivalent to a couple about an axis at right angles to the plane of bending. Hence the theories are inapplicable to any case of bending by a transverse load. Saint-Venant[88] adopted from the older theories two assumptions. He assumed that the extensions and contractions of the longitudinal filaments are proportional to their distances from the plane which is drawn through the line of centroids of the normal sections (the "central-line") and at right angles to the plane of bending. He assumed also that there is no normal traction across any plane drawn parallel to the central-line. The states of stress and strain which satisfy these conditions in a prismatic body can be maintained by forces and couples applied at the ends only, and include two cases. One case is that of uniform bending of a bar by couples applied at its ends. In this case the stress is correctly given by the older theories and the curvature of the central-line is proportional to the bending couple, as in those theories; but the lateral contractions and extensions have the effect of distorting those longitudinal sections which are at right angles to the plane of bending into anticlastic surfaces. The second

[86] J. Boussinesq, *J. de Math.* (*Liouville*), (Sér. 2), t. 16 (1871).

[87] Kelvin and Tait, *Nat. Phil.*, Part 2, p. 242.

[88] See the memoirs of 1855 and 1856 cited in footnote 50.

case of bending which is included in Saint-Venant's theory is that of a cantilever, or beam fixed in a horizontal position at one end, and bent by a vertical load applied at the other end. In this case the stress given by the older theories requires to be corrected by the addition of shearing stresses. The normal tractions across any normal section are statically equivalent to a couple, which is proportional to the curvature of the central-line at the section, as in the theory of simple bending. The tangential tractions across any normal section are statically equivalent to the terminal load, but the magnitude and direction of the tangential traction at any point are entirely determinate and follow rather complex laws. The strain given by the older theories requires to be corrected by the addition of lateral contractions and extensions, as in the theory of simple bending, and also by shearing strains corresponding with the shearing stresses.

In Saint-Venant's theories of torsion and flexure the couples and forces applied to produce twisting and bending are the resultants of tractions exerted across the terminal sections, and these tractions are distributed in perfectly definite ways. The forces and couples that are applied to actual structures are seldom distributed in these ways. The application of the theories to practical problems rests upon a principle introduced by Saint-Venant which has been called the "principle of the elastic equivalence of statically equipollent systems of load." According to this principle the effects produced by deviations from the assigned laws of loading are unimportant except near the ends of the bent beam or twisted bar, and near the ends they produce merely "local perturbations." The condition for the validity of the results in practice is that the length of the beam should be a considerable multiple of the greatest diameter of its cross-section.

Later researches by A. Clebsch[53] and W. Voigt[89] have resulted in considerable simplifications of Saint-Venant's analysis. Clebsch showed that the single assumption that there is no normal traction across any plane parallel to the central-line leads to four cases of equilibrium of a prismatic body, viz., (1) simple extension under terminal tractive load, (2) simple bending by couples, (3) torsion, (4) bending of a cantilever by terminal transverse load. Voigt showed that the single assumption that the stress at any point is independent of the coordinate measured along the bar led to the first three cases, and that the assumption that the stress is a linear function of that coordinate leads to the fourth case. When a quadratic function is taken instead of a linear one, the case of a beam supported at the ends and bent by a load which is distributed uniformly along its length can be included[90]. The case where the load is not uniform but is applied by means of surface tractions which, so far as they depend on the coordinate measured along the beam, are rational integral

[89] 'Theoretische Studien über die Elasticitätsverhältnisse der Krystalle,' *Göttingen Abhandlungen*, Bd. 34 (1887).

[90] J. H. Michell, *Quart. J. of Math.*, vol. 32 (1901).

functions, can be reduced to the case where the load is uniform[91]. It appears from these theories that, when lateral forces are applied to the beam, the relation of proportionality between the curvature of the central-line and the bending moment, verified in Saint-Venant's theory, is no longer exact[92]. Unless the conditions of loading are rather unusual, the modification that ought to be made in this relation is, however, of little practical importance.

Saint-Venant's theories of torsion and of simple bending have found their way into technical treatises, but in some current books on applied Mechanics the theory of bending by transverse load is treated by a method invented by Jouravski[93] and Rankine[94], and subsequently developed by Grashof[95]. The components of stress determined by this method do not satisfy the conditions which are necessary to secure that they shall correspond with any possible displacement[73]. The distribution of stress that is found by this method is, however, approximately correct in the case of a beam of which the breadth is but a small fraction of the depth[96].

The most important practical application of the theory of flexure is that which was made by Navier[97] to the bending of a beam resting on supports. The load may consist of the weight of the beam and of weights attached to the beam. Young's modulus is usually determined by observing the deflexion of a bar supported at its ends and loaded in the middle. All such applications of the theory depend upon the proportionality of the curvature to the bending moment. The problem of a continuous beam resting on several supports was at first very difficult, as a solution had to be obtained for each span by Navier's method, and the solutions compared in order to determine the constants of integration. The analytical complexity was very much diminished when Clapeyron[98] noticed that the bending moments at three consecutive supports are connected by an invariable relation, but in many particular cases the analysis is still formidable. A method of graphical solution has, however, been invented by Mohr[99], and it has, to a great extent, superseded the calculations

[91] E. Almansi, *Roma, Acc. Lincei Rend.* (Ser. 6), t. 10 (1901), pp. 333, 400. In the second of these papers a solution of the problem of bending by uniform load is obtained by a method which differs from that used by Michell in the paper just cited.

[92] This result was first noted by K. Pearson, *Quart. J. of Math.*, vol. 24 (1889), in connexion with a particular law for the distribution of the load over the cross-section.

[93] *Ann. des ponts et chaussées*, 1856.

[94] *Applied Mechanics*, 1st edition, London, 1858. The method has been retained in later editions.

[95] *Elasticität und Festigkeit*, 2nd edition, Berlin, 1878. Grashof gives Saint-Venant's theory as well.

[96] Saint-Venant noted this result in his edition of Navier's *Leçons*, p. 394.

[97] In the second edition of his *Leçons* (1833).

[98] *Paris, C. R.*, t. 45 (1857). The history of Clapeyron's theorem is given by J. M. Heppel, *London, Roy. Soc. Proc.*, vol. 19 (1871).

[99] 'Beitrag zur Theorie des Fachwerks,' *Zeitschrift des Architekten- und Ingenieur-Vereins zu Hannover*, 1874. This is the reference given by Müller-Breslau. Lévy gives an account of the method in his *Statique Graphique*, t. 2, and attributes it to Mohr. A slightly different account is given by Canevazzi in *Memorie dell' Accademia di Bologna* (Ser. 4), t. 1 (1880). The method

that were formerly conducted by means of Clapeyron's "Theorem of Three Moments." Many other applications of the theory of flexure to problems of frameworks will be found in such books as Müller-Breslau's *Die Neueren Methoden der Festigkeitslehre* (Leipzig, 1886), Weyrauch's *Theorie Elastischer Körper* (Leipzig, 1884), Ritter's *Anwendungen der graphischen Statik* (Zürich, 1888). A considerable literature has sprung up in this subject, but the use made of the Theory of Elasticity is small.

The theory of the bending and twisting of thin rods and wires—including the theory of spiral springs—was for a long time developed, independently of the general equations of Elasticity, by methods akin to those employed by Euler. At first it was supposed that the flexural couple must be in the osculating plane of the curve formed by the central-line; and, when the equation of moments about the tangent was introduced by Binet[100], Poisson[101] concluded from it that the moment of torsion was constant. It was only by slow degrees that the notion of two flexural couples in the two principal planes sprang up, and that the measure of twist came to be understood. When these elements of the theory were made out it could be seen that a knowledge of the expressions for the flexural and torsional couples in terms of the curvature and twist[102] would be sufficient, when combined with the ordinary conditions of equilibrium, to determine the form of the curve assumed by the central-line, the twist of the wire around that line, and the tension and shearing forces across any section. The flexural and torsional couples, as well as the resultant forces across a section, must arise from tractions exerted across the elements of the section, and the correct expressions for them must be sought by means of the general theory. But here a difficulty arises from the fact that the general equations are applicable to small displacements only, while the displacements in such a body as a spiral spring are by no means small. Kirchhoff[103] was the first to face this difficulty. He pointed out that the general equations are strictly applicable to any small portion of a thin rod if all the linear dimensions of the portion are of the same order of magnitude as the diameters of the cross-sections. He held that the equations of equilibrium or motion of such a portion could be simplified, for a first approximation, by the omission of kinetic reactions and forces distributed through the volume. The process by which Kirchhoff developed his theory was, to a great extent, kinematical. When a thin rod is bent and twisted, every element of it undergoes a strain analogous to that in one of

has been extended by Culman, *Die graphische Statik*, Bd. 1, Zürich, 1875. See also Ritter, *Die elastische Linie und ihre Anwendung auf den continuirlichen Balken*, Zürich, 1883.

100 *J. de l'École polytechnique*, t. 10 (1815).

101 *Correspondance sur l'École polytechnique*, t. 3 (1816).

102 They are due to Saint-Venant, *Paris, C. R.*, tt. 17, 19 (1843, 1844).

103 'Über das Gleichgewicht und die Bewegung eines unendlich dünnen elastischen Stabes,' *J. f. Math.* (*Crelle*), Bd. 56 (1859). The theory is also given in Kirchhoff's *Vorlesungen über math Physik, Mechanik* (3rd edition, Leipzig, 1883).

Saint-Venant's prisms, but neighbouring elements must continue to fit. To express this kind of continuity certain conditions are necessary, and these conditions take the form of differential equations connecting the relative displacements of points within a small portion of the rod with the relative coordinates of the points, and with the quantities that define the position of the portion relative to the rod as a whole. From these differential equations Kirchhoff deduced an approximate account of the strain in an element of the rod, and thence an expression for the potential energy per unit of length, in terms of the extension, the components of curvature and the twist. He obtained the equations of equilibrium and vibration by varying the energy-function. In the case of a thin rod subjected to terminal forces only he showed that the equations by which the form of the central-line is determined are identical with the equations of motion of a heavy rigid body about a fixed point. This theorem is known as "Kirchhoff's kinetic analogue."

Kirchhoff's theory has given rise to much discussion. Clebsch[53] proposed to replace that part of it by which the flexural and torsional couples can be evaluated by an appeal to the results of Saint-Venant's theories of flexure and torsion. Kelvin and Tait[54] proposed to establish Kirchhoff's formula for the potential energy by general reasoning. J. Boussinesq[104] proposed to obtain by the same kind of reasoning Kirchhoff's approximate expression for the extension of a longitudinal filament. Clebsch[53] gave the modified formulæ for the flexural and torsional couples when the central-line of the rod in the unstressed state is curved, and his results have been confirmed by later independent investigations. The discussions which have taken place have cleared up many difficulties, and the results of the theory, as distinguished from the methods by which they were obtained, have been confirmed by the later writers[105].

The applications of Kirchhoff's theory of thin rods include the theory of the *elastica* which has been investigated in detail by means of the theorem of the kinetic analogue[106], the theory of spiral springs worked out in detail by Kelvin and Tait[54], and various problems of elastic stability. Among the latter we may mention the problem of the buckling of an elastic ring subjected to pressure directed radially inwards and the same at all points of the circumference[107].

The theory of the vibrations of thin rods was brought under the general equations of vibratory motion of elastic solid bodies by Poisson[36]. He regarded the rod as a circular cylinder of small section, and expanded all the quantities that occur in powers of the distance of a particle from the

[104] *J. de Math.* (*Liouville*), (Sér. 2), t. 16 (1871).

[105] See, for example, A. B. Basset, *London Math. Soc. Proc.*, vol. 23 (1892), and *Amer. J. of Math.*, vol. 17 (1895), and J. H. Michell, *London Math. Soc. Proc.*, vol. 31 (1900), p. 130.

[106] W. Hess, *Math. Ann.*, Bde. 23 (1884) and 25 (1885).

[107] This problem appears to have been discussed first by Bresse, *Cours de mécanique appliquée, Première partie*, Paris, 1859.

axis of the cylinder. When terms above a certain order (the fourth power of the radius) are neglected, the equations for flexural vibrations are identical with Euler's equations of lateral vibration. The equation found for the longitudinal vibrations had been obtained by Navier[108]. The equation for the torsional vibrations was obtained first by Poisson[36]. The chief point of novelty in Poisson's results in regard to the vibrations of rods is that the coefficients on which the frequencies depend are expressed in terms of the constants that occur in the general equations; but the deduction of the generally admitted special differential equations, by which these modes of vibration are governed, from the general equations of Elasticity constituted an advance in method. Reference has already been made to L. Pochhammer's more complete investigation[77]. Poisson's theory is verified as an approximate theory by an application of Kirchhoff's results. This application has been extended to the vibrations of curved bars, the first problem to be solved being that of the flexural vibrations of a circular ring which vibrates in its own plane[109].

An important problem arising in connexion with the theory of longitudinal vibrations is the problem of impact. When two bodies collide each is thrown into a state of internal vibration, and it appears to have been hoped that a solution of the problem of the vibrations set up in two bars which impinge longitudinally would throw light on the laws of impact. Poisson[110] was the first to attempt a solution of the problem from this point of view. His method of integration in trigonometric series vastly increases the difficulty of deducing general results, and, by an unfortunate error in the analysis, he arrived at the paradoxical conclusion that, when the bars are of the same material and section, they never separate unless they are equal in length. Saint-Venant[111] treated the problem by means of the solution of the equation of vibration in terms of arbitrary functions, and arrived at certain results, of which the most important relate to the duration of impact, and to the existence of an apparent "coefficient of restitution" for perfectly elastic bodies[112]. This theory is not confirmed by experiment. A correction suggested by Voigt[113], when worked out, led to little better agreement, and it thus appears that the attempt to trace the phenomena of impact to vibrations must be abandoned. Much more successful was the theory of Hertz[114], obtained from a solution of the problem which we have named the problem

[108] *Bulletin des Sciences à la Société philomathique*, 1824.

[109] R. Hoppe, *J. f. Math.* (*Crelle*), Bd. 73 (1871).

[110] In his *Traité de Mécanique*, 1833.

[111] 'Sur le choc longitudinal de deux barres élastiques...,' *J. de Math.* (*Liouville*), (Sér. 2), t. 12 (1867).

[112] Cf. Hopkinson, *Messenger of Mathematics*, vol. 4, 1874.

[113] *Ann. Phys. Chem.* (*Wiedemann*), Bd. 19 (1882). See also Hausmaninger in the same *Annalen*, Bd. 25 (1885).

[114] 'Ueber die Berührung fester elastischer Körper,' *J. f. Math.* (*Crelle*), Bd. 92 (1882).

of the transmission of force. Hertz made an independent investigation of a particular case of this problem—that of two bodies pressed together. He proposed to regard the strain produced in each by impact as a local statical effect, produced gradually and subsiding gradually; and he found means to determine the duration of impact and the size and shape of the parts that come into contact. The theory yielded a satisfactory comparison with experiment.

The theory of vibrations can be applied to problems concerning various kinds of shocks and the effects of moving loads. The inertia as well as the elastic reactions of bodies come into play in the resistances to strain under rapidly changing conditions, and the resistances called into action are sometimes described as "dynamical resistances." The special problem of the longitudinal impact of a massive body upon one end of a rod was discussed by Sébert and Hugoniot[115] and by Boussinesq[116]. The conclusions which they arrived at are tabulated and illustrated graphically by Saint-Venant[117]. But problems of dynamical resistance under impulses that tend to produce flexure are perhaps practically of more importance. When a body strikes a rod perpendicularly the rod will be thrown into vibration, and, if the body moves with the rod, the ordinary solution in terms of the normal functions for the vibrations of the rod becomes inapplicable. Solutions of several problems of this kind, expressed in terms of the normal functions for the compound system consisting of the rod and the striking body, were given by Saint-Venant[118].

Among problems of dynamical resistance we must note especially Willis's problem of the travelling load. When a train crosses a bridge, the strain is not identical with the statical strain which is produced when the same train is standing on the bridge. To illustrate the problem thus presented Willis[119] proposed to consider the bridge as a straight wire and the train as a heavy particle deflecting it. Neglecting the inertia of the wire he obtained a certain differential equation, which was subsequently solved by Stokes[120]. Later writers have shown that the effects of the neglected inertia are very important. A more complete solution has been obtained by E. Phillips[121] and Saint-Venant[122], and an admirable *précis* of their results may be read

115 *Paris, C. R.*, t. 95 (1882).

116 *Applications des Potentiels...*, Paris, 1885. The results were given in a note in *Paris, C. R.*, t. 97 (1883).

117 In papers in *Paris, C. R.*, t. 97 (1883), reprinted as an appendix to his Translation of Clebsch's Treatise (Paris, 1883).

118 In the 'Annotated Clebsch' just cited, *Note du* § 61. Cf. Lord Rayleigh, *Theory of Sound*, Chapter VIII.

119 Appendix to the *Report of the Commissioners...to enquire into the Application of Iron to Railway Structures* (1849).

120 *Cambridge Phil. Soc. Trans.*, vol. 8 (1849), or Stokes, *Math. and Phys. Papers*, vol. 2 (Cambridge, 1883), p. 178.

121 *Paris, Ann. des Mines*, t. 7 (1855).

122 In the 'Annotated Clebsch,' *Note du* § 61.

in the second volume of Todhunter and Pearson's *History* (Articles 373 *et seq.*).

We have seen already how problems of the equilibrium and vibrations of plane plates and curved shells were attempted before the discovery of the general equations of Elasticity, and how these problems were among those which led to the investigation of such equations. After the equations had been formulated little advance seems to have been made in the treatment of the problem of shells for many years, but the more special problem of plates attracted much attention. Poisson[123] and Cauchy[124] both treated this problem, proceeding from the general equations of Elasticity, and supposing that all the quantities which occur can be expanded in powers of the distance from the middle-surface. The equations of equilibrium and free vibration which hold when the displacement is directed at right angles to the plane of the plate were deduced. Much controversy has arisen concerning Poisson's boundary conditions. These expressed that the resultant forces and couples applied at the edge must be equal to the forces and couples arising from the strain. In a famous memoir Kirchhoff[125] showed that these conditions are too numerous and cannot in general be satisfied. His method rests on two assumptions: (1) that linear filaments of the plate initially normal to the middle-surface remain straight and normal to the middle-surface after strain, and (2) that all the elements of the middle-surface remain unstretched. These assumptions enabled him to express the potential energy of the bent plate in terms of the curvatures produced in its middle-surface. The equations of motion and boundary conditions were then deduced by the principle of virtual work, and they were applied to the problem of the flexural vibrations of a circular plate.

The problem of plates can be attacked by means of considerations of the same kind as those which were used by Kirchhoff in his theory of thin rods. An investigation of the problem by this method was made by Gehring[126] and was afterwards adopted in an improved form by Kirchhoff[127]. The work is very similar in detail to that in Kirchhoff's theory of thin rods, and it leads to an expression for the potential energy per unit of area of the middle-surface of the plate. This expression consists of two parts: one a quadratic function of the quantities defining the extension of the middle-surface with a coefficient proportional to the thickness of the plate, and the other a quadratic function

123 In the memoir of 1828. A large part of the investigation is reproduced in Todhunter and Pearson's *History*.

124 In an Article 'Sur l'équilibre et le mouvement d'une plaque solide' in the *Exercices de mathématique*, vol. 3 (1828). Most of this Article also is reproduced by Todhunter and Pearson.

125 *J. f. Math.* (*Crelle*), Bd. 40 (1850).

126 'De Æquationibus differentialibus quibus æquilibrium et motus laminæ crystallinæ definiuntur' (Diss.), Berlin, 1860. The analysis may be read in Kirchhoff's *Vorlesungen über math. Phys.*, *Mechanik*, and parts of it also in Clebsch's Treatise.

127 *Vorlesungen über math. Phys.*, *Mechanik*.

of the quantities defining the flexure of the middle-surface with a coefficient proportional to the cube of the thickness. The equations of small motion are deduced by an application of the principle of virtual work. When the displacement of a point on the middle-surface is very small the flexure depends only on displacements directed at right angles to the plane of the plate, and the extension only on displacements directed parallel to the plane of the plate, and the equations fall into two sets. The equation of normal vibration and the boundary conditions are those previously found and discussed by Kirchhoff[125].

As in the theory of rods, so also in that of plates, attention is directed rather to tensions, shearing forces and flexural couples, reckoned across the whole thickness, than to the tractions across elements of area which give rise to such forces and couples. To fix ideas we may think of the plate as horizontal, and consider the actions exerted across an imagined vertical dividing plane, and on this plane we may mark out a small area by two vertical lines near together. The distance between these lines may be called the "breadth" of the area. The tractions across the elements of this area are statically equivalent to a force at the centroid of the area and a couple. When the "breadth" is very small, the magnitudes of the force and couple are proportional to the breadth, and we estimate them as so much per unit of length of the line in which our vertical dividing plane cuts the middle plane of the plate. The components of the force and couple thus estimated we call the "stress-resultants" and the "stress-couples." The stress-resultants consist of a tension at right angles to the plane of the area, a horizontal shearing force and a vertical shearing force. The stress-couples have a component about the normal to the dividing plane which we shall call the "torsional couple," and a component in the vertical plane containing this normal which we shall call the "flexural couple." The stress-resultants and stress-couples depend upon the direction of the dividing plane, but they are known for all such directions when they are known for two of them. Clebsch[53] adopted from the Kirchhoff-Gehring theory the approximate account of the strain and stress in a small portion of the plate bounded by vertical dividing planes, and he formed equations of equilibrium of the plate in terms of stress-resultants and stress-couples. His equations fall into two sets, one set involving the tensions and horizontal shearing forces, and the other set involving the stress-couples and the vertical shearing forces. The latter set of equations are those which relate to the bending of the plate, and they have such forms that, when the expressions for the stress-couples are known in terms of the deformation of the middle plane, the vertical shearing forces can be determined, and an equation can be formed for the deflexion of the plate. The expressions for the couples can be obtained from Kirchhoff's theory. Clebsch solved his equation for the deflexion of a circular plate clamped at the edge and loaded in an arbitrary manner.

All the theory of the equations of equilibrium in terms of stress-resultants and stress-couples was placed beyond the reach of criticism by Kelvin and Tait[54]. These authors noticed also, that, in the case of uniform bending, the expressions for the stress-couples could be deduced from Saint-Venant's theory of the anticlastic flexure of a bar; and they explained the union of two of Poisson's boundary conditions in one of Kirchhoff's as an example of the principle of the elastic equivalence of statically equipollent systems of load. More recent researches have assisted in removing the difficulties which had been felt in respect of Kirchhoff's theory[128]. One obstacle to progress has been the lack of exact solutions of problems of the bending of plates analogous to those found by Saint-Venant for beams. The few solutions of this kind which have been obtained[129] tend to confirm the main result of the theory which has not been proved rigorously, viz. the approximate expression of the stress-couples in terms of the curvature of the middle-surface.

The problem of curved plates or shells was first attacked from the point of view of the general equations of Elasticity by H. Aron[130]. He expressed the geometry of the middle-surface by means of two parameters after the manner of Gauss, and he adapted to the problem the method which Clebsch had used for plates. He arrived at an expression for the potential energy of the strained shell which is of the same form as that obtained by Kirchhoff for plates, but the quantities that define the curvature of the middle-surface were replaced by the differences of their values in the strained and unstrained states. E. Mathieu[131] adapted to the problem the method which Poisson had used for plates. He observed that the modes of vibration possible to a shell do not fall into classes characterized respectively by normal and tangential displacements, and he adopted equations of motion that could be deduced from Aron's formula for the potential energy by retaining the terms that depend on the stretching of the middle-surface only. Lord Rayleigh[132] proposed a different theory. He concluded from physical reasoning that the middle-surface of a vibrating shell remains unstretched, and determined the character of the displacement of a point of the middle-surface in accordance with this condition. The direct application of the Kirchhoff-Gehring method[133] led to a formula for the potential energy of the same form as Aron's and to equations of motion and boundary conditions which were difficult to reconcile with Lord Rayleigh's theory. Later investigations have shown that the extensional strain which

[128] See, for example, J. Boussinesq, *J. de Math.* (*Liouville*), (Sér. 2), t. 16 (1871) and (Sér. 3), t. 5 (1879): H. Lamb, *London Math. Soc. Proc.*, vol. 21 (1890); J. H. Michell, *London Math. Soc. Proc.*, vol. 31 (1900), p. 121; J. Hadamard, *Amer. Math. Soc. Trans.*, vol. 3 (1902).

[129] Some solutions were given by Saint-Venant in the 'Annotated Clebsch,' pp. 337 *et seq.* Others will be found in Chapter XXII of this book.

[130] *J. f. Math.* (*Crelle*), Bd. 78 (1874).

[131] *J. de l'École polytechnique*, t. 51 (1883).

[132] *London Math. Soc. Proc.*, vol. 13 (1882).

[133] A. E. H. Love, *Phil. Trans. Roy. Soc.* (Ser. A), vol. 179 (1888).

was thus proved to be a necessary concomitant of the vibrations may be practically confined to a narrow region near the edge of the shell, but that, in this region, it may be so adjusted as to secure the satisfaction of the boundary conditions while the greater part of the shell vibrates according to Lord Rayleigh's type.

Whenever very thin rods or plates are employed in constructions it becomes necessary to consider the possibility of buckling, and thus there arises the general problem of *elastic stability*. We have already seen that the first investigations of problems of this kind were made by Euler and Lagrange. A number of isolated problems have been solved. In all of them two modes of equilibrium with the same type of external forces are possible, and the ordinary proof[134] of the determinacy of the solution of the equations of Elasticity is defective. A general theory of elastic stability has been proposed by G. H. Bryan[135]. He arrived at the result that the theorem of determinacy cannot fail except in cases where large relative displacements can be accompanied by very small strains, as in thin rods and plates, and in cases where displacements differing but slightly from such as are possible in a rigid body can take place, as when a sphere is compressed within a circular ring of slightly smaller diameter. In all cases where two modes of equilibrium are possible the criterion for determining the mode that will be adopted is given by the condition that the energy must be a minimum.

The history of the mathematical theory of Elasticity shows clearly that the development of the theory has not been guided exclusively by considerations of its utility for technical Mechanics. Most of the men by whose researches it has been founded and shaped have been more interested in Natural Philosophy than in material progress, in trying to understand the world than in trying to make it more comfortable. From this attitude of mind it may possibly have resulted that the theory has contributed less to the material advance of mankind than it might otherwise have done. Be this as it may, the intellectual gain which has accrued from the work of these men must be estimated very highly. The discussions that have taken place concerning the number and meaning of the elastic constants have thrown light on most recondite questions concerning the nature of molecules and the mode of their interaction. The efforts that have been made to explain optical phenomena by means of the hypothesis of a medium having the same physical character as an elastic solid body led, in the first instance, to the understanding of a concrete example of a medium which can transmit transverse vibrations, and, at a later stage, to the definite conclusion that there is no luminiferous medium having the physical character assumed in the hypothesis. They have thus issued in an essential widening of our ideas concerning the nature of light. The methods that have been devised for solving the equations of equilibrium

[134] Kirchhoff, *Vorlesungen über math. Phys., Mechanik.*

[135] *Cambridge Phil. Soc. Proc.*, vol. 6 (1889), p. 199.

of an isotropic solid body form part of an analytical theory which is of great importance in pure mathematics. The application of these methods to the problem of the internal constitution of the Earth has led to results which must influence profoundly the course of speculative thought both in Geology and in cosmical Physics. Even in the more technical problems, such as the transmission of force and the resistance of bars and plates, attention has been directed, for the most part, rather to theoretical than to practical aspects of the questions. To get insight into what goes on in impact, to bring the theory of the behaviour of thin bars and plates into accord with the general equations —these and such-like aims have been more attractive to most of the men to whom we owe the theory than endeavours to devise means for effecting economies in engineering constructions or to ascertain the conditions in which structures become unsafe. The fact that much material progress is the indirect outcome of work done in this spirit is not without significance. The equally significant fact that most great advances in Natural Philosophy have been made by men who had a first-hand acquaintance with practical needs and experimental methods has often been emphasized; and, although the names of Green, Poisson, Cauchy show that the rule is not without important exceptions, yet it is exemplified well in the history of our science.

CHAPTER I

ANALYSIS OF STRAIN

1. Extension.

Whenever, owing to any cause, changes take place in the relative positions of the parts of a body the body is said to be "strained." A very simple example of a strained body is a stretched bar. Consider a bar of square section suspended vertically and loaded with a weight at its lower end. Let a line be traced on the bar in the direction of its length, let two points of the line be marked, and let the distance between these points be measured. When the weight is attached the distance in question is a little greater than it was before the weight was attached. Let l_0 be the length before stretching, and l the length when stretched. Then $(l-l_0)/l_0$ is a number (generally a very small fraction) which is called the *extension* of the line in question. If this number is the same for all lines parallel to the length of the bar, it may be called "the extension of the bar." A steel bar of sectional area 1 square inch (= 6·4515 cm.²) loaded with 1 ton (= 1016·05 kilogrammes) will undergo an extension of about 7×10^{-5}. It is clear that for the measurement of such small quantities as this rather elaborate apparatus and refined methods of observation are required*. Without attending to methods of measurement we may consider a little more in detail the state of strain in the stretched bar. Let e denote the extension of the bar, so that its length is increased in the ratio $1+e:1$, and consider the volume of the portion of the bar contained between any two marked sections. This volume is increased by stretching the bar, but not in the ratio $1+e:1$. When the bar is stretched longitudinally in contracts laterally. If the linear lateral contraction is e', the sectional area is diminished in the ratio $(1-e')^2:1$, and the volume in question is increased in the ratio $(1+e)(1-e')^2:1$. In the case of a bar under tension e' is a certain multiple of e, say σe, and σ is about $\frac{1}{3}$ or $\frac{1}{4}$ for very many materials. If e is very small and e^2 is neglected, the areal contraction is $2\sigma e$, and the cubical dilatation is $(1-2\sigma)\,e$.

For the analytical description of the state of strain in the bar we should take an origin of coordinates x, y, z on the axis, and measure the coordinate z along the length of the bar. Any particle of the bar which has the coordinates x, y, z when the weight is not attached will move after the attachment of the weight into a new position. Let the particle which was at the origin move through a distance z_0, then the particle which was at (x, y, z) moves to the point of which the coordinates are

$$x(1-\sigma e), \quad y(1-\sigma e), \quad z_0 + z(1+e).$$

* See, for example, Ewing, *Strength of Materials*, Cambridge, 1899, pp. 73 *et seq.*, or G. F. C. Searle, *Experimental Elasticity*, Cambridge, 1908.

The state of strain is not very simple. If lateral forces could be applied to the bar to prevent the lateral contraction the state of strain would be very much simplified. It would then be described as a "simple extension."

2. Pure shear.

As a second example of strain let us suppose that lateral forces are applied to the bar so as to produce extension of amount ϵ_1 of lines parallel to the axis of x and extension of amount ϵ_2 of lines parallel to the axis of y, and that longitudinal forces are applied, if any are required, to prevent any extension or contraction parallel to the axis of z. The particle which was at (x, y, z) will move to $(x+\epsilon_1 x,\ y+\epsilon_2 y,\ z)$ and the area of the section will be increased in the ratio $(1+\epsilon_1)(1+\epsilon_2):1$. If ϵ_1 and ϵ_2 are related so that this ratio is equal to unity there will be no change in the area of the section or in the volume of any portion of the bar, but the shape of the section will be distorted. Either ϵ_1 or ϵ_2 is then negative, or there is *contraction* of the corresponding set of lines. The strain set up in the bar is called "pure shear." Fig. 1 below shows a square $ABCD$ distorted by pure shear into a rhombus $A'B'C'D'$ of the same area.

3. Simple shear.

As a third example of strain let us suppose that the bar after being distorted by pure shear is turned bodily about its axis. We suppose that the axis of x is the direction in which contraction takes place, and we put

$$\epsilon_2 - \epsilon_1 = 2\tan\alpha.$$

Then we can show that, if the rotation is of amount α in the sense from y to x, the position reached by any particle is one that could have been reached by the sliding of all the particles in the direction of a certain line through distances proportional to the distances of the particles from a certain plane containing this line.

Since $(1+\epsilon_1)(1+\epsilon_2)=1$, and $\epsilon_2-\epsilon_1=2\tan\alpha$, we have

$$1+\epsilon_1=\sec\alpha-\tan\alpha, \quad 1+\epsilon_2=\sec\alpha+\tan\alpha.$$

By the pure shear, the particle which was at (x, y) is moved to (x_1, y_1), where

$$x_1=x(\sec\alpha-\tan\alpha), \quad y_1=y(\sec\alpha+\tan\alpha);$$

and by the rotation it is moved again to (x_2, y_2), where

$$x_2=x_1\cos\alpha+y_1\sin\alpha, \quad y_2=-x_1\sin\alpha+y_1\cos\alpha;$$

so that we have

$$x_2=x+\tan\alpha\{-x\cos\alpha+y(1+\sin\alpha)\},$$

$$y_2=y+\tan\alpha\{-x(1-\sin\alpha)+y\cos\alpha\}.$$

Now, writing β for $\frac{1}{2}\pi-\alpha$, we have

$$x_2=x+2\tan\alpha\cos\tfrac{1}{2}\beta\,(-x\sin\tfrac{1}{2}\beta+y\cos\tfrac{1}{2}\beta),$$

$$y_2=y+2\tan\alpha\sin\tfrac{1}{2}\beta\,(-x\sin\tfrac{1}{2}\beta+y\cos\tfrac{1}{2}\beta);$$

and we can observe that

$$-x_2\sin\tfrac{1}{2}\beta+y_2\cos\tfrac{1}{2}\beta=-x\sin\tfrac{1}{2}\beta+y\cos\tfrac{1}{2}\beta,$$

and that

$$x_2\cos\tfrac{1}{2}\beta+y_2\sin\tfrac{1}{2}\beta=x\cos\tfrac{1}{2}\beta+y\sin\tfrac{1}{2}\beta+2\tan\alpha\,(-x\sin\tfrac{1}{2}\beta+y\cos\tfrac{1}{2}\beta).$$

Hence, taking axes of X and Y which are obtained from those of x and y by a rotation through $\frac{1}{4}\pi - \frac{1}{2}\alpha$ in the sense from x towards y, we see that the particle which was at (X, Y) is moved by the pure shear followed by the rotation to the point (X_2, Y_2), where

$$X_2 = X + 2 \tan \alpha \, . \, Y, \qquad Y_2 = Y.$$

Thus every plane of the material which is parallel to the plane of (X, z) slides along itself in the direction of the axis of X through a distance proportional to the distance of the plane from the plane of (X, z). The kind of strain just described is called a "simple shear," the angle α is the "angle of the shear," and $2 \tan \alpha$ is the "amount of the shear."

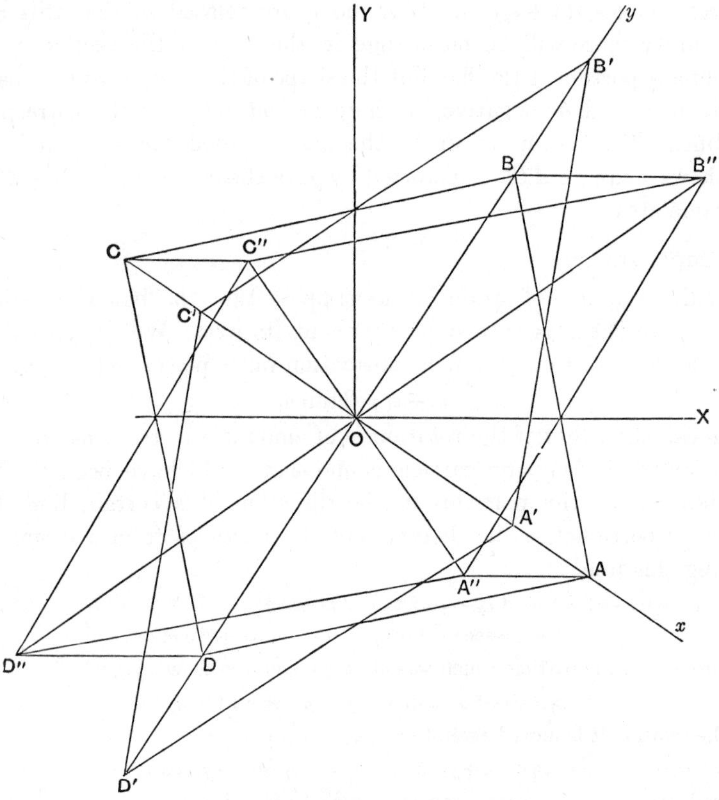

Fig. 1.

Fig. 1 shows a square $ABCD$ distorted by pure shear into a rhombus $A'B'C'D'$ of the same area, which is then rotated into the position $A''B''C''D''$. The angle of the shear is $A'OA''$, and the angle AOX is half the complement of this angle. The lines AA'', BB'', CC'', DD'' are parallel to OX and proportional to their distances from it.

We shall find that all kinds of strain can be described in terms of simple extension and simple shear, but for the discussion of complex states of strain and for the expression of them by means of simpler strains we require a general kinematical theory*.

4. Displacement.

We have, in every case, to distinguish two states of a body—a first state and a second state. The particles of the body pass from their positions in the first state to their positions in the second state by a *displacement.* The displacement may be such that the line joining any two particles of the body has the same length in the second state as it has in the first; the displacement is then one which would be possible in a rigid body. If the displacement alters the length of any line, the second state of the body is described as a "strained state," and then the first state is described as the "unstrained state."

In what follows we shall denote the coordinates of the point occupied by a particle, in the unstrained state of the body, by x, y, z, and the coordinates of the point occupied by the same particle in the strained state by

$$x+u, \quad y+v, \quad z+w.$$

Then u, v, w are the projections on the axes of a vector quantity—the displacement. We must take u, v, w to be continuous functions of x, y, z, and we shall in general assume that they are analytic functions.

It is clear that, if the displacement (u, v, w) is given, the strained state is entirely determined; in particular, the length of the line joining any two particles can be determined.

5. Displacement in simple extension and simple shear.

The displacement in a simple extension parallel to the axis of x is given by the equations

$$u=ex, \quad v=0, \quad w=0.$$

where e is the amount of the extension. If e is negative there is *contraction.*

The displacement in a simple shear of amount $s\ (=2\tan a)$, by which lines parallel to the axis of x slide along themselves, and particles in any plane parallel to the plane of (x, y) remain in that plane, is given by the equations

$$u=sy, \quad v=0, \quad w=0.$$

In Fig. 2, AB is a segment of a line parallel to the axis of x, which subtends an angle $2a$ at O and is bisected by Oy. By the simple shear particles lying on the line OA are displaced so as to lie on OB. The particle at any point P on AB is displaced to Q on AB so that $PQ=AB$, and the particles on OP are displaced to points on OQ. A parallelogram such as $OPNM$ becomes a parallelogram such as $OQKM$.

If the angle $xOP=\theta$ we may prove that

$$\tan POQ=\frac{2\tan a\tan^2\theta}{\sec^2\theta+2\tan a\tan\theta}, \qquad \tan xOQ=\frac{\tan\theta}{1+2\tan a\tan\theta}.$$

In particular, if $\theta=\frac{1}{2}\pi$, $\cot xOQ=s$, so that, if s is small, it is the complement of the angle

* The greater part of the theory is due to Cauchy (see Introduction). Some improvements were made by Clebsch in his treatise of 1862, and others were made by Kelvin and Tait, *Nat. Phil.*, Part I.

in the strained state between two lines of particles which, in the unstrained state, were at right angles to each other.

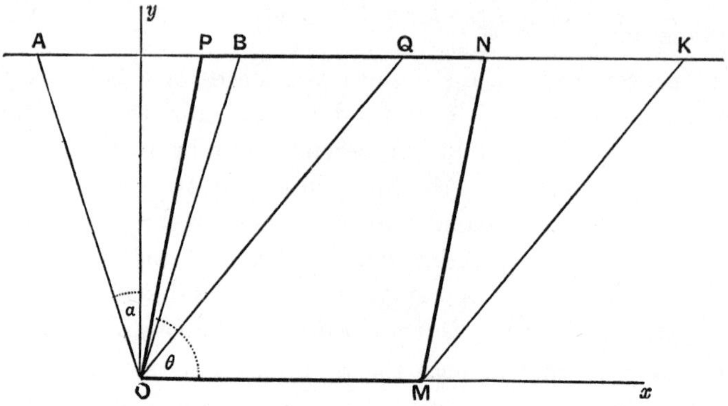

Fig. 2.

6. Homogeneous strain.

In the cases of simple extension and simple shear, the component displacements are expressed as linear functions of the coordinates. In general, if a body is strained so that the component displacement can be expressed in this way, the strain is said to be *homogeneous*.

Let the displacement corresponding with a homogeneous strain be given by the equations

$$u = a_{11}x + a_{12}y + a_{13}z, \qquad v = a_{21}x + a_{22}y + a_{23}z, \qquad w = a_{31}x + a_{32}y + a_{33}z.$$

Since x, y, z are changed into $x+u$, $y+v$, $z+w$, that is, are transformed by a linear substitution, any plane is transformed into a plane, and any ellipsoid is transformed, in general, into an ellipsoid. We infer at once the following characteristics of homogeneous strain:—(i) Straight lines remain straight. (ii) Parallel straight lines remain parallel. (iii) All straight lines in the same direction are extended, or contracted, in the same ratio. (iv) A sphere is transformed into an ellipsoid, and any three orthogonal diameters of the sphere are transformed into three conjugate diameters of the ellipsoid. (v) Any ellipsoid of a certain shape and orientation is transformed into a sphere, and any set of conjugate diameters of the ellipsoid is transformed into a set of orthogonal diameters of the sphere. (vi) There is one set of three orthogonal lines in the unstrained state which remain orthogonal after the strain; the directions of these lines are in general altered by the strain. In the unstrained state they are the principal axes of the ellipsoid referred to in (v); in the strained state, they are the principal axes of the ellipsoid referred to in (iv).

The ellipsoid referred to in (iv) is called the *strain ellipsoid*; it has the property that the ratio of the length of a line, which has a given direction in the strained state, to the length of the corresponding line in the unstrained state, is proportional to the central radius vector of the surface drawn in the given direction. The ellipsoid referred to in (v) may be called the *reciprocal strain ellipsoid*; it has the property that the length of a line, which has a given direction in the unstrained state, is increased by the strain in a ratio inversely proportional to the central radius vector of the surface drawn in the given direction.

The principal axes of the reciprocal strain ellipsoid are called the *principal axes of the strain*. The extensions of lines drawn in these directions, in the unstrained state, are stationary for small variations of direction. One of them is the greatest extension, and another the smallest.

7. Relative displacement.

Proceeding now to the general case, in which the strain is not necessarily homogeneous, we take $(x+\mathbf{x},\ y+\mathbf{y},\ z+\mathbf{z})$ to be a point near to (x, y, z), and $(u+\mathbf{u},\ v+\mathbf{v},\ w+\mathbf{w})$ to be the corresponding displacement. There will be expressions for the components $\mathbf{u}, \mathbf{v}, \mathbf{w}$ of the relative displacement as series in powers of $\mathbf{x}, \mathbf{y}, \mathbf{z}$, viz. we have

$$\left.\begin{aligned} \mathbf{u} &= \mathbf{x}\frac{\partial u}{\partial x} + \mathbf{y}\frac{\partial u}{\partial y} + \mathbf{z}\frac{\partial u}{\partial z} + \ldots, \\ \mathbf{v} &= \mathbf{x}\frac{\partial v}{\partial x} + \mathbf{y}\frac{\partial v}{\partial y} + \mathbf{z}\frac{\partial v}{\partial z} + \ldots, \\ \mathbf{w} &= \mathbf{x}\frac{\partial w}{\partial x} + \mathbf{y}\frac{\partial w}{\partial y} + \mathbf{z}\frac{\partial w}{\partial z} + \ldots, \end{aligned}\right\} \qquad \text{.....................(1)}$$

where the terms that are not written contain powers of $\mathbf{x}, \mathbf{y}, \mathbf{z}$ above the first. When $\mathbf{x}, \mathbf{y}, \mathbf{z}$ are sufficiently small, the latter terms may be neglected. The quantities $\mathbf{u}, \mathbf{v}, \mathbf{w}$ are the displacements of a particle which, in the unstrained state, is at $(x+\mathbf{x},\ y+\mathbf{y},\ z+\mathbf{z})$, relative to the particle which, in the same state, is at (x, y, z). We may accordingly say that, in a sufficiently small neighbourhood of any point, the relative displacements are linear functions of the relative coordinates. In other words, *the strain about any point is sensibly homogeneous.* All that we have said about the effects of homogeneous strain upon straight lines will remain true for linear elements going out from a point. In particular, there will be one set of three orthogonal linear elements, in the unstrained state, which remain orthogonal after the strain, but the directions of these lines are in general altered by the strain. The directions, in the unstrained state, of these linear elements at any point are the "principal axes of the strain" at the point.

8. Analysis of the relative displacement*.

In the discussion of the formulæ (1) we shall confine our attention to the

* Stokes, *Cambridge Phil. Soc. Trans.*, vol. 8 (1845), *Math. and Phys. Papers*, vol. 1, p. 75.

displacement near a point, and shall neglect terms in $\mathbf{x}$, $\mathbf{y}$, $\mathbf{z}$ above the first. It is convenient to introduce the following notations:

$$\left.\begin{aligned}
e_{xx}&=\frac{\partial u}{\partial x}, & e_{yy}&=\frac{\partial v}{\partial y}, & e_{zz}&=\frac{\partial w}{\partial z},\\
e_{yz}&=\frac{\partial w}{\partial y}+\frac{\partial v}{\partial z}, & e_{zx}&=\frac{\partial u}{\partial z}+\frac{\partial w}{\partial x}, & e_{xy}&=\frac{\partial v}{\partial x}+\frac{\partial u}{\partial y},\\
2\varpi_x&=\frac{\partial w}{\partial y}-\frac{\partial v}{\partial z}, & 2\varpi_y&=\frac{\partial u}{\partial z}-\frac{\partial w}{\partial x}, & 2\varpi_z&=\frac{\partial v}{\partial x}-\frac{\partial u}{\partial y}.
\end{aligned}\right\} \quad \text{.........(2)}$$

The formulæ (1) may then be written

$$\left.\begin{aligned}
\mathbf{u}&= e_{xx}\mathbf{x}+\tfrac{1}{2}e_{xy}\mathbf{y}+\tfrac{1}{2}e_{zx}\mathbf{z}-\varpi_z\mathbf{y}+\varpi_y\mathbf{z},\\
\mathbf{v}&=\tfrac{1}{2}e_{xy}\mathbf{x}+ e_{yy}\mathbf{y}+\tfrac{1}{2}e_{yz}\mathbf{z}-\varpi_x\mathbf{z}+\varpi_z\mathbf{x},\\
\mathbf{w}&=\tfrac{1}{2}e_{zx}\mathbf{x}+\tfrac{1}{2}e_{yz}\mathbf{y}+ e_{zz}\mathbf{z}-\varpi_y\mathbf{x}+\varpi_x\mathbf{y}.
\end{aligned}\right\} \quad \text{...............(3)}$$

The relative displacement is thus represented as the resultant of two displacements, expressed respectively by such forms as $e_{xx}\mathbf{x}+\frac{1}{2}e_{xy}\mathbf{y}+\frac{1}{2}e_{zx}\mathbf{z}$ and $-\varpi_z\mathbf{y}+\varpi_y\mathbf{z}$; and there is a fundamental kinematical distinction between the cases in which the latter displacement vanishes and the cases in which it does not vanish. When it vanishes, that is when ϖ_x, ϖ_y, ϖ_z vanish, the component displacements are the partial differential coefficients, with respect to the coordinates, of a single function ϕ, so that

$$u=\frac{\partial\phi}{\partial x},\qquad v=\frac{\partial\phi}{\partial y},\qquad w=\frac{\partial\phi}{\partial z},$$

and the line-integral of the tangential component of the displacement taken round any closed curve vanishes, provided that the curve can be contracted to a point without passing out of the space occupied by the body. Such a function as ϕ would be called a "displacement-potential." Through each point $(\mathbf{x}, \mathbf{y}, \mathbf{z})$ there passes one quadric surface of the family

$$e_{xx}\mathbf{x}^2+e_{yy}\mathbf{y}^2+e_{zz}\mathbf{z}^2+e_{yz}\mathbf{yz}+e_{zx}\mathbf{zx}+e_{xy}\mathbf{xy}=\text{const.} \quad \text{.........(4)}$$

and the displacement that is derived, as above, from a displacement-potential, is, at each point, directed along the normal to that surface of the family (4) which passes through the point. The linear elements that lie along the principal axes of these quadrics in the unstrained state continue to do so in the strained state, or the three orthogonal linear elements which remain orthogonal retain their primitive directions. The strain involved in such displacements is described as a "pure strain." We learn that the relative displacement is always compounded of a displacement involving a pure strain and a displacement represented by such expressions as $-\varpi_z\mathbf{y}+\varpi_y\mathbf{z}$. The line-integral of the latter displacement taken round a closed curve does not vanish (cf. Article 15, *infra*). If the quantities ϖ_x, ϖ_y, ϖ_z are small, the terms such as $-\varpi_z\mathbf{y}+\varpi_y\mathbf{z}$ represent a displacement that would be possible in a rigid body, viz. a small rotation of amount $\sqrt{(\varpi_x^2+\varpi_y^2+\varpi_z^2)}$ about an axis in direction $(\varpi_x : \varpi_y : \varpi_z)$. For this reason the displacement corresponding with a pure strain is often described as "irrotational."

9. Strain corresponding with small displacement*.

It is clear that the changes of size and shape of all parts of a body will be determined when the length, in the strained state, of every line is known. Let l, m, n be the direction cosines of a line going out from the point (x, y, z). Take a very short length r along this line, so that the coordinates of a neighbouring point on the line are $x+lr$, $y+mr$, $z+nr$. After strain the particle that was at (x, y, z) comes to $(x+u, y+v, z+w)$, and the particle that was at the neighbouring point comes to the point of which the coordinates are

$$\left.\begin{aligned} &x+lr+u+r\left(l\frac{\partial u}{\partial x}+m\frac{\partial u}{\partial y}+n\frac{\partial u}{\partial z}\right),\\ &y+mr+v+r\left(l\frac{\partial v}{\partial x}+m\frac{\partial v}{\partial y}+n\frac{\partial v}{\partial z}\right),\\ &z+nr+w+r\left(l\frac{\partial w}{\partial x}+m\frac{\partial w}{\partial y}+n\frac{\partial w}{\partial z}\right),\end{aligned}\right\}\qquad\text{.................. (5)}$$

provided r is so small that we may neglect its square. Let r_1 be the length after strain which corresponds with r before strain. Then we have

$$r_1^2=r^2\left[\left\{l\left(1+\frac{\partial u}{\partial x}\right)+m\frac{\partial u}{\partial y}+n\frac{\partial u}{\partial z}\right\}^2+\left\{l\frac{\partial v}{\partial x}+m\left(1+\frac{\partial v}{\partial y}\right)+n\frac{\partial v}{\partial z}\right\}^2 + \left\{l\frac{\partial w}{\partial x}+m\frac{\partial w}{\partial y}+n\left(1+\frac{\partial w}{\partial z}\right)\right\}^2\right].\qquad\text{............... (6)}$$

When the relative displacements are very small, and squares and products of such quantities as $\frac{\partial u}{\partial x}, \ldots$ can be neglected, this formula passes over into

$$r_1=r\,(1+e_{xx}l^2+e_{yy}m^2+e_{zz}n^2+e_{yz}mn+e_{zx}nl+e_{xy}lm),\qquad\text{...... (7)}$$

where the notation is the same as that in equations (2).

10. Components of strain†.

By the formula (7) we know the length r_1 of a line which, in the unstrained state, has an assigned short length r and an assigned direction (l, m, n), as soon as we know the values of the six quantities $e_{xx}, e_{yy}, e_{zz}, e_{yz}, e_{zx}, e_{xy}$. These six quantities are called the "components of strain." In the case of

* In the applications of the theory to strains in elastic solid bodies, the displacements that have to be considered are in general so small that squares and products of first differential coefficients of u, v, w with respect to x, y, z can be neglected in comparison with their first powers. The more general theory in which this simplification is not made will be discussed in the Appendix to this Chapter.

† When the relative displacement is not small the strain is not specified completely by the quantities $e_{xx}, \ldots e_{yz}, \ldots$. This matter is considered in the Appendix to this Chapter. Lord Kelvin has called attention to the unsymmetrical character of the strain-components here specified. Three of them, in fact, are extensions and the remaining three are shearing strains. He has worked out a symmetrical system of strain-components which would be the extensions of lines parallel to the edges of a tetrahedron. See *Edinburgh Roy. Soc. Proc.*, vol. 24 (1902), and *Phil. Mag.* (Ser. 6), vol. 3 (1902), pp. 95 and 444.

homogeneous strain they are constants; in the more general case they are variable from point to point of a body.

The extension e of the short line in direction (l, m, n) is given at once by (7) in the form

$$e = e_{xx}l^2 + e_{yy}m^2 + e_{zz}n^2 + e_{yz}mn + e_{zx}nl + e_{xy}lm, \quad \text{............(8)}$$

so that the three quantities e_{xx}, e_{yy}, e_{zz} are extensions of linear elements, which, in the unstrained state, are parallel to axes of coordinates.

Again let (l_1, m_1, n_1) be the direction in the strained state of a linear element which, in the unstrained state, has the direction (l, m, n), and let e be the corresponding extension, and let the same letters with accents refer to a second linear element and its extension. From the formulæ (5) it appears that

$$l_1 = \frac{r}{r_1}\left\{l\left(1 + \frac{\partial u}{\partial x}\right) + m\frac{\partial u}{\partial y} + n\frac{\partial u}{\partial z}\right\}$$

with similar expressions for m_1, n_1. The cosine of the angle between the two elements in the strained state is easily found in the form

$$\begin{aligned} l_1l_1' + m_1m_1' + n_1n_1' = (ll' + mm' + nn')(1 - e - e') + 2(e_{xx}ll' + e_{yy}mm' + e_{zz}nn') \\ + e_{yz}(mn' + m'n) + e_{zx}(nl' + n'l) + e_{xy}(lm' + l'm). \quad \text{.........(9)} \end{aligned}$$

If the two lines in the unstrained state are the axes of x and y the cosine of the angle between the corresponding lines in the strained state is e_{xy}. In like manner e_{yz} and e_{zx} are the cosines of the angles, in the strained state, between pairs of lines which, in the unstrained state, are parallel to pairs of axes of coordinates.

Another interpretation of the strain-components of type e_{xy} is afforded immediately by such equations as

$$e_{xy} = \frac{\partial v}{\partial x} + \frac{\partial u}{\partial y},$$

from which it appears that e_{xy} is made up of two simple shears. In one of these simple shears planes of the material which are at right angles to the axis of x slide in the direction of the axis of y, while in the other these axes are interchanged. The strain denoted by e_{xy} will be called the "shearing strain corresponding with the directions of the axes of x and y."

The change of volume of any small portion of the body can be expressed in terms of the components of strain. The ratio of corresponding very small volumes in the strained and unstrained states is expressed by the functional determinant

$$\begin{vmatrix} 1 + \frac{\partial u}{\partial x}, & \frac{\partial u}{\partial y}, & \frac{\partial u}{\partial z} \\ \frac{\partial v}{\partial x}, & 1 + \frac{\partial v}{\partial y}, & \frac{\partial v}{\partial z} \\ \frac{\partial w}{\partial x}, & \frac{\partial w}{\partial y}, & 1 + \frac{\partial w}{\partial z} \end{vmatrix},$$

and, when squares and products of $\partial u/\partial x, \ldots$ are neglected, this becomes $1 + \frac{\partial u}{\partial x} + \frac{\partial v}{\partial y} + \frac{\partial w}{\partial z}$, or say $1 + \Delta$. The quantity Δ which is defined by the equation

$$\Delta = e_{xx} + e_{yy} + e_{zz} = \frac{\partial u}{\partial x} + \frac{\partial v}{\partial y} + \frac{\partial w}{\partial z} \quad \text{.................(10)}$$

is the increment of volume per unit of volume, or the "cubical dilatation," often called the "dilatation."

With the introduction of the components of strain, the interpretation of these components and the expression of the cubical dilatation in terms of them, we have achieved a general kinematical theory of the strains that accompany small displacements. The rest of this Chapter will be devoted to theorems and methods, relating to small strains, which will be useful in the development of the theory of Elasticity.

11. The Strain Quadric.

Through any point in the neighbourhood of (x, y, z) there passes one, and only one, quadric surface of the family

$$e_{xx}\mathbf{x}^2 + e_{yy}\mathbf{y}^2 + e_{zz}\mathbf{z}^2 + e_{yz}\mathbf{yz} + e_{zx}\mathbf{zx} + e_{xy}\mathbf{xy} = \text{const.} \quad \text{......(4 } bis\text{)}$$

Any one of these quadrics is called a *strain quadric*; such a surface has the property that the reciprocal of the square of its central radius vector in any direction is proportional to the extension of a line in that direction.

If the quadric is an ellipsoid, all lines issuing from the point (x, y, z) are extended or else all are contracted; if the quadric is an hyperboloid, some lines are extended and others contracted; and these sets of lines are separated by the common asymptotic cone of the surfaces. Lines which undergo no extension or contraction are generators of this cone.

The directions of lines, in the unstrained state, for which the extension is a maximum or a minimum, or is stationary without being a true maximum or minimum, are the principal axes of the quadrics (4). These axes are therefore the principal axes of the strain (Article 7), and the extensions in the directions of these axes are the "principal extensions." When the quadrics are referred to their principal axes, the left-hand member of (4) takes the form

$$e_1 X^2 + e_2 Y^2 + e_3 Z^2,$$

wherein the coefficients e_1, e_2, e_3 are the values of the principal extensions.

We now see that, in order to specify completely a state of strain, we require to know the directions of the principal axes of the strain, and the magnitudes of the principal extensions at each point of the body. With the point we may associate a certain quadric surface which enables us to express the strain at the point.

The directions of the principal axes of the strain are determined as follows:—let l, m, n be the direction cosines of one of these axes, then we have

$$\frac{e_{xx}l+\frac{1}{2}e_{xy}m+\frac{1}{2}e_{zx}n}{l}=\frac{\frac{1}{2}e_{xy}l+e_{yy}m+\frac{1}{2}e_{yz}n}{m}=\frac{\frac{1}{2}e_{zx}l+\frac{1}{2}e_{yz}m+e_{zz}n}{n},$$

and, if e is written for either of these three quantities, the three possible values of e are the roots of the equation

$$\begin{vmatrix} e_{xx}-e & \frac{1}{2}e_{xy} & \frac{1}{2}e_{zx} \\ \frac{1}{2}e_{xy} & e_{yy}-e & \frac{1}{2}e_{yz} \\ \frac{1}{2}e_{zx} & \frac{1}{2}e_{yz} & e_{zz}-e \end{vmatrix}=0;$$

these roots are real, and they are the values of the principal extensions e_1, e_2, e_3.

12. Transformation of the components of strain.

The same state of strain may be specified by means of its components referred to any system of rectangular axes; and the components referred to any one system must therefore be determinate when the components referred to some other system, and the relative situation of the two systems, are known. The determination can be made at once by using the property of the strain quadric, viz. that the reciprocal of the square of the radius vector in any direction is proportional to the extension of a line in that direction. We shall take the coordinates of a point referred to the first system of axes to be, as before, x, y, z, and those of the same point referred to the second system of axes to be x', y', z', and we shall suppose the second system to be connected with the first by the orthogonal scheme

	x	y	z
x'	l_1	m_1	n_1
y'	l_2	m_2	n_2
z'	l_3	m_3	n_3

Further we shall suppose that the determinant of the transformation is 1 (not -1), so that the second system can be derived from the first by an operation of rotation*. We shall write $e_{x'x'}$, $e_{y'y'}$, $e_{z'z'}$, $e_{y'z'}$, $e_{z'x'}$, $e_{x'y'}$ for the components of strain referred to the second system.

The relative coordinates of points in the neighbourhood of a given point may be denoted by $\mathbf{x}$, $\mathbf{y}$, $\mathbf{z}$ in the first system and $\mathbf{x}'$, $\mathbf{y}'$, $\mathbf{z}'$ in the second system. These quantities are transformed by the same substitutions as x, y, z and x', y', z'.

When the form

$$e_{xx}\mathbf{x}^2+e_{yy}\mathbf{y}^2+e_{zz}\mathbf{z}^2+e_{yz}\mathbf{yz}+e_{zx}\mathbf{zx}+e_{xy}\mathbf{xy}$$

* This restriction makes no difference to the relations between the components of strain referred to the two systems. It affects the components of rotation ϖ_x, ϖ_y, ϖ_z.

is transformed by the above substitution, it becomes

$$e_{x'x'}\mathbf{x}'^2+e_{y'y'}\mathbf{y}'^2+e_{z'z'}\mathbf{z}'^2+e_{y'z'}\mathbf{y}'\mathbf{z}'+e_{z'x'}\mathbf{z}'\mathbf{x}'+e_{x'y'}\mathbf{x}'\mathbf{y}'.$$

It follows that

$$\left.\begin{aligned} e_{x'x'} &= e_{xx}l_1^2+e_{yy}m_1^2+e_{zz}n_1^2+e_{yz}m_1n_1+e_{zx}n_1l_1+e_{xy}l_1m_1,\\ &\dots\\ e_{y'z'} &= 2e_{xx}l_2l_3+2e_{yy}m_2m_3+2e_{zz}n_2n_3+e_{yz}(m_2n_3+m_3n_2)\\ &\quad+e_{zx}(n_2l_3+n_3l_2)+e_{xy}(l_2m_3+l_3m_2),\\ &\dots \end{aligned}\right\} \qquad\dots\dots(11)$$

These are the formulæ of transformation of strain-components.

13. Additional methods and results.

(*a*) The formulæ (11) might have been inferred from the interpretation of $e_{x'x'}$ as the extension of a linear element parallel to the axis of x', and of $e_{y'z'}$ as the cosine of the angle between the positions after strain of the linear elements which before strain are parallel to the axes of y' and z'.

(*b*) The formulæ (11) might also have been obtained by introducing the displacement (u', v', w') referred to the axes of (x', y', z'), and forming $\partial u'/\partial x',\dots$. The displacement being a vector, u, v, w are cogredient with x, y, z, and we have for example

$$e_{x'x'}=\frac{\partial u'}{\partial x'}=\frac{\partial}{\partial x'}(l_1u+m_1v+n_1w)=\left(l_1\frac{\partial}{\partial x}+m_1\frac{\partial}{\partial y}+n_1\frac{\partial}{\partial z}\right)(l_1u+m_1v+n_1w)$$

$$=l_1^2\frac{\partial u}{\partial x}+m_1^2\frac{\partial v}{\partial y}+n_1^2\frac{\partial w}{\partial z}+m_1n_1\left(\frac{\partial w}{\partial y}+\frac{\partial v}{\partial z}\right)+n_1l_1\left(\frac{\partial u}{\partial z}+\frac{\partial w}{\partial x}\right)+l_1m_1\left(\frac{\partial v}{\partial x}+\frac{\partial u}{\partial y}\right).$$

This method may be applied to the transformation of $\varpi_x, \varpi_y, \varpi_z$. We should find for example

$$\varpi_{x'}=l_1\varpi_x+m_1\varpi_y+n_1\varpi_z, \qquad\dots\dots(12)$$

and we might hence infer the vectorial character of $(\varpi_x, \varpi_y, \varpi_z)$. The same inference might be drawn from the interpretation of $\varpi_x, \varpi_y, \varpi_z$ as components of rotation.

(*c*) According to a well-known theorem* concerning the transformation of quadratic expressions, the following quantities are invariant in respect of transformations from one set of rectangular axes to another:

$$\left.\begin{aligned} &e_{xx}+e_{yy}+e_{zz},\\ &e_{yy}e_{zz}+e_{zz}e_{xx}+e_{xx}e_{yy}-\tfrac{1}{4}(e_{yz}^2+e_{zx}^2+e_{xy}^2),\\ &e_{xx}e_{yy}e_{zz}+\tfrac{1}{4}(e_{yz}e_{zx}e_{xy}-e_{xx}e_{yz}^2-e_{yy}e_{zx}^2-e_{zz}e_{xy}^2). \end{aligned}\right\} \qquad\dots\dots(13)$$

The first of these invariants is the expression for the cubical dilatation.

(*d*) It may be shown directly that the following quantities are invariants:

(i) $\varpi_x^2+\varpi_y^2+\varpi_z^2$,

(ii) $e_{xx}\varpi_x^2+e_{yy}\varpi_y^2+e_{zz}\varpi_z^2+e_{yz}\varpi_y\varpi_z+e_{zx}\varpi_z\varpi_x+e_{xy}\varpi_x\varpi_y$;

and the direct verification may serve as an exercise for the student. These invariants could be inferred from the fact that $\varpi_x, \varpi_y, \varpi_z$ are cogredient with x, y, z.

(*e*) It may be shown also that the following quantities are invariants†:

(iii) $\left(\frac{\partial w}{\partial y}\frac{\partial v}{\partial z}-\frac{\partial w}{\partial z}\frac{\partial v}{\partial y}\right)+\left(\frac{\partial u}{\partial z}\frac{\partial w}{\partial x}-\frac{\partial u}{\partial x}\frac{\partial w}{\partial z}\right)+\left(\frac{\partial v}{\partial x}\frac{\partial u}{\partial y}-\frac{\partial v}{\partial y}\frac{\partial u}{\partial x}\right)$,

(iv) $e_{xx}^2+e_{yy}^2+e_{zz}^2+\tfrac{1}{2}(e_{yz}^2+e_{zx}^2+e_{xy}^2)+2(\varpi_x^2+\varpi_y^2+\varpi_z^2)$.

* Salmon, *Geometry of three dimensions*, 4th ed., Dublin, 1882, p. 66.

† The invariant (iii) will be used in a subsequent investigation (Chapter VII).

(*f*) It may be shown* also that, in the notation of Article 7, the invariant (iv) is equal to

$$3\frac{\iiint(\mathbf{u}^2+\mathbf{v}^2+\mathbf{w}^2)\,d\mathbf{x}\,d\mathbf{y}\,d\mathbf{z}}{\iiint(\mathbf{x}^2+\mathbf{y}^2+\mathbf{z}^2)\,d\mathbf{x}\,d\mathbf{y}\,d\mathbf{z}},$$

where the integrations are taken through a very small sphere with its centre at the point (x, y, z).

(*g*) The following result is of some importance†:—If the strain can be expressed by shears e_{zx}, e_{yz} only, the remaining components being zero, then the strain is a shearing strain $e_{zx'}$; and the magnitude of this shear, and the direction of the axis x' in the plane of x, y, are to be found from e_{zx} and e_{yz} by treating these quantities as the projections of a vector on the axes of x and y.

14. Types of strain.

(*a*) *Uniform dilatation.*

When the strain quadric is a sphere, the principal axes of the strain are indeterminate, and the extension (or contraction) of all linear elements issuing from a point is the same; or we have

$$e_{xx}=e_{yy}=e_{zz}=\tfrac{1}{3}\Delta, \quad e_{yz}=e_{zx}=e_{xy}=0,$$

where Δ is the cubical dilatation, and the axes of x, y, z are any three orthogonal lines. In this case the linear extension in any direction is one-third of the cubical dilatation—a result which does not hold in general.

(*b*) *Simple extension.*

We may exemplify the use of the methods and formulæ of Article 12 by finding the components, referred to the axes of x, y, z, of a strain which is a simple extension, of amount e, parallel to the direction (l, m, n). If this direction were that of the axis of x' the form (4) would be $e\mathbf{x}'^2$; and we have therefore

$$e_{xx}=el^2, \quad e_{yy}=em^2, \quad e_{zz}=en^2,$$
$$e_{yz}=2emn, \quad e_{zx}=2enl, \quad e_{xy}=2elm.$$

A simple extension is accordingly equivalent to a strain specified by these six components.

It has been proposed‡ to call any kind of quantity, related to directions, which is equivalent to components in the same way as a simple extension, a *tensor*. Any strain is, as we have already seen, equivalent to three simple extensions parallel to the principal axes of the strain. It has been proposed to call any kind of quantity, related to directions, which is equivalent to components in the same way as a strain, a *tensor-triad*. The discussion in Articles 12 and 13 (*b*) brings out clearly the distinction between tensors and vectors.

In the theory of tensors§, as developed by Ricci and Levi-Civita, the components of strain $e_{xx}, \dots e_{yz}, \dots$ are not components of a tensor, but $e_{yz}, \dots$ must be given the coefficient $\frac{1}{2}$. There is a tensor whose components are expressed approximately by $e_{xx}, \dots \frac{1}{2}e_{yz}, \dots$ when terms of the second order in the first differential coefficients of u, v, w are neglected.

* E. Betti, *Il Nuovo Cimento* (Ser. 2), t. 7 (1872).

† Cf. Chapter XIV *infra*.

‡ W. Voigt, *Göttingen Nachr.* (1900), p. 117. Cf. M. Abraham in *Ency. d. math. Wiss.*, Bd. 4, Art. 14.

§ Reference may be made to A. S. Eddington, *Mathematical Theory of Relativity*, Cambridge, 1923, Ch. II.

(c) *Shearing strain.*

The strain denoted by e_{xy} is called "the shearing strain corresponding with the directions of the axes of x and y." We have already observed that it is equal to the cosine of the angle, in the strained state, between two linear elements which, in the unstrained state, are parallel to these axes, and that it is equivalent to two simple shears, consisting of the relative sliding, parallel to each of these directions, of planes at right angles to the other. The "shearing strain" is measured by the sum of the two simple shears and is independent of their ratio. The change in the length of any line and the change in the angle between any two lines depend upon the sum of the two simple shears and not on the ratio of their amounts.

The components of a strain, which is a shearing strain corresponding with the directions of the axes of x' and y', are given by the equations

$$e_{xx}=sl_1l_2, \qquad e_{yy}=sm_1m_2, \qquad e_{zz}=sn_1n_2,$$
$$e_{yz}=s(m_1n_2+m_2n_1), \quad e_{zx}=s(n_1l_2+n_2l_1), \quad e_{xy}=s(l_1m_2+l_2m_1),$$

where s is the amount of the shearing strain. The strain involves no cubical dilatation.

If we take the axes of x' and y' to be in the plane of x, y, and suppose that the axes of x, y, z are parallel to the principal axes of the strain, we find that e_{zz} vanishes, or there is no extension at right angles to the plane of the two directions concerned. In this case we have the form $sx'y'$ equivalent to the form $e_{xx}x^2+e_{yy}y^2$. It follows that $e_{xx}=-e_{yy}=\pm\frac{1}{2}s$, and that the principal axes of the strain bisect the angles between the two directions concerned. In other words equal extension and contraction of two linear elements at right angles to each other are equivalent to shearing strain, which is numerically equal to twice the extension or contraction, and corresponds with directions bisecting the angles between the elements.

We may enquire how to choose two directions so that the shearing strain corresponding with them may be as great as possible. It may be shown that the greatest shearing strain is equal to the difference between the algebraically greatest and least principal extensions, and that the corresponding directions bisect the angles between those principal axes of the strain for which the extensions are the maximum and minimum extensions*.

(d) *Plane strain.*

A more general type, which includes simple extension and shearing strain as particular cases, is obtained by assuming that *one* of the principal extensions is zero. If the corresponding principal axis is the axis of z, the strain quadric becomes a cylinder, standing on a conic in the plane of $\mathbf{x}$, $\mathbf{y}$, which may be called the strain conic; and its equation can be written

$$e_{xx}\mathbf{x}^2+e_{yy}\mathbf{y}^2+e_{xy}\mathbf{xy}=\text{const.};$$

so that the shearing strains e_{yz} and e_{zx} vanish, as well as the extension e_{zz}. In the particular case of simple extension, the conic consists of two parallel lines; in the case of shearing strain, it is a rectangular hyperbola. If it is a circle, there is extension or contraction, of the same amount, of all linear elements issuing from the point (x, y, z) in directions at right angles to the axis of z.

The relative displacement corresponding with plane strain is parallel to the plane of the strain; or we have $w=$const., while u and v are functions of x and y only. The axis of the resultant rotation is normal to the plane of the strain. The cubical dilatation, Δ, and the rotation, ϖ, are connected with the displacement by the equations

$$\Delta=\frac{\partial u}{\partial x}+\frac{\partial v}{\partial y}, \qquad 2\varpi=\frac{\partial v}{\partial x}-\frac{\partial u}{\partial y}.$$

* The theorem here stated is due to W. Hopkins, *Cambridge Phil. Soc. Trans.*, vol. 8 (1849).

We can have states of plane strain for which both Δ and ϖ vanish; the strain is pure shear, i.e. shearing strain combined with such a rotation that the principal axes of the strain retain their primitive directions. In any such state the displacement components v, u are conjugate functions of x and y, or $v+\iota u$ is a function of the complex variable $x+\iota y$.

15. Relations connecting the dilatation, the rotation and the displacement.

The cubical dilatation Δ is connected with the displacement (u, v, w) by the equation

$$\Delta=\frac{\partial u}{\partial x}+\frac{\partial v}{\partial y}+\frac{\partial w}{\partial z}.$$

A scalar quantity derived from a vector by means of this formula is described as the *divergence* of the vector. We write

$$\Delta=\operatorname{div}(u, v, w). \qquad \text{...(14)}$$

This relation is independent of coordinates, and may be expressed as follows:—Let any closed surface S be drawn in the field of the vector, and let N denote the projection of the vector on the normal drawn outwards at any point on S, also let $d\tau$ denote any element of volume within S, then

$$\iint N dS=\iiint \Delta d\tau, \qquad \text{...(15)}$$

the integration on the right-hand side being taken through the volume within S, and that on the left being taken over the surface S*.

The rotation $(\varpi_x, \varpi_y, \varpi_z)$ is connected with the displacement (u, v, w) by the equations

$$2\varpi_x=\frac{\partial w}{\partial y}-\frac{\partial v}{\partial z}, \quad 2\varpi_y=\frac{\partial u}{\partial z}-\frac{\partial w}{\partial x}, \quad 2\varpi_z=\frac{\partial v}{\partial x}-\frac{\partial u}{\partial y}.$$

A vector quantity derived from another vector by the process here indicated is described as the *curl* of the other vector. We write

$$2(\varpi_x, \varpi_y, \varpi_z)=\operatorname{curl}(u, v, w). \qquad \text{.............................(16)}$$

This relation is independent of coordinates†, and may be expressed as follows:—Let any closed curve s be drawn in the field of the vector, and let any surface S be described so as to have the curve s for an edge; let T be the resolved part of the vector (u, v, w) along the tangent at any point of s, and let $2\varpi_\nu$ be the projection of the vector $2(\varpi_x, \varpi_y, \varpi_z)$ on the normal at any point of S, then

$$\int T ds=\iint 2\varpi_\nu dS, \qquad \text{...................................(17)}$$

the integration on the right being taken over the surface S, and that on the left being taken along the curve s‡.

16. Resolution of any strain into dilatation and shearing strains.

When the strain involves no cubical dilatation the invariant $e_{xx}+e_{yy}+e_{zz}$ vanishes, and it is possible to choose rectangular axes of x', y', z' so that the form

$$e_{xx}x^2+e_{yy}y^2+e_{zz}z^2+e_{yz}yz+e_{zx}zx+e_{xy}xy$$

* The result is a particular case of the theorem known as "Green's theorem." See *Ency. d. math. Wiss.* II. A 2, Nos. 45—47.

† It is assumed that the axes of x, y, z form a right-handed system. If a transformation to a left-handed system is admitted a convention must be made as to the sign of the curl of a vector.

‡ The result is generally attributed to Stokes. Cf. *Ency. d. math. Wiss.* II. A 2, No. 46. It implies that there is a certain relation between the sense in which the integration along ds is taken and that in which the normal ν is drawn. This relation is the same as the relation of rotation to translation in a right-handed screw.

is transformed into the form

$$e_{y'z'}y'z' + e_{z'x'}z'x' + e_{x'y'}x'y',$$

in which there are no terms in x'^2, y'^2, z'^2. The strain is then equivalent to shearing strains corresponding with the pairs of directions

$$(y', z'),\quad (z', x'),\quad (x', y').$$

When the strain involves cubical dilatation the displacement can be analysed into two constituent displacements, in such a way that the cubical dilatation corresponding with one of them is zero; the strains derived from this constituent are shearing strains only, when the axes of reference are chosen suitably. The displacement which gives rise to the cubical dilatation is the gradient* of a scalar potential (ϕ), and the remaining part of the displacement is the curl of a vector potential (F, G, H), of which the divergence vanishes. To prove this statement we have to show that any vector (u, v, w) can be expressed in the form

$$(u, v, w) = \text{gradient of } \phi + \text{curl}\,(F, G, H), \qquad \text{............(18)}$$

involving the three equations of the type

$$u = \frac{\partial\phi}{\partial x} + \frac{\partial H}{\partial y} - \frac{\partial G}{\partial z}, \qquad \text{..........................(19)}$$

in which F, G, H satisfy the equation

$$\frac{\partial F}{\partial x} + \frac{\partial G}{\partial y} + \frac{\partial H}{\partial z} = 0. \qquad \text{..........................(20)}$$

In the case of displacement in a body this resolution must be valid at all points within the surface bounding the body.

There are many different ways of effecting this resolution of (u, v, w)†. We observe that if it is effected the dilatation and rotation will be expressed in the forms

$$\Delta = \nabla^2\phi,\quad 2\varpi_x = -\nabla^2 F,\quad 2\varpi_y = -\nabla^2 G,\quad 2\varpi_z = -\nabla^2 H, \quad \text{......(21)}$$

the last three holding good because $\partial F/\partial x + \partial G/\partial y + \partial H/\partial z = 0$. Now solutions of (21) can be written in the forms

$$\phi = -\frac{1}{4\pi}\iiint \frac{\Delta'}{r}\,dx'dy'dz',\quad F = \frac{1}{2\pi}\iiint \frac{\varpi_x'}{r}\,dx'dy'dz',\ \ldots \quad \text{...(22)}$$

where r is the distance between the point (x', y', z') and the point (x, y, z) at which ϕ, F, ... are estimated, Δ' and (ϖ_x', ϖ_y', ϖ_z') are the values of Δ and (ϖ_x, ϖ_y, ϖ_z) at the point (x', y', z'), and the integration extends through the body. But the solutions given in (22) do not always satisfy the equation $\text{div}\,(F, G, H) = 0$. A case in which they do satisfy this equation is presented

* The gradient of ϕ is the vector $\left(\frac{\partial\phi}{\partial x}, \frac{\partial\phi}{\partial y}, \frac{\partial\phi}{\partial z}\right)$.

† See, e.g., E. Betti, *Il Nuovo Cimento* (Ser. 2), t. 7 (1872), or P. Duhem, *J. de Math.* (*Liouville*), (Sér. 5), t. 6 (1900). The resolution was first effected by Stokes in his memoir on Diffraction. (See Introduction, footnote 80.)

when the body extends indefinitely in all directions, and the displacements at infinite distances tend to zero in the order r^{-2} at least. To see this we take the body to be bounded by a surface S, and write the first of equations (22), viz.

$$\phi = -\frac{1}{4\pi}\iiint\left(\frac{\partial u'}{\partial x'}+\frac{\partial v'}{\partial y'}+\frac{\partial w'}{\partial z'}\right)\frac{1}{r}\,dx'\,dy'\,dz',$$

in the equivalent form

$$\phi = -\frac{1}{4\pi}\iint\frac{1}{r}\{u'\cos(x,\nu)+v'\cos(y,\nu)+w'\cos(z,\nu)\}\,dS$$

$$+\frac{1}{4\pi}\iiint\left\{u'\frac{\partial r^{-1}}{\partial x'}+v'\frac{\partial r^{-1}}{\partial y'}+w'\frac{\partial r^{-1}}{\partial z'}\right\}dx'\,dy'\,dz',$$

and omit the surface-integral when S is infinitely distant. In the same case we may put

$$F = -\frac{1}{4\pi}\iiint\left(w'\frac{\partial r^{-1}}{\partial y'}-v'\frac{\partial r^{-1}}{\partial z'}\right)dx'\,dy'\,dz', \ldots$$

or, since $\partial r^{-1}/\partial x' = -\partial r^{-1}/\partial x, \ldots$ we have

$$F = \frac{\partial}{\partial y}\left\{\frac{1}{4\pi}\iiint\frac{w'}{r}\,dx'\,dy'\,dz'\right\}-\frac{\partial}{\partial z}\left\{\frac{1}{4\pi}\iiint\frac{v'}{r}\,dx'\,dy'\,dz'\right\}$$

with similar forms for G and H. From these forms it is clear that

$$\operatorname{div}(F, G, H) = 0.$$

The expressions into which the right-hand members of equations (22) have been transformed in the special case are possible forms for ϕ, F, G, H in every case, that is to say one mode of resolution is always given by the equations

$$\left.\begin{aligned}
\phi &= -\frac{1}{4\pi}\iiint\left(u'\frac{\partial r^{-1}}{\partial x}+v'\frac{\partial r^{-1}}{\partial y}+w'\frac{\partial r^{-1}}{\partial z}\right)dx'\,dy'\,dz',\\
F &= \frac{1}{4\pi}\iiint\left(w'\frac{\partial r^{-1}}{\partial y}-v'\frac{\partial r^{-1}}{\partial z}\right)dx'\,dy'\,dz',\\
G &= \frac{1}{4\pi}\iiint\left(u'\frac{\partial r^{-1}}{\partial z}-w'\frac{\partial r^{-1}}{\partial x}\right)dx'\,dy'\,dz',\\
H &= \frac{1}{4\pi}\iiint\left(v'\frac{\partial r^{-1}}{\partial x}-u'\frac{\partial r^{-1}}{\partial y}\right)dx'\,dy'\,dz',
\end{aligned}\right\} \quad \ldots\ldots\ldots(23)$$

where the integration extends throughout the body; for it is clear that these make $\operatorname{div}(F, G, H) = 0$ and also make

$$\frac{\partial\phi}{\partial x}+\frac{\partial H}{\partial y}-\frac{\partial G}{\partial z} = -\frac{1}{4\pi}\nabla^2\iiint\frac{u'}{r}\,dx'\,dy'\,dz' = u,$$

$$\ldots \qquad \ldots \qquad \ldots$$

$$\ldots \qquad \ldots \qquad \ldots$$

17. Identical relations between components of strain.

The components of strain $e_{xx}, \ldots, e_{yz}, \ldots$ cannot be given arbitrarily as functions of x, y, z, but are necessarily subject to such relations as follow from the expression of them in terms of displacement according to the formulæ

$$e_{xx} = \frac{\partial u}{\partial x}, \ \ldots, \ e_{yz} = \frac{\partial w}{\partial y} + \frac{\partial v}{\partial z}. \quad \ldots\ldots\ldots\ldots\ldots\ldots(24)$$

On substitution from (24) it will be seen that each of the six following equations (25) is satisfied identically:

$$\left.\begin{aligned} &\frac{\partial^2 e_{yy}}{\partial z^2} + \frac{\partial^2 e_{zz}}{\partial y^2} = \frac{\partial^2 e_{yz}}{\partial y \partial z}, \quad 2\frac{\partial^2 e_{xx}}{\partial y \partial z} = \frac{\partial}{\partial x}\left(-\frac{\partial e_{yz}}{\partial x} + \frac{\partial e_{zx}}{\partial y} + \frac{\partial e_{xy}}{\partial z}\right), \\ &\frac{\partial^2 e_{zz}}{\partial x^2} + \frac{\partial^2 e_{xx}}{\partial z^2} = \frac{\partial^2 e_{zx}}{\partial z \partial x}, \quad 2\frac{\partial^2 e_{yy}}{\partial z \partial x} = \frac{\partial}{\partial y}\left(\frac{\partial e_{yz}}{\partial x} - \frac{\partial e_{zx}}{\partial y} + \frac{\partial e_{xy}}{\partial z}\right), \\ &\frac{\partial^2 e_{xx}}{\partial y^2} + \frac{\partial^2 e_{yy}}{\partial x^2} = \frac{\partial^2 e_{xy}}{\partial x \partial y}, \quad 2\frac{\partial^2 e_{zz}}{\partial x \partial y} = \frac{\partial}{\partial z}\left(\frac{\partial e_{yz}}{\partial x} + \frac{\partial e_{zx}}{\partial y} - \frac{\partial e_{xy}}{\partial z}\right). \end{aligned}\right\} \ldots(25)$$

The above remark proves the *necessity* of the formulæ (25). Various proofs have been given that they are also *sufficient* to secure the existence of quantities u, v, w connected with e_{xx}, ... e_{yz}, ... by the formulæ (24). The simplest of these proofs introduces the components of rotation by the equations of the type

$$2\varpi_x = \frac{\partial w}{\partial y} - \frac{\partial v}{\partial z}.$$

All the first differential coefficients of u, v, w can then be expressed in terms of the nine quantities ϖ_x, ..., e_{xx}, ... e_{yz}, ... For example we have

$$\frac{\partial u}{\partial x} = e_{xx}, \quad \frac{\partial u}{\partial y} = \tfrac{1}{2}e_{xy} - \varpi_z, \quad \frac{\partial u}{\partial z} = \tfrac{1}{2}e_{zx} + \varpi_y.$$

The conditions of compatibility of these nine equations give six equations of the type

$$\frac{\partial e_{xx}}{\partial y} = \frac{1}{2}\frac{\partial e_{xy}}{\partial x} - \frac{\partial \varpi_z}{\partial x}$$

and three equations of the type

$$\frac{1}{2}\left(\frac{\partial e_{zx}}{\partial y} - \frac{\partial e_{xy}}{\partial z}\right) = -\frac{\partial \varpi_y}{\partial y} - \frac{\partial \varpi_z}{\partial z} = \frac{\partial \varpi_x}{\partial x}.$$

All the first differential coefficients of ϖ_x, ϖ_y, ϖ_z can thus be expressed in terms of those of e_{xx}, ... e_{yz}, ... For example we have

$$2\frac{\partial \varpi_x}{\partial x} = \frac{\partial e_{zx}}{\partial y} - \frac{\partial e_{xy}}{\partial z}, \quad 2\frac{\partial \varpi_x}{\partial y} = \frac{\partial e_{yz}}{\partial y} - 2\frac{\partial e_{yy}}{\partial z}, \quad 2\frac{\partial \varpi_x}{\partial z} = 2\frac{\partial e_{zz}}{\partial y} - \frac{\partial e_{yz}}{\partial z},$$

and the conditions of compatibility of these nine equations are the six equations (25).

The identical relations (25) between components of strain were obtained first by Saint-Venant* (1864) without introducing the components of rotation. The proof given above is due to Beltrami†. Another way of obtaining them can be worked out as an application of the theory of the transformation of quadratic differential forms. If dx, dy, dz are the

* See Introduction, footnote 73. Saint-Venant indicated a proof which was afterwards developed by Kirchhoff, *Mechanik*, Vorlesung 27.

† *Paris, C. R.*, t. 108 (1889), cf. Koenigs, *Leçons de Cinématique*, Paris, 1897, p. 411.

projections on the axes of a linear element in the unstrained state, and dx_1, dy_1, dz_1 are the projections on the axes of the same linear element in the strained state, equation (7) of Article 9 gives approximately

$$(1+2e_{xx})(dx)^2+(1+2e_{yy})(dy)^2+(1+2e_{zz})(dz)^2+2e_{yz}\,dy\,dz+2e_{zx}\,dz\,dx+2e_{xy}\,dx\,dy$$
$$=(dx_1)^2+(dy_1)^2+(dz_1)^2,$$

where terms of the second order in e_{xx}, ... e_{yz}, ... are neglected; and therefore the coefficients in the quadratic form on the left must be such that this form can be transformed into the form on the right. The conditions for this to be possible are well known*, and can be shown to be the same as equations (25), when terms of the second order are neglected.

18. Displacement corresponding with given strain†.

When the components of strain are given functions, which satisfy the identical relations of the last Article, the components of displacement are to be deduced by solving the equations (24) as differential equations for u, v, w. These equations are linear, and the complete solutions of them are compounded of (1) any set of particular solutions, (2) complementary solutions containing arbitrary constants. The complementary solutions satisfy the equations

$$\frac{\partial u}{\partial x}=\frac{\partial v}{\partial y}=\frac{\partial w}{\partial z}=\frac{\partial w}{\partial y}+\frac{\partial v}{\partial z}=\frac{\partial u}{\partial z}+\frac{\partial w}{\partial x}=\frac{\partial v}{\partial x}+\frac{\partial u}{\partial y}=0. \quad \text{.........(26)}$$

If we differentiate the left-hand members of these equations with respect to x, y, z we shall obtain eighteen linear equations connecting the eighteen second differential coefficients of u, v, w, from which it follows that all these second differential coefficients vanish. Hence the complementary u, v, w are linear functions of x, y, z, and, in virtue of equations (26), they must be expressed by equations of the forms

$$u=u_0-ry+qz, \quad v=v_0-pz+rx, \quad w=w_0-qx+py, \quad \text{......(27)}$$

which are the formulæ for the displacement of a rigid body by a translation (u_0, v_0, w_0) and a small rotation (p, q, r).

In the complementary solutions thus obtained, the constants p, q, r must be small quantities of the same order of magnitude as the given functions $e_{xx}, \ldots$, as otherwise the equations (6) of Art. 9 show that these functions would not express the strain in the body correctly, and the terms of (27) that contain p, q, r would not represent a displacement possible in a rigid body. Bearing this restriction in mind, we conclude that, if the six components of strain are given, the corresponding displacement is arbitrary to the extent of an additional displacement of the type expressed by (27); but, if we impose six independent conditions, such as that, at the origin, the displacement

* The most convenient references are J. E. Wright's *Invariants of Quadratic Differential Forms*, Cambridge, 1908, pp. 11, 23, and A. S. Eddington, *Mathematical Theory of Relativity*, Cambridge, 1923, p. 72. The theory is due to Riemann (1861) and Christoffel (1869).

† Kirchhoff, *Mechanik*, Vorlesung 27.

(u, v, w) and the rotation $(\varpi_x, \varpi_y, \varpi_z)$ vanish, or again that, at the same point

$$u=0,\ v=0,\ w=0,\ \frac{\partial u}{\partial z}=0,\ \frac{\partial v}{\partial z}=0,\ \frac{\partial v}{\partial x}=0, \quad\text{..............(28)}$$

the expression for the displacement with given strains will be unique. The particular set of equations (28) indicate that one point of the body (the origin), one linear element of the body (that along the axis of z issuing from the origin) and one plane-element of the body (that in the plane of z, x containing the origin) retain their positions after the strain. It is manifestly possible, after straining a body in any way, to bring it back by translation and rotation so that a given point, a given linear element through the point and a given plane-element through the line shall recover their primitive positions.

19. Curvilinear orthogonal coordinates *.

For many problems it is convenient to use systems of curvilinear coordinates instead of the ordinary Cartesian coordinates. These may be introduced as follows:—Let $f(x, y, z)=\alpha$, some constant, be the equation of a surface. If α is allowed to vary we obtain a family of surfaces. In general one surface of the family will pass through a chosen point, and a neighbouring point will in general lie on a neighbouring surface of the family, so that α is a function of x, y, z, viz., the function denoted by f. If $\alpha+d\alpha$ is the parameter of that surface of the family which passes through $(x+dx, y+dy, z+dz)$, we have

$$d\alpha=\frac{\partial f}{\partial x}dx+\frac{\partial f}{\partial y}dy+\frac{\partial f}{\partial z}dz=\frac{\partial \alpha}{\partial x}dx+\frac{\partial \alpha}{\partial y}dy+\frac{\partial \alpha}{\partial z}dz.$$

If we have three independent families of surfaces given by the equations

$$f_1(x, y, z)=\alpha,\quad f_2(x, y, z)=\beta,\quad f_3(x, y, z)=\gamma,$$

so that in general one surface of each family passes through a chosen point, then a point may be determined by the values of α, β, γ which belong to the surfaces that pass through it†, and a neighbouring point will be determined by the neighbouring values $\alpha+d\alpha$, $\beta+d\beta$, $\gamma+d\gamma$. Such quantities as α, β, γ are called "curvilinear coordinates" of the point.

The most convenient systems of curvilinear coordinates for applications to the theory of Elasticity are determined by families of surfaces which cut each other everywhere at right angles. In such a case we have a triply-orthogonal family of surfaces. It is well known that there exists an infinite number of sets of such surfaces, and, according to a celebrated theorem due to Dupin, the line of intersection of two surfaces belonging to different families of such

* The theory is due to Lamé. See his *Leçons sur les coordonnées curvilignes*, Paris, 1859.

† The determination of the point may not be free from ambiguity, e.g., in elliptic coordinates, an ellipsoid and two confocal hyperboloids pass through any point, and they meet in seven other points. The ambiguity is removed if the region of space considered is suitably limited, e.g., in the case of elliptic coordinates, if it is an octant bounded by principal planes.

a set is a line of curvature on each*. In what follows we shall take α, β, γ to be the parameters of such a set of surfaces, so that the following relations hold:

$$\frac{\partial\beta}{\partial x}\frac{\partial\gamma}{\partial x}+\frac{\partial\beta}{\partial y}\frac{\partial\gamma}{\partial y}+\frac{\partial\beta}{\partial z}\frac{\partial\gamma}{\partial z}=0,$$

$$\frac{\partial\gamma}{\partial x}\frac{\partial\alpha}{\partial x}+\frac{\partial\gamma}{\partial y}\frac{\partial\alpha}{\partial y}+\frac{\partial\gamma}{\partial z}\frac{\partial\alpha}{\partial z}=0,$$

$$\frac{\partial\alpha}{\partial x}\frac{\partial\beta}{\partial x}+\frac{\partial\alpha}{\partial y}\frac{\partial\beta}{\partial y}+\frac{\partial\alpha}{\partial z}\frac{\partial\beta}{\partial z}=0.$$

The length of the normal, dn_1, to a surface of the family α intercepted between the surfaces α and $\alpha+d\alpha$ is determined by the observation that the direction-cosines of the normal to α at the point (x, y, z) are

$$\frac{1}{h_1}\frac{\partial\alpha}{\partial x},\quad \frac{1}{h_1}\frac{\partial\alpha}{\partial y},\quad \frac{1}{h_1}\frac{\partial\alpha}{\partial z},\quad\text{.....................(29)}$$

where h_1 is expressed by the first of equations (31) below. For, by projecting the line joining two neighbouring points on the normal to α, we obtain the equation

$$dn_1=\frac{1}{h_1}\left(\frac{\partial\alpha}{\partial x}dx+\frac{\partial\alpha}{\partial y}dy+\frac{\partial\alpha}{\partial z}dz\right)=\frac{d\alpha}{h_1}.\quad\text{..............(30)}$$

In like manner the elements dn_2, dn_3 of the normals to β and γ are $d\beta/h_2$ and $d\gamma/h_3$, where

$$\left.\begin{aligned}h_1^2&=\left(\frac{\partial\alpha}{\partial x}\right)^2+\left(\frac{\partial\alpha}{\partial y}\right)^2+\left(\frac{\partial\alpha}{\partial z}\right)^2,\\ h_2^2&=\left(\frac{\partial\beta}{\partial x}\right)^2+\left(\frac{\partial\beta}{\partial y}\right)^2+\left(\frac{\partial\beta}{\partial z}\right)^2,\\ h_3^2&=\left(\frac{\partial\gamma}{\partial x}\right)^2+\left(\frac{\partial\gamma}{\partial y}\right)^2+\left(\frac{\partial\gamma}{\partial z}\right)^2.\end{aligned}\right\}\quad\text{.....................(31)}$$

The distance between two neighbouring points being $(dn_1^2+dn_2^2+dn_3^2)^{\frac{1}{2}}$, we have the expression for the "line-element," ds, i.e. the distance between the points (α, β, γ) and $(\alpha+d\alpha, \beta+d\beta, \gamma+d\gamma)$, in the form

$$(ds)^2=(d\alpha/h_1)^2+(d\beta/h_2)^2+(d\gamma/h_3)^2.\quad\text{..................(32)}$$

In general h_1, h_2, h_3 are regarded as functions of α, β, γ.

The quantities h_1, h_2, h_3, considered as functions of α, β, γ, are not independent, but are connected by the six conditions which secure that the quadratic differential form

$$h_1^{-2}(d\alpha)^2+h_2^{-2}(d\beta)^2+h_3^{-2}(d\gamma)^2$$

may be transformable into the form $(dx)^2+(dy)^2+(dz)^2$. These conditions† are three equations of the type

$$\frac{\partial^2}{\partial\beta\,\partial\gamma}\left(\frac{1}{h_1}\right)=h_2\frac{\partial}{\partial\beta}\left(\frac{1}{h_1}\right)\frac{\partial}{\partial\gamma}\left(\frac{1}{h_2}\right)+h_3\frac{\partial}{\partial\gamma}\left(\frac{1}{h_1}\right)\frac{\partial}{\partial\beta}\left(\frac{1}{h_3}\right),$$

* Salmon, *Geometry of three dimensions*, 4th ed., p. 269.

† The conditions were given by Lamé, *loc. cit.*, p. 51, before the invention of the theory of quadratic differential forms.

and three equations of the type

$$\frac{\partial}{\partial\beta}\left\{h_2\frac{\partial}{\partial\beta}\left(\frac{1}{h_3}\right)\right\}+\frac{\partial}{\partial\gamma}\left\{h_3\frac{\partial}{\partial\gamma}\left(\frac{1}{h_2}\right)\right\}+h_1{}^2\frac{\partial}{\partial\alpha}\left(\frac{1}{h_2}\right)\frac{\partial}{\partial\alpha}\left(\frac{1}{h_3}\right)=0.$$

20. Components of strain referred to curvilinear orthogonal coordinates*.

Let P, (α, β, γ), and Q, $(\alpha+a, \beta+b, \gamma+c)$, be two points at a short distance r apart, and let the direction-cosines of PQ, referred to the normals at P to those surfaces of the α, β, and γ families which pass through P, be l, m, n. Then, to the first order in r,

$$a=lrh_1,\quad b=mrh_2,\quad c=nrh_3.$$

Let the particles which are at P, Q in the unstrained state be displaced to P_1, Q_1, let u_α, u_β, u_γ be the projections of the displacement PP_1 on the same three normals, and let $\alpha+\xi$, $\beta+\eta$, $\gamma+\zeta$ be the curvilinear coordinates of P_1. If the displacement is small, so that u_α, u_β, u_γ and ξ, η, ζ are small quantities of the same order, then we have the equations

$$\xi=h_1u_\alpha,\quad \eta=h_2u_\beta,\quad \zeta=h_3u_\gamma,$$

which are correct to this order. The curvilinear coordinates of Q_1 are expressed with sufficient approximation by such formulæ as

$$\alpha+a+\xi+a\frac{\partial\xi}{\partial\alpha}+b\frac{\partial\xi}{\partial\beta}+c\frac{\partial\xi}{\partial\gamma},$$

and the values of $1/h_1, \ldots$ at P_1 are expressed with sufficient approximation by such formulæ as

$$\frac{1}{h_1}+\xi\frac{\partial}{\partial\alpha}\left(\frac{1}{h_1}\right)+\eta\frac{\partial}{\partial\beta}\left(\frac{1}{h_1}\right)+\zeta\frac{\partial}{\partial\gamma}\left(\frac{1}{h_1}\right).$$

It follows that the projections of P_1Q_1 on the normals at P_1, to those surfaces of the α, β, and γ families which pass through P_1, are expressed with sufficient approximation by three formulæ of the type

$$\left\{a\left(1+\frac{\partial\xi}{\partial\alpha}\right)+b\frac{\partial\xi}{\partial\beta}+c\frac{\partial\xi}{\partial\gamma}\right\}\left\{\frac{1}{h_1}+\xi\frac{\partial}{\partial\alpha}\left(\frac{1}{h_1}\right)+\eta\frac{\partial}{\partial\beta}\left(\frac{1}{h_1}\right)+\zeta\frac{\partial}{\partial\gamma}\left(\frac{1}{h_1}\right)\right\},\quad\ldots(33)$$

which may be simplified by omission of the terms of order higher than the first in ξ, η, ζ, and their derivatives. On substituting for a, b, c and ξ, η, ζ, and squaring and adding the three formulæ of this type, we obtain an expression for the square of the length of P_1Q_1. This length is $r(1+e)$, where e is the extension of a linear element along PQ. It is thus proved that e is given by the equation

$$(1+e)^2=\left[l\left\{1+h_1\frac{\partial u_\alpha}{\partial\alpha}+h_1h_2u_\beta\frac{\partial}{\partial\beta}\left(\frac{1}{h_1}\right)+h_1h_3u_\gamma\frac{\partial}{\partial\gamma}\left(\frac{1}{h_1}\right)\right\}\right.$$
$$\left.+m\frac{h_2}{h_1}\frac{\partial}{\partial\beta}(h_1u_\alpha)+n\frac{h_3}{h_1}\frac{\partial}{\partial\gamma}(h_1u_\alpha)\right]^2+\ldots+\ldots.\quad\ldots\ldots(34)$$

* The method here given is due to Borchardt, *J. f. Math.* (*Crelle*), Bd. 76 (1873), reprinted in *C. W. Borchardt's Ges. Werke*, Berlin, 1888, p. 289. Other methods will be given in Article 22 C, *infra*, and in the 'Note on the Applications of Moving Axes' at the end of this book.

Neglecting squares and products of u_α, u_β, u_γ, we may write the result in the form

$$e = e_{\alpha\alpha}l^2 + e_{\beta\beta}m^2 + e_{\gamma\gamma}n^2 + e_{\beta\gamma}mn + e_{\gamma\alpha}nl + e_{\alpha\beta}lm, \quad \text{.........(35)}$$

in which

$$\left.\begin{aligned}
e_{\alpha\alpha} &= h_1\frac{\partial u_\alpha}{\partial\alpha} + h_1h_2u_\beta\frac{\partial}{\partial\beta}\left(\frac{1}{h_1}\right) + h_3h_1u_\gamma\frac{\partial}{\partial\gamma}\left(\frac{1}{h_1}\right),\\
e_{\beta\beta} &= h_2\frac{\partial u_\beta}{\partial\beta} + h_2h_3u_\gamma\frac{\partial}{\partial\gamma}\left(\frac{1}{h_2}\right) + h_1h_2u_\alpha\frac{\partial}{\partial\alpha}\left(\frac{1}{h_2}\right),\\
e_{\gamma\gamma} &= h_3\frac{\partial u_\gamma}{\partial\gamma} + h_3h_1u_\alpha\frac{\partial}{\partial\alpha}\left(\frac{1}{h_3}\right) + h_2h_3u_\beta\frac{\partial}{\partial\beta}\left(\frac{1}{h_3}\right),\\
e_{\beta\gamma} &= \frac{h_2}{h_3}\frac{\partial}{\partial\beta}(h_3u_\gamma) + \frac{h_3}{h_2}\frac{\partial}{\partial\gamma}(h_2u_\beta),\\
e_{\gamma\alpha} &= \frac{h_3}{h_1}\frac{\partial}{\partial\gamma}(h_1u_\alpha) + \frac{h_1}{h_3}\frac{\partial}{\partial\alpha}(h_3u_\gamma),\\
e_{\alpha\beta} &= \frac{h_1}{h_2}\frac{\partial}{\partial\alpha}(h_2u_\beta) + \frac{h_2}{h_1}\frac{\partial}{\partial\beta}(h_1u_\alpha).
\end{aligned}\right\} \quad \text{.........(36)}$$

The quantities $e_{\alpha\alpha}$, ... $e_{\beta\gamma}$, ... are the six components of strain referred to the orthogonal coordinates. In fact $e_{\alpha\alpha}$ is the extension of a linear element which, in the unstrained state, lies along the normal to the surface α; and $e_{\beta\gamma}$ is the cosine of the angle between the linear elements which, in the unstrained state, lie along the normals to the surfaces β and γ.

21. Dilatation and Rotation referred to curvilinear orthogonal coordinates.

The results of Art. 15 can be utilized to express the cubical dilatation Δ, and the component rotations ϖ_α, ϖ_β, ϖ_γ about the normals to the three surfaces, in terms of the components u_α, u_β, u_γ of the displacement.

To obtain the expression for Δ we form the surface integral of the normal component of the displacement* over the surface of an element of the body bounded by the three pairs of surfaces $(\alpha, \alpha+d\alpha)$, $(\beta, \beta+d\beta)$, $(\gamma, \gamma+d\gamma)$, the normal being drawn away from the interior of the element. The contributions of the faces of the element can be put down in such forms as

$$\text{contribution of} \quad \alpha = -u_\alpha\frac{d\beta}{h_2}\frac{d\gamma}{h_3},$$

$$\text{,,} \quad \text{,,} \quad \alpha+d\alpha = u_\alpha\frac{d\beta}{h_2}\frac{d\gamma}{h_3} + d\alpha\frac{\partial}{\partial\alpha}\left(u_\alpha\frac{d\beta}{h_2}\frac{d\gamma}{h_3}\right),$$

and, on adding the six contributions, we obtain

$$d\alpha\, d\beta\, d\gamma\left\{\frac{\partial}{\partial\alpha}\left(\frac{u_\alpha}{h_2h_3}\right) + \frac{\partial}{\partial\beta}\left(\frac{u_\beta}{h_3h_1}\right) + \frac{\partial}{\partial\gamma}\left(\frac{u_\gamma}{h_1h_2}\right)\right\};$$

this must be the same as $\Delta\,.\,d\alpha\, d\beta\, d\gamma/h_1h_2h_3$. We therefore have

$$\Delta = h_1h_2h_3\left\{\frac{\partial}{\partial\alpha}\left(\frac{u_\alpha}{h_2h_3}\right) + \frac{\partial}{\partial\beta}\left(\frac{u_\beta}{h_3h_1}\right) + \frac{\partial}{\partial\gamma}\left(\frac{u_\gamma}{h_1h_2}\right)\right\}. \quad \text{..................(37)}$$

This result is the same as would be found by adding the expressions for $e_{\alpha\alpha}$, $e_{\beta\beta}$, $e_{\gamma\gamma}$ in (36).

* This method is due to Lord Kelvin. (Sir W. Thomson, *Math. and Phys. Papers*, Vol. 1, p. 25. The date of the investigation is 1843.)

To obtain the expression for $2\varpi_\gamma$ we form the line integral of the tangential component of the displacement along the edge of the element in the face $\gamma+d\gamma$. The contributions of the four portions of the edge can be written down by the help of Fig. 3 as follows:

$$\text{contribution of } RP = u_\alpha \frac{d\alpha}{h_1},$$

$$\text{,,} \quad \text{,,} \quad R'Q = -u_\alpha \frac{d\alpha}{h_1} - d\beta \frac{\partial}{\partial\beta}\left(u_\alpha \frac{d\alpha}{h_1}\right),$$

$$\text{,,} \quad \text{,,} \quad QR = -u_\beta \frac{d\beta}{h_2},$$

$$\text{,,} \quad \text{,,} \quad PR' = u_\beta \frac{d\beta}{h_2} + d\alpha \frac{\partial}{\partial\alpha}\left(u_\beta \frac{d\beta}{h_2}\right).$$

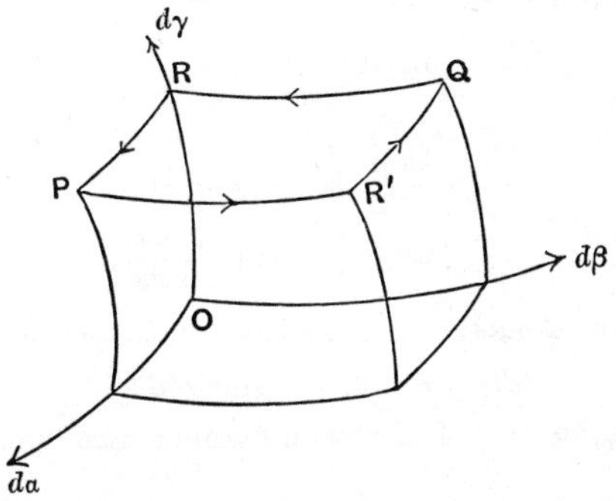

Fig. 3.

On adding these contributions, we obtain

$$d\alpha\, d\beta \left\{\frac{\partial}{\partial\alpha}\left(\frac{u_\beta}{h_2}\right) - \frac{\partial}{\partial\beta}\left(\frac{u_\alpha}{h_1}\right)\right\}.$$

This must be the same as $2\varpi_\gamma d\alpha\, d\beta/h_1 h_2$, and we have thus an expression for ϖ_γ which is given in the third of equations (38); the other equations of this set can be obtained in the same way. The formulæ* are

$$\left.\begin{aligned} 2\varpi_\alpha &= h_2 h_3 \left\{\frac{\partial}{\partial\beta}\left(\frac{u_\gamma}{h_3}\right) - \frac{\partial}{\partial\gamma}\left(\frac{u_\beta}{h_2}\right)\right\}, \\ 2\varpi_\beta &= h_3 h_1 \left\{\frac{\partial}{\partial\gamma}\left(\frac{u_\alpha}{h_1}\right) - \frac{\partial}{\partial\alpha}\left(\frac{u_\gamma}{h_3}\right)\right\}, \\ 2\varpi_\gamma &= h_1 h_2 \left\{\frac{\partial}{\partial\alpha}\left(\frac{u_\beta}{h_2}\right) - \frac{\partial}{\partial\beta}\left(\frac{u_\alpha}{h_1}\right)\right\}. \end{aligned}\right\} \quad \text{.........................(38)}$$

* The formulæ (38), as also (36) and (37), are due to Lamé. The method here used to obtain (38), and used also in a slightly more analytical form by Cesàro, *Introduzione alla teoria matematica della Elasticità* (Turin, 1894), p. 193, is familiar in Electrodynamics. Cf. H. Lamb, *Phil. Trans. Roy. Soc.*, vol. 178 (1888), p. 150, or J. J. Thomson, *Recent Researches in Electricity and Magnetism*, Oxford, 1893, p. 367. The underlying physical notion is, of course, identical with the relation of "circulation" to "vortex strength" brought to light in Lord Kelvin's memoir 'On Vortex Motion,' *Edinburgh Roy. Soc. Trans.*, vol. 25 (1869).

22. Cylindrical and polar coordinates.

In the case of *cylindrical coordinates* r, θ, z we have the line-element

$$\{(dr)^2+r^2(d\theta)^2+(dz)^2\}^{\frac{1}{2}},$$

and the displacements u_r, u_θ, u_z. The general formulæ take the following forms:

(1) for the strains

$$e_{rr}=\frac{\partial u_r}{\partial r},\quad e_{\theta\theta}=\frac{1}{r}\frac{\partial u_\theta}{\partial \theta}+\frac{u_r}{r},\quad e_{zz}=\frac{\partial u_z}{\partial z},$$

$$e_{\theta z}=\frac{1}{r}\frac{\partial u_z}{\partial \theta}+\frac{\partial u_\theta}{\partial z},\quad e_{zr}=\frac{\partial u_r}{\partial z}+\frac{\partial u_z}{\partial r},\quad e_{r\theta}=\frac{\partial u_\theta}{\partial r}-\frac{u_\theta}{r}+\frac{1}{r}\frac{\partial u_r}{\partial \theta};$$

(2) for the cubical dilatation

$$\Delta=\frac{1}{r}\frac{\partial}{\partial r}(ru_r)+\frac{1}{r}\frac{\partial u_\theta}{\partial \theta}+\frac{\partial u_z}{\partial z};$$

(3) for the components of rotation

$$2\varpi_r=\frac{1}{r}\frac{\partial u_z}{\partial \theta}-\frac{\partial u_\theta}{\partial z},$$

$$2\varpi_\theta=\frac{\partial u_r}{\partial z}-\frac{\partial u_z}{\partial r},$$

$$2\varpi_z=\frac{1}{r}\frac{\partial}{\partial r}(ru_\theta)-\frac{1}{r}\frac{\partial u_r}{\partial \theta}.$$

In the case of *polar coordinates* r, θ, ϕ, we have the line-element

$$\{(dr)^2+r^2(d\theta)^2+r^2\sin^2\theta\,(d\phi)^2\}^{\frac{1}{2}},$$

and the displacements u_r, u_θ, u_ϕ. The general formulæ take the following forms:

(1) for the strains

$$e_{rr}=\frac{\partial u_r}{\partial r},\quad e_{\theta\theta}=\frac{1}{r}\frac{\partial u_\theta}{\partial \theta}+\frac{u_r}{r},\quad e_{\phi\phi}=\frac{1}{r\sin\theta}\frac{\partial u_\phi}{\partial \phi}+\frac{u_\theta}{r}\cot\theta+\frac{u_r}{r},$$

$$e_{\theta\phi}=\frac{1}{r}\left(\frac{\partial u_\phi}{\partial \theta}-u_\phi\cot\theta\right)+\frac{1}{r\sin\theta}\frac{\partial u_\theta}{\partial \phi},\quad e_{\phi r}=\frac{1}{r\sin\theta}\frac{\partial u_r}{\partial \phi}+\frac{\partial u_\phi}{\partial r}-\frac{u_\phi}{r},\quad e_{r\theta}=\frac{\partial u_\theta}{\partial r}-\frac{u_\theta}{r}+\frac{1}{r}\frac{\partial u_r}{\partial \theta};$$

(2) for the cubical dilatation

$$\Delta=\frac{1}{r^2\sin\theta}\left\{\frac{\partial}{\partial r}(r^2u_r\sin\theta)+\frac{\partial}{\partial \theta}(ru_\theta\sin\theta)+\frac{\partial}{\partial \phi}(ru_\phi)\right\};$$

(3) for the components of rotation

$$2\varpi_r=\frac{1}{r^2\sin\theta}\left\{\frac{\partial}{\partial \theta}(ru_\phi\sin\theta)-\frac{\partial}{\partial \phi}(ru_\theta)\right\},$$

$$2\varpi_\theta=\frac{1}{r\sin\theta}\left\{\frac{\partial u_r}{\partial \phi}-\frac{\partial}{\partial r}(ru_\phi\sin\theta)\right\},$$

$$2\varpi_\phi=\frac{1}{r}\left\{\frac{\partial}{\partial r}(ru_\theta)-\frac{\partial u_r}{\partial \theta}\right\}.$$

The verification of these formulæ may serve as exercises for the student.

22 C. Further theory of curvilinear orthogonal coordinates.

(*a*) In Article 19 the theory was developed by regarding α, β, γ as functions of x, y, z, but it is often more convenient to regard x, y, z as functions of α, β, γ.

We can write down three equations of the type

$$\frac{\partial \alpha}{\partial x}\frac{\partial x}{\partial \alpha}+\frac{\partial \alpha}{\partial y}\frac{\partial y}{\partial \alpha}+\frac{\partial \alpha}{\partial z}\frac{\partial z}{\partial \alpha}=1,$$

and six equations of the type $\frac{\partial\alpha}{\partial x}\frac{\partial x}{\partial\beta}+\frac{\partial\alpha}{\partial y}\frac{\partial y}{\partial\beta}+\frac{\partial\alpha}{\partial z}\frac{\partial z}{\partial\beta}=0$,

and solve them as linear equations to determine the derivatives of x, y, z with respect to α, β, γ. Being linear, they possess a unique solution, and they do possess the obvious solution

$$\frac{\partial x}{\partial\alpha}=\left(\frac{1}{h_1}\right)^2\frac{\partial\alpha}{\partial x},\quad \frac{\partial x}{\partial\beta}=\left(\frac{1}{h_2}\right)^2\frac{\partial\beta}{\partial x},\ \ldots\ \frac{\partial y}{\partial\alpha}=\left(\frac{1}{h_1}\right)^2\frac{\partial\alpha}{\partial y},\ \ldots,$$

where the h's are given by equations (31) of Article 19. From these it appears that the h's are given also by equivalent equations of the type

$$\frac{1}{h_1^2}=\left(\frac{\partial x}{\partial\alpha}\right)^2+\left(\frac{\partial y}{\partial\alpha}\right)^2+\left(\frac{\partial z}{\partial\alpha}\right)^2. \qquad\qquad (39)$$

(b) These results may also be expressed by the statement that the nine direction-cosines of the normals at (α, β, γ), to the surfaces of the α, β and γ families that pass through this point, are given by formulæ of the type

$$\cos(\alpha, x)=h_1\frac{\partial x}{\partial\alpha},\quad \cos(\alpha, y)=h_1\frac{\partial y}{\partial\alpha},\quad \cos(\alpha, z)=h_1\frac{\partial z}{\partial\alpha},$$

as well as by formulæ of the type

$$\cos(\alpha, x)=\frac{1}{h_1}\frac{\partial\alpha}{\partial x},\quad \cos(\alpha, y)=\frac{1}{h_1}\frac{\partial\alpha}{\partial y},\quad \cos(\alpha, z)=\frac{1}{h_1}\frac{\partial\alpha}{\partial z}.$$

(c) Since the nine quantities of the type $h_1\frac{\partial x}{\partial\alpha}$ are the direction-cosines of three lines which are mutually at right angles, we have three equations of the type

$$\frac{\partial x}{\partial\alpha}\frac{\partial x}{\partial\beta}+\frac{\partial y}{\partial\alpha}\frac{\partial y}{\partial\beta}+\frac{\partial z}{\partial\alpha}\frac{\partial z}{\partial\beta}=0,$$

as well as the three equations of the type (39) above. By differentiation with respect to α, β, γ in turn, 18 equations containing second derivatives of x, y, z are obtained, and these can be solved for the second derivatives. The solution is known*, and can be expressed in such forms as

$$\frac{\partial^2 x}{\partial\alpha^2}=-\frac{1}{h_1}\frac{\partial h_1}{\partial\alpha}\frac{\partial x}{\partial\alpha}+\frac{h_2^2}{h_1^3}\frac{\partial h_1}{\partial\beta}\frac{\partial x}{\partial\beta}+\frac{h_3^2}{h_1^3}\frac{\partial h_1}{\partial\gamma}\frac{\partial x}{\partial\gamma},$$

$$\frac{\partial^2 x}{\partial\alpha\partial\beta}=-\frac{1}{h_1}\frac{\partial h_1}{\partial\beta}\frac{\partial x}{\partial\alpha}-\frac{1}{h_2}\frac{\partial h_2}{\partial\alpha}\frac{\partial x}{\partial\beta}.$$

It is easy, after forming any one of the 18 equations, to substitute these values for the second derivatives, and thus to verify these values.

(d) The results in (c) may be expressed in terms of the direction-cosines $\cos(\alpha, x), \ldots$, giving nine equations†: three of the type

$$\frac{\partial}{\partial\alpha}\cos(\alpha, x)=-h_2\frac{\partial}{\partial\beta}\left(\frac{1}{h_1}\right).\cos(\beta, x)-h_3\frac{\partial}{\partial\gamma}\left(\frac{1}{h_1}\right).\cos(\gamma, x), \qquad (40)$$

and six of the type $$\frac{\partial}{\partial\beta}\cos(\alpha, x)=h_1\frac{\partial}{\partial\alpha}\left(\frac{1}{h_2}\right)\cos(\beta, x). \qquad (41)$$

(e) The foregoing results may be utilized to obtain a new proof of the important formulæ (36) of Article 20.

Let u, v, w be the components, in the directions of the axes of x, y, z, of the displacement whose components, in the directions of the normals to the surfaces α, β, γ, are

* See J. E. Wright, *loc. cit. ante* p. 50.

† Another proof of these equations will be found in the 'Note on the Applications of Moving Axes' at the end of this book.

u_α, u_β, u_γ, and let $\cos(\alpha, x)$, $\cos(\alpha, y)$, ... $\cos(\gamma, z)$ be denoted by l_1, m_1, ... n_3. We shall have three equations of the type

$$u_\alpha = l_1 u + m_1 v + n_1 w,$$

and $e_{\alpha\alpha}$, ... $e_{\beta\gamma}$, ... will be given by the right-hand members of (11) in Article 12.

Thus we have by direct transformation

$$\begin{aligned}
e_{\alpha\alpha} &= h_1^2 \left\{ \frac{\partial u}{\partial x}\left(\frac{\partial x}{\partial \alpha}\right)^2 + \frac{\partial v}{\partial y}\left(\frac{\partial y}{\partial \alpha}\right)^2 + \frac{\partial w}{\partial z}\left(\frac{\partial z}{\partial \alpha}\right)^2 + \left(\frac{\partial w}{\partial y} + \frac{\partial v}{\partial z}\right)\frac{\partial y}{\partial \alpha}\frac{\partial z}{\partial \alpha} \right. \\
&\qquad \left. + \left(\frac{\partial u}{\partial z} + \frac{\partial w}{\partial x}\right)\frac{\partial z}{\partial \alpha}\frac{\partial x}{\partial \alpha} + \left(\frac{\partial v}{\partial x} + \frac{\partial u}{\partial y}\right)\frac{\partial x}{\partial \alpha}\frac{\partial y}{\partial \alpha} \right\} \\
&= h_1^2 \left(\frac{\partial x}{\partial \alpha}\frac{\partial u}{\partial \alpha} + \frac{\partial y}{\partial \alpha}\frac{\partial v}{\partial \alpha} + \frac{\partial z}{\partial \alpha}\frac{\partial w}{\partial \alpha}\right) \\
&= h_1 \left\{ \frac{\partial}{\partial \alpha}\left(u h_1 \frac{\partial x}{\partial \alpha} + v h_1 \frac{\partial y}{\partial \alpha} + w h_1 \frac{\partial z}{\partial \alpha}\right) \right. \\
&\qquad \left. - u \frac{\partial}{\partial \alpha}\left(h_1 \frac{\partial x}{\partial \alpha}\right) - v \frac{\partial}{\partial \alpha}\left(h_1 \frac{\partial y}{\partial \alpha}\right) - w \frac{\partial}{\partial \alpha}\left(h_1 \frac{\partial z}{\partial \alpha}\right) \right\} \\
&= h_1 \left[\frac{\partial u_\alpha}{\partial \alpha} - \left\{ u \frac{\partial}{\partial \alpha}\cos(\alpha, x) + v \frac{\partial}{\partial \alpha}\cos(\alpha, y) + w \frac{\partial}{\partial \alpha}\cos(\alpha, z) \right\} \right],
\end{aligned}$$

and, on substituting from the equations of type (40), and writing u_β for

$$u\cos(\beta, x) + v\cos(\beta, y) + w\cos(\beta, z)$$

and u_γ for $u\cos(\gamma, x) + \dots$, the formula for $e_{\alpha\alpha}$ given in (36) of Article 20 is obtained.

In like manner we have

$$\begin{aligned}
e_{\beta\gamma} &= h_2 h_3 \left\{ 2\left(\frac{\partial u}{\partial x}\frac{\partial x}{\partial \beta}\frac{\partial x}{\partial \gamma} + \frac{\partial v}{\partial y}\frac{\partial y}{\partial \beta}\frac{\partial y}{\partial \gamma} + \frac{\partial w}{\partial z}\frac{\partial z}{\partial \beta}\frac{\partial z}{\partial \gamma}\right) \right. \\
&\qquad \left. + \left(\frac{\partial w}{\partial y} + \frac{\partial v}{\partial z}\right)\left(\frac{\partial y}{\partial \beta}\frac{\partial z}{\partial \gamma} + \frac{\partial z}{\partial \beta}\frac{\partial y}{\partial \gamma}\right) + \dots + \dots \right\} \\
&= h_2 h_3 \left(\frac{\partial x}{\partial \beta}\frac{\partial u}{\partial \gamma} + \frac{\partial y}{\partial \beta}\frac{\partial v}{\partial \gamma} + \frac{\partial z}{\partial \beta}\frac{\partial w}{\partial \gamma} + \frac{\partial x}{\partial \gamma}\frac{\partial u}{\partial \beta} + \frac{\partial y}{\partial \gamma}\frac{\partial v}{\partial \beta} + \frac{\partial z}{\partial \gamma}\frac{\partial w}{\partial \beta}\right) \\
&= h_3 \frac{\partial}{\partial \gamma}\left(u h_2 \frac{\partial x}{\partial \beta} + v h_2 \frac{\partial y}{\partial \beta} + w h_2 \frac{\partial z}{\partial \beta}\right) + h_2 \frac{\partial}{\partial \beta}\left(u h_3 \frac{\partial x}{\partial \gamma} + v h_3 \frac{\partial y}{\partial \gamma} + w h_3 \frac{\partial z}{\partial \gamma}\right) \\
&\qquad - h_3 \left\{ u \frac{\partial}{\partial \gamma}\left(h_2 \frac{\partial x}{\partial \beta}\right) + v \frac{\partial}{\partial \gamma}\left(h_2 \frac{\partial y}{\partial \beta}\right) + \dots \right\} - h_2 \left\{ u \frac{\partial}{\partial \beta}\left(h_3 \frac{\partial x}{\partial \gamma}\right) + \dots + \dots \right\} \\
&= h_3 \frac{\partial u_\beta}{\partial \gamma} + h_2 \frac{\partial u_\gamma}{\partial \beta} - h_3 \left\{ u \frac{\partial}{\partial \gamma}\cos(\beta, x) + v \frac{\partial}{\partial \gamma}\cos(\beta, y) + w \frac{\partial}{\partial \gamma}\cos(\beta, z) \right\} \\
&\qquad - h_2 \left\{ u \frac{\partial}{\partial \beta}\cos(\gamma, x) + v \frac{\partial}{\partial \beta}\cos(\gamma, y) + w \frac{\partial}{\partial \beta}\cos(\gamma, z) \right\},
\end{aligned}$$

and from this the formula for $e_{\beta\gamma}$ can be obtained in the same way.

(*f*) It may be remarked that it is very easy, but quite worth while, to apply this method step by step to the important case of plane strain expressed in terms of polar coordinates.

APPENDIX TO CHAPTER I

GENERAL THEORY OF STRAIN

23. THE preceding part of this Chapter contains all the results, relating to strains, which are of importance in the mathematical theory of Elasticity, as at present developed. The discussion of strains that correspond with displacements in general, as opposed to small displacements, is an interesting branch of kinematics; and some account of it will now be given*. It may be premised that the developments here described will not be required in the remainder of this treatise.

It is customary, in recent books on Kinematics, to base the theory of strains in general on the result, stated in Article 7, that the strain about a point is sensibly homogeneous, and to develop the theory of finite strain in the case of homogeneous strain only. From the point of view of a rigorous analysis, it appears to be desirable to establish the theory of strains in general on an independent basis. We shall begin with an account of the theory of the strain corresponding with any displacement, and shall afterwards investigate homogeneous strain in some detail.

24. Strain corresponding with any displacement.

We consider the effect of the displacement on aggregates of particles forming given curves in the unstrained state. Any chosen particle occupies, in the unstrained state, a point (x, y, z). The same particle occupies, in the strained state, a point $(x+u,\ y+v,\ z+w)$. The particles which lie on a given curve in the first state lie in general on a different curve in the second state. If ds is the differential element of arc of a curve in the first state, the direction-cosines of the tangent to this curve at any point are $\frac{dx}{ds}, \frac{dy}{ds}, \frac{dz}{ds}$.

* Reference may be made to Cauchy, *Exercices de mathématique*, Année 1827, the Article 'Sur la condensation et la dilatation des corps solides'; Green's memoir on the reflexion of light quoted in the Introduction (footnote 42); Saint-Venant, 'Mémoire sur l'équilibre des corps solides... quand les déplacements...ne sont pas très petits,' *Paris, C. R.*, t. 24 (1847); Kelvin and Tait, *Nat. Phil.*, Part I. pp. 115—144; Todhunter and Pearson, *History*, vol. 1, Articles 1619—1622; J. Hadamard, *Leçons sur la propagation des ondes*, Paris, 1903, Chapter VI. An interesting extension of the theory, involving the introduction of secondary elements of strain, has been made by J. Le Roux, *Paris, Ann. Éc. norm.*, t. 28, 1911, p. 523 and t. 30, 1913, p. 193. The secondary elements of strain are the curvature and twist of slender filaments of the material, and the curvature of thin sheets of the material, the filaments and sheets being straight and plane in the unstrained state.

If ds_1 is the differential element of arc of the corresponding curve in the second state, the direction-cosines of the tangent to this curve are

$$\frac{d(x+u)}{ds_1}, \quad \frac{d(y+v)}{ds_1}, \quad \frac{d(z+w)}{ds_1}.$$

Herein, for example,

$$\frac{d(x+u)}{ds_1} = \frac{ds}{ds_1}\left(\frac{dx}{ds} + \frac{\partial u}{\partial x}\frac{dx}{ds} + \frac{\partial u}{\partial y}\frac{dy}{ds} + \frac{\partial u}{\partial z}\frac{dz}{ds}\right), \quad \text{...........(1)}$$

with similar formulæ for the other two.

Let l, m, n be the direction-cosines of a line in the unstrained state, l_1, m_1, n_1 the direction-cosines of the corresponding line in the strained state, ds, ds_1 the differential elements of arc of corresponding curves having these lines respectively as tangents. In the notation used above

$$l = \frac{dx}{ds}, \qquad m = \frac{dy}{ds}, \qquad n = \frac{dz}{ds},$$

$$l_1 = \frac{d(x+u)}{ds_1}, \quad m_1 = \frac{d(y+v)}{ds_1}, \quad n_1 = \frac{d(z+w)}{ds_1},$$

and the equations of type (1) may be written in such forms as

$$l_1 = \frac{ds}{ds_1}\left\{l\left(1 + \frac{\partial u}{\partial x}\right) + m\frac{\partial u}{\partial y} + n\frac{\partial u}{\partial z}\right\} \quad \text{.....................(2)}$$

On squaring and adding the right-hand and left-hand members, and remembering the equations

$$l^2 + m^2 + n^2 = 1, \quad l_1^2 + m_1^2 + n_1^2 = 1,$$

we find an equation which can be written

$$\left(\frac{ds_1}{ds}\right)^2 = (1 + 2\epsilon_{xx})\, l^2 + (1 + 2\epsilon_{yy})\, m^2 + (1 + 2\epsilon_{zz})\, n^2 + 2\epsilon_{yz}\, mn + 2\epsilon_{zx}\, nl + 2\epsilon_{xy}\, lm, \quad \text{.........(3)}$$

where $\epsilon_{xx}, \ldots$ are given by the formulæ

$$\left.\begin{aligned}
\epsilon_{xx} &= \frac{\partial u}{\partial x} + \tfrac{1}{2}\left\{\left(\frac{\partial u}{\partial x}\right)^2 + \left(\frac{\partial v}{\partial x}\right)^2 + \left(\frac{\partial w}{\partial x}\right)^2\right\}, \\
\epsilon_{yy} &= \frac{\partial v}{\partial y} + \tfrac{1}{2}\left\{\left(\frac{\partial u}{\partial y}\right)^2 + \left(\frac{\partial v}{\partial y}\right)^2 + \left(\frac{\partial w}{\partial y}\right)^2\right\}, \\
\epsilon_{zz} &= \frac{\partial w}{\partial z} + \tfrac{1}{2}\left\{\left(\frac{\partial u}{\partial z}\right)^2 + \left(\frac{\partial v}{\partial z}\right)^2 + \left(\frac{\partial w}{\partial z}\right)^2\right\}, \\
\epsilon_{yz} &= \frac{\partial w}{\partial y} + \frac{\partial v}{\partial z} + \frac{\partial u}{\partial y}\frac{\partial u}{\partial z} + \frac{\partial v}{\partial y}\frac{\partial v}{\partial z} + \frac{\partial w}{\partial y}\frac{\partial w}{\partial z}, \\
\epsilon_{zx} &= \frac{\partial u}{\partial z} + \frac{\partial w}{\partial x} + \frac{\partial u}{\partial z}\frac{\partial u}{\partial x} + \frac{\partial v}{\partial z}\frac{\partial v}{\partial x} + \frac{\partial w}{\partial z}\frac{\partial w}{\partial x}, \\
\epsilon_{xy} &= \frac{\partial v}{\partial x} + \frac{\partial u}{\partial y} + \frac{\partial u}{\partial x}\frac{\partial u}{\partial y} + \frac{\partial v}{\partial x}\frac{\partial v}{\partial y} + \frac{\partial w}{\partial x}\frac{\partial w}{\partial y}.
\end{aligned}\right\} \quad \text{..............(4)}$$

The state of strain is entirely determined when we know the lengths in the strained and unstrained states of corresponding lines*. The quantity $\frac{ds_1}{ds} - 1$ is the *extension* of the linear element ds. This is determined by the formula (3). We observe that the extensions of linear elements which, in the unstrained state, are parallel to the axes of coordinates are respectively

$$\sqrt{(1 + 2\epsilon_{xx})} - 1, \quad \sqrt{(1 + 2\epsilon_{yy})} - 1, \quad \sqrt{(1 + 2\epsilon_{zz})} - 1,$$

where the positive values of the square roots are taken. We thus obtain an interpretation of the quantities ϵ_{xx}, ϵ_{yy}, ϵ_{zz}. We shall presently obtain an interpretation of the quantities ϵ_{yz}, ϵ_{zx}, ϵ_{xy}, in terms of the angles, in the strained state, between linear elements, which, in the unstrained state, are parallel to the axes of coordinates. In the meantime, we observe that the strain at any point is entirely determined by the six quantities ϵ_{xx}, ϵ_{yy}, ϵ_{zz}, ϵ_{yz}, ϵ_{zx}, ϵ_{xy}. These quantities will be called the *components of strain*. The quantities e_{xx}, ... which were called "components of strain" in previous Articles are sufficiently exact equivalents of ϵ_{xx}, ... when the squares and products of such quantities as $\partial u/\partial x$ are neglected.

25. Cubical Dilatation.

The ratio of a differential element of volume in the strained state to the corresponding differential element of volume in the unstrained state is equal to the functional determinant

$$\frac{\partial (x+u,\ y+v,\ z+w)}{\partial (x,\ y,\ z)},$$

or it is

$$\begin{vmatrix} 1+\dfrac{\partial u}{\partial x}, & \dfrac{\partial u}{\partial y}, & \dfrac{\partial u}{\partial z} \\ \dfrac{\partial v}{\partial x}, & 1+\dfrac{\partial v}{\partial y}, & \dfrac{\partial v}{\partial z} \\ \dfrac{\partial w}{\partial x}, & \dfrac{\partial w}{\partial y}, & 1+\dfrac{\partial w}{\partial z} \end{vmatrix}.$$

This will be denoted by $1 + \Delta$. Then Δ is the increment of volume per unit volume at a point, or it is the *cubical dilatation*. The quantity $e_{xx} + e_{yy} + e_{zz}$ is a sufficiently exact equivalent of Δ when the displacement is small.

We may express Δ in terms of the components of strain. We find by the process of squaring the determinant that

$$(1 + \Delta)^2 = (1 + 2\epsilon_{xx})(1 + 2\epsilon_{yy})(1 + 2\epsilon_{zz}) + 2\epsilon_{yz}\epsilon_{zx}\epsilon_{xy} - (1 + 2\epsilon_{xx})\epsilon_{yz}^2 - (1 + 2\epsilon_{yy})\epsilon_{zx}^2 - (1 + 2\epsilon_{zz})\epsilon_{xy}^2 \quad\text{.........(5)}$$

* Lord Kelvin's method (Article 10, footnote) is applicable, as he points out, to strains of unrestricted magnitude.

26. Reciprocal strain ellipsoid.

The ratio $ds_1 : ds$, on which the extension of a linear element issuing from a point depends, is expressed in the formula (3) in terms of the direction-cosines of the element, in the unstrained state, and the components of strain at the point. The formula shows that, for any direction, the ratio in question is inversely proportional to the central radius vector, in that direction, of an ellipsoid which is given by the equation

$$(1+2\epsilon_{xx})x^2+(1+2\epsilon_{yy})y^2+(1+2\epsilon_{zz})z^2+2\epsilon_{yz}yz+2\epsilon_{zx}zx+2\epsilon_{xy}xy=\text{const.} \quad \text{.........(6)}$$

This is the *reciprocal strain ellipsoid* already defined (Article 6) in the case of homogeneous strains. Its axes are called the *principal axes of the strain*; they are in the directions of those linear elements in the unstrained state which undergo stationary (maximum or minimum or minimax) extension. The extensions of linear elements in these directions are called the *principal extensions*, ϵ_1, ϵ_2, ϵ_3. The values of $1+\epsilon_1$, $1+\epsilon_2$, $1+\epsilon_3$ are the positive square roots of the three values of κ, which satisfy the equation

$$\begin{vmatrix} 1+2\epsilon_{xx}-\kappa, & \epsilon_{xy}, & \epsilon_{zx} \\ \epsilon_{xy}, & 1+2\epsilon_{yy}-\kappa, & \epsilon_{yz} \\ \epsilon_{zx}, & \epsilon_{yz}, & 1+2\epsilon_{zz}-\kappa \end{vmatrix} = 0. \quad \text{.........(7)}$$

The invariant relation of the reciprocal strain ellipsoid to the state of strain may be utilized for the purpose of transforming the components of strain from one set of rectangular axes to another, in the same way as the strain quadric was transformed in Article 12. It would thus appear that the quantities $\epsilon_{xx}, \dots \epsilon_{xy}$ are components of a "tensor-triad." Three invariants would thus be found, viz.:

$$\left.\begin{aligned} &\epsilon_{xx}+\epsilon_{yy}+\epsilon_{zz}, \quad \epsilon_{yy}\epsilon_{zz}+\epsilon_{zz}\epsilon_{xx}+\epsilon_{xx}\epsilon_{yy}-\tfrac{1}{4}(\epsilon^2_{yz}+\epsilon^2_{zx}+\epsilon^2_{xy}), \\ &\epsilon_{xx}\epsilon_{yy}\epsilon_{zz}+\tfrac{1}{4}(\epsilon_{yz}\epsilon_{zx}\epsilon_{xy}-\epsilon_{xx}\epsilon^2_{yz}-\epsilon_{yy}\epsilon^2_{zx}-\epsilon_{zz}\epsilon^2_{xy}). \end{aligned}\right\} \quad \text{...(8)}$$

27. Angle between two curves altered by strain.

The effect of the strain on the angle between any two linear elements, issuing from the point (x, y, z), can be calculated. Let l, m, n and l', m', n' be the direction-cosines of the two lines in the unstrained state, and θ the angle between them; let l_1, m_1, n_1 and l_1', m_1', n_1' be the direction-cosines of the corresponding lines in the strained state, and θ_1 the angle between them. From the formulæ such as (2) we find

$$\begin{aligned} \cos\theta_1 = \frac{ds}{ds_1}\frac{ds'}{ds_1'}\{\cos\theta + 2(\epsilon_{xx}ll'+\epsilon_{yy}mm'+\epsilon_{zz}nn')+\epsilon_{yz}(mn'+m'n) \\ +\epsilon_{zx}(nl'+n'l)+\epsilon_{xy}(lm'+l'm)\}, \quad \text{.........(9)} \end{aligned}$$

where ds_1/ds and ds_1'/ds' are the ratios of the lengths, after and before strain, of corresponding linear elements in the two directions.

We observe that, if the two given directions are the positive directions of the axes of y and z, the formula becomes

$$\epsilon_{yz} = \sqrt{\{(1+2\epsilon_{xx})(1+2\epsilon_{yy})\}} \cos\theta_1, \quad \text{..................(10)}$$

and we thus obtain an interpretation of the quantity ϵ_{yz}. Similar interpretations can be found for ϵ_{zx} and ϵ_{xy}. From the above formula it appears also that, if the axes of x, y, z are parallel to the principal axes of the strain at a point, linear elements, issuing from the point, in the direction of these axes continue to cut each other at right angles after the strain.

We may show that, in general, this is the only set of three orthogonal linear elements, issuing from a point, which remain orthogonal after the strain. For the condition that linear elements which cut at right angles in the unstrained state should also cut at right angles in the strained state is obtained by putting $\cos\theta$ and $\cos\theta_1$ both equal to zero in equation (9). We thus find the equation

$$\{(1+2\epsilon_{xx})\,l + \epsilon_{xy}\,m + \epsilon_{zx}\,n\}\,l' + \{\epsilon_{xy}\,l + (1+2\epsilon_{yy})\,m + \epsilon_{yz}n\}\,m' + \{\epsilon_{zx}l + \epsilon_{yz}m + (1+2\epsilon_{zz})\,n\}\,n' = 0,$$

wherein $ll' + mm' + nn' = 0$. This equation shows that each of two such linear elements, (besides being at right angles to the other), is parallel to the plane which is conjugate to the other with respect to the reciprocal strain ellipsoid. Any set of three such elements must therefore, (besides being at right angles to each other), be parallel to conjugate diameters of this ellipsoid.

The formulæ so far obtained may be interpreted in the sense that a small element of the body, which has, in the unstrained state, the shape and orientation of the reciprocal strain ellipsoid, corresponding with that point which is at the centre of the element, will, after strain, have the shape of a sphere, and that any set of conjugate diameters of the ellipsoid will become three orthogonal diameters of the sphere.

28. Strain ellipsoid.

We might express the ratio $ds_1 : ds$ in terms of the direction of the linear element in the strained state instead of the unstrained. If we solved the equations of type (2) for l, m, n we should find that these are linear functions of l_1, m_1, n_1 with coefficients containing ds_1/ds as a factor; and, on squaring and adding and replacing $l^2+m^2+n^2$ by unity, we should find an equation of the form

$$\left(\frac{ds}{ds_1}\right)^2 = (a_1 l_1 + b_1 m_1 + c_1 n_1)^2 + (a_2 l_1 + b_2 m_1 + c_2 n_1)^2 + (a_3 l_1 + b_3 m_1 + c_3 n_1)^2,$$

where a_1, ... depend only on $\dfrac{\partial u}{\partial x}, \dfrac{\partial u}{\partial y}, \ldots \dfrac{\partial w}{\partial z}$.

The ellipsoid represented by the equation

$$(a_1x + b_1y + c_1z)^2 + (a_2x + b_2y + c_2z)^2 + (a_3x + b_3y + c_3z)^2 = \text{const.}$$

would have the property that its central radius vector, in any direction, is proportional to the ratio $ds_1 : ds$ for the linear element which, in the strained state, lies along that direction. This ellipsoid is called the *strain ellipsoid.* The lengths of the principal axes of this ellipsoid and of the reciprocal strain ellipsoid are inverse to each other, so that, as regards shape, the ellipsoids are reciprocal to each other; but their principal axes are not in general in the same directions. In fact the principal axes of the strain ellipsoid are in the directions of those linear elements in the strained state which have undergone stationary (maximum or minimum or minimax) extension. The simplest way of finding these directions is to observe that the corresponding linear elements in the unstrained state are parallel to the principal axes of the strain, so that their directions are known. The formulæ of type (2) express the direction-cosines, in the strained state, of any linear element of which the direction-cosines, in the unstrained state, are given. The direction-cosines of the principal axes of the strain ellipsoid can thus be found from these formulæ.

29. Alteration of direction by the strain.

The correspondence of directions of linear elements in the strained and unstrained states can be made clearer by reference to the principal axes of the strain. When the axes of coordinates are parallel to the principal axes, the equation of the reciprocal strain ellipsoid is of the form

$$(1 + \epsilon_1)^2 x^2 + (1 + \epsilon_2)^2 y^2 + (1 + \epsilon_3)^2 z^2 = \text{const.},$$

where ϵ_1, ϵ_2, ϵ_3 are the principal extensions. In the formula (9) for the cosine of the angle between the strained positions of two linear elements we have to put

$$1 + 2\epsilon_{xx} = (1 + \epsilon_1)^2, \quad 1 + 2\epsilon_{yy} = (1 + \epsilon_2)^2, \quad 1 + 2\epsilon_{zz} = (1 + \epsilon_3)^2, \quad \epsilon_{yz} = \epsilon_{zx} = \epsilon_{xy} = 0.$$

Let the line (l', m', n') of the formula (9) take successively the positions of the three principal axes, and let the line (l, m, n) be any chosen line in the unstrained state.

We have to equate ds'/ds_1' in turn to $(1 + \epsilon_1)^{-1}$, $(1 + \epsilon_2)^{-1}$, $(1 + \epsilon_3)^{-1}$, and we have to put for ds/ds_1 the expression

$$[(1 + \epsilon_1)^2 l^2 + (1 + \epsilon_2)^2 m^2 + (1 + \epsilon_3)^2 n^2]^{-\frac{1}{2}}.$$

The formula then gives the cosines of the angles which the corresponding linear element in the strained state makes with the principal axes of the strain ellipsoid. Denoting these cosines by λ, μ, ν, we find

$$(\lambda, \mu, \nu) = [(1 + \epsilon_1)^2 l^2 + (1 + \epsilon_2)^2 m^2 + (1 + \epsilon_3)^2 n^2]^{-\frac{1}{2}} \{(1 + \epsilon_1)\, l, (1 + \epsilon_2)\, m, (1 + \epsilon_3)\, n\}. \quad \text{.........(11)}$$

By solving these for l, m, n we find

$$(l, m, n) = \left[\frac{\lambda^2}{(1+\epsilon_1)^2} + \frac{\mu^2}{(1+\epsilon_2)^2} + \frac{\nu^2}{(1+\epsilon_3)^2}\right]^{-\frac{1}{2}} \left(\frac{\lambda}{1+\epsilon_1}, \frac{\mu}{1+\epsilon_2}, \frac{\nu}{1+\epsilon_3}\right) \ldots\ldots(12)$$

Here l, m, n are the direction-cosines of a line in the unstrained state referred to the principal axes of the strain, and λ, μ, ν are the direction-cosines of the corresponding line in the strained state referred to the principal axes of the strain ellipsoid. The operation of deriving the second of these directions from the first may therefore be made in two steps. The first step* is the operation of deriving a set of direction-cosines (λ, μ, ν) from the set (l, m, n); and the second step is a rotation of the principal axes of the strain into the positions of the principal axes of the strain ellipsoid.

The formulæ also admit of interpretation in the sense that any small element of the body, which is spherical in the unstrained state, and has a given point as centre, assumes after strain the shape and orientation of the strain ellipsoid with its centre at the corresponding point, and any set of three orthogonal diameters of the sphere becomes a set of conjugate diameters of the ellipsoid.

30. Application to cartography.

The methods of this Chapter would admit of application to the problem of constructing maps. The surface to be mapped and the plane map of it are the analogues of a body in the unstrained and strained states. The theorem that the strain about any point is sensibly homogeneous is the theorem that any small portion of the map is similar to one of the orthographic projections of the corresponding portion of the original surface. The analogue of the properties of the strain-ellipsoid is found in the theorem that with any small circle on the original surface there corresponds a small ellipse on the map; the dimensions and orientation of the ellipse, with its centre at any point, being known, the scale of the map near the point, and all distortions of length, area and angle are determinate. These theorems form the foundation of the theory of cartography. [Cf. Tissot, *Mémoire sur la représentation des surfaces et les projections des cartes géographiques*, Paris, 1881.]

31. Conditions satisfied by the displacement.

The components of displacement u, v, w are not absolutely arbitrary functions of x, y, z. In the foregoing discussion it has been assumed that they are subject to such conditions of differentiability and continuity as will secure the validity of the "theorem of the total differential†." For our purpose this theorem is expressed by such equations as

$$\frac{du}{ds} = \frac{\partial u}{\partial x}\frac{dx}{ds} + \frac{\partial u}{\partial y}\frac{dy}{ds} + \frac{\partial u}{\partial z}\frac{dz}{ds}.$$

Besides this analytical restriction, there are others imposed by the assumed condition that the displacement must be such as can be conceived to take place in a continuous body. Thus, for example, a displacement, by which every

* This operation is one of homogeneous pure strain. See Article 33, *infra*.

† Cf. Harnack, *Introduction to the Calculus*, London, 1891, p. 92.

point is replaced by its optical image in a plane, would be excluded. The expression of any component displacement by functions, which become infinite at any point within the region of space occupied by the body, is also excluded. Any analytically possible displacement, by which the length of any line would be reduced to zero, is also to be excluded. We are thus concerned with real transformations which, within a certain region of space, have the following properties:—(i) The new coordinates

$$(x+u,\ y+v,\ z+w)$$

are continuous functions of the old coordinates (x, y, z) which obey the theorem of the total differential. (ii) The real functions u, v, w are such that the quadratic function

$$(1+2\epsilon_{xx})\,l^2+(1+2\epsilon_{yy})\,m^2+(1+2\epsilon_{zz})\,n^2+2\epsilon_{yz}mn+2\epsilon_{zx}nl+2\epsilon_{xy}lm$$

is definite and positive. (iii) The functional determinant denoted by $1+\Delta$ is positive and does not vanish.

The condition (iii) secures that the strained state is such as can be produced from the unstrained state, by a continuous series of small real displacements. It can be shown that it includes the condition (ii) when the transformation is real. From a geometrical point of view, this amounts to the observation that, if the volume of a variable tetrahedron is never reduced to zero, none of its edges can ever be reduced to zero.

In the particular case of homogeneous strain, the displacements are linear functions of the coordinates. Thus all homogeneous strains are included among linear homogeneous transformations. The condition (iii) then excludes such transformations as involve the operation of reflexion in a plane in addition to transformations which can be produced by a continuous series of small displacements. Some linear homogeneous transformations, which obey the condition (iii), express rotations about axes passing through the origin. All others involve the extension of some line. In discussing homogeneous strains and rotations it will be convenient to replace $(x+u,\ y+v,\ z+w)$ by $(x_1,\ y_1,\ z_1)$.

32. Finite homogeneous strain.

We shall take the equations by which the coordinates in the strained state are connected with the coordinates in the unstrained state to be

$$\left.\begin{aligned} x_1 &= (1+a_{11})\,x + a_{12}y + a_{13}\,z,\\ y_1 &= a_{21}x + (1+a_{22})\,y + a_{23}\,z,\\ z_1 &= a_{31}x + a_{32}y + (1+a_{33})\,z.\end{aligned}\right\} \quad\ldots\ldots\ldots\ldots(13)$$

The corresponding components of strain are given by the equations

$$\left.\begin{aligned} \epsilon_{xx} &= a_{11} + \tfrac{1}{2}\left(a_{11}{}^2 + a_{21}{}^2 + a_{31}{}^2\right),\\ &\ldots\ldots\ldots\ldots\ldots\ldots,\\ \epsilon_{yz} &= a_{32} + a_{23} + a_{12}a_{13} + a_{22}a_{23} + a_{32}a_{33},\\ &\ldots\ldots\ldots\ldots\ldots\ldots\end{aligned}\right\} \quad\ldots\ldots\ldots\ldots(14)$$

The quantities e_{xx}, ..., defined in Article 8, do not lose their importance when the displacements are not small. The notation used here may be identified with that of Article 8 by writing, for the expressions

$$a_{11},\ a_{22},\ a_{33},\ a_{23}+a_{32}, a_{31}+a_{13},\ a_{12}+a_{21},\ a_{32}-a_{23},\ a_{13}-a_{31},\ a_{21}-a_{12},$$

the expressions $e_{xx},\ e_{yy},\ e_{zz},\ e_{yz},\ e_{zx},\ e_{xy},\ 2\varpi_x,\ 2\varpi_y,\ 2\varpi_z$.

Denoting the radius vector from the origin to any point P, or (x, y, z), by r, we may resolve the displacement of P in the direction of r, and consider the ratio of the component displacement to the length r. Let E be this ratio. We may define E to be the *elongation* of the material in the direction of r. We find

$$E=\frac{1}{r}\left\{(x_1-x)\frac{x}{r}+(y_1-y)\frac{y}{r}+(z_1-z)\frac{z}{r}\right\};\ldots\ldots\ldots\ldots\ldots(15)$$

and this is the same as

$$Er^2=e_{xx}x^2+e_{yy}y^2+e_{zz}z^2+e_{yz}yz+e_{zx}zx+e_{xy}xy.\ \ldots\ldots\ldots(16)$$

A quadric surface obtained by equating the right-hand member of this equation to a constant may be called an *elongation quadric*. It has the property that the elongation in any direction is inversely proportional to the square of the central radius vector in that direction. In the case of very small displacements, the elongation quadric becomes the strain quadric previously discussed (Article 11). The invariant expressions noted in Article 13 (*c*) do not cease to be invariant when the displacements are not small.

The displacement expressed by (13) can be analysed into two constituent displacements. One constituent is derived from a potential, equal to half the right-hand member of (16); this displacement is directed, at each point, along the normal to the elongation quadric which passes through the point. The other constituent may be derived from a vector potential

$$-\tfrac{1}{2}[\varpi_x(y^2+z^2),\ \varpi_y(z^2+x^2),\ \varpi_z(x^2+y^2)]\ \ldots\ldots\ldots\ldots(17)$$

by the operation *curl*.

33. Homogeneous pure strain.

The direction of a line passing through the origin is unaltered by the strain if the coordinates x, y, z of any point on the line satisfy the equations

$$\frac{(1+a_{11})x+a_{12}y+a_{13}z}{x}=\frac{a_{21}x+(1+a_{22})y+a_{23}z}{y}$$
$$=\frac{a_{31}x+a_{32}y+(1+a_{33})z}{z}.\ \ldots\ldots(18)$$

If each of these quantities is put equal to λ, then λ is a root of the cubic equation

$$\begin{vmatrix} 1+a_{11}-\lambda & a_{12} & a_{13} \\ a_{21} & 1+a_{22}-\lambda & a_{23} \\ a_{31} & a_{32} & 1+a_{33}-\lambda \end{vmatrix}=0.\ \ldots\ldots\ldots(19)$$

The cubic has always one real root, so that there is always one line of which the direction is unaltered by the strain, and if the root is positive the *sense* of the line also is unaltered. When there are three such lines, they are not necessarily orthogonal; but, if they are orthogonal, they are by definition the principal axes of the strain. In this case the strain is said to be *pure*. It is worth while to give a formal definition, as follows:—Pure strain is such that the set of three orthogonal lines which remain orthogonal retain their directions and senses.

We may prove that the sufficient and necessary conditions that the strain corresponding with the equations (13), may be pure, are (i) that the quadratic form on the left-hand side of (20) below is definite and positive, (ii) that ϖ_x, ϖ_y, ϖ_z vanish. That these conditions are *sufficient* may be proved as follows:—When ϖ_x, ϖ_y, ϖ_z vanish, or $a_{23}=a_{32}$, ..., the equation (19) is the discriminating cubic of the quadric

$$(1+a_{11})x^2+(1+a_{22})y^2+(1+a_{33})z^2+2a_{23}yz+2a_{31}zx+2a_{12}xy=\text{const.}; \quad (20)$$

the left-hand member being positive, the cubic has three real positive roots, which determine three real directions according to equations (18); and these directions are orthogonal for they are the directions of the principal axes of the surface (20). Further they are the principal axes of the elongation quadric

$$a_{11}x^2+a_{22}y^2+a_{33}z^2+2a_{23}yz+2a_{31}zx+2a_{12}xy=\text{const.}, \quad \text{......(21)}$$

for this surface and (20) have their principal axes in the same directions.

The vanishing of ϖ_x, ϖ_y and ϖ_z are *necessary* conditions in order that the strain may be pure. To prove this we suppose that equations (13) represent a pure strain, and that the principal axes of the strain are a set of axes of coordinates ξ, η, ζ. The effect of the strain is to transform any point (ξ, η, ζ) into (ξ_1, η_1, ζ_1) in such a way that when, for example, η and ζ vanish, η_1 and ζ_1 also vanish. Referred to principal axes, the equations (13) must be equivalent to three equations of the form

$$\xi_1=(1+\epsilon_1)\xi, \quad \eta_1=(1+\epsilon_2)\eta, \quad \zeta_1=(1+\epsilon_3)\zeta, \quad \text{........(22)}$$

where ϵ_1, ϵ_2, ϵ_3 are the principal extensions. We may express the coordinates ξ, η, ζ in terms of x, y, z by means of an orthogonal scheme of substitution. We take this scheme to be

	x	y	z
ξ	l_1	m_1	n_1
η	l_2	m_2	n_2
ζ	l_3	m_3	n_3

Then we have

$$\begin{aligned} x_1 &= l_1\xi_1+l_2\eta_1+l_3\zeta_1 \\ &= (1+\epsilon_1)l_1(l_1x+m_1y+n_1z)+(1+\epsilon_2)l_2(l_2x+m_2y+n_2z) \\ &\qquad +(1+\epsilon_3)l_3(l_3x+m_3y+n_3z). \end{aligned}$$

Hence $a_{12} = (1 + \epsilon_1) l_1 m_1 + (1 + \epsilon_2) l_2 m_2 + (1 + \epsilon_3) l_3 m_3.$

We should find the same expression for a_{21}, and in the same way we should find identical expressions for the pairs of coefficients a_{23}, a_{32} and a_{31}, a_{13}.

It appears from this discussion that a homogeneous pure strain is equivalent to three simple extensions, in three directions mutually at right angles. These directions are those of the principal axes of the strain.

34. Analysis of any homogeneous strain into a pure strain and a rotation.

It is geometrically obvious that any homogeneous strain may be produced in a body by a suitable pure strain followed by a suitable rotation. To determine these we may proceed as follows:—When we have found the strain-components corresponding with the given strain, we can find the equation of the reciprocal strain ellipsoid. The lengths of the principal axes determine the principal extensions, and the directions of these axes are those of the principal axes of the strain. The required pure strain has these principal extensions and principal axes, and it is therefore completely determined. The required rotation is that by which the principal axes of the given strain are brought into coincidence with the principal axes of the strain ellipsoid. According to Article 28, this rotation turns three orthogonal lines of known position respectively into three other orthogonal lines of known position. The required angle and axis of rotation can therefore be determined by a well-known geometrical construction. [Cf. Kelvin and Tait, *Nat. Phil.* Part I. p. 69.]

35. Rotation*.

When the components of strain vanish, the displacement expressed by (13) of Articl 32 is a rotation about an axis passing through the origin. We shall take θ to be the angle of rotation and shall suppose the direction-cosines l, m, n of the axis to be taken so that the rotation is right-handed. Any point P, or (x, y, z), moves on a circle having its centre (C) on the axis, and comes into a position P_1, or (x_1, y_1, z_1). Let λ, μ, ν be the direction-cosines of CP in the sense from C to P, and let λ_1, μ_1, ν_1 be those of CP_1 in the sense from C to P_1. From P_1 let fall P_1N perpendicular to CP. The direction-cosines of NP_1 in the sense from N to P_1 are†

$$m\nu - n\mu, \quad n\lambda - l\nu, \quad l\mu - m\lambda.$$

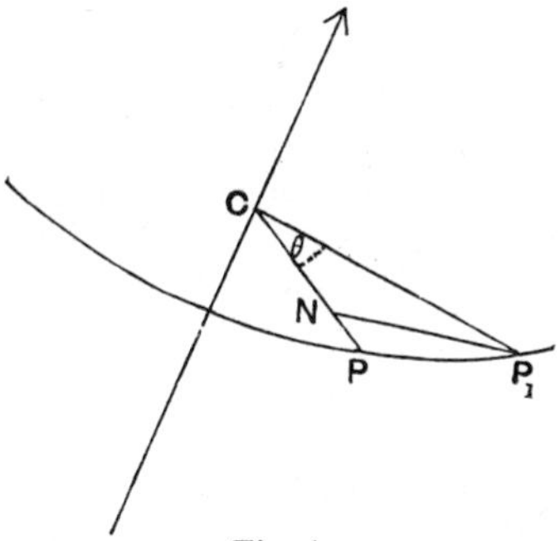

Fig. 4.

Let ξ, η, ζ be the coordinates of C. Then these satisfy the equations

$$\frac{\xi}{l} = \frac{\eta}{m} = \frac{\zeta}{n}, \quad l(\xi - x) + m(\eta - y) + n(\zeta - z) = 0,$$

so that $\xi = l(lx + my + nz)$ with similar expressions for η, ζ.

* Cf. Kelvin and Tait, *Nat. Phil.*, Part I. p. 69, and Minchin, *Statics*, Third Edn., Oxford, 1886, vol. 2, p. 103.

† The coordinate axes are taken to be a right-handed system.

The coordinates of P_1 are obtained by equating the projection of CP_1 on any coordinate axis to the sums of the projections of CN and NP_1. Projecting on the axis of x we find, taking ρ for the length of CP or CP_1,

$$\lambda_1 \rho = \lambda \rho \cos\theta + (m\nu - n\mu)\,\rho \sin\theta,$$

or

$$x_1 - \xi = (x-\xi)\cos\theta + \{m(z-\zeta) - n(y-\eta)\}\sin\theta,$$

or

$$x_1 = x + (mz - ny)\sin\theta - \{x - l(lx+my+nz)\}(1-\cos\theta). \qquad (23)$$

Similar expressions for y_1 and z_1 can be written down by symmetry.

The coefficients of the linear transformation (13) become in this case

$$\left.\begin{aligned} a_{11} &= -(1-l^2)(1-\cos\theta),\\ a_{12} &= -n\sin\theta + lm(1-\cos\theta),\\ a_{13} &= \quad m\sin\theta + ln(1-\cos\theta),\\ &\ldots\ldots \end{aligned}\right\} \qquad (24)$$

and it appears, on calculation, that the components of strain vanish, as they ought to do.

36. Simple extension.

In the example of simple extension given by the equations

$$x_1 = (1+e)\,x, \quad y_1 = y, \quad z_1 = z,$$

the components of strain, with the exception of ϵ_{xx} vanish, and

$$\epsilon_{xx} = e + \tfrac{1}{2}e^2.$$

The invariant property of the reciprocal strain ellipsoid may be applied to find the components of a strain which is a simple extension of amount e and direction l, m, n. We should find

$$\frac{\epsilon_{xx}}{l^2} = \ldots = \ldots = \frac{\epsilon_{yz}}{2mn} = \ldots = \ldots = e + \tfrac{1}{2}e^2.$$

The same property may be applied to determine the conditions that a strain specified by six components may be a simple extension. These conditions are that the invariants

$$\epsilon_{yy}\epsilon_{zz} + \ldots + \ldots - \tfrac{1}{4}(\epsilon^2_{yz} + \ldots + \ldots),$$

$$\epsilon_{xx}\epsilon_{yy}\epsilon_{zz} + \tfrac{1}{4}(\epsilon_{yz}\epsilon_{zx}\epsilon_{xy} - \epsilon_{xx}\epsilon^2_{yz} - \ldots - \ldots)$$

vanish. The amount of the extension is expressed in terms of the remaining invariant by the formula $\surd\{1 + 2(\epsilon_{xx} + \epsilon_{yy} + \epsilon_{zz})\} - 1$, the positive value of the square root being taken. Two roots of the cubic in κ, (7) of Article 26, are equal to unity, and the third is equal to $1 + 2(\epsilon_{xx} + \epsilon_{yy} + \epsilon_{zz})$. The direction of the extension is the direction (l, m, n) that is given by the equations

$$\frac{2\epsilon_{xx}l + \epsilon_{xy}m + \epsilon_{zx}n}{2l} = \frac{\epsilon_{xy}l + 2\epsilon_{yy}m + \epsilon_{yz}n}{2m} = \frac{\epsilon_{zx}l + \epsilon_{yz}m + 2\epsilon_{zz}n}{2n} = \epsilon_{xx} + \epsilon_{yy} + \epsilon_{zz}.$$

37. Simple shear.

In the example of simple shear given by the equations

$$x_1 = x + sy, \quad y_1 = y, \quad z_1 = z,$$

the components of strain are given by the equations

$$\epsilon_{xx} = \epsilon_{zz} = 0, \quad \epsilon_{yz} = \epsilon_{zx} = 0, \quad \epsilon_{yy} = \tfrac{1}{2}s^2, \quad \epsilon_{xy} = s.$$

By putting $s = 2\tan\alpha$ we may prove that the two principal extensions which are not zero are given, as in Article 3, by the equations

$$1 + \epsilon_1 = \sec\alpha - \tan\alpha, \quad 1 + \epsilon_2 = \sec\alpha + \tan\alpha.$$

We may prove that the area of a figure in the plane of x, y is unaltered by the shear and that the difference of the two principal extensions is equal to the amount of the shear. Further we may show that the directions of the principal axes of the strain are the bisectors of the angle AOx in Fig. 2 of Article 5, and that the angle through which the principal axes are turned is the angle α. So that the simple shear is equivalent to a "pure shear" followed by a rotation through an angle α, as was explained before.

By using the invariants noted in Article 26, we may prove that the conditions that a strain with given components ϵ_{xx}, ... may be a shearing strain are

$$2(\epsilon_{xx}+\epsilon_{yy}+\epsilon_{zz})+4(\epsilon_{yy}\epsilon_{zz}+\epsilon_{zz}\epsilon_{xx}+\epsilon_{xx}\epsilon_{yy})-(\epsilon^2_{yz}+\epsilon^2_{zx}+\epsilon^2_{xy})=0,$$

$$4\epsilon_{xx}\epsilon_{yy}\epsilon_{zz}+\epsilon_{yz}\epsilon_{zx}\epsilon_{xy}-\epsilon_{xx}\epsilon^2_{yz}-\epsilon_{yy}\epsilon^2_{zx}-\epsilon_{zz}\epsilon^2_{xy}=0,$$

and that the amount of the shear is $\sqrt{\{2(\epsilon_{xx}+\epsilon_{yy}+\epsilon_{zz})\}}$.

38. Additional results relating to shear.

A good example of shear* is presented by a sphere built up of circular cards in parallel planes. If each card is shifted in its own plane, so that the line of centres becomes a straight line inclined obliquely to the planes of the cards, the sphere becomes an ellipsoid, and the cards coincide with one set of circular sections of the ellipsoid. It is an instructive exercise to determine the principal axes of the strain and the principal extensions.

We may notice the following methods† of producing any homogeneous strain by a sequence of operations:

(*a*) Any such strain can be produced by a simple shear parallel to one axis of planes perpendicular to another, a simple extension in the direction at right angles to both axes, an uniform dilatation and a rotation.

(*b*) Any such strain can be produced by three simple shears each of which is a shear parallel to one axis of planes at right angles to another, the three axes being at right angles to each other, an uniform dilatation and a rotation.

39. Composition of strains.

After a body has been subjected to a homogeneous strain, it may again be subjected to a homogeneous strain; and the result is a displacement of the body, which, in general, could be effected by a single homogeneous strain. More generally, when any aggregate of points is transformed by two homogeneous linear transformations successively, the resulting displacement is equivalent to the effect of a single linear homogeneous transformation. This statement may be expressed by saying that linear homogeneous transformations form a *group*. The particular linear homogeneous transformations with which we are concerned are subjected to the conditions stated in Article 31, and they form a *continuous group*. The transformations of rotation, described in Article 35, also form a group; and this group is a *sub-group* included in the linear homogeneous group. The latter group also includes all homogeneous strains; but these do not by themselves form a group, for two successive homogeneous strains‡ may be equivalent to a rotation.

* Suggested by Mr R. R. Webb. Cf. Kelvin and Tait, *Nat. Phil.*, Part I. p. 122.

† Cf. Kelvin and Tait, *Nat. Phil.*, Part I. §§ 178 *et seq.*

‡ A transformation such as (13) of Article 32, supposed to satisfy condition (iii) of Article 31, expresses a rotation if all the components of strain (14) vanish. In any other case it expresses a homogeneous strain.

The result of two successive linear homogeneous transformations may be expressed conveniently in the notation of matrices. In this notation the equations of transformation (13) would be written

$$(x_1, y_1, z_1) = \begin{pmatrix} 1+a_{11} & a_{12} & a_{13} \\ a_{21} & 1+a_{22} & a_{23} \\ a_{31} & a_{32} & 1+a_{33} \end{pmatrix} (x, y, z), \quad \text{.........(25)}$$

and the equations of a second such transformation could in the same way be written

$$(x_2, y_2, z_2) = \begin{pmatrix} 1+b_{11} & b_{12} & b_{13} \\ b_{21} & 1+b_{22} & b_{23} \\ b_{31} & b_{32} & 1+b_{33} \end{pmatrix} (x_1, y_1, z_1). \quad \text{......(26)}$$

By the first transformation a point (x, y, z) is replaced by (x_1, y_1, z_1), and by the second (x_1, y_1, z_1) is replaced by (x_2, y_2, z_2). The result of the two operations is that (x, y, z) is replaced by (x_2, y_2, z_2); and we have

$$(x_2, y_2, z_2) = \begin{pmatrix} 1+c_{11} & c_{12} & c_{13} \\ c_{21} & 1+c_{22} & c_{23} \\ c_{31} & c_{32} & 1+c_{33} \end{pmatrix} (x, y, z), \quad \text{.........(27)}$$

where

$$\left.\begin{aligned} c_{11} &= b_{11} + a_{11} + b_{11}a_{11} + b_{12}a_{21} + b_{13}a_{31}, \\ c_{12} &= b_{12} + a_{12} + b_{11}a_{12} + b_{12}a_{22} + b_{13}a_{32}, \\ &\ldots\ldots \end{aligned}\right\} \quad \text{...............(28)}$$

In regard to this result, we notice (i) that the transformations are not in general commutative; (ii) that the result of two successive pure strains is not in general a pure strain; (iii) that the result of two successive transformations, involving very small displacements, is obtained by simple superposition, that is by the addition of corresponding coefficients. The result (ii) may be otherwise expressed by the statement that pure strains do not form a group.

40. Additional results relating to the composition of strains.

When the transformation (26) is equivalent to a rotation about an axis, so that its coefficients are those given in Article 35, we may show that the components of strain corresponding with the transformation (27) are the same as those corresponding with the transformation (25), as it is geometrically evident they ought to be.

In the particular case where the transformation (25) is a pure strain referred to its principal axes, [so that $a_{11}=\epsilon_1$, $a_{22}=\epsilon_2$, $a_{33}=\epsilon_3$, and the remaining coefficients vanish], and the transformation (26) is a rotation about an axis, [so that its coefficients are those given in Article 35], the coefficients of the resultant strain are given by such equations as

$$\begin{aligned} 1+c_{11} &= (1+\epsilon_1)\{1-(1-l^2)(1-\cos\theta)\}, \\ c_{12} &= (1+\epsilon_2)\{-n\sin\theta + lm(1-\cos\theta)\}, \\ &\ldots\ldots \end{aligned}$$

The quantities ϖ_x, ϖ_y, ϖ_z corresponding with this strain are not components of rotation, the displacement not being small. We should find for example

$$2\varpi_x = c_{32} - c_{23} = 2l \sin\theta + (\epsilon_2 + \epsilon_3)\, l \sin\theta + (\epsilon_2 - \epsilon_3)\, mn\,(1 - \cos\theta).$$

We may deduce the result that, if the components of strain corresponding with the transformation (27) vanish, and the condition (iii) of Article 31 is satisfied, the rotation expressed by (27) is of amount θ about an axis (l, m, n) determined by the equations

$$\frac{c_{32} - c_{23}}{l} = \frac{c_{13} - c_{31}}{m} = \frac{c_{21} - c_{12}}{n} = 2\sin\theta.$$

We may show that the transformation expressed by the equations

$$x_1 = x - \varpi_z y + \varpi_y z, \quad y_1 = y - \varpi_x z + \varpi_z x, \quad z_1 = z - \varpi_y x + \varpi_x y$$

represents a homogeneous strain compounded of uniform extension of all lines which are at right angles to the direction $(\varpi_x : \varpi_y : \varpi_z)$ and rotation about a line in this direction. The amount of the extension is $\sqrt{(1 + \varpi_x^2 + \varpi_y^2 + \varpi_z^2)} - 1$, and the tangent of the angle of rotation is $\sqrt{(\varpi_x^2 + \varpi_y^2 + \varpi_z^2)}$.

In the general case of the composition of strains, we may seek expressions for the resultant strain-components in terms of the strain-components of the constituent strains and the coefficients of the transformations. If we denote the components of strain corresponding with (25), (26), (27) respectively by $(\epsilon_{xx})_a, \ldots \epsilon_{x_1 x_1}, \ldots (\epsilon_{xx})_c, \ldots$, we find such formulæ as

$$(\epsilon_{xx})_c = (\epsilon_{xx})_a + (1 + a_{11})^2 \epsilon_{x_1 x_1} + a^2_{21} \epsilon_{y_1 y_1} + a^2_{31} \epsilon_{z_1 z_1}$$
$$+ a_{21} a_{31} \epsilon_{y_1 z_1} + (1 + a_{11})\, a_{31} \epsilon_{z_1 x_1} + (1 + a_{11})\, a_{21} \epsilon_{x_1 y_1},$$

$$(\epsilon_{yz})_c = (\epsilon_{yz})_a + 2a_{12} a_{13} \epsilon_{x_1 x_1} + 2(1 + a_{22})\, a_{23} \epsilon_{y_1 y_1} + 2(1 + a_{33})\, a_{32} \epsilon_{z_1 z_1}$$
$$+ \{(1 + a_{22})(1 + a_{33}) + a_{23} a_{32}\}\, \epsilon_{y_1 z_1} + \{(1 + a_{33})\, a_{12} + a_{32} a_{13}\}\, \epsilon_{z_1 x_1} + \{(1 + a_{22})\, a_{13} + a_{12} a_{23}\}\, \epsilon_{x_1 y_1}.$$

CHAPTER II

ANALYSIS OF STRESS

41. THE notion of stress in general is simply that of balancing internal action and reaction between two parts of a body, the force which either part exerts on the other being one aspect of a stress*. A familiar example is that of tension in a bar; the part of the bar on one side of any normal section exerts tension on the other part across the section. Another familiar example is that of hydrostatic pressure. At any point within a fluid, pressure is exerted across any plane drawn through the point, and this pressure is estimated as a force per unit of area. For the complete specification of the stress at any point of a body we should require to know the force per unit of area across every plane drawn through the point, and the direction of the force as well as its magnitude would be part of the specification. For a complete specification of the state of stress within a body we should require to know the stress at every point of the body. The object of an analysis of stress is to determine the nature of the quantities by which the stress at a point can be specified†. In this Chapter we shall develop also those consequences in regard to the theory of the equilibrium and motion of a body which follow directly from the analysis of stress.

42. Traction across a plane at a point.

We consider any area S in a given plane, and containing a point O within a body. We denote the normal to the plane drawn in a specified sense by ν, and we think of the portion of the body, which is on the side of the plane towards which ν is drawn, as exerting force on the remaining portion across the plane, this force being one aspect of a stress. We suppose that the force, which is thus exerted across the particular area S, is statically equivalent to a force R, acting at O in a definite direction, and a couple G, about a definite axis. If we contract the area S by any continuous process, keeping the point O always within it, the force R and the couple G tend towards zero limits, and the direction of the force tends to a limiting direction (l, m, n). We assume that the number obtained by dividing the number of units of force in the force R by the number of units of area in the area S (say R/S) tends to a limit F, which is not zero, and that on the other hand G/S tends to zero as a

* For a discussion of the notion of stress from the point of view of Rational Mechanics, see Note B at the end of this book.

† The theory of the specification of stress was given by Cauchy in the Article 'De la pression ou tension dans un corps solide' in the volume for 1827 of the *Exercices de mathématiques*.

limit. We define a vector quantity by the direction (l, m, n), the numerical measure F, and the dimension symbol

$$(\text{mass})\,(\text{length})^{-1}\,(\text{time})^{-2}.$$

This quantity is a force per unit of area; we call it the *traction* across the plane ν at the point O. We write X_ν, Y_ν, Z_ν for the projections of this vector on the axes of coordinates. The projection on the normal ν is

$$X_\nu \cos(x, \nu) + Y_\nu \cos(y, \nu) + Z_\nu \cos(z, \nu).$$

If this component traction is positive it is a *tension*; if it is negative it is a *pressure*. If dS is a very small area of the plane normal to ν at the point O, the portion of the body, which is on the side of the plane towards which ν is drawn, acts upon the portion on the other side with a force at the point O, specified by

$$(X_\nu dS, \quad Y_\nu dS, \quad Z_\nu dS);$$

this is the *traction upon the element of area* dS.

In the case of pressure in a fluid at rest, the direction (l, m, n) of the vector (X_ν, Y_ν, Z_ν) is always exactly opposite to the direction ν. In the cases of viscous fluids in motion and elastic solids, this direction is in general obliquely inclined to ν.

43. Surface Tractions and Body Forces.

When two bodies are in contact, the nature of the action between them over the surfaces in contact is assumed to be the same as the nature of the action between two portions of the same body, separated by an imagined surface. If we begin with any point O within a body, and any direction for ν, and allow O to move up to a point O' on the bounding surface, and ν to coincide with the outward drawn normal to this surface at O', then X_ν, Y_ν, Z_ν tend to limiting values, which are the components of the *surface traction* at O'; and $X_\nu \delta S$, $Y_\nu \delta S$, $Z_\nu \delta S$ are the forces exerted across the element δS of the bounding surface by some other body having contact with the body in question in the neighbourhood of the point O'.

In general other forces act upon a body, or upon each part of the body, in addition to the tractions on its surface. The type of such forces is the force of gravitation, and such forces are in general proportional to the masses of particles on which they act, and, further, they are determined as to magnitude and direction by the positions of these particles in the field of force. If X, Y, Z are the components of the intensity of the field at any point, m the mass of a particle at the point, then mX, mY, mZ are the forces of the field that act on the particle. The forces of the field may arise from the action of particles forming part of the body, as in the case of a body subject to its own gravitation, or of particles outside the body, as in the case of a body subject to the gravitational attraction of another body. In either case we call them *body forces*.

44. Equations of Motion.

The body forces, applied to any portion of a body, are statically equivalent to a single force, applied at one point, together with a couple. The components, parallel to the axes, of the single force are

$$\iiint \rho X\,dx\,dy\,dz,\quad \iiint \rho Y\,dx\,dy\,dz,\quad \iiint \rho Z\,dx\,dy\,dz,$$

where ρ is the density of the body at the point (x, y, z), and the integration is taken through the volume of the portion of the body. In like manner, the tractions on the elements of area of the surface of the portion are equivalent to a resultant force and a couple, and the components of the former are

$$\iint X_\nu dS,\quad \iint Y_\nu dS,\quad \iint Z_\nu dS,$$

where the integration is taken over the surface of the portion. The centre of mass of the portion moves like a particle under the action of these two sets of forces, for they are all the *external* forces acting on the portion. If then (f_x, f_y, f_z) is the acceleration of the particle which is at the point (x, y, z) at time t, the equations of motion of the portion are three of the type*

$$\iiint \rho f_x\,dx\,dy\,dz = \iiint \rho X\,dx\,dy\,dz + \iint X_\nu dS, \quad\text{...............(1)}$$

where the volume-integrations are taken through the volume of the portion, and the surface-integration is taken over its surface.

Again the equations, which determine the changes of moment of momentum of the portion of the body, are three of the type

$$\iiint \rho\,(yf_z - zf_y)\,dx\,dy\,dz = \iiint \rho\,(yZ - zY)\,dx\,dy\,dz + \iint (yZ_\nu - zY_\nu)\,dS\,; \quad\text{............(2)}$$

and, in accordance with the theorem† of the independence of the motion of the centre of mass and the motion relative to the centre of mass, the origin of the coordinates x, y, z may be taken to be at the centre of mass of the portion.

The above equations (1) and (2) are the types of the *general equations of motion of all bodies* for which the notion of stress is valid.

45. Equilibrium.

When a body is at rest under the action of body forces and surface tractions, these are subject to the conditions of equilibrium, which are obtained from equations (1) and (2) by omission of the terms containing f_x, f_y, f_z. We have thus six equations, viz.: three of the type

$$\iiint \rho X\,dx\,dy\,dz + \iint X_\nu dS = 0, \quad\text{.............................(3)}$$

and three of the type

$$\iiint \rho\,(yZ - zY)\,dx\,dy\,dz + \iint (yZ_\nu - zY_\nu)\,dS = 0. \quad\text{..................(4)}$$

* The equation (1) is the form assumed by the equations of the type $\Sigma m\ddot{x} = \Sigma X$, of my *Theoretical Mechanics*, Chapter VI.; and the equation (2) is the form assumed by the equations of the type $\Sigma m\,(y\ddot{z} - z\ddot{y}) = \Sigma\,(yZ - zY)$ of the same Chapter.

† *Theoretical Mechanics*, Chapter VI.

It follows that if the body forces and surface tractions are given arbitrarily, there will not be equilibrium.

In the particular case where there are no body forces, equilibrium cannot be maintained unless the surface tractions satisfy six equations of the types

$$\iint X_\nu dS = 0, \quad \text{and} \quad \iint (yZ_\nu - zY_\nu)\, dS = 0.$$

46. Law of equilibrium of surface tractions on small volumes.

From the forms alone of equations (1) and (2) we can deduce a result of great importance. Let the volume of integration be very small in all its dimensions, and let l^3 denote this volume. If we divide both members of equation (1) by l^2, and then pass to a limit by diminishing l indefinitely, we find the equation

$$\lim_{l=0} l^{-2} \iint X_\nu dS = 0.$$

Again, if we take the origin within the volume of integration, we obtain by a similar process from (2) the equation

$$\lim_{l=0} l^{-3} \iint (yZ_\nu - zY_\nu)\, dS = 0.$$

The equations of which these are types can be interpreted in the statement:

The tractions on the elements of area of the surface of any portion of a body, which is very small in all its dimensions, are ultimately, to a first approximation, a system of forces in equilibrium.

47. Specification of stress at a point.

Through any point O in a body, there passes a doubly infinite system of planes, and the complete specification of the stress at O involves the knowledge of the traction at O across all these planes. We may use the results obtained in the last Article to express all these tractions in terms of the component tractions across planes parallel to the coordinate planes, and to obtain relations between these components. We denote the traction across a plane $x = \text{const.}$ by its vector components (X_x, Y_x, Z_x) and use a similar notation for the tractions across planes $y = \text{const.}$ and $z = \text{const.}$ The capital letters show the directions of the component tractions, and the suffixes the planes across which they act. The sense is such that X_x is positive when it is a tension, negative when it is a pressure. If the axis of x is supposed drawn upwards from the paper (cf. Fig. 5), and the paper is placed so as to pass through O, the traction in question is exerted by the part of the body above the paper upon the part below.

We consider the equilibrium of a tetrahedral portion of the body, having one vertex at O, and the three edges that meet at this vertex parallel to the axes of coordinates. The remaining vertices are the intersections of these edges with a plane near to O. We denote the direction of the normal to this plane, drawn away from the interior of the tetrahedron, by ν, so that its direction-cosines are $\cos(x, \nu)$, $\cos(y, \nu)$, $\cos(z, \nu)$. Let Δ be the area of the face of the tetrahedron that is in this plane; the areas of the remaining faces are

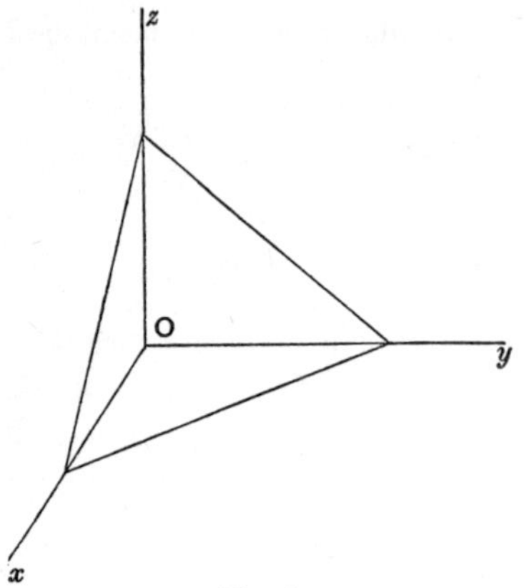

Fig. 5.

$$\Delta\cos(x, \nu),\ \Delta\cos(y, \nu),\ \Delta\cos(z, \nu).$$

For a first approximation, when all the edges of the tetrahedron are small, we may take the resultant tractions across the face ν to be $X_\nu\Delta$, ..., and those on the remaining faces to be $-X_x\Delta\cos(x, \nu)$, ... The sum of the tractions parallel to x on all the faces of the tetrahedron can be taken to be

$$X_\nu\Delta - X_x\Delta\cos(x, \nu) - X_y\Delta\cos(y, \nu) - X_z\Delta\cos(z, \nu).$$

By dividing by Δ, in accordance with the process of the last Article, we obtain the first of equations (5), and the other equations of this set are obtained by similar processes; we thus find the three equations

$$\left.\begin{aligned} X_\nu &= X_x\cos(x, \nu) + X_y\cos(y, \nu) + X_z\cos(z, \nu),\\ Y_\nu &= Y_x\cos(x, \nu) + Y_y\cos(y, \nu) + Y_z\cos(z, \nu),\\ Z_\nu &= Z_x\cos(x, \nu) + Z_y\cos(y, \nu) + Z_z\cos(z, \nu).\end{aligned}\right\} \quad \text{...........(5)}$$

By these equations the traction across any plane through O is expressed in terms of the tractions across planes parallel to the coordinate planes. By these equations also the component tractions across planes, parallel to the coordinate planes, at any point on the bounding surface of a body, are connected with the tractions exerted upon the body, across the surface, by any other body in contact with it.

Again, consider a very small cube (Fig. 6) of the material with its edges parallel to the coordinate axes. To a first approximation, the resultant tractions exerted upon the cube across the faces perpendicular to the axis of x are ΔX_x, ΔY_x, ΔZ_x, for the face for which x is greater, and $-\Delta X_x$, $-\Delta Y_x$, $-\Delta Z_x$, for the opposite face, Δ being the area of any face. Similar expressions hold for the other faces. The value of $\iint(yZ_\nu - zY_\nu)\,dS$ for the cube can be taken to be $l\Delta(Z_y - Y_z)$, where l is the length of any edge. By the process of the last Article we obtain the first of equations (6), and the other equations of this set are obtained by similar processes; we thus find the three equations

$$Z_y = Y_z,\quad X_z = Z_x,\quad Y_x = X_y. \quad \text{....................(6)}$$

By equations (6) the number of quantities which must be specified, in order that the stress at a point may be determined, is reduced to six, viz. three normal component tractions X_x, Y_y, Z_z, and three tangential tractions Y_z, Z_x, X_y. These six quantities are called the *components of stress** at the point.

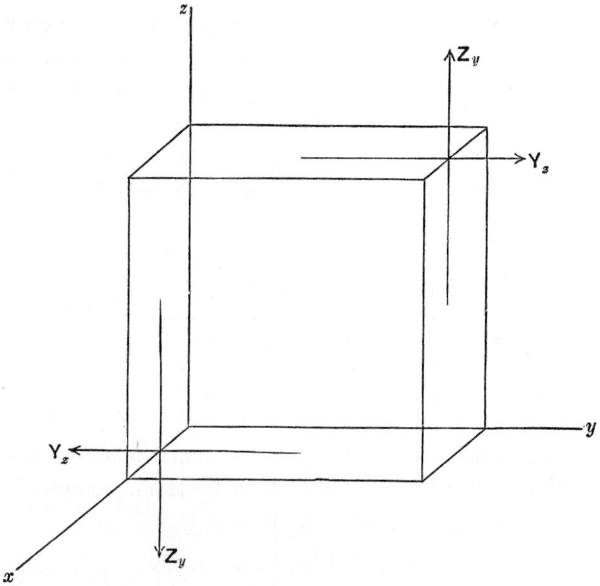

Fig. 6.

The six components of stress are sometimes written $\widehat{xx}$, $\widehat{yy}$, $\widehat{zz}$, $\widehat{yz}$, $\widehat{zx}$, $\widehat{xy}$. A notation of this kind is especially convenient when use is made of the orthogonal curvilinear coordinates of Article 19. The six components of stress referred to the normals to the surfaces α, β, γ at a point will hereafter be denoted by $\widehat{\alpha\alpha}$, $\widehat{\beta\beta}$, $\widehat{\gamma\gamma}$, $\widehat{\beta\gamma}$, $\widehat{\gamma\alpha}$, $\widehat{\alpha\beta}$.

48. Measure of stress.

The state of stress within a body is determined when we know the values at each point of the six components of stress. Each of these stress-components is a traction of the kind described in Article 42, so that it is measured as a force per unit area. The dimension symbol of any stress-component is $ML^{-1}T^{-2}$.

A stress may accordingly be measured as so many "tons per square inch," or so many "dynes per square centimetre," or more generally, as so many units of force per unit of area. [One ton per square inch $= 1{\cdot}545 \times 10^8$ dynes per square centimetre.]

* A symmetrical method of specifying the stress is worked out by Lord Kelvin (Article 10, footnote). The method is equivalent to taking as the six components of stress at a point the tensions per unit of area across six planes which are perpendicular respectively to the six edges of a chosen tetrahedron.

For example, the pressure of the atmosphere is about 10^6 dynes per square centimetre. As exemplifying the stresses which have to be allowed for by engineers we may note the statement of W. C. Unwin* that the Conway bridge is daily subjected to stresses reaching 7 tons per square inch.

49. Transformation of stress-components.

Since the traction at a given point across any plane is determined when the six components of stress at the point are given, it must be possible to express the six components of stress, referred to any system of axes, in terms of those referred to another system. Let the components of stress referred to axes of x', y', z' be denoted by $X'_{x'}, \ldots$; and let the new coordinates be given in terms of the old by the orthogonal scheme of transformation

	x	y	z
x'	l_1	m_1	n_1
y'	l_2	m_2	n_2
z'	l_3	m_3	n_3

Then equations (5) show that the component tractions across the plane x' (in the directions of the axes of x, y, z) are given by the equations

$$\left.\begin{aligned} X_{x'} &= l_1 X_x + m_1 X_y + n_1 X_z, \\ Y_{x'} &= l_1 Y_x + m_1 Y_y + n_1 Y_z, \\ Z_{x'} &= l_1 Z_x + m_1 Z_y + n_1 Z_z. \end{aligned}\right\} \qquad \ldots\ldots(7)$$

Also, since the traction across any plane is a vector, we have the equations

$$\left.\begin{aligned} X'_{x'} &= l_1 X_{x'} + m_1 Y_{x'} + n_1 Z_{x'}, \\ Y'_{x'} &= l_2 X_{x'} + m_2 Y_{x'} + n_2 Z_{x'}, \\ Z'_{x'} &= l_3 X_{x'} + m_3 Y_{x'} + n_3 Z_{x'}. \end{aligned}\right\} \qquad \ldots\ldots(8)$$

On substituting from (7) in (8), and taking account of (6), we find formulæ of the type

$$\left.\begin{aligned} X'_{x'} &= l_1^2 X_x + m_1^2 Y_y + n_1^2 Z_z + 2m_1 n_1 Y_z + 2n_1 l_1 Z_x + 2l_1 m_1 X_y, \\ X'_{y'} &= l_1 l_2 X_x + m_1 m_2 Y_y + n_1 n_2 Z_z + (m_1 n_2 + m_2 n_1) Y_z \\ &\qquad + (n_1 l_2 + n_2 l_1) Z_x + (l_1 m_2 + l_2 m_1) X_y. \end{aligned}\right\} \qquad \ldots\ldots(9)$$

These are the formulæ for the transformation of stress-components.

50. The stress quadric.

The formulæ (9) show that, if the equation of the quadric surface

$$X_x x^2 + Y_y y^2 + Z_z z^2 + 2Y_z yz + 2Z_x zx + 2X_y xy = \text{const.} \qquad \ldots\ldots(10)$$

is transformed by an orthogonal substitution so that the left-hand member becomes a function of x', y', z', the coefficients of $x'^2, \ldots\ 2y'z', \ldots$ in the left-hand member are $X'_{x'}, \ldots\ Y'_{z'}, \ldots$.

* *The Testing of Materials of Construction*, London 1888, p. 9.

The quadric surface (10) is called the *stress quadric.* It has the property that the normal stress across any plane through its centre is inversely proportional to the square of that radius vector of the quadric which is normal to the plane. If the quadric were referred to its principal axes, the tangential tractions across the coordinate planes would vanish. The normal tractions across these planes are called *principal stresses.* We learn that there exist, at any point of a body, three orthogonal planes, across each of which the traction is purely normal. These are called the *principal planes of stress.* We also learn that to specify completely the state of stress at any point of a body we require to know the directions of the principal planes of stress, and the magnitudes of the principal stresses; and that we may then obtain the six components of stress, referred to any set of orthogonal planes, by the process of transforming the equation of a quadric surface from one set of axes to another. The stress at a point may be regarded as a single quantity related to directions; this quantity is not a vector, but has six components in much the same way as a strain*.

51. Types of stress.

(*a*) *Purely normal stress.*

If the traction across every plane at a point is normal to the plane, the terms containing products yz, zx, xy are always absent from the equation of the stress quadric, however the rectangular axes of coordinates may be chosen. In this case any set of orthogonal lines passing through the point can be taken to be the principal axes of the quadric. It follows that the quadric is a sphere, and thence that the normal stress-components are all equal in magnitude and have the same sign. If they are positive the stress is a tension, the same in all directions round the point. If they are negative the stress is pressure, with the like property of equality in all directions†.

(*b*) *Simple tension or pressure.*

A simple tension or pressure is a state of stress at a point, which is such that the traction across one plane through the point is normal to the plane, and the traction across any perpendicular plane vanishes. The equation of the stress quadric referred to its principal axes would be of the form

$$X'_{x'}x'^2 = \text{const.},$$

so that the quadric consists of a pair of planes normal to the direction of the tension, or pressure. The components of stress referred to arbitrary axes of x, y, z would be

$$X_x = X'_{x'}l^2, \quad Y_y = X'_{x'}m^2, \quad Z_z = X'_{x'}n^2, \quad Y_z = X'_{x'}mn, \quad Z_x = X'_{x'}nl, \quad X_y = X'_{x'}lm,$$

where (l, m, n) is the direction of the tension, or pressure, and $X'_{x'}$ is its magnitude. If the stress is tension $X'_{x'}$ is positive; if the stress is pressure $X'_{x'}$ is negative.

(*c*) *Shearing stress.*

The result expressed by equations (6) is independent of the directions of the axes of coordinates, and may be stated as follows:—The tangential traction, parallel to a line l, across a plane at right angles to a line l', the two lines being at right angles to each other, is equal to the tangential traction, parallel

* In the language of Voigt it is a tensor-triad. Cf. Article 14 (*b*) *supra.*

† This is a fundamental theorem of rational Hydrodynamics, cf. Lamb, *Hydrodynamics*, p. 2. It was proved first by Cauchy, see *Ency. d. math. Wiss.*, Bd. 4, Art. 15, p. 52.

to l', across a plane at right angles to l. It follows that the existence of tangential traction across any plane implies the existence of tangential traction across a perpendicular plane. The term *shearing stress* is used to express the stress at a point specified by a pair of equal tangential tractions on two perpendicular planes.

We may use the analysis of Article 49 to determine the corresponding principal stresses and principal planes of stress. Let the stress quadric be $2X'_{y'}x'y'=\text{const.}$, so that there is tangential traction parallel to the axis x' on a plane $y'=\text{const.}$, and equal tangential traction parallel to the axis y' on a plane $x'=\text{const.}$ Let the axes of x, y, z be the principal axes of the stress. The form $2X'_{y'}x'y'$ is the same as

$$X'_{y'}\left\{\left(\frac{x'+y'}{\sqrt{2}}\right)^2-\left(\frac{x'-y'}{\sqrt{2}}\right)^2\right\},$$

and this ought to be the same as

$$X_x x^2+Y_y y^2+Z_z z^2.$$

We therefore have $$Z_z=0,\quad X_x=-Y_y=X'_{y'};$$

and we find that the shearing stress is equivalent to tension across one of the planes, that bisect the angles between the two perpendicular planes concerned, and pressure across the other of these planes. The tension and the pressure are equal in absolute magnitude, and each of them is equal to either tangential traction of the shearing stress.

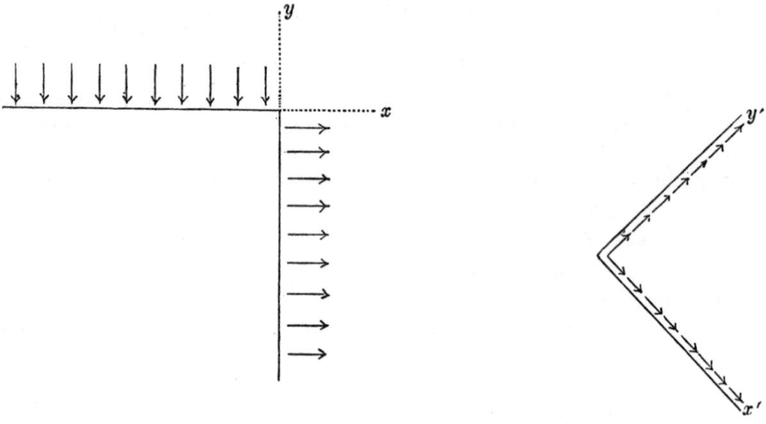

Fig. 7.

The diagram (Fig. 7) illustrates the equivalence of the shearing stress and the principal stresses. Shearing stress equivalent to such principal stresses as those shown in the left-hand figure may be expected to produce shearing strains in which planes of the material that are perpendicular to the axis of y' before the application of the stress slide in a direction parallel to the axis of x', and planes perpendicular to the axis of x' slide in a direction parallel to the axis of y'. Thus shearing stress of the type X_y may be expected to produce shearing strain of the type e_{xy}. (See Article 14 (*c*).)

(*d*) *Plane Stress.*

A more general type of stress, which includes simple tension and shearing stress as particular cases, is obtained by assuming that *one* principal stress is zero. The stress quadric is then a cylinder standing on a conic as base, and the latter may be called the *stress conic*; its plane contains the directions of the two principal stresses which do not vanish. If this plane is at right angles to the axis of z, the equation of the stress conic is of the form

$$X_x x^2 + Y_y y^2 + 2X_y xy = \text{const.}$$

and the shearing stresses Z_x and Y_z are zero, as well as the tension Z_z. In the particular case of simple tension the stress conic consists of a pair of parallel lines, in the case of shearing stress it is a rectangular hyperbola. If it is a circle there is tension or pressure the same in all directions in the plane of the circle.

52. Resolution of any stress-system into uniform tension and shearing stress.

The quantity $X_x + Y_y + Z_z$ is invariant as regards transformations from one set of rectangular axes to another. When the stress-system is uniform normal pressure of amount p, this quantity is $-3p$. In general, we may call the quantity $\frac{1}{3}(X_x + Y_y + Z_z)$ the "mean tension at a point"; and we may resolve the stress-system into components characterized respectively by the existence and non-existence of mean tension. For this purpose we may put

$$X_x = \tfrac{1}{3}(X_x + Y_y + Z_z) + \tfrac{2}{3}X_x - \tfrac{1}{3}(Y_y + Z_z),$$

......

Then the stress-system expressed by $\frac{2}{3}X_x - \frac{1}{3}(Y_y + Z_z)$, ... involves no mean tension. This system has the property that the sum of the principal stresses vanishes; and it is possible to choose rectangular axes of coordinates x', y', z' in such a way that the normal tractions $X'_{x'}$, $Y'_{y'}$, $Z'_{z'}$, corresponding with these axes, vanish. Accordingly, stress-systems, which involve no mean tension at a point, are equivalent to shearing stresses only, in the sense that three orthogonal planes can be found across which the tractions are purely tangential. It follows that any stress-system at a point is equivalent to tension (or pressure), the same in all directions round the point, together with tangential tractions across three planes which cut each other at right angles.

53. Additional results.

The proofs of the following results* may serve as exercises for the student:

(i) The quantities

$$X_x + Y_y + Z_z, \quad Y_y Z_z + Z_z X_x + X_x Y_y - Y_z^2 - Z_x^2 - X_y^2,$$
$$X_x Y_y Z_z + 2Y_z Z_x X_y - X_x Y_z^2 - Y_y Z_x^2 - Z_z X_y^2$$

are invariant as regards orthogonal transformations of coordinates.

(ii) If X_x, Y_y, Z_z are principal stresses, the traction across any plane is proportional to the central perpendicular on the parallel tangent plane of the ellipsoid

$$x^2/X_x^2 + y^2/Y_y^2 + z^2/Z_z^2 = \text{const.}$$

This is Lamé's *stress-ellipsoid*. The reciprocal surface was discussed by Cauchy; its central radius vector in any direction is inversely proportional to the traction across the plane at right angles to that direction.

* The results (i)—(v) are due to Cauchy and Lamé.

(iii) The quadric surface $x^2/X_x+y^2/Y_y+z^2/Z_z=\text{const.}$ (in which $X_x, \ldots$ are principal stresses), called Lamé's *stress-director quadric*, is the reciprocal of the stress quadric with respect to its centre; the radius vector from the centre to any point of the surface is in the direction of the traction across a plane parallel to the tangent plane at the point.

(iv) The planes across which there is no normal traction at a point envelope a cone of the second degree which is the reciprocal of the asymptotic cone of the stress quadric at the point. The former cone is Lamé's *cone of shearing stress*. When it is real, it separates the planes across which the normal traction is tension from those across which it is pressure; when it is imaginary the normal traction across all planes is tension or pressure according as the mean tension $\frac{1}{3}(X_x+Y_y+Z_z)$ is positive or negative.

(v) If any two lines x and x' are drawn from any point of a body in a state of stress, and planes at right angles to them are drawn at the point, the component parallel to x' of the traction across the plane perpendicular to x is equal to the component parallel to x of the traction across the plane perpendicular to x'.

This theorem, which may be expressed by the equation $x'_x=x_{x'}$, is a generalization of the results (6) of Article 47.

(vi) Maxwell's electrostatic stress-system*.

Let V be the potential of a system of electric charges, and let a stress-system be determined by the equations

$$X_x=\frac{1}{8\pi}\left\{\left(\frac{\partial V}{\partial x}\right)^2-\left(\frac{\partial V}{\partial y}\right)^2-\left(\frac{\partial V}{\partial z}\right)^2\right\}, \qquad Y_z=\frac{1}{4\pi}\frac{\partial V}{\partial y}\frac{\partial V}{\partial z},$$

$$Y_y=\frac{1}{8\pi}\left\{-\left(\frac{\partial V}{\partial x}\right)^2+\left(\frac{\partial V}{\partial y}\right)^2-\left(\frac{\partial V}{\partial z}\right)^2\right\}, \quad Z_x=\frac{1}{4\pi}\frac{\partial V}{\partial z}\frac{\partial V}{\partial x},$$

$$Z_z=\frac{1}{8\pi}\left\{-\left(\frac{\partial V}{\partial x}\right)^2-\left(\frac{\partial V}{\partial y}\right)^2+\left(\frac{\partial V}{\partial z}\right)^2\right\}, \quad X_y=\frac{1}{4\pi}\frac{\partial V}{\partial x}\frac{\partial V}{\partial y}.$$

It may be shown, by taking the axis of x to be parallel to the normal at (x, y, z) to the equipotential surface at the point, that one principal plane of the stress at any point is the tangent plane to the equipotential surface at the point, and that the traction across this plane is tension of amount $R^2/8\pi$, while the traction across any perpendicular plane is pressure of the same amount, R being the resultant electric force at the point so that

$$R^2=\left(\frac{\partial V}{\partial x}\right)^2+\left(\frac{\partial V}{\partial y}\right)^2+\left(\frac{\partial V}{\partial z}\right)^2.$$

(vii) If u, v, w are the components of any vector quantity, and $X_x, \ldots$ are the components of any stress, the three quantities

$$X_xu+X_yv+Z_xw, \quad X_yu+Y_yv+Y_zw, \quad Z_xu+Y_zv+Z_zw$$

are the components of a vector, i.e. they are transformed from one set of rectangular axes to another by the same substitution as u, v, w.

54. The stress-equations of motion and of equilibrium.

In the equations of the type (1) of Article 44, we substitute for $X_\nu, \ldots$ from equations (5). We then have, as the equation obtained by resolving all the forces parallel to the axis of x,

$$\iiint \rho f_x\,dx\,dy\,dz=\iiint \rho X\,dx\,dy\,dz$$
$$+\iint \{X_x\cos(x,\nu)+X_y\cos(y,\nu)+X_z\cos(z,\nu)\}\,dS. \quad \text{......(11)}$$

* Maxwell, *Electricity and Magnetism*, 2nd Edn., Oxford, 1881, vol. 1, ch. 5.

We apply Green's transformation* to the surface-integral, and transpose, thus obtaining the equation

$$\iiint\left(\frac{\partial X_x}{\partial x}+\frac{\partial X_y}{\partial y}+\frac{\partial X_z}{\partial z}+\rho X-\rho f_x\right)dx\,dy\,dz=0. \quad \text{.........(12)}$$

In this equation the integration may be taken through any volume within the body, and it follows that the equation cannot be satisfied unless the subject of integration vanishes at every point within the body. Similar results would follow by transforming the equations obtained by resolving all the forces parallel to the axes of y and z. We thus obtain three *equations of motion* of the type

$$\frac{\partial X_x}{\partial x}+\frac{\partial X_y}{\partial y}+\frac{\partial X_z}{\partial z}+\rho X=\rho f_x. \quad \text{....................(13)}$$

If the body is held in equilibrium, f_x, f_y, f_z are zero, and the *equations of equilibrium* are

$$\left.\begin{aligned}\frac{\partial X_x}{\partial x}+\frac{\partial X_y}{\partial y}+\frac{\partial Z_x}{\partial z}+\rho X=0,\\ \frac{\partial X_y}{\partial x}+\frac{\partial Y_y}{\partial y}+\frac{\partial Y_z}{\partial z}+\rho Y=0,\\ \frac{\partial Z_x}{\partial x}+\frac{\partial Y_z}{\partial y}+\frac{\partial Z_z}{\partial z}+\rho Z=0,\end{aligned}\right\} \quad \text{....................(14)}$$

wherein Y_z, Z_x, X_y have been written for the equivalent Z_y, X_z, Y_x.

If the body moves so that the displacement (u, v, w) of any particle is always very small, we may put

$$\frac{\partial^2 u}{\partial t^2},\quad \frac{\partial^2 v}{\partial t^2},\quad \frac{\partial^2 w}{\partial t^2}$$

instead of f_x, f_y, f_z, the time being denoted by t; the *equations of small motion* are therefore

$$\left.\begin{aligned}\frac{\partial X_x}{\partial x}+\frac{\partial X_y}{\partial y}+\frac{\partial Z_x}{\partial z}+\rho X=\rho\frac{\partial^2 u}{\partial t^2},\\ \frac{\partial X_y}{\partial x}+\frac{\partial Y_y}{\partial y}+\frac{\partial Y_z}{\partial z}+\rho Y=\rho\frac{\partial^2 v}{\partial t^2},\\ \frac{\partial Z_x}{\partial x}+\frac{\partial Y_z}{\partial y}+\frac{\partial Z_z}{\partial z}+\rho Z=\rho\frac{\partial^2 w}{\partial t^2}.\end{aligned}\right\} \quad \text{..................(15)}$$

Other forms of equations of equilibrium and of motion, containing fewer unknown quantities, will be given hereafter. We distinguish the above forms (14) and (15) as the *stress-equations*.

55. Uniform stress and uniformly varying stress.

We observe that the stress-equations of equilibrium (14) hold within a body, and equations (5) hold at its boundary, provided that, in the latter equations, ν is the direction of

* The transformation is that expressed by the equation

$$\iint\{\xi\cos(x,\nu)+\eta\cos(y,\nu)+\zeta\cos(z,\nu)\}\,dS=\iiint\left(\frac{\partial\xi}{\partial x}+\frac{\partial\eta}{\partial y}+\frac{\partial\zeta}{\partial z}\right)dx\,dy\,dz.$$

the normal to the bounding surface drawn outwards and X_ν, ... are the surface tractions. The equations may be used to determine the forces that must be applied to a body to maintain a given state of stress.

When the components of stress are independent of the coordinates, or the stress is the same at all points of the body, the body forces vanish. In other words, any state of uniform stress can be maintained by surface tractions only.

We shall consider two cases:

(*a*) *Uniform pressure.* In this case we have

$$X_x = Y_y = Z_z = -p, \quad Y_z = Z_x = X_y = 0,$$

where p is the pressure, supposed to be the same at all points and in all directions round each point. The surface tractions are equal to the components of a pressure p exerted across the surface of the body, whatever the shape of the body may be. We may conclude that, when a body is subjected to constant pressure p, the same at all points of its surface, and is free from the action of body forces, the state of stress in the interior can be a state of mean pressure, equal to p at each point, unaccompanied by any shearing stress.

(*b*) *Simple tension.* Let T be the amount of the tension, and the axis of x its direction. Then we have $X_x = T$, and the remaining stress-components vanish. We take T to be the same at all points. The surface traction at any point is directed parallel to the axis of x, and its amount is $T \cos(x, \nu)$. If the body is in the shape of a cylinder or prism, of any form of section, with its length in the direction of the axis of x, there will be tensions on its ends of amount T per unit area, and there will be no tractions across its cylindrical surface. We may conclude that when a bar is subjected to equal and opposite uniform normal tensions over its ends, and is free from the action of any other forces, the state of stress in the interior can be a state of tension across the normal sections of the same amount at all points.

Uniform traction across a plane area is statically equivalent to a force at the centroid of the area. The force has the same direction as the traction, and its magnitude is measured by the product of the measures of the area and of the magnitude of the traction.

If the traction across an area is uniform as regards direction and, as regards magnitude, is proportional to distance, measured in a definite sense, from a definite line in the plane of the area, we have an example of *uniformly varying stress.* The traction across the area is statically equivalent to a single force acting at a certain point of the plane, which is identical with the "centre of pressure" investigated in treatises on Hydrostatics. There is an exceptional case, in which the line of zero traction passes through the centroid of the area; the traction across the area is then statically equivalent to a couple. When the line of zero traction does not intersect the boundary of the area, the traction has the same sign at all points of the area; and the centre of pressure must then lie within a certain curve surrounding the centroid. If the area is of rectangular shape, and the line of zero traction is parallel to one side, the greatest distance of the centre of pressure from the centroid is $\frac{1}{6}$th of that side. This result is the engineers' "rule of the middle third*."

56. Observations concerning the stress-equations.

(*a*) The equations of type (13) may be obtained by applying the equations of type (1) [Article 44] to a small parallelepiped bounded by planes parallel to the coordinate planes. The contributions of the faces x and $x + dx$ to $\iint X_\nu dS$ can be taken to be $-X_x dy dz$ and $\{X_x + (\partial X_x/\partial x)dx\} dy dz$, and similar expressions for the contributions of the remaining pairs of faces can be written down.

* Ewing, *Strength of Materials*, p. 104.

(*b*) The equations of moments of type (2) are already satisfied in consequence of equations (6). In fact (2) may be written

$$\iiint \left\{ y \left(\frac{\partial Z_x}{\partial x} + \frac{\partial Z_y}{\partial y} + \frac{\partial Z_z}{\partial z} + \rho Z \right) - z \left(\frac{\partial Y_x}{\partial x} + \frac{\partial Y_y}{\partial y} + \frac{\partial Y_z}{\partial z} + \rho Y \right) \right\} dx\, dy\, dz$$

$$= \iiint \rho \left(yZ - zY \right) dx\, dy\, dz$$

$$+ \iint [y \{ Z_x \cos (x, \nu) + Z_y \cos (y, \nu) + Z_z \cos (z, \nu) \}$$

$$- z \{ Y_x \cos (x, \nu) + Y_y \cos (y, \nu) + Y_z \cos (z, \nu) \}]\, dS,$$

by substituting for f_x, ... from the equations of type (13), and for Y_ν, Z_ν from (5). By help of Green's transformation, this equation becomes

$$\iiint (Z_y - Y_z)\, dx\, dy\, dz = 0;$$

and thus the equations of moments are satisfied identically in virtue of equations (6). It will be observed that, equations (6) might be proved by the above analysis instead of that in Article 47.

(*c*) When the equations (14) are satisfied at all points of a body, the conditions of equilibrium of the body as a whole (Article 45) are necessarily satisfied, and the resultant of all the body forces, acting upon elements of volume of the body, is balanced by the resultant of all the tractions, acting upon elements of its surface. The like statement is true of the resultant moments of the body forces and surface tractions.

(*d*) An example of the application of this remark is afforded by Maxwell's stress-system described in (vi) of Article 53. We should find for example

$$\frac{\partial X_x}{\partial x} + \frac{\partial X_y}{\partial y} + \frac{\partial Z_x}{\partial z} - \frac{1}{4\pi} \nabla^2 V \frac{\partial V}{\partial x} = 0,$$

where ∇^2 stands for $\partial^2/\partial x^2 + \partial^2/\partial y^2 + \partial^2/\partial z^2$. It follows that, in any region throughout which $\nabla^2 V = 0$, this stress-system is self-equilibrating, and that, in general, this stress-system is in equilibrium with body force specified by $-\frac{1}{4\pi} \nabla^2 V \left(\frac{\partial V}{\partial x}, \frac{\partial V}{\partial y}, \frac{\partial V}{\partial z} \right)$ per unit volume. Hence the tractions over any closed surface, which would be deduced from the formulæ for X_x, ..., are statically equivalent to body forces, specified by $\frac{1}{4\pi} \nabla^2 V \left(\frac{\partial V}{\partial x}, \frac{\partial V}{\partial y}, \frac{\partial V}{\partial z} \right)$ per unit volume of the volume within the surface.

(*e*) ~~*Stress-functions.*~~

In the development of the theory we shall be much occupied with bodies in equilibrium under forces applied over their surfaces only. In this case there are no body forces and no accelerations, and the equations of equilibrium are

$$\frac{\partial X_x}{\partial x} + \frac{\partial X_y}{\partial y} + \frac{\partial Z_x}{\partial z} = 0, \quad \frac{\partial X_y}{\partial x} + \frac{\partial Y_y}{\partial y} + \frac{\partial Y_z}{\partial z} = 0, \quad \frac{\partial Z_x}{\partial x} + \frac{\partial Y_z}{\partial y} + \frac{\partial Z_z}{\partial z} = 0; \quad \text{......(16)}$$

while the surface tractions are equal to the values of (X_ν, Y_ν, Z_ν) at the surface of the body. The differential equations (16) are three independent relations between the six components of stress at any point; by means of them we might express these six quantities in terms of three independent functions of position. Such functions would be called "stress-functions." So long as we have no information about the state of the body, besides that contained in equations (16), such functions are arbitrary functions.

One way of expressing the stress-components in terms of stress-functions is to assume*

$$Y_z = -\frac{\partial^2 \chi_1}{\partial y \partial z}, \quad Z_x = -\frac{\partial^2 \chi_2}{\partial z \partial x}, \quad X_y = -\frac{\partial^2 \chi_3}{\partial x \partial y},$$

and then it is clear that the equations (16) are satisfied if

$$X_x = \frac{\partial^2 \chi_3}{\partial y^2} + \frac{\partial^2 \chi_2}{\partial z^2}, \quad Y_y = \frac{\partial^2 \chi_1}{\partial z^2} + \frac{\partial^2 \chi_3}{\partial x^2}, \quad Z_z = \frac{\partial^2 \chi_2}{\partial x^2} + \frac{\partial^2 \chi_1}{\partial y^2}.$$

Another way is to assume†

$$X_x = \frac{\partial^2 \psi_1}{\partial y \partial z}, \quad Y_y = \frac{\partial^2 \psi_2}{\partial z \partial x}, \quad Z_z = \frac{\partial^2 \psi_3}{\partial x \partial y},$$

$$Y_z = -\frac{1}{2}\frac{\partial}{\partial x}\left(-\frac{\partial \psi_1}{\partial x} + \frac{\partial \psi_2}{\partial y} + \frac{\partial \psi_3}{\partial z}\right), \quad Z_x = -\frac{1}{2}\frac{\partial}{\partial y}\left(\frac{\partial \psi_1}{\partial x} - \frac{\partial \psi_2}{\partial y} + \frac{\partial \psi_3}{\partial z}\right),$$

$$X_y = -\frac{1}{2}\frac{\partial}{\partial z}\left(\frac{\partial \psi_1}{\partial x} + \frac{\partial \psi_2}{\partial y} - \frac{\partial \psi_3}{\partial z}\right).$$

These formulæ may be readily verified. It will be observed that the relations between the χ functions and the ψ functions are the same as those between the quantities $e_{xx}, \ldots$ and the quantities $e_{yz}, \ldots$ in Article 17.

57. Graphic representation of stress.

States of stress may be illustrated in various ways by means of diagrams, but complete diagrammatic representations cannot easily be found. There are cases in which the magnitude and direction of the stress at a point can be determined by inspection of a drawing of a family of curves, just as magnetic force may be found by aid of a diagram of lines of force. But such cases are rare, the most important being the stress in a twisted bar.

In the case of plane stress, in a body held by forces applied at its boundary, a complete representation of the stress at any point can be obtained by using two diagrams‡. The stress is determined by means of a stress-function χ, so that

$$X_x = \frac{\partial^2 \chi}{\partial y^2}, \quad Y_y = \frac{\partial^2 \chi}{\partial x^2}, \quad X_y = -\frac{\partial^2 \chi}{\partial x \partial y}, \quad \ldots\ldots\ldots\ldots(17)$$

the plane of the stress being the plane of x, y, and χ being a function of x, y, z. If the curves $\frac{\partial \chi}{\partial x}=$const. and $\frac{\partial \chi}{\partial y}=$const. are traced for the same value of z and for equidifferent values of the constants, then the tractions at any point, across planes parallel to the planes of (x, z) and (y, z), are directed respectively along the tangents to the curves $\frac{\partial \chi}{\partial x}=$const. and $\frac{\partial \chi}{\partial y}=$const. which pass through the point, and their magnitudes are proportional to the closeness of consecutive curves of the respective families.

Partial representations by graphic means have sometimes been used in cases where a complete representation cannot be obtained. Of this kind are tracings or models of the "lines of stress." These lines are such that the tangent to any one of them at any point is normal to a principal plane of stress at the point. Through any point there pass three such lines, cutting each other at right angles. These lines *may* determine a triply orthogonal set of surfaces, but in general no such set exists. When such surfaces exist they are described

* Maxwell, *Edinburgh Roy. Soc. Trans.*, vol. 26 (1870), or *Scientific Papers*, vol. 2, p. 161. The particular case of plane stress was discussed by G. B. Airy, *Brit. Assoc. Rep.* 1862.

† G. Morera, *Roma, Acc. Lincei Rend.* (Ser. 5), t. 1 (1892). The relations between the two systems of stress-functions were discussed by Beltrami and Morera in the same volume.

‡ J. H. Michell, *London Math. Soc. Proc.*, vol. 32 (1901).

as "isostatic surfaces*," and from a knowledge of them the directions of the principal stresses at any point can be inferred. In two-dimensional systems there is always a set of isostatic surfaces.

Distributions of stress may also be studied by the aid of polarized light. The method† is based on the experimental fact that an isotropic transparent body, when stressed, becomes doubly refracting, with its optical principal axes at any point in the directions of the principal axes of stress at the point.

58. Stress-equations referred to curvilinear orthogonal coordinates‡.

The required equations may be obtained by finding the transformed expression for $\iint X_\nu dS$ in the general equation (1) of Article 44. Now we have, by equations (5),

$$X_\nu = X_x \cos(x, \nu) + X_y \cos(y, \nu) + X_z \cos(z, \nu),$$

and $$\cos(x, \nu) = \cos(\alpha, \nu)\cos(x, \alpha) + \cos(\beta, \nu)\cos(x, \beta) + \cos(\gamma, \nu)\cos(x, \gamma),$$

so that $$X_\nu = \{X_x \cos(x, \alpha) + X_y \cos(y, \alpha) + X_z \cos(z, \alpha)\}\cos(\alpha, \nu)$$
$$+ \text{ two similar expressions}$$
$$= X_\alpha \cos(\alpha, \nu) + X_\beta \cos(\beta, \nu) + X_\gamma \cos(\gamma, \nu),$$

where, for example, X_α denotes the traction in direction x, at a point (α, β, γ), across the tangent plane at the point to that surface of the α family which passes through the point. According to the result (v) of Article 53 this is the same as α_x, the traction in the direction of the normal to the α surface at the point, exerted across the plane $x=$const. which passes through the point. Further we have, by equations (5),

$$\alpha_x = \widehat{\alpha\alpha}\cos(\alpha, x) + \widehat{\alpha\beta}\cos(\beta, x) + \widehat{\gamma\alpha}\cos(\gamma, x).$$

Again, $\cos(\alpha, \nu)\, dS$ is the projection of the surface element dS, about any point of S, upon the tangent plane to the α surface which passes through the point, and this projection is $d\beta d\gamma / h_2 h_3$. Hence

$$\iint X_\nu dS = \iint \{\widehat{\alpha\alpha}\cos(\alpha, x) + \widehat{\alpha\beta}\cos(\beta, x) + \widehat{\gamma\alpha}\cos(\gamma, x)\}\frac{d\beta d\gamma}{h_2 h_3}$$
$$+ \iint \{\widehat{\alpha\beta}\cos(\alpha, x) + \widehat{\beta\beta}\cos(\beta, x) + \widehat{\beta\gamma}\cos(\gamma, x)\}\frac{d\gamma d\alpha}{h_3 h_1}$$
$$+ \iint \{\widehat{\gamma\alpha}\cos(\alpha, x) + \widehat{\beta\gamma}\cos(\beta, x) + \widehat{\gamma\gamma}\cos(\gamma, x)\}\frac{d\alpha d\beta}{h_1 h_2}.$$

* These surfaces were first discussed by Lamé, *J. de Math.* (*Liouville*), t. 6 (1841), and *Leçons sur les coordonnées curvilignes*. The fact that they do not in general exist was pointed out by Boussinesq, *Paris, C. R.*, t. 74 (1872). Cf. Weingarten, *J. f. Math.* (*Crelle*), Bd. 90 (1881).

† The method originated with D. Brewster, *Phil. Trans. Roy. Soc.*, 1816. It was developed by F. E. Neumann, *Berlin Abh.* 1841, and by Maxwell, *Edinburgh Roy. Soc. Trans.*, vol. 20 (1853), or *Scientific Papers*, vol. 1, p. 30. For a more recent experimental investigation, see J. Kerr, *Phil. Mag.* (Ser. 5), vol. 26 (1888). Reference may also be made to M. E. Mascart, *Traité d'Optique*, t. 2 (Paris 1891), pp. 229 *et seq.* The method has been developed further by various physicists, among whom may be named E. G. Coker, *Phil. Mag.* (Ser. 6), vol. 20, 1909, p. 740, and *London, Roy. Soc. Proc.* (Ser. A), vol. 86, 1912, p. 86, and L. N. G. Filon, *Phil. Mag.* (Ser. 6), vol. 23, 1912, p. 1. Further references will be found in a Report by Filon and Coker in *Brit. Assoc. Rep.* 1914, pp. 201–210. Improved methods are described by Filon in *Brit. Assoc. Rep.* 1919, p. 475, and 1923, p. 350.

‡ Other methods of obtaining these equations will be given in Article 116 *infra* and in the 'Note on the Applications of Moving Axes' at the end of this book.

When we apply Green's transformation to this expression we find

$$\iint X_\nu\,dS = \iiint d\alpha\,d\beta\,d\gamma \left\{ \frac{\partial}{\partial\alpha}\left[\frac{1}{h_2h_3}\{\widehat{\alpha\alpha}\cos(\alpha,x)+\widehat{\alpha\beta}\cos(\beta,x)+\widehat{\gamma\alpha}\cos(\gamma,x)\}\right] + \frac{\partial}{\partial\beta}\left[\frac{1}{h_3h_1}\{\widehat{\alpha\beta}\cos(\alpha,x)+\widehat{\beta\beta}\cos(\beta,x)+\widehat{\beta\gamma}\cos(\gamma,x)\}\right] + \frac{\partial}{\partial\gamma}\left[\frac{1}{h_1h_2}\{\widehat{\gamma\alpha}\cos(\alpha,x)+\widehat{\beta\gamma}\cos(\beta,x)+\widehat{\gamma\gamma}\cos(\gamma,x)\}\right]\right\},$$

and since $(h_1h_2h_3)^{-1}d\alpha\,d\beta\,d\gamma$ is the element of volume, we deduce from (1) the equation

$$\rho f_x = \rho X + h_1h_2h_3 \left\{ \frac{\partial}{\partial\alpha}\left[\frac{1}{h_2h_3}\{\widehat{\alpha\alpha}\cos(\alpha,x)+\widehat{\alpha\beta}\cos(\beta,x)+\widehat{\gamma\alpha}\cos(\gamma,x)\}\right] + \frac{\partial}{\partial\beta}\left[\frac{1}{h_3h_1}\{\widehat{\alpha\beta}\cos(\alpha,x)+\widehat{\beta\beta}\cos(\beta,x)+\widehat{\beta\gamma}\cos(\gamma,x)\}\right] + \frac{\partial}{\partial\gamma}\left[\frac{1}{h_1h_2}\{\widehat{\gamma\alpha}\cos(\alpha,x)+\widehat{\beta\gamma}\cos(\beta,x)+\widehat{\gamma\gamma}\cos(\gamma,x)\}\right]\right\} \quad\text{..........(18)}$$

The angles denoted by (α, x), ... are variable with α, β, γ because the normals to the surfaces α=const., ... vary from point to point. Equations (40) and (41) of Article 22 C show that, for any fixed direction of x, the differential coefficients of $\cos(\alpha, x)$, ... are given by nine equations of the type

$$\frac{\partial}{\partial\alpha}\cos(\alpha,x) = -h_2\frac{\partial}{\partial\beta}\left(\frac{1}{h_1}\right).\cos(\beta,x) - h_3\frac{\partial}{\partial\gamma}\left(\frac{1}{h_1}\right).\cos(\gamma,x),$$

$$\frac{\partial}{\partial\beta}\cos(\alpha,x) = h_1\frac{\partial}{\partial\alpha}\left(\frac{1}{h_2}\right).\cos(\beta,x), \qquad \frac{\partial}{\partial\gamma}\cos(\alpha,x) = h_1\frac{\partial}{\partial\alpha}\left(\frac{1}{h_3}\right).\cos(\gamma,x).$$

We now take the direction of the axis of x to be that of the normal to the surface α=const. which passes through the point (α, β, γ). After the differentiations have been performed we put

$$\cos(\alpha,x)=1, \quad \cos(\beta,x)=0, \quad \cos(\gamma,x)=0.$$

We take f_α for the component acceleration along the normal to the surface α=const., and F_α for the component of body force in the same direction. Equation (18) then becomes

$$\rho f_\alpha = \rho F_\alpha + h_1h_2h_3\left(\frac{\partial}{\partial\alpha}\frac{\widehat{\alpha\alpha}}{h_2h_3} + \frac{\partial}{\partial\beta}\frac{\widehat{\alpha\beta}}{h_3h_1} + \frac{\partial}{\partial\gamma}\frac{\widehat{\gamma\alpha}}{h_1h_2}\right) + \widehat{\alpha\beta}\,h_1h_2\frac{\partial}{\partial\beta}\left(\frac{1}{h_1}\right) + \widehat{\gamma\alpha}\,h_1h_3\frac{\partial}{\partial\gamma}\left(\frac{1}{h_1}\right) - \widehat{\beta\beta}\,h_1h_2\frac{\partial}{\partial\alpha}\left(\frac{1}{h_2}\right) - \widehat{\gamma\gamma}\,h_1h_3\frac{\partial}{\partial\alpha}\left(\frac{1}{h_3}\right). \quad\text{........................(19)}$$

The two similar equations containing components of acceleration and body force in the directions of the normals to β=const. and γ=const. can be written down by symmetry.

59. Special cases of stress-equations referred to curvilinear coordinates.

(i) In the case of cylindrical coordinates r, θ, z (cf. Article 22) the stress-equations are

$$\frac{\partial\widehat{rr}}{\partial r} + \frac{1}{r}\frac{\partial\widehat{r\theta}}{\partial\theta} + \frac{\partial\widehat{rz}}{\partial z} + \frac{\widehat{rr}-\widehat{\theta\theta}}{r} + \rho F_r = \rho f_r,$$

$$\frac{\partial\widehat{r\theta}}{\partial r} + \frac{1}{r}\frac{\partial\widehat{\theta\theta}}{\partial\theta} + \frac{\partial\widehat{\theta z}}{\partial z} + \frac{2\widehat{r\theta}}{r} + \rho F_\theta = \rho f_\theta,$$

$$\frac{\partial\widehat{rz}}{\partial r} + \frac{1}{r}\frac{\partial\widehat{\theta z}}{\partial\theta} + \frac{\partial\widehat{zz}}{\partial z} + \frac{\widehat{rz}}{r} + \rho F_z = \rho f_z.$$

(ii) In the case of plane stress referred to cylindrical coordinates, when there is equilibrium under surface tractions only, the stress-components, when expressed in terms of the stress-function χ of equations (17), are given by the equations*

$$\widehat{rr}=\frac{1}{r^2}\frac{\partial^2\chi}{\partial\theta^2}+\frac{1}{r}\frac{\partial\chi}{\partial r},\quad \widehat{\theta\theta}=\frac{\partial^2\chi}{\partial r^2},\quad \widehat{r\theta}=-\frac{\partial}{\partial r}\left(\frac{1}{r}\frac{\partial\chi}{\partial\theta}\right).$$

(iii) In the more general case of plane stress referred to coordinates α, β, which are such that $\alpha+\iota\beta$ is a function of the complex variable $x+\iota y$, the stress-components are expressed in terms of χ by the formulæ†

$$\frac{\widehat{\alpha\alpha}}{h}=\frac{\partial}{\partial\beta}\left(h\frac{\partial\chi}{\partial\beta}\right)-\frac{\partial h}{\partial\alpha}\frac{\partial\chi}{\partial\alpha},\quad \frac{\widehat{\beta\beta}}{h}=\frac{\partial}{\partial\alpha}\left(h\frac{\partial\chi}{\partial\alpha}\right)-\frac{\partial h}{\partial\beta}\frac{\partial\chi}{\partial\beta},$$

$$\frac{\widehat{\alpha\beta}}{h}=-\frac{\partial}{\partial\alpha}\left(h\frac{\partial\chi}{\partial\beta}\right)-\frac{\partial h}{\partial\beta}\frac{\partial\chi}{\partial\alpha},\quad h=\left|\frac{d(\alpha+\iota\beta)}{d(x+\iota y)}\right|.$$

(iv) In the case of polar coordinates r, θ, ϕ the stress-equations are

$$\frac{\partial\widehat{rr}}{\partial r}+\frac{1}{r}\frac{\partial\widehat{r\theta}}{\partial\theta}+\frac{1}{r\sin\theta}\frac{\partial\widehat{r\phi}}{\partial\phi}+\frac{1}{r}(2\widehat{rr}-\widehat{\theta\theta}-\widehat{\phi\phi}+\widehat{r\theta}\cot\theta)+\rho F_r=\rho f_r,$$

$$\frac{\partial\widehat{r\theta}}{\partial r}+\frac{1}{r}\frac{\partial\widehat{\theta\theta}}{\partial\theta}+\frac{1}{r\sin\theta}\frac{\partial\widehat{\theta\phi}}{\partial\phi}+\frac{1}{r}\{(\widehat{\theta\theta}-\widehat{\phi\phi})\cot\theta+3\widehat{r\theta}\}+\rho F_\theta=\rho f_\theta,$$

$$\frac{\partial\widehat{r\phi}}{\partial r}+\frac{1}{r}\frac{\partial\widehat{\theta\phi}}{\partial\theta}+\frac{1}{r\sin\theta}\frac{\partial\widehat{\phi\phi}}{\partial\phi}+\frac{1}{r}\{3\widehat{r\phi}+2\widehat{\theta\phi}\cot\theta\}+\rho F_\phi=\rho f_\phi.$$

(v) When the surfaces α, β, γ are isostatic so that $\widehat{\beta\gamma}=\widehat{\gamma\alpha}=\widehat{\alpha\beta}=0$, the equations can be written in such forms‡ as

$$h_1\frac{\partial\widehat{\alpha\alpha}}{\partial\alpha}+\frac{\widehat{\alpha\alpha}-\widehat{\beta\beta}}{\rho_{13}}-\frac{\widehat{\alpha\alpha}-\widehat{\gamma\gamma}}{\rho_{12}}+\rho F_\alpha=\rho f_\alpha,$$

where ρ_{12} and ρ_{13} are the principal radii of curvature of the surface α=const. which correspond respectively with the curves of intersection of that surface and the surfaces β=const. and γ=const.

* J. H. Michell, *London Math. Soc. Proc.*, vol. 31 (1899), p. 100.

† G. B. Jeffery, *Phil. Trans. Roy. Soc.* (Ser. A), vol. 221, 1920, p. 265.

‡ Lamé, *Coordonnées curvilignes*, p. 274. The equations, of this type, which hold in the case of plane stress, have been utilized by L. N. G. Filon, *Brit. Assoc. Rep.* 1923, p. 351.

CHAPTER III

THE ELASTICITY OF SOLID BODIES

60. In the preceding Chapters we have developed certain kinematical and dynamical notions, which are necessary for the theoretical discussion of the physical behaviour of material bodies in general. We have now to explain how these notions are adapted to elastic solid bodies in particular.

An ordinary solid body is constantly subjected to forces of gravitation, and, if it is in equilibrium, it is supported by other forces. We have no experience of a body which is free from the action of all external forces. From the equations of Article 54 we know that the application of forces to a body necessitates the existence of *stress* within the body.

Again, solid bodies are not absolutely rigid. By the application of suitable forces they can be made to change both in size and shape. When the induced changes of size and shape are considerable, the body does not, in general, return to its original size and shape after the forces which induced the change have ceased to act. On the other hand, when the changes are not too great the recovery may be apparently complete. The property of recovery of an original size and shape is the property that is termed *elasticity*. The changes of size and shape are expressed by specifying *strains*. The "unstrained state" (Article 4), with reference to which strains are specified, is, as it were, an arbitrary zero of reckoning, and the choice of it is in our power. When the unstrained state is chosen, and the strain is specified, the internal configuration of the body is known.

We shall suppose that the differential coefficients of the *displacement* (u, v, w), by which the body could pass from the unstrained state to the strained state, are sufficiently small to admit of the calculation of the strain by the simplified methods of Article 9; and we shall regard the configuration as specified by this displacement.

For the complete specification of any state of the body, it is necessary to know the *temperature* of every part, as well as the configuration. A change of configuration may, or may not, be accompanied by changes of temperature.

61. Work and energy.

Unless the body is in equilibrium under the action of the external forces, it will be moving through the configuration that is specified by the displacement, towards a new configuration which could be specified by a slightly different displacement. As the body moves from one configuration to another, the external forces (body forces and surface tractions) in general do some work; and we can estimate the quantity of work done per unit of time, that is to say the *rate* at which work is done.

Any body, or any portion of a body, can possess energy in various ways. If it is in motion, it possesses kinetic energy, which depends on the distribution of mass and velocity. In the case of small displacements, to which we are restricting the discussion, the kinetic energy per unit of volume is expressed with sufficient approximation by the formula

$$\tfrac{1}{2}\rho\left\{\left(\frac{\partial u}{\partial t}\right)^2+\left(\frac{\partial v}{\partial t}\right)^2+\left(\frac{\partial w}{\partial t}\right)^2\right\},$$

in which ρ denotes the density in the unstrained state. In addition to the molar kinetic energy, possessed by the body in bulk, the body possesses energy which depends upon its state, i.e. upon its configuration and the temperatures of its parts. This energy is called "intrinsic energy"; it is to be calculated by reference to a standard state of chosen uniform temperature and zero displacement. The total energy of any portion of the body is the sum of the kinetic energy of the portion and the intrinsic energy of the portion. The total energy of the body is the sum of the total energies of any parts*, into which it can be imagined to be divided.

As the body passes from one state to another, the total energy, in general, is altered; but the change in the total energy is not, in general, equal to the work done by the external forces. To produce the change of state it is, in general, necessary that heat should be supplied to the body or withdrawn from it. The quantity of heat is measured by its equivalent in work.

The First Law of Thermodynamics states that the increment of the total energy of the body is equal to the sum of the work done by the external forces and the quantity of heat supplied.

We may calculate the rate at which work is done by the external forces. The rate at which work is done by the body forces is expressed by the formula

$$\iiint\rho\left(X\frac{\partial u}{\partial t}+Y\frac{\partial v}{\partial t}+Z\frac{\partial w}{\partial t}\right)dx\,dy\,dz, \quad\text{.................(1)}$$

where the integration is taken through the volume of the body in the unstrained state. The rate at which work is done by the surface tractions is expressed by the formula

$$\iint\left(X_\nu\frac{\partial u}{\partial t}+Y_\nu\frac{\partial v}{\partial t}+Z_\nu\frac{\partial w}{\partial t}\right)dS,$$

where the integration is taken over the surface of the body in the unstrained

* For the validity of the analysis of the energy into molar kinetic energy and intrinsic energy it is necessary that the dimensions of the *parts* in question should be large compared with molecular dimensions.

state. This expression may be transformed into an integral taken through the volume of the body, by the use of Green's transformation and of the formulæ of the type

$$X_\nu = X_x \cos(x, \nu) + X_y \cos(y, \nu) + X_z \cos(z, \nu),$$
$$\ldots\ldots$$

We use also the results of the type $Y_z = Z_y$, and the notation for strain-components $e_{xx}, \ldots$. We find that the rate at which work is done by the surface tractions is expressed by the formula

$$\iiint\left[\left(\frac{\partial X_x}{\partial x} + \frac{\partial X_y}{\partial y} + \frac{\partial Z_x}{\partial z}\right)\frac{\partial u}{\partial t} + \left(\frac{\partial X_y}{\partial x} + \frac{\partial Y_y}{\partial y} + \frac{\partial Y_z}{\partial z}\right)\frac{\partial v}{\partial t}\right.$$
$$\left. + \left(\frac{\partial Z_x}{\partial x} + \frac{\partial Y_z}{\partial y} + \frac{\partial Z_z}{\partial z}\right)\frac{\partial w}{\partial t}\right] dx\,dy\,dz$$
$$+ \iiint\left[X_x \frac{\partial e_{xx}}{\partial t} + Y_y \frac{\partial e_{yy}}{\partial t} + Z_z \frac{\partial e_{zz}}{\partial t} + Y_z \frac{\partial e_{yz}}{\partial t} + Z_x \frac{\partial e_{zx}}{\partial t} + X_y \frac{\partial e_{xy}}{\partial t}\right] dx\,dy\,dz. \quad \ldots(2)$$

We may calculate also the rate at which the kinetic energy increases. This rate is expressed with sufficient approximation by the formula

$$\iiint \rho\left(\frac{\partial^2 u}{\partial t^2}\frac{\partial u}{\partial t} + \frac{\partial^2 v}{\partial t^2}\frac{\partial v}{\partial t} + \frac{\partial^2 w}{\partial t^2}\frac{\partial w}{\partial t}\right) dx\,dy\,dz, \quad \ldots\ldots\ldots\ldots\ldots\ldots(3)$$

where the integration is taken through the volume of the body in the unstrained state. If we use the equations of motion, (15) of Article 54, we can express this in the form

$$\iiint\left[\left(\rho X + \frac{\partial X_x}{\partial x} + \frac{\partial X_y}{\partial y} + \frac{\partial Z_x}{\partial z}\right)\frac{\partial u}{\partial t} + \ldots + \ldots\right] dx\,dy\,dz.$$

It appears hence that the expression

$$\iiint\left[X_x \frac{\partial e_{xx}}{\partial t} + Y_y \frac{\partial e_{yy}}{\partial t} + Z_z \frac{\partial e_{zz}}{\partial t} + Y_z \frac{\partial e_{yz}}{\partial t} + Z_x \frac{\partial e_{zx}}{\partial t} + X_y \frac{\partial e_{xy}}{\partial t}\right] dx\,dy\,dz \quad \ldots(4)$$

represents the excess of the rate at which work is done by the external forces above the rate of increase of the kinetic energy.

62. Existence of the strain-energy-function.

Now let δT_1 denote the increment of kinetic energy per unit of volume, which is acquired in a short interval of time δt. Let δU be the increment of intrinsic energy per unit of volume, which is acquired in the same interval. Let δW_1 be the work done by the external forces in the interval, and let δQ be the mechanical value of the heat supplied in the interval. Then the First Law of Thermodynamics is expressed by the formula

$$\iiint(\delta T_1 + \delta U)\, dx\,dy\,dz = \delta W_1 + \delta Q. \quad \ldots\ldots\ldots\ldots\ldots\ldots(5)$$

Now, according to the final result (4) obtained in Article 61, we have

$$\delta W_1 - \iiint \delta T_1 \, dx dy dz$$

$$= \iiint (X_x \delta e_{xx} + Y_y \delta e_{yy} + Z_z \delta \epsilon_{zz} + Y_z \delta e_{yz} + Z_x \delta e_{zx} + X_y \delta e_{xy}) \, dx dy dz, \quad \ldots(6)$$

where δe_{xx}, ... represent the increments of the components of strain in the interval of time δt. Hence we have

$$\iiint \delta U \, dx dy dz = \delta Q + \iiint (X_x \delta e_{xx} + \ldots) \, dx dy dz. \quad \ldots\ldots\ldots\ldots(7)$$

The differential quantity δU is the differential of a function U, which is a one-valued function of the temperature and the quantities that determine the configuration. The value of this function U, corresponding with any state, is the measure of the intrinsic energy in that state. In the standard state, the value of U is zero.

If the change of state takes place adiabatically, that is to say in such a way that no heat is gained or lost by any element of the body, δQ vanishes, and we have

$$\delta U = X_x \delta e_{xx} + Y_y \delta e_{yy} + Z_z \delta e_{zz} + Y_z \delta e_{yz} + Z_x \delta e_{zx} + X_y \delta e_{xy}. \quad \ldots\ldots\ldots(8)$$

Thus the expression on the right-hand side is, in this case, an exact differential; and there exists a function W, which has the properties expressed by the equations

$$X_x = \frac{\partial W}{\partial e_{xx}}, \ \ldots \ Y_z = \frac{\partial W}{\partial e_{yz}}, \ \ldots \quad \ldots\ldots\ldots\ldots\ldots\ldots(9)$$

The function W represents potential energy, per unit of volume, stored up in the body by the strain; and its variations, when the body is strained adiabatically, are identical with those of the intrinsic energy of the body. It is probable that the changes that actually take place in bodies executing small and rapid vibrations are practically adiabatic.

A function which has the properties expressed by equations (9) is called a "strain-energy-function."

If the changes of state take place isothermally, i.e. so that the temperature of every element of the body remains constant, a function W having the properties expressed by equations (9) exists. To prove this we utilize the Second Law of Thermodynamics in the form that, in any reversible cycle of changes of state performed without variation of temperature, the sum of the elements δQ vanishes*. The sum of the elements δU also vanishes; and it follows that the sum of the elements expressed by the formula

$$\Sigma (X_x \delta e_{xx} + Y_y \delta e_{yy} + Z_z \delta e_{zz} + Y_z \delta e_{yz} + Z_x \delta e_{zx} + X_y \delta e_{xy})$$

* Cf. Kelvin, *Math. and Phys. Papers*, vol. 1, p. 291.

also vanishes in a reversible cycle of changes of state without variation of temperature. Hence the differential expression

$$X_x \delta e_{xx} + Y_y \delta e_{yy} + Z_z \delta e_{zz} + Y_z \delta e_{yz} + Z_x \delta e_{zx} + X_y \delta e_{xy}$$

is an exact differential, and the strain-energy-function W exists.

When a body is strained slowly by gradual increase of the load, and is in continual equilibrium of temperature with surrounding bodies, the changes of state are practically isothermal.

63. Indirectness of experimental results.

The object of experimental investigations of the behaviour of elastic bodies may be said to be the discovery of numerical relations between the quantities that can be measured, which shall be sufficiently varied and sufficiently numerous to serve as a basis for the inductive determination of the form of the intrinsic energy-function, viz. the function U of Article 62. This object has not been achieved, except in the case of gases in states that are far removed from critical states. In the case of elastic solids, the conditions are much more complex, and the results of experiment are much less complete; and the indications which we have at present are not sufficient for the formation of a theory of the physical behaviour of a solid body in any circumstances other than those in which a strain-energy-function exists.

When such a function exists, and its form is known, we can deduce from it the relations between the components of stress and the components of strain; and, conversely, if, from any experimental results, we are able to infer such relations, we acquire thereby data which can serve for the construction of the function.

The components of stress or of strain within a solid body can never, from the nature of the case, be measured directly. If their values can be found, it must always be by a process of inference from measurements of quantities that are not, in general, components of stress or of strain.

Instruments can be devised for measuring average strains in bodies of ordinary size, and others for measuring particular strains of small superficial parts. For example, the average cubical compression can be measured by means of a piezometer; the extension of a short length of a longitudinal filament on the outside of a bar can be measured by means of an extensometer. Sometimes, as for example in experiments on torsion and flexure, a displacement is measured*.

External forces applied to a body can often be measured with great exactness, e.g. when a bar is extended or bent by hanging a weight at one end. In such cases it is a resultant force that is measured directly, not the component

* For an account of experimental methods, which are commonly used, reference may be made to J. H. Poynting and J. J. Thomson, *Properties of Matter*, London, 1902, and G. F. C. Searle, *Experimental Elasticity*, Cambridge, 1908.

tractions per unit of area that are applied to the surface of the body. In the case of a body under normal pressure, as in the experiments with the piezometer, the pressure per unit of area can be measured.

In any experiment designed to determine a relation between stress and strain, some displacement is brought about, in a body partially fixed, by the application of definite forces which can be varied in amount. We call these forces collectively "the load."

64. Hooke's Law.

Most hard solids show the same type of relation between load and measurable strain. It is found that, over a wide range of load, the measured strain is proportional to the load. This statement may be expressed more fully by saying that

(1) when the load increases the measured strain increases in the same ratio,

(2) when the load diminishes the measured strain diminishes in the same ratio,

(3) when the load is reduced to zero no strain can be measured.

The most striking exception to this statement is found in the behaviour of cast metals. It appears to be impossible to assign any finite range of load, within which the measurable strains of such metals increase and diminish in the same proportion as the load.

The experimental results which hold for most hard solids, other than cast metals, lead by a process of inductive reasoning to the *Generalized Hooke's Law of the proportionality of stress and strain.* The general form of the law is expressed by the statement:

Each of the six components of stress at any point of a body is a linear function of the six components of strain at the point.

It is necessary to pay some attention to the way in which this law represents the experimental results. In most experiments the load that is increased, or diminished, or reduced to zero consists of part only of the external forces. The weight of the body subjected to experiment must be balanced; and neither the weight, nor the force employed to balance it, is, in general, included in the load. At the beginning and end of the experiment the body is in a state of stress; but there is no measured strain. For the strain that is measured is reckoned from the state of the body at the beginning of the experiment as standard state. The strain referred to in the statement of the law must be reckoned from a different state as standard or "unstrained" state. This state is that in which the body would be if it were freed from the action of *all* external forces, and if there were no internal stress at any point of it. We call this state of the body the "unstressed state." Reckoned from this state as standard, the body is in a state of strain at the beginning of the experiment; it is also in a state of stress. When the load is applied, the stress is altered in amount and distribution; and the strain also is altered. After the application of the load, the stress consists of two stress-systems: the stress-system in the initial state, and a stress-system by which the load would be balanced all through the body. The strain, reckoned from the unstressed state, is likewise compounded of two strains: the strain from the unstressed state to the initial state, and the strain from the initial state to the state assumed under the load. The only things, about which the experiments can tell us anything, are the second stress-system and the second strain; and it is consonant with the result of the experiments to assume that the law of proportionality holds for this stress and strain. The general statement of the law of proportionality implies that the stress in the initial state also is proportional to the strain in that state. It also implies that both the initial state, and the state assumed under the load, are derivable from the unstressed state by displacements, of amount sufficiently small to admit of the calculation of the strains by the simplified methods of Article 9. If this were not the case, the strains would not be compounded by simple superposition; and the proportionality of load and measured strain would not imply the proportionality of stress-components and strain-components.

65. Form of the strain-energy-function.

The experiments which lead to the enunciation of Hooke's Law do not constitute a proof of the truth of the law. The law formulates in abstract terms the results of many observations and experiments, but it is much more precise than these results. The mathematical consequences which can be deduced by assuming the law to be true are sometimes capable of experimental verification; and, whenever this verification can be made, fresh evidence of the truth of the law is obtained. We shall be occupied in subsequent chapters with the deduction of these consequences; here we note some results which can be deduced immediately.

When a body is slightly strained by gradual application of a load, and the temperature remains constant, the stress-components are linear functions of the strain-components, and they are also partial differential coefficients of a function (W) of the strain-components. The strain-energy-function, W, is therefore a homogeneous quadratic function of the strain-components.

The known theory of sound waves* leads us to expect that, when a body is executing small vibrations, the motion takes place too quickly for any portion of the body to lose or gain any sensible quantity of heat. In this case also there is a strain-energy-function; and, if we assume that Hooke's Law holds, the function is a homogeneous quadratic function of the strain-components. When the stress-components are eliminated from the equations of motion (15) of Article 54, these equations become linear equations for the determination of the displacement. The linearity of them, and the way in which the time enters into them, make it possible for them to possess solutions which represent isochronous vibrations. The fact that all solid bodies admit of being thrown into states of isochronous vibration has been emphasized by Stokes† as a peremptory proof of the truth of Hooke's Law for the very small strains involved.

The proof of the existence of W given in Article 62 points to different coefficients for the terms of W expressed as a quadratic function of strain-components, in the two cases of isothermal and adiabatic changes of state.

* See Rayleigh, *Theory of Sound*, Chapter XI.

† See Introduction, footnote 37.

These coefficients are the "elastic constants," and discrepancies have actually been found in experimental determinations of the constants by statical methods, involving isothermal changes of state, and dynamical methods, involving adiabatic changes of state *. The discrepancies are not, however, very serious.

To secure the stability of the body it is necessary that the coefficients of the terms in the homogeneous quadratic function W should be adjusted so that the function is always positive †. This condition involves certain relations of inequality among the elastic constants.

If Hooke's Law is regarded as a first approximation, valid in the case of very small strains, it is natural to assume that the terms of the second order in the strain-energy-function constitute likewise a first approximation. If terms of higher order could be taken into account, an extension of the theory might be made to circumstances which are at present excluded from its scope. Such extensions have been suggested and partially worked out by several writers ‡.

66. Elastic constants.

According to the generalized Hooke's Law, the six components of stress at any point of an elastic solid body are connected with the six components of strain at the point by equations of the form

$$\left.\begin{aligned} X_x &= c_{11}e_{xx} + c_{12}e_{yy} + c_{13}e_{zz} + c_{14}e_{yz} + c_{15}e_{zx} + c_{16}e_{xy}, \\ &\cdots\cdots \\ Y_z &= c_{41}e_{xx} + c_{42}e_{yy} + c_{43}e_{zz} + c_{44}e_{yz} + c_{45}e_{zx} + c_{46}e_{xy}, \\ &\cdots\cdots \end{aligned}\right\} \quad \text{.........(10)}$$

The coefficients in these equations, $c_{11}, \ldots$, are the *elastic constants* of the substance. They are the coefficients of a homogeneous quadratic function $2W$, where W is the strain-energy-function; and they are therefore connected by the relations which ensure the existence of the function. These relations are of the form

$$c_{rs} = c_{sr}, \quad (r, s = 1, 2, \ldots 6), \quad \text{.......................(11)}$$

and the number of constants is reduced by these equations from 36 to 21.

* The discrepancies appear to have been noticed first by P. Lagerhjelm in 1827, see Todhunter and Pearson's *History*, vol. 1, p. 189. They were made the subject of extensive experiments by G. Wertheim, *Ann. de Chimie*, t. 12 (1844). Information concerning the results of more recent experimental researches is given by Lord Kelvin (Sir W. Thomson) in the Article 'Elasticity' in *Ency. Brit.*, 9th edition, reprinted in *Math. and Phys. Papers*, vol. 3. See also W. Voigt, *Ann. Phys. Chem.* (*Wiedemann*), Bd. 52 (1894).

† Kirchhoff, *Vorlesungen über...Mechanik*, Vorlesung 27. For a discussion of the theory of stability reference may be made to a paper by R. Lipschitz, *J. f. Math.* (*Crelle*), Bd. 78 (1874).

‡ Reference may be made, in particular, to W. Voigt, *Ann. Phys. Chem.* (*Wiedemann*), Bd. 52, 1894, p. 536, and *Berlin Berichte*, 1901.

We write the expression for $2W$ in the form

$$\begin{aligned}2W = c_{11}e^2_{xx} &+ 2c_{12}e_{xx}e_{yy} + 2c_{13}e_{xx}e_{zz} + 2c_{14}e_{xx}e_{yz} + 2c_{15}e_{xx}e_{zx} + 2c_{16}e_{xx}e_{xy}\\ &+ c_{22}e^2_{yy} + 2c_{23}e_{yy}e_{zz} + 2c_{24}e_{yy}e_{yz} + 2c_{25}e_{yy}e_{zx} + 2c_{26}e_{yy}e_{xy}\\ &+ c_{33}e^2_{zz} + 2c_{34}e_{zz}e_{yz} + 2c_{35}e_{zz}e_{zx} + 2c_{36}e_{zz}e_{xy}\\ &+ c_{44}e^2_{yz} + 2c_{45}e_{yz}e_{zx} + 2c_{46}e_{yz}e_{xy}\\ &+ c_{55}e^2_{zx} + 2c_{56}e_{zx}e_{xy}\\ &+ c_{66}e^2_{xy}.\end{aligned} \qquad \text{.........(12)}$$

The theory of Elasticity has sometimes been based on that hypothesis concerning the constitution of matter, according to which bodies are regarded as made up of material points, and these points are supposed to act on each other at a distance, the law of force between a pair of points being that the force is a function of the distance between the points, and acts in the line joining the points. It is a consequence of this hypothesis* that the coefficients in the function W are connected by six additional relations, whereby their number is reduced to 15. These relations are

$$\left.\begin{aligned}c_{23} = c_{44},\ c_{31} = c_{55},\ c_{12} = c_{66},\\ c_{14} = c_{56},\ c_{25} = c_{46},\ c_{45} = c_{36}.\end{aligned}\right\} \qquad \text{.........................(13)}$$

We shall refer to these as "Cauchy's relations"; but we shall not assume that they hold good.

67. Methods of determining the stress in a body.

If we wish to know the state of stress in a body to which given forces are applied, either as body forces or as surface tractions, we have to solve the stress-equations of equilibrium (14) of Article 54, viz.

$$\left.\begin{aligned}\frac{\partial X_x}{\partial x} + \frac{\partial X_y}{\partial y} + \frac{\partial Z_x}{\partial z} + \rho X = 0,\\ \frac{\partial X_y}{\partial x} + \frac{\partial Y_y}{\partial y} + \frac{\partial Y_z}{\partial z} + \rho Y = 0,\\ \frac{\partial Z_x}{\partial x} + \frac{\partial Y_z}{\partial y} + \frac{\partial Z_z}{\partial z} + \rho Z = 0;\end{aligned}\right\} \qquad \text{.....................(14)}$$

and the solutions must be of such forms that they give rise to the right expressions for the surface tractions, when the latter are calculated from the formulæ (5) of Article 47, viz.

$$\left.\begin{aligned}X_\nu = X_x \cos(x, \nu) + X_y \cos(y, \nu) + Z_x \cos(z, \nu),\\ \ldots\ldots\end{aligned}\right\} \qquad \text{...........(15)}$$

The equations (14) with the conditions (15) are not sufficient to determine the stress, and a stress-system may satisfy these equations and conditions and yet fail to be the correct solution of the problem; for the stress-components are

* See Note B at the end of this book.

functions of the strain-components, and the latter satisfy the six equations of compatibility (25) of Article 17, viz. three equations of the type

$$\frac{\partial^2 e_{yy}}{\partial z^2} + \frac{\partial^2 e_{zz}}{\partial y^2} = \frac{\partial^2 e_{yz}}{\partial y \partial z},$$

and three of the type

$$2\frac{\partial^2 e_{xx}}{\partial y \partial z} = \frac{\partial}{\partial x}\left(-\frac{\partial e_{yz}}{\partial x} + \frac{\partial e_{zx}}{\partial y} + \frac{\partial e_{xy}}{\partial z}\right).$$

When account is taken of these relations, there are sufficient equations to determine the stress.

Whenever the forces are such that the stress-components are either constants or linear functions of the coordinates, the same is true of the strain-components, and the equations of compatibility are satisfied identically. We shall consider such cases in the sequel.

In the general case, the problem may in various ways be reduced to that of solving certain systems of differential equations. One way is to form, by the method described above, a system of equations for the stress-components in which account is taken of the identical relations between strain-components. Another way is to eliminate the stress-components and express the strain-components in terms of displacements by using the formulæ

$$\left.\begin{aligned} e_{xx} &= \frac{\partial u}{\partial x}, \quad e_{yy} = \frac{\partial v}{\partial y}, \quad e_{zz} = \frac{\partial w}{\partial z}, \\ e_{yz} &= \frac{\partial w}{\partial y} + \frac{\partial v}{\partial z}, \quad e_{zx} = \frac{\partial u}{\partial z} + \frac{\partial w}{\partial x}, \quad e_{xy} = \frac{\partial v}{\partial x} + \frac{\partial u}{\partial y}. \end{aligned}\right\} \quad \text{.........(16)}$$

Both these methods will be illustrated in the sequel.

If the displacement can be obtained, the strain-components can be found by differentiation, and the stress-components can be deduced. If, on the other hand, the stress can be determined, the strains can be deduced, and the displacement can be found by the method indicated in Article 18.

It will be proved in Chapter VII that the solution of any problem of the kind considered here is effectively unique. We shall assume for the present that any solution, which satisfies all the conditions, is *the* solution.

68. Form of the strain-energy-function for isotropic solids.

If we refer the stress-components and strain-components to a new system of axes of coordinates x', y', z', instead of x, y, z, the stress-components must be transformed according to the formulæ of Article 49, and the strain-components must be transformed according to the formulæ of Article 12. When we substitute for X_x, ... and e_{xx}, ... in the equations of the types (10) we find that the stress-components $X'_{x'}$, ... and the strain-components $e_{x'x'}$, ... are connected by linear equations. These may be solved for the $X'_{x'}$, ... and the result will be that the $X'_{x'}$, ... are expressed as linear functions of $e_{x'x'}$, ... with coefficients, which depend on the coefficients c_{11}, ... in the formula (12), and also on the quantities by which the relative situations of the old and new axes are determined. The results might be found more rapidly by transforming the expression $2W$ according to the formulæ of Article 12. The general result is that the elastic behaviour of a material has reference to certain directions fixed relatively to the material. If, however, the elastic constants are connected by certain relations, the formulæ connecting stress-components with strain-components are independent of direction. The material is then said to be *isotropic* as regards elasticity. In this case the function W is invariant for all transformations from one set of orthogonal axes to another. If we knew that there were no invariants of the strain, of the first or second degrees, independent of the two which were found in Article 13 (*c*), we could conclude that the strain-energy-function for an isotropic solid must be of the form

$$\tfrac{1}{2}A(e_{xx}+e_{yy}+e_{zz})^2+\tfrac{1}{2}B(e^2_{yz}+e^2_{zx}+e^2_{xy}-4e_{yy}e_{zz}-4e_{zz}e_{xx}-4e_{xx}e_{yy}).$$

This result may be obtained from Hooke's Law. The most general forms that equations (10) can take in an isotropic solid are included in the following:

$$\begin{aligned}
X_x &= Ae_{xx}+A'(e_{yy}+e_{zz})+Ce_{yz}+C'(e_{zx}+e_{xy}),\\
Y_y &= Ae_{yy}+A'(e_{zz}+e_{xx})+Ce_{zx}+C'(e_{xy}+e_{yz}),\\
Z_z &= Ae_{zz}+A'(e_{xx}+e_{yy})+Ce_{xy}+C'(e_{yz}+e_{zx}),\\
Y_z &= De_{xx}+D'(e_{yy}+e_{zz})+Be_{yz}+B'(e_{zx}+e_{xy}),\\
Z_x &= De_{yy}+D'(e_{zz}+e_{xx})+Be_{zx}+B'(e_{xy}+e_{yz}),\\
X_y &= De_{zz}+D'(e_{xx}+e_{yy})+Be_{xy}+B'(e_{yz}+e_{zx}),
\end{aligned}$$

for the stress-strain relations must not be altered by interchanging any two of the axes. The relations must not be altered by reversing the sense of any axis; but, when the axis of x is reversed, e_{xy}, e_{zx}, X_y and Z_x are changed in sign while the remaining components of stress and strain are unaltered. It follows that C, C', D, D', B' must vanish.

The stress-strain relations must also be unaltered by rotating the axes into new positions. Let the axes be turned through an angle θ about the axis of z into positions denoted by x', y', z. The relation $X'_{y'}=Be_{x'y'}$ gives, by (9) of Article 49 and (11) of Article 12,

$$\begin{aligned}
&-\sin\theta\cos\theta\{(A-A')e_{xx}+A'\Delta\}+\sin\theta\cos\theta\{(A-A')e_{yy}+A'\Delta\}+(\cos^2\theta-\sin^2\theta)Be_{xy}\\
&=B\{-2e_{xx}\sin\theta\cos\theta+2e_{yy}\sin\theta\cos\theta+e_{xy}(\cos^2\theta-\sin^2\theta)\},
\end{aligned}$$

an equation which must hold for all values of θ. Hence

$$A-A'=2B,$$

and the expressions for $X_x, \ldots$ in terms of $e_{xx}, \ldots$ are the derivatives of the function

$$\tfrac{1}{2}A\Delta^2+\tfrac{1}{2}B(e^2_{yz}+\ldots\ 4e_{yy}e_{zz}-\ldots).$$

In what follows $\lambda+2\mu$ and μ will be written in place of A and B. When the material is homogeneous λ and μ are the same at all points.

69. Elastic constants and moduluses of isotropic solids.

When W is expressed by the equation

$$2W=(\lambda+2\mu)(e_{xx}+e_{yy}+e_{zz})^2 + \mu(e^2_{yz}+e^2_{zx}+e^2_{xy}-4e_{yy}e_{zz}-4e_{zz}e_{xx}-4e_{xx}e_{yy}), \quad\ldots\ldots(17)$$

the stress-components are given by the equations

$$\left.\begin{aligned}
X_x&=\lambda\Delta+2\mu e_{xx}, & Y_y&=\lambda\Delta+2\mu e_{yy}, & Z_z&=\lambda\Delta+2\mu e_{zz},\\
Y_z&=\mu e_{yz}, & Z_x&=\mu e_{zx}, & X_y&=\mu e_{xy},
\end{aligned}\right\}\quad\ldots(18)$$

where Δ is written for $e_{xx}+e_{yy}+e_{zz}$.

A body of any form subjected to the action of a constant pressure p, the same at all points of its surface, will be in a certain state of stress. As we have seen in Article 55, this state will be given by the equations

$$X_x = Y_y = Z_z = -p, \quad Y_z = Z_x = X_y = 0.$$

According to equations (18), the body is in a state of strain such that

$$e_{xx} = e_{yy} = e_{zz} = -p/(3\lambda + 2\mu),$$
$$e_{yz} = e_{zx} = e_{xy} = 0.$$

The cubical compression is $p/(\lambda + \frac{2}{3}\mu)$.

We write $$k = \lambda + \tfrac{2}{3}\mu. \qquad \text{.........(19)}$$

Then k is the quantity obtained by dividing the measure of an uniform pressure by the measure of the cubical compression produced by it. It is called the *modulus of compression.*

Whatever the stress-system may be, it can be resolved, as in Article 52, into mean tension, or pressure, and shearing stresses on three orthogonal planes. The mean tension is measured by $\frac{1}{3}(X_x + Y_y + Z_z)$. We learn that the quantity obtained by dividing the measure of the mean tension at a point by the measure of the cubical dilatation at the point is a constant quantity —the modulus of compression.

A cylinder or prism of any form, subjected to tension T which is uniform over its plane ends, and free from traction on its lateral surfaces, will be in a certain state of stress. As we have seen in Article 55, this state will be given by the equations

$$X_x = T, \quad Y_y = Z_z = Y_z = Z_x = X_y = 0.$$

According to equations (18) the body will be in a state of strain such that

$$e_{xx} = \frac{T(\lambda + \mu)}{\mu(3\lambda + 2\mu)}, \quad e_{yy} = e_{zz} = -\frac{\lambda T}{2\mu(3\lambda + 2\mu)}.$$

We write $$E = \frac{\mu(3\lambda + 2\mu)}{\lambda + \mu}, \qquad \text{.........(20)}$$

$$\sigma = \frac{\lambda}{2(\lambda + \mu)}. \qquad \text{.........(21)}$$

Then E is the quantity obtained by dividing the measure of a simple longitudinal tension by the measure of the extension produced by it. It is known as *Young's modulus.* The number σ is the ratio of lateral contraction to longitudinal extension of a bar under terminal tension. It is known as *Poisson's ratio.*

Whatever the stress-system may be, the extensions in the directions of the axes and the normal tractions across planes at right angles to the axes are connected by the equations

$$\left.\begin{aligned} e_{xx} &= E^{-1}\{X_x - \sigma(Y_y + Z_z)\}, \\ e_{yy} &= E^{-1}\{Y_y - \sigma(Z_z + X_x)\}, \\ e_{zz} &= E^{-1}\{Z_z - \sigma(X_x + Y_y)\}. \end{aligned}\right\} \qquad \text{.........(22)}$$

Whatever the stress-system may be, the shearing strain corresponding with a pair of rectangular axes and the shearing stress on the pair of planes at right angles to those axes are connected by an equation of the form

$$X_y = \mu e_{xy}. \qquad \text{.............................(23)}$$

This relation is independent of the directions of the axes. The quantity μ is called the *rigidity*.

70. Observations concerning the stress-strain relations in isotropic solids.

(*a*) We may note the relations

$$\lambda = \frac{E\sigma}{(1+\sigma)(1-2\sigma)}, \quad \mu = \frac{E}{2(1+\sigma)}, \quad k = \frac{E}{3(1-2\sigma)}. \qquad \text{..............(24)}$$

(*b*) If σ were $> \frac{1}{2}$, k would be negative, or the material would expand under pressure. If σ were < -1, μ would be negative, and the function W would not be a positive quadratic function. We may show that this would also be the case if k were negative*. Negative values for σ are not excluded by the condition of stability, but such values have not been found for any isotropic material.

(*c*) The constant k is usually determined by experiments on compression, the constant E sometimes directly by experiments on stretching, and sometimes by experiments on bending, the constant μ usually by experiments on torsion. The value of the constant σ is usually inferred from a knowledge of two among the quantities E, k, μ†.

(*d*) If Cauchy's relations (13) of Article 66 are true, $\lambda = \mu$ and $\sigma = \frac{1}{4}$.

(*e*) Instead of assuming the form of the strain-energy-function, we might assume some of the relations between stress-components and strain-components and deduce the relations (18). For example‡ we may assume (i) that the mean tension and the cubical dilatation are connected by the equation $\frac{1}{3}(X_x + Y_y + Z_z) = k\Delta$, (ii) that the relation $X'_{y'} = \mu e_{x'y'}$ holds for all pairs of rectangular axes of x' and y'. From the second assumption we should find, by taking the axes of x, y, z to be the principal axes of strain, that the principal planes of stress are at right angles to these axes. With the same choice of axes we should then find, by means of the formulæ of transformation of Articles 12 and 49, that the relation

$$X_x l_1 l_2 + Y_y m_1 m_2 + Z_z n_1 n_2 = \mu\,(2e_{xx} l_1 l_2 + 2e_{yy} m_1 m_2 + 2e_{zz} n_1 n_2)$$

holds for all values of $l_1, \ldots$ which satisfy the equation

$$l_1 l_2 + m_1 m_2 + n_1 n_2 = 0.$$

It follows that we must have

$$X_x - 2\mu e_{xx} = Y_y - 2\mu e_{yy} = Z_z - 2\mu e_{zz}.$$

Then the first assumption shows that each of these quantities is equal to $(k - \frac{2}{3}\mu)\,\Delta$. The relations (18) are thus found to hold for principal axes of strain, and, by a fresh application of the formulæ of transformation, we may prove that they hold for any axes.

(*f*) Instead of making the assumptions just described we might assume that the principal planes of stress are at right angles to the principal axes of strain and that the relations (22) hold for principal axes, and we might deduce the relations (18) for any axes. The working out of this assumption may serve as an exercise for the student.

* $2W$ may be written

$$(\lambda + \tfrac{2}{3}\mu)\,(e_{xx} + e_{yy} + e_{zz})^2 + \tfrac{2}{3}\mu\,\{(e_{yy} - e_{zz})^2 + (e_{zz} - e_{xx})^2 + (e_{xx} - e_{yy})^2\} + \mu\,(e_{yz}^2 + e_{zx}^2 + e_{xy}^2).$$

† Experiments for the direct determination of Poisson's ratio have been made by P. Cardani, *Phys. Zeitschr.*, Bd. 4, 1903, and J. Morrow, *Phil. Mag.* (Ser. 6), vol. 6 (1903). M. A. Cornu, *Paris, C. R.*, t. 69 (1869), and A. Mallock, *London, Roy. Soc. Proc.*, vol. 29 (1879), determined σ by experiments on bending.

‡ This is the method of Stokes. See Introduction, footnote 37.

(*g*) We may show that, in the problem of the compression of a body by pressure uniform over its surface which was associated with the definition of k, the displacement is expressed by the equations*

$$\frac{u}{x}=\frac{v}{y}=\frac{w}{z}=-\frac{p}{3k}.$$

(*h*) We may show that, in the problem of the bar stretched by simple tension T which was associated with the definitions of E and σ, the displacement is expressed by the equations

$$\frac{v}{y}=\frac{w}{z}=-\frac{\sigma T}{E}=-\frac{\lambda T}{2\mu(3\lambda+2\mu)},\qquad \frac{u}{x}=\frac{T}{E}=\frac{(\lambda+\mu)T}{\mu(3\lambda+2\mu)}.$$

71. Magnitude of elastic constants and moduluses of some isotropic solids.

To give an idea of the order of magnitude of the elastic constants and moduluses of some of the materials in everyday use a few of the results of experiments are tabulated here. The table gives the density (ρ) of the material as well as the elastic constants, the constants being expressed as multiples of an unit stress of one dyne per square centimetre. Poisson's ratio is also given. The results marked "E" are taken from J. D. Everett's *Illustrations of the C.G.S. system of units*, London, 1891, where the authorities for them will be found. Those marked "A" are reduced from results of more recent researches recorded in a paper by Amagat in the *Journal de Physique* (Sér. 2), t. 8 (1889). It must be understood that considerable differences are found in the elastic constants of different samples of nominally the same substance, and that such a designation as "steel," for example, is far from being precise.

Material	ρ	E	k	μ	σ	Reference
Steel	7·849	$2{\cdot}139\times10^{12}$	$1{\cdot}841\times10^{12}$	$8{\cdot}19\times10^{11}$	·310	E
"		$2{\cdot}041\times10^{12}$	$1{\cdot}43\times10^{12}$		·268	A
Iron (wrought)	7·677	$1{\cdot}963\times10^{12}$	$1{\cdot}456\times10^{12}$	$7{\cdot}69\times10^{11}$	·275	E
Brass (drawn)	8·471	$1{\cdot}075\times10^{12}$		$3{\cdot}66\times10^{11}$		E
Brass		$1{\cdot}085\times10^{12}$	$1{\cdot}05\times10^{12}$		·327	A
Copper	8·843	$1{\cdot}234\times10^{12}$	$1{\cdot}684\times10^{12}$	$4{\cdot}47\times10^{11}$	·378	E
"		$1{\cdot}215\times10^{12}$	$1{\cdot}166\times10^{12}$		·327	A
Lead		$1{\cdot}57\times10^{11}$	$3{\cdot}62\times10^{11}$		·428	A
Glass	2·942	$6{\cdot}03\times10^{11}$	$4{\cdot}15\times10^{11}$	$2{\cdot}40\times10^{11}$	·258	E
"		$6{\cdot}77\times10^{11}$	$4{\cdot}54\times10^{11}$		·245	A

72. Elastic constants in general.

Materials such as natural crystals or wood which are not isotropic are said to be *æolotropic*. The analytical expression of Hooke's Law in an æolotropic

* A displacement which would be possible in a rigid body may be superposed on that given in the text. A like remark applies to the Observation (*h*). Cf. Article 18, *supra*.

solid body is effected by the equations (10) of Article 66. In matrix notation we may write the equations

$$(X_x, Y_y, Z_z, Y_z, Z_x, X_y) = \begin{pmatrix} c_{11} & c_{12} & c_{13} & c_{14} & c_{15} & c_{16} \\ c_{21} & c_{22} & c_{23} & c_{24} & c_{25} & c_{26} \\ c_{31} & c_{32} & c_{33} & c_{34} & c_{35} & c_{36} \\ c_{41} & c_{42} & c_{43} & c_{44} & c_{45} & c_{46} \\ c_{51} & c_{52} & c_{53} & c_{54} & c_{55} & c_{56} \\ c_{61} & c_{62} & c_{63} & c_{64} & c_{65} & c_{66} \end{pmatrix} (e_{xx}, e_{yy}, e_{zz}, e_{yz}, e_{zx}, e_{xy}), \quad \ldots\ldots(25)$$

where $c_{rs} = c_{sr}$, $(r, s = 1, 2, \ldots 6)$.

These equations may be solved, so as to express the strain-components in terms of the stress-components. If Π denotes the determinant of the quantities c_{rs}, and C_{rs} denotes the minor determinant that corresponds with c_{rs}, so that

$$\Pi = c_{r1}C_{r1} + c_{r2}C_{r2} + c_{r3}C_{r3} + c_{r4}C_{r4} + c_{r5}C_{r5} + c_{r6}C_{r6}, \quad \ldots\ldots\ldots(26)$$

the equations that give the strain-components in terms of the stress-components can be written

$$\Pi\,(e_{xx}, e_{yy}, e_{zz}, e_{yz}, e_{zx}, e_{xy}) = \begin{pmatrix} C_{11} & C_{12} & C_{13} & C_{14} & C_{15} & C_{16} \\ C_{21}\ldots\ldots & & & & & \\ \vdots & & & & & \end{pmatrix} (X_x, Y_y, Z_z, Y_z, Z_x, X_y), \quad \ldots\ldots(27)$$

where $C_{rs} = C_{sr}$, $(r, s = 1, 2, \ldots 6)$.

The quantities $\frac{1}{2}c_{11}, \ldots c_{12}, \ldots$ are the coefficients of a homogeneous quadratic function of $e_{xx}, \ldots$. This function is the strain-energy-function expressed in terms of strain-components.

The quantities $\frac{1}{2}C_{11}/\Pi, \ldots C_{12}/\Pi, \ldots$ are the coefficients of a homogeneous quadratic function of $X_x, \ldots$. This function is the strain-energy-function expressed in terms of stress-components.

73. Moduluses of elasticity.

We may in various ways define types of stress and types of strain. For example, simple tension $[X_x]$, shearing stress $[Y_z]$, mean tension $[\frac{1}{3}(X_x+Y_y+Z_z)]$ are types of stress. The corresponding types of strain are simple extension $[e_{xx}]$, shearing strain $[e_{yz}]$, cubical dilatation $[e_{xx}+e_{yy}+e_{zz}]$. We may express the strain of any of these types that accompanies a stress of the corresponding type, *when there is no other stress*, by an equation of the form

$$\text{stress} = M \times (\text{corresponding strain}).$$

Then M is called a "modulus of elasticity." The quantities Π/C_{11}, Π/C_{44} are examples of such moduluses.

The modulus that corresponds with simple tension is known as *Young's modulus* for the direction of the related tension. The modulus that corresponds with shearing stress on a pair of orthogonal planes is known as the *rigidity* for the related pair of directions (the normals to the planes). The modulus that corresponds with mean tension or pressure is known as the *modulus of compression*.

We shall give some examples of the calculation of moduluses.

(*a*) *Modulus of compression.*

We have to assume that $X_x = Y_y = Z_z$, and the remaining stress-components vanish; the corresponding strain is cubical dilatation, and we must therefore calculate $e_{xx}+e_{yy}+e_{zz}$. We find for the modulus the expression

$$\Pi/(C_{11}+C_{22}+C_{33}+2C_{23}+2C_{31}+2C_{12}). \qquad \text{.........................(28)}$$

As in Article 68, we see that the cubical compression produced in a body of any form by the application of uniform normal pressure, p, to its surface is p/k, where k now denotes the above expression (28).

(*b*) *Rigidity.*

We may suppose that all the stress-components vanish except Y_z, and then we have $\Pi e_{yz} = C_{44} Y_z$, so that Π/C_{44} is the rigidity corresponding with the pair of directions y, z.

If the shearing stress is related to the two orthogonal directions (l, m, n) and (l', m', n'), the rigidity can be shown to be expressed by

$$\Pi \div (C_{11}, C_{22}, \ldots C_{12}, \ldots)(2ll', 2mm', 2nn', mn'+m'n, nl'+n'l, lm'+l'm)^2, \quad \text{...(29)}$$

where the denominator is a complete quadratic function of the six arguments $2ll'$, ... with coefficients C_{11}, C_{22}, ...

(*c*) *Young's modulus and Poisson's ratio.*

We may suppose that all the stress-components vanish except X_x, and then we have $\Pi e_{xx} = C_{11} X_x$, so that Π/C_{11} is the Young's modulus corresponding with the direction x. In the same case the Poisson's ratio of the contraction in the direction of the axis of y to the extension in the direction of the axis of x is $-C_{12}/C_{11}$. The value of Poisson's ratio depends on the direction of the contracted transverse linear elements as well as on that of the extended longitudinal ones.

In the general case we may take the stress to be tension $X'_{x'}$ across the planes $x' = \text{const.}$, of which the normal is in the direction (l, m, n). Then we have

$$X_x = l^2 X'_{x'}, \qquad Y_y = m^2 X'_{x'}, \qquad Z_z = n^2 X'_{x'},$$
$$Y_z = mn X'_{x'}, \qquad Z_x = nl X'_{x'}, \qquad X_y = lm X'_{x'},$$

and we have also

$$e_{x'x'} = e_{xx} l^2 + e_{yy} m^2 + e_{zz} n^2 + e_{yz} mn + e_{zx} nl + e_{xy} lm;$$

it follows that the Young's modulus E corresponding with this direction is

$$\Pi \div (C_{11}, C_{22}, \ldots C_{12}, \ldots)(l^2, m^2, n^2, mn, nl, lm)^2, \qquad \text{..................(30)}$$

where the denominator is a complete quadratic function of the six arguments l^2, ... with coefficients C_{11}, ...

If (l', m', n') is any direction at right angles to x', the contraction, $-e_{y'y'}$, in this direction is given by the equation

$$e_{y'y'} = e_{xx} l'^2 + e_{yy} m'^2 + e_{zz} n'^2 + e_{yz} m'n' + e_{zx} n'l' + e_{xy} l'm',$$

and the corresponding Poisson's ratio σ is expressible in the form

$$\sigma = -\frac{1}{2\phi}\left[l'^2 \frac{\partial\phi}{\partial(l^2)} + m'^2 \frac{\partial\phi}{\partial(m^2)} + n'^2 \frac{\partial\phi}{\partial(n^2)} + m'n' \frac{\partial\phi}{\partial(mn)} + n'l' \frac{\partial\phi}{\partial(nl)} + l'm' \frac{\partial\phi}{\partial(lm)}\right], \quad \text{...(31)}$$

where ϕ is the above-mentioned quadratic function of the arguments l^2, ..., and the differential coefficients are formed as if these arguments were independent. It may be observed that σ/E is related symmetrically to the two directions in which the corresponding contraction and extension occur.

If we construct the surface of the fourth order of which the equation is

$$(C_{11}, C_{22}, \ldots C_{12}, \ldots)(x^2, y^2, z^2, yz, zx, xy)^2 = \text{const.}, \quad \text{.................(32)}$$

then the radius vector of this surface in any direction is proportional to the positive fourth root of the Young's modulus of the material corresponding with that direction*.

74. Thermo-elastic equations.

The application of the two fundamental laws of Thermodynamics to the problem of determining the stress and strain in elastic solid bodies when variations of temperature occur has been discussed by Lord Kelvin†. The results at which he arrived do not permit of the formulation of a system of differential equations to determine the state of stress in the body in the manner explained in Article 67.

At an earlier date Duhamel‡ had obtained a set of equations of the required kind by developing the theory of an elastic solid regarded as a system of material points, and F. E. Neumann, starting from certain assumptions§, had arrived at the same system of equations. These assumptions may, when the body is isotropic, be expressed in the following form:

When the temperature in a small portion of a body is increased by θ, dilatation of amount proportional to θ can be produced without any corresponding change of pressure. This implies extension of all linear elements of amount $\frac{1}{3}c\theta$, where c is a constant, the *coefficient of expansion*. If forces are applied to the body the strain at a point consists of such extension superposed upon a strain connected with the stress by the usual stress-strain equations.

According to these assumptions the stress and strain in a body strained by change of temperature do not obey Hooke's Law, but are connected by three equations of the type

$$e_{xx} = \tfrac{1}{3}c\theta + E^{-1}\{X_x - \sigma(Y_y + Z_z)\}, \quad \text{..................(33)}$$

as well as three of the type

$$e_{yz} = \mu^{-1} Y_z.$$

On solving these equations we have

$$\left.\begin{array}{l} X_x = \lambda\Delta + 2\mu e_{xx} - \beta\theta, \quad Y_y = \lambda\Delta + 2\mu e_{yy} - \beta\theta, \quad Z_z = \lambda\Delta + 2\mu e_{zz} - \beta\theta, \\ Y_z = \mu e_{yz}, \quad Z_x = \mu e_{zx}, \quad X_y = \mu e_{xy}, \end{array}\right\} \quad \text{......(34)}$$

where

$$\beta = (\lambda + \tfrac{2}{3}\mu)\, c.$$

The result is that the displacement in the body is the same as if it were subject to body force (per unit volume, not per unit mass), expressed as the

* The result is due to Cauchy, *Exercices de mathématique*, t. 4 (1829), p. 30.

† See Introduction, footnote 43.

‡ *Paris, Mém....par divers savans*, t. 5 (1838).

§ See his *Vorlesungen über die Theorie der Elasticität der festen Körper*, Leipzig, 1885, and cf. the memoir by Maxwell cited in Article 57, footnote.

gradient of a potential $-\beta\theta$, and to normal surface pressure $\beta\theta$, in addition to the body forces and surface tractions that are actually applied to it. The equations of equilibrium are sufficient to determine this displacement, and the corresponding strain and stress, when θ is given. When it is not given an additional equation is required, and this may be obtained from the theory of conduction of heat, as was done by Duhamel and Neumann.

The theory thus arrived at has not been very much developed. Attention has been directed especially to the fact that a plate of glass strained by unequal heating becomes doubly refracting, and to the explanation of this effect by the inequality of the stresses in different directions. The reader who wishes to pursue the subject is referred to the following memoirs in addition to those already cited:—C. W. Borchardt, *Berlin Monatsberichte,* 1873; J. Hopkinson, *Messenger of Math.* vol. 8 (1879); Lord Rayleigh, *Phil. Mag.* (Ser. 6) vol. 1 (1901), or *Scientific Papers,* vol. 4, p. 502; E. Almansi, *Torino Atti,* t. 32 (1897); P. Alibrandi, *Giornale di matem.* t. 38 (1900).

A modification of the theory is needed when the changes of temperature are so great that the dilatation due to the rise θ is not proportional to θ. This has been worked out, for the cases of spherical and cylindrical shells concentrically heated, by C. H. Lees, *London, Roy. Soc. Proc.* (Ser. A), vol. 100 (1922), p. 379, and vol. 101 (1922), p. 411.

It must be observed that the elastic "constants" themselves are functions of the temperature. In general, they are diminished by a rise of temperature; this result has been established by the experiments of Wertheim*, Kohlrausch† and Macleod and Clarke‡. References to more recent experimental researches on this subject, with some new results, will be found in papers by K. Iokibe and S. Sakai, *Phil. Mag.* (Ser. 6), vol. 42 (1921), p. 397, and by H. M. Dadourian, *ibid.*, p. 442.

75. Initial stress.

The initial state of a body may be too far removed from the unstressed state to permit of the stress and strain being calculated by the principle of superposition as explained in Article 64. Such initial states may be induced by processes of preparation, or of manufacture, or by the action of body forces. In cast iron the exterior parts cool more rapidly than the interior, and the unequal contractions that accompany the unequally rapid rates of cooling give rise to considerable initial stress in the iron when cold. If a sheet of metal is rolled up into a cylinder and the edges welded together the body so formed is in a state of initial stress, and the unstressed state cannot be attained without cutting the cylinder open. A body in equilibrium under the mutual

* *Ann. de Chimie,* t. 12 (1844).

† *Ann. Phys. Chem.* (*Poggendorff*), Bd. 141 (1870).

‡ A result obtained by these writers is explained in the sense stated in the text by Lord Kelvin in the Article 'Elasticity' in *Ency. Brit.* quoted in the footnote to Article 65.

gravitation of its parts is in a state of stress, and when the body is large the stress may be enormous. The Earth is an example of a body which must be regarded as being in a state of initial stress, for the stress that must exist in the interior is much too great to permit of the calculation, by the ordinary methods, of strains reckoned from the unstressed state as unstrained state.

If a body is given in a state of initial stress, and is subjected to forces, changes of volume and shape will be produced which can be specified by a displacement reckoned from the given initial state as unstrained state. We may specify the initial stress at a point by the components

$$X_x^{(0)},\ Y_y^{(0)},\ Z_z^{(0)},\ Y_z^{(0)},\ Z_x^{(0)},\ X_y^{(0)},$$

and we may specify the stress at the point when the forces are in action by $X_x^{(0)} + X_x', \ldots$. In like manner we may specify the density in the initial state by ρ_0 and that in the strained state by $\rho_0 + \rho'$, and we may specify the body force in the initial state by (X_0, Y_0, Z_0) and that in the strained state by $(X_0 + X', Y_0 + Y', Z_0 + Z')$. Then the conditions of equilibrium in the initial state are three equations of the type

$$\frac{\partial X_x^{(0)}}{\partial x} + \frac{\partial X_y^{(0)}}{\partial y} + \frac{\partial Z_x^{(0)}}{\partial z} + \rho_0 X_0 = 0 \quad \ldots\ldots\ldots\ldots(35)$$

and three boundary conditions of the type

$$X_x^{(0)} \cos(x, \nu_0) + X_y^{(0)} \cos(y, \nu_0) + Z_x^{(0)} \cos(z, \nu_0) = 0, \quad \ldots\ldots(36)$$

in which ν_0 denotes the direction of the normal to the initial boundary.

The conditions of equilibrium in the strained state are three equations of the form

$$\frac{\partial}{\partial x}(X_x^{(0)} + X_x') + \frac{\partial}{\partial y}(X_y^{(0)} + X_y') + \frac{\partial}{\partial z}(Z_x^{(0)} + Z_x') + (\rho_0 + \rho')(X_0 + X') = 0 \quad \ldots\ldots(37)$$

and three boundary conditions of the type

$$(X_x^{(0)} + X_x') \cos(x, \nu) + (X_y^{(0)} + X_y') \cos(y, \nu) + (Z_x^{(0)} + Z_x') \cos(z, \nu) = X_\nu, \quad \ldots\ldots(38)$$

in which (X_ν, Y_ν, Z_ν) is the surface traction at any point of the displaced boundary. These equations may be transformed, when the displacement is small, by using the results (35) and (36), so as to become three equations of the type

$$\frac{\partial X_x'}{\partial x} + \frac{\partial X_y'}{\partial y} + \frac{\partial Z_x'}{\partial z} + \rho_0 X' + \rho' X_0 = 0 \quad \ldots\ldots\ldots\ldots(39)$$

and three boundary conditions of the type

$$\left.\begin{aligned} X_x' \cos(x, \nu) + X_y' \cos(y, \nu) + Z_x' \cos(z, \nu) \\ = X_\nu - X_x^{(0)} \{\cos(x, \nu) - \cos(x, \nu_0)\} \\ - X_y^{(0)} \{\cos(y, \nu) - \cos(y, \nu_0)\} \\ - Z_x^{(0)} \{\cos(z, \nu) - \cos(z, \nu_0)\}. \end{aligned}\right\} \quad \ldots\ldots(40)$$

If the initial stress is not known the equations (35) and conditions (36) are not sufficient to determine it, and no progress can be made. If the initial stress is known the determination of the additional stress (X_x', ...) cannot be effected by means of equations (39) and conditions (40), without knowledge of the relations between these stress-components and the displacement. To obtain such knowledge recourse must be had either to experiment or to some more general theory. Experimental evidence appears to be entirely wanting*.

Cauchy† worked out the consequences of applying that theory of material points to which reference has been made in Article 66. He found for X_x', ... expressions of the form

$$\left.\begin{aligned} X_x' &= X_x^{(0)}\left(\frac{\partial u}{\partial x}-\frac{\partial v}{\partial y}-\frac{\partial w}{\partial z}\right)+2X_y^{(0)}\frac{\partial u}{\partial y}+2Z_x^{(0)}\frac{\partial u}{\partial z}+X_x'',\\ Y_z' &= Y_y^{(0)}\frac{\partial w}{\partial y}+Z_z^{(0)}\frac{\partial v}{\partial z}-Y_z^{(0)}\frac{\partial u}{\partial x}+Z_x^{(0)}\frac{\partial v}{\partial x}+X_y^{(0)}\frac{\partial w}{\partial x}+Y_z'',\\ &\dots\dots \end{aligned}\right\}\quad\dots(41)$$

where (u, v, w) is the displacement reckoned from the initial state, and $(X_x'', \dots)$ is a stress-system related to this displacement by the same equations as would hold if there were no initial stress. In the case of isotropy these equations would be (18) of Article 69 with λ put equal to μ. It may be observed that the terms of X_x', ... that contain $X_x^{(0)}$, ... arise from the changes in the distances between Cauchy's material points, and from changes in the directions of the lines joining them in pairs, and these changes are expressed by means of the displacement (u, v, w).

Saint-Venant‡ has obtained Cauchy's result by adapting the method of Green, that is to say by the use of the energy-function. His deduction has been criticized by K. Pearson§, and it cannot be accepted as valid. Green's original discussion|| appears to be restricted to the case of uniform initial stress in an unlimited elastic medium, and the same restriction characterizes Lord Kelvin's discussion of Green's theory¶.

* Reference may be made to a paper by F. H. Cilley, *Amer. J. of Science* (*Silliman*), (Ser. 4), vol. 11 (1901).

† See Introduction and cf. Note B at the end of this book.

‡ *J. de Math.* (*Liouville*), (Sér. 2), t. 8 (1863).

§ Todhunter and Pearson's *History*, vol. 2, pp. 84, 85.

|| See the paper quoted in the Introduction, footnote 81.

¶ *Baltimore Lectures on Molecular Dynamics and the Wave Theory of Light*, London, 1904, pp. 228 *et seq.*

CHAPTER IV

THE RELATION BETWEEN THE MATHEMATICAL THEORY OF ELASTICITY AND TECHNICAL MECHANICS

76. Limitations of the mathematical theory.

The object of this Chapter is to present as clear an idea as possible of the scope and limitations of the mathematical theory in its application to practical questions. The theory is worked out for bodies strained gradually at a constant temperature, from an initial state of no stress to a final state which differs so little from the unstressed state that squares and products of the displacements can be neglected; and further it is worked out on the basis of Hooke's Law, as generalized in the statements in Article 64. It is known that many materials used in engineering structures, e.g. cast iron, building stone, cement, do not obey Hooke's Law for any strains that are large enough to be observed. It is known also that those materials which do obey the law for small measurable strains do not obey it for larger ones. The statement of the law in Article 64 included the statement that the strain disappears on removal of the load, and this part of it is absolutely necessary to the mathematical theory; but it is known that the limits of strain, or of load, in which this condition holds good are relatively narrow. Although there exists much experimental knowledge* in regard to the behaviour of bodies which are not in the conditions to which the mathematical theory is applicable, yet it appears that the appropriate extensions of the theory which would be needed

* Information in regard to experimental results will be found in treatises on Applied Mechanics. The following may be mentioned:—W. J. M. Rankine, *Applied Mechanics*, 1st edition, London, 1858 (there have been numerous later editions); W. C. Unwin, *The Testing of Materials of Construction*, London, 1888; J. A. Ewing, *The Strength of Materials*, Cambridge, 1899; Flamant, *Stabilité des constructions, Résistance des matériaux*, Paris, 1896; C. Bach, *Elasticität und Festigkeit*, 2nd edition, Berlin, 1894; A. Föppl, *Vorlesungen über technische Mechanik*, Bd. 3, *Festigkeitslehre*, Leipzig, 1900. Very valuable experimental researches were made by J. Bauschinger and recorded by him in *Mittheilungen aus dem mechanischtechnischen Laboratorium...in München* (especially those dated 1886 and 1891); these researches were continued by A. Föppl. New facts in regard to the nature of permanent set in metals, which have proved to be very important, were brought to light by J. A. Ewing and W. Rosenhain, *Phil. Trans. Roy. Soc.* (Ser. A), vols. 193, 195 (1900, 1901). A later development of the theory there described, relating to the structure of metals and the changes of structure that accompany overstrain, is given by W. Rosenhain and S. L. Archbutt in *London, Roy. Soc. Proc.* (Ser. A), vol. 96, 1919, p. 55, where references will also be found to the work of G. T. Beilby and others. Reference may also be made to C. F. Jenkin, *London, Roy. Soc. Proc.* (Ser. A), vol. 103, 1923, p. 121 and H. J. Gough and D. Hanson, *London, Roy. Soc. Proc.* (Ser. A), vol. 104, 1923, p. 538. Important reports on the state of knowledge in regard to many of the matters discussed in this Chapter, including a number of records of new experimental researches, as well as very complete references to previous work, will be found in *Brit. Assoc. Rep.* 1913, pp. 168—224, 1915, pp. 159—170, 1916, pp. 280—291, 1919, pp. 465—495, 1921, pp. 291—358, and 1923, pp. 345—411.

in order to incorporate such knowledge within it cannot be made until much fuller experimental knowledge has been obtained.

The restriction of the theory to conditions in which the strain disappears on removal of the load is usually expressed by saying that the body must be strained within the limits of "perfect elasticity." The restriction to conditions in which the measurable strain is proportional to the load is sometimes expressed by saying that the body must be strained within the limits of "linear elasticity." The expression "limits of elasticity" is used sometimes in one of these senses and sometimes in the other, and the limits are sometimes specified by means of a "stress" or a "traction," i.e. by a load per unit of area, and sometimes by the measurable strain.

When the strain does not disappear after removal of the load, the strain which remains when the load is removed is called "set," and the excess of the strain which occurs under the load above the set is called "elastic strain." The strain is then compounded of set and elastic strain. A body which can be strained without taking any set is sometimes said to be in a "state of ease" up to the strain at which set begins.

77. Stress-strain diagrams.

One of the greatest aids to scientific investigation of the properties of matter subjected to stress is the use of these diagrams. They are usually constructed by taking the strain developed as abscissa, and the stress producing it as the corresponding ordinate. For most materials the case selected for this kind of treatment is the extension of bars, and, in the diagram, the ordinate represents the applied traction, and the abscissa the extension of a line traced on the bar parallel to its length and rather near the middle. The extension is measured by some kind of extensometer*. The load at any instant is known, and the traction is estimated by assuming this load to be distributed uniformly over the area of the cross-section of the specimen in the initial state. If any considerable contraction of the section were to occur the traction would be underestimated. The testing machine, by means of which the experiments are made, is sometimes fitted with an automatic recording apparatus† by which the curve is drawn; but this cannot be done satisfactorily with some types of machine‡.

It is clear that, in general, the quantities recorded by such arrangements are the traction, estimated as stated, and the extension which it produces immediately. Special methods of experimenting and observing are required

* Several kinds of extensometers are described by Ewing and Unwin. The possibility of using the double refraction, produced by loading, to examine stress-strain relations, in specimens strained beyond their elastic limits, has been explored, to some extent, by E. G. Coker and K. C. Chakko, *Phil. Trans. Roy. Soc.* (Ser. A), vol. 221, 1920, p. 139, and by L. N. G. Filon and H. T. Jessop, *Phil. Trans. Roy. Soc.* (Ser. A), vol. 223, 1922, p. 89.

† Unwin, *loc. cit.*

‡ Bauschinger, *Mittheilungen*, xx. (1891).

if elastic strain is to be distinguished from set, and if the various effects that depend upon time are to be calculated.

The general character of the curve for moderately hard metals under extension is now well known. It is for a considerable range of stress very nearly straight. Then comes a stage in which the curve is generally concave downwards, so that the strain increases faster than it would do if it were proportional to the traction; in this stage the strain is largely a permanent set. As the traction increases there comes a region of well-marked discontinuity, in which a small increase of traction produces a large increase of set. The traction at the beginning of this region is called the *Yield-Point.* After a further considerable increase of traction the bar begins to thin down at some section, determined apparently by accidental circumstances, and there it ultimately breaks. When this local thinning down begins the load is usually eased off somewhat before rupture occurs, and the bar breaks with less than the maximum traction. The maximum traction before rupture is called the "breaking stress" of the material, sometimes also the "ultimate strength" or "tenacity."

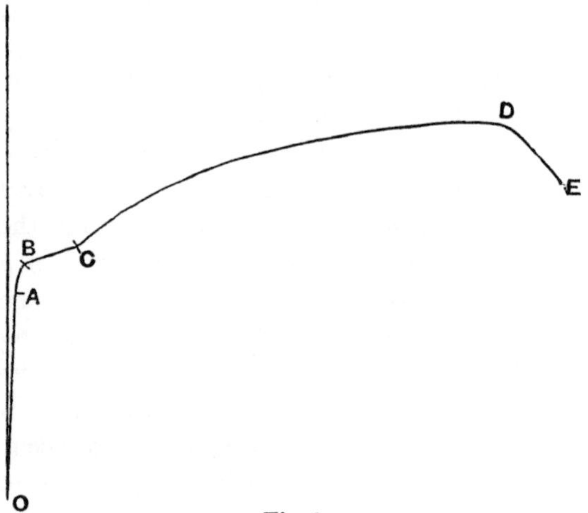

Fig. 8.

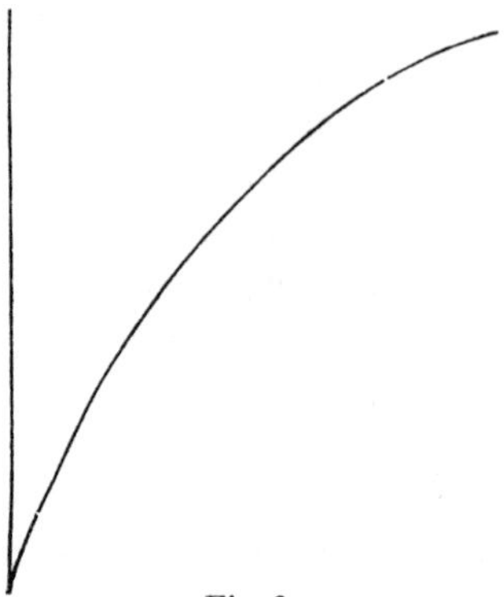

Fig. 9.

Figure 8 shows the character of the diagram for "weld iron." It is reduced from one of Bauschinger's curves. Similar diagrams for mild steel are drawn in many books. A is the limit of linear elasticity; between A and B the strain increases rather faster than between O and A and at a varying rate, B is the yield-point* and D represents the maximum traction. Fig. 9 is reduced from one of Bauschinger's curves for cast iron. There is no sensible range, and so no limit, of linear elasticity, and no yield-point.

Diagrams may be constructed in the same way for thrust and contraction, but the forms of them are in general different from the above. For some

* In a curve recorded by W. E. Dalby, *Phil. Trans. Roy. Soc.* (Ser. A), vol. 221 (1920), p. 117, the part of the curve answering to the arc BC in Fig. 8 is very decidedly concave upwards.

examples of the determination of the yield-point under thrust reference may be made to Bauschinger, *Mittheilungen*, XIII. In the case of cast iron it has been verified that the curve is continuous through the origin, where there is an inflexion*.

78. Elastic limits.

The diagrams do not show the limits of perfect elasticity when these are different from the limits of linear elasticity. These limits usually are different, and the former are lower than the latter†. The numerical measures of the limits for extension and contraction are usually different for the same specimen. The limits are not very well defined. The limit of perfect elasticity for any type of stress would be determined by the greatest traction which produces no set, but all that experiment can tell us is the smallest traction for which set can be measured by means of our instruments. The limits of linear elasticity are shown by the diagrams, but they are liable to the same kind of uncertainty as the limits of perfect elasticity, inasmuch as the determination of them depends upon the degree of accuracy with which the diagrams can be drawn.

The limits of linear elasticity can be raised by overstrain‡. If a bar of steel, not specially hard, is subjected to a load above the elastic limit, and even above the yield-point, and this load is maintained until a permanent state is reached, it is found afterwards to possess linear elasticity up to a higher limit than before. If the load is removed, and the bar remains for some time unloaded, the limit is found to be raised still further, and may be above the load which produced the overstrain.

On the other hand, the limits of elasticity can be lowered by overstrain§. If a bar of iron or mild steel is subjected to a load above the yield-point, and then unloaded and immediately reloaded, its elasticity is found to be very imperfect, and the limit of linear elasticity very low; but if the bar remains unloaded for a few days it is found to have recovered partially from the effects of the previous overstraining, and the longer the period of rest the more complete is the recovery. Wrought iron recovers much more rapidly than steel.

In the case of cast iron, not previously subjected to tests, any load that produces a measurable strain produces some set, and there is no appreciable range of linear elasticity. After several times loading and unloading, the behaviour of the metal approaches more closely to that of other metals as exemplified in Fig. 8. These results suggest that the set produced in the first tests consists in the removal of a state of initial stress.

* See e.g. Ewing, *loc. cit.*, p. 31.

† Bauschinger, *Mittheilungen*, XIII. (1886). See, however, Article 82 A. *infra*.

‡ *Ibid.*

§ See e.g. Ewing, *loc. cit.*, pp. 33 *et seq.*, and the tables in Bauschinger's *Mittheilungen*, XIII.

The yield-point also is raised by overstrain, if the original load is above the original yield-point, and the amount by which it is raised is increased by allowing a period of rest; it is increased still more by maintaining constant the load which produced the original overstrain. This effect is described as "hardening by overstrain."

The following table* gives some examples of the limit of linear elasticity and the yield-point for some kinds of iron. The results, given in atmospheres, are in each case those for a single specimen not previously tested.

Metal	Elastic limit	Yield-point
Weld-iron	1410	1920
,,	1830	2180
Ingot iron	2390	2780
,,	2660	2960
Steel (Bessemer)	1780	2650

79. Time-effects. Plasticity.

The length of time that a body has been subjected to considerable load generally affects the strain produced, and the length of time that a strained body has been free from load generally affects the extent of the elastic recovery. The latter effect was discovered by W. Weber† in 1835 and has been called *Elastische Nachwirkung* or *elastic after-working*; the former appears to have been first noted by Vicat‡ in 1834. When a body has been strained by a load surpassing the limit of perfect elasticity, and is set free, the set gradually diminishes. The body never returns to its primitive condition, and the ultimate deformation is the "permanent set," the part of the strain that gradually disappears is called "elastic after-strain." To produce the effect noted by Vicat very considerable stress is generally required. He found that wires held stretched, with a tension equal to one quarter of the breaking stress, retained the length to which this tension brought them throughout the whole time of his experiments (33 months), while similar wires stretched with a tension equal to half the breaking stress exhibited a notable gradual increase of extension. The gradual flow of solids under great stress, indicated by these experiments, has been made the subject of exhaustive investigation by H. Tresca§. He found, in his experiments on the

* Extracted from results given by Bauschinger, *Mittheilungen*, XIII. We may take 1000 atmospheres = 6·56 tons per square inch = $1{\cdot}0136 \times 10^9$ C.G.S. units of stress.

† *De fili Bombycini vi Elastica.* Göttingen, 1841. An off-print of a paper communicated to the *Königliche Gesellschaft der Wissenschaften zu Göttingen*, 1835, and practically translated in *Ann. Phys. Chem.* (*Poggendorff*), Bde. 34 (1835) and 54 (1841).

‡ *Note sur l'allongement progressif du fil de fer soumis à diverses tensions. Annales des ponts et chaussées*, 1er *semestre*, 1834.

§ *Paris, Mém.…par divers savants*, tt. 18 (1868) and 20 (1872). An account of some of Tresca's experiments is given by Unwin, *loc. cit.*, pp. 46 *et seq.*

punching and crushing of metals, results which point to the conclusion that all solids when subjected to very great pressure ultimately flow, i.e. take a set which increases with the time. This capacity of solids to flow under great stress is called *plasticity*. A solid is said to be "hard" when the force required to produce considerable set is great, "soft" or "plastic" when it is small. A substance must be termed "fluid" if considerable set can be produced by any force, however small, provided it is applied for a sufficient time.

In experiments on extension some plasticity of the material is shown as soon as the limit of linear elasticity is exceeded*. If the load exceeding this limit is removed some set can be observed, but this set diminishes at a rate which itself diminishes. If the load is maintained the strain gradually increases and reaches a constant value after the lapse of some time. If the load is removed and reapplied several times, both the set and the elastic strain increase. None of these effects is observed when the load is below the limit of linear elasticity. The possibility of these plastic effects tends to complicate the results of testing, for if two like specimens are loaded at different rates, the one which is loaded more rapidly will show a greater breaking stress and a smaller ultimate extension than the other. Such differences have in fact been observed†, but it has been shown‡ that under ordinary conditions of testing the variations in the rate of loading do not affect the results appreciably.

79 A. Momentary stress.

A time-effect of the opposite kind has been observed in connexion with impact. It appears that very great stress acting for a very short time, of the order one-thousandth of a second, or less, does not necessarily cause any dangerous set, or fracture, when the stress exceeds that answering to statical limits of elasticity, or even when it exceeds the statical yield-point. Such stresses may, without sensible error, be calculated by the Mathematical Theory of Elasticity, as if there were no such things as limits of elasticity. This result has been established by B. Hopkinson and J. E. Sears§.

80. Viscosity of solids.

"Viscosity" is a general term for all those properties of matter in virtue of which the resistance, which a body offers to any change, depends upon the rate at which the change is effected. The existence of viscous resistances involves a dissipation of the energy of the substance, the kinetic energy of molar motion being transformed, as is generally supposed, into kinetic energy of molecular agitation. The most marked effect of this property, if it exists

* Bauschinger, *Mittheilungen*, XIII. (1886). † Cf. Unwin, *loc. cit.*, p. 89.

‡ Bauschinger, *Mittheilungen*, XX. (1891).

§ B. Hopkinson, *London, Roy. Soc. Proc.*, vol. 74, 1905, p. 498, and *Phil. Trans. Roy. Soc.* Ser. A), vol. 213, 1914, p. 437; J. E. Sears, *Cambridge, Phil. Soc. Proc.*, vol. 14, 1908, p. 257, and *Cambridge, Phil. Soc. Trans.*, vol. 21, 1912, p. 49.

in the case of elastic solids, would be the subsidence of vibrations set up in the solid. Suppose a solid of any form to be struck, or otherwise suddenly disturbed. It will be thrown into more or less rapid vibration, and the stresses developed in it would, if there is genuine viscosity, depend partly on the displacements, and partly on the rates at which they are effected. The parts of the stresses depending on the rates of change would be viscous resistances, and they would ultimately destroy the vibratory motion. Now the vibratory motion of elastic solid bodies is actually destroyed, but the decay appears not to be the effect of viscous resistances of the ordinary type, that is to say such as are proportional to the rates of strain. It has been pointed out by Lord Kelvin* that, if this type of resistance alone were involved, the proportionate diminution of the amplitude of the oscillations per unit of time would be inversely proportional to the square of the period; but a series of experiments on the torsional oscillations of wires showed that this law does not hold good.

Lord Kelvin pointed out that the decay of vibrations could be accounted for by supposing that, even for the very small strains involved in vibratory motions, the effects of elastic after-working and plasticity are not wholly absent. These effects, as well as viscous resistances of the ordinary type, are included in the class of *hysteresis* phenomena. All of them show that the state of the body concerned depends at any instant on its previous states as well as on the external conditions (forces, temperature, &c.) which obtain at the instant. Hysteresis always implies irreversibility in the sequence of states through which a body passes, and is generally traced to the molecular structure of matter. Accordingly, theories of molecular action have been devised by various investigators† to account for viscosity and elastic after-working.

81. Æolotropy induced by permanent set.

One of the changes produced in a solid, which has received a permanent set, may be that the material, previously isotropic, becomes æolotropic. The best known example is that of a bar rendered æolotropic by permanent torsion. Warburg‡ found that, in a copper wire to which a permanent twist had been given, the elastic phenomena observed could all be explained on the supposition that the substance of the wire was rendered æolotropic like a rhombic crystal. When a weight was hung on the wire it produced, in

* Sir W. Thomson, Article 'Elasticity,' *Ency. Brit.* or *Math. and Phys. Papers*, vol. 3, Cambridge, 1890, p. 27.

† The following may be mentioned:—J. C. Maxwell, Article 'Constitution of Bodies,' *Ency. Brit.* or *Scientific Papers*, vol. 2, Cambridge, 1890; J. G. Butcher, *London Math. Soc. Proc.*, vol. 8 (1877); O. E. Meyer, *J. f. Math.* (*Crelle*), Bd. 78 (1874); L. Boltzmann, *Ann. Phys. Chem.* (*Poggendorff*), Ergzgsbd. 7 (1878). For a good account of the theories the reader may be referred to the Article by F. Braun in Winkelmann's *Handbuch der Physik*, Bd. 1 (Breslau, 1891), pp. 321—342. For a more recent discussion of the viscosity of metals and crystals, see W. Voigt, *Ann. Phys. Chem.* (*Wiedemann*), Bd. 47 (1892).

‡ *Ann. Phys. Chem.* (*Wiedemann*), Bd. 10 (1880).

addition to extension, a small shear, equivalent to a partial untwisting* of the wire; this was an elastic strain, and disappeared on the removal of the load. This experiment is important as showing that processes of manufacture may induce considerable æolotropy in materials which in the unworked stage are isotropic, and consequently that estimates of strength, founded on the employment of the equations of isotropic elasticity, cannot be strictly interpreted†.

82. Repeated loading.

A body strained within its elastic limits may be strained again and again without receiving any injury; thus a watch-spring may be coiled and uncoiled one hundred and twenty millions of times a year for several years without deterioration. But it is different when a body is strained repeatedly by rapidly varying loads which exceed the limits of elasticity. Wöhler's‡ experiments on this point have been held to show that the resistance of a body to any kind of deformation can be seriously diminished, by rapidly repeated applications of a load. The result appears to point to a gradual deterioration§ of the quality of the material subjected to repeated loading, which can be verified by the observation that after a large number of applications and removals of the load, bars may be broken by a stress much below the statical breaking stress.

Bauschinger|| made several independent series of experiments on the same subject. In these the load was reversed 100 times a minute, and the specimens which endured so long were submitted to some millions of repetitions of alternating stress. In some cases these severe tests revealed the existence of flaws in the material, but the general result obtained was that the strength of a piece is not diminished by repeated loading, provided that the load always lies within the limits of linear elasticity.

An analogous property of bodies is that to which Lord Kelvin¶ has called attention under the name "fatigue of elasticity**." He observed that the torsional vibrations of wires subsided much more rapidly when the wires had been kept vibrating for several hours or days, than when, after being at rest for some days, they were set in vibration and immediately left to themselves.

Experimental results of this kind point to the importance of taking into account the manner and frequency of the application of force to a structure in estimating its strength.

* Cf. Lord Kelvin, *loc. cit.*, *Math. and Phys. Papers*, vol. 3, p. 82.

† Cf. Unwin, *loc. cit.*, p. 25.

‡ *Ueber Festigkeitsversuche mit Eisen und Stahl*, Berlin, 1870. An account of Wöhler's experiments is given by Unwin, *loc. cit.*, pp. 356 *et seq.*

§ A different explanation has been proposed by K. Pearson, *Messenger of Math.*, vol. 20 (1890).

|| *Mittheilungen*, xx. (1891) and xxv. (1897) edited by Föppl.

¶ *Loc. cit.*, *Math. and Phys. Papers*, vol. 3, p. 22.

** Discussions of "fatigue failure" will be found in the papers by Rosenhain and Archbutt, Jenkin, and Gough and Hanson, cited on p. 112.

82 A. Elastic Hysteresis.

It has been known for a long time that there may be a defect of Hooke's Law (Article 64) even within the limits of perfect elasticity. For example, in tensile tests, a specimen which has been loaded gradually, and then unloaded gradually, may show no measurable subsequent extension, that is to say, it may be perfectly elastic within the limits of the applied load; and, nevertheless, the extension under a given load, during the process of unloading, may be appreciably different from the extension, under the same load, during the process of loading. Thus the limits of sensibly linear elasticity may be narrower than those of sensibly perfect elasticity. When this is the case it is found that the strain during unloading is greater, not less, than that, at the same load, during loading. The earliest account of this phenomenon, which I have found, is in a paper by Ewing*, describing experiments made on steel wire. They showed that the effect in question, described by the author as "hysteresis," is more marked when the loading and unloading are rapid than when they are slow, but it is sensible when they are performed very slowly, so that there appears to be a true statical hysteresis. It appeared later that with very rapid alternations of stress the observable amount of hysteresis is less than the statical amount†. For hard metals it seems that there is no hysteresis with moderate load, but for rocks, such as granite and marble‡, there is hysteresis at quite moderate loads. The effect in metals is especially important in torsion tests§. The general nature of the effect may be described in the words—The stress-strain diagram is a closed curve. It appears to follow that some energy is dissipated in putting a specimen through a cycle of stress-changes, and Ewing (*loc. cit.*) calls attention to the bearing of this conclusion upon Wöhler's experiments on repeated loading and alternating stress. The subject, however, is still rather obscure‖.

It is perhaps a little unfortunate that the term "elastic hysteresis" should have been appropriated to describe the special phenomenon noticed by Ewing, because, as has been already observed, elastic after-working, plasticity, and viscosity are also properties which indicate hysteresis, in the general sense of the word, and the same may be said of the property called fatigue of elasticity, and of those brought to light in experiments on repeated loading and alternating stress. They all imply a dependence of the instantaneous state of a body upon its previous states as well as upon the instantaneous conditions.

* J. A. Ewing, *Brit. Assoc. Rep.*, 1889, p. 502.

† B. Hopkinson and G. T. Williams, *London, Roy. Soc. Proc.* (Ser. A), vol. 87, 1912, p. 502.

‡ F. D. Adams and E. G. Coker, *An investigation into the elastic constants of rocks, more especially with reference to cubic compressibility* (Washington, 1906).

§ Cf. Searle, *Experimental Elasticity*, p. 152.

‖ Cf. the 'Report on Alternating Stress' by W. Mason in *Brit. Assoc. Rep.*, 1913, p. 183, the Report by the same author 'On the Hysteresis of Steel under repeated Torsion' in *Brit. Assoc. Rep.*, 1916, p. 285, and further Reports by the same author in *Brit. Assoc. Rep.*, 1921, p. 329 and 1923, p. 386. Interesting diagrams, illustrating the stress-strain relations in pieces subjected to repeated loading, will be found in the paper by W. E. Dalby cited on p. 114. Reference may also be made to the paper by Gough and Hanson cited on p. 112.

A rather promising beginning of a mathematical theory of elastic after-working, possibly applicable also to other phenomena involving hysteresis, in the general sense of the word, has been made by Volterra, starting with the physical theory developed by Boltzmann, cited in Article 80. He describes the physical circumstances by the epithet "ereditario" (hereditary) and shows that the theory leads to equations of a type, which he names "integro-differential," and by aid of the theory of integral equations he has obtained some special solutions of his integro-differential equations. We shall not pursue the matter, but refer the reader to the papers cited below*.

83. Hypotheses concerning the conditions of rupture.

Various hypotheses have been advanced as to the conditions under which a body is ruptured, or a structure becomes unsafe. Thus Lamé† supposed it to be necessary that the greatest tension should be less than a certain limit. Poncelet‡, followed by Saint-Venant§, assumed that the greatest extension must be less than a certain limit. These measures of *tendency to rupture* agree for a bar under extension, but in general they lead to different limits of safe loading‖. Again, Tresca followed by G. H. Darwin¶ makes the maximum difference of the greatest and least principal stresses the measure of tendency to rupture, and not a very different limit would be found by following Coulomb's** suggestion, that the greatest shear produced in the material is a measure of this tendency. An interesting modification of this view has been suggested and worked out geometrically by O. Mohr††. It would enable us to take account of the possible dependence of the condition of safety upon the nature of the load, i.e. upon the kind of stress which is developed within the body. The manner and frequency of application of the load are matters which ought also to be taken into account. The conditions of rupture are but vaguely understood,

* V. Volterra, *Roma, Acc. Linc. Rend.* (Ser. 5), t. 18 (2), 1909, pp. 295 and 577, t. 19 (1), 1910, pp. 107 and 239, t. 21 (2), 1912, p. 3, t. 22 (1), 1913, p. 529; G. Lauricella, *Roma, Acc. Linc. Rend.* (Ser. 5), t. 21 (1), p. 165; R. Serini, *Roma, Acc. Linc. Rend.* (Ser. 5), tt. 23 (2), 1914, p. 1112 and 25 (1), 1916, p. 155; A. M. Molinari, *Roma, Acc. Linc. Rend.*, t. 23 (2), 1914, pp. 106, 163.

† See e.g. the memoir of Lamé and Clapeyron, quoted in the Introduction (footnote 39).

‡ See Todhunter and Pearson's *History*, vol. 1, art. 995.

§ See especially the *Historique Abrégé* in Saint-Venant's edition of the *Leçon sde Navier*, pp. cxcix—ccv.

‖ For examples see Todhunter and Pearson's *History*, vol. 1, p. 550 footnote.

¶ 'On the stresses produced in the interior of the Earth by the weight of Continents and Mountains,' *Phil. Trans. Roy. Soc.*, vol. 173 (1882). The same measure is adopted in the account of Prof. Darwin's work in Kelvin and Tait's *Nat. Phil.*, Part II. art. 832′.

** 'Essai sur une application des règles de Maximis etc.,' *Mém....par divers savans*, 1776, Introduction.

†† *Zeitschr. des Vereines Deutscher Ingenieure*, Bd. 44 (1900). A discussion by Voigt of the views of Mohr and other writers will be found in *Ann. Phys.* (Ser. 4), Bd. 4 (1901). The subject is discussed further in the light of new experimental researches by Th. v. Kármán, 'Festigkeitsversuche unter allseitigem Druck,' *Zeitschr. des Vereines Deutscher Ingenieure*, 1911, also by W. A. Scoble, 'Report on Combined Stress,' *Brit. Assoc. Rep.*, 1913. P. B. Haigh, *Brit. Assoc. Rep.*, 1919, p. 486, proposes a 'criterion of elastic failure' based on the strain-energy function, and develops his theory further in *Brit. Assoc. Rep.*, 1921, p. 324 and 1923, p. 358.

and may depend largely on these and other accidental circumstances. At the same time the question is very important, as a satisfactory answer to it might suggest in many cases causes of weakness previously unsuspected, and, in others, methods of economizing material that would be consistent with safety.

In all these hypotheses it is supposed that the stress or strain actually produced in a body of given form, by a given load, is somehow calculable. The only known method of calculating these effects is by the use of the mathematical theory of Elasticity, or by some more or less rough and ready rule obtained from some result of this theory. Suppose the body to be subject to a given system of load, and suppose that we know how to solve the equations of elastic equilibrium with the given boundary-conditions. Then the stress and strain at every point of the body can be determined, and the principal stresses and principal extensions can be found. Let T be the greatest principal tension, S the greatest difference of two principal tensions at the same point, e the greatest principal extension. Let T_0 be the breaking stress as determined by tensile tests. On the greatest tension hypothesis T must not exceed a certain fraction of T_0. On the stress-difference hypothesis S must not exceed a certain fraction of T_0. On the greatest extension hypothesis e must not exceed a certain fraction of T_0/E, where E is Young's modulus for the material. These conditions may be written

$$T < T_0/\Phi, \quad S < T_0/\Phi, \quad e < T_0/\Phi E$$

and the number Φ which occurs in them is called the "factor of safety."

Most English and American engineers adopt the first of these hypotheses, but take Φ to depend on the kind of strain to which the body is likely to be subjected in use. A factor 6 is allowed for boilers, 10 for pillars, 6 for axles, 6 to 10 for railway-bridges, and 12 for screw-propeller-shafts and parts of other machines subjected to sudden reversals of load. In France and Germany the greatest extension hypothesis is often adopted.

Recently attempts have been made to determine which of these hypotheses best represents the results of experiments. The fact that short pillars can be crushed by longitudinal pressure excludes the greatest tension hypothesis. If it were proposed to replace this by a greatest stress hypothesis, according to which rupture would occur when any principal stress (tension *or pressure*) exceeds a certain limit, then the experiments of A. Föppl* on bodies subjected to very great pressures uniform over their surfaces would be very important, as it appeared that rupture is not produced by such pressures as he could apply. These experiments would also forbid us to replace the greatest extension hypothesis by a greatest strain hypothesis. There remain for examination the greatest extension hypothesis and the stress-difference hypothesis. Wehage's experiments† on specimens of wrought iron subjected to equal tensions (or

* *Mittheilungen* (München), XXVII. (1899).

† *Mittheilungen der mechanisch-technischen Versuchsanstalt zu Berlin*, 1888.

pressures) in two directions at right angles to each other have thrown doubt on the greatest extension hypothesis. From experiments on metal tubes subjected to various systems of combined stress J. J. Guest* has concluded that the stress-difference hypothesis is the one which accords best with observed results. The general tendency of modern technical writings seems to be to attach more importance to the limits of linear elasticity and the yield-point than to the limits of perfect elasticity and the breaking stress, and to emphasize the importance of dynamical tests in addition to the usual statical tests of tensile and bending strength.

84. Scope of the mathematical theory of elasticity.

Numerical values of the quantities that can be involved in practical problems may serve to show the smallness of the strains that occur in structures which are found to be safe. Examples of such values have been given in Articles 1, 48, 71, 78. A piece of iron or steel with a limit of linear elasticity equal to $10\frac{1}{2}$ tons per square inch, a yield-point equal to 14 tons per square inch and a Young's modulus equal to 13,000 tons per square inch would take, under a load of 6 tons per square inch, an extension 0·00046. Even if loaded nearly up to the yield-point the extension would be small enough to require very refined means of observation. The neglect of squares and products of the strains in iron and steel structures within safe limits of loading cannot be the cause of any serious error. The fact that for loads much below the limit of linear elasticity the elasticity of metals is very imperfect may perhaps be a more serious cause of error, since set and elastic after-working are unrepresented in the mathematical theory; but the sets that occur within the limit of linear elasticity are always extremely small. The effects produced by unequal heating, with which the theory cannot deal satisfactorily, are very important in practice. Some examples of the application of the theory to questions of strength may be cited here:—By Saint-Venant's theory of the torsion of prisms, it can be predicted that a shaft transmitting a couple by torsion is seriously weakened by the existence of a dent having a curvature approaching to that in a re-entrant angle, or by the existence of a flaw parallel to the axis of the shaft. By the theory of equilibrium of a mass with a spherical boundary, it can be predicted that the shear in the neighbourhood of a flaw of spherical form may be as great as twice that at a distance. The result of such theories would be that the factor of safety should be doubled for shafts transmitting a couple when such flaws may occur. Again it can be shown that, in certain cases, a load suddenly applied may cause a strain twice† as great as that produced by a gradual application of the same

* *Phil. Mag.* (Ser. 5), vol. 48 (1900). Mohr (*loc. cit.*) has criticized Guest.

† This point appears to have been first expressly noted by Poncelet in his *Introduction à la Mécanique industrielle, physique et expérimentale* of 1839, see Todhunter and Pearson's *History*, vol. 1, art. 988.

load, and that a load suddenly reversed may cause a strain three times as great as that produced by the gradual application of the same load. These results lead us to expect that additional factors of safety will be required for sudden applications and sudden reversals, and they suggest that these extra factors may be 2 and 3. Again, a source of weakness in structures, some parts of which are very thin bars or plates subjected to thrust, is a possible buckling of the parts. The conditions of buckling can sometimes be determined from the theory of Elastic Stability, and this theory can then be made to suggest some method of supporting the parts by stays, and the best places for them, so as to secure the greatest strength with the least expenditure of materials; but the result, at any rate in structures that may receive small permanent sets, is only a suggestion and requires to be verified by experiment. Further, as has been pointed out before, all calculations of the strength of structures rest on some result or other deduced from the mathematical theory.

More precise indications as to the behaviour of solid bodies can be deduced from the theory when applied to obtain corrections to very exact physical measurements*. For example, it is customary to specify the temperature at which standards of length are correct; but it appears that the effects of such changes of atmospheric pressure as actually occur are not too small to have a practical significance. As more and more accurate instruments come to be devised for measuring lengths the time is probably not far distant when the effects produced in the length of a standard by different modes of support will have to be taken into account. Another example is afforded by the result that the cubic capacity of a vessel intended to contain liquid is increased when the liquid is put into it in consequence of excess of pressure in the parts of the liquid near the bottom of the vessel. Again, the bending of the deflexion-bars of magnetometers affects the measurement of magnetic force. Many of the simpler results of the mathematical theory are likely to find important applications in connexion with the improvement of measuring apparatus.

* Cf. C. Chree, *Phil. Mag.* (Ser. 6), vol. 2 (1901).

CHAPTER V

EQUILIBRIUM OF ISOTROPIC ELASTIC SOLID BODIES

85. Recapitulation of the general theory.

As a preliminary to the further study of the theory of elasticity some parts of the general theory will here be recapitulated briefly.

(*a*) *Stress.* The state of stress at a point of a body is determined when the traction across every plane through the point is known. The traction is estimated as a force per unit of area. If ν denotes the direction of the normal to a plane the traction across the plane is specified by means of rectangular components X_ν, Y_ν, Z_ν parallel to axes of coordinates. The traction across the plane that is normal to ν is expressed in terms of the tractions across planes that are normal to the axes of coordinates by the equations

$$\left.\begin{aligned} X_\nu &= X_x \cos(x, \nu) + X_y \cos(y, \nu) + X_z \cos(z, \nu), \\ Y_\nu &= Y_x \cos(x, \nu) + Y_y \cos(y, \nu) + Y_z \cos(z, \nu), \\ Z_\nu &= Z_x \cos(x, \nu) + Z_y \cos(y, \nu) + Z_z \cos(z, \nu). \end{aligned}\right\} \qquad \text{(1)}$$

The quantities X_x, ... are connected by the equations

$$Y_z = Z_y, \quad Z_x = X_z, \quad X_y = Y_x. \qquad \text{(2)}$$

The six quantities X_x, Y_y, Z_z, Y_z, Z_x, X_y are the "components of stress." Their values at any point depend in general upon the position of the point.

(*b*) *Stress-equations.* In a body in equilibrium under body forces and surface tractions the components of stress satisfy the following equations at every point in the body:

$$\left.\begin{aligned} \frac{\partial X_x}{\partial x} + \frac{\partial X_y}{\partial y} + \frac{\partial Z_x}{\partial z} + \rho X = 0, \\ \frac{\partial X_y}{\partial x} + \frac{\partial Y_y}{\partial y} + \frac{\partial Y_z}{\partial z} + \rho Y = 0, \\ \frac{\partial Z_x}{\partial x} + \frac{\partial Y_z}{\partial y} + \frac{\partial Z_z}{\partial z} + \rho Z = 0. \end{aligned}\right\} \qquad \text{(3)}$$

In these equations ρ is the density and (X, Y, Z) the body force per unit of mass.

The components of stress also satisfy certain equations at the surface of the body. If ν denotes the direction of the normal drawn outwards from the body at any point of its surface and $(\bar{X}_\nu, \bar{Y}_\nu, \bar{Z}_\nu)$ denotes the surface traction at the point, the values of the components of stress at the point must satisfy the equations (1), in which $\bar{X}_\nu$, ... are written for X_ν, ...

(*c*) *Displacement.* Under the action of the forces the body is displaced from the configuration that it would have if the stress-components were zero throughout. If (x, y, z) denotes the position of a point of the body in the unstressed state, and $(x+u, y+v, z+w)$ denotes the position of the same point of the body when under the action of the forces, (u, v, w) denotes the displacement, and the components of displacement u, v, w are functions of x, y, z.

(*d*) *Strain.* The strain at a point is determined when the extension of every linear element issuing from the point is known. If the relative displacement is small, the extension of a linear element in direction (l, m, n) is

$$e_{xx}l^2+e_{yy}m^2+e_{zz}n^2+e_{yz}mn+e_{zx}nl+e_{xy}lm, \qquad \text{.........(4)}$$

where e_{xx}, ... denote the following:

$$\left.\begin{aligned} e_{xx}&=\frac{\partial u}{\partial x}, & e_{yy}&=\frac{\partial v}{\partial y}, & e_{zz}&=\frac{\partial w}{\partial z}, \\ e_{yz}&=\frac{\partial w}{\partial y}+\frac{\partial v}{\partial z}, & e_{zx}&=\frac{\partial u}{\partial z}+\frac{\partial w}{\partial x}, & e_{xy}&=\frac{\partial v}{\partial x}+\frac{\partial u}{\partial y}. \end{aligned}\right\} \qquad \text{.........(5)}$$

The quantities e_{xx}, ... e_{xy} are the "components of strain."

The quantities ϖ_x, ϖ_y, ϖ_z determined by the equations

$$2\varpi_x=\frac{\partial w}{\partial y}-\frac{\partial v}{\partial z}, \quad 2\varpi_y=\frac{\partial u}{\partial z}-\frac{\partial w}{\partial x}, \quad 2\varpi_z=\frac{\partial v}{\partial x}-\frac{\partial u}{\partial y} \qquad \text{.........(6)}$$

are the components of a vector quantity, the "rotation." The quantity Δ determined by the equation

$$\Delta=\frac{\partial u}{\partial x}+\frac{\partial v}{\partial y}+\frac{\partial w}{\partial z} \qquad \text{.........(7)}$$

is the "dilatation."

(*e*) *Stress-strain relations.* In an elastic solid slightly strained from the unstressed state the components of stress are linear functions of the components of strain. When the material is isotropic we have

$$\left.\begin{aligned} X_x&=\lambda\Delta+2\mu e_{xx}, & Y_y&=\lambda\Delta+2\mu e_{yy}, & Z_z&=\lambda\Delta+2\mu e_{zz}, \\ Y_z&=\mu e_{yz}, & Z_x&=\mu e_{zx}, & X_y&=\mu e_{xy}; \end{aligned}\right\} \qquad \text{.........(8)}$$

and by solving these we have

$$\left.\begin{aligned} e_{xx}&=\frac{1}{E}\{X_x-\sigma(Y_y+Z_z)\}, & e_{yy}&=\frac{1}{E}\{Y_y-\sigma(Z_z+X_x)\}, & e_{zz}&=\frac{1}{E}\{Z_z-\sigma(X_x+Y_y)\}, \\ e_{yz}&=\frac{2(1+\sigma)}{E}Y_z, & e_{zx}&=\frac{2(1+\sigma)}{E}Z_x, & e_{xy}&=\frac{2(1+\sigma)}{E}X_y, \end{aligned}\right\} \qquad \text{...(9)}$$

where

$$E=\frac{\mu(3\lambda+2\mu)}{\lambda+\mu}, \quad \sigma=\frac{\lambda}{2(\lambda+\mu)}. \qquad \text{.........(10)}$$

The quantity E is "Young's modulus," the number σ is "Poisson's ratio," the quantity μ is the "rigidity," the quantity $\lambda+\frac{2}{3}\mu$, $=k$, is the "modulus of compression."

86. Uniformly varying stress.

We considered some examples of uniform stress in connexion with the definitions of E, k, etc. (Article 69). The cases which are next in order of simplicity are those in which the stress-components are linear functions of the coordinates. We shall record the results in regard to some particular distributions of stress.

(*a*) Let the axis of z be directed vertically upwards, let all the stress-components except Z_z vanish, and let $Z_z=g\rho z$, where ρ is the density of the body and g is the acceleration due to gravity.

The stress-equations of equilibrium (3) are satisfied if $X=0$, $Y=0$, $Z=-g$. Hence this state of stress can be maintained in a body of any form by its own weight provided that suitable tractions are applied at its surface. The traction applied at the surface must be of amount $g\rho z\cos(z, \nu)$, and it must be directed vertically upwards. If the body is a cylinder or prism of any form of cross-section, and the origin is at the lower end, the cylinder is supported by tension uniformly distributed over its upper end. If l is the length of the cylinder this tension is $g\rho l$, and the resultant tension is equal to the weight of the cylinder. The lower end and the curved surface are free from traction.

The strain is given by the equations

$$e_{xx}=e_{yy}=-\frac{\sigma g\rho z}{E},\quad e_{zz}=\frac{g\rho z}{E},\quad e_{yz}=e_{zx}=e_{xy}=0.$$

To find the displacement* we take first the equation

$$\frac{\partial w}{\partial z}=\frac{g\rho z}{E},$$

which gives

$$w=\frac{1}{2}\frac{g\rho}{E}z^2+w_0,$$

where w_0 is a function of x and y. The equations $e_{yz}=e_{zx}=0$ give

$$\frac{\partial u}{\partial z}=-\frac{\partial w_0}{\partial x},\quad \frac{\partial v}{\partial z}=-\frac{\partial w_0}{\partial y};$$

and therefore we must have

$$u=-z\frac{\partial w_0}{\partial x}+u_0,\quad v=-z\frac{\partial w_0}{\partial y}+v_0,$$

where u_0 and v_0 are functions of x and y. The equations

$$\frac{\partial u}{\partial x}=\frac{\partial v}{\partial y}=-\frac{\sigma g\rho z}{E}$$

give

$$\frac{\partial u_0}{\partial x}=0,\quad \frac{\partial v_0}{\partial y}=0,\quad \frac{\partial^2 w_0}{\partial x^2}=\frac{\sigma g\rho}{E},\quad \frac{\partial^2 w_0}{\partial y^2}=\frac{\sigma g\rho}{E}.$$

The equation $e_{xy}=0$ gives

$$\frac{\partial u_0}{\partial y}+\frac{\partial v_0}{\partial x}=0,\quad \frac{\partial^2 w_0}{\partial x\,\partial y}=0.$$

The equations containing w_0 can be satisfied only by an equation of the form

$$w_0=\frac{1}{2}\frac{\sigma g\rho}{E}(x^2+y^2)+\alpha' x+\beta' y+\gamma,$$

where α', β', γ are constants. The equations containing u_0, v_0 show that u_0 is a function of y, say $F_1(y)$, and v_0 is a function of x, say $F_2(x)$, and that these functions satisfy the equation

$$\frac{\partial F_1(y)}{\partial y}+\frac{\partial F_2(x)}{\partial x}=0,$$

and this equation requires that $\partial F_1(y)/\partial y$ and $\partial F_2(x)/\partial x$ should be constants, γ' and $-\gamma'$ say. Hence we have

$$F_1(y)=\gamma' y+\alpha,\quad F_2(x)=-\gamma' x+\beta,$$

where α and β are constants. The complete expressions for the displacements are therefore

$$\left.\begin{aligned} u&=-\frac{\sigma g\rho}{E}zx-\alpha' z+\gamma' y+\alpha,\\ v&=-\frac{\sigma g\rho}{E}zy-\beta' z-\gamma' x+\beta,\\ w&=\frac{1}{2}\frac{g\rho}{E}(z^2+\sigma x^2+\sigma y^2)+\alpha' x+\beta' y+\gamma. \end{aligned}\right\}$$

* The work is given at length as an example of method.

The terms containing α, β, γ, α', β', γ' represent a displacement which would be possible in a rigid body. If the cylinder is not displaced by rotation we may omit α', β', γ'. If it is not displaced laterally we may omit α, β. If the point $(0, 0, l)$ is not displaced vertically, we must have $\gamma = -\frac{1}{2}\frac{g\rho l^2}{E}$. The displacement is then given by the equations

$$u = -\frac{\sigma g\rho zx}{E}, \quad v = -\frac{\sigma g\rho yz}{E}, \quad w = \frac{1}{2}\frac{g\rho}{E}(z^2 + \sigma x^2 + \sigma y^2 - l^2). \quad \text{.........(11)}$$

Any cross-section of the cylinder is distorted into a paraboloid of revolution about the vertical axis of the cylinder, and the sections shrink laterally by amounts proportional to their distances from the free (lower) end.

(b) A more general case* is obtained by taking

$$X_x = Y_y = -p + g\rho' z, \quad Z_z = -p + g(\rho - \rho')l + g\rho z,$$
$$Y_z = Z_x = X_y = 0.$$

This state of stress can be maintained in a cylinder or prism of any form of length $2l$ suspended in fluid of density ρ' so as to have its axis vertical and the highest point $(0, 0, l)$ of its axis fixed; then p is the pressure of the fluid at the level of the centre of gravity of the cylinder.

The displacement may be shown to be given by the equations

$$\left.\begin{aligned} \frac{u}{x} = \frac{v}{y} &= -\frac{1}{E}[(1-2\sigma)p + \sigma g(\rho-\rho')l + g\{\sigma\rho - (1-\sigma)\rho'\}z], \\ w &= -\frac{z-l}{E}[(1-2\sigma)p - g(\rho-\rho')l] + \tfrac{1}{2}g(\rho - 2\sigma\rho')(z^2 - l^2) \\ &\quad + \frac{1}{2}\frac{x^2+y^2}{E}g\{\sigma\rho - (1-\sigma)\rho'\}. \end{aligned}\right\} \quad \text{.........(12)}$$

(c) By putting

$$X_x = Y_y = Z_z = -p + g\rho z, \quad Y_z = Z_x = X_y = 0,$$

we obtain the state of stress in a body of any form immersed in liquid of the same density, p being the pressure at the level of the origin†. The displacement may be shown to be given by the equations

$$\left.\begin{aligned} u &= \frac{1}{3\lambda + 2\mu}(-px + g\rho zx), \quad v = \frac{1}{3\lambda + 2\mu}(-py + g\rho zy), \\ w &= \frac{1}{3\lambda + 2\mu}\{-pz + \tfrac{1}{2}g\rho(z^2 - x^2 - y^2)\}. \end{aligned}\right\} \quad \text{...............(13)}$$

(d) Let all the stress-components except Y_z and Z_x vanish, and let these be given by the equations

$$\frac{Y_z}{x} = \frac{Z_x}{-y} = \mu\tau,$$

where τ is a constant and μ is the rigidity.

This state of stress can be maintained in a bar of circular section with its axis coinciding with the axis of z by tractions applied at its ends only. If a is the radius of the circle the tractions on the terminal sections are statically equivalent to couples of moment $\frac{1}{2}\pi a^4\mu\tau$ about the axis of z, so that we have the problem of a round bar held twisted by opposing couples.

* C. Chree, *Phil. Mag.* (Ser. 6), vol. 2 (1901).
† E. and F. Cosserat, *Paris, C. R.*, t. 133 (1901).

The displacement may be shown to be given by the equations

$$u = -\tau yz, \quad v = \tau zx, \quad w = 0, \quad \text{.................................(14)}$$

so that any section is turned in its own plane through an angle τz, which is proportional to the distance from a fixed section. The constant τ measures the twist of the bar.

87. Bar bent by couples*.

Our next example of uniformly varying stress is of very great importance. We take the stress-component Z_z to be equal to $-ER^{-1}x$, where R is a constant, and we take the remaining stress-components to vanish. If this state of stress existed within a body, in the shape of a cylinder or prism having its generators in the direction of the axis of z, there would be no body force, and there would be no tractions on the cylindrical boundary. The resultant traction over any cross-section is of amount $\iint Z_z dxdy$; and this vanishes if the axis of z coincides with the line of centroids of the normal sections in the unstressed state. We take this to be the case. Then the bar is held in the specified state of stress by tractions over its terminal sections only, and the traction across any section is statically equivalent to a couple.

The component of the couple about the axis of z vanishes. The component about the axis of y is $\iint ER^{-1}x^2 dxdy$, or it is EI/R, where I is the moment of inertia of the section about an axis through its centroid parallel to the axis of y. The component of the couple about the axis of x is $\iint -ER^{-1}xydxdy$, and this vanishes if the axes of x and y are parallel to principal axes of inertia of the cross-sections. We shall suppose that this is the case.

The strain-components are given by the equations

$$\frac{\partial u}{\partial x} = \frac{\partial v}{\partial y} = \frac{\sigma x}{R}, \quad \frac{\partial w}{\partial z} = -\frac{x}{R},$$

$$\frac{\partial w}{\partial y} + \frac{\partial v}{\partial z} = \frac{\partial u}{\partial z} + \frac{\partial w}{\partial x} = \frac{\partial v}{\partial x} + \frac{\partial u}{\partial y} = 0;$$

and the displacement may be shown to be given by the equations

$$u = \tfrac{1}{2}R^{-1}(z^2 + \sigma x^2 - \sigma y^2), \quad v = \sigma R^{-1}xy, \quad w = -R^{-1}xz. \quad \text{......(15)}$$

This example corresponds with the *bending of a bar by couples*. The line of centroids of the cross-sections is displaced according to the law $u = \tfrac{1}{2}R^{-1}z^2$, so that it becomes very approximately an arc of a circle of large radius R, in the plane (x, z), which is the plane of the *bending couple* EI/R; the centre of the circle is at $x = R$, $z = 0$.

* The theory was given by Saint-Venant in his memoir on Torsion of 1855. See Introduction, footnote 50 and p. 20.

88. Discussion of the solution for the bending of a bar by terminal couple.

The forces applied at either end of the bar are statically equivalent to a couple of moment EI/R. This couple, called the "bending moment," is proportional to the curvature $1/R$. When the bar is bent by a given couple M the line of centroids of its cross-sections, called the "central-line," takes a curvature M/EI in the plane of the couple. The formulæ for the components of strain show that the linear elements of the material which, in the unstressed state, are in the plane $x=0$ undergo no extension or contraction. This plane is called the "neutral plane"; it is the plane that passes through the central-line and is at right angles to the plane of bending. The same formulæ show that linear elements of the material which, in the unstressed state, are parallel to the central-line are contracted or extended according as they lie on the same side of the neutral plane as the centre of curvature or on the opposite side. The amount of the extension or contraction of a longitudinal linear element at a distance x from the neutral plane is the absolute value of Mx/EI or x/R. The stress consists of tensions and pressures across the elements of the normal sections. It is tension at a point where the longitudinal filament passing through the point is extended, and pressure at a point where the longitudinal filament passing through the point is contracted. The amount of the tension or pressure is the absolute value of Mx/I, or Ex/R.

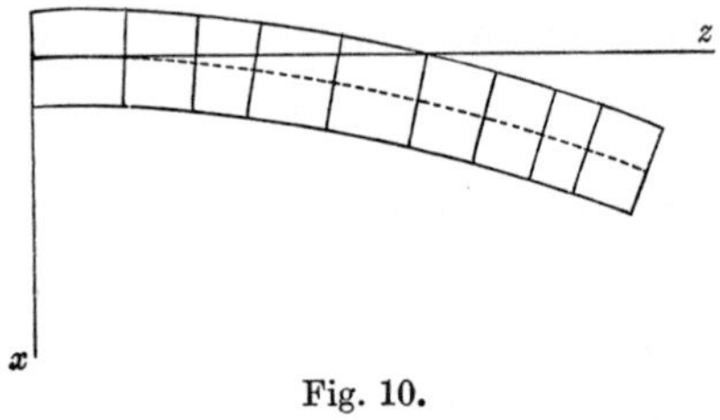

Fig. 10.

The formulæ for the displacement show that the cross-sections remain plane, but that their planes are rotated so as to pass through the centre of curvature, as shown in Figure 10. The formulæ for the displacement also show that the shapes of the sections are changed. If, for example, the section is originally a rectangle with boundaries given by the equations

$$x = \pm\alpha, \quad y = \pm\beta,$$

in a plane $z=\gamma$, these boundaries will become the curves that are given respectively by the equations

$$x \mp \alpha - \tfrac{1}{2}\gamma^2/R - \tfrac{1}{2}\sigma(\alpha^2 - y^2)/R = 0, \quad y \mp \beta \mp \sigma\beta x/R = 0.$$

The latter are straight lines slightly inclined to their original directions; the former are approximately arcs of circles of radii R/σ, with their planes parallel to the plane of (x, y), and their curvatures turned in the opposite sense to that of the line of centroids. The change of shape of the cross-sections is shown in Figure 11. The neutral plane, and every parallel plane, is strained into an

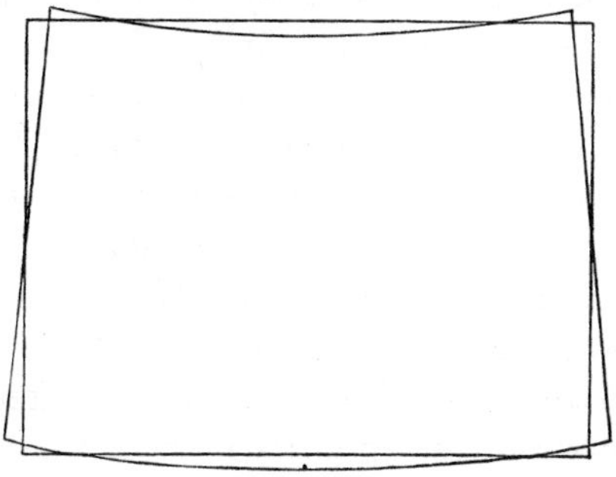

Fig. 11.

anticlastic surface, with principal curvatures of magnitudes R^{-1} in the plane of (x, z), and σR^{-1} in the plane of (x, y), so that the shape of the bent bar is of the kind illustrated in Figure 12, in which the front face is parallel to the plane of bending (x, z).

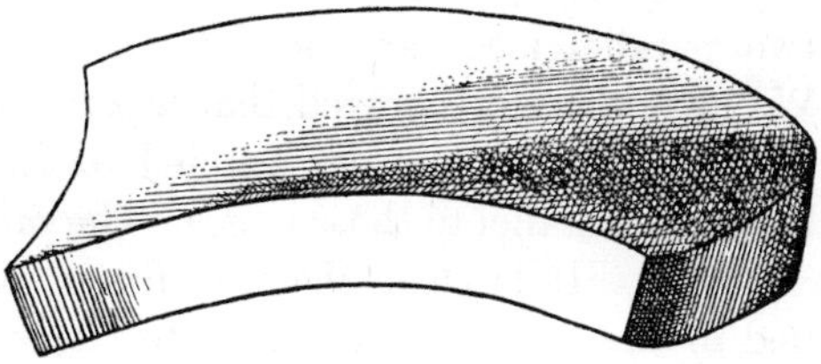

Fig. 12.

The distortion of the bounding surfaces $x = \pm a$ into anticlastic surfaces, admits of very exact verification by means of the interference fringes which are produced by light transmitted through a plate of glass held parallel and very close to these surfaces of the bent bar. Cornu* has used this method for an experimental determination of Poisson's ratio for glass by means of the bending of glass bars. The value obtained was almost exactly $\frac{1}{4}$.

It is worth while to calculate the potential energy of strain. The value of the strain-energy-function at any point is easily found to be $\frac{1}{2} Ex^2/R^2$. The potential energy of strain of the part of the bar between two normal sections distant l apart is $\frac{1}{2}(EI/R^2)\, l$, so that the potential energy per unit of length is $\frac{1}{2} EI/R^2$.

89. Saint-Venant's principle†.

In the problem of Article 87, the tractions, of which the bending moment EI/R is the statical equivalent, are distributed over the terminal sections in the manner of tensions and pressures on the elements of area, these tensions

* *Paris, C. R.*, t. 69 (1869). The method has been used for several materials by Mallock. See Article 70 (*c*), footnote. Reference may also be made to a paper by H. T. Jessop, *Phil. Mag.* (Ser. 6), vol. 42, 1921, p. 551.

† Stated in the memoir on Torsion of 1855.

and pressures being proportional to the distance from the neutral plane. But the practical utility of the solution is not confined to the case where this distribution of terminal traction is exactly realized. The extension to other cases is made by means of a principle, first definitely enunciated by Saint-Venant, and known as the "principle of the elastic equivalence of statically equipollent systems of load." According to this principle, the strains that are produced in a body by the application, to a small part of its surface, of a system of forces statically equivalent to zero force and zero couple, are of negligible magnitude at distances which are large compared with the linear dimensions of the part. In the problem in hand, we infer that, when the length of the bar is large compared with any diameter of its cross-section, the state of stress and strain set up in its interior by the terminal couple is practically independent of the distribution of the tractions, of which the couple is the resultant, in all the portions of the bar except comparatively small portions near its ends.

90. Rectangular plate bent by couples*.

The problem solved in Article 87 admits of generalization in another direction. A bar of rectangular section is a particular case of a brick-shaped body; and, when two parallel faces are near together, such a body is a rectangular plate. We have therefore proved that a plate can be held, so that its faces are anticlastic surfaces, by couples applied to one pair of opposite edges, and having their axes parallel to those edges. The ratio of the principal curvatures is the number σ. It is clear that, by means of suitable couples simultaneously applied to the other pair of opposite edges, the plate can be bent into a cylindrical form, or the ratio of curvatures can be altered in any desired way.

It is most convenient to take the faces of the plate to be given by the equations

$$z = \pm h,$$

so that the thickness is $2h$. The coordinate z thus takes the place of the coordinate which we called x in the case of the bar. The requisite stress-components are X_x and Y_y, and both are proportional to the coordinate z. If we assume that all the stress-components except X_x and Y_y vanish, and that these are given by the equations

$$X_x = E\alpha z, \quad Y_y = E\beta z, \qquad \text{(16)}$$

where α and β are constants, we find that the displacement is given by the equations

$$\left. \begin{aligned} u &= (\alpha - \sigma\beta)\, xz, \quad v = (\beta - \sigma\alpha)\, yz, \\ w &= -\tfrac{1}{2}(\alpha - \sigma\beta)\, x^2 - \tfrac{1}{2}(\beta - \sigma\alpha)\, y^2 - \tfrac{1}{2}\sigma(\alpha + \beta)\, z^2. \end{aligned} \right\} \qquad \text{(17)}$$

Hence any surface which in the unstrained state was parallel to the faces becomes curved so that the curvatures in the planes of (x, z) and (y, z) are

* Kelvin and Tait, *Nat. Phil.*, Part II, pp. 265, 266.

respectively $\sigma\beta - \alpha$ and $\sigma\alpha - \beta$. These are the principal curvatures of the surface. If these quantities are positive, the corresponding centres of curvature lie in the direction in which z is positive. Let R_1 and R_2 be the radii of curvature so that

$$\frac{1}{R_1} = \frac{\partial^2 w}{\partial x^2} = \sigma\beta - \alpha, \quad \frac{1}{R_2} = \frac{\partial^2 w}{\partial y^2} = \sigma\alpha - \beta,$$

then $$\alpha = -\frac{1}{1-\sigma^2}\left(\frac{1}{R_1} + \frac{\sigma}{R_2}\right), \quad \beta = -\frac{1}{1-\sigma^2}\left(\frac{1}{R_2} + \frac{\sigma}{R_1}\right). \quad \text{.........(18)}$$

The state of curvature expressed by R_1 and R_2 is maintained by couples applied to the edges. The couple per unit of length, applied to that edge x = const. for which x has the greater value, has its axis parallel to the axis of y, and its amount is

$$\int_{-h}^{h} zX_x dz, \text{ which is } -\frac{2}{3}\frac{Eh^3}{1-\sigma^2}\left(\frac{1}{R_1} + \frac{\sigma}{R_2}\right).$$

An equal and opposite couple must be applied to the opposite edge. The corresponding couple for the other pair of edges is given by

$$\int_{-h}^{h} -zY_y dz, \text{ which is } \frac{2}{3}\frac{Eh^3}{1-\sigma^2}\left(\frac{1}{R_2} + \frac{\sigma}{R_1}\right).$$

The value of the strain-energy-function at any point can be shown without difficulty to be

$$\frac{1}{2}z^2\frac{E}{1-\sigma^2}\left[\left(\frac{1}{R_1} + \frac{1}{R_2}\right)^2 - 2(1-\sigma)\frac{1}{R_1 R_2}\right],$$

and the potential energy of the bent plate per unit of area is

$$\frac{1}{3}\frac{Eh^3}{1-\sigma^2}\left[\left(\frac{1}{R_1} + \frac{1}{R_2}\right)^2 - 2(1-\sigma)\frac{1}{R_1 R_2}\right].$$

It is noteworthy that this expression contains the sum and the product of the principal curvatures.

91. Equations of equilibrium in terms of displacements.

In the equations of type

$$\frac{\partial X_x}{\partial x} + \frac{\partial X_y}{\partial y} + \frac{\partial Z_x}{\partial z} + \rho X = 0,$$

we substitute for the normal stress-components X_x, ... such expressions as $\lambda\Delta + 2\mu\partial u/\partial x$, and for the tangential stress-components Y_z, ... such expressions as $\mu(\partial w/\partial y + \partial v/\partial z)$; and we thus obtain three equations of the type

$$(\lambda + \mu)\frac{\partial \Delta}{\partial x} + \mu\nabla^2 u + \rho X = 0, \quad \text{....................(19)}$$

where $$\Delta = \frac{\partial u}{\partial x} + \frac{\partial v}{\partial y} + \frac{\partial w}{\partial z}, \quad \nabla^2 = \frac{\partial^2}{\partial x^2} + \frac{\partial^2}{\partial y^2} + \frac{\partial^2}{\partial z^2}.$$

These equations may be written in a compact form

$$(\lambda + \mu)\left(\frac{\partial}{\partial x}, \frac{\partial}{\partial y}, \frac{\partial}{\partial z}\right)\Delta + \mu\nabla^2(u, v, w) + \rho(X, Y, Z) = 0. \quad \text{......(20)}$$

If we introduce the rotation

$$(\varpi_x, \varpi_y, \varpi_z) = \tfrac{1}{2} \text{ curl } (u, v, w),$$
$$= \frac{1}{2}\left(\frac{\partial w}{\partial y} - \frac{\partial v}{\partial z}, \frac{\partial u}{\partial z} - \frac{\partial w}{\partial x}, \frac{\partial v}{\partial x} - \frac{\partial u}{\partial y}\right),$$

and make use of the identity

$$\nabla^2 (u, v, w) = \left(\frac{\partial}{\partial x}, \frac{\partial}{\partial y}, \frac{\partial}{\partial z}\right) \Delta - 2 \text{ curl } (\varpi_x, \varpi_y, \varpi_z),$$

the above equations (20) take the form

$$(\lambda + 2\mu)\left(\frac{\partial}{\partial x}, \frac{\partial}{\partial y}, \frac{\partial}{\partial z}\right) \Delta - 2\mu \text{ curl } (\varpi_x, \varpi_y, \varpi_z) + \rho (X, Y, Z) = 0. \quad \text{...(21)}$$

We may note that the equations of small motion (Article 54) can be expressed in either of the forms

$$(\lambda+\mu) \left(\frac{\partial}{\partial x}, \frac{\partial}{\partial y}, \frac{\partial}{\partial z}\right) \Delta + \mu\nabla^2 (u, v, w) + \rho (X, Y, Z) = \rho \frac{\partial^2}{\partial t^2} (u, v, w),$$

or

$$(\lambda+2\mu) \left(\frac{\partial}{\partial x}, \frac{\partial}{\partial y}, \frac{\partial}{\partial z}\right) \Delta - 2\mu \text{ curl } (\varpi_x, \varpi_y, \varpi_z) + \rho (X, Y, Z) = \rho \frac{\partial^2}{\partial t^2} (u, v, w). \quad \text{...(22)}$$

The traction (X_ν, Y_ν, Z_ν) across a plane of which the normal is in the direction ν, is given by formulæ of the type

$$X_\nu = \cos (x, \nu) \left(\lambda\Delta + 2\mu \frac{\partial u}{\partial x}\right) + \cos (y, \nu) \mu \left(\frac{\partial v}{\partial x} + \frac{\partial u}{\partial y}\right) + \cos (z, \nu) \mu \left(\frac{\partial u}{\partial z} + \frac{\partial w}{\partial x}\right);$$

and this may be written in either of the forms

$$X_\nu = \lambda\Delta \cos (x, \nu) + \mu \left\{\frac{\partial u}{\partial \nu} + \cos (x, \nu) \frac{\partial u}{\partial x} + \cos (y, \nu) \frac{\partial v}{\partial x} + \cos (z, \nu) \frac{\partial w}{\partial x}\right\}, \quad (23)$$

or

$$X_\nu = \lambda\Delta \cos (x, \nu) + 2\mu \left\{\frac{\partial u}{\partial \nu} - \varpi_y \cos (z, \nu) + \varpi_z \cos (y, \nu)\right\}, \quad \text{......(24)}$$

where

$$\frac{\partial u}{\partial \nu} = \cos (x, \nu) \frac{\partial u}{\partial x} + \cos (y, \nu) \frac{\partial u}{\partial y} + \cos (z, \nu) \frac{\partial u}{\partial z}.$$

If ν is the normal to the bounding surface drawn outwards from the body, and the values of Δ, $\partial u/\partial x, \ldots$ are calculated at a point on the surface, the right-hand members of (23) and the similar expressions represent the component tractions per unit area exerted upon the body across the surface.

92. Relations between components of stress.

When there are no body forces the displacement equations are

$$(\lambda + \mu) \left(\frac{\partial}{\partial x}, \frac{\partial}{\partial y}, \frac{\partial}{\partial z}\right) \Delta + \mu\nabla^2 (u, v, w) = 0, \quad \text{...........(25)}$$

and the result of differentiating the left-hand members with respect to x, y, z and adding the differential coefficients is

$$\nabla^2 \Delta = 0, \quad \text{.................................(26)}$$

so that Δ is an *harmonic* function, i.e. a function satisfying Laplace's equation, at all points within the body.

From equations (8) of Article 85 we have

$$(3\lambda+2\mu)\,\Delta = X_x + Y_y + Z_z = \Theta \text{ say}, \quad\text{.................}(27)$$

and thence it appears that Θ is an harmonic function.

The first of equations (25) gives, on differentiation with respect to x,

$$(\lambda+\mu)\frac{\partial^2\Delta}{\partial x^2} + \mu\nabla^2 e_{xx} = 0.$$

On substituting from (8) for e_{xx} and from (27) for Δ, and utilizing (26), this equation becomes

$$\nabla^2 X_x + \frac{2(\lambda+\mu)}{3\lambda+2\mu}\frac{\partial^2\Theta}{\partial x^2} = 0. \quad\text{......................}(28)$$

The result of differentiating the left-hand members of the second and third of equations (25) with respect to z and y respectively, adding the differential coefficients, and substituting from equations (8) and (27), is

$$\nabla^2 Y_z + \frac{2(\lambda+\mu)}{3\lambda+2\mu}\frac{\partial^2\Theta}{\partial y\,\partial z} = 0. \quad\text{......................}(29)$$

We learn that in addition to the three stress-equations of equilibrium of the type

$$\frac{\partial X_x}{\partial x} + \frac{\partial X_y}{\partial y} + \frac{\partial Z_x}{\partial z} = 0, \quad\text{..........................}(30)$$

the stress-components in an isotropic solid body, in equilibrium and free from body forces, satisfy six independent conditions: three of the type (28), and three of the type (29)*. The coefficient $2(\lambda+\mu)/(3\lambda+2\mu)$ is $1/(1+\sigma)$.

93. Additional results.

(i) It may be proved that, when there are no body forces, each of the components of rotation is an harmonic function.

(ii) In the same case it may be proved that each of u, v, w satisfies the equation

$$\nabla^4\phi = 0 \quad\text{...}(31)$$

at all points within the body. All the components of strain and stress also satisfy this equation. A function satisfying this equation is sometimes described as *biharmonic*.

(iii) The equations of the types (28) and (29) can be deduced† from the equations of equilibrium in forms such as (30), the stress-strain relations in the form (9), and the identical relations between components of stress given in Article 17.

For example the equation

$$\frac{\partial^2 e_{yy}}{\partial z^2} + \frac{\partial^2 e_{zz}}{\partial y^2} = \frac{\partial^2 e_{yz}}{\partial y\,\partial z}$$

gives

$$\frac{\partial^2}{\partial z^2}\{(1+\sigma)Y_y - \sigma\Theta\} + \frac{\partial^2}{\partial y^2}\{(1+\sigma)Z_z - \sigma\Theta\} = 2(1+\sigma)\frac{\partial^2 Y_z}{\partial y\,\partial z},$$

* The result is due to Beltrami, *Roma, Acc. Lincei Rend.* (Ser. 5), t. 1 (1892).

† J. H. Michell, *London Math. Soc. Proc.*, vol. 31 (1900), p. 100.

and the equations of type (30) give

$$\frac{\partial Y_z}{\partial y} = -\frac{\partial Z_x}{\partial x} - \frac{\partial Z_z}{\partial z}, \quad \frac{\partial Y_z}{\partial z} = -\frac{\partial X_y}{\partial x} - \frac{\partial Y_y}{\partial y},$$

so that

$$2\frac{\partial^2 Y_z}{\partial y \partial z} = -\frac{\partial}{\partial x}\left(\frac{\partial X_y}{\partial y} + \frac{\partial Z_x}{\partial x}\right) - \frac{\partial^2 Y_y}{\partial y^2} - \frac{\partial^2 Z_z}{\partial z^2}$$

$$= \frac{\partial^2 X_x}{\partial x^2} - \frac{\partial^2 Y_y}{\partial y^2} - \frac{\partial^2 Z_z}{\partial z^2}.$$

With the notation $\Theta = X_x + Y_y + Z_z$ we have therefore

$$(1+\sigma)\left\{\left(\nabla^2 - \frac{\partial^2}{\partial x^2}\right)(\Theta - X_x) - \frac{\partial^2 X_x}{\partial x^2}\right\} - \sigma\left(\nabla^2 - \frac{\partial^2}{\partial x^2}\right)\Theta = 0,$$

or

$$\nabla^2\Theta - \frac{\partial^2\Theta}{\partial x^2} - (1+\sigma)\nabla^2 X_x = 0;$$

and, on adding the left-hand members of the three equations of this type, we find that $\nabla^2\Theta$ must vanish, and obtain equation (28).

Equation (29) can be deduced in the same way from the equation

$$2\frac{\partial^2 e_{xx}}{\partial y \partial z} = \frac{\partial}{\partial x}\left(-\frac{\partial e_{yz}}{\partial x} + \frac{\partial e_{zx}}{\partial y} + \frac{\partial e_{xy}}{\partial z}\right).$$

(iv) As an example of the application of these formulæ, it may be observed that Maxwell's stress-system, described in (vi) of Article 53, cannot be the stress in an isotropic elastic solid free from the action of body force*, and slightly strained from a state of zero stress, for Θ, as given for that system, is not an harmonic function.

(v) It may be shown† that the stress-functions χ_1, χ_2, χ_3 of Article 56 satisfy three equations of the type

$$(1+\sigma)\nabla^2\left(\frac{\partial^2\chi_2}{\partial z^2} + \frac{\partial^2\chi_3}{\partial y^2}\right) + \frac{\partial^2\Theta}{\partial x^2} = 0, \quad \text{.........................(32)}$$

and three equations of the type

$$\frac{\partial^2}{\partial y \partial z}\left[(1+\sigma)\nabla^2\chi_1 - \Theta\right] = 0, \quad \text{...............................(33)}$$

where Θ is written for

$$\nabla^2(\chi_1+\chi_2+\chi_3) - \frac{\partial^2\chi_1}{\partial x^2} - \frac{\partial^2\chi_2}{\partial y^2} - \frac{\partial^2\chi_3}{\partial z^2}. \quad \text{.........................(34)}$$

It may be shown also that the stress-functions ψ_1, ψ_2, ψ_3 of the same Article satisfy three equations of the type

$$(1+\sigma)\nabla^2\frac{\partial^2\psi_1}{\partial y \partial z} + \frac{\partial^2\Theta}{\partial x^2} = 0, \quad \text{...................................(35)}$$

and three equations of the type

$$(1+\sigma)\nabla^2\frac{\partial}{\partial x}\left(\frac{\partial\psi_1}{\partial x} - \frac{\partial\psi_2}{\partial y} - \frac{\partial\psi_3}{\partial z}\right) + 2\frac{\partial^2\Theta}{\partial y \partial z} = 0, \quad \text{....................(36)}$$

where Θ is written for

$$\frac{\partial^2\psi_1}{\partial y \partial z} + \frac{\partial^2\psi_2}{\partial z \partial x} + \frac{\partial^2\psi_3}{\partial x \partial y}. \quad \text{...................................(37)}$$

* G. M. Minchin, *Statics*, 3rd edn. Oxford 1886, vol. 2, ch. 18.

† Ibbetson, *Mathematical Theory of Elasticity*, London 1887.

(vi) It may be shown* also that, when there are body forces, the stress-components satisfy equations of the types

$$\nabla^2 X_x + \frac{1}{1+\sigma}\frac{\partial^2 \Theta}{\partial x^2} = -\frac{\sigma}{1-\sigma}\rho\left(\frac{\partial X}{\partial x}+\frac{\partial Y}{\partial y}+\frac{\partial Z}{\partial z}\right) - 2\rho\frac{\partial X}{\partial x} \quad\text{..............(38)}$$

and

$$\nabla^2 Y_z + \frac{1}{1+\sigma}\frac{\partial^2 \Theta}{\partial y\,\partial z} = -\rho\frac{\partial Z}{\partial y} - \rho\frac{\partial Y}{\partial z}. \quad\text{..........................(39)}$$

The equations of these two types with the equations (3) are a complete system of equations satisfied by the stress-components.

94. Plane strain and plane stress.

States of plane strain and of plane stress can be maintained in bodies of cylindrical form by suitable forces. We take the generators of the cylindrical bounding surface to be parallel to the axis of z, and suppose that the terminal sections are at right angles to this axis. The body forces, if any, must be at right angles to this axis. When the lengths of the generators are small in comparison with the linear dimensions of the cross-section the body becomes a *plate* and the terminal sections are its *faces*.

In a state of plane strain, the displacements u, v are functions of x, y only and the displacement w vanishes (Article 15). All the components of strain and of stress are independent of z; the stress-components Z_x, Y_z vanish, and the strain-components e_{zx}, e_{yz}, e_{zz} vanish. The stress-component Z_z does not in general vanish. Thus the maintenance of a state of plane strain requires the application of tension or pressure, over the terminal sections, adjusted so as to keep constant the lengths of all the longitudinal filaments.

Without introducing any additional complication, we may allow for an *uniform* extension or contraction of all longitudinal filaments, by taking w to be equal to ez, where e is constant. The stress-components are then expressed by the equations

$$X_x = (\lambda + 2\mu)\frac{\partial u}{\partial x} + \lambda\left(\frac{\partial v}{\partial y} + e\right), \quad Y_z = 0,$$

$$Y_y = (\lambda + 2\mu)\frac{\partial v}{\partial y} + \lambda\left(\frac{\partial u}{\partial x} + e\right), \quad Z_x = 0,$$

$$Z_z = (\lambda + 2\mu)\,e + \lambda\left(\frac{\partial u}{\partial x} + \frac{\partial v}{\partial y}\right), \quad X_y = \mu\left(\frac{\partial v}{\partial x} + \frac{\partial u}{\partial y}\right).$$

The functions u, v are to be determined by solving the equations of equilibrium. We shall discuss the theory of plane strain more fully in Chapter IX.

In a state of plane stress parallel to the plane of (x, y) the stress-components Z_x, Y_z, Z_z vanish, but the displacements u, v, w are not in general independent of z. In particular the strain-component e_{zz} does not vanish, and in general it is not constant, but we have

$$e_{zz} = \frac{\partial w}{\partial z} = -\frac{\lambda}{\lambda + 2\mu}\left(\frac{\partial u}{\partial x} + \frac{\partial v}{\partial y}\right) = -\frac{\lambda}{2\mu}\Delta. \quad\text{..............(40)}$$

* Michell, *loc. cit.*

The maintenance, in a plate, of a state of plane stress does not require the application of traction to the faces of the plate, but it requires the body forces and tractions at the edge to be distributed in certain special ways. We shall discuss the theory more fully in Chapter IX.

An important generalization* can be made by supposing that the normal traction Z_z vanishes throughout the plate, but that the tangential tractions Z_x, Y_z vanish at the faces $z = \pm h$ only. If the plate is thin the determination of the average values of the components of displacement, strain and stress, taken over the thickness of the plate, may lead to knowledge nearly as useful as that of the actual values at each point. We denote these average values by $\bar{u}$, ... $\bar{e}_{xx}$, ... $\bar{X}_x$, ... so that we have for example

$$\bar{u} = (2h)^{-1} \int_{-h}^{h} u dz. \qquad \text{.......................(41)}$$

We integrate both members of the equations of equilibrium over the thickness of the plate, and observe that Z_x and Y_z vanish at the faces. We thus find that, if there are no body forces, the average stress-components $\bar{X}_x$, $\bar{X}_y$, $\bar{Y}_y$ satisfy the equations

$$\frac{\partial \bar{X}_x}{\partial x} + \frac{\partial \bar{X}_y}{\partial y} = 0, \quad \frac{\partial \bar{X}_y}{\partial x} + \frac{\partial \bar{Y}_y}{\partial y} = 0. \qquad \text{..............(42)}$$

Since Z_z vanishes, equations (40) hold, and it follows that the average displacements $\bar{u}, \bar{v}$ are connected with the average stress-components $\bar{X}_x$, $\bar{X}_y$, $\bar{Y}_y$ by the equations

$$\left.\begin{aligned} \bar{X}_x &= \frac{2\lambda\mu}{\lambda + 2\mu}\left(\frac{\partial \bar{u}}{\partial x} + \frac{\partial \bar{v}}{\partial y}\right) + 2\mu \frac{\partial \bar{u}}{\partial x}, \\ \bar{Y}_y &= \frac{2\lambda\mu}{\lambda + 2\mu}\left(\frac{\partial \bar{u}}{\partial x} + \frac{\partial \bar{v}}{\partial y}\right) + 2\mu \frac{\partial \bar{v}}{\partial y}, \\ \bar{X}_y &= \mu\left(\frac{\partial \bar{v}}{\partial x} + \frac{\partial \bar{u}}{\partial y}\right). \end{aligned}\right\} \qquad \text{..................(43)}$$

States of stress such as are here described will be termed states of "generalized plane stress."

95. Bending of narrow rectangular beam by terminal load.

A simple example of the generalized type of plane stress, described in Article 94, is afforded by a beam of rectangular section and small breadth ($2h$), bent by forces which act in directions parallel to the plane containing the length and the depth. We shall take the plane of (x, y) to be the mid-plane of the beam (parallel to length and depth); and, to fix ideas, we shall regard the beam as horizontal in the unstressed state. The top and bottom surfaces of the beam will be given by $y = \mp c$, so that $2c$ is the depth of the beam, and we shall denote the length of the beam by l. We shall take the origin at one end, and consider that end to be fixed.

* Cf. L. N. G. Filon, *Phil. Trans. Roy. Soc.* (Ser. A), vol. 201 (1903).

From the investigation in Article 87, we know a state of stress in the beam, given by $X_x = -Ey/R$; and we know that the beam can be held in this state by terminal couples of moment $\frac{4}{3}hc^3E/R$ about axes parallel to the axis of z. The central-line of the beam is bent into an arc of a circle of radius R. The traction across any section of the beam is then statically equivalent to a couple, the same for all sections, and equal to the terminal couple, or bending moment.

Let us now suppose that the beam is bent by a load W applied at the end $x=l$ as in Fig. 13. This force cannot be balanced by a couple at any section, but the traction across any section is equivalent to a force W and a couple of moment $W(l-x)$. The stress-system is therefore not so simple as in the case of bending by couples. The couple of moment $W(l-x)$ could be balanced by tractions X_x, given by the equation

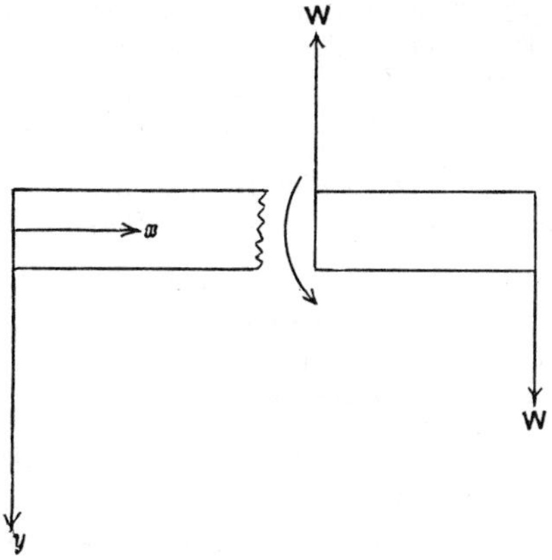

Fig. 13.

$$X_x = -\frac{3}{4hc^3} W(l-x)\,y; \quad \text{.......................(44)}$$

and the average traction $\overline{X}_x$ across the breadth would be the same as X_x. We seek to combine with this traction $\overline{X}_x$ a tangential traction $\overline{X}_y$, so that the load W may be equilibrated. The conditions to be satisfied by $\overline{X}_y$ are the following:

(i) $\overline{X}_y$ must satisfy the equations of equilibrium

$$\frac{\partial \overline{X}_x}{\partial x} + \frac{\partial \overline{X}_y}{\partial y} = 0, \qquad \frac{\partial \overline{X}_y}{\partial x} = 0,$$

(ii) $\overline{X}_y$ must vanish when $y = \pm c$,

(iii) $2h\int_{-c}^{c} \overline{X}_y \, dy$ must be equal to W.

These are all satisfied by putting

$$\overline{X}_y = \frac{3}{8hc^3} W(c^2 - y^2). \quad \text{.........................(45)}$$

It follows that the load W can be equilibrated by tractions $\overline{X}_x$ and $\overline{X}_y$, without $\overline{Y}_y$, provided that the terminal tractions, of which W is the resultant, are distributed over the end so as to be proportional to $c^2 - y^2$. As in Article 89, the distribution of the load is important near the ends only, if the length of the beam is great in comparison with its depth.

We may show that a system of average displacements which would correspond with this system of average stresses is given by the equations

$$\left.\begin{aligned} 2\mu\bar{u} &= \frac{W}{8hc^3}(3c^2y - y^3) - \frac{\lambda+\mu}{3\lambda+2\mu}\frac{W}{4hc^3}(6lxy + y^3 - 3x^2y), \\ 2\mu\bar{v} &= \frac{3W}{8hc^3}\{c^2x + (l-x)\,y^2\} + \frac{\lambda+\mu}{3\lambda+2\mu}\frac{W}{4hc^3}\{3l(x^2-y^2) - x^3 + 3xy^2\}. \end{aligned}\right\} \quad \ldots\ldots\ldots(46)$$

Since these are deduced from known stress-components a displacement possible in a rigid body might be added, so as to satisfy conditions of fixity at the origin.

These conclusions may be compared with those found in the case of bending by couples (Article 88). We note the following results:

(i) The tension per unit area across the normal sections (X_x) is connected with the bending moment, $W(l-x)$, by the equation

$$\text{tension} = -\,(\text{bending moment})\,(y/I),$$

where y is distance from the neutral plane, and I is the appropriate moment of inertia.

(ii) The curvature $(d^2\bar{v}/dx^2)_{y=0}$ is $\dfrac{3(\lambda+\mu)\,W(l-x)}{4hc^3\mu(3\lambda+2\mu)}$; so that we have the equation

$$\text{curvature} = (\text{bending moment})/(EI).$$

(iii) The surface of particles which, in the unstressed state, is a normal section does not continue to cut at right angles the line of particles which, in the same state, is the line of centroids of normal sections. The cosine of the angle at which they cut when the beam is bent is $(\partial\bar{v}/\partial x + \partial\bar{u}/\partial y)_{y=0}$, and this is $3W/8\mu hc$.

(iv) The normal sections do not remain plane, but are distorted into curved surfaces. A line of particles which, in the unstressed state, is vertical becomes a curved line, of

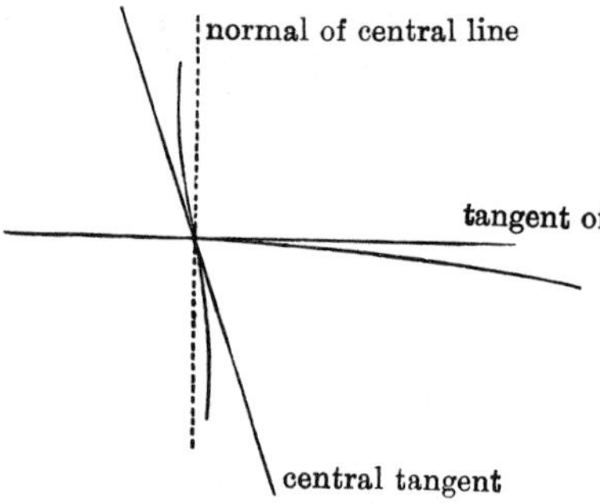

Fig. 14.

which the equation is determined by the expression for u as a function of y when x is constant. This equation is of the form

$$\bar{u} = \alpha y + \beta y^3,$$

and the corresponding displacement consists of a part αy which does not alter the planeness of the section combined with a part which does. If we construct the curve $x = \beta y^3$ and place it with its origin ($x=0$, $y=0$) on the strained central-line, and its tangent at the origin along the tangent to the line of particles which, in the unstressed state, is vertical, the curve will be the locus of these particles in the strained state.

Fig. 14 shows the form into which an initially vertical filament is bent and the relative situation of the central tangent of this line and the normal of the strained central-line.

96. Equations referred to orthogonal curvilinear coordinates.

The equations such as (21) expressed in terms of dilatation and rotation can be transformed immediately by noticing the vectorial character of the terms. In fact the terms $\left(\frac{\partial}{\partial x}, \frac{\partial}{\partial y}, \frac{\partial}{\partial z}\right)\Delta$ may be read as "the gradient of Δ," and then the equations (22) may be read

$$(\lambda + 2\mu)\,(\text{gradient of } \Delta) - 2\mu\,(\text{curl of } \varpi) + \rho\,(\text{body force}) = \rho\,(\text{acceleration}), \quad \text{......(47)}$$

where ϖ stands temporarily for the rotation $(\varpi_x, \varpi_y, \varpi_z)$, and the factors such as $\lambda + 2\mu$ are scalar.

Now the gradient of Δ is the vector of which the component, in any direction, is the rate of increase of Δ per unit of length in that direction; and the components of this vector, in the directions of the normals to three orthogonal surfaces α, β, γ (Article 19), are accordingly

$$h_1 \frac{\partial \Delta}{\partial \alpha}, \quad h_2 \frac{\partial \Delta}{\partial \beta}, \quad h_3 \frac{\partial \Delta}{\partial \gamma}.$$

We have already transformed the operation curl, and the components of rotation, as well as the dilatation (Article 21); and we may therefore regard Δ and ϖ_α, ϖ_β, ϖ_γ as known in terms of the displacement. The equation (47) is then equivalent to three of the form

$$(\lambda + 2\mu)\,h_1 \frac{\partial \Delta}{\partial \alpha} - 2\mu h_2 h_3 \frac{\partial}{\partial \beta}\left(\frac{\varpi_\gamma}{h_3}\right) + 2\mu h_2 h_3 \frac{\partial}{\partial \gamma}\left(\frac{\varpi_\beta}{h_2}\right) + \rho F_\alpha = \rho \frac{\partial^2 u_\alpha}{\partial t^2} \quad \text{...(48)}$$

where F_α, F_β, F_γ are, as in Article 58, the components of the body force in the directions of the normals to the three surfaces.

97. Polar coordinates.

As an example of the equations (48) we may show that the equations of equilibrium under no body forces when referred to polar coordinates take the forms

$$\left.\begin{aligned}
(\lambda+2\mu)\sin\theta \frac{\partial \Delta}{\partial \theta} - 2\mu \left\{\frac{\partial \varpi_r}{\partial \phi} - \frac{\partial}{\partial r}(r\varpi_\phi \sin\theta)\right\} &= 0,\\
(\lambda+2\mu)\frac{1}{\sin\theta}\frac{\partial \Delta}{\partial \phi} - 2\mu\left\{\frac{\partial}{\partial r}(r\varpi_\theta) - \frac{\partial \varpi_r}{\partial \theta}\right\} &= 0,\\
(\lambda+2\mu)\, r\sin\theta \frac{\partial \Delta}{\partial r} - 2\mu\left\{\frac{\partial}{\partial \theta}(\varpi_\phi \sin\theta) - \frac{\partial \varpi_\theta}{\partial \phi}\right\} &= 0.
\end{aligned}\right\} \quad \text{..................(49)}$$

We may show also that the radial components of displacement and rotation and the dilatation satisfy the equations

$$\mu\nabla^2(ru_r) + (\lambda+\mu)\,r\frac{\partial \Delta}{\partial r} - 2\mu\Delta = 0,$$

$$\nabla^2\Delta = 0, \quad \nabla^2(r\varpi_r) = 0;$$

but that some solutions of these equations correspond with states of stress that would require body force for their maintenance*.

* Michell, *London Math. Soc. Proc.*, vol. 32 (1901), p. 24.

98. Radial displacement*.

The simplest applications of polar coordinates relate to problems involving purely radial displacements. We suppose that the displacements u_θ, u_ϕ vanish, and we write U in place of u_r. Then we find from the formulæ of Articles 22 and 96 the following results:

(i) The strain-components are given by

$$e_{rr}=\frac{\partial U}{\partial r}, \quad e_{\theta\theta}=e_{\phi\phi}=\frac{U}{r}, \quad e_{\theta\phi}=e_{\phi r}=e_{r\theta}=0.$$

(ii) The dilatation and rotation are given by

$$\Delta=\frac{\partial U}{\partial r}+2\frac{U}{r}, \quad \varpi_r=\varpi_\theta=\varpi_\phi=0.$$

(iii) The stress-components are given by

$$\widehat{rr}=(\lambda+2\mu)\frac{\partial U}{\partial r}+2\lambda\frac{U}{r}, \quad \widehat{\theta\theta}=\widehat{\phi\phi}=\lambda\frac{\partial U}{\partial r}+2(\lambda+\mu)\frac{U}{r}, \quad \widehat{\theta\phi}=\widehat{\phi r}=\widehat{r\theta}=0.$$

(iv) The general equation of equilibrium, under radial body force R, is

$$(\lambda+2\mu)\frac{\partial}{\partial r}\left(\frac{\partial U}{\partial r}+2\frac{U}{r}\right)+\rho R=0.$$

(v) If $R=0$, the complete primitive of the equation just written is

$$U=Ar+Br^{-2},$$

where A and B are arbitrary constants. The first term corresponds with the problem of compression by uniform normal pressure [Article 70 (g)]. The complete primitive cannot represent a displacement in a solid body containing the origin of r. The origin must either be outside the body or inside a cavity within the body.

(vi) The solution in (v) may be adapted to the case of a shell bounded by concentric spherical surfaces, and held strained by internal and external pressure. We must have

$$(\lambda+2\mu)\frac{\partial U}{\partial r}+2\lambda\frac{U}{r}=\begin{cases}-p_0 \text{ when } r=r_0,\\ -p_1 \text{ when } r=r_1,\end{cases}$$

where p_0 is the pressure at the external boundary ($r=r_0$), and p_1 is the pressure at the internal boundary ($r=r_1$). We should find

$$U=\frac{1}{3\lambda+2\mu}\frac{p_1r_1^3-p_0r_0^3}{r_0^3-r_1^3}r+\frac{1}{4\mu}\frac{r_0^3r_1^3(p_1-p_0)}{r_0^3-r_1^3}\frac{1}{r^2}.$$

The radial pressure at any point is

$$p_1\frac{r_1^3}{r^3}\frac{r_0^3-r^3}{r_0^3-r_1^3}+p_0\frac{r_0^3}{r^3}\frac{r^3-r_1^3}{r_0^3-r_1^3},$$

and the tension in any direction at right angles to the radius is

$$\frac{1}{2}p_1\frac{r_1^3}{r^3}\frac{r_0^3+2r^3}{r_0^3-r_1^3}-\frac{1}{2}p_0\frac{r_0^3}{r^3}\frac{2r^3+r_1^3}{r_0^3-r_1^3}.$$

In case $p_0=0$, the greatest tension is the superficial tension at the inner surface, of amount $\frac{1}{2}p_1(r_0^3+2r_1^3)/(r_0^3-r_1^3)$; and the greatest extension is the extension at right angles to the radius at the inner surface, of amount

$$\frac{p_1}{r_0^3-r_1^3}\left(\frac{r_1^3}{3\lambda+2\mu}+\frac{r_0^3}{4\mu}\right).$$

* Most of the results given in this Article are due to Lamé, *Leçons sur la théorie...de l'élasticité*, Paris 1852.

(vii) If in the general equation of (iv) $R=-gr/r_0$, where g is constant, the surface $r=r_0$ is free from traction, and the sphere is complete up to the centre, we find

$$U=-\frac{1}{10}\frac{g\rho r_0 r}{\lambda+2\mu}\left(\frac{5\lambda+6\mu}{3\lambda+2\mu}-\frac{r^2}{r_0^2}\right).$$

This corresponds with the problem of a sphere held strained by the mutual gravitation of its parts. It is noteworthy that the radial strain is contraction within the surface $r=r_0\sqrt{\{(3-\sigma)/(3+3\sigma)\}}$, but it is *extension* outside this surface.

The application of this result to the case of the Earth is beset by the serious difficulty which has been pointed out in Article 75.

99. Displacement symmetrical about an axis.

The conditions that the displacement may take place in planes through an axis, and be the same in all such planes, would be expressed, by reference to cylindrical coordinates r, θ, z, by the equations

$$u_\theta=0,\quad \partial u_r/\partial\theta=\partial u_z/\partial\theta=0.$$

It will be convenient to write U for u_r, and w for u_z. The strain-components are then expressed by the equations

$$\left.\begin{aligned} e_{rr}&=\frac{\partial U}{\partial r},\quad e_{\theta\theta}=\frac{U}{r},\quad e_{zz}=\frac{\partial w}{\partial z},\\ e_{rz}&=\frac{\partial U}{\partial z}+\frac{\partial w}{\partial r},\quad e_{r\theta}=e_{\theta z}=0.\end{aligned}\right\}\quad\text{..................(50)}$$

The cubical dilatation and the rotation are expressed by the equations

$$\Delta=\frac{\partial U}{\partial r}+\frac{U}{r}+\frac{\partial w}{\partial z},\quad 2\varpi_\theta=\frac{\partial U}{\partial z}-\frac{\partial w}{\partial r},\quad \varpi_r=\varpi_z=0.\text{ ....(51)}$$

It will be convenient to write ϖ for ϖ_θ. The equations of motion in terms of displacements take the forms

$$\left.\begin{aligned}(\lambda+2\mu)\frac{\partial\Delta}{\partial r}+2\mu\frac{\partial\varpi}{\partial z}+\rho F_r&=\rho f_r,\\ (\lambda+2\mu)\frac{\partial\Delta}{\partial z}-\frac{2\mu}{r}\frac{\partial}{\partial r}(r\varpi)+\rho F_z&=\rho f_z;\end{aligned}\right\}\quad\text{..............(52)}$$

and the stress-equations of equilibrium take the forms

$$\left.\begin{aligned}\frac{\partial\widehat{rr}}{\partial r}+\frac{\partial\widehat{rz}}{\partial z}+\frac{\widehat{rr}-\widehat{\theta\theta}}{r}+\rho F_r&=0,\\ \frac{\partial\widehat{rz}}{\partial r}+\frac{\partial\widehat{zz}}{\partial z}+\frac{\widehat{rz}}{r}+\rho F_z&=0.\end{aligned}\right\}\quad\text{..................(53)}$$

In case $w=ez$, where e is constant, and $\partial U/\partial z=0$, we have a state of plane strain, with an uniform longitudinal extension superposed. In this case $\widehat{rz}=0$. In case $\widehat{zz}$, $\widehat{rz}$, F_z vanish, we have a state of plane stress.

100. Tube under pressure.

In the case of plane strain, under no body forces, the displacement U satisfies the equation

$$\frac{\partial}{\partial r}\left(\frac{\partial U}{\partial r}+\frac{U}{r}\right)=0 \qquad (54)$$

of which the complete primitive is of the form

$$U = Ar + B/r. \qquad (55)$$

We may adapt this solution to the problem of a cylindrical tube under internal and external pressure, and we may allow for an uniform longitudinal extension e. With a notation similar to that in (vi) of Article 98, we should find for the stress-components

$$\left.\begin{aligned}\widehat{rr} &= \frac{p_1 r_1^2 - p_0 r_0^2}{r_0^2 - r_1^2} - \frac{p_1 - p_0}{r_0^2 - r_1^2}\frac{r_0^2 r_1^2}{r^2},\\ \widehat{\theta\theta} &= \frac{p_1 r_1^2 - p_0 r_0^2}{r_0^2 - r_1^2} + \frac{p_1 - p_0}{r_0^2 - r_1^2}\frac{r_0^2 r_1^2}{r^2},\\ \widehat{zz} &= \frac{\lambda}{\lambda+\mu}\frac{p_1 r_1^2 - p_0 r_0^2}{r_0^2 - r_1^2} + e\frac{(3\lambda+2\mu)\mu}{\lambda+\mu},\end{aligned}\right\} \qquad (56)$$

and for the constants A and B in (55)

$$A = \frac{p_1 r_1^2 - p_0 r_0^2}{2(\lambda+\mu)(r_0^2 - r_1^2)} - \frac{\lambda e}{2(\lambda+\mu)}, \qquad B = \frac{(p_1 - p_0) r_0^2 r_1^2}{2\mu(r_0^2 - r_1^2)}. \qquad (57)$$

The constant e may be adjusted so that the length is maintained constant; then $e = 0$, and there is longitudinal tension $\widehat{zz}$ of amount

$$\frac{\lambda}{\lambda+\mu}\frac{p_1 r_1^2 - p_0 r_0^2}{r_0^2 - r_1^2}.$$

It may also be adjusted so that there is no longitudinal tension; then $\widehat{zz} = 0$ and

$$e = -\frac{\lambda(p_1 r_1^2 - p_0 r_0^2)}{\mu(3\lambda+2\mu)(r_0^2 - r_1^2)}.$$

When p_0 vanishes, and e is not too great, the greatest tension is the circumferential tension, $\widehat{\theta\theta}$, at the inner surface, $r = r_1$, and its amount is

$$p_1(r_0^2 + r_1^2)/(r_0^2 - r_1^2).$$

The greatest extension is the circumferential extension, $e_{\theta\theta}$, at the same surface.

If a closed cylindrical vessel is under internal pressure p_1 and external pressure p_0, the resultant tension $\pi(r_0^2 - r_1^2)\,\widehat{zz}$ must balance the resultant pressure on the ends, and we must therefore have the equation

$$\pi(r_0^2 - r_1^2)\,\widehat{zz} = \pi(r_1^2 p_1 - r_0^2 p_0).$$

This equation gives for e the value*

$$e=\frac{1}{3\lambda+2\mu}\frac{p_1r_1^2-p_0r_0^2}{r_0^2-r_1^2}. \qquad \text{(58)}$$

If we assume that the ends of the vessel are plane, and neglect the alteration of their shape under pressure, the volume of the vessel will be increased by $\pi r_1 l_1(er_1+2U_1)$, where l_1 denotes the length of the inside of the cylinder, and U_1 is the value of U at $r=r_1$. With the above value of e this is

$$\pi r_1^2 l_1\left[\frac{3}{3\lambda+2\mu}\frac{p_1r_1^2-p_0r_0^2}{r_0^2-r_1^2}+\frac{1}{\mu}\frac{(p_1-p_0)\,r_0^2}{r_0^2-r_1^2}\right]. \qquad \text{(59)}$$

In like manner, if we denote by l_0 the length of the outside of the cylinder, and neglect the change of volume of the ends, the volume within the external boundary of the vessel will be increased by

$$\pi r_0^2 l_0\left[\frac{3}{3\lambda+2\mu}\frac{p_1r_1^2-p_0r_0^2}{r_0^2-r_1^2}+\frac{1}{\mu}\frac{(p_1-p_0)\,r_1^2}{r_0^2-r_1^2}\right]. \qquad \text{(60)}$$

The quantity l_0 differs from l_1 by the sum of the thicknesses of the ends. In the case of a long cylinder this difference is unimportant. The constant $3/(3\lambda+2\mu)$ is $1/k$, the reciprocal of the modulus of compression. When the difference between l_0 and l_1 is neglected, the result accords with a more general result†, which can be proved for a closed vessel of any form under internal and external pressure, viz. if V_1 and V_0 are the internal and external volumes in the unstressed state, then V_0-V_1 is increased by the amount $(p_1V_1-p_0V_0)/k$, when internal and external pressures p_1, p_0 are applied. In obtaining the results (59) and (60) we have not taken proper account of the action of the ends of the cylinder, for we have assumed that these ends are stretched in their own planes so as to fit the distended cylinder, and we have neglected the changes of shape and volume of the ends; further, we have supposed that the action of the ends upon the walls of the vessel is equivalent to a tension uniformly distributed over the thickness of the walls. The results will provide a good approximation if the length of the cylinder is great in comparison with its radii and if the walls are very thin.

101. Application to gun-construction.

In equations (56), the stress-components $\widehat{rr}$ and $\widehat{\theta\theta}$ are expressed by formulæ of the type

$$\widehat{rr}=A-\frac{B}{r^2}, \quad \widehat{\theta\theta}=A+\frac{B}{r^2},$$

where A and B are constants. These constants are determined by the internal and external pressures. We have therefore a solution of the stress-equations in a tube under

* The problem has been discussed by numerous writers including Lamé, *loc. cit. ante* p. 142. It is important in the theory of the piezometer. Cf. Poynting and Thomson, *Properties of Matter*, London 1902, p. 116. The fact that e depends on k $(=\lambda+\frac{2}{3}\mu)$ and not on any other elastic constant has been utilized for the determination of k by A. Mallock, *London, Roy. Soc. Proc.*, vol 74 (1904).

† See Chapter VII, *infra*.

internal and external pressure which is applicable in other cases besides the case where the material would, in the absence of the pressures, be in the unstressed state. The solution has been taken to be applicable to states of initial stress, and has been applied to the theory of the construction of cannon*. Cannon are sometimes constructed in the form of a series of tubes, each tube being heated so that it can slip over the next interior tube; the outer tube contracts by cooling and exerts pressure on the inner. Cannon so constructed have been found to be stronger than single tubes of the same thickness. If, for example, we take the case of two tubes between which there is a pressure P, and suppose r' to be the radius of the common surface, the initial stress may be taken to be given by the equations

$$\widehat{rr} = -P\frac{r'^2}{r^2}\frac{r_0^2-r^2}{r_0^2-r'^2}, \quad \widehat{\theta\theta} = P\frac{r'^2}{r^2}\frac{r_0^2+r^2}{r_0^2-r'^2}, \quad (r_0>r>r')$$

and

$$\widehat{rr} = -P\frac{r'^2}{r^2}\frac{r^2-r_1^2}{r'^2-r_1^2}, \quad \widehat{\theta\theta} = -P\frac{r'^2}{r^2}\frac{r^2+r_1^2}{r'^2-r_1^2}, \quad (r'>r>r_1).$$

The additional stress when the compound tube is subjected to internal pressure p may be taken to be given by the equations

$$\widehat{rr} = -p\frac{r_1^2}{r^2}\frac{r_0^2-r^2}{r_0^2-r_1^2}, \quad \widehat{\theta\theta} = p\frac{r_1^2}{r^2}\frac{r_0^2+r^2}{r_0^2-r_1^2}.$$

The diminution of the hoop tension $\widehat{\theta\theta}$ at the inner surface $r=r_1$ may be taken as an index of the increased strength of the compound tube.

102. Rotating cylinder†.

An example of equations of motion is afforded by a rotating cylinder. In equations (52) we have to put $f_r = -\omega^2 r$, where ω is the angular velocity.

The equations for the displacements are

$$\left.\begin{aligned}(\lambda+2\mu)\frac{\partial}{\partial r}\left(\frac{\partial U}{\partial r}+\frac{U}{r}+\frac{\partial w}{\partial z}\right)+\mu\frac{\partial}{\partial z}\left(\frac{\partial U}{\partial z}-\frac{\partial w}{\partial r}\right) &= -\omega^2\rho r,\\ (\lambda+2\mu)\frac{\partial}{\partial z}\left(\frac{\partial U}{\partial r}+\frac{U}{r}+\frac{\partial w}{\partial z}\right)-\mu\frac{\partial}{\partial r}\left(\frac{\partial U}{\partial z}-\frac{\partial w}{\partial r}\right)-\frac{\mu}{r}\left(\frac{\partial U}{\partial z}-\frac{\partial w}{\partial r}\right) &= 0,\end{aligned}\right\} \quad \text{......(61)}$$

with the conditions $\widehat{rr} = \widehat{rz} = 0$ when $r=a$ or $r=a'$,

$$\widehat{rz} = \widehat{zz} = 0 \text{ when } z = \pm l.$$

The cylindrical bounding surface is here taken to be $r=a$, and it is supposed that there is an axle-hole given by $r=a'$; the terminal sections are taken to be given by $z=\pm l$, so that the cylinder is a shaft of length $2l$, or a disk of thickness $2l$.

Case (a). Rotating shaft.

An approximate solution can be obtained in the case of a long shaft, by treating the problem as one of plane strain, with an allowance for uniform longitudinal extension, e. We regard the cylinder as complete, i.e. without an axle-hole; and then the approximate solution satisfies the equations

$$\widehat{rz} = 0 \text{ throughout,}$$

$$\widehat{rr} = 0 \text{ when } r = a,$$

* A. G. Greenhill, *Nature*, vol. 42 (1890). Cf. Boltzmann, *Wien Berichte*, Bd. 59 (1870).

† See papers by C. Chree in *Cambridge Phil. Soc. Proc.*, vol. 7 (1892), pp. 201, 283. The problem had been discussed previously by several writers among whom Maxwell (*loc. cit.* Article 57), and Hopkinson, *Messenger of Math.* (Ser. 2), vol. 2 (1871), may be mentioned.

but it does not satisfy $\widehat{zz}=0$ when $z=\pm l$. The uniform longitudinal extension e can be adjusted so that the tractions $\widehat{zz}$ on the ends shall have no statical resultant, i.e.

$$\int_0^a \widehat{zz}\, r\, dr=0;$$

and then the solution represents the state of the shaft with sufficient exactness over the greater part of the length, but is defective near the ends. [Cf. Article 89.]

We shall state the results in terms of E and σ. We should find

$$U=Ar-\frac{\omega^2\rho r^3}{8E}\frac{(1+\sigma)(1-2\sigma)}{1-\sigma}, \quad w=ez, \quad\text{.........................(62)}$$

where the constants A and e are given by the equations

$$A=\frac{\omega^2\rho a^2}{8E}\frac{3-5\sigma}{1-\sigma}, \quad e=-\frac{\omega^2\rho a^2\sigma}{2E}. \quad\text{.........................(63)}$$

The stress-components are given by the equations

$$\left.\begin{aligned}\widehat{rr}&=\frac{\omega^2\rho(a^2-r^2)}{8}\frac{3-2\sigma}{1-\sigma}, \quad \widehat{\theta\theta}=\frac{\omega^2\rho}{8}\left(\frac{3-2\sigma}{1-\sigma}a^2-\frac{1+2\sigma}{1-\sigma}r^2\right),\\ \widehat{zz}&=\frac{\omega^2\rho(a^2-2r^2)}{4}\frac{\sigma}{1-\sigma}.\end{aligned}\right\}\quad\text{............(64)}$$

Instead of making the resultant longitudinal tension vanish, we might suppose that the tension is adjusted so that the length is maintained constant. Then we should have

$$e=0, \quad A=\frac{\omega^2\rho a^2}{8E}\frac{(3-2\sigma)(1+\sigma)(1-2\sigma)}{1-\sigma}; \quad\text{.....................(65)}$$

the first two of equations (64) would still hold, and the longitudinal tension would be given by the equation

$$\widehat{zz}=\frac{\omega^2\rho\{(3-2\sigma)a^2-2r^2\}}{4}\frac{\sigma}{1-\sigma}. \quad\text{..........................(66)}$$

Case (*b*). *Rotating disk.*

An approximate solution can be obtained in the case of a thin disk, by treating the problem as one of plane stress. If the disk is complete, the approximate solution satisfies the equations $\widehat{zz}=0$, $\widehat{rz}=0$ throughout, so that the plane faces of the disk are free from traction; but it does not satisfy the condition $\widehat{rr}=0$ when $r=a$. Instead of this it makes $\int_{-l}^{l}\widehat{rr}\,dz$ vanish at $r=a$, so that the resultant radial tension on any portion of the rim between the two plane faces vanishes*; and it represents the state of the disk in the parts that are not too near the edge.

In this case U, as a function of r, satisfies the equation

$$\frac{4\mu(\lambda+\mu)}{\lambda+2\mu}\frac{\partial}{\partial r}\left(\frac{\partial U}{\partial r}+\frac{U}{r}\right)=-\omega^2\rho r; \quad\text{.........................(67)}$$

and we also have

$$\frac{\partial w}{\partial z}=-\frac{\lambda}{\lambda+2\mu}\left(\frac{\partial U}{\partial r}+\frac{U}{r}\right), \quad \frac{\partial w}{\partial r}=-\frac{\partial U}{\partial z}, \quad\text{.....................(68)}$$

from which we may deduce the equation

$$\frac{\partial^2 U}{\partial z^2}=-\frac{\lambda\omega^2\rho r}{4\mu(\lambda+\mu)}. \quad\text{...................................(69)}$$

* A small supplementary displacement corresponding with traction $-\widehat{rr}$ at the edge surface and zero traction over the plane faces would be required for the complete solution of the problem. See a paper by F. Purser in *Dublin, R. Irish Acad. Trans.*, vol. 32 (1902).

These equations, with the condition that $\int_{-l}^{l} \widehat{rr}\, dz$ vanishes when $r=a$, determine U and w, apart from a displacement which would be possible in a rigid body; and we may impose the conditions that U and w vanish at the origin ($r=0$, $z=0$), and that 2ϖ, which is equal to $\partial U/\partial z - \partial w/\partial r$, also vanishes there. We should then find that U, w are given by the equations

$$\left.\begin{aligned} U &= \frac{\omega^2\rho r}{8E}(1-\sigma)\{(3+\sigma)a^2-(1+\sigma)r^2\}+\frac{\omega^2\rho r}{6E}\sigma(1+\sigma)(l^2-3z^2),\\ w &= -\frac{\omega^2\rho z}{4E}\sigma\{(3+\sigma)a^2-2(1+\sigma)r^2\}-\frac{\omega^2\rho z}{3E}\sigma^2\frac{1+\sigma}{1-\sigma}(l^2-z^2);\end{aligned}\right\} \quad \text{.........(70)}$$

from these equations we should deduce the following expressions for the stress-components:

$$\left.\begin{aligned} \widehat{rr} &= \frac{\omega^2\rho}{8}(3+\sigma)(a^2-r^2)+\frac{\omega^2\rho}{6}\sigma\frac{1+\sigma}{1-\sigma}(l^2-3z^2),\\ \widehat{\theta\theta} &= \frac{\omega^2\rho}{8}\{(3+\sigma)a^2-(1+3\sigma)r^2\}+\frac{\omega^2\rho}{6}\sigma\frac{1+\sigma}{1-\sigma}(l^2-3z^2).\end{aligned}\right\} \quad \text{...............(71)}$$

When there is a circular axle-hole of radius a' we have the additional condition that $\int_{-l}^{l}\widehat{rr}\,dz=0$ when $r=a'$, but now the displacement may involve terms which would be infinite at the axis. We should obtain the complete solution by adding to the above expressions for U and w terms U' and w', given by the equations

$$\left.\begin{aligned} U' &= \frac{\omega^2\rho r}{8E}(3+\sigma)\left[(1-\sigma)a'^2+(1+\sigma)\frac{a^2a'^2}{r^2}\right],\\ w' &= -\frac{\omega^2\rho z}{4E}\sigma(3+\sigma)a'^2,\end{aligned}\right\} \quad \text{.....................(72)}$$

and these displacements correspond with additional stresses given by the equations

$$\widehat{rr}=\frac{\omega^2\rho}{8}(3+\sigma)\left(a'^2-\frac{a^2a'^2}{r^2}\right),\quad \widehat{\theta\theta}=\frac{\omega^2\rho}{8}(3+\sigma)\left(a'^2+\frac{a^2a'^2}{r^2}\right); \quad \text{.........(73)}$$

these are to be added to the expressions given in (71) for $\widehat{rr}$ and $\widehat{\theta\theta}$.

CHAPTER VI

EQUILIBRIUM OF ÆOLOTROPIC ELASTIC SOLID BODIES

103. Symmetry of structure.

The dependence of the stress-strain relations (25) of Article 72 upon the directions of the axes of reference has been pointed out in Article 68. The relations are simplified when the material exhibits certain kinds of symmetry, and the axes of reference are suitably chosen. It is necessary to explain the geometrical characters of the kinds of symmetry that are observed in various materials. The nature of the æolotropy of the material is not completely determined by its elastic behaviour alone. The material may be æolotropic in regard to other physical actions, e.g. the refraction of light. If, in an æolotropic body, two lines can be found, relatively to which all the physical characters of the material are the same, such lines are said to be "equivalent." Different materials may be distinguished by the distributions in them of equivalent lines. For the present, we shall confine our attention to the case of homogeneous materials, for which parallel lines in like senses are equivalent; and we have then to consider the distribution of equivalent lines meeting in a point. For some purposes it is important to observe that oppositely directed lines are not always equivalent. When certain crystals are undergoing changes of temperature, opposite ends of particular axes become oppositely electrified; this is the phenomenon of *pyro-electricity*. When certain crystals are compressed between parallel planes, which are at right angles to particular axes, opposite ends of these axes become oppositely electrified; this is the phenomenon of *piezo-electricity**. We accordingly consider the properties of a material relative to *rays* or *directions* of lines going out from a point; and we determine the nature of the symmetry of a material by the distribution in it of equivalent directions. A figure made up of a set of equivalent directions is a geometrical figure exhibiting some kind of symmetry.

104. Geometrical symmetry†.

When a surface of revolution is turned through any angle about the axis of revolution, the position of every point, which is on the surface but not on the axis, is changed; but the position of the figure as a whole is unchanged.

* For an outline of the main facts in regard to pyro- and piezo-electricity the reader may consult Mascart, *Leçons sur l'électricité et le magnétisme*, t. 1, Paris, 1896, or Liebisch, *Physikalische Krystallographie*, Leipzig, 1891.

† The facts are stated in greater detail and the necessary proofs are given by Schoenflies, *Krystallsysteme und Krystallstructur*, Leipzig, 1891. Reference may also be made to H. Hilton, *Mathematical Crystallography and the Theory of Groups of Movements*, Oxford, 1903.

In other words, the surface can be made to coincide with itself, after an operation which changes the positions of some of its points. Any geometrical figure which can be brought to coincidence with itself, by an operation which changes the position of any of its points, is said to possess "symmetry." The operations in question are known as "covering operations"; and a figure, which is brought to coincidence with itself by any such operation, is said to "allow" the operation. The possible covering operations include (1) rotation, either through a definite angle or through any angle whatever, about an axis, (2) reflexion in a plane. A figure, which allows a rotation about an axis, is said to possess an "axis of symmetry"; a figure, which allows reflexion in a plane, is said to possess a "plane of symmetry."

It can be shown that every covering operation, which is neither a rotation about an axis nor a reflexion in a plane, is equivalent to a combination of such operations. Of such combinations one is specially important. It consists of a rotation about an axis combined with a reflexion in the perpendicular plane. As an example, consider an ellipsoid of semiaxes a, b, c; and suppose that it is cut in half along the plane (a, b), and thereafter let one half be rotated, relatively to the other, through $\frac{1}{2}\pi$ about the axis (c). The ellipsoid allows a rotation of amount π about each principal axis, and also allows a reflexion in each principal plane; the solid formed from the ellipsoid in the manner explained allows a rotation of amount $\frac{1}{2}\pi$ about the c axis, combined with a reflexion in the perpendicular plane, but does not allow either the rotation alone or the reflexion alone. A figure which allows the operation of rotation about an axis combined with reflexion in a perpendicular plane is said to possess an "axis of alternating symmetry."

A special case of the operation just described arises when the angle of rotation about the axis of alternating symmetry is π. The effect of the operation, consisting of this rotation and reflexion in a perpendicular plane, is to replace every ray going out from a point by the opposite ray. This operation is known as "central perversion," and the direction of the corresponding axis of alternating symmetry is arbitrary; a figure which allows this operation is said to possess a "centre of symmetry."

It can be shown that the effect of any two, or more, covering operations, performed successively, in any order, is either the same as the effect of a single covering operation, or else the first and last positions of every point of the figure are identical. We include the latter case in the former by introducing the "identical operation" as a covering operation; it is the operation of not moving any point. With this convention the above statement may be expressed in the form:—The covering operations allowed by any symmetrical figure form a *group*.

With every covering operation there corresponds an orthogonal linear transformation of coordinates. When the operation is a rotation about an axis, the determinant of the transformation is $+1$; for any other covering operation, the determinant is -1. All the transformations, that correspond with covering operations allowed by the same figure, form a *group of linear substitutions.*

105. Elastic symmetry.

In an isotropic elastic solid all rays going out from a point are equivalent. If an æolotropic elastic solid shows any kind of symmetry, some equivalent directions can be found; and the figure formed with them is a symmetrical figure, which allows all the covering operations of a certain group. With this group of operations, there corresponds a group of orthogonal linear substitutions; and the strain-energy-function is unaltered by all the substitutions of this group. The effect of any such substitution is that the components of strain, referred to the new coordinates, are linear functions of the components of strain, referred to the old coordinates. It will be convenient to determine the relations between elastic constants, which must be satisfied if the strain-energy-function is unaltered, when the strain-components are transformed according to such a substitution.

Let the coordinates be transformed according to the orthogonal scheme

	x	y	z
x'	l_1	m_1	n_1
y'	l_2	m_2	n_2
z'	l_3	m_3	n_3

We know from Article 12 that the components of strain are transformed according to formulæ of the types

$$\left.\begin{aligned} e_{x'x'} &= e_{xx}l_1^2 + e_{yy}m_1^2 + e_{zz}n_1^2 + e_{yz}m_1n_1 + e_{zx}n_1l_1 + e_{xy}l_1m_1,\\ e_{y'z'} &= 2(e_{xx}l_2l_3 + e_{yy}m_2m_3 + e_{zz}n_2n_3) + e_{yz}(m_2n_3 + m_3n_2) + e_{zx}(n_2l_3 + n_3l_2)\\ &\qquad + e_{xy}(l_2m_3 + l_3m_2). \end{aligned}\right\} \quad \text{...(1)}$$

If the material possesses, at each point, a centre of symmetry, a figure consisting of equivalent rays going out from the point allows the operation of central perversion. The corresponding substitution is given by the equations

$$x' = -x, \quad y' = -y, \quad z' = -z.$$

This substitution does not affect any component of strain, and we may conclude that the elastic behaviour of a material is in no way dependent upon the presence or absence of central symmetry. The absence of such symmetry in a material could not be detected by experiments on the relation between stress and strain.

It remains to determine the conditions which must hold if the strain-energy-function is unaltered, when the strain-components are transformed by the substitutions that correspond with the following operations:—(1) reflexion in a plane, (2) rotation about an axis, (3) rotation about an axis combined with reflexion in the plane at right angles to the axis. We shall take the plane of symmetry to be the plane of x, y, and the axis of symmetry, or of alternating symmetry, to be the axis of z. The angle of rotation will be taken to be a given angle θ, which will not in the first instance be thought of as subject to any restrictions.

The conditions that the strain-energy-function may be unaltered, by any of the substitutions to be considered, are obtained by substituting for $e_{x'x'}, \ldots$, in the form $c_{11}e^2_{x'x'} + \ldots$, their values in terms of $e_{xx}, \ldots$, and equating the coefficients of the several terms to their coefficients in the form $c_{11}e^2_{xx} + \ldots$.

The substitution which corresponds with reflexion in the plane of (x, y) is given by the equations

$$x' = x, \quad y' = y, \quad z' = -z;$$

and the formulæ connecting the components of strain referred to the two systems of axes are

$$e_{x'x'} = e_{xx}, \quad e_{y'y'} = e_{yy}, \quad e_{z'z'} = e_{zz},$$
$$e_{y'z'} = -e_{yz}, \quad e_{z'x'} = -e_{zx}, \quad e_{x'y'} = e_{xy}.$$

The conditions that the strain-energy-function may be unaltered by this substitution are

$$c_{14} = c_{15} = c_{24} = c_{25} = c_{34} = c_{35} = c_{46} = c_{56} = 0. \quad \ldots\ldots\ldots\ldots\ldots\ldots(2)$$

The substitution which corresponds with rotation through an angle θ about the axis of z is given by the equations

$$x' = x\cos\theta + y\sin\theta, \quad y' = -x\sin\theta + y\cos\theta, \quad z' = z; \quad \ldots\ldots(3)$$

and the formulæ that connect the components of strain referred to the two systems of axes are

$$\left.\begin{aligned}
e_{x'x'} &= e_{xx}\cos^2\theta + e_{yy}\sin^2\theta + e_{xy}\sin\theta\cos\theta,\\
e_{y'y'} &= e_{xx}\sin^2\theta + e_{yy}\cos^2\theta - e_{xy}\sin\theta\cos\theta,\\
e_{z'z'} &= e_{zz},\\
e_{y'z'} &= e_{yz}\cos\theta - e_{zx}\sin\theta,\\
e_{z'x'} &= e_{yz}\sin\theta + e_{zx}\cos\theta,\\
e_{x'y'} &= -2e_{xx}\sin\theta\cos\theta + 2e_{yy}\sin\theta\cos\theta + e_{xy}(\cos^2\theta - \sin^2\theta).
\end{aligned}\right\} \quad \ldots\ldots(4)$$

The algebraic work required to determine the conditions that the strain-energy-function may be unaltered by this substitution is more complicated than in the cases of central perversion and reflexion in a plane. The equations fall into sets connecting a small number of coefficients, and the relations between the coefficients involved in a set of equations can be obtained without much difficulty. We proceed to sketch the process. We have the set of equations

$$c_{11}=c_{11}\cos^4\theta+2c_{12}\sin^2\theta\cos^2\theta+c_{22}\sin^4\theta-4c_{16}\cos^3\theta\sin\theta-4c_{26}\sin^3\theta\cos\theta+4c_{66}\sin^2\theta\cos^2\theta,$$

$$c_{22}=c_{11}\sin^4\theta+2c_{12}\sin^2\theta\cos^2\theta+c_{22}\cos^4\theta+4c_{16}\sin^3\theta\cos\theta+4c_{26}\cos^3\theta\sin\theta+4c_{66}\sin^2\theta\cos^2\theta,$$

$$c_{12}=c_{11}\sin^2\theta\cos^2\theta+c_{12}(\cos^4\theta+\sin^4\theta)+c_{22}\sin^2\theta\cos^2\theta+2(c_{16}-c_{26})\sin\theta\cos\theta(\cos^2\theta-\sin^2\theta)$$
$$-4c_{66}\sin^2\theta\cos^2\theta,$$

$$c_{66}=c_{11}\sin^2\theta\cos^2\theta-2c_{12}\sin^2\theta\cos^2\theta+c_{22}\sin^2\theta\cos^2\theta+2(c_{16}-c_{26})\sin\theta\cos\theta(\cos^2\theta-\sin^2\theta)$$
$$+c_{66}(\cos^2\theta-\sin^2\theta)^2,$$

$$c_{16}=c_{11}\cos^3\theta\sin\theta-c_{12}\sin\theta\cos\theta(\cos^2\theta-\sin^2\theta)-c_{22}\sin^3\theta\cos\theta+c_{16}\cos^2\theta(\cos^2\theta-3\sin^2\theta)$$
$$+c_{26}\sin^2\theta(3\cos^2\theta-\sin^2\theta)-2c_{66}\sin\theta\cos\theta(\cos^2\theta-\sin^2\theta),$$

$$c_{26}=c_{11}\sin^3\theta\cos\theta+c_{12}\sin\theta\cos\theta(\cos^2\theta-\sin^2\theta)-c_{22}\cos^3\theta\sin\theta+c_{16}\sin^2\theta(3\cos^2\theta-\sin^2\theta)$$
$$+c_{26}\cos^2\theta(\cos^2\theta-3\sin^2\theta)+2c_{66}\sin\theta\cos\theta(\cos^2\theta-\sin^2\theta).$$

The equations in this set are not independent, as is seen by adding the first four. We form the following combinations:

$$c_{16}+c_{26}=(c_{11}-c_{22})\sin\theta\cos\theta+(c_{16}+c_{26})(\cos^4\theta-\sin^4\theta),$$
$$c_{11}-c_{22}=(c_{11}-c_{22})(\cos^4\theta-\sin^4\theta)-4(c_{16}+c_{26})\sin\theta\cos\theta,$$

from which it follows that, unless $\sin\theta=0$, we must have

$$c_{11}=c_{22},\quad c_{26}=-c_{16}.$$

When we use these results in any of the first four equations of the set of six we find

$$(c_{11}-c_{12}-2c_{66})\sin^2\theta\cos^2\theta+2c_{16}\sin\theta\cos\theta(\cos^2\theta-\sin^2\theta)=0,$$

and when we use them in either of the last two equations of the same set we find

$$-8c_{16}\sin^2\theta\cos^2\theta+(c_{11}-c_{12}-2c_{66})\sin\theta\cos\theta(\cos^2\theta-\sin^2\theta)=0;$$

and it follows that, if neither $\sin\theta$ nor $\cos\theta$ vanishes, we must have

$$c_{66}=\tfrac{1}{2}(c_{11}-c_{12}),\quad c_{16}=0.$$

Again we have the set of equations

$$c_{13}=c_{13}\cos^2\theta+c_{23}\sin^2\theta-2c_{36}\sin\theta\cos\theta,$$
$$c_{23}=c_{13}\sin^2\theta+c_{23}\cos^2\theta+2c_{36}\sin\theta\cos\theta,$$
$$c_{36}=(c_{13}-c_{23})\sin\theta\cos\theta+c_{36}(\cos^2\theta-\sin^2\theta);$$

from which it follows that, unless $\sin\theta=0$, we must have

$$c_{13}=c_{23},\quad c_{36}=0.$$

In like manner we have the set of equations

$$c_{44}=c_{44}\cos^2\theta+c_{55}\sin^2\theta+2c_{45}\sin\theta\cos\theta,$$
$$c_{55}=c_{44}\sin^2\theta+c_{55}\cos^2\theta-2c_{45}\sin\theta\cos\theta,$$
$$c_{45}=-(c_{44}-c_{55})\sin\theta\cos\theta+c_{45}(\cos^2\theta-\sin^2\theta);$$

from which it follows that, unless $\sin\theta=0$, we must have

$$c_{44}=c_{55},\quad c_{45}=0.$$

In like manner we have the set of equations

$$c_{34}=c_{34}\cos\theta+c_{35}\sin\theta,$$
$$c_{35}=-c_{34}\sin\theta+c_{35}\cos\theta;$$

from which it follows, since $\cos\theta\neq 1$, that we must have

$$c_{34}=c_{35}=0.$$

Finally we have the set of equations

$$c_{14}=c_{14}\cos^3\theta+c_{15}\cos^2\theta\sin\theta+c_{24}\sin^2\theta\cos\theta+c_{25}\sin^3\theta-2c_{46}\cos^2\theta\sin\theta-2c_{56}\sin^2\theta\cos\theta,$$
$$c_{15}=-c_{14}\cos^2\theta\sin\theta+c_{15}\cos^3\theta-c_{24}\sin^3\theta+c_{25}\sin^2\theta\cos\theta+2c_{46}\sin^2\theta\cos\theta-2c_{56}\cos^2\theta\sin\theta,$$
$$c_{24}=c_{14}\sin^2\theta\cos\theta+c_{15}\sin^3\theta+c_{24}\cos^3\theta+c_{25}\cos^2\theta\sin\theta+2c_{46}\cos^2\theta\sin\theta+2c_{56}\sin^2\theta\cos\theta,$$
$$c_{25}=-c_{14}\sin^3\theta+c_{15}\sin^2\theta\cos\theta-c_{24}\cos^2\theta\sin\theta+c_{25}\cos^3\theta-2c_{46}\sin^2\theta\cos\theta+2c_{56}\cos^2\theta\sin\theta$$
$$c_{46}=c_{14}\cos^2\theta\sin\theta+c_{15}\sin^2\theta\cos\theta-c_{24}\cos^2\theta\sin\theta-c_{25}\sin^2\theta\cos\theta$$
$$+(c_{46}\cos\theta+c_{56}\sin\theta)(\cos^2\theta-\sin^2\theta),$$
$$c_{56}=-c_{14}\sin^2\theta\cos\theta+c_{15}\cos^2\theta\sin\theta+c_{24}\sin^2\theta\cos\theta-c_{25}\cos^2\theta\sin\theta$$
$$-(c_{46}\sin\theta-c_{56}\cos\theta)(\cos^2\theta-\sin^2\theta).$$

From these we form the combinations

$$c_{14}+c_{24}=(c_{14}+c_{24})\cos\theta+(c_{15}+c_{25})\sin\theta,$$
$$c_{15}+c_{25}=-(c_{14}+c_{24})\sin\theta+(c_{15}+c_{25})\cos\theta;$$

and it follows, since $\cos\theta\neq 1$, that we must have

$$c_{14}+c_{24}=0,\quad c_{15}+c_{25}=0.$$

Assuming these results, we form the combinations

$$(c_{14}-c_{56})=(c_{14}-c_{56})\cos\theta-(c_{15}+c_{46})\sin\theta,$$
$$(c_{15}+c_{46})=(c_{14}-c_{56})\sin\theta+(c_{15}+c_{46})\cos\theta;$$

from which it follows that

$$c_{14}=c_{56},\quad c_{15}=-c_{46}.$$

Assuming these results, we express all the coefficients in the above set of equations in terms of c_{46} and c_{56}, and the equations are equivalent to two:

$$c_{46}(1-\cos^3\theta+3\sin^2\theta\cos\theta)-c_{56}(3\cos^2\theta\sin\theta-\sin^3\theta)=0,$$
$$c_{46}(3\cos^2\theta\sin\theta-\sin^3\theta)+c_{56}(1-\cos^3\theta+3\sin^2\theta\cos\theta)=0.$$

The condition that these may be compatible is found to reduce to $(1-\cos\theta)(1+2\cos\theta)^2=0$; so that, unless $\cos\theta=-\frac{1}{2}$, we must have

$$c_{46}=c_{56}=0.$$

We have thus found that, if the strain-energy-function is unaltered by a substitution which corresponds with rotation about the axis z, through any angle other than π, $\frac{1}{2}\pi$, $\frac{2}{3}\pi$, the following coefficients must vanish:

$$c_{16},\ c_{26},\ c_{36},\ c_{46},\ c_{56},\ c_{45},\ c_{14},\ c_{24},\ c_{15},\ c_{25},\ c_{34},\ c_{35};\ \ldots\ldots\ldots(5)$$

and the following equations must hold among the remaining coefficients:

$$c_{11}=c_{22},\quad c_{13}=c_{23},\quad c_{44}=c_{55},\quad c_{66}=\tfrac{1}{2}(c_{11}-c_{12}).\ \ldots\ldots\ldots\ldots(6)$$

When the angle of rotation is π, the following coefficients vanish:

$$c_{14},\ c_{24},\ c_{15},\ c_{25},\ c_{46},\ c_{56},\ c_{34},\ c_{35};\ \ldots\ldots\ldots\ldots\ldots(7)$$

no relations between the remaining coefficients are involved. When the angle of rotation is $\frac{1}{2}\pi$, the following coefficients vanish:

$$c_{36},\ c_{46},\ c_{56},\ c_{45},\ c_{14},\ c_{24},\ c_{15},\ c_{25},\ c_{34},\ c_{35};\ \ldots\ldots\ldots(8)$$

and the following equations connect the remaining coefficients:

$$c_{11}=c_{22},\quad c_{13}=c_{23},\quad c_{44}=c_{55},\quad c_{26}=-c_{16}.\ \ldots\ldots\ldots\ldots\ldots(9)$$

When the angle of rotation is $\frac{2}{3}\pi$, the following coefficients vanish:

$$c_{16},\quad c_{26},\quad c_{36},\quad c_{45},\quad c_{34},\quad c_{35};\quad \text{.....................(10)}$$

and the following equations connect the remaining coefficients:

$$\left.\begin{array}{l} c_{11}=c_{22},\quad c_{13}=c_{23},\quad c_{44}=c_{55},\quad c_{66}=\frac{1}{2}(c_{11}-c_{12}), \\ c_{14}=-c_{24}=c_{56},\quad -c_{15}=c_{25}=c_{46}. \end{array}\right\} \text{............(11)}$$

In like manner, when the axis of z is an axis of alternating symmetry, and the angle of rotation is not one of the angles π, $\frac{1}{2}\pi$, $\frac{1}{3}\pi$, the same coefficients vanish as in the general case of an axis of symmetry, and the same relations connect the remaining coefficients. When the angle is π, we have the case of central perversion, which has been discussed already. When the angle is $\frac{1}{2}\pi$, the results are the same as for direct symmetry. When the angle is $\frac{1}{3}\pi$, the results are the same as for an axis of direct symmetry with angle of rotation $\frac{2}{3}\pi$.

106. Isotropic solid.

In the case of an isotropic solid every plane is a plane of symmetry, and every axis is an axis of symmetry, and the corresponding rotation may be of any amount. The following coefficients must vanish:

$$c_{14},\quad c_{15},\quad c_{16},\quad c_{24},\quad c_{25},\quad c_{26},\quad c_{34},\quad c_{35},\quad c_{36},\quad c_{45},\quad c_{46},\quad c_{56},\ \text{...(12)}$$

and the following relations must hold between the remaining coefficients:

$$c_{11}=c_{22}=c_{33},\quad c_{23}=c_{31}=c_{12},\quad c_{44}=c_{55}=c_{66}=\tfrac{1}{2}(c_{11}-c_{12}).\ \text{......(13)}$$

Thus the strain-energy-function is reduced to the form

$$\tfrac{1}{2}c_{11}(e^2_{xx}+e^2_{yy}+e^2_{zz})+c_{12}(e_{yy}e_{zz}+e_{zz}e_{xx}+e_{xx}e_{yy}) + \tfrac{1}{4}(c_{11}-c_{12})(e^2_{yz}+e^2_{zx}+e^2_{xy}),\ \text{......(14)}$$

which is the same as that obtained in Article 68.

107. Symmetry of crystals.

Among æolotropic materials, some of the most important are recognized as crystalline. The structural symmetries of crystalline materials have been studied chiefly by examining the shapes of the crystals. This examination has led to the construction, in each case, of a figure, bounded by planes, and having the same symmetry as is possessed in common by the figures of all crystals, formed naturally in the crystallization of a material. The figure in question is the "crystallographic form" corresponding with the material.

F. Neumann* propounded a fundamental principle in regard to the physical behaviour of crystalline materials. It may be stated as follows:—Any kind of symmetry, which is possessed by the crystallographic form of a material, is possessed by the material in respect of every physical quality. In other words

* See his *Vorlesungen über die Theorie der Elasticität*, Leipzig, 1885.

we may say that a figure consisting of a system of rays, going out from a point, and having the same symmetry as the crystallographic form, is a set of equivalent rays for the material. The law is an induction from experience, and the evidence for it consists partly in *a posteriori* verifications.

It is to be noted that a crystal may, and generally does, possess, in respect of some physical qualities, kinds of symmetry which are not possessed by the crystallographic form. For example, cubic crystals are optically isotropic. Other examples are afforded by results obtained in Article 105.

The laws of the symmetry of crystals are laws which have been observed to be obeyed by crystallographic forms. They may be expressed most simply in terms of equivalent rays, as follows:

(1) The number of rays, equivalent to a chosen ray, is finite.

(2) The number of rays, equivalent to a chosen ray, is, in general, the same for all positions of the chosen ray. We take this number to be $N-1$, so that there is a set of N equivalent rays. For special positions, e.g. when one of the rays is an axis of symmetry, the number of rays in a set of equivalent rays can be less than N.

(3) A figure, formed of N equivalent rays, is a symmetrical figure, allowing all the covering operations of a certain group. By these operations, the N equivalent rays are interchanged, so that each ray comes at least once into the position of any equivalent ray. Any figure formed of equivalent rays allows all the covering operations of the same group.

(4) When a figure, formed of N equivalent rays, possesses an axis of symmetry, or an axis of alternating symmetry, the corresponding angle of rotation is one of the angles π, $\frac{2}{3}\pi$, $\frac{1}{2}\pi$, $\frac{1}{3}\pi$*.

It can be shown that there are 32 groups of covering operations, and no more, which obey the laws of the symmetry of crystals. With each of these groups there corresponds a class of crystals. The strain-energy-function corresponding with each class may be written down by making use of the results of Article 105; but each of the forms which the function can take corresponds with more than one class of crystals. It is necessary to describe briefly the symmetries of the classes. For this purpose we shall now introduce a few definitions and geometrical theorems relating to axes of symmetry:

The angle of rotation about an axis of symmetry, or of alternating symmetry, is $2\pi/n$, where n is one of the numbers: 2, 3, 4, 6. The axis is described as "n-gonal." For $n=2, 3, 4, 6$ respectively, the axis is described as "digonal," "trigonal," "tetragonal," "hexagonal." Unless otherwise stated it is to be understood that the n-gonal axis is an axis of symmetry, not of alternating symmetry.

The existence of a digonal axis, at right angles to an n-gonal axis, implies the existence of n such axes; e.g. if the axis z is tetragonal, and the axis x digonal, then the axis y and the lines that bisect the angles between the axes of x and y also are digonal axes.

The existence of a plane of symmetry, passing through an n-gonal axis, implies the existence of n such planes; e.g. if the axis z is digonal, and the plane $x=0$ is a plane of symmetry, then the plane $y=0$ also is a plane of symmetry.

If the n-gonal axis is an axis of alternating symmetry, the two results just stated still hold if n is uneven; but, if n is even, the number of axes or planes implied is $\frac{1}{2}n$.

* The restriction to these angles is the expression of the "law of rational indices."

108. Classification of crystals.

The symmetries of the classes of crystals may now be described by reference to the groups of covering operations which correspond with them severally:

One group consists of the identical operation alone; the corresponding figure has no symmetry; it will be described as "asymmetric." The identical operation is one of the operations contained in all the groups. A second group contains, besides the identical operation, the operation of central perversion only; the symmetry of the corresponding figure will be described as "central." A third group contains, besides the identical operation, the operation of reflexion in a plane only; the symmetry of the corresponding figure will be described as "equatorial." Besides these three groups, there are 24 groups for which there is a "principal axis"; that is to say, every axis of symmetry, other than the principal axis, is at right angles to the principal axis; and every plane of symmetry either passes through the principal axis or is at right angles to that axis. The five remaining groups are characterized by the presence of four axes of trigonal symmetry equally inclined to one another, like the diagonals of a cube.

When there is an n-gonal principal axis, and no plane of symmetry through it, the symmetry is described as "n-gonal"; in case there are digonal axes at right angles to the principal axis, the symmetry is further described as "holoaxial"; in case there is a plane of symmetry at right angles to the principal axis, the symmetry is further described as "equatorial"; when the symmetry is neither holoaxial nor equatorial it is further described as "polar." When there is a plane of symmetry through the n-gonal principal axis, the symmetry is described as "di-n-gonal"; it is further described as "equatorial" or "polar," according as there is, or is not, a plane of symmetry at right angles to the principal axis.

When the principal axis is an axis of alternating symmetry, the symmetry is described as "di-n-gonal alternating," or "n-gonal alternating," according as there is, or is not, a plane of symmetry through the principal axis.

The appended table shows the names* of the classes of crystals so far described, the symbols† of the corresponding groups of covering operations, and the numbers of the classes as given by Voigt‡. It shows also the grouping of the classes in systems and the names of the classes as given by Lewis§.

The remaining groups, for which there is not a principal axis, may be described by reference to a cube; and the corresponding crystals are frequently called "cubic," or "tesseral," crystals. All such crystals possess, at any point, axes of symmetry which are distributed like the diagonals of a cube, having its centre at the point, and others, which are parallel to the edges of the cube. The latter may be called the "cubic axes." The symmetry about the diagonals is trigonal, so that the cubic axes are equivalent. The symmetry with respect to the cubic axes is of one of the types previously named. There are five classes of cubic crystals, which may be distinguished by their symmetries with respect to these axes. The table shows the names of the classes (Miers, Lewis), the symbols of the corresponding groups (Schoenflies), the numbers of the classes (Voigt), and the character of the symmetry with respect to the cubic axes.

* The names are those adopted by H. A. Miers, *Mineralogy*, Oxford, 1902.

† The symbols are those used by Schoenflies in his book *Krystallsysteme und Krystallstructur*.

‡ *Rapports présentées au Congrès International de Physique*, t. 1, Paris, 1900.

§ W. J. Lewis, *Treatise on Crystallography*, Cambridge, 1899. The older classification in six (sometimes seven) "systems" as opposed to the 32 "classes" is supported by some modern authorities. See V. Goldschmidt, *Zeitschr. f. Krystallographie*, Bde. 31 and 32 (1899).

System	Name of class [Miers]	Symbol of group [Schoenflies]	Number of class [Voigt]	Name of class [Lewis]
Triclinic or Anorthic	Asymmetric	C_1	2	Anorthic I
	Central	S_2	1	Anorthic II
Monoclinic or Oblique	Equatorial	S	4	Oblique II
	Digonal polar	C_2	5	Oblique I
	Digonal equatorial	C_2^h	3	Oblique III
Rhombic or Prismatic	Digonal holoaxial	V	7	Prismatic I
	Didigonal polar	C_2^v	8	Prismatic III
	Didigonal equatorial	V^h	6	Prismatic II
Hexagonal and Rhombohedral	Trigonal polar	C_3	13	Rhombohedral I
	Trigonal holoaxial	D_3	10	Rhombohedral IV
	Trigonal equatorial	C_3^h	27	Rhombohedral VI
	Ditrigonal polar	C_3^v	11	Rhombohedral V
	Ditrigonal equatorial	D_3^h	26	Rhombohedral VII
	Hexagonal polar	C_6	25	Hexagonal I
	Hexagonal alternating	S_6	12	Rhombohedral II
	Hexagonal holoaxial	D_6	23	Hexagonal V
	Hexagonal equatorial	C_6^h	24	Hexagonal II
	Dihexagonal polar	C_6^v	22	Hexagonal III
	Dihexagonal alternating	S_6^u	9	Rhombohedral III
	Dihexagonal equatorial	D_6^h	21	Hexagonal IV
Tetragonal	Tetragonal polar	C_4	18	Tetragonal III
	Tetragonal alternating	S_4	20	Tetragonal VII
	Tetragonal holoaxial	D_4	15	Tetragonal V
	Tetragonal equatorial	C_4^h	17	Tetragonal IV
	Ditetragonal polar	C_4^v	16	Tetragonal VI
	Ditetragonal alternating	S_4^u	19	Tetragonal I
	Ditetragonal equatorial	D_4^h	14	Tetragonal II

Name of class [Miers]	[Lewis]	Symbol of group [Schoenflies]	Number [Voigt]	Symmetry with respect to the cubic axes
tesseral polar	Cubic III	T	32	digonal
tesseral holoaxial	Cubic I	O	29	tetragonal
tesseral central	Cubic IV	$T^{(h)}$	31	digonal equatorial
ditesseral polar	Cubic V	$T^{(d)}$	30	tetragonal alternating
ditesseral central	Cubic II	$O^{(h)}$	28	tetragonal equatorial

109. Elasticity of crystals.

We can now put down the forms of the strain-energy-function for the different classes of crystals. For the classes which have a principal axis we shall take this axis as axis of z; when there is a plane of symmetry through the principal axis we shall take this plane as the plane (x, z); when there is no such plane of symmetry but there is a digonal axis at right angles to the principal axis we shall take this axis as axis of y. For the crystals of the cubic system we shall take the cubic axes as coordinate axes. The classes will be described by their group symbols as in the tables of Article 108; we shall first write down the symbol or symbols, and then the corresponding strain-energy-function; the omitted terms have zero coefficients, and the constants with different suffixes are independent. The results* are as follows:

Groups C_1, S_2—(21 constants)

$$\begin{aligned}\tfrac{1}{2}c_{11}e^2_{xx} &+ c_{12}e_{xx}e_{yy} + c_{13}e_{xx}e_{zz} + c_{14}e_{xx}e_{yz} + c_{15}e_{xx}e_{zx} + c_{16}e_{xx}e_{xy}\\ &+ \tfrac{1}{2}c_{22}e^2_{yy} + c_{23}e_{yy}e_{zz} + c_{24}e_{yy}e_{yz} + c_{25}e_{yy}e_{zx} + c_{26}e_{yy}e_{xy}\\ &+ \tfrac{1}{2}c_{33}e^2_{zz} + c_{34}e_{zz}e_{yz} + c_{35}e_{zz}e_{zx} + c_{36}e_{zz}e_{xy}\\ &+ \tfrac{1}{2}c_{44}e^2_{yz} + c_{45}e_{yz}e_{zx} + c_{46}e_{yz}e_{xy}\\ &+ \tfrac{1}{2}c_{55}e^2_{zx} + c_{56}e_{zx}e_{xy}\\ &+ \tfrac{1}{2}c_{66}e^2_{xy}.\end{aligned}$$

Groups S, C_2, C_2^h—(13 constants)

$$\begin{aligned}\tfrac{1}{2}c_{11}e^2_{xx} &+ c_{12}e_{xx}e_{yy} + c_{13}e_{xx}e_{zz} + c_{16}e_{xx}e_{xy}\\ &+ \tfrac{1}{2}c_{22}e^2_{yy} + c_{23}e_{yy}e_{zz} + c_{26}e_{yy}e_{xy}\\ &+ \tfrac{1}{2}c_{33}e^2_{zz} + c_{36}e_{zz}e_{xy}\\ &+ \tfrac{1}{2}c_{44}e^2_{yz} + c_{45}e_{yz}e_{zx}\\ &+ \tfrac{1}{2}c_{55}e^2_{zx}\\ &+ \tfrac{1}{2}c_{66}e^2_{xy}.\end{aligned}$$

Groups V, C_2^v, V^h—(9 constants)

$$\begin{aligned}\tfrac{1}{2}c_{11}e^2_{xx} &+ c_{12}e_{xx}e_{yy} + c_{13}e_{xx}e_{zz}\\ &+ \tfrac{1}{2}c_{22}e^2_{yy} + c_{23}e_{yy}e_{zz}\\ &+ \tfrac{1}{2}c_{33}e^2_{zz} + \tfrac{1}{2}c_{44}e^2_{yz} + \tfrac{1}{2}c_{55}e^2_{zx} + \tfrac{1}{2}c_{66}e^2_{xy}.\end{aligned}$$

Groups C_3, S_6—(7 constants)

$$\begin{aligned}\tfrac{1}{2}c_{11}e^2_{xx} &+ c_{12}e_{xx}e_{yy} + c_{13}e_{xx}e_{zz} + c_{14}e_{xx}e_{yz} + c_{15}e_{xx}e_{zx}\\ &+ \tfrac{1}{2}c_{11}e^2_{yy} + c_{13}e_{yy}e_{zz} - c_{14}e_{yy}e_{yz} - c_{15}e_{yy}e_{zx}\\ &+ \tfrac{1}{2}c_{33}e^2_{zz} + \tfrac{1}{2}c_{44}e^2_{yz} - c_{15}e_{yz}e_{xy}\\ &+ \tfrac{1}{2}c_{44}e^2_{zx} + c_{14}e_{zx}e_{xy} + \tfrac{1}{4}(c_{11} - c_{12})\, e^2_{xy}.\end{aligned}$$

* The results are due to Voigt.

Groups D_3, C_3^v, S_6^u—(6 constants)

$$\tfrac{1}{2}c_{11}e^2_{xx} + c_{12}e_{xx}e_{yy} + c_{13}e_{xx}e_{zz} + c_{15}e_{xx}e_{zx} + \tfrac{1}{2}c_{11}e^2_{yy} + c_{13}e_{yy}e_{zz} - c_{15}e_{yy}e_{zx} + \tfrac{1}{2}c_{33}e^2_{zz} + \tfrac{1}{2}c_{44}e^2_{yz} + \tfrac{1}{2}c_{44}e^2_{zx} - c_{15}e_{yz}e_{xy} + \tfrac{1}{4}(c_{11}-c_{12})e^2_{xy}.$$

Groups C_3^h, D_3^h, C_6, D_6, C_6^h, C_6^v, D_6^h—(5 constants)

$$\tfrac{1}{2}c_{11}e^2_{xx} + c_{12}e_{xx}e_{yy} + c_{13}e_{xx}e_{zz} + \tfrac{1}{2}c_{11}e^2_{yy} + c_{13}e_{yy}e_{zz} + \tfrac{1}{2}c_{33}e^2_{zz} + \tfrac{1}{2}c_{44}e^2_{yz} + \tfrac{1}{2}c_{44}e^2_{zx} + \tfrac{1}{4}(c_{11}-c_{12})e^2_{xy}.$$

Groups C_4, S_4, C_4^h—(7 constants)

$$\tfrac{1}{2}c_{11}e^2_{xx} + c_{12}e_{xx}e_{yy} + c_{13}e_{xx}e_{zz} + c_{16}e_{xx}e_{xy} + \tfrac{1}{2}c_{11}e^2_{yy} + c_{13}e_{yy}e_{zz} - c_{16}e_{yy}e_{xy} + \tfrac{1}{2}c_{33}e^2_{zz} + \tfrac{1}{2}c_{44}e^2_{yz} + \tfrac{1}{2}c_{44}e^2_{zx} + \tfrac{1}{2}c_{66}e^2_{xy}.$$

Groups D_4, C_4^v, S_4^u, D_4^h—(6 constants)

$$\tfrac{1}{2}c_{11}e^2_{xx} + c_{12}e_{xx}e_{yy} + c_{13}e_{xx}e_{zz} + \tfrac{1}{2}c_{11}e^2_{yy} + c_{13}e_{yy}e_{zz} + \tfrac{1}{2}c_{33}e^2_{zz} + \tfrac{1}{2}c_{44}e^2_{yz} + \tfrac{1}{2}c_{44}e^2_{zx} + \tfrac{1}{2}c_{66}e^2_{xy}.$$

Groups T, O, T^h, T^d, O^h—(3 constants)

$$\tfrac{1}{2}c_{11}(e^2_{xx} + e^2_{yy} + e^2_{zz}) + c_{12}(e_{yy}e_{zz} + e_{zz}e_{xx} + e_{xx}e_{yy}) + \tfrac{1}{2}c_{44}(e^2_{yz} + e^2_{zx} + e^2_{xy}).$$

110. Various types of symmetry.

Besides the kinds of symmetry shown by crystals there are others which merit special attention. We note the following cases:

(1) The material may possess at each point three planes of symmetry at right angles to each other. Taking these to be the coordinate planes the formula for the strain-energy-function would be

$$2W = Ae^2_{xx} + Be^2_{yy} + Ce^2_{zz} + 2Fe_{yy}e_{zz} + 2Ge_{zz}e_{xx} + 2He_{xx}e_{yy} + Le^2_{yz} + Me^2_{zx} + Ne^2_{xy}. \quad\text{.......................(15)}$$

This formula contains a number of those which have been obtained for various classes of crystals.

(2) The material may possess an axis of symmetry in the sense that all rays at right angles to this axis are equivalent. Taking the axis of symmetry to be the axis of z, the formula for the strain-energy-function would be

$$2W = A(e^2_{xx} + e^2_{yy}) + Ce^2_{zz} + 2F(e_{yy} + e_{xx})e_{zz} + 2(A-2N)e_{xx}e_{yy} + L(e^2_{yz} + e^2_{zx}) + Ne^2_{xy}. \quad\text{.......................(16)}$$

Bodies which show this kind of symmetry may be described as "transversely isotropic." It is to be noted that cubic crystals are not transversely isotropic.

For a cubic crystal $A=B=C$, $F=G=H$, $L=M=N$, but the relation $H=A-2N$ does not hold.

(3) The material may possess symmetry of one of the kinds already discussed, or of some other kind, but the axes of symmetry may be directed differently at different points*. In such cases we may be able to choose a system of orthogonal curvilinear coordinates so that the normals to the orthogonal surfaces at a point become lines with reference to which the strain-energy-function is simplified. For example, formula (15) might hold for axes x, y, z directed along the normals to the surfaces of reference at a point, or the material might be transversely isotropic with reference to the normals and tangent planes of a family of surfaces. This kind of symmetry of structure may be possessed by curved plates of metal. When a body possesses symmetry in this way it is said to possess "curvilinear æolotropy."

111. Material with three orthogonal planes of symmetry. Moduluses.

In the cases where formula (15) holds, Young's modulus E for an arbitrary direction (l_1, m_1, n_1) is given by the equation

$$\frac{1}{E}=\frac{l_1^4}{E_1}+\frac{m_1^4}{E_2}+\frac{n_1^4}{E_3}+\frac{2m_1^2n_1^2}{F_1}+\frac{2n_1^2l_1^2}{F_2}+\frac{2l_1^2m_1^2}{F_3}, \qquad (17)$$

where E_1, E_2, E_3 are the Young's moduluses for the three principal directions, and the E's and F's are given by such equations as

$$\frac{1}{E_1}=\frac{BC-F^2}{\begin{vmatrix} A & H & G \\ H & B & F \\ G & F & C \end{vmatrix}}, \qquad \frac{2}{F_1}=\frac{2(GH-AF)}{\begin{vmatrix} A & H & G \\ H & B & F \\ G & F & C \end{vmatrix}}+\frac{1}{L}. \qquad (18)$$

This case has been discussed by Saint-Venant†. He showed that there are in general 13 directions for which E becomes a maximum or minimum. Of these 3 are the axes of (x, y, z), 2 others lie in each of the coordinate planes between the axes, and the remaining 4 lie one in each of the trihedral angles formed by the coordinate planes. He also found that all these directions except the first three will be imaginary if F_1 lies between E_2 and E_3, F_2 lies between E_3 and E_1, and F_3 lies between E_1 and E_2, and if the 3 quantities such as $\left(\frac{1}{E_2}-\frac{1}{F_3}\right)\left(\frac{1}{E_3}-\frac{1}{F_2}\right)+\left(\frac{1}{F_3}-\frac{1}{F_1}\right)\left(\frac{1}{F_1}-\frac{1}{F_2}\right)$ have not all the same sign.

In the notation of this Article the rigidity for directions (l_2, m_2, n_2) and (l_3, m_3, n_3) is the reciprocal of the expression

$$4\left[\frac{l_2^2l_3^2}{E_1}+\frac{m_2^2m_3^2}{E_2}+\frac{n_2^2n_3^2}{E_3}+\left(\frac{2}{F_1}-\frac{1}{L}\right)m_2m_3n_2n_3+\left(\frac{2}{F_2}-\frac{1}{M}\right)n_2n_3l_2l_3+\left(\frac{2}{F_3}-\frac{1}{N}\right)l_2l_3m_2m_3\right]$$
$$+\frac{(m_2n_3+m_3n_2)^2}{L}+\frac{(n_2l_3+n_3l_2)^2}{M}+\frac{(l_2m_3+l_3m_2)^2}{N}. \qquad (19)$$

* This kind of æolotropy was noted by Saint-Venant, *J. de Math.* (*Liouville*), (Sér. 2), t. 10 (1865), who worked out some examples of its application. The case of a cylindrical distribution has been discussed by Voigt, *Göttingen Nachrichten*, 1886.

† See the 'Annotated Clebsch,' pp. 95 *et seq.*

The rigidities for the pairs of axes at right angles to the planes of symmetry are L, M, N.

With the same notation we could show that the Poisson's ratios for contractions parallel to the axes of y and z respectively, when the stress is tension across the planes $x=$const., are

$$\text{for } y,\ E_1(1/2N-1/F_3), \text{ and for } z,\ E_1(1/2M-1/F_2). \quad\text{.................(20)}$$

The values for other pairs of directions can be written down without difficulty (Article 73).

With the same notation we may show that the modulus of compression is the reciprocal of

$$\frac{1}{E_1}+\frac{1}{E_2}+\frac{1}{E_3}+\frac{2}{F_1}+\frac{2}{F_2}+\frac{2}{F_3}-\frac{1}{L}-\frac{1}{M}-\frac{1}{N}. \quad\text{.....................(21)}$$

In the case of cubic crystals we may show that the value of E, Young's modulus for tension in direction (l, m, n), is given by the equation*

$$\frac{1}{E}=\frac{1}{E_1}+\left\{\frac{1}{N}-\frac{2(1+\sigma)}{E_1}\right\}(m^2n^2+n^2l^2+l^2m^2). \quad\text{.....................(22)}$$

Provided that the coefficient of the second term is positive, E is a maximum in the directions of the principal axes, and a minimum in the directions of lines equally inclined to the three principal axes; further it is stationary without being a maximum or a minimum in the directions of lines bisecting the angles between two principal axes, and remains constant for all lines given by $l\pm m\pm n=0$.

112. Extension and bending of a bar.

As examples of distributions of stress in an æolotropic solid body, we may take the problems of extension of a bar and bending of a bar by terminal couples. We shall suppose that the material has, at each point, three planes of symmetry of structure, so that the strain-energy-function is given by the formula (15); we shall suppose also that the bar is of uniform section, that the axis of z is the line of centroids of its normal sections, and that the axes of x and y are parallel to principal axes of inertia of its normal sections, so that the line of centroids and the said principal axes are at right angles to planes of symmetry.

(*a*) *Extension.*

We suppose that all the stress-components except Z_z vanish, and take $Z_z=E\epsilon$, where ϵ is constant, and E is the Young's modulus of the material corresponding with tension Z_z.

We find the displacement in the form

$$u=-\sigma_1\epsilon x, \quad v=-\sigma_2\epsilon y, \quad w=\epsilon z, \quad\text{..............................(23)}$$

where σ_1 is the Poisson's ratio for contraction parallel to the axis of x when there is tension Z_z, and σ_2 is the corresponding ratio for contraction parallel to the axis of y.

(*b*) *Bending by couples.*

We assume that all the stress-components vanish except Z_z, and take $Z_z=-ER^{-1}x$, where R is constant.

We find that the displacement is given by the equations

$$u=\tfrac{1}{2}R^{-1}(z^2+\sigma_1x^2-\sigma_2y^2), \quad v=\sigma_2R^{-1}xy, \quad w=-R^{-1}xz, \quad\text{...........(24)}$$

and that the traction across a normal section is statically equivalent to a couple about an axis parallel to the axis of y, of moment EI/R, where $I=\iint x^2\,dx\,dy$, the integration being taken over the cross-section.

The interpretation of the result is similar to that in Article 88.

* A figure showing the variation of $1/E$ with direction is drawn by Liebisch, *Physikalische Krystallographie* (Leipzig, 1891), p. 564.

113. Elastic constants of crystals. Results of experiments.

The elastic constants of a number of minerals have been determined by W. Voigt* by experiments on the twisting and bending of rods. Some of his principal results are stated here. The constants are expressed in terms of an unit stress of 10^6 grammes' weight per square centimetre.

For Pyrites (cubic), the constants are

$$c_{11}=3680, \quad c_{44}=1075, \quad c_{12}=-483,$$

and we have

$$\text{Principal Young's modulus, } E=3530,$$

$$\text{Principal Rigidity, } c_{44}=\mu=1075;$$

also by calculation we find Principal Poisson's ratio $\sigma=-\frac{1}{7}$ nearly.

These results are very remarkable, since they show that these moduluses of pyrites are much greater than those of steel †, and further that a bar of the material cut in the direction of a principal axis when extended *expands* slightly in a lateral direction ‡. The modulus of compression is about 905×10^6 grammes' weight per square centimetre, which is considerably smaller than that of steel.

The table shows the values of the constants for three other minerals for which the energy-function has the same form as for Pyrites. In this table c_{44} is the principal rigidity, and E is the principal Young's modulus.

Material	E	c_{11}	c_{12}	c_{44}
Fluor Spar	1470	1670	457	345
Rock-salt	418	477	132	129
Potassium Chloride	372	375	198	65·5

Except in the case of rock-salt, Cauchy's condition ($c_{12}=c_{44}$) is not even approximately verified, and the differences are much greater than could be accounted for by assuming experimental errors.

Beryl is a hexagonal crystal of the class specified by the group $D_6{}^h$ for which the constants are

$$c_{11}=2746, \quad c_{33}=2409, \quad c_{12}=980, \quad c_{13}=674, \quad c_{44}=666.$$

For a bar whose axis is in the direction of the principal axis of symmetry $E=2100$. For a bar whose axis is in the direction of a secondary axis of symmetry $E=2300$. The first of these is about the same as that for steel, and the second is rather greater. The principal rigidities are 666 and 883, of which the first is less and the second considerably greater than the rigidity of steel. Cauchy's relations are approximately verified.

Quartz is a rhombohedral crystal of the class specified by the group D_3. The constants are

$$c_{11}=868, \quad c_{33}=1074, \quad c_{13}=143, \quad c_{12}=70, \quad c_{44}=582, \quad c_{15}=-171,$$

and E in the direction of the principal axis is 1030.

* For references see Introduction, footnote 55.

† See table, Article 71.

‡ It has been suggested that these somewhat paradoxical results may be due to "twinning" of the crystals.

Topaz is a rhombic crystal (of the class specified by the group V^h) whose principal Young's moduluses and rigidities are greater than those of ordinary steel. The constants of formula (15) are for this mineral

$$A=2870,\quad B=3560,\quad C=3000,\quad F=900,\quad G=860,\quad H=1280,$$
$$L=1100,\quad M=1350,\quad N=1330.$$

The principal Young's moduluses are 2300, 2890, 2650.

Barytes is a crystal of the same class, and its constants are

$$A=907,\quad B=800,\quad C=1074,\quad F=273,\quad G=275,\quad H=468,$$
$$L=122,\quad M=293,\quad N=283.$$

These results show that for these materials Cauchy's reduction is not valid.

114. Curvilinear æolotropy.

As examples of curvilinear æolotropy (Article 110) we may take the problems of a tube (Article 100) and a spherical shell (Article 98) under pressure, when there is transverse isotropy about the radius vector*.

(*a*) In the case of the *tube* we should have

$$\left.\begin{aligned}\widehat{rr}&=C\frac{\partial U}{\partial r}+F\left(\frac{U}{r}+e\right),\\ \widehat{\theta\theta}&=A\frac{U}{r}+F\frac{\partial U}{\partial r}+He,\\ \widehat{zz}&=Ae+F\frac{\partial U}{\partial r}+H\frac{U}{r},\end{aligned}\right\}\qquad\text{.........(25)}$$

where H is written for $A-2N$. The displacement U is given by the equation

$$C\frac{\partial^2 U}{\partial r^2}+\frac{C}{r}\frac{\partial U}{\partial r}-\frac{AU}{r^2}+\frac{(F-H)\,e}{r}=0,\qquad\text{.........(26)}$$

of which the complete primitive is

$$U=\alpha r^n+\beta r^{-n}+\frac{F-H}{A-C}er,\qquad\text{.........(27)}$$

n being written for $\sqrt{(A/C)}$, and α and β being arbitrary constants. The constants can be adjusted so that $\widehat{rr}$ has the value $-p_0$ at the outer surface $r=r_0$, and $-p_1$ at the inner surface $r=r_1$. The constant e can be adjusted so as to make the resultant of the longitudinal tension $\widehat{zz}$ over the annulus $r_0>r>r_1$ balance the pressure $\pi(p_1r_1^2-p_0r_0^2)$ on an end of the cylinder.

(*b*) In the case of the *sphere* we should find in like manner that the radial displacement U satisfies the equation

$$C\frac{d^2U}{dr^2}+\frac{2C}{r}\frac{dU}{dr}-2(A+H-F)\frac{U}{r^2}=0;\qquad\text{.........(28)}$$

so that
$$U=\alpha r^{n-\frac{1}{2}}+\beta r^{-n-\frac{1}{2}},$$

where
$$n^2=\tfrac{1}{4}\left\{1+8\frac{A+H-F}{C}\right\},$$

* Saint-Venant, *J. de Math.* (*Liouville*), (Sér. 2), t. 10 (1865).

and we can find the formula

$$U = \frac{1}{r_0^{2n} - r_1^{2n}} \left\{ \frac{p_1 r_1^{n+\frac{3}{2}} - p_0 r_0^{n+\frac{3}{2}}}{(n-\frac{1}{2})\, C + 2F} r^{n-\frac{1}{2}} + (r_0 r_1)^{2n} \frac{p_1 r_1^{\frac{3}{2}-n} - p_0 r_0^{\frac{3}{2}-n}}{(n+\frac{1}{2})\, C - 2F} r^{-n-\frac{1}{2}} \right\}, \quad \text{...(29)}$$

which agrees with the result obtained in (vi) of Article 98 in the case of isotropy.

The cubical dilatation of the spherical cavity is the value of $3U/r$ when $r = r_1$, and this is

$$\frac{3 r_1^{n-\frac{3}{2}}}{r_0^{2n} - r_1^{2n}} \left\{ \frac{p_1 r_1^{n+\frac{3}{2}} - p_0 r_0^{n+\frac{3}{2}}}{(n-\frac{1}{2})\, C + 2F} + r_0^{2n} \frac{p_1 r_1^{\frac{3}{2}-n} - p_0 r_0^{\frac{3}{2}-n}}{(n+\frac{1}{2})\, C - 2F} \right\}. \quad \text{............(30)}$$

This result has been applied by Saint-Venant to the theory of piezometer experiments, in which a discrepancy appears to have been observed between the results obtained and the dilatation that should theoretically be found to occur if the material were isotropic. The solution in (30) contains three independent constants and Saint-Venant held that these could be adjusted so as to accord with the experiments in question.

CHAPTER VII

GENERAL THEOREMS

115. The variational equation of motion*.

Whenever a strain-energy-function, W, exists, we may deduce the equations of motion from the Hamiltonian principle. For the expression of this principle, we take T to be the total kinetic energy of the body, and V to be the potential energy of deformation, so that V is the volume-integral of W. We form, by the rules of the Calculus of Variations, the variation of the integral $\int (T-V)\,dt$, taken between fixed initial and final values (t_0 and t_1) for t. In varying the integral we assume that the displacement alone is subject to variation, and that its values at the initial and final instants are given. We denote the variation so formed by

$$\delta \int (T-V)\,dt.$$

We denote by δW_1 the work done by the external forces when the displacement is varied. Then the principle is expressed by the equation

$$\delta \int (T-V)\,dt + \int \delta W_1\,dt = 0. \qquad \text{.....................(1)}$$

We may carry out the variation of $\int T dt$. We have

$$T = \iiint \frac{1}{2}\rho \left\{ \left(\frac{\partial u}{\partial t}\right)^2 + \left(\frac{\partial v}{\partial t}\right)^2 + \left(\frac{\partial w}{\partial t}\right)^2 \right\} dx\,dy\,dz;$$

and therefore

$$\begin{aligned}\delta \int T dt &= \int dt \iiint \rho \left(\frac{\partial u}{\partial t}\frac{\partial \delta u}{\partial t} + \ldots + \ldots\right) dx\,dy\,dz \\ &= \Big/_{t_0}^{t_1} \iiint \rho \left(\frac{\partial u}{\partial t}\delta u + \frac{\partial v}{\partial t}\delta v + \frac{\partial w}{\partial t}\delta w\right) dx\,dy\,dz \\ &\quad - \int dt \iiint \rho \left(\frac{\partial^2 u}{\partial t^2}\delta u + \frac{\partial^2 v}{\partial t^2}\delta v + \frac{\partial^2 w}{\partial t^2}\delta w\right) dx\,dy\,dz. \qquad \text{...........(2)}\end{aligned}$$

Here t_0 and t_1 are the initial and final values of t, and $\delta u, \ldots$ vanish for both these values. The first term may therefore be omitted; and the equation (1)

* Cf. Kirchhoff, *Vorlesungen über...Mechanik*, Vorlesung 11.

is then transformed into a *variational equation of motion*. Further, δV is $\iiint \delta W\,dx\,dy\,dz$, and δW_1 is given by the equation

$$\delta W_1 = \iiint \rho\,(X\delta u + Y\delta v + Z\delta w)\,dx\,dy\,dz + \iint (X_\nu \delta u + Y_\nu \delta v + Z_\nu \delta w)\,dS.$$

Hence the variational equation of motion is of the form

$$\iiint \left\{ \rho \left(\frac{\partial^2 u}{\partial t^2}\,\delta u + \frac{\partial^2 v}{\partial t^2}\,\delta v + \frac{\partial^2 w}{\partial t^2}\,\delta w \right) + \delta W \right\} dx\,dy\,dz$$

$$-\iiint \rho\,(X\delta u + Y\delta v + Z\delta w)\,dx\,dy\,dz - \iint (X_\nu \delta u + Y_\nu \delta v + Z_\nu \delta w)\,dS = 0. \quad \ldots(3)$$

Again, δW is $\dfrac{\partial W}{\partial e_{xx}}\,\delta e_{xx} + \dfrac{\partial W}{\partial e_{yy}}\,\delta e_{yy} + \ldots + \dfrac{\partial W}{\partial e_{xy}}\,\delta e_{xy}$,

where, for example, δe_{xx} is $\partial \delta u / \partial x$. Hence $\iiint \delta W\,dx\,dy\,dz$ may be transformed, by integration by parts, into the sum of a surface integral and a volume integral. We find

$$\iiint \delta W\,dx\,dy\,dz = \iint \left[\left\{ \frac{\partial W}{\partial e_{xx}} \cos(x, \nu) + \frac{\partial W}{\partial e_{xy}} \cos(y, \nu) + \frac{\partial W}{\partial e_{zx}} \cos(z, \nu) \right\} \delta u + \ldots + \ldots \right] dS$$

$$- \iiint \left[\left(\frac{\partial}{\partial x} \frac{\partial W}{\partial e_{xx}} + \frac{\partial}{\partial y} \frac{\partial W}{\partial e_{xy}} + \frac{\partial}{\partial z} \frac{\partial W}{\partial e_{zx}} \right) \delta u + \ldots + \ldots \right] dx\,dy\,dz. \quad \ldots(4)$$

The coefficients of the variations $\delta u, \ldots$ under the signs of volume integration and surface integration in equation (3), when transformed by means of (4), must vanish separately, and we thus deduce three differential equations of motion which hold at all points of the body, and three conditions which hold at the boundary. The equations of motion are of the type

$$\rho \frac{\partial^2 u}{\partial t^2} = \rho X + \frac{\partial}{\partial x} \frac{\partial W}{\partial e_{xx}} + \frac{\partial}{\partial y} \frac{\partial W}{\partial e_{xy}} + \frac{\partial}{\partial z} \frac{\partial W}{\partial e_{zx}}; \quad \ldots\ldots\ldots\ldots\ldots(5)$$

and the surface conditions are of the type

$$\frac{\partial W}{\partial e_{xx}} \cos(x, \nu) + \frac{\partial W}{\partial e_{xy}} \cos(y, \nu) + \frac{\partial W}{\partial e_{zx}} \cos(z, \nu) = X_\nu. \quad \ldots\ldots\ldots(6)$$

116. Applications of the variational equation.

(i) As an example* of the application of this method we may obtain the equations (19) of Article 58. We have

$$\delta W = \frac{\partial W}{\partial e_{\alpha\alpha}}\,\delta e_{\alpha\alpha} + \frac{\partial W}{\partial e_{\beta\beta}}\,\delta e_{\beta\beta} + \ldots + \frac{\partial W}{\partial e_{\alpha\beta}}\,\delta e_{\alpha\beta};$$

* Cf. J. Larmor, *Cambridge Phil. Soc. Trans.*, vol. 14 (1885).

and, by the formulæ (36) of Article 20, we have also

$$\delta e_{aa} = h_1 \frac{\partial \delta u_a}{\partial a} + h_1 h_2 \frac{\partial}{\partial \beta}\left(\frac{1}{h_1}\right) \delta u_\beta + h_1 h_3 \frac{\partial}{\partial \gamma}\left(\frac{1}{h_1}\right) \delta u_\gamma,$$

......

$$\delta e_{\beta\gamma} = \frac{h_2}{h_3} \frac{\partial}{\partial \beta} (h_3 \delta u_\gamma) + \frac{h_3}{h_2} \frac{\partial}{\partial \gamma} (h_2 \delta u_\beta),$$

......

Every term of $\iiint \delta W \frac{da\, d\beta\, d\gamma}{h_1 h_2 h_3}$ is now to be transformed by the aid of the formulæ of the type

$$\iiint \frac{\partial \xi}{\partial a} da\, d\beta\, d\gamma = \iint h_2 h_3 \xi \cos(a, \nu)\, dS,$$

and the integral will then be transformed into the sum of a surface integral and a volume integral, in such a way that no differential coefficients of δu_a, δu_β, δu_γ occur. We may collect, for example, the terms containing δu_a in the volume integral. They are

$$-\iiint \left[\frac{\partial}{\partial a}\left(\frac{1}{h_2 h_3} \frac{\partial W}{\partial e_{aa}}\right) - \frac{1}{h_3} \frac{\partial}{\partial a}\left(\frac{1}{h_2}\right) \frac{\partial W}{\partial e_{\beta\beta}} - \frac{1}{h_2} \frac{\partial}{\partial a}\left(\frac{1}{h_3}\right) \frac{\partial W}{\partial e_{\gamma\gamma}} \right.$$
$$\left. + h_1 \frac{\partial}{\partial \gamma}\left(\frac{1}{h_1^2 h_2} \frac{\partial W}{\partial e_{\gamma a}}\right) + h_1 \frac{\partial}{\partial \beta}\left(\frac{1}{h_1^2 h_3} \frac{\partial W}{\partial e_{a\beta}}\right)\right] \delta u_a\, da\, d\beta\, d\gamma.$$

The equations in question can be deduced without difficulty.

(ii) As another example, we may obtain equations (21) of Article 91 and the second forms of equations (22) of the same Article. For this purpose we observe that

$$e_{yz}^2 - 4e_{yy} e_{zz} = 4\varpi_x^2 + 4\left(\frac{\partial w}{\partial y}\frac{\partial v}{\partial z} - \frac{\partial v}{\partial y}\frac{\partial w}{\partial z}\right).$$

Hence the strain-energy-function in an isotropic body may be expressed in the form

$$W = \tfrac{1}{2}(\lambda + 2\mu)\Delta^2 + 2\mu(\varpi_x^2 + \varpi_y^2 + \varpi_z^2) + 2\mu\left[\left(\frac{\partial w}{\partial y}\frac{\partial v}{\partial z} - \frac{\partial v}{\partial y}\frac{\partial w}{\partial z}\right) + \text{two similar terms}\right].$$

Now
$$\iiint \delta\left(\frac{\partial w}{\partial y}\frac{\partial v}{\partial z} - \frac{\partial v}{\partial y}\frac{\partial w}{\partial z}\right) dx\, dy\, dz$$
$$= \iiint \left[\left(\frac{\partial w}{\partial y}\frac{\partial \delta v}{\partial z} - \frac{\partial w}{\partial z}\frac{\partial \delta v}{\partial y}\right) + \left(\frac{\partial v}{\partial z}\frac{\partial \delta w}{\partial y} - \frac{\partial v}{\partial y}\frac{\partial \delta w}{\partial z}\right)\right] dx\, dy\, dz$$
$$= \iint \left[\left\{\cos(z, \nu)\frac{\partial w}{\partial y} - \cos(y, \nu)\frac{\partial w}{\partial z}\right\} \delta v + \left\{\cos(y, \nu)\frac{\partial v}{\partial z} - \cos(z, \nu)\frac{\partial v}{\partial y}\right\} \delta w\right] dS;$$

and therefore the terms of the type $2\mu\left(\frac{\partial w}{\partial y}\frac{\partial v}{\partial z} - \frac{\partial v}{\partial y}\frac{\partial w}{\partial z}\right)$ in W do not contribute anything to the volume integral in the transformed expression for $\iiint \delta W\, dx\, dy\, dz$. Hence the equations of motion or of equilibrium can be obtained by forming the variation of

$$\iiint \left[\tfrac{1}{2}(\lambda + 2\mu)\Delta^2 + 2\mu(\varpi_x^2 + \varpi_y^2 + \varpi_z^2)\right] dx\, dy\, dz$$

instead of the variation of $\iiint W\, dx\, dy\, dz$. The equations (21) and the second forms of equations (22) of Article 91 are the equations that would be obtained by this process.

The result here found is that the differential equations of vibration, or of equilibrium, of an isotropic solid are the same as those of a body possessing potential energy of deformation per unit of volume expressed by the formula

$$\tfrac{1}{2}(\lambda + 2\mu)\Delta^2 + 2\mu(\varpi_x^2 + \varpi_y^2 + \varpi_z^2).$$

The surface conditions are different in the two cases. In MacCullagh's theory of optics* it was shown that, if the luminiferous æther is incompressible and possesses potential energy according to the formula $2\mu(\varpi_x^2+\varpi_y^2+\varpi_z^2)$, the observed facts about reflexion and refraction of light are accounted for; the surface conditions which are required to hold for the purposes of the optical theory are precisely those which arise from the variation of the volume integral of this expression. Larmor† has described a medium, which possesses potential energy in the required manner, as "rotationally elastic." The equations of motion of a rotationally elastic medium are formally identical with those which govern the propagation of electric waves *in vacuo*.

117. The general problem of equilibrium.

We seek to determine the state of stress, and strain, in a body of given shape which is held strained by body forces and surface tractions. For this purpose we have to express the equations of the type

$$\frac{\partial}{\partial x}\left(\frac{\partial W}{\partial e_{xx}}\right)+\frac{\partial}{\partial y}\left(\frac{\partial W}{\partial e_{xy}}\right)+\frac{\partial}{\partial z}\left(\frac{\partial W}{\partial e_{zx}}\right)+\rho X=0 \quad \ldots\ldots\ldots\ldots\ldots(7)$$

as a system of equations to determine the components of displacement, u, v, w; and the solutions of them must be adapted to satisfy certain conditions at the surface S of the body. In general we shall take these conditions to be, either (*a*) that the displacement is given at all points of S, or (*b*) that the surface tractions are given at all points of S. In case (*a*), the quantities u, v, w have given values at S; in case (*b*) the quantities of the type

$$X_\nu,=\frac{\partial W}{\partial e_{xx}}\cos(x,\nu)+\frac{\partial W}{\partial e_{xy}}\cos(y,\nu)+\frac{\partial W}{\partial e_{zx}}\cos(z,\nu),$$

have given values at S. It is clear that, if any displacement has been found, which satisfies the equations of type (7), and yields the prescribed values for the surface tractions, a small displacement which would be possible in a rigid body may be superposed and the equations will still be satisfied; the strain and stress are not altered by the superposition of this displacement. It follows that, in case (*b*), the solution of the equations is indeterminate, in the sense that a small displacement which would be possible in a rigid body may be superposed upon any displacement that satisfies the equations.

The question of the existence of solutions of the equations of type (7) which also satisfy the given boundary conditions will not be discussed here. It is of more importance to remark that, when the surface tractions are given, the equations and conditions are incompatible unless these tractions, with the body forces, are a system of forces which would keep a rigid body in equilibrium. Suppose in fact that u, v, w are a system of functions which satisfy the equations of type (7). If we integrate the left-hand member of (7) through the volume

* *Dublin, R. Irish Acad. Trans.*, vol. 21 (1839), or *Collected Works of James MacCullagh*, Dublin, 1880, p. 145.

† *Phil. Trans. Roy. Soc.* (Ser. A), vol. 185 (1894).

of the body, and transform the volume integrals of such terms as $\frac{\partial}{\partial x}\left(\frac{\partial W}{\partial e_{xx}}\right)$ by Green's transformation, we find the equation

$$\iint X_\nu dS + \iiint \rho X dx dy dz = 0. \quad \text{.....................(8)}$$

If we multiply the equation of type (7) which contains Z by y, and that which contains Y by z, and subtract, we obtain the equation

$$\iiint \left[y \left\{ \frac{\partial}{\partial x}\left(\frac{\partial W}{\partial e_{zx}}\right) + \frac{\partial}{\partial y}\left(\frac{\partial W}{\partial e_{yz}}\right) + \frac{\partial}{\partial z}\left(\frac{\partial W}{\partial e_{zz}}\right) \right\} - z \left\{ \frac{\partial}{\partial x}\left(\frac{\partial W}{\partial e_{xy}}\right) + \frac{\partial}{\partial y}\left(\frac{\partial W}{\partial e_{yy}}\right) + \frac{\partial}{\partial z}\left(\frac{\partial W}{\partial e_{yz}}\right) \right\} + \rho (yZ - zY) \right] dx dy dz = 0;$$

and, on transforming this by Green's transformation, we find the equation

$$\iint (yZ_\nu - zY_\nu) dS + \iiint \rho (yZ - zY) dx dy dz = 0. \quad \text{...............(9)}$$

In this way all the conditions of statical equilibrium may be shown to hold.

118. Uniqueness of solution*.

We shall prove the following theorem: If either the surface displacements or the surface tractions are given the solution of the problem of equilibrium is unique, in the sense that the state of stress (and strain) is determinate without ambiguity.

We observe in the first place that the function W, being a homogeneous quadratic function which is always positive for real values of its arguments, cannot vanish unless all its arguments vanish. These arguments are the six components of strain; and, when they vanish, the displacement is one which would be possible in a rigid body. Thus, if W vanishes, the body is only moved as a whole.

Now, if possible, let u', v', w' and u'', v'', w'' be two systems of displacements which satisfy the equations of type (7), and also satisfy the given conditions at the surface S of the body. Then $u' - u''$, $v' - v''$, $w' - w''$ is a system of displacements which satisfies the equations of the type

$$\frac{\partial}{\partial x}\left(\frac{\partial W}{\partial e_{xx}}\right) + \frac{\partial}{\partial y}\left(\frac{\partial W}{\partial e_{xy}}\right) + \frac{\partial}{\partial z}\left(\frac{\partial W}{\partial e_{zx}}\right) = 0 \quad \text{..................(10)}$$

throughout the body, and also satisfies conditions at the surface. Denote this displacement by (u, v, w). Then we can write down the equation

$$\iiint \left[u \left\{ \frac{\partial}{\partial x}\left(\frac{\partial W}{\partial e_{xx}}\right) + \frac{\partial}{\partial y}\left(\frac{\partial W}{\partial e_{xy}}\right) + \frac{\partial}{\partial z}\left(\frac{\partial W}{\partial e_{zx}}\right) \right\} + v \left\{ \frac{\partial}{\partial x}\left(\frac{\partial W}{\partial e_{xy}}\right) + \frac{\partial}{\partial y}\left(\frac{\partial W}{\partial e_{yy}}\right) + \frac{\partial}{\partial z}\left(\frac{\partial W}{\partial e_{yz}}\right) \right\} + w \left\{ \frac{\partial}{\partial x}\left(\frac{\partial W}{\partial e_{zx}}\right) + \frac{\partial}{\partial y}\left(\frac{\partial W}{\partial e_{yz}}\right) + \frac{\partial}{\partial z}\left(\frac{\partial W}{\partial e_{zz}}\right) \right\} \right] dx dy dz = 0,$$

* Cf. Kirchhoff, *J. f. Math.* (*Crelle*), Bd. 56 (1859).

and this is the same as

$$\iint \left[u \left\{ \cos(x, \nu) \frac{\partial W}{\partial e_{xx}} + \cos(y, \nu) \frac{\partial W}{\partial e_{xy}} + \cos(z, \nu) \frac{\partial W}{\partial e_{zx}} \right\} \right.$$

$$\left. + \text{two similar expressions} \right] dS$$

$$- \iiint \left[\frac{\partial W}{\partial e_{xx}} e_{xx} + \frac{\partial W}{\partial e_{yy}} e_{yy} + \frac{\partial W}{\partial e_{zz}} e_{zz} + \frac{\partial W}{\partial e_{yz}} e_{yz} + \frac{\partial W}{\partial e_{zx}} e_{zx} + \frac{\partial W}{\partial e_{xy}} e_{xy} \right] dx\,dy\,dz = 0.$$

When the surface conditions are of displacement u, v, w vanish at all points of S; and when they are of traction the tractions calculated from u, v, w vanish at all points of S. In either case, the surface integral in the above equation vanishes. The volume integral is $\iiint 2W\,dx\,dy\,dz$; and since W is necessarily positive, this cannot vanish unless W vanishes. Hence (u, v, w) is a displacement possible in a rigid body. When the surface conditions are of displacement u, v, w must vanish, for they vanish at all points of S.

119. Theorem of minimum energy.

The theorem of uniqueness of solution is associated with a theorem of minimum potential energy. We consider the case where there are no body forces, and the surface displacements are given. The potential energy of deformation of the body is the volume integral of the strain-energy-function taken through the volume of the body. We may state the theorem in the form:

The displacement which satisfies the differential equations of equilibrium, as well as the conditions at the bounding surface, yields a smaller value for the potential energy of deformation than any other displacement, which satisfies the same conditions at the bounding surface.

Let (u, v, w) be the displacement which satisfies the equations of equilibrium throughout the body and the conditions at the bounding surface, and let any other displacement which satisfies the conditions at the surface be denoted by $(u+u', v+v', w+w')$. The quantities u', v', w' vanish at the surface. We denote collectively by e the strain-components calculated from u, v, w, and by e' the strain-components calculated from u', v', w'; we denote by $f(e)$ the strain-energy-function calculated from the displacements u, v, w, with a similar notation for the strain-energy-function calculated from the other displacements. We write V for the potential energy of deformation corresponding with the displacement (u, v, w), and V_1 for the potential energy of deformation corresponding with the displacement $(u+u', v+v', w+w')$. Then we show that $V_1 - V$ must be positive.

We have

$$V_1 - V = \iiint \{f(e+e') - f(e)\}\, dx\,dy\,dz,$$

and this is the same as

$$V_1 - V = \iiint \left[\Sigma e' \frac{\partial f(e)}{\partial e} + f(e') \right] dx\,dy\,dz,$$

because $f(e)$ is a homogeneous quadratic function of the arguments denoted collectively by e. Herein $f(e')$ is necessarily positive, for it is the strain-energy-function calculated from the displacement (u', v', w'). Also we have, in the ordinary notation,

$$\Sigma e' \frac{\partial f(e)}{\partial e} = \frac{\partial u'}{\partial x}\frac{\partial W}{\partial e_{xx}} + \frac{\partial v'}{\partial y}\frac{\partial W}{\partial e_{yy}} + \frac{\partial w'}{\partial z}\frac{\partial W}{\partial e_{zz}}$$
$$+ \left(\frac{\partial w'}{\partial y} + \frac{\partial v'}{\partial z}\right)\frac{\partial W}{\partial e_{yz}} + \left(\frac{\partial u'}{\partial z} + \frac{\partial w'}{\partial x}\right)\frac{\partial W}{\partial e_{zx}} + \left(\frac{\partial v'}{\partial x} + \frac{\partial u'}{\partial y}\right)\frac{\partial W}{\partial e_{xy}}.$$

We transform the volume integral of this expression into a surface integral and a volume integral, neither of which involves differential coefficients of u', v', w'. The surface integral vanishes because u', v', w' vanish at the surface. The coefficient of u' in the volume integral is

$$\frac{\partial}{\partial x}\left(\frac{\partial W}{\partial e_{xx}}\right) + \frac{\partial}{\partial y}\left(\frac{\partial W}{\partial e_{xy}}\right) + \frac{\partial}{\partial z}\left(\frac{\partial W}{\partial e_{zx}}\right),$$

and this vanishes in virtue of the equations of equilibrium. In like manner the coefficients of v' and w' vanish. It follows that

$$V_1 - V = \iiint f(e')\, dx\,dy\,dz,$$

which is necessarily positive, and therefore $V < V_1$.

The converse of this theorem has been employed to prove that there exists a solution of the equations of equilibrium which yields given values for the displacements at the boundary*. If we knew independently that among all the sets of functions u, v, w, which take the given values on the boundary, there must be one which gives a smaller value to $\iiint W\,dx\,dy\,dz$ than any other gives, we could infer the truth of this converse theorem. The same difficulty occurs in the proof of the existence-theorem in the Theory of Potential†. In that theory it has been attempted to turn the difficulty by devising an explicit process for constructing the required function‡. In the case of two-dimensional potential functions the existence of a minimum for the integral concerned has been proved by Hilbert§.

* Lord Kelvin (Sir W. Thomson), *Phil. Trans. Roy. Soc.*, vol. 153 (1863), or *Math. and Phys. Papers*, vol. 3, p. 351.

† The difficulty appears to have been pointed out first by Weierstrass in his lectures on the Calculus of Variations. See the Article 'Variation of an integral' in *Ency. Brit. Supplement*, [*Ency. Brit.*, 10th ed., vol. 33 (1902)].

‡ See, e.g., C. Neumann, *Untersuchungen über das logarithmische und Newton'sche Potential*, Leipzig, 1877.

§ 'Ueber das Dirichlet'sche Princip' (*Festschrift zur Feier des 150 jährigen Bestehens d. Königl. Ges. d. Wiss. zu Göttingen*), Berlin, 1901.

120. Theorem concerning the potential energy of deformation*.

The potential energy of deformation of a body, which is in equilibrium under given load, is equal to half the work done by the external forces, acting through the displacements from the unstressed state to the state of equilibrium.

The work in question is

$$\iiint \rho\,(uX + vY + wZ)\,dxdydz + \iint (uX_\nu + vY_\nu + wZ_\nu)\,dS.$$

The surface integral is the sum of three such terms as

$$\iint u\left\{\frac{\partial W}{\partial e_{xx}}\cos(x,\nu) + \frac{\partial W}{\partial e_{xy}}\cos(y,\nu) + \frac{\partial W}{\partial e_{zx}}\cos(z,\nu)\right\}dS;$$

and the work in question is therefore equal to

$$\iiint\left\{u\left(\rho X + \frac{\partial}{\partial x}\frac{\partial W}{\partial e_{xx}} + \frac{\partial}{\partial y}\frac{\partial W}{\partial e_{xy}} + \frac{\partial}{\partial z}\frac{\partial W}{\partial e_{zx}}\right) + \ldots + \ldots\right\}dxdydz$$
$$+ \iiint\left(e_{xx}\frac{\partial W}{\partial e_{xx}} + e_{yy}\frac{\partial W}{\partial e_{yy}} + e_{zz}\frac{\partial W}{\partial e_{zz}} + e_{yz}\frac{\partial W}{\partial e_{yz}} + e_{zx}\frac{\partial W}{\partial e_{zx}} + e_{xy}\frac{\partial W}{\partial e_{xy}}\right)dxdydz.$$

The first line of this expression vanishes in virtue of the equations of equilibrium, and the second line is equal to $2\iiint W dxdydz$. Hence the theorem follows at once.

121. The reciprocal theorem†.

Let u, v, w be any functions of x, y, z, t which are one-valued and free from discontinuity throughout the space occupied by a body; and let us suppose that u, v, w are not too great at any point to admit of their being displacements within the range of "small displacements" contemplated in the theory of elasticity founded on Hooke's Law. Then suitable forces could maintain the body in the state of displacement determined by u, v, w. The body forces and surface tractions that would be required can be determined by calculating the strain-components and strain-energy-function from the displacement (u, v, w) and substituting in the equations of the types

$$\rho X + \frac{\partial}{\partial x}\left(\frac{\partial W}{\partial e_{xx}}\right) + \frac{\partial}{\partial y}\left(\frac{\partial W}{\partial e_{xy}}\right) + \frac{\partial}{\partial z}\left(\frac{\partial W}{\partial e_{zx}}\right) = \rho\frac{\partial^2 u}{\partial t^2},$$

$$X_\nu = \cos(x,\nu)\left(\frac{\partial W}{\partial e_{xx}}\right) + \cos(y,\nu)\left(\frac{\partial W}{\partial e_{xy}}\right) + \cos(z,\nu)\left(\frac{\partial W}{\partial e_{zx}}\right).$$

* In some books the potential energy of deformation is called the "resilience" of the body.

† The theorem is due to E. Betti, *Il nuovo Cimento* (Ser. 2), tt. 7 and 8 (1872). It is a special case of a more general theorem given by Lord Rayleigh, *London Math. Soc. Proc.*, vol. 4 (1873), or *Scientific Papers*, vol. 1, p. 179. For a general discussion of reciprocal theorems in Dynamics reference may be made to a paper by H. Lamb, *London Math. Soc. Proc.*, vol. 19 (1889), p. 144.

The displacement u, v, w is one that could be produced by these body forces and surface tractions.

Now let (u, v, w), (u', v', w') be two sets of displacements, (X, Y, Z) and (X', Y', Z') the corresponding body forces, (X_ν, Y_ν, Z_ν) and (X'_ν, Y'_ν, Z'_ν) the corresponding surface tractions. The reciprocal theorem is as follows:

The whole work done by the forces of the first set (including kinetic reactions), acting over the displacements produced by the second set, is equal to the whole work done by the forces of the second set, acting over the displacements produced by the first.

The analytical statement of the theorem is expressed by the equation

$$\iiint \rho \left\{\left(X - \frac{\partial^2 u}{\partial t^2}\right) u' + \left(Y - \frac{\partial^2 v}{\partial t^2}\right) v' + \left(Z - \frac{\partial^2 w}{\partial t^2}\right) w'\right\} dx\,dy\,dz$$
$$+ \iint (X_\nu u' + Y_\nu v' + Z_\nu w')\, dS$$
$$= \iiint \rho \left\{\left(X' - \frac{\partial^2 u'}{\partial t^2}\right) u + \left(Y' - \frac{\partial^2 v'}{\partial t^2}\right) v + \left(Z' - \frac{\partial^2 w'}{\partial t^2}\right) w\right\} dx\,dy\,dz$$
$$+ \iint (X'_\nu u + Y'_\nu v + Z'_\nu w)\, dS. \qquad \text{......(11)}$$

In virtue of the equations of motion and the equations which connect the surface tractions with stress-components, we may express the left-hand member of (11) in terms of stress-components in the form of a sum of terms containing u', v', w' explicitly. The terms in u' are

$$-\iiint u' \left\{\frac{\partial}{\partial x}\left(\frac{\partial W}{\partial e_{xx}}\right) + \frac{\partial}{\partial y}\left(\frac{\partial W}{\partial e_{xy}}\right) + \frac{\partial}{\partial z}\left(\frac{\partial W}{\partial e_{zx}}\right)\right\} dx\,dy\,dz$$
$$+ \iint u' \left\{\cos(x, \nu)\left(\frac{\partial W}{\partial e_{xx}}\right) + \cos(y, \nu)\left(\frac{\partial W}{\partial e_{xy}}\right) + \cos(z, \nu)\left(\frac{\partial W}{\partial e_{zx}}\right)\right\} dS.$$

It follows that the left-hand member of (11) may be expressed as a volume integral; and it takes the form

$$\iiint \left[e'_{xx}\frac{\partial W}{\partial e_{xx}} + e'_{yy}\frac{\partial W}{\partial e_{yy}} + e'_{zz}\frac{\partial W}{\partial e_{zz}} + e'_{yz}\frac{\partial W}{\partial e_{yz}} + e'_{zx}\frac{\partial W}{\partial e_{zx}} + e'_{xy}\frac{\partial W}{\partial e_{xy}}\right] dx\,dy\,dz.$$

By a general property of quadratic functions, this expression is symmetrical in the components of strain of the two systems, $e_{xx}, \ldots$ and $e'_{xx}, \ldots$. It is therefore the same as the result of transforming the right-hand member of (11).

122. Determination of average strains*.

We may use the reciprocal theorem to find the average values of the strains produced in a body by any system of forces by which equilibrium can be maintained. For this purpose we have only to suppose that u', v', w' are

* The method is due to Betti, *loc. cit.*

displacements corresponding with a homogeneous strain. The stress-components calculated from u', v', w' are then constant throughout the body. Equation (11) can be expressed in the form

$$\iiint(e_{xx}X'_x + e_{yy}Y'_y + e_{zz}Z'_z + e_{yz}Y'_z + e_{zx}Z'_x + e_{xy}X'_y)\,dx\,dy\,dz$$

$$= \iiint \rho\,(Xu' + Yv' + Zw')\,dx\,dy\,dz + \iint (X_\nu u' + Y_\nu v' + Z_\nu w')\,dS \text{....(12)}$$

If X'_x is the only stress-component of the uniform stress that is different from zero the corresponding strain-components can be calculated from the stress-strain relations, and the displacements (u', v', w') can be found. Thus the quantity $\iiint e_{xx}\,dx\,dy\,dz$ can be determined, and this quantity is the product of the volume of the body and the average value of the strain-component e_{xx} taken through the body. In the same way the average of any other strain can be determined. To find the average value of the cubical dilatation we take the uniform stress-system to consist of uniform tension the same in all directions round a point.

123. Average strains in an isotropic solid body.

In the case of an isotropic solid of volume V the average value of e_{xx} is

$$\frac{1}{EV}\iiint \rho\,\{Xx - \sigma(Yy + Zz)\}\,dx\,dy\,dz + \frac{1}{EV}\iint\{X_\nu x - \sigma(Y_\nu y + Z_\nu z)\}\,dS;\ \text{...(13)}$$

the average value of e_{yz} is

$$\frac{1}{2\mu V}\iiint \rho\,(Yz + Zy)\,dx\,dy\,dz + \frac{1}{2\mu V}\iint \rho\,(Y_\nu z + Z_\nu y)\,dS;\ \text{.......(14)}$$

the average value of Δ is

$$\frac{1}{3kV}\iiint \rho\,(Xx + Yy + Zz)\,dx\,dy\,dz + \frac{1}{3kV}\iint (X_\nu x + Y_\nu y + Z_\nu z)\,dS\text{....(15)}$$

The following results* may be obtained easily from these formulæ:

(i) A solid cylinder of any form of section resting on one end on a horizontal plane is shorter than it would be in the unstressed state by a length $Wl/2E\omega$, where W is its weight, l its length, ω the area of its cross-section. The volume of the cylinder is less than it would be in the unstressed state by $Wl/6k$.

(ii) When the same cylinder lies on its side, it is longer than it would be in the unstressed state by $\sigma Wh/E\omega$, where h is the height of the centre of gravity above the plane. The volume of the cylinder is less than it would be in the unstressed state by $Wh/3k$.

(iii) A body of any form compressed between two parallel planes, at a distance c apart, will have its volume diminished by $pc/3k$, where p is the resultant pressure on either plane.

* Numerous examples of the application of these formulæ, and the corresponding formulæ for an æolotropic body, have been given by C. Chree, *Cambridge Phil. Soc. Trans.*, vol. 15 (1892), p. 313.

If the body is a cylinder with plane ends at right angles to its generators, and these ends are in contact with the compressing planes, its length will be diminished by $pc/E\omega$, where ω is the area of the cross-section.

(iv) A vessel of any form, of internal volume V_1 and external volume V_0, when subjected to internal pressure p_1 and external pressure p_0, will be deformed so that the volume $V_0 - V_1$ of the material of the vessel is diminished by the amount $(p_0 V_0 - p_1 V_1)/k$.

124. The general problem of vibrations. Uniqueness of solution.

When a solid body is held in a state of strain, and the forces that maintain the strain cease to act, internal relative motion is generally set up. Such motions can also be set up by the action of forces which vary with the time. In the latter case they may be described as "forced motions." In problems of forced motions the conditions at the surface may be conditions of displacement or conditions of traction. When there are no forces, and the surface of the body is free from traction, the motions that can take place are "free vibrations." They are to be determined by solving the equations of the type

$$\frac{\partial}{\partial x}\left(\frac{\partial W}{\partial e_{xx}}\right) + \frac{\partial}{\partial y}\left(\frac{\partial W}{\partial e_{xy}}\right) + \frac{\partial}{\partial z}\left(\frac{\partial W}{\partial e_{zx}}\right) = \rho \frac{\partial^2 u}{\partial t^2}, \quad \ldots\ldots\ldots\ldots\ldots\ldots(16)$$

in a form adapted to satisfy the conditions of the type

$$\cos(x, \nu)\frac{\partial W}{\partial e_{xx}} + \cos(y, \nu)\frac{\partial W}{\partial e_{xy}} + \cos(z, \nu)\frac{\partial W}{\partial e_{zx}} = 0 \quad \ldots\ldots\ldots(17)$$

at the surface of the body. There is an infinite number of modes of free vibration, and we can adapt the solution of the equations to satisfy given conditions of displacement and velocity in the initial state.

When there are variable body forces, and the surface is free from traction, free vibrations can coexist with forced motions, and the like holds good for forced motions produced by variable surface tractions.

The methods of integration of the equations of free vibration will occupy us immediately. We shall prove here that a solution of the equations of free vibration which also satisfies given initial conditions of displacement and velocity is unique*.

If possible, let there be two sets of displacements (u', v', w') and (u'', v'', w'') which both satisfy the equations of type (16) and the conditions of type (17), and, at a certain instant, $t = t_0$, let $(u', v', w') = (u'', v'', w'')$ and

$$\left(\frac{\partial u'}{\partial t}, \frac{\partial v'}{\partial t}, \frac{\partial w'}{\partial t}\right) = \left(\frac{\partial u''}{\partial t}, \frac{\partial v''}{\partial t}, \frac{\partial w''}{\partial t}\right).$$

The difference $(u' - u'', v' - v'', w' - w'')$ would be a displacement which would also satisfy the equations of type (16) and the conditions of type (17), and,

* Cf. F. Neumann, *Vorlesungen über...Elasticität*, p. 125.

at the instant $t = t_0$, this displacement and the corresponding velocity would vanish. Let (u, v, w) denote this displacement. We form the equation

$$\int_{t_0}^{t} dt \iiint \left[\frac{\partial u}{\partial t} \left\{ \rho \frac{\partial^2 u}{\partial t^2} - \frac{\partial}{\partial x}\left(\frac{\partial W}{\partial e_{xx}}\right) - \frac{\partial}{\partial y}\left(\frac{\partial W}{\partial e_{xy}}\right) - \frac{\partial}{\partial z}\left(\frac{\partial W}{\partial e_{zx}}\right) \right\} \right.$$
$$+ \frac{\partial v}{\partial t} \left\{ \rho \frac{\partial^2 v}{\partial t^2} - \frac{\partial}{\partial x}\left(\frac{\partial W}{\partial e_{xy}}\right) - \frac{\partial}{\partial y}\left(\frac{\partial W}{\partial e_{yy}}\right) - \frac{\partial}{\partial z}\left(\frac{\partial W}{\partial e_{yz}}\right) \right\}$$
$$\left. + \frac{\partial w}{\partial t} \left\{ \rho \frac{\partial^2 w}{\partial t^2} - \frac{\partial}{\partial x}\left(\frac{\partial W}{\partial e_{zx}}\right) - \frac{\partial}{\partial y}\left(\frac{\partial W}{\partial e_{yz}}\right) - \frac{\partial}{\partial z}\left(\frac{\partial W}{\partial e_{zz}}\right) \right\} \right] dx\,dy\,dz = 0, \quad \ldots(18)$$

in which the components of strain, $e_{xx} \ldots$, and the strain-energy-function, W, are to be calculated from the displacement (u, v, w). The terms containing ρ can be integrated with respect to t, and the result is that these terms are equal to the kinetic energy at time t calculated from $\partial u/\partial t, \ldots$, for the kinetic energy at time t_0 vanishes. The terms containing W can be transformed into a surface integral and a volume integral. The surface integral is the sum of three terms of the type

$$-\int_{t_0}^{t} dt \iint dS \frac{\partial u}{\partial t} \left\{ \cos(x, \nu)\left(\frac{\partial W}{\partial e_{xx}}\right) + \cos(y, \nu)\left(\frac{\partial W}{\partial e_{xy}}\right) + \cos(z, \nu)\left(\frac{\partial W}{\partial e_{zx}}\right) \right\};$$

and this vanishes because the surface tractions calculated from (u, v, w) vanish. The volume integral is

$$\int_{t_0}^{t} dt \iiint \left[\frac{\partial W}{\partial e_{xx}} \frac{\partial e_{xx}}{\partial t} + \frac{\partial W}{\partial e_{yy}} \frac{\partial e_{yy}}{\partial t} + \frac{\partial W}{\partial e_{zz}} \frac{\partial e_{zz}}{\partial t} + \frac{\partial W}{\partial e_{yz}} \frac{\partial e_{yz}}{\partial t} + \frac{\partial W}{\partial e_{zx}} \frac{\partial e_{zx}}{\partial t} + \frac{\partial W}{\partial e_{xy}} \frac{\partial e_{xy}}{\partial t} \right] dx\,dy\,dz,$$

and this is the value of $\iiint W\,dx\,dy\,dz$ at time t, for W vanishes at the instant $t = t_0$, because the displacement vanishes throughout the body at that instant. Our equation (18) is therefore

$$\iiint \left\{ \tfrac{1}{2}\rho \left[\left(\frac{\partial u}{\partial t}\right)^2 + \left(\frac{\partial v}{\partial t}\right)^2 + \left(\frac{\partial w}{\partial t}\right)^2 \right] + W \right\} dx\,dy\,dz = 0, \quad \ldots\ldots(19)$$

and this equation cannot hold unless, at the time t, the velocity $(\partial u/\partial t, \ldots)$ and the strain-energy-function W vanish. There would then be no velocity and no strain, and any displacement (u, v, w) that could exist would be possible in a rigid body and independent of the time. Since (u, v, w) vanishes throughout the body at the instant $t = t_0$, it vanishes throughout the body at all subsequent instants.

125. Flux of energy in vibratory motion.

The kinetic energy T and potential energy V of the portion of the body within a closed surface S are expressed by the formulæ

$$T = \iiint \tfrac{1}{2}\rho\,(\dot{u}^2 + \dot{v}^2 + \dot{w}^2)\,dx\,dy\,dz, \qquad V = \iiint W\,dx\,dy\,dz,$$

in which the dots denote differentiation with respect to t, and the integration extends through the volume within S. We have at once

$$\frac{d}{dt}(T+V)=\iiint\left\{\rho(\ddot{u}\dot{u}+\ddot{v}\dot{v}+\ddot{w}\dot{w})+\frac{\partial W}{\partial e_{xx}}\frac{\partial \dot{u}}{\partial x}+\frac{\partial W}{\partial e_{yy}}\frac{\partial \dot{v}}{\partial y}+\frac{\partial W}{\partial e_{zz}}\frac{\partial \dot{w}}{\partial z}\right.$$
$$\left.+\frac{\partial W}{\partial e_{yz}}\left(\frac{\partial \dot{w}}{\partial y}+\frac{\partial \dot{v}}{\partial z}\right)+\frac{\partial W}{\partial e_{zx}}\left(\frac{\partial \dot{u}}{\partial z}+\frac{\partial \dot{w}}{\partial x}\right)+\frac{\partial W}{\partial e_{xy}}\left(\frac{\partial \dot{v}}{\partial x}+\frac{\partial \dot{u}}{\partial y}\right)\right\}dx\,dy\,dz. \quad\text{......(20)}$$

The right-hand member may be transformed into a volume integral and a surface integral. The terms of the volume integral which contain $\dot{u}$ are

$$\iiint \dot{u}\left(\rho\ddot{u}-\frac{\partial}{\partial x}\frac{\partial W}{\partial e_{xx}}-\frac{\partial}{\partial y}\frac{\partial W}{\partial e_{xy}}-\frac{\partial}{\partial z}\frac{\partial W}{\partial e_{zx}}\right)dx\,dy\,dz;$$

and the terms of the surface integral which contain $\dot{u}$ are

$$\iint \dot{u}\left\{\frac{\partial W}{\partial e_{xx}}\cos(x,\nu)+\frac{\partial W}{\partial e_{xy}}\cos(y,\nu)+\frac{\partial W}{\partial e_{zx}}\cos(z,\nu)\right\}dS.$$

When there are no body forces, we deduce the equation

$$\frac{d}{dt}(T+V)=\iint(\dot{u}X_\nu+\dot{v}Y_\nu+\dot{w}Z_\nu)\,dS. \quad\text{........................(21)}$$

This equation may be expressed in words in the form :—The rate of increase of the energy within S is equal to the rate at which work is done by the tractions across S.

According to the theorem (vii) of Article 53 the expression $-(\dot{u}X_\nu+\dot{v}Y_\nu+\dot{w}Z_\nu)$ is the normal component of a vector quantity, of which the components parallel to the axes are

$$-(\dot{u}X_x+\dot{v}X_y+\dot{w}Z_x),\quad -(\dot{u}X_y+\dot{v}Y_y+\dot{w}Y_z),\quad -(\dot{u}Z_x+\dot{v}Y_z+\dot{w}Z_z).$$

This vector therefore may be used to calculate the flux of energy.

126. Free vibrations of elastic solid bodies.

In the theory of the small oscillations of dynamical systems with a finite number of degrees of freedom, it is shown that the most general small motion of a system, which is slightly disturbed from a position of stable equilibrium, is capable of analysis into a number of small periodic motions, each of which could be executed independently of the others. The number of these special types of motion is equal to the number of degrees of freedom of the system. Each of them is characterized by the following properties:

(i) The motion of every particle of the system is simple harmonic.

(ii) The period and phase of the simple harmonic motion are the same for all the particles.

(iii) The displacement of any particle from its equilibrium position, estimated in any direction, bears a definite ratio to the displacement of any chosen particle in any specified direction.

When the system is moving in one of these special ways it is said to be oscillating in a "principal" (or "normal") mode. The motion consequent upon any small disturbance can be represented as the result of superposed motions in the different normal modes.

When we attempt to generalize this theory, so as to apply it to systems with infinite freedom, we begin by seeking for normal modes of vibration*. Taking $p/2\pi$ for the frequency of such a mode of motion, we assume for the displacement the formulæ

$$u = u' \cos(pt + \epsilon), \quad v = v' \cos(pt + \epsilon), \quad w = w' \cos(pt + \epsilon), \ \ldots(22)$$

in which u' v', w' are functions of x, y, z, but not of t, and p and ϵ are constants. Now let W' be what the strain-energy-function, W, would become if u', v', w' were the displacement, and let $X'_x, \ldots$ be what the stress components would become in the same case. The equations of motion under no body forces take such forms as

$$\frac{\partial X'_x}{\partial x} + \frac{\partial X'_y}{\partial y} + \frac{\partial Z'_x}{\partial z} + \rho p^2 u' = 0; \ \ldots\ldots\ldots\ldots\ldots\ldots(23)$$

and the boundary conditions, when the surface is free from traction, take such forms as

$$\cos(x, \nu) X'_x + \cos(y, \nu) X'_y + \cos(z, \nu) Z'_x = 0. \ \ \ldots\ldots\ldots(24)$$

These equations and conditions suffice to determine u', v', w' as functions of x, y, z with an arbitrary constant multiplier, and these functions also involve p. The boundary conditions lead to an equation for p, in general transcendental and having an infinite number of roots. This equation is known as the "frequency equation."

It thus appears that an elastic solid body possesses an infinite number of normal modes of vibration.

Let p_1, p_2, ... be the roots of the frequency equation, and let the normal mode of vibration with period $2\pi/p_r$ be expressed by the equations

$$u = A_r u_r \cos(p_r t + \epsilon_r), \quad v = A_r v_r \cos(p_r t + \epsilon_r), \quad w = A_r w_r \cos(p_r t + \epsilon_r), \ \ldots(25)$$

in which A_r is an arbitrary constant multiplier. The functions u_r, v_r, w_r are called "normal functions."

The result of superposing motions in the different normal modes would be a motion expressed by equations of the type

$$u = \Sigma u_r \phi_r, \quad v = \Sigma v_r \phi_r, \quad w = \Sigma w_r \phi_r, \ \ldots\ldots\ldots\ldots\ldots\ldots(26)$$

in which ϕ_r stands for the function $A_r \cos(p_r t + \epsilon_r)$, The statement that every small motion of the system can be represented as the result of superposed motions in normal modes is equivalent to a theorem, viz.: that any arbitrary displacement (or velocity) can be represented as the sum of a finite or infinite series of normal functions. Such theorems concerning the expansions of functions are generalizations of Fourier's theorem, and, from the point of view of a rigorous analysis, they require independent proof. Every problem of free vibrations suggests such a theorem of expansion.

* See Clebsch, *Elasticität*, or Lord Rayleigh, *Theory of Sound*, vol. 1.

127. General theorems relating to free vibrations*.

(i) In the variational equation of motion

$$\iiint \delta W\,dx\,dy\,dz + \iiint \rho\left(\frac{\partial^2 u}{\partial t^2}\,\delta u + \frac{\partial^2 v}{\partial t^2}\,\delta v + \frac{\partial^2 w}{\partial t^2}\,\delta w\right) dx\,dy\,dz = 0 \;\ldots(27)$$

let u, v, w have the forms $u_r\phi_r$, $v_r\phi_r$, $w_r\phi_r$, and let δu, δv, δw have the forms $u_s\phi_s$, $v_s\phi_s$, $w_s\phi_s$, where ϕ_r and ϕ_s stand for $A_r \cos(p_r t + \epsilon_r)$ and $A_s \cos(p_s t + \epsilon_s)$, and the constants A_r and A_s may be as small as we please. Let W become W_r when u_r, v_r, w_r are substituted for u, v, w, and become W_s when u_s, v_s, w_s are substituted for u, v, w. Let e denote any one of the six strain-components, and let e_r and e_s denote what e becomes when u_r, v_r, w_r and u_s, v_s, w_s respectively are substituted for u, v, w. Then the variational equation takes the form

$$\iiint \Sigma\left(\frac{\partial W_r}{\partial e_r}\,e_s\right) dx\,dy\,dz = p_r^2 \iiint \rho\,(u_r u_s + v_r v_s + w_r w_s)\,dx\,dy\,dz.$$

The left-hand member is unaltered when e_r and e_s are interchanged, i.e. when u, v, w are taken to have the forms $u_s\phi_s, \ldots$ and δu, δv, δw are taken to have the forms $u_r\phi_r, \ldots$ and then the right-hand member contains p_s^2 instead of p_r^2. Since p_r and p_s are unequal it follows that

$$\iiint \rho\,(u_r u_s + v_r v_s + w_r w_s)\,dx\,dy\,dz = 0. \;\ldots\ldots\ldots\ldots\ldots\ldots(28)$$

This result is known as the "conjugate property" of the normal functions.

(ii) We may write ϕ_r in the form $A_r \cos p_r t + B_r \sin p_r t$, and then the conjugate property of the normal functions enables us to determine the constants A_r, B_r in terms of the initial displacement and velocity. We assume that the displacement at any time can be represented in the form (26). Then initially we have

$$u_0 = \Sigma A_r u_r, \quad v_0 = \Sigma A_r v_r, \quad w_0 = \Sigma A_r w_r, \;\ldots\ldots\ldots\ldots(29)$$

$$\dot{u}_0 = \Sigma B_r p_r u_r, \quad \dot{v}_0 = \Sigma B_r p_r v_r, \quad \dot{w}_0 = \Sigma B_r p_r w_r, \;\ldots\ldots\ldots(30)$$

where (u_0, v_0, w_0) is the initial displacement and $(\dot{u}_0, \dot{v}_0, \dot{w}_0)$ is the initial velocity. On multiplying the three equations of (29) by ρu_r, ρv_r, ρw_r respectively, and integrating through the volume of the body, we obtain the equation

$$A_r \iiint \rho\,(u_r^2 + v_r^2 + w_r^2)\,dx\,dy\,dz = \iiint \rho\,(u_0 u_r + v_0 v_r + w_0 w_r)\,dx\,dy\,dz. \;\ldots(31)$$

The other coefficients are determined by a similar process.

(iii) The conjugate property of the normal functions may be used to show that the frequency equation cannot have imaginary roots. If there were

* These theorems were given by Clebsch as a generalization of Poisson's theory of the vibrations of an elastic sphere. See Introduction.

a root p_r^2 of the form $\alpha+\iota\beta$, there would also be a root p_s^2 of the form $\alpha-\iota\beta$ With these there would correspond two sets of normal functions u_r, v_r, w_r and u_s, v_s, w_s which also would be conjugate imaginaries. The equation

$$\iiint \rho\,(u_r u_s + v_r v_s + w_r w_s)\,dx\,dy\,dz = 0$$

could not then be satisfied, for the subject of integration would be the product of the positive quantity ρ and a sum of positive squares.

It remains to show that p_r^2 cannot be negative. For this purpose we consider the integral

$$\iiint \rho\,(u_r^2 + v_r^2 + w_r^2)\,dx\,dy\,dz,$$

which is equal to

$$-p_r^{-2}\iiint \left\{u_r\left(\frac{\partial X_x^{(r)}}{\partial x} + \frac{\partial X_y^{(r)}}{\partial y} + \frac{\partial Z_x^{(r)}}{\partial z}\right) + \ldots + \ldots\right\} dx\,dy\,dz,$$

where $X_x^{(r)}, \ldots$ are what $X_x, \ldots$ become when u_r, v_r, w_r are substituted for u, v, w. The expression last written can be transformed into

$$-p_r^{-2}\iint [u_r\{\cos(x,\nu)\,X_x^{(r)} + \cos(y,\nu)\,X_y^{(r)} + \cos(z,\nu)\,Z_x^{(r)}\} + \ldots + \ldots]\,dS$$

$$+\,p_r^{-2}\iiint 2W_r\,dx\,dy\,dz,$$

in which the surface integral vanishes and the volume integral is necessarily positive. It follows that p_r^2 is positive.

128. Load suddenly applied or suddenly reversed.

The theory of the vibrations of solids may be used to prove two theorems of great importance in regard to the strength of materials. The first of these is that the strain produced by a load suddenly applied may be twice as great as that produced by the gradual application of the same load; the second is that, if the load is suddenly reversed, the strain may be trebled.

To prove the first theorem, we observe that, if a load is suddenly applied to an elastic system, the system will be thrown into a state of vibration about a certain equilibrium configuration, viz. that which the system would take if the load were applied gradually. The initial state is one in which the energy is purely potential, and, as there is no elastic stress, this energy is due simply to the position of the elastic solid in the field of force constituting the load. If the initial position is a possible position of instantaneous rest in a normal mode of oscillation of the system, then the system will oscillate in that normal mode, and the configuration at the end of a quarter of a period will be the equilibrium configuration, i.e. the displacement from the equilibrium configuration will then be zero; at the end of a half-period, it will be equal and opposite to that in the initial position. The maximum displacement from the initial configuration will therefore be twice that in the equilibrium configuration. If the system, when left to itself under the suddenly applied load, does not oscillate in a normal mode the strain will be less than twice that in the equilibrium configuration, since the system never passes into a configuration in which the energy is purely potential.

The proof of the second theorem is similar. The system being held strained in a configuration of equilibrium, the load is suddenly reversed, and the new position of equilibrium is one in which all the displacements are reversed. This is the position about which the system oscillates. If it oscillates in a normal mode the maximum displacement from the equilibrium configuration is double the initial displacement from the configuration of no strain; and, at the instant when the displacement from the equilibrium configuration is a maximum, the displacement from the configuration of no strain is three times that which would occur in the equilibrium configuration.

A typical example of the first theorem is the case of an elastic string, to which a weight is suddenly attached. The greatest extension of the string is double that which it has, when statically supporting the weight.

A typical example of the second theorem is the case of a cylindrical shaft held twisted. If the twisting couple is suddenly reversed the greatest shear can be three times that which originally accompanied the twist.

CHAPTER VIII

THE TRANSMISSION OF FORCE

129. In this Chapter we propose to investigate some special problems of the equilibrium of an isotropic solid body under no body forces. We shall take the equations of equilibrium in the forms

$$(\lambda+\mu)\left(\frac{\partial}{\partial x}, \frac{\partial}{\partial y}, \frac{\partial}{\partial z}\right)\Delta+\mu\nabla^2(u, v, w)=0, \quad \text{...........(1)}$$

and shall consider certain particular solutions which tend to become infinite in the neighbourhood of chosen points. These points must be outside the body, or in cavities within the body. We have a theory of the solution of the equations, by a synthesis of solutions having certain points as singular points, analogous to the theory of harmonic functions regarded as the potentials due to point masses. From the physical point of view the simplest singular point is a point at which a force acts on the body.

130. Force operative at a point*.

When body forces (X, Y, Z) act on the body the equations of equilibrium are

$$(\lambda+\mu)\left(\frac{\partial}{\partial x}, \frac{\partial}{\partial y}, \frac{\partial}{\partial z}\right)\Delta+\mu\nabla^2(u, v, w)+\rho(X, Y, Z)=0, \quad \text{...(2)}$$

and the most general solution of these equations will be obtained by adding to any particular solution of them the general solution of equations (1). The effects of the body forces are represented by the particular solution. We seek such a solution in the case where (X, Y, Z) are different from zero within a finite volume T and vanish outside T. The volume T may be that of the body or that of a part of the body. For the purpose in hand we may think of the body as extended indefinitely in all directions and the volume T as a part of it. We pass to a limit by diminishing T indefinitely.

We express the displacement by means of a scalar potential ϕ and a vector potential (F, G, H) (cf. Article 16) by means of formulæ of the type

$$u=\frac{\partial\phi}{\partial x}+\frac{\partial H}{\partial y}-\frac{\partial G}{\partial z}, \quad \text{..........................(3)}$$

* The results obtained in this Article are due to Lord Kelvin. See Introduction, footnote 66.

and we express the body force in like manner by means of formulæ of the type

$$X = \frac{\partial \Phi}{\partial x} + \frac{\partial N}{\partial y} - \frac{\partial M}{\partial z}. \quad \text{.........................(4)}$$

Since $\Delta = \nabla^2 \phi$, ..., the equations (2) can be written in such forms as

$$(\lambda + 2\mu)\frac{\partial}{\partial x}\nabla^2\phi + \mu\left(\frac{\partial}{\partial y}\nabla^2 H - \frac{\partial}{\partial z}\nabla^2 G\right) + \rho\left(\frac{\partial \Phi}{\partial x} + \frac{\partial N}{\partial y} - \frac{\partial M}{\partial z}\right) = 0, \quad \text{...(5)}$$

and particular solutions can be obtained by writing down particular solutions of the four equations

$$\left.\begin{aligned} (\lambda + 2\mu)\nabla^2\phi + \rho\Phi = 0, \quad \mu\nabla^2 F + \rho L = 0, \\ \mu\nabla^2 G + \rho M = 0, \quad \mu\nabla^2 H + \rho N = 0. \end{aligned}\right\} \quad \text{...............(6)}$$

Now X, Y, Z can be expressed in forms of the type (4) by putting

$$\left.\begin{aligned} \Phi &= -\frac{1}{4\pi}\iiint\left(X'\frac{\partial r^{-1}}{\partial x} + Y'\frac{\partial r^{-1}}{\partial y} + Z'\frac{\partial r^{-1}}{\partial z}\right)dx'\,dy'\,dz', \\ L &= \frac{1}{4\pi}\iiint\left(Z'\frac{\partial r^{-1}}{\partial y} - Y'\frac{\partial r^{-1}}{\partial z}\right)dx'\,dy'\,dz', \\ M &= \frac{1}{4\pi}\iiint\left(X'\frac{\partial r^{-1}}{\partial z} - Z'\frac{\partial r^{-1}}{\partial x}\right)dx'\,dy'\,dz', \\ N &= \frac{1}{4\pi}\iiint\left(Y'\frac{\partial r^{-1}}{\partial x} - X'\frac{\partial r^{-1}}{\partial y}\right)dx'\,dy'\,dz', \end{aligned}\right\} \quad \text{......(7)}$$

where X', Y', Z' denote the values of X, Y, Z at any point (x', y', z') within T, r is the distance of this point from x, y, z, and the integration extends through T. It is at once obvious that these forms yield the correct values for X, Y, Z at any point within T, and zero values at any point outside T.

We now pass to a limit by diminishing all the linear dimensions of T indefinitely, but supposing that $\iiint X'\,dx'\,dy'\,dz'$ has a finite limit. We pass in this way to the case of a force X_0 acting at (x', y', z') in the direction of the axis of x. We have to put

$$\rho\iiint X'\,dx'\,dy'\,dz' = X_0, \quad \text{.......................(8)}$$

and then we have

$$\Phi = -\frac{1}{4\pi\rho}X_0\frac{\partial r^{-1}}{\partial x}, \quad L = 0, \quad M = \frac{1}{4\pi\rho}X_0\frac{\partial r^{-1}}{\partial z}, \quad N = -\frac{1}{4\pi\rho}X_0\frac{\partial r^{-1}}{\partial y}. \quad \text{...(9)}$$

Now $\nabla^2(\partial r/\partial x) = 2\partial r^{-1}/\partial x$, and we may therefore put

$$\phi = \frac{X_0}{8\pi(\lambda + 2\mu)}\frac{\partial r}{\partial x}, \quad F = 0, \quad G = -\frac{X_0}{8\pi\mu}\frac{\partial r}{\partial z}, \quad H = \frac{X_0}{8\pi\mu}\frac{\partial r}{\partial y}. \quad \text{...(10)}$$

The corresponding forms for u, v, w are

$$\left.\begin{aligned} u &= -\frac{(\lambda+\mu) X_0}{8\pi\mu(\lambda+2\mu)} \frac{\partial^2 r}{\partial x^2} + \frac{X_0}{4\pi\mu r}, \\ v &= -\frac{(\lambda+\mu) X_0}{8\pi\mu(\lambda+2\mu)} \frac{\partial^2 r}{\partial x \partial y}, \\ w &= -\frac{(\lambda+\mu) X_0}{8\pi\mu(\lambda+2\mu)} \frac{\partial^2 r}{\partial x \partial z}. \end{aligned}\right\} \qquad \text{.................(11)}$$

More generally, the displacement due to force (X_0, Y_0, Z_0) acting at the point (x', y', z'), is expressed by the equation

$$(u, v, w) = \frac{\lambda+3\mu}{8\pi\mu(\lambda+2\mu)} \left(\frac{X_0}{r}, \frac{Y_0}{r}, \frac{Z_0}{r}\right)$$
$$+ \frac{\lambda+\mu}{8\pi\mu(\lambda+2\mu)} \left(\frac{x-x'}{r}, \frac{y-y'}{r}, \frac{z-z'}{r}\right) \frac{X_0(x-x') + Y_0(y-y') + Z_0(z-z')}{r^2}.$$
$$\text{...........(12)}$$

When the forces X, Y, Z act through a volume T of finite size, particular integrals of the equations (2) can be expressed in such forms as

$$u = \frac{\lambda+\mu}{8\pi\mu(\lambda+2\mu)} \times$$
$$\iiint \left\{ \frac{\lambda+3\mu}{\lambda+\mu} \rho \frac{X'}{r} + \rho(x-x') \frac{X'(x-x') + Y'(y-y') + Z'(z-z')}{r^3} \right\} dx' dy' dz', \text{...(13)}$$

where the integration extends through the volume T.

It may be observed that the dilatation and rotation corresponding with the displacement (11) are given by the equations

$$\Delta = \frac{X_0}{4\pi(\lambda+2\mu)} \frac{\partial r^{-1}}{\partial x}, \quad 2\varpi_x = 0, \quad 2\varpi_y = \frac{X_0}{4\pi\mu} \frac{\partial r^{-1}}{\partial z}, \quad 2\varpi_z = -\frac{X_0}{4\pi\mu} \frac{\partial r^{-1}}{\partial y}. \quad \text{...(14)}$$

131. First type of simple solutions*.

When the force acts at the origin parallel to the axis of z we may write the expressions for the displacement in the forms

$$u = A\frac{xz}{r^3}, \quad v = A\frac{yz}{r^3}, \quad w = A\left(\frac{z^2}{r^3} + \frac{\lambda+3\mu}{\lambda+\mu}\frac{1}{r}\right). \text{.....................(15)}$$

It may be verified immediately that these constitute a solution of equations (1) in all space except at the origin. We suppose that the origin is in a cavity within a body, and calculate the traction across the surface of the cavity. The tractions corresponding with (15) over any surfaces bounding a body are a system of forces in statical equilibrium when the origin is not a point of the body [cf. Article 117]. It follows that, in the case of the body with the cavity, the resultant and resultant moment of these tractions at the outer boundary of the body are equal and opposite to the resultant and resultant moment of the tractions at the surface of the cavity. The values of these tractions at the outer boundary do not depend upon the shape or size of the cavity, and they may therefore be calculated by

* The solution expressed in equations (15) has received this title at the hands of Boussinesq, *Applications des Potentiels*....

taking the cavity to be spherical and passing to a limit by diminishing the radius of the sphere indefinitely. In this way we may verify that the displacement expressed by (15) is produced by a single force of magnitude $8\pi\mu(\lambda+2\mu)A/(\lambda+\mu)$ applied at the origin in the direction of the axis of z.

We write equations (15) in the form

$$u=-A\frac{\partial^2 r}{\partial x\partial z},\quad v=-A\frac{\partial^2 r}{\partial y\partial z},\quad w=-A\left(\frac{\partial^2 r}{\partial z^2}-\frac{\lambda+2\mu}{\lambda+\mu}\nabla^2 r\right)\;\text{.............(16)}$$

The cubical dilatation Δ corresponding with the displacement (16) is $A\dfrac{2\mu}{\lambda+\mu}\dfrac{\partial r^{-1}}{\partial z}$, and the stress-components can be calculated readily in the forms

$$X_x=2\mu A\frac{\partial r^{-1}}{\partial z}\left\{3\left(\frac{\partial r}{\partial x}\right)^2-\frac{\mu}{\lambda+\mu}\right\},\quad Y_z=2\mu A\frac{\partial r^{-1}}{\partial y}\left\{3\left(\frac{\partial r}{\partial z}\right)^2+\frac{\mu}{\lambda+\mu}\right\},$$

$$Y_y=2\mu A\frac{\partial r^{-1}}{\partial z}\left\{3\left(\frac{\partial r}{\partial y}\right)^2-\frac{\mu}{\lambda+\mu}\right\},\quad Z_x=2\mu A\frac{\partial r^{-1}}{\partial x}\left\{3\left(\frac{\partial r}{\partial z}\right)^2+\frac{\mu}{\lambda+\mu}\right\},$$

$$Z_z=2\mu A\frac{\partial r^{-1}}{\partial z}\left\{3\left(\frac{\partial r}{\partial z}\right)^2+\frac{\mu}{\lambda+\mu}\right\},\quad X_y=6\mu A\frac{\partial r}{\partial x}\frac{\partial r}{\partial y}\frac{\partial r^{-1}}{\partial z}.$$

The tractions across any plane (of which the normal is in direction ν) are given by the equations

$$X_\nu=2\mu A\left[3\frac{\partial r}{\partial x}\frac{\partial r}{\partial z}\frac{\partial r^{-1}}{\partial \nu}+\frac{\mu}{\lambda+\mu}\left\{\cos(z,\nu)\frac{\partial r^{-1}}{\partial x}-\cos(x,\nu)\frac{\partial r^{-1}}{\partial z}\right\}\right],$$

$$Y_\nu=2\mu A\left[3\frac{\partial r}{\partial y}\frac{\partial r}{\partial z}\frac{\partial r^{-1}}{\partial \nu}+\frac{\mu}{\lambda+\mu}\left\{\cos(z,\nu)\frac{\partial r^{-1}}{\partial y}-\cos(y,\nu)\frac{\partial r^{-1}}{\partial z}\right\}\right],$$

$$Z_\nu=2\mu A\frac{\partial r^{-1}}{\partial \nu}\left\{3\left(\frac{\partial r}{\partial z}\right)^2+\frac{\mu}{\lambda+\mu}\right\};$$

and, when ν is the inwards drawn normal to a spherical surface with its centre at the origin, these are

$$X_\nu=\frac{6\mu Axz}{r^4},\quad Y_\nu=\frac{6\mu Ayz}{r^4},\quad Z_\nu=\frac{2\mu A}{r^2}\left(3\frac{z^2}{r^2}+\frac{\mu}{\lambda+\mu}\right).\;\text{..............(17)}$$

Whatever the radius of the cavity may be, this system of tractions is statically equivalent to a single force, applied at the origin, directed along the axis of z in the positive sense, and of magnitude $8\pi\mu A(\lambda+2\mu)/(\lambda+\mu)$.

Some additional results in regard to the state of stress set up in a body by the application of force at a point will be given in Article 141 *infra*.

132. Typical nuclei of strain.

Various solutions which possess singular points can be derived from that discussed in Article 131. In particular, we may suppose two points at which forces act to coalesce, and obtain new solutions by a limiting process. It is convenient to denote the displacement due to force (X_0, Y_0, Z_0) applied at the origin by

$$(X_0u_1+Y_0u_2+Z_0u_3,\quad X_0v_1+Y_0v_2+Z_0v_3,\quad X_0w_1+Y_0w_2+Z_0w_3),$$

so that for example (u_1, v_1, w_1) is the displacement obtained by replacing X_0 by unity in equations (11). We consider some examples* of the synthesis of singularities:

(*a*) Let a force $h^{-1}P$ be applied at the origin in the direction of the axis of x, and let an equal and opposite force be applied at the point $(h, 0, 0)$, and let us pass to a limit

* In most of these the leading steps only of the analysis are given. The results (a') and (b') are due to J. Dougall, *Edinburgh Math. Soc. Proc.*, vol. 16 (1898).

by supposing that h is diminished indefinitely while P remains constant. The displacement is

$$P\left(\frac{\partial u_1}{\partial x}, \frac{\partial v_1}{\partial x}, \frac{\partial w_1}{\partial x}\right).$$

We may describe the singularity as a "double force without moment." It is related to an axis, in this case the axis of x, and is specified as regards magnitude by the quantity P.

(a') We may combine three double forces without moment, having their axes parallel to the axes of coordinates, and specified by the same quantity P. The resultant displacement is

$$P\left\{\left(\frac{\partial u_1}{\partial x}+\frac{\partial u_2}{\partial y}+\frac{\partial u_3}{\partial z}\right), \left(\frac{\partial v_1}{\partial x}+\frac{\partial v_2}{\partial y}+\frac{\partial v_3}{\partial z}\right), \left(\frac{\partial w_1}{\partial x}+\frac{\partial w_2}{\partial y}+\frac{\partial w_3}{\partial z}\right)\right\}. \quad \text{.........(18)}$$

Now the result (12) shows that we have

$$v_3 = w_2, \quad w_1 = u_3, \quad u_2 = v_1, \quad \text{..............................(19)}$$

and thus (18) may be written $P(\Delta_1, \Delta_2, \Delta_3)$, where Δ_1 is the dilatation when the displacement is (u_1, v_1, w_1), and so on. Hence the displacement (18) is

$$\frac{P}{4\pi(\lambda+2\mu)}\left\{\frac{\partial r^{-1}}{\partial x}, \frac{\partial r^{-1}}{\partial y}, \frac{\partial r^{-1}}{\partial z}\right\}. \quad \text{.........................(20)}$$

We may describe the singularity as a "centre of compression"; when P is negative it may be called a "centre of dilatation." The point must be in a cavity within the body; when the cavity is spherical and has its centre at the point, it may be verified that the traction across the cavity is normal tension of amount

$$\{\mu P/(\lambda+2\mu)\,\pi\}\, r^{-3}.$$

(b) We may suppose a force $h^{-1}P$ to act at the origin in the positive direction of the axis of x, and an equal and opposite force to act at the point $(0, h, 0)$, and we may pass to a limit as before. The resultant displacement is

$$P\left(\frac{\partial u_1}{\partial y}, \frac{\partial v_1}{\partial y}, \frac{\partial w_1}{\partial y}\right).$$

We may describe the singularity as a "double force with moment." The forces applied to the body in the neighbourhood of this point are statically equivalent to a couple of moment P about the axis of z. The singularity is related to this axis and also to the direction of the forces, in this case the axis of x.

(b') We may combine two double forces with moment, the moments being about the same axis and of the same sign, and the directions of the forces being at right angles to each other. We take the forces to be $h^{-1}P$ and $-h^{-1}P$ parallel to the axes of x and y at the origin, $-h^{-1}P$ parallel to the axis of x at the point $(0, h, 0)$, and $h^{-1}P$ parallel to the axis of y at the point $(h, 0, 0)$, and we pass to a limit as before. The resulting displacement is

$$P\left\{\left(\frac{\partial u_1}{\partial y}-\frac{\partial u_2}{\partial x}\right), \left(\frac{\partial v_1}{\partial y}-\frac{\partial v_2}{\partial x}\right), \left(\frac{\partial w_1}{\partial y}-\frac{\partial w_2}{\partial x}\right)\right\},$$

or it is

$$\frac{P}{4\pi\mu}\left(\frac{\partial r^{-1}}{\partial y}, -\frac{\partial r^{-1}}{\partial x}, 0\right). \quad \text{..............................(21)}$$

We may describe the singularity as a "centre of rotation about the axis of z." The forces applied to the body in the neighbourhood of this point are statically equivalent to a couple of moment $2P$ about the axis of z; the singularity is not related to the directions of the forces. In like manner we may have singularities which are centres of rotation about the axes of x and y, for which the displacements have the forms

$$\frac{P}{4\pi\mu}\left(0,\ \frac{\partial r^{-1}}{\partial z},\ -\frac{\partial r^{-1}}{\partial y}\right), \qquad\qquad (22)$$

and

$$\frac{P}{4\pi\mu}\left(-\frac{\partial r^{-1}}{\partial z},\ 0,\ \frac{\partial r^{-1}}{\partial x}\right). \qquad\qquad (23)$$

(*c*) We suppose that centres of dilatation are distributed uniformly along a semi-infinite line. The line may be taken to be the portion of the axis of z on which z is negative. The displacement is given by equations of the form

$$u=Bx\int_0^\infty \frac{dz'}{R^3},\quad v=By\int_0^\infty \frac{dz'}{R^3},\quad w=B\int_0^\infty \frac{z+z'}{R^3}\,dz',$$

where B is a constant, and $R^2=x^2+y^2+(z+z')^2$.

Now
$$\int_0^\infty \frac{dz'}{R^3}=\frac{1}{x^2+y^2}\Big/_0^\infty\left[\frac{z+z'}{R}\right]=\frac{1}{r^2-z^2}\left(1-\frac{z}{r}\right)=\frac{1}{r(z+r)},$$

and
$$\int_0^\infty \frac{z+z'}{R^3}\,dz'=\Big/_0^\infty\left[-\frac{1}{R}\right]=\frac{1}{r};$$

and the displacement is given by the equations

$$u=B\frac{x}{r(z+r)},\quad v=B\frac{y}{r(z+r)},\quad w=\frac{B}{r}. \qquad\qquad (24)$$

These displacements constitute the "simple solutions of the second type*." The result may be expressed in the form

$$(u,\ v,\ w)=B\left(\frac{\partial}{\partial x},\ \frac{\partial}{\partial y},\ \frac{\partial}{\partial z}\right)\log(z+r). \qquad\qquad (25)$$

A singularity of the type here described might be called a "line of dilatation," and B might be called its "strength." If B is negative, the singularity might be called a "line of compression."

(*d*) A line of dilatation may be terminated at both ends, and its strength may be variable. If its extremities are the origin and the point $(0,\ 0,\ -k)$, and its strength is proportional to the distance from the origin, we have

$$u=C'x\int_0^k \frac{z'dz'}{R^3},\quad v=C'y\int_0^k \frac{z'dz'}{R^3},\quad w=C'\int_0^k \frac{(z+z')\,z'dz'}{R^3}, \qquad\qquad (26)$$

where C' is constant. Now we have

$$\int_0^k \frac{z'dz'}{R^3}=\int_0^k\left(\frac{z+z'}{R^3}-\frac{z}{R^3}\right)dz'=\frac{1}{r}-\frac{1}{R_1}-\frac{z}{x^2+y^2}\left(\frac{z+k}{R_1}-\frac{z}{r}\right),$$

where $R_1{}^2=x^2+y^2+(z+k)^2$. The integral remains finite when k is increased indefinitely, and we have

$$\int_0^\infty \frac{z'dz'}{R^3}=\frac{1}{r}-\frac{z}{r^2-z^2}\left(1-\frac{z}{r}\right)=\frac{1}{z+r}.$$

Again we have

$$\int_0^k \frac{(z+z')\,z'}{R^3}\,dz'=-\frac{k}{R_1}+\int_0^k \frac{dz'}{R}=-\frac{k}{R_1}+\log\frac{z+k+R_1}{z+r}.$$

This does not tend to a limit when k is increased indefinitely. Let $C'(U,\ V,\ W)$ denote the displacement (26); and, in addition to the line of dilatation which gives rise to the

* Boussinesq, *loc. cit.*

displacement (U, V, W), let there be a line of compression, with the same law of strength, extending from the point $(h, 0, 0)$ to the point $(h, 0, -k)$. We pass to a limit by taking h to diminish indefinitely and C' to increase indefinitely, in such a way that $C'h$ has a finite limit, C say. The displacement is given by the equations

$$u=C\frac{\partial U}{\partial x},\quad v=C\frac{\partial V}{\partial x},\quad w=C\frac{\partial W}{\partial x}.$$

Now

$$\frac{\partial W}{\partial x}=\frac{kx}{R_1{}^3}+\frac{x}{R_1(z+k+R_1)}-\frac{x}{r(z+r)};$$

and this has a finite limit when k is increased indefinitely, viz. $-x/r(z+r)$. The displacement due to such a semi-infinite double line of singularities as we have described here is expressed by the equations

$$u=C\left(\frac{1}{z+r}-\frac{x^2}{r(z+r)^2}\right),\quad v=-C\frac{xy}{r(z+r)^2},\quad w=-C\frac{x}{r(z+r)},\qquad \text{.........(27)}$$

or, as they may be written,

$$(u, v, w)=-C\left(\frac{\partial^2}{\partial x^2}, \frac{\partial^2}{\partial x\,\partial y}, \frac{\partial^2}{\partial x\,\partial z}\right)\{z\log(z+r)-r\}.\qquad \text{..............(28)}$$

In like manner we may have

$$(u, v, w)=-C\left(\frac{\partial^2}{\partial x\,\partial y}, \frac{\partial^2}{\partial y^2}, \frac{\partial^2}{\partial y\,\partial z}\right)\{z\log(z+r)-r\}.\qquad \text{..................(29)}$$

(*e*) Instead of a line-distribution of centres of dilatation, we may take a line-distribution of centres of rotation. From the result of example (*b'*) we should find

$$u=0,\quad v=-D\int_0^\infty\frac{z+z'}{R^3}dz',\quad w=D\int_0^\infty\frac{y}{R^3}dz',$$

where D is a constant, and the axes of the centres of rotation are parallel to the axis of x. This gives

$$u=0,\quad v=-\frac{D}{r},\quad w=D\frac{y}{r(z+r)}.\qquad \text{.........................(30)}$$

In like manner we may have

$$u=\frac{D}{r},\quad v=0,\quad w=-D\frac{x}{r(z+r)},\qquad \text{.........................(31)}$$

or, as they may be written,

$$(u, v, w)=D\left(\frac{\partial}{\partial z}, 0, -\frac{\partial}{\partial x}\right)\{\log(z+r)\}.\qquad \text{.......................(32)}$$

Other formulæ of the same kind might be obtained by taking the line of singularities in directions other than the axis of z.

The reader will observe that, in all the examples of this Article, except (*a*) and (*b*), the components of displacement are harmonic functions, and the cubical dilatation vanishes. The only strains involved are shearing strains, and the displacements are independent of the ratio of elastic constants $\lambda:\mu$.

133. Local Perturbations.

Examples (*a*) and (*a'*) of the last Article show in particular instances how the application of equilibrating forces to a small portion of a body sets up strains which are unimportant at a distance from the portion. The displacement due to a distribution of force having a finite resultant for a small volume varies inversely as the distance; that due to forces having zero resultant for the small volume varies inversely as the square of the distance, and directly as the linear dimension of the small volume. We may conclude that the strain produced at a distance, by forces applied locally, depends upon the resultant of the forces, and is practically independent of the mode of distribution of the forces which are statically equivalent to this resultant. The effect of the mode of distribution of the forces is practically confined to a comparatively small portion of the body near to the place of application of the forces. Such local effects are called by Boussinesq "perturbations locales*."

The statement that the mode of distribution of forces applied locally gives rise to local perturbations only, includes Saint-Venant's "Principle of the elastic equivalence of statically equipollent systems of load," which is used in problems relating to bars and plates. In these cases, the falling off of the local perturbations, as the distance from the place of application of the load increases, is much more rapid than in the case of a solid body of which all the dimensions are large compared with those of the part subjected to the direct action of the forces. We may cite the example of a very thin rectangular plate under uniform torsional couple along its edges. The local perturbations diminish according to an exponential function of the distance from the edge†.

134. Second type of simple solutions.

The displacement is expressed by the equations given in Article 132 (*c*), viz.:

$$u = B\frac{x}{r(z+r)}, \quad v = B\frac{y}{r(z+r)}, \quad w = \frac{B}{r}, \qquad \text{.........(24 } bis\text{)}$$

or, as they may be written,

$$u = B\frac{\partial \log(z+r)}{\partial x}, \quad v = B\frac{\partial \log(z+r)}{\partial y}, \quad w = B\frac{\partial \log(z+r)}{\partial z}.$$

It may be verified immediately that these expressions are solutions of the equations (1) at all points except the origin and points on the axis of z at which z is negative. There is no dilatation, and the stress components are given by the equations

$$X_x = 2\mu B\left\{\frac{y^2+z^2}{r^3(z+r)} - \frac{x^2}{r^2(z+r)^2}\right\}, \quad Y_z = -2\mu B\frac{y}{r^3},$$

$$Y_y = 2\mu B\left\{\frac{z^2+x^2}{r^3(z+r)} - \frac{y^2}{r^2(z+r)^2}\right\}, \quad Z_x = -2\mu B\frac{x}{r^3},$$

$$Z_z = -2\mu B\frac{z}{r^3}, \qquad X_y = -2\mu B\frac{xy(z+2r)}{r^3(z+r)^2}.$$

* Boussinesq, *loc. cit.*

† Kelvin and Tait, *Nat. Phil.*, Part II. pp. 267 *et seq.* Cf. Articles 226 B. and 245 A. *infra.*

At the surface of a hemisphere, for which r is constant and z is positive, these give rise to tractions

$$X_\nu = 2\mu B \frac{x}{r^2(z+r)}, \quad Y_\nu = 2\mu B \frac{y}{r^2(z+r)}, \quad Z_\nu = \frac{2\mu B}{r^2}, \quad \ldots\ldots(33)$$

the normal (ν) being drawn towards the centre.

135. Pressure at a point on a plane boundary.

We consider an elastic solid body to which forces are applied in the neighbourhood of a single point on the surface. If all the linear dimensions of the body are large compared with those of the area subjected to the load, we may regard the body as bounded by an infinite plane.

We take the origin to be the point at which the load is applied, the plane $z=0$ to be the bounding surface of the body, and the positive direction of the axis of z to be that which goes into the interior of the body. The local effect of force applied at the origin being very great, we suppose the origin to be excluded by a hemispherical surface.

The displacement expressed by (15) could be maintained in the body by tractions over the plane boundary, which are expressed by the equations

$$X_z = -\frac{2\mu^2}{\lambda+\mu} A \frac{x}{r^3}, \quad Y_z = -\frac{2\mu^2}{\lambda+\mu} A \frac{y}{r^3}, \quad Z_z = 0,$$

and by tractions over the hemispherical boundary, which are expressed by the equations (17). The resultant of the latter for the hemispherical surface is a force in the positive direction of the axis of z of amount

$$4\pi\mu A(\lambda+2\mu)/(\lambda+\mu).$$

The displacement expressed by (24) could be maintained in the body by tractions over the plane boundary, which are expressed by the equations

$$X_z = -2\mu B \frac{x}{r^3}, \quad Y_z = -2\mu B \frac{y}{r^3}, \quad Z_z = 0, \quad \ldots\ldots\ldots\ldots(34)$$

and by tractions over the hemispherical boundary, which are expressed by the equations (33). The resultant of the latter is a force in the positive direction of the axis of z of amount $4\pi\mu B$.

If we put $B = -A\mu/(\lambda+\mu)$, the state of displacement expressed by the sum of the displacements (15) and (24) will be maintained by forces applied to the hemispherical surface only; and, if the resultant of these forces is P, the displacement is given by the equations

$$\left.\begin{aligned} u &= \frac{P}{4\pi\mu}\frac{xz}{r^3} - \frac{P}{4\pi(\lambda+\mu)}\frac{x}{r(z+r)}, \\ v &= \frac{P}{4\pi\mu}\frac{yz}{r^3} - \frac{P}{4\pi(\lambda+\mu)}\frac{y}{r(z+r)}, \\ w &= \frac{P}{4\pi\mu}\frac{z^2}{r^3} + \frac{P(\lambda+2\mu)}{4\pi\mu(\lambda+\mu)}\frac{1}{r}. \end{aligned}\right\} \quad \ldots\ldots\ldots\ldots\ldots\ldots(35)$$

At all points not too near to the origin, these equations express the displacement due to a pressure of magnitude P applied at the origin.

For the discussion of this solution, it is convenient to regard the plane boundary as horizontal, and the body as supporting a weight P at the origin. We observe that the tractions across a horizontal plane are

$$X_z = -\frac{3P}{2\pi}\frac{z^2 x}{r^5}, \quad Y_z = -\frac{3P}{2\pi}\frac{z^2 y}{r^5}, \quad Z_z = -\frac{3P}{2\pi}\frac{z^3}{r^5},$$

so that the resultant traction per unit area exerted from the upper side across the plane at any point is a force directed along the radius vector drawn from the origin and of magnitude $\frac{3}{2}(P/\pi r^2)\cos^2\theta$, where θ is the angle which the radius vector drawn from the origin makes with the vertical drawn downwards. The tractions across horizontal planes are the same at all points of any sphere which touches the bounding plane at the origin, and their magnitude is $\frac{3}{2}P/\pi D^2$, where D is the diameter of the sphere. These expressions for the tractions across horizontal planes are independent of the elastic constants.

The displacement may be resolved into a horizontal component and a vertical component. The former is

$$\frac{P\sin\theta}{4\pi\mu r}\left[\cos\theta - \frac{\mu}{\lambda+\mu}\frac{1}{(1+\cos\theta)}\right];$$

it is directed towards or away from the line of action of the weight according as the radius vector is without or within the cone which is given by the equation

$$(\lambda+\mu)\cos\theta\,(1+\cos\theta) = \mu.$$

When Poisson's ratio for the material is $\frac{1}{4}$ the angle of the cone is about 68° 32′. At any point on the bounding plane the horizontal displacement is directed towards the axis and is of amount $\frac{1}{4}P/\pi r(\lambda+\mu)$. The vertical displacement at any point is

$$\frac{P}{4\pi\mu r}\left(\frac{\lambda+2\mu}{\lambda+\mu} + \cos^2\theta\right);$$

it is always directed downwards. Its magnitude at a point on the bounding plane is $\frac{1}{4}P(\lambda+2\mu)/\pi r\mu(\lambda+\mu)$. The initially plane boundary is deformed into a curved surface. The parts which are not too near the origin come to lie on the surface formed by the revolution of the hyperbola

$$xz = \tfrac{1}{4}P(\lambda+2\mu)/\pi\mu(\lambda+\mu)$$

about the axis of z.

136. Distributed pressure.

Instead of supposing the pressure to be applied at one point, we may suppose it to be distributed over an area on the bounding plane. Let $(x', y', 0)$ be any point of this plane, P' the pressure per unit of area at this point, r the distance of a point (x, y, z) within the body from the point $(x', y', 0)$. Let ψ denote the *direct potential* of a distribution P' over the area, χ the *logarithmic potential* of the same distribution, so that

$$\psi = \iint P' r\, dx' dy', \quad \chi = \iint P' \log(z+r)\, dx' dy', \quad \text{...........(36)}$$

where the integrations are taken over the area subjected to pressure. We observe that

$$\nabla^2\chi = 0, \quad \nabla^2\psi = 2\frac{\partial\chi}{\partial z} = 2\iint\frac{P'}{r}\, dx' dy' = 2\phi, \text{ say}, \quad \text{...........(37)}$$

where ϕ is the ordinary or *inverse potential* of the distribution P'. We observe also that $\frac{\partial \psi}{\partial z} = z\phi$.

The displacement at any point of the body produced by the distributed pressure P' is expressed by the equations

$$u = -\frac{1}{4\pi(\lambda+\mu)}\frac{\partial \chi}{\partial x} - \frac{1}{4\pi\mu}\frac{\partial^2 \psi}{\partial x \partial z},$$

$$v = -\frac{1}{4\pi(\lambda+\mu)}\frac{\partial \chi}{\partial y} - \frac{1}{4\pi\mu}\frac{\partial^2 \psi}{\partial y \partial z},$$

$$w = -\frac{1}{4\pi(\lambda+\mu)}\frac{\partial \chi}{\partial z} - \frac{1}{4\pi\mu}\frac{\partial^2 \psi}{\partial z^2} + \frac{\lambda+2\mu}{4\pi\mu(\lambda+\mu)}\nabla^2\psi.$$

These expressions can be simplified by introducing a new function Ω determined by the equation

$$\Omega = -\frac{z\phi}{4\pi\mu} - \frac{\chi}{4\pi(\lambda+\mu)}; \quad \text{.........................(38)}$$

and we have the expressions* for the displacement

$$u = \frac{\partial \Omega}{\partial x}, \quad v = \frac{\partial \Omega}{\partial y}, \quad w = \frac{\partial \Omega}{\partial z} + \frac{\lambda+2\mu}{2\pi\mu(\lambda+\mu)}\phi. \quad \text{............(39)}$$

We observe that these expressions are finite and determinate for all values of (x, y, z), provided z is positive; and that, as the point (x, y, z) approaches any point $(x', y', 0)$, they tend to definite finite limits. They represent the displacement at all points of the body, bounded by the infinite plane $z = 0$, to which pressure is applied over any area†. The normal component, w, of the displacement at any point on the surface of the body is $(\lambda + 2\mu)\phi/4\pi\mu(\lambda + \mu)$.

137. Pressure between two bodies in contact.—Geometrical Preliminaries.

Let two bodies be pressed together so that the resultant pressure between them is P. The parts of the bodies near the points of contact will be compressed, so that there is contact over a small area of the surface of each. This common area will be called the *compressed area*, and the curve that bounds it the *curve of compression*. We propose to determine the curve of compression and the distribution of pressure over the compressed area‡.

The shapes, in the unstressed state, of the two bodies near the parts that come into contact can be determined, with sufficient approximation, by equations of the form

$$\left.\begin{aligned} z_1 &= A_1x^2 + B_1y^2 + 2H_1xy, \\ z_2 &= A_2x^2 + B_2y^2 + 2H_2xy, \end{aligned}\right\} \quad \text{.........................(40)}$$

* These formulæ are due to Hertz, *J. f. Math.* (*Crelle*), Bd. 92 (1881), reprinted in *Ges. Werke von Heinrich Hertz*, Bd. 1, Leipzig 1895, p. 155.

† A number of special cases are worked out by Boussinesq, *loc. cit.*

‡ The theory is due to Hertz, *loc. cit.*

the axes of z_1 and z_2 being directed along the normals drawn towards the interiors of the bodies respectively. In the unstressed state, the bodies are in contact at the origin of (x, y), they have a common tangent plane there, and the distance apart of two points of them, estimated along the common normal, is expressed with sufficient approximation by the quadratic form $(A_1+A_2)x^2+(B_1+B_2)y^2+2(H_1+H_2)xy$. This expression must be positive in whatever way the axes of x and y are chosen, and we may choose these axes so that H_1+H_2 vanishes. Then A_1+A_2 and B_1+B_2 must be positive. We may therefore write

$$A_1+A_2=A, \quad B_1+B_2=B, \quad H_1=-H_2, \qquad \text{..........(41)}$$

A and B being positive.

If R_1, R_1' are the principal radii of curvature at the point of contact for the body (1), and R_2, R_2' those for the body (2), and if these have positive signs when the corresponding centres of curvature are inside the bodies respectively, we have

$$2(A+B)=1/R_1+1/R_1'+1/R_2+1/R_2'. \qquad \text{..............(42)}$$

The angle (ω) between those normal sections of the two surfaces in which the radii of curvature are R_1, R_2 is given by the equation

$$4(A-B)^2=\left(\frac{1}{R_1}-\frac{1}{R_1'}\right)^2+\left(\frac{1}{R_2}-\frac{1}{R_2'}\right)^2+2\left(\frac{1}{R_1}-\frac{1}{R_1'}\right)\left(\frac{1}{R_2}-\frac{1}{R_2'}\right)\cos 2\omega. \text{...(43)}$$

The angle (ω') between the (x, z) plane, chosen so that $H_2=-H_1$, and the normal section in which the radius of curvature is R_1 is given by the equation

$$\left(\frac{1}{R_2}-\frac{1}{R_2'}\right)\sin 2(\omega-\omega')=\left(\frac{1}{R_1}-\frac{1}{R_1'}\right)\sin 2\omega'. \qquad \text{..........(44)}$$

If we introduce an angle τ by the equation

$$\cos\tau=\frac{B-A}{B+A}, \qquad \text{...........................(45)}$$

so that $\quad 2A\operatorname{cosec}^2\tfrac{1}{2}\tau=2B\sec^2\tfrac{1}{2}\tau=1/R_1+1/R_1'+1/R_2+1/R_2', \quad$ ......(46)

the shape of the "relative indicatrix," $Ax^2+By^2=\text{const.}$, depends on the angle τ only.

When the bodies are pressed together there will be displacement of both. We take the displacement of the body (1) to be (u_1, v_1, w_1) relative to the axes of (x, y, z_1), and that of the body (2) to be (u_2, v_2, w_2) relative to the axes of (x, y, z_2). Since the parts within the compressed area are in contact after the compression, we must have, at all points of this area,

$$z_1+w_1=-(z_2+w_2)+\alpha,$$

where α is the value of $w_1 + w_2$ at the origin*. Hence within the compressed area we have

$$w_1 + w_2 = \alpha - Ax^2 - By^2, \quad \text{.....................(47)}$$

and outside the compressed area we must have

$$w_1 + w_2 > \alpha - Ax^2 - By^2, \quad \text{.....................(48)}$$

in order that the surfaces may be separated from each other.

138. Solution of the problem of the pressure between two bodies in contact.

We denote by λ_1, μ_1 the elastic constants of the body (1), and by λ_2, μ_2 those of the body (2). The pressure P between the bodies is the resultant of a distributed pressure (P' per unit of area) over the compressed area. We may form functions ϕ_1, χ_1, Ω_1 for the body (1) in the same way as ϕ, χ, Ω were formed in Article 136, and we may form corresponding functions for the body (2). The values of w_1 and w_2 at the common surface can then be written,

$$w_1 = \vartheta_1 \phi_0, \quad w_2 = \vartheta_2 \phi_0, \quad \text{..........................(49)}$$

where $\vartheta_1 = (\lambda_1 + 2\mu_1)/4\pi\mu_1(\lambda_1 + \mu_1)$, $\vartheta_2 = (\lambda_2 + 2\mu_2)/4\pi\mu_2(\lambda_2 + \mu_2)$, ...(50)

and ϕ_0 is the value of ϕ_1 or ϕ_2 at the surface, i.e. the value of the convergent integral $\iint P' r^{-1} dx' dy'$ at a point on the surface. The value of ϕ_0 at any point within the compressed area is determined in terms of the quantity α and the coordinates of the point by the equation

$$\phi_0 = \frac{1}{\vartheta_1 + \vartheta_2}(\alpha - Ax^2 - By^2). \quad \text{..................(51)}$$

This result suggests the next step in the solution of the problem. The functions denoted by ϕ_1 and ϕ_2 are the potentials, on the two sides of the plane $z = 0$, of a superficial distribution of density P' within the compressed area, and the potential at a point of this area is a quadratic function of the coordinates of the point. We recall the result that the potential of a homogeneous ellipsoid at an internal point is a quadratic function of the coordinates

* If the points (x_1, y_1, z_1) of the body (1) and (x_2, y_2, z_2) of the body (2) come into contact, we must have

$$x_1 + u_1 = x_2 + u_2, \quad y_1 + v_1 = y_2 + v_2, \quad z_1 + w_1 = -(z_2 + w_2) + \alpha;$$

and in equation (47) we identify (x_1, y_1) with (x_2, y_2). We may show that, without making this identification, we should have

$$w_1 + w_2 = \alpha - Ax_1^2 - By_1^2 - 2\left[A_2 \tfrac{1}{2}(x_1 + x_2)(u_1 - u_2) + B_2 \tfrac{1}{2}(y_1 + y_2)(v_1 - v_2) + H_2\{x_1(v_1 - v_2) + y_1(u_1 - u_2)\}\right].$$

In the result we shall find for $w_1 + w_2$ an expression of the order Aa^2, where a is the greatest diameter of the compressed area, and $u_1, u_2, \ldots$ will be of the same order in a as $w_1 + w_2$; thus the terms neglected are of a higher order of small quantities than those retained. If the bodies are of the same material we have $u_1 = u_2$ and $v_1 = v_2$ when $x_1 = x_2$ and $y_1 = y_2$, and thus the identification of (x_1, y_1) with (x_2, y_2) leads in this case to an exact result.

of the point. We therefore seek to satisfy the conditions of the problem by assuming that the compressed area is the area within an ellipse, regarded as an ellipsoid very much flattened, and that the pressure P' may be obtained by a limiting process, the whole mass of the ellipsoid remaining finite, and one of its principal axes being diminished indefinitely. In the case of an ellipsoid of density ρ, whose equation referred to its principal axes is

$$x^2/a^2 + y^2/b^2 + z^2/c^2 = 1,$$

the mass would be $\frac{4}{3}\pi\rho abc$; the part of this mass that would be contained in a cylinder standing on the element of area $dx'dy'$ would be

$$2\rho\, dx'dy'c\sqrt{(1 - x'^2/a^2 - y'^2/b^2)},$$

and the potential at any external point would be

$$\pi\rho abc\int_\nu^\infty \left(1 - \frac{x^2}{a^2+\psi} - \frac{y^2}{b^2+\psi} - \frac{z^2}{c^2+\psi}\right)\frac{d\psi}{\{(a^2+\psi)(b^2+\psi)(c^2+\psi)\}^{\frac{1}{2}}},$$

where ν is the positive root of the equation

$$x^2/(a^2+\nu) + y^2/(b^2+\nu) + z^2/(c^2+\nu) = 1.$$

At an internal point we should have the same form for the potential with 0 written for ν. We have now to pass to a limit by taking c to diminish indefinitely, and ρ to increase indefinitely, while a and b remain finite, in such a way that

(i) $\frac{4}{3}\pi(\rho c)\, ab = P$,

(ii) $2(\rho c)\sqrt{(1 - x'^2/a^2 - y'^2/b^2)} = P'$,

(iii) $\phi_0 = \pi ab(\rho c)\int_0^\infty \left(1 - \frac{x^2}{a^2+\psi} - \frac{y^2}{b^2+\psi}\right)\frac{d\psi}{\{(a^2+\psi)(b^2+\psi)\psi\}^{\frac{1}{2}}}$,

the third of these conditions being satisfied at all points within the compressed area. Hence we have

$$P' = \frac{3P}{2\pi ab}\sqrt{\left(1 - \frac{x'^2}{a^2} - \frac{y'^2}{b^2}\right)}, \quad \text{.....................(52)}$$

and $\frac{1}{\vartheta_1+\vartheta_2}(\alpha - Ax^2 - By^2)$

$$= \frac{3}{4}P\int_0^\infty \left(1 - \frac{x^2}{a^2+\psi} - \frac{y^2}{b^2+\psi}\right)\frac{d\psi}{\{(a^2+\psi)(b^2+\psi)\psi\}^{\frac{1}{2}}}. \quad \text{......(53)}$$

The equation (52) determines the law of distribution of the pressure P' over the compressed area, when the dimensions of this area are known. The equation (53) must hold for all values of x and y within this area, and it is therefore equivalent to three equations, viz.

$$\left.\begin{aligned} \alpha &= \tfrac{3}{4}P(\vartheta_1+\vartheta_2)\int_0^\infty \frac{d\psi}{\{(a^2+\psi)(b^2+\psi)\psi\}^{\frac{1}{2}}}, \\ A &= \tfrac{3}{4}P(\vartheta_1+\vartheta_2)\int_0^\infty \frac{d\psi}{(a^2+\psi)^{\frac{3}{2}}\{(b^2+\psi)\psi\}^{\frac{1}{2}}}, \\ B &= \tfrac{3}{4}P(\vartheta_1+\vartheta_2)\int_0^\infty \frac{d\psi}{(b^2+\psi)^{\frac{3}{2}}\{(a^2+\psi)\psi\}^{\frac{1}{2}}}. \end{aligned}\right\} \quad \text{............(54)}$$

The second and third of these equations determine a and b, and the first of them determines α when a and b are known. If we express the results in terms of the eccentricity (e) of the ellipse, e will be determined by the equation

$$B\int_0^\infty \frac{d\zeta}{(1+\zeta)^{\frac{3}{2}}\{\zeta(1-e^2+\zeta)\}^{\frac{1}{2}}} = A\int_0^\infty \frac{d\zeta}{(1-e^2+\zeta)^{\frac{3}{2}}\{\zeta(1+\zeta)\}^{\frac{1}{2}}}, \quad\ldots(55)$$

a will be given by the equation

$$Aa^3 = \tfrac{3}{4}P(\vartheta_1+\vartheta_2)\int_0^\infty \frac{d\zeta}{(1+\zeta)^{\frac{3}{2}}\{\zeta(1-e^2+\zeta)\}^{\frac{1}{2}}}, \quad\ldots\ldots\ldots(56)$$

and α will be given by the equation

$$\alpha = \frac{3P}{4a}(\vartheta_1+\vartheta_2)\int_0^\infty \frac{d\zeta}{\{\zeta(1+\zeta)(1-e^2+\zeta)\}^{\frac{1}{2}}}. \quad\ldots\ldots\ldots\ldots(57)$$

We observe that e depends on the ratio $A:B$ only. Hertz has tabulated the values of b/a, $=(1-e^2)^{\frac{1}{2}}$, in terms of the angle τ, of which the cosine is $(B-A)/(B+A)$. He found the following results:

$\tau=$	90°	80°	70°	60°	50°	40°	30°	20°	10°	0°
$b/a=$	1	0·79	0·62	0·47	0·36	0·26	0·18	0·10	0·05	0

At points on the plane $z=0$ which are outside the compressed area, ϕ_0 is the potential, at external points in this plane, due to the distribution P' over the compressed area. It follows from (49) that at points on the surfaces of the bodies, outside the compressed area and not far from it, we may write, with sufficient approximation

$$w_1+w_2 = (\vartheta_1+\vartheta_2)\frac{3P}{4}\int_\nu^\infty \left(1-\frac{x^2}{a^2+\psi}-\frac{y^2}{b^2+\psi}\right)\frac{d\psi}{\{(a^2+\psi)(b^2+\psi)\psi\}^{\frac{1}{2}}},$$

where ν is the positive root of the equation

$$x^2/(a^2+\nu)+y^2/(b^2+\nu)=1. \quad\ldots\ldots\ldots\ldots\ldots\ldots\ldots(58)$$

Hence we have

$$(w_1+w_2)-(\alpha-Ax^2-By^2)$$
$$=-(\vartheta_1+\vartheta_2)\frac{3P}{4}\int_0^\nu\left(1-\frac{x^2}{a^2+\psi}-\frac{y^2}{b^2+\psi}\right)\frac{d\psi}{\{(a^2+\psi)(b^2+\psi)\psi\}^{\frac{1}{2}}}.\ \ldots(59)$$

Now, when ψ lies between 0 and ν, the point (x, y), which is on the ellipse (58), is outside the ellipse $x^2/(a^2+\psi)+y^2/(b^2+\psi)=1$, and therefore the expression on the right-hand side of equation (59) is positive. The condition of inequality (48) is therefore satisfied.

The assumptions that the compressed area is bounded by an ellipse $x^2/a^2+y^2/b^2=1$, where a and b are determined by the second and third of equations (54), and that the pressure P' over this area is expressed by the formula (52), satisfy all the conditions of the problem. When P' is known the functions ϕ, χ, Ω for each of the bodies can be calculated, and hence we may determine the displacement and the distribution of stress in each body.

Hertz* has drawn the lines of principal stress in the (x, z) plane for the case in which $\lambda = 2\mu$ (Poisson's ratio $= \frac{1}{3}$). His drawing was in part conjectural, as the differential equation determining the directions of the lines of principal stress cannot be integrated exactly. A more exact result has been obtained by S. Fuchs†, by a method of approximate integration, in the case of a sphere resting on a plane. The lines of principal stress in the body with the spherical boundary are represented in Fig. 15, where the full curved lines

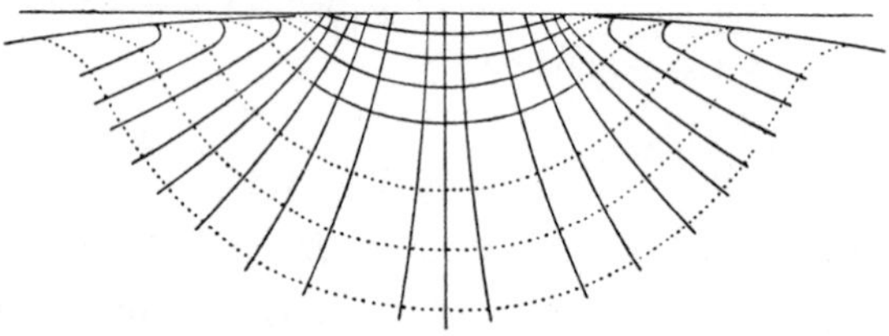

Fig. 15.

are lines of principal stress along which the traction is pressure, and the dotted lines are lines of principal stress along which the traction is tension. It will be observed that near the compressed area both the principal stresses are pressures. A little further away one set of lines shows tension near the surface and pressure in the central portions. Still further away the same set of lines shows tension throughout. The other set of lines are always lines of pressure.

Hertz made a series of experiments with the view of testing the theory. The result that the linear dimensions of the compressed area are proportional to the cube root of the pressure between the bodies was verified very exactly; the dependence of the form of the compressed area upon the form of the relative indicatrix was also verified in cases in which the latter could be determined with fair accuracy.

139. Hertz's theory of impact.

The results obtained in the last Article have been applied to the problem of the impact of two solid bodies‡. The ordinary theory of impact, founded by Newton, divides bodies into two classes, "perfectly elastic" and "imperfectly elastic." In the case of the former class there is no loss of kinetic energy in impact. In the other case energy is dissipated in impact. Many actual bodies are not very far from being perfectly elastic in the Newtonian sense. Hertz's theory of impact takes no account of the dissipation of energy; the compression at the place of contact is regarded as gradually produced and as subsiding completely by reversal of the process by which it is produced. The local compression is thus regarded as a statical effect. In order that such a theory may hold it is necessary that the duration of the impact should be a large

* *Verhandlungen des Vereins zur Beförderung des Gewerbefleisses*, 1882, reprinted in Hertz, *Ges. Werke*, Bd. 1, p. 174.

† *Physikalische Zeitschr.*, 1913, p. 1282. Further discussion of the case considered by Fuchs will be found in a paper by W. B. Morton and L. J. Close, *Phil. Mag.* (Ser. 6), vol. 43, 1922, p. 320.

‡ Hertz, *J. f. Math.* (*Crelle*), Bd. 92 (1881), reprinted in Hertz, *Ges. Werke*, Bd. 1, p. 170.

multiple of the gravest period of free vibration of either body which involves compression at the place in question. A formula for the duration of the impact, which satisfies this requirement when the bodies impinge on each other with moderate velocities, has been given by Hertz, and the result has been verified experimentally*.

At any instant during the impact, the quantity α is the relative displacement of the centres of mass of the two bodies, estimated from their relative positions at the instant when the impact commences, and resolved in the direction of the common normal. The pressure P between the bodies is the rate of destruction of the momentum of either. We therefore have the equation

$$\frac{d}{dt}\left(m_1 \frac{m_2 \dot{\alpha}}{m_1 + m_2}\right) = -P, \qquad \text{.........(60)}$$

where $\dot{\alpha}$ stands for $d\alpha/dt$, and m_1, m_2 are the masses of the bodies. Now P is a function of t, so that the principal semi-diameters a and b of the compressed area at any instant are also functions of t, determined in terms of P by the second and third of equations (54); in fact a and b are each of them proportional to $P^{\frac{1}{3}}$. Equation (57) shows that α is proportional to $P^{\frac{2}{3}}$, or that P is proportional to $\alpha^{\frac{3}{2}}$; we write

$$P = k_2 \alpha^{\frac{3}{2}}, \qquad \text{.........(61)}$$

where

$$(\tfrac{3}{4})^2 k_2^2 A (\vartheta_1 + \vartheta_2)^2 \left[\int_0^\infty \frac{d\zeta}{\{\zeta(1+\zeta)(1-e^2+\zeta)\}^{\frac{1}{2}}}\right]^3 = \int_0^\infty \frac{d\zeta}{(1+\zeta)^{\frac{3}{2}}\{\zeta(1-e^2+\zeta)\}^{\frac{1}{2}}} \qquad \text{.........(62)}$$

Equation (60) may now be written

$$\ddot{\alpha} = -k_1 k_2 \alpha^{\frac{3}{2}}, \qquad \text{.........(63)}$$

where $k_1 = (m_1 + m_2)/m_1 m_2$. This equation may be integrated in the form

$$\tfrac{1}{2}(\dot{\alpha}^2 - v^2) = -\tfrac{2}{5} k_1 k_2 \alpha^{\frac{5}{2}}, \qquad \text{.........(64)}$$

where v is the initial value of $\dot{\alpha}$, i.e. the velocity of approach of the bodies before impact. The value of α at the instant of greatest compression is

$$\left(\frac{5}{k_1 k_2}\right)^{\frac{2}{5}} \left(\frac{v}{2}\right)^{\frac{4}{5}}; \qquad \text{.........(65)}$$

and, if this quantity is denoted by α_1, the duration of the impact is

$$2\int_0^{\alpha_1} \frac{d\alpha}{[v^2 - \frac{4}{5}k_1 k_2 \alpha^{\frac{5}{2}}]^{\frac{1}{2}}},$$

which is $\quad 2\dfrac{\alpha_1}{v}\displaystyle\int_0^1 \frac{dx}{(1-x^{\frac{5}{2}})^{\frac{1}{2}}}$, or $\tfrac{4}{5}\sqrt{\pi}\,\dfrac{\alpha_1}{v}\dfrac{\Gamma(\frac{2}{5})}{\Gamma(\frac{9}{10})}$, or $(2{\cdot}9432\ldots)\dfrac{\alpha_1}{v}$.

* Schneebeli, *Arch. des sci. phys., Geneva*, t. 15 (1885). Investigations of the duration of impact in the case of high velocities were made by Tait, *Edinburgh Roy. Soc. Trans.*, vols. 36, 37 (1890, 1892), reprinted in P. G. Tait, *Scientific Papers*, vol. 2, Cambridge 1900, pp. 222, 249. The theory will be discussed further in Chapter XX *infra*.

We may express α_1 in terms of the shapes and masses of the bodies and the velocities of propagation of waves of compression in them; let V_1 and V_2 be these velocities*, ρ_1 and ρ_2 the densities of the bodies, σ_1 and σ_2 the values of Poisson's ratio for the two materials; then

$$\vartheta_1 = \frac{(1-\sigma_1)^2}{\pi V_1^2 \rho_1 (1-2\sigma_1)}, \quad \vartheta_2 = \frac{(1-\sigma_2)^2}{\pi V_2^2 \rho_2 (1-2\sigma_2)}, \qquad \text{............(66)}$$

so that

$$\alpha_1 = \left[\frac{5m_1 m_2 v^2}{4(m_1+m_2)} \frac{3\sqrt{A}}{4\pi} \left\{\frac{(1-\sigma_1)^2}{V_1^2\rho_1(1-2\sigma_1)} + \frac{(1-\sigma_2)^2}{V_2^2\rho_2(1-2\sigma_2)}\right\} I\right]^{\frac{2}{5}}, \quad \text{..(67)}$$

where

$$I^2 \int_0^\infty \frac{d\zeta}{(1+\zeta)^{\frac{3}{2}} \{\zeta(1-e^2+\zeta)\}^{\frac{1}{2}}} = \left[\int_0^\infty \frac{d\zeta}{\{\zeta(1+\zeta)(1-e^2+\zeta)\}^{\frac{1}{2}}}\right]^3 \text{.......(68)}$$

It appears that the duration of the impact varies inversely as the fifth root of the relative velocity of approach before impact. The order of magnitude of the gravest period of free vibration that would involve compression is $1/A_1 V_1$, and thus the duration of impact bears to this period a ratio of which the order of magnitude is $(V_1/v)^{\frac{1}{5}}$.

140. Impact of spheres.

When the bodies are spheres of radii r_1, r_2, we have

$$\left.\begin{aligned} &A = B = \tfrac{1}{2}(1/r_1 + 1/r_2), \quad e = 0, \quad a = b, \\ &a^3 = \frac{3\pi}{4}\frac{r_1 r_2}{r_1+r_2}(\vartheta_1+\vartheta_2) P, \\ &\alpha = \frac{3\pi}{4a}(\vartheta_1+\vartheta_2) P; \end{aligned}\right\} \text{........................(69)}$$

from which we find

$$\left.\begin{aligned} &k_2 = \frac{4}{3\pi}\left(\frac{r_1 r_2}{r_1+r_2}\right)^{\frac{1}{2}} \frac{1}{\vartheta_1+\vartheta_2}, \quad a = \{\alpha(r_1 r_2)/(r_1+r_2)\}^{\frac{1}{2}}, \\ &\alpha_1 = \left[\frac{15\pi v^2(\vartheta_1+\vartheta_2) m_1 m_2}{16(m_1+m_2)}\right]^{\frac{2}{5}} \left(\frac{r_1+r_2}{r_1 r_2}\right)^{\frac{1}{5}}. \end{aligned}\right\} \text{..................(70)}$$

Hence the duration of the impact and the radius of the (circular) compressed area are determined.

In the particular case of equal spheres of the same material the duration of the impact is

$$(2\cdot9432...)\left\{\frac{25\pi^2}{8}\frac{(1-\sigma)^4}{(1-2\sigma)^2}\right\}^{\frac{1}{5}} \frac{r}{v^{\frac{1}{5}} V^{\frac{4}{5}}}, \quad \text{........................(71)}$$

where r is the radius of either sphere, σ is the Poisson's ratio of the material, and V is the velocity of propagation of waves of compression. The radii of the circular patches that come into contact are each equal to

$$r\left(\frac{v}{V}\right)^{\frac{2}{5}} \left[\frac{5\pi}{16}\frac{(1-\sigma)^2}{1-2\sigma}\right]^{\frac{1}{5}}. \quad \text{..................................(72)}$$

These results have been verified experimentally†.

* V_1^2 is $(\lambda_1+2\mu_1)/\rho_1$ and V_2^2 is $(\lambda_2+2\mu_2)/\rho_2$. See Chapter XIII *infra*.

† Schneebeli, *Rep. d. Phys.*, Bd. 22 (1886), and Hamburger, *Tageblatt d. Nat. Vers. in Wiesbaden*, 1887.

141. Effects of nuclei of strain referred to polar coordinates.

We may seek solutions of the equations (1) in terms of polar coordinates, the displacement being taken to be inversely proportional to the radius vector r. The displacement must satisfy equations (49) of Article 97. If we take u_r and u_θ to be proportional to $\cos n\phi$, and u_ϕ to be proportional to $\sin n\phi$, we may show that*

$$\Delta = \frac{\cos n\phi}{r^2}\left\{A(n+\cos\theta)\tan^n\frac{\theta}{2} + B(n-\cos\theta)\cot^n\frac{\theta}{2}\right\},$$

$$2\varpi_r = \frac{\sin n\phi}{r^2}\left\{C\tan^n\frac{\theta}{2} - D\cot^n\frac{\theta}{2}\right\},$$

$$u_r = \frac{\cos n\phi}{r}\left\{-\frac{\lambda+2\mu}{\mu}\frac{r^2\Delta}{\cos n\phi} + C\tan^n\frac{\theta}{2} + D\cot^n\frac{\theta}{2}\right\},$$

where A, B, C, D are arbitrary constants; and then we may show that

$$u_\theta = \frac{\cos n\phi}{r\sin\theta}\left\{-\frac{\lambda+3\mu}{2\mu}\sin\theta\frac{d}{d\theta}\left(\frac{r^2\Delta}{\cos n\phi}\right) + \cos\theta\left(C\tan^n\frac{\theta}{2} + D\cot^n\frac{\theta}{2}\right) + G\tan^n\frac{\theta}{2} + H\cot^n\frac{\theta}{2}\right\},$$

$$u_\phi = \frac{\sin n\phi}{r\sin\theta}\left\{n\frac{\lambda+3\mu}{2\mu}\frac{r^2\Delta}{\cos n\phi} - \cos\theta\left(C\tan^n\frac{\theta}{2} - D\cot^n\frac{\theta}{2}\right) - G\tan^n\frac{\theta}{2} + H\cot^n\frac{\theta}{2}\right\},$$

where G and H are arbitrary constants. In the particular cases where $n=0$ or 1 some of the solutions require independent investigation. These cases include the first type of simple solutions for any direction of the applied force, the second type of simple solutions, and the solutions arrived at in Article 132, examples (d), (e). We give the expressions for the displacements and stress-components in a series of cases.

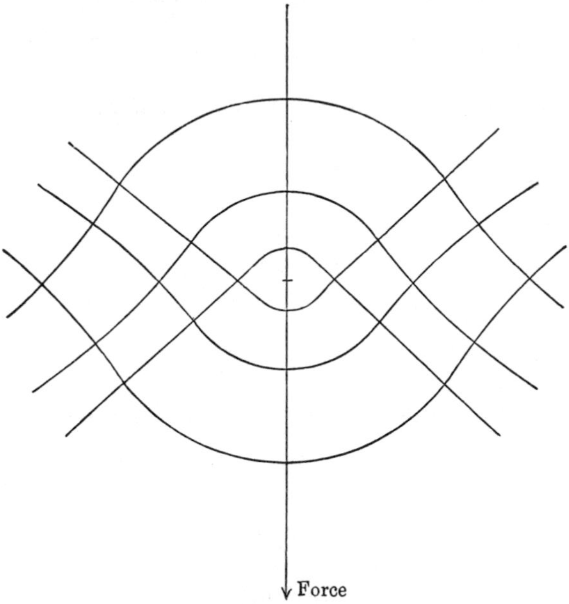

Fig. 16.

* J. H. Michell, *London Math. Soc. Proc.*, vol. 32 (1900), p. 23.

(α) The first type of simple solutions, corresponding with a force F parallel to the axis of z, is expressed by the equations

$$u_r = \frac{F}{4\pi\mu}\frac{\cos\theta}{r}, \quad u_\theta = -\frac{\lambda+3\mu}{2(\lambda+2\mu)}\frac{F}{4\pi\mu}\frac{\sin\theta}{r}, \quad u_\phi = 0;$$

the stress-components are expressed by the equations

$$\widehat{rr} = -\frac{3\lambda+4\mu}{\lambda+2\mu}\frac{F}{4\pi}\frac{\cos\theta}{r^2}, \quad \widehat{\theta\theta} = \widehat{\phi\phi} = \frac{\mu}{\lambda+2\mu}\frac{F}{4\pi}\frac{\cos\theta}{r^2},$$

$$\widehat{\theta\phi} = \widehat{\phi r} = 0, \quad \widehat{r\theta} = \frac{\mu}{\lambda+2\mu}\frac{F}{4\pi}\frac{\sin\theta}{r^2}.$$

The meridian planes (ϕ=const.) are principal planes of stress; and the lines of principal stress, which are in any meridian plane, make with the radius vector at any point angles ψ determined by the equation

$$\tan 2\psi = -\{2\mu/(3\lambda+5\mu)\}\tan\theta.$$

These lines have been traced by Michell, for the case where $\lambda=\mu$, with the result shown in Fig. 16, in which the central point is the point of application of the force.

(β) When the line of action of the force F' is parallel to the axis of x, the displacement is expressed by the equations

$$u_r = \frac{F'}{4\pi\mu}\frac{\sin\theta\cos\phi}{r}, \quad u_\theta = \frac{\lambda+3\mu}{2(\lambda+2\mu)}\frac{F'}{4\pi\mu}\frac{\cos\theta\cos\phi}{r}, \quad u_\phi = -\frac{\lambda+3}{2(\lambda+2\mu)}\frac{F'}{4\pi\mu}\frac{\sin\phi}{r};$$

the stress-components are expressed by the equations

$$\widehat{rr} = -\frac{3\lambda+4\mu}{\lambda+2\mu}\frac{F'}{4\pi}\frac{\sin\theta\cos\phi}{r^2}, \quad \widehat{\theta\theta} = \widehat{\phi\phi} = \frac{\mu}{\lambda+2\mu}\frac{F'}{4\pi}\frac{\sin\theta\cos\phi}{r^2},$$

$$\widehat{\theta\phi} = 0, \quad \widehat{\phi r} = \frac{\mu}{\lambda+2\mu}\frac{F'}{4\pi}\frac{\sin\phi}{r^2}, \quad \widehat{r\theta} = -\frac{\mu}{\lambda+2\mu}\frac{F'}{4\pi}\frac{\cos\theta\cos\phi}{r^2}.$$

(γ) The second type of simple solutions is expressed by the equations

$$u_r = \frac{B}{r}, \quad u_\theta = -\frac{B}{r}\frac{\sin\theta}{1+\cos\theta}, \quad u_\phi = 0;$$

the stress-components are expressed by the equations

$$\widehat{rr} = -2\mu\frac{B}{r^2}, \quad \widehat{\theta\theta} = 2\mu\frac{B}{r^2}\frac{\cos\theta}{1+\cos\theta}, \quad \widehat{\phi\phi} = 2\mu\frac{B}{r^2}\frac{1}{1+\cos\theta},$$

$$\widehat{\theta\phi} = \widehat{\phi r} = 0, \quad \widehat{r\theta} = 2\mu\frac{B}{r^2}\frac{\sin\theta}{1+\cos\theta}.$$

(δ) The solution (28) obtained in Article 132 (d) is expressed by the equations

$$u_r = 0, \quad u_\theta = -\frac{C}{r}\frac{\cos\phi}{1+\cos\theta}, \quad u_\phi = \frac{C}{r}\frac{\sin\phi}{1+\cos\theta};$$

the stress-components are expressed by the equations

$$\widehat{rr} = 0, \quad \widehat{\theta\theta} = -\widehat{\phi\phi} = -2\mu\frac{C}{r^2}\frac{(1-\cos\theta)\cos\phi}{(1+\cos\theta)\sin\theta},$$

$$\widehat{\theta\phi} = 2\mu\frac{C}{r^2}\frac{(1-\cos\theta)\sin\phi}{(1+\cos\theta)\sin\theta}, \quad \widehat{\phi r} = -2\mu\frac{C}{r^2}\frac{\sin\phi}{1+\cos\theta}, \quad \widehat{r\theta} = 2\mu\frac{C}{r^2}\frac{\cos\phi}{1+\cos\theta}.$$

(ϵ) The solution (31) obtained in Article 132 (e) is expressed by the equations

$$u_r = \frac{D}{r}\frac{\sin\theta\cos\phi}{1+\cos\theta}, \quad u_\theta = \frac{D}{r}\cos\phi, \quad u_\phi = -\frac{D}{r}\sin\phi;$$

the stress-components are expressed by the equations

$$\widehat{rr} = -\widehat{\theta\theta} = -2\mu\frac{D}{r^2}\frac{\sin\theta\cos\phi}{1+\cos\theta}, \quad \widehat{\phi\phi}=0,$$

$$\widehat{\theta\phi} = -\mu\frac{D}{r^2}\frac{\sin\theta\sin\phi}{1+\cos\theta}, \quad \widehat{\phi r} = \mu\frac{D}{r^2}\left(2-\frac{1}{1+\cos\theta}\right)\sin\phi, \quad \widehat{r\theta} = -\mu\frac{D}{r^2}\left(2-\frac{1}{1+\cos\theta}\right)\cos\phi.$$

142. Problems relating to the equilibrium of cones*.

(i) We may combine the solutions expressed in (α) and (γ) of the last Article so as to obtain the distribution of stress in a cone, subjected to a force at its vertex directed along its axis, when the parts at a great distance from the vertex are held fixed. If $\theta=a$ is the equation of the surface of the cone, the stress-components $\widehat{\theta\theta}$, $\widehat{\theta\phi}$, $\widehat{r\theta}$ must vanish when $\theta=a$, and we have therefore

$$\frac{\mu}{\lambda+2\mu}\frac{F}{4\pi}+\frac{2\mu B}{1+\cos a}=0.$$

The resultant force at the vertex of the cone may be found by considering the traction in the direction of the axis of the cone across a spherical surface with its centre at the vertex; it would be found that the force is

$$\frac{F}{2(\lambda+2\mu)}\{\lambda(1-\cos^3 a)+\mu(1-\cos a)(1+\cos^2 a)\},$$

and, when F is positive, it is directed towards the interior of the cone.

By putting $a=\frac{1}{2}\pi$ we obtain the solution for a point of pressure on a plane boundary (Article 135).

(ii) We may combine the solutions expressed in (β), (δ), (ϵ) of the last Article so as to obtain the distribution of stress in a cone, subjected to a force at its vertex directed at right angles to its axis. The conditions that the surface of the cone may be free from traction are

$$2C\frac{1-\cos a}{\sin a}-D\sin a=0,$$

$$2C-D(1+2\cos a)-\frac{F'}{4\pi(\lambda+2\mu)}\cos a(1+\cos a)=0,$$

$$-2C\frac{1-\cos a}{\sin a}+2D\sin a+\frac{F'}{4\pi(\lambda+2\mu)}\sin a(1+\cos a)=0,$$

giving

$$C=-\frac{F'(1+\cos a)^2}{8\pi(\lambda+2\mu)}, \quad D=-\frac{F'(1+\cos a)}{4\pi(\lambda+2\mu)}.$$

The resultant force at the vertex is in the positive direction of the axis of x, when F' is positive, and is of magnitude

$$\frac{F'}{4}\frac{(2+\cos a)\lambda+2\mu}{\lambda+2\mu}(1-\cos a)^2.$$

By combining the results of problems (i) and (ii) we may obtain the solution for force acting in a given direction at the vertex of a cone; and by putting $a=\frac{1}{2}\pi$ we may obtain the solution for force acting in a given direction at a point of a plane boundary.

* Michell, *loc. cit.*

CHAPTER IX

TWO-DIMENSIONAL ELASTIC SYSTEMS

143. METHODS of the kind considered in the last Chapter, depending upon simple solutions which tend to become infinite at a point, may be employed also in the case of two-dimensional elastic systems. We have already had occasion (Chapter V) to remark that there are various ways in which such systems present themselves naturally for investigation. They are further useful for purposes of illustration. As in other departments of mathematical physics which have relations to the theory of potential, it frequently happens that the analogues, in two dimensions, of problems which cannot be solved in three dimensions are capable of exact solution; so it will appear that in the theory of Elasticity a two-dimensional solution can often be found which throws light upon some wider problem that cannot be solved completely.

144. Displacement corresponding with plane strain.

In a state of plane strain parallel to the plane (x, y), the displacement w vanishes, and the displacements u, v are functions of the coordinates x, y only. The components of rotation ϖ_x and ϖ_y vanish, and we shall write ϖ for ϖ_z. When there are no body forces, the stress-equations of equilibrium show that the stress-components X_x, Y_y, X_y can be expressed in terms of a stress-function χ, which is a function of x and y, but not of z, by the formulæ

$$X_x = \frac{\partial^2 \chi}{\partial y^2}, \quad Y_y = \frac{\partial^2 \chi}{\partial x^2}, \quad X_y = -\frac{\partial^2 \chi}{\partial x \partial y} \qquad \text{.................(1)}$$

Since

$$X_x + Y_y = 2(\lambda + \mu)\Delta \qquad \text{...... ....(2)}$$

and Δ is an harmonic function, we see that χ must satisfy the equation

$$\frac{\partial^4 \chi}{\partial x^4} + \frac{\partial^4 \chi}{\partial y^4} + 2\frac{\partial^4 \chi}{\partial x^2 \partial y^2} = 0. \qquad \text{.........................(3)}$$

We shall denote the operator $\partial^2/\partial x^2 + \partial^2/\partial y^2$ by ∇_1^2, and then this equation is $\nabla_1^4 \chi = 0$. It shows that $\nabla_1^2 \chi$ is a plane harmonic function.

The equations of equilibrium in terms of dilatation and rotation are

$$(\lambda + 2\mu)\frac{\partial \Delta}{\partial x} - 2\mu\frac{\partial \varpi}{\partial y} = 0, \quad (\lambda + 2\mu)\frac{\partial \Delta}{\partial y} - 2\mu\frac{\partial \varpi}{\partial x} = 0. \qquad \text{........(4)}$$

From these we deduce that Δ and ϖ are plane harmonic functions, and that $(\lambda + 2\mu)\Delta + \iota 2\mu\varpi$ is a function of the complex variable $x + \iota y$. The plane harmonic function $\nabla_1^2\chi$ is equal to $2(\lambda+\mu)\Delta$. We introduce a new function $\xi+\iota\eta$ of $x+\iota y$ by means of the equation

$$\xi+\iota\eta=\int\{(\lambda+2\mu)\Delta+\iota 2\mu\varpi\}\,d(x+\iota y), \quad \text{..............(5)}$$

so that

$$\left.\begin{aligned}\frac{\partial\xi}{\partial x}&=\frac{\partial\eta}{\partial y}=(\lambda+2\mu)\Delta=\frac{\lambda+2\mu}{2(\lambda+\mu)}\nabla_1^2\chi,\\ -\frac{\partial\xi}{\partial y}&=\frac{\partial\eta}{\partial x}=2\mu\varpi.\end{aligned}\right\} \quad \text{...............(6)}$$

Then we have

$$2\mu\frac{\partial u}{\partial x}=\frac{\partial^2\chi}{\partial y^2}-\frac{\lambda}{2(\lambda+\mu)}\nabla_1^2\chi=-\frac{\partial^2\chi}{\partial x^2}+\frac{\partial\xi}{\partial x},$$

$$2\mu\frac{\partial v}{\partial y}=\frac{\partial^2\chi}{\partial x^2}-\frac{\lambda}{2(\lambda+\mu)}\nabla_1^2\chi=-\frac{\partial^2\chi}{\partial y^2}+\frac{\partial\eta}{\partial y}.$$

Also we have

$$2\mu\frac{\partial u}{\partial y}=-\frac{\partial^2\chi}{\partial x\partial y}-2\mu\varpi=-\frac{\partial^2\chi}{\partial x\partial y}+\frac{\partial\xi}{\partial y},$$

$$2\mu\frac{\partial v}{\partial x}=-\frac{\partial^2\chi}{\partial x\partial y}+2\mu\varpi=-\frac{\partial^2\chi}{\partial x\partial y}+\frac{\partial\eta}{\partial x}.$$

It follows that

$$2\mu u=-\frac{\partial\chi}{\partial x}+\xi,\quad 2\mu v=-\frac{\partial\chi}{\partial y}+\eta. \quad \text{........................(7)}$$

These equations enable us to express the displacement when the stress-function χ is known.

Again, when Δ and ϖ are known, we may find expressions for u, v. We have the equations

$$\frac{\partial u}{\partial x}+\frac{\partial v}{\partial y}=\Delta,\quad \frac{\partial v}{\partial x}-\frac{\partial u}{\partial y}=2\varpi. \quad \text{........................(8)}$$

These, with (6), give

$$u=\frac{\partial}{\partial x}\left(\frac{y\eta}{2(\lambda+2\mu)}\right)+\frac{\partial}{\partial y}\left(\frac{y\xi}{2\mu}\right)+u',$$

$$v=\frac{\partial}{\partial y}\left(\frac{y\eta}{2(\lambda+2\mu)}\right)-\frac{\partial}{\partial x}\left(\frac{y\xi}{2\mu}\right)+v',$$

in which [Article 14 (*d*)] $v'+\iota u'$ is a function of $x+\iota y$. We may put

$$u'=\frac{\partial f}{\partial x},\quad v'=\frac{\partial f}{\partial y},$$

where f is a plane harmonic function, and then u, v can be expressed in the forms

$$\left.\begin{aligned}u&=\frac{\xi}{2\mu}+\frac{\lambda+\mu}{2\mu(\lambda+2\mu)}y\frac{\partial\xi}{\partial y}+\frac{\partial f}{\partial x},\\ v&=\frac{\eta}{2(\lambda+2\mu)}-\frac{\lambda+\mu}{2\mu(\lambda+2\mu)}y\frac{\partial\eta}{\partial y}+\frac{\partial f}{\partial y}.\end{aligned}\right\} \quad \text{..............(9)}$$

We may show without difficulty that the corresponding form of χ is

$$\chi = -2\mu f + \frac{\lambda+\mu}{\lambda+2\mu} y\eta, \quad \text{.................................(10)}$$

and we may verify that the forms (7) for u, v are identical with the forms (9).

145. Displacement corresponding with plane stress.

In the case of plane stress, when every plane parallel to the plane of x, y is free from traction, we have $Z_x = Y_z = Z_z = 0$. We wish to determine the most general forms for the remaining stress-components, and for the corresponding displacement, when these conditions are satisfied and no body forces are in action. We recall the results of Article 92. It was there shown that, if $\Theta = X_x + Y_y + Z_z$, the function Θ is harmonic, and that, besides satisfying the three equations of the type

$$\frac{\partial X_x}{\partial x} + \frac{\partial X_y}{\partial y} + \frac{\partial Z_x}{\partial z} = 0, \quad \text{.........................(11)}$$

the stress-components also satisfy six equations of the types

$$\nabla^2 X_x + \frac{1}{1+\sigma}\frac{\partial^2\Theta}{\partial x^2} = 0, \quad \nabla^2 Y_z + \frac{1}{1+\sigma}\frac{\partial^2\Theta}{\partial y \partial z} = 0. \quad \text{.........(12)}$$

Since Z_x, Y_z, Z_z are zero, $\partial\Theta/\partial z$ is a constant, β say, and we have

$$\Theta = \Theta_0 + \beta z, \quad \text{.............................(13)}$$

where Θ_0 is a function of x and y, which must be a plane harmonic function since Θ is harmonic, or we have

$$\nabla_1^2 \Theta_0 = 0. \quad \text{...................................(14)}$$

The stress-components X_x, Y_y, X_y are derived from a stress-function χ, which is a function of x, y, z, in accordance with the formulæ (1), and we have

$$\nabla_1^2 \chi = \Theta_0 + \beta z. \quad \text{............................(15)}$$

The first of equations (12) gives us

$$\nabla^2 \frac{\partial^2 \chi}{\partial y^2} + \frac{1}{1+\sigma}\frac{\partial^2 \Theta_0}{\partial x^2} = 0,$$

or, in virtue of (14) and (15),

$$\frac{\partial^2}{\partial y^2}\left(\frac{\partial^2\chi}{\partial z^2} + \Theta_0\right) - \frac{1}{1+\sigma}\frac{\partial^2\Theta_0}{\partial y^2} = 0,$$

or

$$\frac{\partial^2}{\partial y^2}\left(\frac{\partial^2\chi}{\partial z^2} + \frac{\sigma}{1+\sigma}\Theta_0\right) = 0.$$

In like manner the remaining equations of (12) are

$$\frac{\partial^2}{\partial x^2}\left(\frac{\partial^2\chi}{\partial z^2} + \frac{\sigma}{1+\sigma}\Theta_0\right) = 0, \quad \frac{\partial^2}{\partial x \partial y}\left(\frac{\partial^2\chi}{\partial z^2} + \frac{\sigma}{1+\sigma}\Theta_0\right) = 0.$$

It follows that $\dfrac{\partial^2\chi}{\partial z^2}+\dfrac{\sigma}{1+\sigma}\Theta_0$ is a linear function of x and y, and this function may be taken to be zero without altering the values of X_x, Y_y, X_y. We therefore find the following form for χ:

$$\chi=\chi_0+\chi_1 z-\tfrac{1}{2}\frac{\sigma}{1+\sigma}\Theta_0 z^2, \qquad (16)$$

where χ_0 and χ_1 are independent of z and satisfy the equations

$$\nabla_1^2\chi_0=\Theta_0,\quad \nabla_1^2\chi_1=\beta. \qquad (17)$$

We may introduce a pair of conjugate functions ξ and η of x and y which are such that

$$\frac{\partial\xi}{\partial x}=\frac{\partial\eta}{\partial y}=\Theta_0,\quad \frac{\partial\xi}{\partial y}=-\frac{\partial\eta}{\partial x}, \qquad (18)$$

and then the most general forms for χ_0 and χ_1 can be written

$$\chi_0=\tfrac{1}{2}x\xi+f,\quad \chi_1=\tfrac{1}{4}\beta(x^2+y^2)+F, \qquad (19)$$

where f and F are plane harmonic functions. The general form for χ being known, formulæ for the stress can be found, and the displacement can be deduced.

The displacement (u, v, w) must satisfy the equations

$$\left.\begin{aligned}\frac{\partial u}{\partial x}=\frac{1}{E}(X_x-\sigma Y_y),\quad \frac{\partial v}{\partial y}=\frac{1}{E}(Y_y-\sigma X_x),\quad \frac{\partial w}{\partial z}=-\frac{\sigma}{E}(X_x+Y_y),\\ \frac{\partial w}{\partial y}+\frac{\partial v}{\partial z}=0,\quad \frac{\partial u}{\partial z}+\frac{\partial w}{\partial x}=0,\quad \frac{\partial v}{\partial x}+\frac{\partial u}{\partial y}=\frac{2(1+\sigma)}{E}X_y.\end{aligned}\right\} \qquad (20)$$

There is no difficulty in obtaining the formulæ*

$$\left.\begin{aligned}u&=\frac{1}{E}\left(\xi+\beta xz+\tfrac{1}{2}\sigma z^2\frac{\partial\Theta_0}{\partial x}\right)-\frac{1+\sigma}{E}\frac{\partial}{\partial x}(\chi_0+z\chi_1),\\ v&=\frac{1}{E}\left(\eta+\beta yz+\tfrac{1}{2}\sigma z^2\frac{\partial\Theta_0}{\partial y}\right)-\frac{1+\sigma}{E}\frac{\partial}{\partial y}(\chi_0+z\chi_1),\\ w&=-\frac{1}{E}\left\{\tfrac{1}{2}\beta(x^2+y^2+\sigma z^2)+\sigma z\Theta_0\right\}+\frac{1+\sigma}{E}\chi_1.\end{aligned}\right\} \qquad (21)$$

Any small displacement possible in a rigid body may, of course, be superposed on this displacement.

146. Generalized plane stress.

We have shown in Article 94 that, when the stress-component Z_z vanishes everywhere, and the stress-components Z_x and Y_z vanish at two plane boundaries $z=\pm h$, the average values of the remaining stress-components X_x, Y_y, X_y

* Equivalent formulæ were obtained by Clebsch, *Elasticität*, § 39.

are determined by the equations

$$\frac{\partial \bar{X}_x}{\partial x}+\frac{\partial \bar{X}_y}{\partial y}=0, \quad \frac{\partial \bar{X}_y}{\partial x}+\frac{\partial \bar{Y}_y}{\partial y}=0, \quad \text{.................(22)}$$

and that the average values of the displacements u, v are connected with the average values of the stress-components by the equations

$$\left.\begin{aligned}\bar{X}_x &= \lambda'\left(\frac{\partial \bar{u}}{\partial x}+\frac{\partial \bar{v}}{\partial y}\right)+2\mu\frac{\partial \bar{u}}{\partial x},\\ \bar{Y}_y &= \lambda'\left(\frac{\partial \bar{u}}{\partial x}+\frac{\partial \bar{v}}{\partial y}\right)+2\mu\frac{\partial \bar{v}}{\partial y},\\ \bar{X}_y &= \mu\left(\frac{\partial \bar{u}}{\partial y}+\frac{\partial \bar{v}}{\partial x}\right),\end{aligned}\right\} \quad \text{....................(23)}$$

where

$$\lambda' = 2\lambda\mu/(\lambda+2\mu). \text{ ....(24)}$$

It follows that $\bar{u}$, $\bar{v}$ are determined by the same equations as if the problem were one of plane strain, provided that λ is replaced by λ'. The quantities $\bar{X}_x$, $\bar{Y}_y$, $\bar{X}_y$ are derived from a stress-function exactly in the same way as in problems of plane strain.

The average values of the displacements in any problem of plane stress are independent of the quantities β and F of Article 145, and are the same as if the problem were one of generalized plane stress. It appears from this statement that the investigation of states of plane strain may be applied to give an account of the effects produced by some distributions of forces which do not produce states of plane strain. The problems to which this method is applicable are problems of the equilibrium of a thin plate which is deformed in its own plane by forces applied in the plane. The actual values of the stresses and displacements produced in the plate are not determined, unless the forces are so distributed that the state is one of plane stress, but the average values across the thickness of the plate are determined. Any such problem can be solved by treating it as a problem of plane strain, and, in the results, substituting λ' for λ.

147. Introduction of nuclei of strain.

We may investigate solutions of the equations of plane strain which tend to become infinite at specified points. Such points must not be in the substance of the body, but they may be in cavities within the body. When this is the case, it is necessary to attend to the conditions which ensure that the displacement, rotation and strain are one-valued. When the points are outside the body, or on its boundary, these conditions do not in general need to be investigated. The displacement being determined by certain functions of $x + \iota y$, the singular points are singularities of these functions. Without making an exhaustive investigation of the possible singular points and their bearing upon the theory of Elasticity, we shall consider the states of stress that correspond with certain simple types of singular points.

148. Force operative at a point.

The simplest singularity is arrived at by taking

$$(\lambda + 2\mu)\Delta + \iota 2\mu\varpi = A(x + \iota y)^{-1}, \quad \text{.................(25)}$$

so that the origin is a simple pole. Equation (5) becomes in this case

$$\xi + \iota\eta = A\log(x + \iota y) = A(\log r + \iota\theta), \quad \text{..............(26)}$$

where r, θ are polar coordinates in the plane of (x, y). The corresponding formulæ for u, v are

$$\left.\begin{aligned} u &= \frac{A}{2\mu}\log r \qquad + \frac{\lambda+\mu}{2\mu(\lambda+2\mu)}A\frac{y^2}{r^2} + u', \\ v &= \frac{A}{2(\lambda+2\mu)}\theta - \frac{\lambda+\mu}{2\mu(\lambda+2\mu)}A\frac{xy}{r^2} + v'. \end{aligned}\right\} \quad \text{..............(27)}$$

To make v one-valued we must put

$$v' = -\frac{A}{2(\lambda+2\mu)}\theta, \quad u' = \frac{A}{2(\lambda+2\mu)}\log r.$$

The formulæ for u, v then become

$$\left.\begin{aligned} u &= \frac{\lambda+3\mu}{2\mu(\lambda+2\mu)}A\log r + \frac{\lambda+\mu}{2\mu(\lambda+2\mu)}A\frac{y^2}{r^2}, \\ v &= -\frac{\lambda+\mu}{2\mu(\lambda+2\mu)}A\frac{xy}{r^2}. \end{aligned}\right\} \quad \text{...........(28)}$$

The stress-components X_x, Y_y, X_y are given by the equations

$$\left.\begin{aligned} X_x &= A\frac{x}{r^2}\left(\frac{2\lambda+3\mu}{\lambda+2\mu} - \frac{2(\lambda+\mu)}{\lambda+2\mu}\frac{y^2}{r^2}\right), \\ Y_y &= A\frac{x}{r^2}\left(-\frac{\mu}{\lambda+2\mu} + \frac{2(\lambda+\mu)}{\lambda+2\mu}\frac{y^2}{r^2}\right), \\ X_y &= A\frac{y}{r^2}\left(\frac{\mu}{\lambda+2\mu} + \frac{2(\lambda+\mu)}{\lambda+2\mu}\frac{x^2}{r^2}\right). \end{aligned}\right\} \quad \text{..............(29)}$$

The origin must be in a cavity within the body; and the statical resultant of the tractions at the surface of the cavity is independent of the shape of the cavity. The resultant may be found by taking the cavity to be bounded (in the plane) by a circle with its centre at the origin. The component in the direction of the axis of x is expressed by the integral

$$\int_0^{2\pi} -\left(X_x\frac{x}{r} + X_y\frac{y}{r}\right) r\,d\theta,$$

which is equal to $-2A\pi$. The component in the direction of the axis of y vanishes, and the moment of the tractions about the centre of the cavity also vanishes. It follows that the state of stress expressed by (29) is that produced by a single force, of magnitude $2\pi A$, acting at the origin in the negative sense of the axis of x.

The effect of force at a point of a plate may be deduced by writing λ' in place of λ and replacing u, X_x, ... by $\bar{u}$, $\bar{X}_x$, ...

149. Force operative at a point of a boundary.

If the origin is at a point on a boundary, the term of (27) which contains θ can be one-valued independently of any adjustment of u', v'. It is merely necessary to fix the meaning of θ. In Fig. 17, OX is the initial line, drawn into the plate, and the angle $XOT = \alpha$. Then θ may be taken to lie in the interval

$$\alpha \geqslant \theta \geqslant -(\pi - \alpha).$$

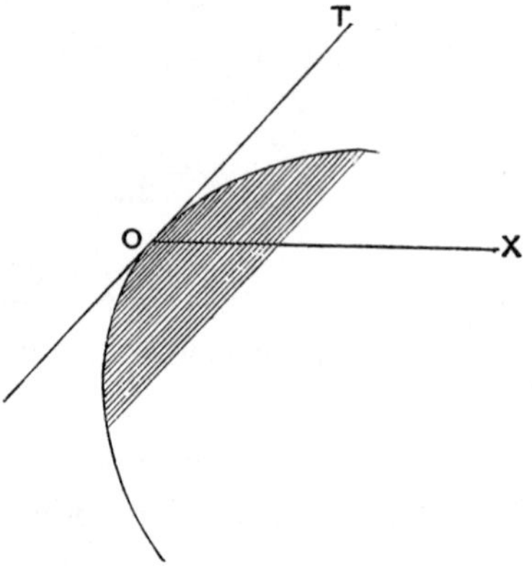

Fig. 17.

We may seek the stress-system that would correspond with (27) if u' and v' were put equal to zero. We should find

$$X_x = \frac{2(\lambda+\mu)}{\lambda+2\mu} A \frac{x^3}{r^4},$$

$$Y_y = \frac{2(\lambda+\mu)}{\lambda+2\mu} A \frac{xy^2}{r^4}, \quad X_y = \frac{2(\lambda+\mu)}{\lambda+2\mu} A \frac{x^2 y}{r^4}. \quad \text{...........(30)}$$

In polar coordinates the same stress-system is expressed by the equations

$$\widehat{rr} = \frac{2(\lambda+\mu)}{\lambda+2\mu} A \frac{\cos\theta}{r}, \quad \widehat{\theta\theta} = 0, \quad \widehat{r\theta} = 0. \quad \text{..............(31)}$$

This distribution of stress is described by Michell* as a "simple radial distribution." Such a distribution about a point cannot exist if the point is within the body. When the origin is a point on a boundary, the state of stress expressed by (31) is that due to a single force at the point. We calculate the resultant traction across a semicircle with its centre at the origin. The x-component of the resultant is

$$-\int_{-\pi+\alpha}^{\alpha} \widehat{rr} \,.\, \cos\theta \,.\, r d\theta,$$

or it is $-A \dfrac{\lambda+\mu}{\lambda+2\mu}\pi$. The y-component of the resultant is

$$-\int_{-\pi+\alpha}^{\alpha} \widehat{rr} \,.\, \sin\theta \,.\, r d\theta,$$

or it is zero. Thus the resultant applied force acts along the initial line and its amount is $\pi A(\lambda+\mu)/(\lambda+2\mu)$; the sense is that of the continuation of the initial line outwards from the body when A is positive.

* *London Math. Soc. Proc.*, vol. 32 (1900), p. 35.

This result gives us the solution of the problem of a plate with a straight boundary, to which force is applied at one point in a given direction. Taking that direction as initial line, and F as the amount of the force, the stress-system is expressed by the equations

$$\widehat{rr} = -\frac{2}{\pi} F \frac{\cos\theta}{r}, \quad \widehat{r\theta} = 0, \quad \widehat{\theta\theta} = 0, \quad \dots\dots\dots\dots\dots\dots(32)$$

and these quantities are of course averages taken through the thickness of the plate.

150. Case of a straight boundary.

In the particular case where the boundary is the axis of x, the axis of y penetrates into the plate, and the force at the origin is pressure F directed normally inwards, the average stresses and displacements are expressed by the equations

$$\overline{X}_x = -\frac{2}{\pi} F \frac{x^2 y}{r^4}, \quad \overline{Y}_y = -\frac{2}{\pi} F \frac{y^3}{r^4}, \quad \overline{X}_y = -\frac{2}{\pi} F \frac{xy^2}{r^4}, \quad \dots\dots\dots\dots(33)$$

and

$$\left.\begin{aligned} \overline{u} &= \frac{F}{2\pi(\lambda'+\mu)}\left(\theta - \frac{\pi}{2}\right) + \frac{F}{2\pi\mu}\frac{xy}{r^2}, \\ \overline{v} &= -\frac{F(\lambda'+2\mu)}{2\pi\mu(\lambda'+\mu)}\log r - \frac{F}{2\pi\mu}\frac{x^2}{r^2}. \end{aligned}\right\} \quad \dots\dots\dots\dots\dots\dots\dots\dots(34)$$

This solution* is the two-dimensional analogue of the solution of the problem of Boussinesq (Article 135). Since $\overline{u}$, $\overline{v}$ do not tend to zero at infinite distances, there is some difficulty in the application of the result to an infinite plate; but it may be regarded as giving correctly the local effect of force applied at a point of the boundary.

151. Additional results.

(i) The stress-function corresponding with (32) of Article 149 is $-\pi^{-1}Fr\theta\sin\theta$.

(ii) The effect of pressure distributed uniformly over a finite length of a straight boundary can be obtained by integration. If p is the pressure per unit of length, and the axis of x is the boundary, the axis of y being drawn into the body, the stress-function is found to be $\frac{1}{2}\pi^{-1}p\{(r_2^2\theta_2 - r_1^2\theta_1)\}$, where r_1, θ_1 and r_2, θ_2 are polar coordinates with the axis of x for initial line and the extremities of the part subject to pressure for origins. It may be shown that the lines of stress are confocal conics having these points as foci†.

(iii) *Force at an angle.*

The results obtained in Article 149 may be generalized by supposing that the boundary is made up of two straight edges meeting at the origin. Working, as before, with the case of plane strain, we have to replace the limit $-\pi+a$ of integration in the calculation of the force by $-\gamma+a$, where γ is the angle between the two straight edges. We find for the x-component of force at the origin the expression

$$-A\frac{\lambda+\mu}{\lambda+2\mu}\{\gamma + \sin\gamma\cos(2a-\gamma)\};$$

and, for the y-component of force at the origin, we find the expression

$$-A\frac{\lambda+\mu}{\lambda+2\mu}\{\sin\gamma\sin(2a-\gamma)\}.$$

* Flamant, *Paris, C. R.*, t. 114, 1892. For the verification by means of polarized light see Mesnager in *Rapports présentés au congrès international de physique*, t. 1, Paris 1900, p. 348. Cf. Carus Wilson, *Phil. Mag.* (Ser. 5), vol. 32 (1891), where an equivalent result obtained by Boussinesq is recorded.

† Michell, *London Math. Soc. Proc.*, vol. 34 (1902), p. 134.

The direction of maximum radial stress is not, in this case, that of the resultant force. The former of these is the initial line, making angles a and $a-\gamma$ with the edges; the latter makes with the same edges angles ϕ and $\gamma-\phi$, where

$$\tan\phi=\frac{\gamma\sin a-\sin\gamma\sin(a-\gamma)}{\gamma\cos a+\sin\gamma\cos(a-\gamma)}.$$

It follows that the angle a is given by the equation

$$\tan a=\frac{\gamma\sin\phi-\sin\gamma\sin(\gamma-\phi)}{\gamma\cos\phi-\sin\gamma\cos(\gamma-\phi)}.$$

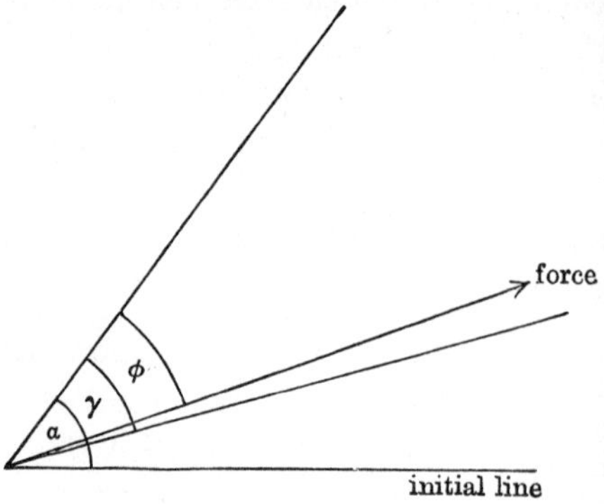

Fig. 18.

When a given force F is applied in a given direction, ϕ will be known, and a can be found from this equation; and the constant A can be determined in terms of the resultant force F. The conditions that the radial stress may be pressure everywhere are $a<\frac{\pi}{2}$, $\gamma-a<\frac{\pi}{2}$; and, in the extreme case $a=\frac{\pi}{2}$, we should have

$$\tan\phi=\frac{\gamma-\sin\gamma\cos\gamma}{\sin^2\gamma}.$$

The solution is due to Michell*, who remarks that for values of γ not exceeding $\frac{\pi}{2}$, the last result is nearly equivalent to a "rule of the middle third," that is to say, the extreme value of ϕ is nearly equal to $\frac{2}{3}\gamma$. If the line of action of the applied force lies within the middle third of the angle, the radial stress is one-signed.

The stress is given by (32), so that the laws of transmission of stress from an angle are (i) that the stress is purely radial, (ii) that it is inversely proportional to the distance from the angle, (iii) that it is proportional to the cosine of the angle made by the radius vector with a certain line in the plane of the angle.

(iv) *Pressure on faces of wedge.*

Equation (3) of Article 144 is satisfied if χ is a cubic function of x and y, say

$$\chi=ax^3+bx^2y+cxy^2+dy^3, \qquad \text{(34 A)}$$

and the constants can be adjusted so that the tractions on two given plane boundaries $y=m_1x$ and $y=m_2x$ may be proportional to x. Suppose, for example, that the axis of y is vertical, and its positive sense downwards, and that a wedge-shaped solid body occupies the region of space below the origin and between the two planes $y=-x\tan a$ and $y=x\tan\beta$. Let ρ be the density of the solid, σ that of fluid in contact with it along the plane $y=-x\tan a$, the plane $y=0$ being the free surface of the fluid, and the plane $y=x\tan\beta$ being free. The system being supposed to be in a state of plane strain the stress-components X_x, Y_y, X_y are given by the equations

$$X_x=\frac{\partial^2\chi}{\partial y^2},\quad Y_y=\frac{\partial^2\chi}{\partial x^2}-g\rho y,\quad X_y=-\frac{\partial^2\chi}{\partial x\,\partial y},$$

where χ has the above form (34 A), and the constants are determined by the conditions

$$-X_x\cos a-X_y\sin a=g\sigma y\cos a,\quad -X_y\cos a-Y_y\sin a=g\sigma y\sin a$$

at the plane $y=-x\tan a$, and the conditions

$$X_x\cos\beta-X_y\sin\beta=0,\quad X_y\cos\beta-Y_y\sin\beta=0$$

at the plane $y=x\tan\beta$.

* *loc. cit.*, p. 210.

These conditions give

$$\left.\begin{aligned}
a&=\frac{g}{6}\left\{\rho\frac{\tan\beta-\tan a}{(\tan a+\tan\beta)^3}-\sigma\frac{2-3\tan a\tan\beta-\tan^2 a}{(\tan a+\tan\beta)^3}\right\},\\
b&=\tfrac{1}{4}\left\{g\rho-\frac{g\sigma\tan a}{\tan a+\tan\beta}-6a(\tan\beta-\tan a)\right\},\\
c&=\tfrac{1}{2}\tan a\tan\beta\left(\frac{g\sigma}{\tan a+\tan\beta}-6a\right),\\
d&=\tfrac{1}{12}\tan^2\beta\left\{-g\rho-\frac{3g\sigma\tan a}{\tan a+\tan\beta}+6a(3\tan a+\tan\beta)\right\}.
\end{aligned}\right\}\quad\text{.............(34B)}$$

The solution is due to M. Lévy (*Paris, C. R.*, t. 127, 1898, p. 10), who proposed to utilize it in the discussion of the technically important problem of determining the stress in a masonry dam. In regard to this problem the reader may be referred to L. W. Atcherley and K. Pearson "On some disregarded points in the stability of Masonry Dams," *Drapers' Company Research Memoirs, Technical Series II.*, London 1904, K. Pearson and A. F. C. Pollard "An experimental study of the stresses in Masonry Dams," *Drapers' Company Research Memoirs, Technical Series V.*, London 1907, and L. F. Richardson, *London, Phil. Trans. R. Soc.* (Ser. A), vol. 210, 1911, p. 307. Lévy's solution leads to the result that there is a linear distribution of pressure and tangential traction over the base of the dam, but in the investigations here cited this result is shown to be improbable. Richardson gives an approximate numerical solution for a two-dimensional system having the contour of an actual dam.

152. Typical nuclei of strain in two dimensions.

(*a*) The formulæ (28) express the displacements in plane strain, corresponding with a single force of magnitude $2A\pi$ acting at the origin in the negative direction of the axis of x. We may obtain a new type of singular point by supposing that the following forces are applied near the origin:

parallel to the axis of x, $-2A\pi$ at the origin and $2A\pi$ at $(h, 0)$;

parallel to the axis of y, $-2A\pi$ at the origin and $2A\pi$ at $(0, h)$;

and we may pass to a limit by supposing that Ah remains constantly equal to B while h is diminished without limit. The resulting displacement is given by the equations

$$u=B\frac{\lambda+3\mu}{2\mu(\lambda+2\mu)}\frac{\partial}{\partial x}(\log r)+B\frac{\lambda+\mu}{2\mu(\lambda+2\mu)}\left(\frac{\partial}{\partial x}\frac{y^2}{r^2}-\frac{\partial}{\partial y}\frac{xy}{r^2}\right),$$

$$v=B\frac{\lambda+3\mu}{2\mu(\lambda+2\mu)}\frac{\partial}{\partial y}(\log r)+B\frac{\lambda+\mu}{2\mu(\lambda+2\mu)}\left(\frac{\partial}{\partial y}\frac{x^2}{r^2}-\frac{\partial}{\partial x}\frac{xy}{r^2}\right),$$

or

$$(u, v)=\frac{B}{\lambda+2\mu}\left(\frac{\partial}{\partial x}, \frac{\partial}{\partial y}\right)\log r. \quad\text{..............................(35)}$$

This displacement is expressible in polar coordinates by the formulæ

$$u_r=\frac{B}{\lambda+2\mu}\frac{1}{r},\quad u_\theta=0; \quad\text{....................................(36)}$$

it involves no dilatation or rotation. The stress is expressed by the formulæ

$$-\widehat{rr}=\widehat{\theta\theta}=\frac{2\mu}{\lambda+2\mu}\frac{B}{r^2},\quad \widehat{r\theta}=0, \quad\text{....................................(37)}$$

so that the origin is a point of pressure. If the origin is in a circular cavity there is uniform pressure of amount $2\mu Br^{-2}/(\lambda+2\mu)$ over the cavity.

(b) Again we may obtain a different type of singular point by supposing that the following forces are applied near the origin:

parallel to the axis of x, $2A\pi$ at the origin, $-2A\pi$ at the point $(0, h)$,

parallel to the axis of y, $-2A\pi$ at the origin, $2A\pi$ at the point $(h, 0)$;

and we may pass to a limit as in case (a). We thus obtain the following displacement:

$$u = -B\frac{\lambda+3\mu}{2\mu(\lambda+2\mu)}\frac{\partial}{\partial y}(\log r) - B\frac{\lambda+\mu}{2\mu(\lambda+2\mu)}\left(\frac{\partial}{\partial y}\frac{y^2}{r^2}+\frac{\partial}{\partial x}\frac{xy}{r^2}\right),$$

$$v = B\frac{\lambda+3\mu}{2\mu(\lambda+2\mu)}\frac{\partial}{\partial x}(\log r) + B\frac{\lambda+\mu}{2\mu(\lambda+2\mu)}\left(\frac{\partial}{\partial x}\frac{x^2}{r^2}+\frac{\partial}{\partial y}\frac{xy}{r^2}\right),$$

or

$$(u, v) = \frac{B}{\mu}\left(-\frac{\partial}{\partial y}, \frac{\partial}{\partial x}\right)\log r. \quad \text{.........(38)}$$

This displacement is expressible in polar coordinates by the formulæ

$$u_r = 0, \quad u_\theta = B/\mu r; \quad \text{.........(39)}$$

it involves no dilatation or rotation. The stress is expressed by the formulæ

$$\widehat{rr} = \widehat{\theta\theta} = 0, \quad \widehat{r\theta} = -2Br^{-2}, \quad \text{.........(40)}$$

so that the state of stress is that produced by a couple of magnitude $4\pi B$ applied at the origin.

(c) We may take $(\lambda+2\mu)\Delta + \iota 2\mu\varpi = C\log(x+\iota y)$. Since ϖ is not one-valued in a region containing the origin, we shall suppose the origin to be on the boundary. Equation (5) becomes

$$\xi + \iota\eta = C(x\log r - y\theta - x) + \iota C(y\log r + x\theta - y),$$

and the displacement may be taken to be given by the formulæ

$$u = \frac{C}{2\mu}(x\log r - x) - \frac{(2\lambda+3\mu)C}{2\mu(\lambda+2\mu)}y\theta,$$

$$v = \frac{C}{2(\lambda+2\mu)}(x\theta - y) - \frac{\lambda C}{2\mu(\lambda+2\mu)}y\log r.$$

The stress is then given by the formulæ

$$X_x = \frac{\lambda+\mu}{\lambda+2\mu}C\left(2\log r + \frac{y^2}{r^2}\right), \quad Y_y = -\frac{\lambda+\mu}{\lambda+2\mu}C\frac{y^2}{r^2}, \quad X_y = -\frac{\lambda+\mu}{\lambda+2\mu}C\left(\theta + \frac{xy}{r^2}\right).$$

We may take $\pi \geqslant \theta \geqslant 0$, the axis of x to be the boundary, and the axis of y to be drawn into the body. Then the traction on the boundary is tangential traction on the part of the boundary for which x is negative; and the traction is of amount $C\pi(\lambda+\mu)/(\lambda+2\mu)$, and it acts towards the origin if C is positive, and away from the origin if C is negative. The most important parts of v, near the origin, are the terms containing $\log r$ and θ, and if x is negative both these have the opposite sign to C, so that they are positive when C is negative. We learn from this example that tangential traction over a portion of a surface tends to depress the material on the side towards which it acts*.

153. Transformation of plane strain.

We have seen that states of plane strain are determined in terms of functions of a complex variable $x + \iota y$, and that the poles and logarithmic infinities of these functions correspond with points of application of force to the body which undergoes the plane strain. If the two-dimensional region occupied by the body is conformally represented upon a different two-dimensional region by

* Cf. L. N. G. Filon, *London, Phil. Trans. R. Soc.* (Ser. A), vol. 198 (1902).

means of a functional relation between complex variables $x' + \iota y'$ and $x + \iota y$, a new state of plane strain, in a body of a different shape from that originally treated, will be found by transforming the function $(\lambda + 2\mu)\Delta + \iota 2\mu\varpi$ into a function of $x' + \iota y'$ by means of the same functional relation. Since poles and logarithmic infinities are conserved in such conformal transformations, the points of application of isolated forces in the two states will be corresponding points. We have found in Article 149 the state of plane strain, in a body bounded by a straight edge and otherwise unlimited, which would be produced by isolated forces acting in given directions at given points of the edge. We may therefore determine a state of plane strain in a cylindrical body of any form of section, subjected to isolated forces at given points of its boundary, whenever we can effect a conformal representation of the cross-section of the body upon a half-plane. It will in general be found, however, that the isolated forces are not the only forces acting on the body; in fact, a boundary free from traction is not in general transformed into a boundary free from traction. This defect of correspondence is the main difficulty in the way of advance in the theory of two-dimensional elastic systems.

We may approach the matter from a different point of view, by considering the stress-function as a solution of $\nabla_1^4\chi = 0$. If we change the independent variables from x, y to x', y', where x' and y' are conjugate functions of x and y, the form of the equation is not conserved, and thus the form of the stress-function in the (x', y') region cannot be inferred from its form in the (x, y) region*.

154. Inversion†.

The transformation of inversion, $x' + \iota y' = (x + \iota y)^{-1}$, constitutes an exception to the statement at the end of Article 153. It will be more convenient in this case to avoid complex variables, and to change the independent variables by means of the equations

$$x' = k^2x/r^2, \quad y' = k^2y/r^2,$$

in which k is the constant of inversion, and r^2 stands for $x^2 + y^2$. We write in like manner r'^2 for $x'^2 + y'^2$. Expressed in polar coordinates the equation $\nabla_1^4\chi = 0$ becomes

$$\left[\frac{1}{r}\frac{\partial}{\partial r}\left(r\frac{\partial}{\partial r}\right) + \frac{1}{r^2}\frac{\partial^2}{\partial\theta^2}\right]\left[\frac{1}{r}\frac{\partial}{\partial r}\left(r\frac{\partial\chi}{\partial r}\right) + \frac{1}{r^2}\frac{\partial^2\chi}{\partial\theta^2}\right] = 0; \quad \text{.........(41)}$$

and when the variables are changed from r, θ to r', θ, this equation may be shown to become

$$\frac{r'^6}{k^8}\left[\frac{1}{r'}\frac{\partial}{\partial r'}\left(r'\frac{\partial}{\partial r'}\right) + \frac{1}{r'^2}\frac{\partial^2}{\partial\theta^2}\right]\left[\frac{1}{r'}\frac{\partial}{\partial r'}\left\{r'\frac{\partial}{\partial r'}(r'^2\chi)\right\} + \frac{1}{r'^2}\frac{\partial^2}{\partial\theta^2}(r'^2\chi)\right] = 0. \quad \text{...(42)}$$

* The direct determination of stress, in two-dimensional elastic systems referred to orthogonal curvilinear coordinates, is discussed by S. D. Carothers, *London, Roy. Soc. Proc.* (Ser. A), vol. 97 (1920), p. 110. Additional references will be found in Article 187 *infra*.

† Michell, *loc. cit.*, p. 211.

It follows that, when χ is expressed in terms of x', y', $r'^2\chi$ satisfies the equation

$$\left(\frac{\partial^4}{\partial x'^4}+\frac{\partial^4}{\partial y'^4}+2\frac{\partial^4}{\partial x'^2\partial y'^2}\right)(r'^2\chi)=0;\quad\ldots\ldots(43)$$

and therefore $r'^2\chi$ is a stress-function in the plane of (x', y').

The stress-components derived from $r'^2\chi$ are given by the equations*

$$\left.\begin{aligned}\widehat{r'r'}&=\frac{1}{r'^2}\frac{\partial^2}{\partial\theta^2}(r'^2\chi)+\frac{1}{r'}\frac{\partial}{\partial r'}(r'^2\chi),\\ \widehat{\theta'\theta'}&=\frac{\partial^2}{\partial r'^2}(r'^2\chi),\quad \widehat{r'\theta'}=-\frac{\partial}{\partial r'}\frac{1}{r'}\frac{\partial}{\partial\theta}(r'^2\chi),\end{aligned}\right\}\quad\ldots\ldots(44)$$

where θ' is the same as θ; and we find

$$\left.\begin{aligned}\widehat{r'r'}&=\ \ r^2.\widehat{rr}+2\left(\chi-r\frac{\partial\chi}{\partial r}\right),\\ \widehat{\theta'\theta'}&=\ \ r^2.\widehat{\theta\theta}+2\left(\chi-r\frac{\partial\chi}{\partial r}\right),\\ \widehat{r'\theta'}&=-r^2.\widehat{r\theta},\end{aligned}\right\}\quad\ldots\ldots(45)$$

where $\widehat{rr}$, $\widehat{\theta\theta}$, $\widehat{r\theta}$ are the stress-components derived from χ, expressed in terms of r, θ. Thus the stress in the (r', θ') system differs from that in the (r, θ) system by the factor r^2, by the reversal of the shearing stress $\widehat{r\theta}$, and by the superposition of a normal traction $2\{\chi-r(\partial\chi/\partial r)\}$, the same in all directions round a point. It follows that lines of stress are transformed into lines of stress, and a boundary free from stress is transformed into a boundary under normal traction only. Further this normal traction is constant. To prove this, we observe that the conditions of zero traction across a boundary are

$$\cos(x,\nu)\frac{\partial^2\chi}{\partial y^2}-\cos(y,\nu)\frac{\partial^2\chi}{\partial x\partial y}=0,\quad -\cos(x,\nu)\frac{\partial^2\chi}{\partial x\partial y}+\cos(y,\nu)\frac{\partial^2\chi}{\partial x^2}=0,$$

and these are the same as

$$\frac{\partial}{\partial s}\left(\frac{\partial\chi}{\partial y}\right)=0,\quad \frac{\partial}{\partial s}\left(\frac{\partial\chi}{\partial x}\right)=0,$$

where ds denotes an element of the boundary. Hence $\partial\chi/\partial x$ and $\partial\chi/\partial y$ are constant along the boundary, and we have

$$\frac{d}{ds}\left(\chi-r\frac{\partial\chi}{\partial r}\right)=\frac{d}{ds}\left(\chi-x\frac{\partial\chi}{\partial x}-y\frac{\partial\chi}{\partial y}\right)=\frac{d\chi}{ds}-\frac{dx}{ds}\frac{\partial\chi}{\partial x}-\frac{dy}{ds}\frac{\partial\chi}{\partial y}=0.$$

It follows that a boundary free from traction in the (r, θ) system is transformed into a boundary subject to normal tension in the (r', θ') system. This tension has the same value at all points of the transformed boundary, and its effect is known and can be allowed for.

* See the theorem (ii) of Article 59.

155. Equilibrium of a circular disk under forces in its plane*.

(i) We may now apply the transformation of inversion to the problem of Articles 149, 150.

Let O' be a point of a fixed straight line $O'A$ (Fig. 19). If $O'A$ were the boundary of the section of a body in which there was plane strain produced by a force F directed along

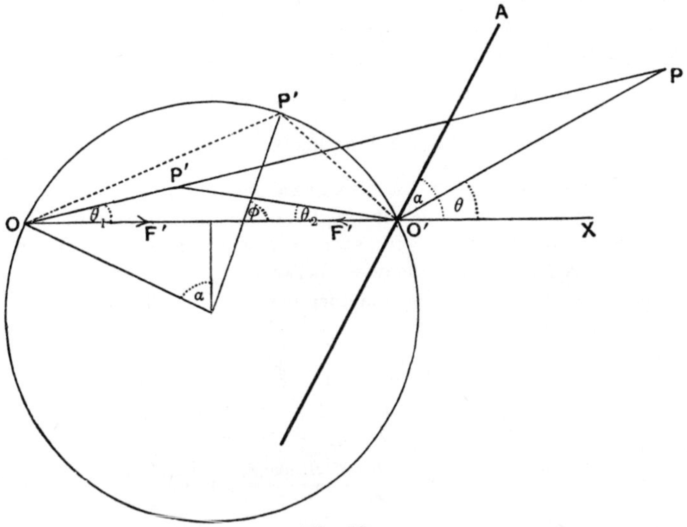

Fig. 19.

$OO'X$, the stress-function at P would be $-\pi^{-1}Fr\theta\sin\theta$, where r stands for $O'P$; and this may be written $-\pi^{-1}F\theta y$, where y is the ordinate of P referred to $O'X$. When we invert the system with respect to O, taking $k=OO'$, P is transformed to P', and the new stress-function is $-\pi^{-1}r_1{}^2F(\theta_1+\theta_2)k^2y'/r_1{}^2$, where θ_1 and $\pi-\theta_2$ are the angles XOP', $XO'P'$, and we have written r_1 for OP', and y' for the ordinate of P' referred to OX. Further the line $O'A$ is transformed into a circle through O, O', and the angle $2a$ which OO' subtends at the centre is equal to twice the angle $AO'X$. Hence the function $-\pi^{-1}F'y'(\theta_1+\theta_2)$ is the stress-function corresponding with equal and opposite isolated forces, each of magnitude F', acting as thrust in the line OO', together with a certain constant normal tension round the bounding circle.

To find the magnitude of this tension, we observe that, when P' is on the circle,

$$r_1 \operatorname{cosec}\theta_2 = r_2 \operatorname{cosec}\theta_1 = k \operatorname{cosec}(\theta_1+\theta_2) = 2R,$$

where R is the radius of the circle. Further, the formulæ (1) of Article 144 give for the stress-components

$$X_x = -\frac{2F'}{\pi}\left(\frac{\cos^3\theta_1}{r_1}+\frac{\cos^3\theta_2}{r_2}\right), \quad Y_y = -\frac{2F'}{\pi}\left(\frac{\cos\theta_1\sin^2\theta_1}{r_1}+\frac{\cos\theta_2\sin^2\theta_2}{r_2}\right),$$

$$X_y = -\frac{2F'}{\pi}\left(\frac{\cos^2\theta_1\sin\theta_1}{r_1}-\frac{\cos^2\theta_2\sin\theta_2}{r_2}\right).$$

* The results of (i) and (ii) are due to Hertz, *Zeitschr. f. Math. u. Physik*, Bd. 28 (1883), or *Ges. Werke*, Bd. 1, p. 283, and Michell, *London Math. Soc. Proc.*, vol. 32 (1900), p. 35, and vol. 34 (1902), p. 134.

Also the angle (ϕ in the figure) which the central radius vector (R) to P' makes with the axis of x, when P' is on the circle, is $\frac{1}{2}\pi - a + 2\theta_1$, or $\frac{1}{2}\pi + \theta_1 - \theta_2$. Hence the normal tension across the circle is

$$X_x \sin^2(\theta_2 - \theta_1) + Y_y \cos^2(\theta_2 - \theta_1) + 2X_y \sin(\theta_2 - \theta_1)\cos(\theta_2 - \theta_1),$$

and this is $-(F' \sin a)/\pi R$.

If the circle is subjected to the two forces F' only there is stress compounded of mean tension, equal at all points to $(F' \sin a)/\pi R$, and the simple radial distributions about the points O and O' in which the radial components are

$$-(2F' \cos\theta_1)/\pi r_1 \text{ and } -(2F' \cos\theta_2)/\pi r_2.$$

(ii) Circular plate subjected to forces acting on its rim.

If the force F' is applied at O in the direction OO' (see Fig. 19) and suitable tractions are applied over the rest of the rim the stress-function may consist of the single term $-\pi^{-1}F'y\theta_1$. Let r and θ be polar coordinates with origin at the centre of the circle and initial line parallel to OO'. The angle (r, r_1) between the radii vectores drawn from the centre and from O to any point on the circumference is $\frac{1}{2}\pi - \theta_2$. The stress-system referred to (r_1, θ_1) is given by the equations

$$\widehat{r_1r_1} = -(2F' \cos\theta_1)/(\pi r_1), \quad \widehat{\theta_1\theta_1} = 0, \quad \widehat{r_1\theta_1} = 0;$$

and therefore, when referred to (r, θ), it is given, at any point of the boundary, by the equations

$$\widehat{rr} = -\frac{2F'}{\pi}\frac{\cos\theta_1 \sin^2\theta_2}{r_1}, \quad \widehat{\theta\theta} = -\frac{2F'}{\pi}\frac{\cos\theta_1\cos^2\theta_2}{r_1}, \quad \widehat{r\theta} = \frac{2F'}{\pi}\frac{\cos\theta_1\cos\theta_2\sin\theta_2}{r_1},$$

or we have at the boundary

$$\widehat{rr} = -\frac{F'}{\pi}\frac{\cos\theta_1\sin\theta_2}{R}, \quad \widehat{r\theta} = \frac{F'}{\pi}\frac{\cos\theta_1\cos\theta_2}{R},$$

and this is the same as

$$\widehat{rr} = -\frac{F'\sin a}{2\pi R} - \frac{F'}{2\pi R}\sin(\theta_2 - \theta_1), \quad \widehat{r\theta} = \frac{F'\cos a}{2\pi R} + \frac{F'}{2\pi R}\cos(\theta_2 - \theta_1),$$

where a, $=\theta_1 + \theta_2$, is the acute angle subtended at a point on the circumference by the chord OO'. Hence the traction across the boundary can be regarded as compounded of

(i) uniform tension $-\frac{1}{2}(F' \sin a)/\pi R$ in the direction of the normal,

(ii) uniform tangential traction $\frac{1}{2}(F' \cos a)/\pi R$,

(iii) uniform traction $-\frac{1}{2}F'/\pi R$ in the direction OO'.

Let any number of forces be applied to various points of the boundary. If they would keep a rigid body in equilibrium they satisfy the condition $\Sigma F' \cos a = 0$, for $\Sigma F'R \cos a$ is the sum of their moments about the centre. Also the uniform tractions corresponding with (iii) in the above solution would have a zero resultant at every point of the rim. Hence the result of superposing the stress-systems of type (32) belonging to each of the forces would be to give us the state of stress in the plate under the actual forces and a normal tension of amount $-\Sigma(F' \sin a)/2\pi R$ at all points of the rim. The terms $F' \sin a$ of this summation are equal to the normal (inward) components of the applied forces. Mean tension, equal at all points to $\Sigma(F' \sin a)/2\pi R$, could be superposed upon this distribution of stress, and then the plate would be subject to the action of the forces F' only.

(iii) Heavy disk*.

The state of stress in a heavy disk resting on a horizontal plane can also be found. Let w be the weight per unit of area, and let r, θ be polar coordinates with origin at the point of contact A and initial line drawn vertically upwards, as in Fig. 20.

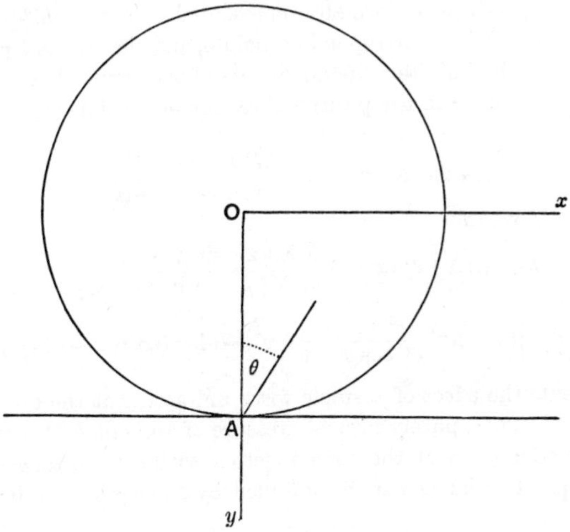

Fig. 20.

The stress can be shown to be compounded of the systems

(i) $X_x = \frac{1}{2}w(y+R), \quad Y_y = -\frac{1}{2}w(y-R), \quad X_y = -\frac{1}{2}wx,$

(ii) $\widehat{rr} = -2wR^2r^{-1}\cos\theta, \quad \widehat{\theta\theta}=0, \quad \widehat{r\theta}=0.$

The traction across any horizontal section is pressure directed radially from A, and is of amount $\frac{1}{2}wr^{-1}(4R^2\cos^2\theta - r^2)$; the traction across any section drawn through A is horizontal tension of amount

$$\tfrac{1}{2}w(2R\cos\theta - r).$$

156. Examples of transformation.

(i) The direct method of Article 153 will lead, by the substitution $x+\iota y = k^2/(x'+\iota y')$ in the formula

$$(\lambda+2\mu)\Delta + 2\mu\iota\varpi = A(x+\iota y-k)^{-1}, \quad \text{.........................(46)}$$

to a stress-system in the plane of (x', y'), in which simple radial stress at the point $(k, 0)$ is superposed upon a constant simple tension (X_x) in the direction of the axis x'. If the boundary in the (x, y) plane is given by the equation $y=(x-k)\tan\alpha$, the boundary in the (x', y') plane will be a circle, and the results given in (i) and (ii) of Article 155 can be deduced.

(ii) By the transformation $x+\iota y=(x'+\iota y')^n$ the wedge-shaped region between $y'=0$ and $y'/x'=\tan\pi/n$ is conformally represented on the half-plane $y>0$. If we substitute for $x+\iota y$ in (46) we shall obtain a state of stress in the wedge-shaped region bounded by the above two lines in the plane of (x', y'), which would be due to a single force applied at

* The solution is due to Michell, *loc. cit.*, p. 210. Figures showing the distribution of stress in this case and in several other cases, some of which have been discussed in this Chapter, are drawn by Michell.

$(k^{1/n}, 0)$, and certain tractions distributed over the boundaries. When $n=2$ the traction over $y'=0$ vanishes and that on $x'=0$ becomes tension of amount proportional to

$$1/(y'^2+k)^2.$$

(iii) By the transformation $z=(e^{z'}-1)/(e^{z'}+1)$, where $z=x+\iota y$ and $z'=x'+\iota y'$, the strip between $y'=0$ and $y'=\pi$ is conformally represented upon the half-plane $y>0$, so that the origins in the two planes are corresponding points, and the points $(\pm 1, 0)$ in the plane of (x, y) correspond with the infinitely distant points of the strip. Let a single force F act at the origin in the (x, y) plane in the positive direction of the axis of y. Then the solution is given by the equation

$$(\lambda+2\mu)\,\Delta+2\mu\iota\varpi=-\frac{\iota F}{\pi}\frac{\lambda+2\mu}{\lambda+\mu}\frac{1}{x+\iota y}.$$

Transforming to (x', y') we find

$$(\lambda+2\mu)\,\Delta+\iota 2\mu\varpi=-\frac{F}{\pi}\frac{\lambda+2\mu}{\lambda+\mu}\frac{\sin y'+\iota\sinh x'}{\cosh x'-\cos y'},$$

and $$\xi+\iota\eta=\frac{F}{\pi}\frac{\lambda+2\mu}{\lambda+\mu}\left\{\left(2\tan^{-1}\frac{e^{x'}\sin y'}{e^{x'}\cos y'-1}-y'\right)-\iota\log(\cosh x'-\cos y')\right\}+\text{const.}$$

This solution represents the effect of a single force $2F$, acting at the origin in the positive direction of the axis of y', and purely normal pressure of amount $F/(1+\cosh x')$ per unit of length, acting on the edge $y'=\pi$ of the strip, together with certain tangential tractions on the edges of the strip. The latter can be annulled by superposing a displacement (u', v') upon the displacement

$$\left(\frac{\xi}{2\mu}+\frac{\lambda+\mu}{2\mu(\lambda+2\mu)}y'\frac{\partial\xi}{\partial y'},\ \frac{\eta}{2(\lambda+2\mu)}-\frac{\lambda+\mu}{2\mu(\lambda+2\mu)}y'\frac{\partial\eta}{\partial y'}\right),$$

provided that

$$v'+\iota u'=\frac{\lambda+\mu}{2\mu(\lambda+2\mu)}(\eta-\iota\xi),$$

and this additional displacement does not affect the normal tractions on the boundary.

APPENDIX TO CHAPTERS VIII AND IX

VOLTERRA'S THEORY OF DISLOCATIONS

156 A. THE analytical possibility that the stress-function of Article 144 may be many-valued was explicitly treated by J. H. Michell*, under the condition that the displacement must be expressed by one-valued functions. The analytical possibility of displacements expressed by many-valued functions is implicitly present in Article 148, where the ambiguity was removed for the reason that an actual physical displacement would appear to be necessarily one-valued. In a body, such as a hollow cylinder, occupying a multiply-connected region of space, there is, however, a physical possibility of many-valued displacements. Suppose, for example, that a thin slice of material, bounded by two axial planes, is removed from such a cylinder, and the new surfaces thus formed are brought together and joined. The body so formed will be in a state of initial stress (Article 75), which may be determined by assuming the displacement of a point in the hollow cylinder, resolved at right angles to the axial plane through the point, or rather the ratio of this displacement to distance from the axis, to be many-valued with a cyclic constant, and adjusting the constant so that the corresponding points of the two axial planes, after displacement, may coincide. The possibility of such interpretations of many-valued displacements appears to have been first indicated by G. Weingarten†. The subject was discussed with more detail by A. Timpe‡ for two-dimensional systems, such as a plane circular ring. A more general theory was afterwards developed by V. Volterra in a series of notes, and a comprehensive account of the theory with some improvements by E. Cesàro was published by the same author§. He describes the kind of deformations to which the theory is applicable by the name "distorsioni." I have ventured to call them "dislocations‖."

The multiply-connected region occupied by the body can be reduced to a simply-connected region by means of a system of barriers¶. For example, the

* *London, Proc. Math. Soc.*, vol. 30 (1900), p. 103.

† *Roma, Acc. Linc. Rend.* (Ser. 5), t. 10 (1 Sem.), 1901, p. 57.

‡ *Probleme d. Spannungsverteilung in ebenen Systemen einfach gelöst mit Hilfe d. Airyschen Funktion*, Göttingen Diss., Leipzig 1905.

§ V. Volterra, "Sur l'équilibre des corps élastiques multiplement connexes," *Paris, Ann. Éc. norm.* (Sér. 3), t. 24, 1907, pp. 401—517.

‖ A discussion of the theory of dislocations in the case of two-dimensional systems will be found in a paper by L. N. G. Filon, *Brit. Assoc. Rep.*, 1921, p. 305.

¶ In regard to the theory of multiple connectivity reference may be made to J. C. Maxwell, *A treatise on Electricity and Magnetism*, vol. 1, 2nd Edn., Oxford 1881, pp. 16—24, or H. Lamb, *Hydrodynamics*, 4th Edn., Cambridge 1916, pp. 47—55.

region between the bounding cylindrical surfaces of a hollow cylinder can be rendered simply-connected by a plane barrier passing through the axis of the cylinder, and having that axis for an edge. The stress in the body, and therefore also the strain, must be one-valued and continuous, but the displacement may be discontinuous in crossing the barrier. With a view to determining the nature of the possible discontinuities we shall (*a*) prove a general theorem for the expression of a displacement answering to given strain-components, and then (*b*) use this theorem to determine the nature of the discontinuities. We shall then, (*c*) and (*d*), apply the theory to two particular examples.

(*a*) *Displacement answering to given strain.*

The displacement (u, v, w) and the rotation $(\varpi_x, \varpi_y, \varpi_z)$ are not necessarily one-valued, but the strain-components $e_{xx}, \ldots$ have definite values at any point (x, y, z). Let (u_0, v_0, w_0) denote one of the values of the displacement at a point M_0 or (x_0, y_0, z_0). Then one of the values (u_1, v_1, w_1) of the displacement at another point M_1 or (x_1, y_1, z_1) can be obtained by evaluating the line-integral

$$\int_{M_0}^{M} \frac{\partial u}{\partial x} dx + \frac{\partial u}{\partial y} dy + \frac{\partial u}{\partial z} dz$$

taken along any path joining the points M_0, M_1. But different values may be obtained by choosing different paths of integration. Now we have in general

$$\frac{\partial u}{\partial x} = e_{xx}, \quad \frac{\partial u}{\partial y} = \tfrac{1}{2} e_{xy} - \varpi_z, \quad \frac{\partial u}{\partial z} = \tfrac{1}{2} e_{zx} + \varpi_y.$$

Hence
$$u_1 - u_0 = \int_{M_0}^{M_1} e_{xx} dx + \tfrac{1}{2} e_{xy} dy + \tfrac{1}{2} e_{zx} dz + \int_{M_0}^{M_1} \varpi_y dz - \varpi_z dy. \quad \ldots\ldots(1)$$

Let $(\varpi_x^{(0)}, \varpi_y^{(0)}, \varpi_z^{(0)})$ denote one of the values of the rotation at the point M_0, or *the* value if there is only one. Then

$$\int_{M_0}^{M_1} \varpi_y dz - \varpi_z dy = \int_{M_0}^{M_1} \varpi_z d(y_1 - y) - \varpi_y d(z_1 - z)$$

$$= \varpi_y^{(0)} (z_1 - z_0) - \varpi_z^{(0)} (y_1 - y_0) - \int_{M_0}^{M_1} (y_1 - y)\, d\varpi_z - (z_1 - z)\, d\varpi_y,$$

where, for example,

$$d\varpi_z = \frac{\partial \varpi_z}{\partial x} dx + \frac{\partial \varpi_z}{\partial y} dy + \frac{\partial \varpi_z}{\partial z} dz.$$

Now we have identically

$$2\frac{\partial \varpi_z}{\partial x} = \frac{\partial e_{xy}}{\partial x} - 2\frac{\partial e_{xx}}{\partial y}, \quad 2\frac{\partial \varpi_y}{\partial x} = 2\frac{\partial e_{xx}}{\partial z} - \frac{\partial \epsilon_{zx}}{\partial x},$$

$$2\frac{\partial \varpi_z}{\partial y} = 2\frac{\partial e_{yy}}{\partial x} - \frac{\partial e_{xy}}{\partial y}, \quad 2\frac{\partial \varpi_y}{\partial y} = \frac{\partial e_{xy}}{\partial z} - \frac{\partial e_{yz}}{\partial x},$$

$$2\frac{\partial \varpi_z}{\partial z} = \frac{\partial e_{yz}}{\partial x} - \frac{\partial e_{zx}}{\partial y}, \quad 2\frac{\partial \varpi_y}{\partial z} = \frac{\partial e_{zx}}{\partial z} - 2\frac{\partial e_{zz}}{\partial x},$$

and we thus obtain the equation

$$u_1 = u_0 + \varpi_y^{(0)}(z_1 - z_0) - \varpi_z^{(0)}(y_1 - y_0) + \int_{M_0}^{M_1} \xi dx + \eta dy + \zeta dz, \quad \ldots(2)$$

where

$$\left.\begin{aligned} \xi &= e_{xx} + (y_1 - y)\left(\frac{\partial e_{xx}}{\partial y} - \tfrac{1}{2}\frac{\partial e_{xy}}{\partial x}\right) + (z_1 - z)\left(\frac{\partial e_{xx}}{\partial z} - \tfrac{1}{2}\frac{\partial e_{zx}}{\partial x}\right), \\ \eta &= \tfrac{1}{2}e_{xy} + (y_1 - y)\left(\tfrac{1}{2}\frac{\partial e_{xy}}{\partial y} - \frac{\partial e_{yy}}{\partial x}\right) + (z_1 - z)\left(\tfrac{1}{2}\frac{\partial e_{xy}}{\partial z} - \tfrac{1}{2}\frac{\partial e_{yz}}{\partial x}\right), \\ \zeta &= \tfrac{1}{2}e_{zx} + (y_1 - y)\left(\tfrac{1}{2}\frac{\partial e_{zx}}{\partial y} - \tfrac{1}{2}\frac{\partial e_{yz}}{\partial x}\right) + (z_1 - z)\left(\tfrac{1}{2}\frac{\partial e_{zx}}{\partial z} - \frac{\partial e_{zz}}{\partial x}\right). \end{aligned}\right\} \quad \ldots(3)$$

Similar equations can be obtained for v_1 and w_1. The proof is due to Cesàro.

(*b*) *Discontinuity at a barrier.*

Now suppose the multiply-connected region to be reduced to a simply-connected one by means of a system of barriers. We are going to apply equation (1) to a circuit, so that M_1 and M_0 coincide, taking for the path of integration a *non-evanescible* circuit, or one which cannot be contracted to a point without passing out of the region. We shall take the circuit to cut a particular barrier Ω once, at a point M, and not to cut any of the other barriers. To fix ideas we may, if we like, think of the region as the doubly-connected region between two coaxial cylinders, having the axis of z as their common axis, and the barrier Ω as formed by that part of the plane $x = 0$, lying between the two cylinders, on which y is positive. But the result is general, not restricted to this particular example. Then we take M_0 and M_1 to be close to M on opposite sides of Ω, and treat the path of integration as not cutting Ω.

It will be observed that ξ, η, ζ, given by (3), are such that the equations

$$\frac{\partial \zeta}{\partial y} - \frac{\partial \eta}{\partial z} = 0, \quad \frac{\partial \xi}{\partial z} - \frac{\partial \zeta}{\partial x} = 0, \quad \frac{\partial \eta}{\partial x} - \frac{\partial \xi}{\partial y} = 0$$

are satisfied identically in virtue of equations (25) of Article 17, and therefore the value of the integral

$$\int_{M_0}^{M_1} \xi dx + \eta dy + \zeta dz \quad \ldots\ldots\ldots\ldots\ldots\ldots(4)$$

is the same for all *reconcileable* circuits, that is to say such as can be deformed, the one into the other, without passing out of the region. For it is possible to construct a surface S, having any two such circuits for edges, and lying entirely in the region, and then the difference between the values of the integral (4) taken along the two circuits is equal to the integral

$$\iint \left\{\left(\frac{\partial \zeta}{\partial y} - \frac{\partial \eta}{\partial z}\right) l + \left(\frac{\partial \xi}{\partial z} - \frac{\partial \zeta}{\partial x}\right) m + \left(\frac{\partial \eta}{\partial x} - \frac{\partial \xi}{\partial y}\right) n\right\} dS,$$

taken over S, where l, m, n denote the direction-cosines of the normal to S drawn in a determinate sense; and this surface integral vanishes. Hence, whatever point on Ω we take for M, the integral (4) has the same value for all circuits beginning and ending at M, provided they cut the barrier Ω nowhere except at M and do not cut any other barrier.

It follows that $u_1 - u_0$ has, at each point M on Ω, a definite value which may depend upon the position of M. The like holds for $v_1 - v_0$ and $w_1 - w_0$.

We now consider the variation of $u_1 - u_0$ as M moves on Ω. Let M and M' be any two points on Ω, M_0 and M_1 points close to M on opposite sides of Ω, M_0' and M_1' points close to M' on opposite sides of Ω, (u_0', v_0', w_0') the displacement at M_0', (u_1', v_1', w_1') that at M_1'. The theorem expressed by equation (2) may be applied to the path from M_0 to M_0', coinciding with a curve traced on Ω and joining M to M'. It gives

$$u_0' - u_0 = \varpi_y^{(0)} (z_0' - z_0) - \varpi_z^{(0)} (y_0' - y_0) + \int_M^{M'} \xi dx + \eta dy + \zeta dz.$$

The same theorem may be applied to the path from M_1 to M_1', coinciding with the same curve, and gives

$$u_1' - u_1 = \varpi_y^{(1)} (z_1' - z_1) - \varpi_z^{(1)} (y_1' - y_1) + \int_M^{M'} \xi dx + \eta dy + \zeta dz.$$

Since (x_1, y_1, z_1) is the same as (x_0, y_0, z_0) and (x_1', y_1', z_1') is the same as (x_0', y_0', z_0'), these equations give

$$u_1' - u_0' = (u_1 - u_0) + (\varpi_y^{(1)} - \varpi_y^{(0)}) (z_0' - z_0) - (\varpi_z^{(1)} - \varpi_z^{(0)}) (y_0' - y_0),$$

where the coefficients of $z_0' - z_0$ and $y_0' - y_0$ are independent of (x_0', y_0', z_0'). Similar equations hold for $v_1' - v_0'$ and $w_1' - w_0'$.

It thus appears that the discontinuities of u, v, w at Ω are expressed by equations of the form

$$\left.\begin{aligned} u_1 - u_0 &= l_1 + p_2 z - p_3 y, \\ v_1 - v_0 &= l_2 + p_3 x - p_1 z, \\ w_1 - w_0 &= l_3 + p_1 y - p_2 x, \end{aligned}\right\} \quad \text{........................(5)}$$

where l_1, l_2, l_3 and p_1, p_2, p_3 are constant over Ω. This is Weingarten's result. It may be interpreted in the statement that the displacement of the matter on one side of a barrier relative to the matter on the other side is a displacement which would be possible in a rigid body.

Let the multiply-connected region occupied by the body be reduced to a simply-connected region by a system of barriers, and suppose each barrier to be the seat of an actual physical breach of continuity, such as could be effected by cutting the material along the barrier. After such dissection the body will not be divided into parts, but will still be a coherent body. The effect of the dissection will be that the region of space occupied by the body will become a simply-connected region. Let one of the faces of the dissected body formed by any barrier be displaced relatively to the other by a small displacement, which would be possible for a rigid body, that is to say let the face be moved as a whole by translation and rotation. Let this be done for each pair of faces, and thereafter let opposing faces be joined, by removal or insertion of a thin sheet of matter of the same kind as that forming the original body. The new body so formed will, in general, be in a state of initial stress. The operation of deriving the new body from the original body is a *dislocation*.

It appears that, if dislocations are permitted, the theorem of Article 118 requires modification. To secure uniqueness of solution, it is necessary that the six constants of each barrier, occurring in equations (5), should be given.

It is open to us either to regard the displacement in the body, occupying the multiply-connected region, as one-valued and discontinuous at the barriers, or as many-valued and continuous in the region, supposed without barriers. In the latter case the sum of the increments of it taken along any such circuit as has been described is the same for all reconcileable circuits passing through a given point. Thus the position of the barriers is, to a great extent, immaterial. In a body, which has suffered a dislocation, and is consequently in a state of initial stress, there is, in general, nothing to show the seat of the dislocation.

A similar result occurs in the theory of electric currents. The magnetic potential due to a unit current flowing in a closed circuit is many-valued and continuous in the multiply-connected region surrounding the linear conductor, which carries the current. One of its values at any point is the solid angle subtended at the point by any surface having the line of the conductor for an edge, the solid angle being specified as regards sign by a certain conventional rule. The solid angle thus specified is one-valued and discontinuous at the surface. But the magnetic field of the current is in no way dependent upon the choice made among the possible surfaces.

(c) *Hollow cylinder deformed by removal of a slice of uniform thickness.*

Volterra has given a very complete discussion of the problem for a hollow cylinder and for some systems of thin rods. We shall select for detailed treatment one of his examples of dislocation in a hollow cylinder.

A possible formula for a many-valued two-dimensional displacement is given in equations (27) of Article 148 *supra*. In a hollow circular cylinder whose axis is the axis of z a possible displacement is given by the equations

$$u=\frac{A}{2\mu}\log r+\frac{\lambda+\mu}{2\mu(\lambda+2\mu)}A\frac{y^2}{r^2},\quad v=\frac{A}{2(\lambda+2\mu)}\theta-\frac{\lambda+\mu}{2\mu(\lambda+2\mu)}A\frac{xy}{r^2},\quad w=0. \qquad \text{.........(6)}$$

Here r, θ are cylindrical polar coordinates in the plane of a cross-section, and A is a constant. The displacement is many-valued and continuous; but, if we restrict θ by a convention such as $2\pi+\alpha>\theta>\alpha$, it becomes one-valued and discontinuous, the y-component decreasing suddenly by $A\pi/(\lambda+2\mu)$ as θ changes from $2\pi+\alpha$ to α. In particular we may take $\alpha=0$. Then the displacement at the axial section $y=0$, $x>0$ is greater on the negative side

($y < 0$) than on the positive side ($y > 0$) by this amount, and there is a dislocation, equivalent to the removal of a thin slice of thickness $A\pi/(\lambda+2\mu)$, bounded by the parts of two planes $y = \pm \frac{1}{2}A\pi/(\lambda+2\mu)$ on which $x > 0$, and subsequent joining of the plane faces so formed. As in the general theory, so here, the seat of dislocation need not be $y=0$, it may be any plane $y=$ const. which meets the inner boundary in real points.

The state of stress answering to the displacement (6) is expressed by the equations

$$\left.\begin{aligned} X_x &= \frac{2(\lambda+\mu)}{\lambda+2\mu} A \frac{x^3}{r^4}, \quad Y_y = \frac{2(\lambda+\mu)}{\lambda+2\mu} A \frac{xy^2}{r^4}, \quad Z_z = \frac{\lambda}{\lambda+2\mu} A \frac{x}{r^2}, \\ Y_z &= 0, \quad Z_x = 0, \quad X_y = \frac{2(\lambda+\mu)}{\lambda+2\mu} A \frac{x^2 y}{r^4}. \end{aligned}\right\} \quad \ldots(7)$$

Cf. equations (30) of Article 149. The state of the hollow cylinder with the dislocation can be maintained by suitable surface tractions on the inner and outer cylindrical boundaries and on the terminal faces. The traction across any cylindrical surface is normal pressure, or tension, expressed by the equation

$$\widehat{rr} = \frac{2(\lambda+\mu)}{\lambda+2\mu} A \frac{\cos\theta}{r}. \quad \ldots\ldots\ldots\ldots\ldots\ldots\ldots(8)$$

The tractions on the terminal faces are expressed by the value of Z_z.

The tractions across the cylindrical boundaries can be nullified by superposing on the displacement (6) a one-valued displacement. For this purpose we consider in the first place the displacement

$$u = \frac{\lambda+3\mu}{2\mu(\lambda+2\mu)} A_1 \log r + \frac{\lambda+\mu}{2\mu(\lambda+2\mu)} A_1 \frac{y^2}{r^2}, \quad v = \frac{\lambda+\mu}{2\mu(\lambda+2\mu)} A_1 \frac{xy}{r^2}, \quad w = 0. \quad \ldots\ldots\ldots(9)$$

Cf. equations (28) of Article 148. This gives rise to tractions across any cylindrical surface $r =$ const. expressed by the equations

$$X_r = A_1 \left(\frac{2\lambda+3\mu}{\lambda+2\mu} \frac{x^2}{r^3} + \frac{\mu}{\lambda+2\mu} \frac{y^2}{r^3} \right), \quad Y_r = A_1 \frac{2(\lambda+\mu)}{\lambda+2\mu} \frac{xy}{r^3}. \quad \ldots(10)$$

In the second place we consider a displacement expressed by equations of the form

$$\left.\begin{aligned} u &= A_2 \{(\lambda-\mu) x^2 + (3\lambda+5\mu) y^2\} + A_3 \frac{x^2-y^2}{r^4}, \\ v &= -2A_2(\lambda+3\mu) xy + 2A_3 \frac{xy}{r^4}, \quad w = 0, \end{aligned}\right\} \quad \ldots\ldots\ldots(11)$$

which may easily be shown to satisfy the equations of equilibrium under no body force. This displacement gives rise to tractions across any cylindrical surface $r = \text{const.}$ expressed by the equations

$$X_r = -4\mu(\lambda+\mu) A_2 \frac{x^2-y^2}{r} - 4\mu A_3 \frac{x^2-y^2}{r^5},$$

$$Y_r = -8\mu(\lambda+\mu) A_2 \frac{xy}{r} - 8\mu A_3 \frac{xy}{r^5}.$$

Let $r = r_1$ and $r = r_0$ be the inner and outer cylindrical boundaries. When the displacements expressed by equations (6), (9), (11) are superposed, and the resulting tractions on these boundaries equated to zero, the following equations are found to hold:

$$\left.\begin{aligned} A_1 &= -A\frac{\lambda+\mu}{\lambda+2\mu}, \\ A_2 &= \frac{A}{4(\lambda+2\mu)^2(r_1^2+r_0^2)}, \\ A_3 &= \frac{(\lambda+\mu) r_1^2 r_0^2 A}{4(\lambda+2\mu)^2(r_1^2+r_0^2)}. \end{aligned}\right\} \qquad \text{......(12)}$$

The composition of the displacements expressed by equations (6), (9), (11), and substitution of these values for A_1, A_2, A_3, yields a displacement in the dislocated hollow cylinder free from traction over the inner and outer cylindrical boundaries, the length being maintained constant by suitable tractions on the terminal faces. These tractions are normal tensions and pressures expressed by the equation

$$Z_z = \frac{\lambda\mu}{(\lambda+2\mu)^2} Ax\left(\frac{1}{r^2} - \frac{2}{r_1^2+r_0^2}\right). \qquad \text{......(13)}$$

By means of an additional one-valued displacement these tractions also could be nullified. We do not know how to determine this displacement in the general case, but it can be found in the case where $(r_0 - r_1)/r_1$ is small. For this the reader may refer to Volterra's memoir, where will also be found photographs of a hollow cylinder under no external forces, but in a state of initial stress due to the formation of a dislocation of the type here discussed, and described as a "parallel fissure."

(*d*) *Hollow cylinder with radial fissure.*

Another of Volterra's examples is that of a hollow cylinder with a dislocation due to the removal of a thin slice bounded by two axial planes. In polar coordinates the many-valued displacement is expressed by the equations

$$u_r = A\frac{\mu}{\lambda+2\mu} r \log r, \quad u_\theta = Ar\theta. \qquad \text{......(14)}$$

It is a good exercise to obtain these formulæ from those of Article 145 by assuming

$$(\lambda+2\mu)\Delta + \iota 2\mu\varpi = 2\mu A \log(x+\iota y),$$

adjusting the subsidiary displacement u', v', and superposing an additional displacement

$$u'' = \frac{\mu}{\lambda+2\mu} Ax, \quad v'' = Ay,$$

which obviously satisfies the equations of equilibrium under no body force. The displacement expressed by (14) can be shown to give rise to tensions or pressures on the cylindrical boundaries expressed by the equation

$$\widehat{rr} = A\frac{\lambda+\mu}{\lambda+2\mu}(2\mu\log r+\lambda+2\mu),$$

and to terminal tensions or pressures expressed by the equation

$$Z_z = -A\frac{\lambda}{\lambda+2\mu}(2\mu\log r+\lambda+3\mu).$$

The tractions on the cylindrical boundaries can be nullified by combining the displacement expressed by (14) with a suitable displacement of the type considered in Article 100, and the tractions on the terminal faces can also be nullified by superposing an additional displacement, which can be determined approximately when the wall of the hollow cylinder is thin. The question is discussed fully by Volterra.

It will be observed that the problems (*c*) and (*d*) arise by putting in equations (5) either $l_1=l_3=0$ and $p_1=p_2=p_3=0$, or $l_1=l_2=l_3=0$ and $p_1=p_2=0$. The nature of the dislocations expressed by l_1, l_3, p_1, p_2 in a hollow cylinder is also discussed by Volterra.

CHAPTER X

THEORY OF THE INTEGRATION OF THE EQUATIONS OF EQUILIBRIUM OF AN ISOTROPIC ELASTIC SOLID BODY

157. Nature of the problem.

The chief analytical problem of the theory of Elasticity is that of the solution of the equations of equilibrium of an isotropic body with a given boundary when the surface displacements or the surface tractions are given. The case in which body forces act upon the body may be reduced, by means of the particular integral obtained in Article 130, to that in which the body is held strained by surface tractions only. Accordingly our problem is to determine functions u, v, w which within a given boundary are continuous and have continuous differential coefficients, which satisfy the system of partial differential equations

$$(\lambda+\mu)\frac{\partial\Delta}{\partial x}+\mu\nabla^2 u=0,\quad (\lambda+\mu)\frac{\partial\Delta}{\partial y}+\mu\nabla^2 v=0,\quad (\lambda+\mu)\frac{\partial\Delta}{\partial z}+\mu\nabla^2 w=0, \quad \ldots(1)$$

where

$$\Delta=\frac{\partial u}{\partial x}+\frac{\partial v}{\partial y}+\frac{\partial w}{\partial z}, \quad \ldots\ldots(2)$$

and which also satisfy certain conditions at the boundary. When the surface displacements are given, the values of u, v, w at the boundary are prescribed. We know that the solution of the problem is unique if μ and $3\lambda+2\mu$ are positive. When the surface tractions are given the values taken at the surface by the three expressions of the type

$$\lambda\Delta\cos(x,\nu)+\mu\left\{\frac{\partial u}{\partial\nu}+\frac{\partial u}{\partial x}\cos(x,\nu)+\frac{\partial v}{\partial x}\cos(y,\nu)+\frac{\partial w}{\partial x}\cos(z,\nu)\right\} \ldots(3)$$

are prescribed, $d\nu$ denoting an element of the normal to the boundary. We know that the problem has no solution unless the prescribed surface tractions satisfy the conditions of rigid-body-equilibrium (Article 117). We know also that, if these conditions are satisfied, and if μ and $3\lambda+2\mu$ are positive, the solution of the problem is effectively unique, in the sense that the strain and stress are uniquely determinate, but the displacement may have superposed upon it an arbitrary small displacement which would be possible in a rigid body.

158. Résumé of the theory of Potential.

The methods which have been devised for solving these problems have a close analogy to the methods which have been devised for solving corresponding problems in the theory of Potential. In that theory we have the problem of determining a function U which, besides satisfying the usual conditions of continuity, shall satisfy the equation

$$\nabla^2 U = 0 \quad \text{..............................(4)}$$

at all points within a given boundary*, and either (a) shall take an assigned value at every point of this boundary, or (b) shall be such that $\partial U/\partial \nu$ takes an assigned value at every point of this boundary. In case (b) the surface integral $\iint \frac{\partial U}{\partial \nu} dS$ taken over the boundary must vanish, and in this case the function U is determinate to an arbitrary constant *près*.

There are two main lines of attack upon these problems, which may be described respectively as the method of series and the method of singularities. To illustrate the method of series we consider the case of a spherical boundary. There exists an infinite series of functions, each of them rational and integral and homogeneous in x, y, z and satisfying equation (4). Let the origin be the centre of the sphere, let a be the radius of the sphere, and let r denote the distance of any point from the origin. Any one of these functions can be expressed in the form $r^n S_n$, where n is an integer, and S , which is independent of r, is a function of position on the sphere. Then the functions S_n have the property that an arbitrary function of position on the sphere can be expressed by an infinite series of the form $\sum_{n=0}^{\infty} A_n S_n$. The possibility of the expansion is bound up with the possession by the functions S_n of the conjugate property expressed by the equation

$$\iint S_n S_m dS = 0. \quad \text{..........................(5)}$$

The function U which satisfies equation (4) within a sphere $r = a$, and takes on the sphere the values of an arbitrary function, is expressible in the form

$$U = \sum_{n=0}^{\infty} A_n \frac{r^n}{a^n} S_n.$$

If the surface integral of the arbitrary function over the sphere vanishes there is no term of degree zero (constant term) in the expansion. The function U which satisfies equation (4) when $r < a$, and is such that $\partial U/\partial \nu$ has assigned values on the sphere $r = a$, is expressed by an equation of the form

$$U = \sum_{n=1}^{\infty} A_n \frac{r^n}{na^{n-1}} S_n.$$

* A function which has these properties is said to be "harmonic" in the region within the given boundary.

The application of the method of series to the theory of Elasticity will be considered in the next Chapter.

The method of singularities depends essentially upon the reciprocal theorem, known as Green's equation, viz.:

$$\iiint (U\nabla^2 V - V\nabla^2 U)\, dx dy dz = \iint \left(U \frac{\partial V}{\partial \nu} - V \frac{\partial U}{\partial \nu}\right) dS, \quad \text{.........(6)}$$

in which U and V are any two functions which satisfy the usual conditions of continuity in a region of space; the volume-integration is taken through this region (or part of it), and the surface-integration is taken over the boundary of the region (or the part). The normal ν is drawn away from the region (or the part). The method depends also on the existence of a solution of (4) having a simple infinity (pole) at an assigned point; such a solution is $1/r$, where r denotes distance from the point. By taking for V the function $1/r$, and, for the region of space, that bounded externally by a given surface S and internally by a sphere Σ with its centre at the origin of r, and by passing to a limit when the radius of Σ is indefinitely diminished, we obtain from (6) the equation

$$4\pi U = \iint \left(\frac{1}{r}\frac{\partial U}{\partial \nu} - U \frac{\partial r^{-1}}{\partial \nu}\right) dS, \quad \text{....................(7)}$$

so that U is expressed explicitly in terms of the surface values of U and $\partial U/\partial \nu$. The term that contains $\partial U/\partial \nu$ explicitly is the potential of a "simple sheet," and that which contains U explicitly is the potential of a "double sheet." In general the surface values of U and $\partial U/\partial \nu$ cannot both be prescribed, and the next step is to eliminate either U or $\partial U/\partial \nu$—the one that is not given. This is effected by the introduction of certain functions known as "Green's functions." Let a function G be defined by the following conditions:—(1) the condition of being harmonic at all points within S except the origin of r, (2) the possession of a simple pole at this point with residue unity, (3) the condition of vanishing at all points of S. The function G may be called "Green's function for the surface and the point." The function $G - 1/r$ is harmonic within S and equal to $-1/r$ at all points on S, and we have the equation

$$\iint \left[U \frac{\partial}{\partial \nu}\left(G - \frac{1}{r}\right) - \left(G - \frac{1}{r}\right)\frac{\partial U}{\partial \nu}\right] dS = 0.$$

Since G vanishes at all points on S we find that (7) may be written

$$4\pi U = -\iint U \frac{\partial G}{\partial \nu}\, dS. \quad \text{.........................(8)}$$

Hence U can be expressed in terms of its surface values if G can be found.

When the values of $\partial U/\partial \nu$ are given at the boundary we introduce a function Γ defined by the following conditions:—(1) the condition of being harmonic at all points within S except the origin of r and a chosen point A, (2) the possession of simple poles at these points with residues $+1$ and -1, (3) the condition that $\partial\Gamma/\partial\nu$ vanishes at all points of S. We find for U the equation

$$4\pi(U - U_A) = \iint \Gamma \frac{\partial U}{\partial \nu} dS. \quad \text{.........................(9)}$$

Hence U can be expressed effectively in terms of the surface values of $\partial U/\partial\nu$ when Γ is known. The function Γ is sometimes called the "second Green's function."

Green's function G for a surface and a point may be interpreted as the electric potential due to a point charge in presence of an uninsulated conducting surface. The second Green's function Γ for the surface, a point P and a chosen point A may be interpreted as the velocity potential of incompressible fluid due to a source and sink at P and A within a rigid boundary. The functions G and Γ are known for a few surfaces of which the plane and the sphere* are the most important.

The existence of Green's functions for any surface, and the existence of functions which are harmonic within a surface and take prescribed values, or have prescribed normal rates of variation at all points on the surface are not obvious without proof. The efforts that have been made to prove these existence-theorems have given rise to a mathematical theory of great interest. Methods have been devised for constructing the functions by convergent processes†; and these methods, although very complicated, have been successful for certain classes of surfaces (e.g. such as are everywhere convex) when some restrictions are imposed upon the degree of arbitrariness of the prescribed surface values.

Similar existence-theorems are involved in the theory of Elasticity. The subject will not be pursued here, but the reader who wishes for further information in regard to the problem of given surface displacements is referred to the following memoirs:—G. Lauricella, *Roma, Acc. Linc. Rend.* (Ser. 5), t. 15, Sem. 1, 1906, p. 426, and Sem. 2, 1906, p. 75, and t. 16, Sem. 2, 1907, p. 373, also A. Korn, *München, Ber.*, Bd. 36, 1906, p. 37, *Paris, Ann. Éc. Norm.*, t. 24, 1907, p. 9, *Palermo, Circ. Mat. Rend.*, t. 30, 1910, pp. 138, 336. For the problem of given surface tractions reference may be made to A. Korn, *Toulouse, Ann.* (Sér. 2), t. 10, 1908, p. 165. References to writings on another method of attacking these problems will be given in the next Chapter. There is a corresponding theory for vibrations, in regard to which reference may be made to A. Korn, *München, Ber.*, Bd. 26, 1906, p. 351, and *Palermo, Circ. Mat. Rend.*, t. 30, 1910, p. 153. For a general survey of such questions, and the methods proposed for dealing with them up to 1906, reference may be made to the Article by O. Tedone "Allgemeine Theoreme d. math. Elastizitätslehre," *Ency. d. math. Wiss.*, Bd. IV., Art. 24, Leipzig, 1907.

159. Description of Betti's method of integration.

The adaptation of the method of singularities to the theory of Elasticity was made by Betti‡, who showed how to express the dilatation Δ and the

* See e.g. Maxwell, *Electricity and Magnetism*, 2nd edition, Oxford 1881, and W. M. Hicks, *Phil. Trans. Roy. Soc.*, vol. 171 (1880).

† See e.g. Poincaré, *Théorie du potentiel Newtonien*, Paris 1899.

‡ See Introduction, footnote 65. A general account of the extension of the theory to æolotropic solid bodies is given by I. Fredholm, *Acta Math.*, t. 23, 1900, p. 1.

rotation (ϖ_x, ϖ_y, ϖ_z) by means of formulæ analogous to (7) and containing explicitly the surface tractions and surface displacements. These formulæ involve special systems of displacements which have been given in Chapter VIII. Since Δ is harmonic the equations (1) can be written in such forms as

$$\nabla^2 [u + \tfrac{1}{2}(1 + \lambda/\mu) x\Delta] = 0, \quad \text{......................(10)}$$

and thus the determination of u, v, w when Δ is known and the surface values of u, v, w are prescribed is reduced to a problem in the theory of Potential. If the surface tractions (X_ν, Y_ν, Z_ν) are prescribed, we observe that the boundary conditions can be written in such forms as

$$\frac{\partial u}{\partial \nu} = \frac{1}{2\mu} X_\nu - \frac{\lambda}{2\mu} \Delta \cos(x, \nu) + \varpi_y \cos(z, \nu) - \varpi_z \cos(y, \nu), \quad \text{......(11)}$$

so that, when Δ and ϖ_x, ϖ_y, ϖ_z are found, the surface values of $\partial u/\partial\nu$, $\partial v/\partial\nu$, $\partial w/\partial\nu$ are known, and the problem is again reduced to a problem in the theory of Potential. Accordingly Betti's method of integration involves the determination of Δ, and of ϖ_x, ϖ_y, ϖ_z, in terms of the prescribed surface displacements or surface tractions, by the aid of subsidiary special solutions which are analogous to Green's functions.

160. Formula for the dilatation.

The formula analogous to (7) is to be obtained by means of the reciprocal theorem proved in Article 121. When no body forces are in action the theorem takes the form

$$\iint (X_\nu u' + Y_\nu v' + Z_\nu w')\, dS = \iint (X_\nu' u + Y_\nu' v + Z_\nu' w)\, dS, \quad \text{......(12)}$$

in which (u, v, w) is a displacement satisfying equations (1) and X_ν, Y_ν, Z_ν are the corresponding surface tractions, and also (u', v', w') is a second displacement and X_ν', Y_ν', Z_ν' are the corresponding surface tractions. Further, the integration is taken over the boundary of any region within which u, v, w and u', v', w' satisfy the usual conditions of continuity and the equations (1). We take for u', v', w' the expressions given in (20) of Article 132. It will be convenient to denote these, omitting a factor, by u_0, v_0, w_0, and the corresponding surface tractions by $X_\nu^{(0)}$, $Y_\nu^{(0)}$, $Z_\nu^{(0)}$. We write

$$(u_0, v_0, w_0) = \left(\frac{\partial r^{-1}}{\partial x}, \frac{\partial r^{-1}}{\partial y}, \frac{\partial r^{-1}}{\partial z}\right), \quad \text{.................(13)}$$

and then the region in question must be bounded internally by a closed surface surrounding the origin of r. The surface will be taken to be a sphere Σ, and we shall pass to a limit by diminishing the radius of this sphere indefinitely. The external boundary of the region will be taken to be the surface S of the body.

Since the values of $\cos(x, \nu), \dots$ at Σ are $-x/r, -y/r, -z/r$, the contribution of Σ to the left-hand member of (12) is

$$\iint\left\{-\left[\frac{x}{r}\left(\lambda\Delta+2\mu\frac{\partial u}{\partial x}\right)+\frac{y}{r}\mu\left(\frac{\partial v}{\partial x}+\frac{\partial u}{\partial y}\right)+\frac{z}{r}\mu\left(\frac{\partial u}{\partial z}+\frac{\partial w}{\partial x}\right)\right]\frac{\partial r^{-1}}{\partial x}\right.$$
$$-\left[\frac{x}{r}\mu\left(\frac{\partial v}{\partial x}+\frac{\partial u}{\partial y}\right)+\frac{y}{r}\left(\lambda\Delta+2\mu\frac{\partial v}{\partial y}\right)+\frac{z}{r}\mu\left(\frac{\partial w}{\partial y}+\frac{\partial v}{\partial z}\right)\right]\frac{\partial r^{-1}}{\partial y}$$
$$\left.-\left[\frac{x}{r}\mu\left(\frac{\partial u}{\partial z}+\frac{\partial w}{\partial x}\right)+\frac{y}{r}\mu\left(\frac{\partial w}{\partial y}+\frac{\partial v}{\partial z}\right)+\frac{z}{r}\left(\lambda\Delta+2\mu\frac{\partial w}{\partial z}\right)\right]\frac{\partial r^{-1}}{\partial z}\right\}d\Sigma,$$

which is

$$\iint\left[\lambda\frac{\Delta}{r^2}+2\mu\left(\frac{x^2}{r^4}\frac{\partial u}{\partial x}+\frac{y^2}{r^4}\frac{\partial v}{\partial y}+\frac{z^2}{r^4}\frac{\partial w}{\partial z}\right)\right]d\Sigma$$
$$+\iint 2\mu\left[\frac{yz}{r^4}\left(\frac{\partial w}{\partial y}+\frac{\partial v}{\partial z}\right)+\frac{zx}{r^4}\left(\frac{\partial u}{\partial z}+\frac{\partial w}{\partial x}\right)+\frac{xy}{r^4}\left(\frac{\partial v}{\partial x}+\frac{\partial u}{\partial y}\right)\right]d\Sigma.$$

All the integrals of type $\iint yz\,d\Sigma$ vanish, and each of those of type $\iint x^2 d\Sigma$ is equal to $\frac{1}{3}4\pi r^4$, and therefore the limit of the above expression when the radius of Σ is diminished indefinitely is $4\pi(\lambda+\frac{2}{3}\mu)(\Delta)_0$, where $(\Delta)_0$ denotes the value of Δ at the origin of r.

Again, since the values of $X_\nu^{(0)}, Y_\nu^{(0)}, Z_\nu^{(0)}$ are expressed by formulæ of the type

$$X_\nu^{(0)}=2\mu\left[\cos(x, \nu)\frac{\partial}{\partial x}+\cos(y, \nu)\frac{\partial}{\partial y}+\cos(z, \nu)\frac{\partial}{\partial z}\right]\frac{\partial r^{-1}}{\partial x},$$

the contribution of Σ to the right-hand member of (12) is

$$2\mu\iint -2\frac{ux+vy+wz}{r^4}\,d\Sigma.$$

Now such integrals as $\iint x\,d\Sigma$ vanish, and we therefore expand the functions u, v, w in the neighbourhood of the origin of r in such forms as

$$u=(u_0)+x\left(\frac{\partial u}{\partial x}\right)_0+y\left(\frac{\partial u}{\partial y}\right)_0+z\left(\frac{\partial u}{\partial z}\right)_0+\dots$$

and retain first powers of x, y, z. Then in the limit, when the radius of Σ is diminished indefinitely, the above contribution becomes

$$-\tfrac{16}{3}\pi\mu\left[\left(\frac{\partial u}{\partial x}\right)_0+\left(\frac{\partial v}{\partial y}\right)_0+\left(\frac{\partial w}{\partial z}\right)_0\right],$$

or $-\frac{16}{3}\pi\mu(\Delta)_0$. Equation (12) therefore yields the result

$$4\pi(\lambda+2\mu)(\Delta)_0=\iint\left[\left(X_\nu^{(0)}u+Y_\nu^{(0)}v+Z_\nu^{(0)}w\right)-\left(X_\nu u_0+Y_\nu v_0+Z_\nu w_0\right)\right]dS.$$
$$\dots\dots\dots\dots(14)$$

The formula (14) is the analogue of (7) in regard to the dilatation.

This formula has been obtained here by a strictly analytical process, but it may also be arrived at synthetically* by an interpretation of the displacement (u_0, v_0, w_0). This displacement could be produced in a body (held by suitable forces at the boundary) by certain forces applied near the origin of r. Betti's reciprocal theorem shows that the work done by the tractions $X_\nu, \ldots$ on the surface S, acting through the displacement (u_0, v_0, w_0), is equal to the work done by certain forces applied at, and near to, the origin, acting through the displacement (u, v, w), together with the work done by the tractions $X_\nu^{(0)}, \ldots$ on the surface S, acting through the same displacement. Let forces, each of magnitude P, be applied at the origin in the positive directions of the axes of coordinates, and let equal and opposite forces be applied in the negative directions of the axes of x, y, z respectively at the points $(h, 0, 0)$, $(0, h, 0)$, $(0, 0, h)$. Let us pass to a limit by increasing P indefinitely and diminishing h indefinitely in such a way that $\lim Ph = 4\pi(\lambda + 2\mu)$. We know from Article 132 that the displacement (u_0, v_0, w_0) will be produced, and it is clear that the work done by the above system of forces, applied at, and near to, the origin, acting through the displacement (u, v, w) is $-4\pi(\lambda+2\mu)(\Delta)_0$.

161. Calculation of the dilatation from surface data.

(*a*) When the surface displacements are given u, v, w are given at all points of S but X_ν, Y_ν, Z_ν are not given. In this case we seek a displacement which shall satisfy the usual conditions of continuity and the equations (1) at all points within S, and shall become equal to (u_0, v_0, w_0) at all points on S. Let this displacement be denoted by (u_0', v_0', w_0'), and let the corresponding surface tractions be denoted by $X_\nu'^{(0)}$, $Y_\nu'^{(0)}$, $Z_\nu'^{(0)}$. Then we may apply the reciprocal theorem to the displacements (u, v, w) and (u_0', v_0', w_0') which have no singularities within S, and obtain the result

$$\iint (X_\nu'^{(0)} u + Y_\nu'^{(0)} v + Z_\nu'^{(0)} w)\, dS = \iint (X_\nu u_0' + Y_\nu v_0' + Z_\nu w_0')\, dS$$
$$= \iint (X_\nu u_0 + Y_\nu v_0 + Z_\nu w_0)\, dS.$$

We may therefore write equation (14) in the form

$$4\pi(\lambda + 2\mu)(\Delta)_0 = \iint [(X_\nu^{(0)} - X_\nu'^{(0)})\, u + (Y_\nu^{(0)} - Y_\nu'^{(0)})\, v + (Z_\nu^{(0)} - Z_\nu'^{(0)})\, w]\, dS. \quad \text{...........(15)}$$

The quantities $X_\nu^{(0)} - X_\nu'^{(0)}, \ldots$ are the surface tractions calculated from displacements $u_0 - u_0', \ldots$ and they are therefore the tractions required to hold the surface fixed when there is a "centre of compression" at the origin of r. To find the dilatation at any point we must therefore calculate the surface tractions required to hold the surface fixed when there is a centre of compression at the point; and for this we must find a displacement which (1) satisfies the usual conditions of continuity and the equations of equilibrium everywhere except at the point, (2) in the neighbourhood of the point tends to become infinite, as if there were a centre of compression at the point, (3) vanishes at the surface. The latter displacement is analogous to Green's function.

* J. Dougall, *Edinburgh Math. Soc. Proc.*, vol. 16 (1898).

(*b*) When the surface tractions are given, we begin by observing that $X_\nu^{(0)}$, $Y_\nu^{(0)}$, $Z_\nu^{(0)}$ are a system of surface tractions which satisfy the conditions of rigid-body-equilibrium. Let (u_0'', v_0'', w_0'') be the displacement produced in the body by the application of these surface tractions. We may apply the reciprocal theorem to the displacements (u, v, w) and (u_0'', v_0'', w_0''), which have no singularities within S, and obtain the result

$$\iint (X_\nu^{(0)} u + Y_\nu^{(0)} v + Z_\nu^{(0)} w)\, dS = \iint (X_\nu u_0'' + Y_\nu v_0'' + Z_\nu w_0'')\, dS;$$

and then we may write equation (14) in the form

$$4\pi (\lambda + 2\mu)(\Delta)_0 = \iint \{X_\nu (u_0'' - u_0) + Y_\nu (v_0'' - v_0) + Z_\nu (w_0'' - w_0)\}\, dS. \quad \text{...(16)}$$

To find the dilatation at any point we must therefore find the displacement produced in the body when the surface is free from traction and there is a centre of dilatation at the point. This displacement is $(u_0'' - u_0,\ v_0'' - v_0,\ w_0'' - w_0)$; it is an analogue of Green's function.

The dilatation can be determined if the displacement (u_0'', v_0'', w_0'') can be found. The corresponding surface tractions being given, this displacement is indeterminate in the sense that any small displacement possible in a rigid body may be superposed upon it. It is easily seen from equation (16) that this indeterminateness does not affect the value of the dilatation.

162. Formulæ for the components of rotation.

In applying the formula (12) to a region bounded externally by the surface S of the body, and internally by the surface Σ of a small sphere surrounding the origin of r, we take for (u', v', w') the displacement given in (22) of Article 132. It will be convenient to denote this displacement, omitting a factor, by (u_4, v_4, w_4)*, and the corresponding surface tractions by $X_\nu^{(4)}$, $Y_\nu^{(4)}$, $Z_\nu^{(4)}$. We write

$$(u_4, v_4, w_4) = \left(0,\ \frac{\partial r^{-1}}{\partial z},\ -\frac{\partial r^{-1}}{\partial y}\right). \quad \text{.........................(17)}$$

The contributions of Σ to the left-hand and right-hand members of (12) may be calculated by the analytical process of Article 160. We should find that the contribution to the left-hand member vanishes, and that the contribution to the right-hand member is $8\pi\mu(\varpi_x)_0$, where $(\varpi_x)_0$ denotes the value of ϖ_x at the origin of r. We should therefore have the formula

$$8\pi\mu(\varpi_x)_0 = \iint \{(X_\nu u_4 + Y_\nu v_4 + Z_\nu w_4) - (X_\nu^{(4)} u + Y_\nu^{(4)} v + Z_\nu^{(4)} w)\}\, dS, \quad \text{......(18)}$$

which is analogous to (7). The same result may be arrived at by observing that (u_4, v_4, w_4) is the displacement due to forces $4\pi\mu/h$ applied at the origin in the positive and negative directions of the axes of y and z respectively, and to equal and opposite forces applied respectively at the points $(0, 0, h)$ and $(0, h, 0)$, in the limiting condition when h is diminished indefinitely. It is clear that the work done by these forces acting over the displacement (u, v, w) is in the limit equal to $4\pi\mu\left(\frac{\partial w}{\partial y} - \frac{\partial v}{\partial z}\right)_0$. Formulæ of the same type as (18) for ϖ_y and ϖ_z can be written down.

* This notation is adopted in accordance with the notation (u_1, v_1, w_1), ... of Article 132 for the displacement due to unit forces.

163. Calculation of the rotation from surface data.

(*a*) When the surface displacements are given, we introduce a displacement (u_4', v_4', w_4') which satisfies the usual conditions of continuity and the equations of equilibrium (1), and takes at the surface the value (u_4, v_4, w_4); and we denote by $X_\nu'^{(4)}, Y_\nu'^{(4)}, Z_\nu'^{(4)}$ the corresponding surface tractions. Then equation (18) can be written

$$8\pi\mu(\varpi_x)_0 = \iint \{(X_\nu'^{(4)} - X_\nu^{(4)})u + (Y_\nu'^{(4)} - Y_\nu^{(4)})v + (Z_\nu'^{(4)} - Z_\nu^{(4)})w\}\, dS, \quad \text{......(19)}$$

in which the quantities $X_\nu'^{(4)} - X_\nu^{(4)}, \ldots$ are the surface tractions required to hold the surface fixed when a couple of moment $8\pi\mu$ about the axis of x is applied at the origin in such a way that this point becomes "a centre of rotation" about the axis of x. The corresponding displacement $(u_4' - u_4, v_4' - v_4, w_4' - w_4)$ is an analogue of Green's function.

(*b*) When the surface tractions are given we observe that the tractions $X_\nu^{(4)}, Y_\nu^{(4)}, Z_\nu^{(4)}$, being statically equivalent to a couple, do not satisfy the conditions of rigid-body-equilibrium, and that, therefore, no displacement exists which, besides satisfying the usual conditions of continuity and the equations of equilibrium, gives rise to surface tractions equal to $X_\nu^{(4)}, \ldots$*. We must introduce a second centre of rotation at a chosen point A, so that the couple at A is equal and opposite to that at the origin of r. Let $u_4^{(A)}, v_4^{(A)}, w_4^{(A)}$ be the displacement due to a centre of rotation about an axis at A parallel to the axis of x, so that

$$(u_4^{(A)}, v_4^{(A)}, w_4^{(A)}) = \left(0, \frac{\partial r_A^{-1}}{\partial z}, -\frac{\partial r_A^{-1}}{\partial y}\right), \quad \text{....................(20)}$$

where r_A denotes distance from A. Let $X_\nu''^{(4)}, Y_\nu''^{(4)}, Z_\nu''^{(4)}$ denote the surface tractions calculated from the displacement $(u_4 - u_4^{(A)}, v_4 - v_4^{(A)}, w_4 - w_4^{(A)})$. The conditions of rigid-body-equilibrium are satisfied by these tractions. Let (u_4'', v_4'', w_4'') be the displacement which, besides satisfying the usual conditions of continuity and the equations of equilibrium, gives rise to the surface tractions $X_\nu''^{(4)}, \ldots$. Then, denoting by $(\varpi_x)_A$ the value of ϖ_x at the point A, we find by the process already used to obtain (18) the equation

$$8\pi\mu\{(\varpi_x)_0 - (\varpi_x)_A\} = \iint [\{X_\nu(u_4 - u_4^{(A)}) + \ldots\} - \{X_\nu''^{(4)}u + \ldots\}]\, dS;$$

and from this again we obtain the equation

$$8\pi\mu\{(\varpi_x)_0 - (\varpi_x)_A\} = \iint \{X_\nu(u_4 - u_4^{(A)} - u_4'') + Y_\nu(v_4 - v_4^{(A)} - v_4'') + Z_\nu(w_4 - w_4^{(A)} - w_4'')\}\, dS. \quad \text{......(21)}$$

The quantities $u_4 - u_4^{(A)} - u_4'', \ldots$ are the components of displacement, produced in the body by equal and opposite centres of rotation about the axis of x at the origin of r and a parallel axis at the point A, when the surface is free from traction. This displacement is an analogue of the second Green's function.

The rotation can be determined if such a displacement as (u_4'', v_4'', w_4'') can be found. The indeterminateness of this displacement, which is to be found from surface conditions of traction, does not affect the rotation, but the indeterminateness of ϖ_x which arises from the additive constant $(\varpi_x)_A$ is of the kind already noted in Article 157.

164. Body bounded by plane—Formulæ for the dilatation.

The difficulty of proceeding with the integration of the equations in any particular case is the difficulty of discovering the functions which have been denoted above by $u_0', u_0'', u_4', \ldots$. These functions can be obtained when the

* J. Dougall, *loc. cit.*, p. 235.

boundary of the body is a plane*. As already remarked (Article 135) the local effects of forces applied to a small part of the surface of a body are deducible from the solution of the problem of the plane boundary.

Let the bounding plane be $z=0$, and let the body be on that side of it on which $z>0$. Let (x', y', z') be any point of the body, $(x', y', -z')$ the optical image of this point in the plane $z=0$, and let r, R denote the distances of any point (x, y, z) from these two points respectively. For the determination of the dilatation when the surface displacements are given we require a displacement (u_0', v_0', w_0') which, besides satisfying the usual conditions of continuity and the equations of equilibrium (1) in the region $z>0$, shall at the plane $z=0$ have the value (u_0, v_0, w_0), i.e. $(\partial r^{-1}/\partial x, \partial r^{-1}/\partial y, \partial r^{-1}/\partial z)$, or, what is the same thing, $(\partial R^{-1}/\partial x, \partial R^{-1}/\partial y, -\partial R^{-1}/\partial z)$. It can be shown without difficulty† that the functions u_0', v_0', w_0' are given by the equations

$$\left.\begin{aligned} u_0' &= \frac{\partial R^{-1}}{\partial x} + 2\frac{\lambda+\mu}{\lambda+3\mu} z \frac{\partial^2 R^{-1}}{\partial x \partial z}, \\ v_0' &= \frac{\partial R^{-1}}{\partial y} + 2\frac{\lambda+\mu}{\lambda+3\mu} z \frac{\partial^2 R^{-1}}{\partial y \partial z}, \\ w_0' &= -\frac{\partial R^{-1}}{\partial z} + 2\frac{\lambda+\mu}{\lambda+3\mu} z \frac{\partial^2 R^{-1}}{\partial z^2}. \end{aligned}\right\} \qquad \text{.................(22)}$$

The surface tractions $X_\nu^{(0)}, Y_\nu^{(0)}, Z_\nu^{(0)}$ on the plane $z=0$ calculated from the displacement (u_0, v_0, w_0) are, since $\cos(z, \nu) = -1$, given by the equations

$$\left.\begin{aligned} X_\nu^{(0)} &= -2\mu\frac{\partial^2 r^{-1}}{\partial z \partial x} = 2\mu\frac{\partial^2 R^{-1}}{\partial z \partial x}, \\ Y_\nu^{(0)} &= -2\mu\frac{\partial^2 r^{-1}}{\partial z \partial y} = 2\mu\frac{\partial^2 R^{-1}}{\partial z \partial y}, \\ Z_\nu^{(0)} &= -2\mu\frac{\partial^2 r^{-1}}{\partial z^2} = -2\mu\frac{\partial^2 R^{-1}}{\partial z^2}; \end{aligned}\right\} \qquad \text{.................(23)}$$

* The application of Betti's method to the problem of the plane was made by Cerruti. (See Introduction, footnote 68.)

† If in fact we assume for u_0', v_0', w_0' such forms as the following:

$$u_0' = \frac{\partial R^{-1}}{\partial x} + zu', \quad v_0' = \frac{\partial R^{-1}}{\partial y} + zv', \quad w_0' = -\frac{\partial R^{-1}}{\partial z} + zw',$$

we find for u', v', w' the equations

$$z\left\{(\lambda+\mu)\frac{\partial}{\partial x}\left(\frac{\partial u'}{\partial x}+\frac{\partial v'}{\partial y}+\frac{\partial w'}{\partial z}\right)+\mu\nabla^2 u'\right\}+(\lambda+\mu)\frac{\partial w'}{\partial x}+2\mu\frac{\partial u'}{\partial z}=2(\lambda+\mu)\frac{\partial^3 R^{-1}}{\partial x\,\partial z^2},$$

$$z\left\{(\lambda+\mu)\frac{\partial}{\partial y}\left(\frac{\partial u'}{\partial x}+\frac{\partial v'}{\partial y}+\frac{\partial w'}{\partial z}\right)+\mu\nabla^2 v'\right\}+(\lambda+\mu)\frac{\partial w'}{\partial y}+2\mu\frac{\partial v'}{\partial z}=2(\lambda+\mu)\frac{\partial^3 R^{-1}}{\partial y\,\partial z^2},$$

$$z\left\{(\lambda+\mu)\frac{\partial}{\partial z}\left(\frac{\partial u'}{\partial x}+\frac{\partial v'}{\partial y}+\frac{\partial w'}{\partial z}\right)+\mu\nabla^2 w'\right\}+(\lambda+\mu)\left(\frac{\partial u'}{\partial x}+\frac{\partial v'}{\partial y}+2\frac{\partial w'}{\partial z}\right)+2\mu\frac{\partial w'}{\partial z}=2(\lambda+\mu)\frac{\partial^3 R^{-1}}{\partial z^3},$$

which are all satisfied by

$$u' = \frac{2(\lambda+\mu)}{\lambda+3\mu}\frac{\partial^2 R^{-1}}{\partial x\,\partial z}, \quad v' = \frac{2(\lambda+\mu)}{\lambda+3\mu}\frac{\partial^2 R^{-1}}{\partial y\,\partial z}, \quad w' = \frac{2(\lambda+\mu)}{\lambda+3\mu}\frac{\partial^2 R^{-1}}{\partial z^2},$$

for these functions are harmonic and are such that $\frac{\partial u'}{\partial x}+\frac{\partial v'}{\partial y}+\frac{\partial w'}{\partial z}=0$.

and the surface tractions $X_\nu'^{(0)}, \ldots$ on the plane $z=0$ calculated from the displacement (u_0', v_0', w_0') are given by the equations

$$\left.\begin{aligned} X_\nu'^{(0)} &= -\mu\left(\frac{\partial u_0'}{\partial z}+\frac{\partial w_0'}{\partial x}\right) = -2\mu\frac{\lambda+\mu}{\lambda+3\mu}\frac{\partial^2 R^{-1}}{\partial x\partial z},\\ Y_\nu'^{(0)} &= -\mu\left(\frac{\partial w_0'}{\partial y}+\frac{\partial v_0'}{\partial z}\right) = -2\mu\frac{\lambda+\mu}{\lambda+3\mu}\frac{\partial^2 R^{-1}}{\partial y\partial z},\\ Z_\nu'^{(0)} &= -\left\{\lambda\left(\frac{\partial u_0'}{\partial x}+\frac{\partial v_0'}{\partial y}+\frac{\partial w_0'}{\partial z}\right)+2\mu\frac{\partial w_0'}{\partial z}\right\} = 2\mu\frac{\lambda+\mu}{\lambda+3\mu}\frac{\partial^2 R^{-1}}{\partial z^2}. \end{aligned}\right\} \quad \ldots(24)$$

We observe that $X_\nu'^{(0)}, Y_\nu'^{(0)}, Z_\nu'^{(0)}$ are equal respectively to the products of $X_\nu^{(0)}, Y_\nu^{(0)}, Z_\nu^{(0)}$ and the numerical factor $-(\lambda+\mu)/(\lambda+3\mu)$, and hence that

$$(u_0'', v_0'', w_0'') = -\{(\lambda+3\mu)/(\lambda+\mu)\}(u_0', v_0', w_0').$$

It follows that, when the surface displacements are given, the value of Δ at the point (x', y', z') is given by the equation

$$\Delta = -\frac{\mu}{\pi(\lambda+3\mu)}\iint\left(\frac{\partial^2 r^{-1}}{\partial x\partial z}u+\frac{\partial^2 r^{-1}}{\partial y\partial z}v+\frac{\partial^2 r^{-1}}{\partial z^2}w\right)dxdy, \quad \ldots\ldots(25)$$

the integration extending over the plane of (x, y). When the surface tractions are given the value of Δ at the point (x', y', z') is

$$\Delta = -\frac{1}{2\pi(\lambda+\mu)}\iint\left(X_\nu\frac{\partial r^{-1}}{\partial x}+Y_\nu\frac{\partial r^{-1}}{\partial y}+Z_\nu\frac{\partial r^{-1}}{\partial z}\right)dxdy. \quad \ldots\ldots(26)$$

165. Body bounded by plane—Given surface displacements.

The formula (25) for the dilatation at (x', y', z') can be written

$$\Delta = -\frac{\mu}{\pi(\lambda+3\mu)}\frac{\partial}{\partial z'}\left\{\frac{\partial}{\partial x'}\iint\frac{u}{r}dxdy+\frac{\partial}{\partial y'}\iint\frac{v}{r}dxdy+\frac{\partial}{\partial z'}\iint\frac{w}{r}dxdy\right\} \quad \ldots(27)$$

If we introduce four functions L, M, N, ϕ by the definitions

$$\left.\begin{aligned} L=\iint\frac{u}{r}dxdy,\quad M=\iint\frac{v}{r}dxdy,\quad N=\iint\frac{w}{r}dxdy,\\ \phi=\frac{\partial L}{\partial x'}+\frac{\partial M}{\partial y'}+\frac{\partial N}{\partial z'}, \end{aligned}\right\} \quad \ldots\ldots(28)$$

these functions of x', y', z' are harmonic on either side of the plane $z'=0$, and at this plane the values of u, v, w are $\lim_{z'=+0} -\frac{1}{2\pi}\frac{\partial L}{\partial z'}$, $\lim_{z'=+0} -\frac{1}{2\pi}\frac{\partial M}{\partial z'}$, $\lim_{z'=+0} -\frac{1}{2\pi}\frac{\partial N}{\partial z'}$. The value of Δ at (x', y', z') is $-\frac{\mu}{\pi(\lambda+3\mu)}\frac{\partial\phi}{\partial z'}$, and the equations of equilibrium can be written

$$\left.\begin{aligned} \nabla'^2\left[u-\frac{\lambda+\mu}{2\pi(\lambda+3\mu)}z'\frac{\partial\phi}{\partial x'}\right]=0,\\ \nabla'^2\left[v-\frac{\lambda+\mu}{2\pi(\lambda+3\mu)}z'\frac{\partial\phi}{\partial y'}\right]=0,\\ \nabla'^2\left[w-\frac{\lambda+\mu}{2\pi(\lambda+3\mu)}z'\frac{\partial\phi}{\partial z'}\right]=0, \end{aligned}\right\} \quad \ldots\ldots(29)$$

where $$\nabla'^2 = \partial^2/\partial x'^2 + \partial^2/\partial y'^2 + \partial^2/\partial z'^2.$$

The three functions such as

$$u - \{(\lambda+\mu)/2\pi(\lambda+3\mu)\} z' (\partial\phi/\partial x')$$

are harmonic in the region $z' > 0$, and, at the plane $z' = 0$, they take the values $-\frac{1}{2}\pi^{-1}(\partial L/\partial z')$, ..., which are themselves harmonic in the same region. It follows that the values of u, v, w at (x', y', z') are given by the equations*

$$\left.\begin{aligned} u &= -\frac{1}{2\pi}\frac{\partial L}{\partial z'} + \frac{1}{2\pi}\frac{\lambda+\mu}{\lambda+3\mu} z' \frac{\partial\phi}{\partial x'}, \\ v &= -\frac{1}{2\pi}\frac{\partial M}{\partial z'} + \frac{1}{2\pi}\frac{\lambda+\mu}{\lambda+3\mu} z' \frac{\partial\phi}{\partial y'}, \\ w &= -\frac{1}{2\pi}\frac{\partial N}{\partial z'} + \frac{1}{2\pi}\frac{\lambda+\mu}{\lambda+3\mu} z' \frac{\partial\phi}{\partial z'}. \end{aligned}\right\} \qquad \text{..............(30)}$$

The simplest example of these formulæ is afforded by the case in which u and v vanish at all points of the surface, and w vanishes at all such points except those in a very small area near the origin. In this case the only points (x, y, z) that are included in the integration are close to the origin, and ϕ is the potential of a mass at the origin. We may suppress the accents on x', y', z' and obtain the solution

$$u = A\frac{xz}{r^3},\quad v = A\frac{yz}{r^3},\quad w = A\left(\frac{\lambda+3\mu}{\lambda+\mu}\frac{1}{r} + \frac{z^2}{r^3}\right),$$

which was considered in Article 131. In the problem of the plane this solution gives the displacement due to pressure of amount $-4\pi\mu\dfrac{\lambda+2\mu}{\lambda+\mu}A$ exerted at the origin when the plane $z=0$ is held fixed at all points that are not quite close to the origin. In an unlimited solid it is the displacement due to a single force acting at the origin and directed along the axis of z.

A second example is afforded by the case in which v and w vanish at all points of the surface, and u vanishes at all such points except those in a very small area near the origin. The values of u, v, w at any point (x, y, z) are given by equations of the form

$$u = -\frac{B}{2\pi}\frac{\partial}{\partial z}\left(\frac{1}{r} + \frac{\lambda+\mu}{\lambda+3\mu}\frac{x^2}{r^3}\right) + \frac{B}{2\pi}\frac{\lambda+\mu}{\lambda+3\mu}\frac{\partial r^{-1}}{\partial z},$$

$$v = -\frac{B}{2\pi}\frac{\lambda+\mu}{\lambda+3\mu}\frac{\partial}{\partial z}\left(\frac{xy}{r^3}\right),$$

$$w = -\frac{B}{2\pi}\frac{\lambda+\mu}{\lambda+3\mu}\frac{\partial}{\partial z}\left(\frac{xz}{r^3}\right) - \frac{B}{2\pi}\frac{\lambda+\mu}{\lambda+3\mu}\frac{\partial r^{-1}}{\partial x},$$

where $B = \iint u\,dx\,dy$ taken over the area in question. In an unlimited solid this would be the displacement due to (i) a "double force with moment," the forces of the double force being parallel to the axis of x, and the axis of the equivalent couple being parallel to the axis of y [Article 132 (*b*)], and (ii) a "centre of rotation about the axis of y" [Article 132 (*b'*)].

The solution of the example in which u and w vanish at all points of the surface, and v vanishes at all such points except those in a very small area near the origin, may be written down and interpreted in the same way; and the solution expressed by (30) may be built up by synthesis of the solutions of these three examples.

* The results are due to Boussinesq. See Introduction, footnote 67.

166. Body bounded by plane—Given surface tractions*.

It is unnecessary to go through the work of calculating the rotations by the general method.

The formula (26) for Δ can be expressed in the form

$$\Delta = \frac{1}{2\pi(\lambda+\mu)}\frac{\partial\psi}{\partial z'}.$$

To effect this we introduce a function χ such that

$$\partial\chi/\partial z' = 1/r \text{ at } z=0.$$

The required function is expressed by the formula

$$\chi = \log(z+z'+R); \qquad \text{.........................(31)}$$

it is harmonic in the space considered and has the property expressed by the equations

$$\frac{\partial\chi}{\partial z} = \frac{\partial\chi}{\partial z'} = \frac{1}{R}. \qquad \text{.........................(32)}$$

Now at the surface $z=0$ we have

$$\frac{\partial r^{-1}}{\partial x} = \frac{\partial R^{-1}}{\partial x} = -\frac{\partial R^{-1}}{\partial x'} = -\frac{\partial^2\chi}{\partial z'\partial x'}, \quad \frac{\partial r^{-1}}{\partial y} = -\frac{\partial^2\chi}{\partial y'\partial z'}, \quad \frac{\partial r^{-1}}{\partial z} = -\frac{\partial^2\chi}{\partial z'^2}.$$

If therefore we write

$$\left.\begin{aligned} F = \iint X_\nu\chi\,dx\,dy, \quad G = \iint Y_\nu\chi\,dx\,dy, \quad H = \iint Z_\nu\chi\,dx\,dy,\\ \psi = \frac{\partial F}{\partial x'} + \frac{\partial G}{\partial y'} + \frac{\partial H}{\partial z'}, \end{aligned}\right\} \quad \text{...(33)}$$

the value of Δ at (x', y', z') is given by the equation

$$\Delta = \frac{1}{2\pi(\lambda+\mu)}\frac{\partial\psi}{\partial z'}. \qquad \text{.........................(34)}$$

We observe also that the functions F, G, H, ψ are harmonic and that the values of X_ν, Y_ν, Z_ν at $z'=0$ are equal to

$$\lim_{z'=+0} -\frac{1}{2\pi}\frac{\partial^2 F}{\partial z'^2}, \quad \lim_{z'=+0} -\frac{1}{2\pi}\frac{\partial^2 G}{\partial z'^2}, \quad \lim_{z'=+0} -\frac{1}{2\pi}\frac{\partial^2 H}{\partial z'^2}.$$

Now the third of the equations of equilibrium is

$$\nabla'^2\left[w + \frac{1}{4\pi\mu}z'\frac{\partial\psi}{\partial z'}\right] = 0,$$

and the third of the boundary conditions is

$$\lambda\Delta + 2\mu\frac{\partial w}{\partial z'} = -Z_\nu,$$

or

$$\frac{\partial w}{\partial z'} = \frac{1}{4\pi\mu}\frac{\partial^2 H}{\partial z'^2} - \frac{\lambda}{4\pi\mu(\lambda+\mu)}\frac{\partial\psi}{\partial z'}.$$

* The results are due to Cerruti. See Introduction, footnote 68.

Hence at $z'=0$

$$\frac{\partial}{\partial z'}\left\{w+\frac{1}{4\pi\mu}z'\frac{\partial\psi}{\partial z'}\right\}=\frac{\partial}{\partial z'}\left\{\frac{1}{4\pi\mu}\frac{\partial H}{\partial z'}+\frac{1}{4\pi(\lambda+\mu)}\psi\right\}.$$

It follows that w is given by the equation

$$w=\frac{1}{4\pi\mu}\frac{\partial H}{\partial z'}+\frac{1}{4\pi(\lambda+\mu)}\psi-\frac{1}{4\pi\mu}z'\frac{\partial\psi}{\partial z'}. \quad \text{............(35)}$$

Again the first of the equations of equilibrium is

$$\nabla'^2\left[u+\frac{1}{4\pi\mu}z'\frac{\partial\psi}{\partial x'}\right]=0,$$

and the first of the boundary conditions is

$$-\mu\left(\frac{\partial u}{\partial z'}+\frac{\partial w}{\partial x'}\right)=X_\nu.$$

Hence at $z'=0$

$$\frac{\partial}{\partial z'}\left[u+\frac{1}{4\pi\mu}z'\frac{\partial\psi}{\partial x'}\right]=\frac{1}{2\pi\mu}\frac{\partial^2 F}{\partial z'^2}-\frac{1}{4\pi\mu}\frac{\partial^2 H}{\partial x'\partial z'}+\frac{\lambda}{4\pi\mu(\lambda+\mu)}\frac{\partial\psi}{\partial x'},$$

and it follows that u is given by the equation

$$u=\frac{1}{2\pi\mu}\frac{\partial F}{\partial z'}-\frac{1}{4\pi\mu}\frac{\partial H}{\partial x'}+\frac{\lambda}{4\pi\mu(\lambda+\mu)}\frac{\partial\psi_1}{\partial x'}-\frac{1}{4\pi\mu}z'\frac{\partial\psi}{\partial x'}, \quad \text{......(36)}$$

where ψ_1 is an harmonic function which has the property $\partial\psi_1/\partial z'=\psi$. Such a function can be obtained by introducing a function Ω by the equation

$$\Omega=(z+z')\log(z+z'+R)-R. \quad \text{..................(37)}$$

Then Ω is harmonic in the space considered and has the property

$$\frac{\partial\Omega}{\partial z}=\frac{\partial\Omega}{\partial z'}=\chi. \quad \text{..............................(38)}$$

If we write

$$\left.\begin{aligned}F_1=\iint X_\nu\Omega\,dxdy,\quad G_1=\iint Y_\nu\Omega\,dxdy,\quad H_1=\iint Z_\nu\Omega\,dxdy,\\ \psi_1=\frac{\partial F_1}{\partial x'}+\frac{\partial G_1}{\partial y'}+\frac{\partial H_1}{\partial z'},\end{aligned}\right\} \quad \text{...(39)}$$

then all the functions F_1, G_1, H_1, ψ_1 are harmonic in the space considered and

$$\frac{\partial F_1}{\partial z'}=F,\quad \frac{\partial G_1}{\partial z'}=G,\quad \frac{\partial H_1}{\partial z'}=H,\quad \frac{\partial\psi_1}{\partial z'}=\psi. \quad \text{...............(40)}$$

In the same way as we found u we may find v in the form

$$v=\frac{1}{2\pi\mu}\frac{\partial G}{\partial z'}-\frac{1}{4\pi\mu}\frac{\partial H}{\partial y'}+\frac{\lambda}{4\pi\mu(\lambda+\mu)}\frac{\partial\psi_1}{\partial y'}-\frac{1}{4\pi\mu}z'\frac{\partial\psi}{\partial y'}. \quad \text{......(41)}$$

The simplest example of these formulæ is afforded by the case in which X_ν, Y_ν vanish at all points of the surface, and Z_ν vanishes at all such points except those in a very small area near the origin, but $\iint Z_\nu dxdy$ taken over this area $=P$. The values of u, v, w at

(x, y, z) are then given by equations (35) of Article 135. In an unlimited solid this solution represents, as we know, the displacement due to (i) a single force acting at the origin and directed along the axis of z, (ii) a line of centres of dilatation along the axis of z from the origin to $-\infty$ [Article 132 (c)].

A second example is afforded by the case in which Y_ν, Z_ν vanish at all points of the surface, and X_ν vanishes at all such points except those in a very small area near the origin, but $\iint X_\nu dx\,dy$ taken over this area $= S$. The values of u, v, w at (x, y, z) are given by the equations

$$u = \frac{S}{4\pi\mu}\left(\frac{\lambda+3\mu}{\lambda+\mu}\frac{1}{r} + \frac{x^2}{r^3}\right) - \frac{S}{2\pi(\lambda+\mu)}\frac{1}{r} + \frac{S}{4\pi(\lambda+\mu)}\left\{\frac{1}{z+r} - \frac{x^2}{r(z+r)^2}\right\},$$

$$v = \frac{S}{4\pi\mu}\frac{xy}{r^3} - \frac{S}{4\pi(\lambda+\mu)}\frac{xy}{r(z+r)^2},$$

$$w = \frac{S}{4\pi\mu}\frac{xz}{r^3} + \frac{S}{4\pi(\lambda+\mu)}\frac{x}{r(z+r)}.$$

In the solid with a plane boundary these equations express the displacement due to tangential force S applied at the origin, the rest of the boundary being free from traction. In an unlimited solid they express the displacement due to (i) a single force acting at the origin, and directed along the axis of x, (ii) a line of centres of rotation along the axis of z from the origin to $-\infty$, the axes of the equivalent couples being parallel to the axis of y [Article 132 (e)], (iii) a double line of centres of dilatation along the axis of z from the origin to $-\infty$, the axes of the doublets being parallel to the axis of x [Article 132 (d)].

The solution of the example in which X_ν, Z_ν vanish at all points of the surface, and Y_ν vanishes at all such points except those in a very small area near the origin, may be written down and interpreted in the same way; and the solution expressed by equations (35), (36), (41) may be built up by synthesis of the solutions in these three examples.

167. Historical Note.

The problem of the plane—sometimes also called the "problem of Boussinesq and Cerruti"—has been the object of numerous researches. In addition to those mentioned in the Introduction, pp. 15, 16, we may cite the following:—J. Boussinesq, *Paris, C. R.*, t. 106 (1888), gave the solutions for a more general type of boundary conditions, viz.: the normal traction and tangential displacements or normal displacement and tangential tractions are given. These solutions were obtained by other methods by V. Cerruti, *Roma, Acc. Linc. Rend.* (Ser. 4), t. 4 (1888), and by J. H. Michell, *London Math. Soc. Proc.*, vol. 31 (1900), p. 183. The theory was extended by J. H. Michell, *London Math. Soc. Proc.*, vol. 32 (1901), p. 247, to æolotropic solid bodies which are transversely isotropic in planes parallel to the boundary. The solutions given in Articles 165 and 166 were obtained by a new method by C. Somigliana in *Il Nuovo Cimento* (Ser. 3), tt. 17—20 (1885—1886), and this was followed up by G. Lauricella in *Il Nuovo Cimento* (Ser. 3), t. 36 (1894). Other methods of arriving at these solutions have been given by H. Weber, *Part. Diff.-Gleichungen d. math. Physik*, Bd. 2, Brunswick 1901, by H. Lamb, *London Math. Soc. Proc.*, vol. 34 (1902), by O. Tedone, *Ann. di mat.* (Ser. 3), t. 8 (1903), and by R. Marcolongo, *Teoria matematica dello equilibrio dei corpi elastici*, Milan 1904. The extension of the theory to the case of a body bounded by two parallel planes has been discussed briefly by H. Lamb, *loc. cit.*, and more fully by J. Dougall, *Edinburgh Roy. Soc. Trans.*, vol. 41 (1904), and also by O. Tedone, *Palermo, Circ. Mat. Rend.*, t. 18 (1904), and by L. Orlando, *Palermo, Circ. Mat. Rend.*, t. 19 (1905).

168. Body bounded by plane—Additional results.

(*a*) In the calculation of the rotations when the surface tractions are given we ma take the point A of Article 163 (*b*) to be at an infinite distance, and omit $u_4^{(A)}, \ldots$ altogethe We should find for u_4'', v_4'', w_4'' the forms

$$u_4'' = -2z\frac{\partial^3\chi}{\partial x\partial y\partial z} - \frac{2\mu}{\lambda+\mu}\frac{\partial^2\chi}{\partial x\partial y},$$

$$v_4'' = -2z\frac{\partial^3\chi}{\partial y^2\partial z} - \frac{2\mu}{\lambda+\mu}\frac{\partial^2\chi}{\partial y^2} + \frac{\partial^2\chi}{\partial z^2},$$

$$w_4'' = -2z\frac{\partial^3\chi}{\partial y\partial z^2} + \frac{2\mu}{\lambda+\mu}\frac{\partial^2\chi}{\partial y\partial z} + \frac{\partial^2\chi}{\partial y\partial z},$$

and we may deduce the formula

$$\varpi_x = \frac{1}{4\pi\mu}\left[\frac{\lambda+2\mu}{\lambda+\mu}\frac{\partial\psi}{\partial y'} + \frac{\partial}{\partial x'}\left(\frac{\partial G}{\partial x'} - \frac{\partial F}{\partial y'}\right)\right].$$

In like manner we may prove that

$$\varpi_y = \frac{1}{4\pi\mu}\left[-\frac{\lambda+2\mu}{\lambda+\mu}\frac{\partial\psi}{\partial x'} + \frac{\partial}{\partial y'}\left(\frac{\partial G}{\partial x'} - \frac{\partial F}{\partial y'}\right)\right].$$

For the calculation of ϖ_z we should require a subsidiary displacement which would give rise t the same surface tractions as the displacement $(\partial r^{-1}/\partial y, -\partial r^{-1}/\partial x, 0)$, and this displaceme is clearly $(-\partial R^{-1}/\partial y, \partial R^{-1}/\partial x, 0)$, and we can deduce the formula

$$\varpi_z = \frac{1}{4\pi\mu}\frac{\partial}{\partial z'}\left(\frac{\partial G}{\partial x'} - \frac{\partial F}{\partial y'}\right).$$

(*b*) As an example of mixed boundary conditions we may take the case where $u, v,$ are given at $z=0$. To calculate Δ we require a displacement (u', v', w') which at $z=0$ sha satisfy the conditions

$$u' = u_0, \quad v' = v_0, \quad Z_\nu' = Z_\nu^{(0)},$$

where (X_ν', Y_ν', Z_ν') is the surface traction calculated from (u', v', w'). Then we may sho that the value of Δ at the origin of r is given by the equation

$$4\pi(\lambda+2\mu)\Delta = \iint\{(X_\nu^{(0)} - X_\nu')u + (Y_\nu^{(0)} - Y_\nu')v - Z_\nu(w_0 - w')\}\,dx\,dy.$$

We may show further that

$$u' = \frac{\partial R^{-1}}{\partial x}, \quad v' = \frac{\partial R^{-1}}{\partial y}, \quad w' = \frac{\partial R^{-1}}{\partial z},$$

and then that

$$\Delta = \frac{1}{2\pi(\lambda+2\mu)}\frac{\partial}{\partial z'}\left\{\frac{\partial H}{\partial z'} - 2\mu\left(\frac{\partial L}{\partial x'} + \frac{\partial M}{\partial y'}\right)\right\},$$

and we may deduce the value of (u, v, w) at (x', y', z') in the form

$$u = -\frac{1}{2\pi}\frac{\partial L}{\partial z'} - \frac{\lambda+\mu}{4\pi\mu(\lambda+2\mu)}z'\frac{\partial}{\partial x'}\left\{\frac{\partial H}{\partial z'} - 2\mu\left(\frac{\partial L}{\partial x'} + \frac{\partial M}{\partial y'}\right)\right\},$$

$$v = -\frac{1}{2\pi}\frac{\partial M}{\partial z'} - \frac{\lambda+\mu}{4\pi\mu(\lambda+2\mu)}z'\frac{\partial}{\partial y'}\left\{\frac{\partial H}{\partial z'} - 2\mu\left(\frac{\partial L}{\partial x'} + \frac{\partial M}{\partial y'}\right)\right\},$$

$$w = \frac{1}{4\pi\mu}\frac{\partial H}{\partial z'} + \frac{1}{4\pi(\lambda+2\mu)}\left\{\frac{\partial H}{\partial z'} - 2\mu\left(\frac{\partial L}{\partial x'} + \frac{\partial M}{\partial y'}\right)\right\}$$
$$- \frac{\lambda+\mu}{4\pi\mu(\lambda+2\mu)}z'\frac{\partial}{\partial z'}\left\{\frac{\partial H}{\partial z'} - 2\mu\left(\frac{\partial L}{\partial x'} + \frac{\partial M}{\partial y'}\right)\right\}.$$

(c) As a second example we may take the case where X_ν, Y_ν, w are given at $z=0$. To calculate Δ we require a displacement (u'', v'', w'') which at $z=0$ shall satisfy the conditions

$$X_\nu''=X_\nu^{(0)}, \quad Y_\nu''=Y_\nu^{(0)}, \quad w''=w_0,$$

where X_ν'', Y_ν'', Z_ν'' denote the surface tractions calculated from (u'', v'', w''). We can prove that the value of Δ at the origin of r is given by the equation

$$4\pi(\lambda+2\mu)\Delta=\iint\{X_\nu(u''-u_0)+Y_\nu(v''-v_0)+(Z_\nu^{(0)}-Z_\nu'')w\}\,dx\,dy,$$

and that

$$u''=-\frac{\partial R^{-1}}{\partial x}, \quad v''=-\frac{\partial R^{-1}}{\partial y}, \quad w''=-\frac{\partial R^{-1}}{\partial z},$$

and then we can find for Δ the formula

$$\Delta=\frac{1}{2\pi(\lambda+2\mu)}\frac{\partial}{\partial z'}\left(\frac{\partial F}{\partial x'}+\frac{\partial G}{\partial y'}-2\mu\frac{\partial N}{\partial z'}\right);$$

and for (u, v, w) the formulæ

$$u=\frac{1}{2\pi\mu}\frac{\partial F}{\partial z'}+\frac{1}{2\pi}\frac{\partial N}{\partial x'}+\frac{\lambda+\mu}{4\pi\mu(\lambda+2\mu)}\frac{\partial}{\partial x'}\left(\frac{\partial F_1}{\partial x'}+\frac{\partial G_1}{\partial y'}-2\mu N\right)$$
$$-\frac{\lambda+\mu}{4\pi\mu(\lambda+2\mu)}z'\frac{\partial}{\partial x'}\left(\frac{\partial F}{\partial x'}+\frac{\partial G}{\partial y'}-2\mu\frac{\partial N}{\partial z'}\right),$$

$$v=\frac{1}{2\pi\mu}\frac{\partial G}{\partial z'}+\frac{1}{2\pi}\frac{\partial N}{\partial y'}+\frac{\lambda+\mu}{4\pi\mu(\lambda+2\mu)}\frac{\partial}{\partial y'}\left(\frac{\partial F_1}{\partial x'}+\frac{\partial G_1}{\partial y'}-2\mu N\right)$$
$$-\frac{\lambda+\mu}{4\pi\mu(\lambda+2\mu)}z'\frac{\partial}{\partial y'}\left(\frac{\partial F}{\partial x'}+\frac{\partial G}{\partial y'}-2\mu\frac{\partial N}{\partial z'}\right),$$

$$w=-\frac{1}{2\pi}\frac{\partial N}{\partial z'}-\frac{\lambda+\mu}{4\pi\mu(\lambda+2\mu)}z'\frac{\partial}{\partial z'}\left(\frac{\partial F}{\partial x'}+\frac{\partial G}{\partial y'}-2\mu\frac{\partial N}{\partial z'}\right).$$

169. Formulæ for the displacement and strain.

By means of the special solutions which represent the effect of force at a point we may obtain formulæ analogous to (7) for the components of displacement. Thus let (u_1, v_1, w_1) represent the displacement due to unit force acting at (x', y', z') in the direction of the axis of x, so that

$$(u_1, v_1, w_1)=-\frac{\lambda+\mu}{8\pi\mu(\lambda+2\mu)}\left(\frac{\partial^2 r}{\partial x^2}-2\frac{\lambda+2\mu}{\lambda+\mu}\frac{1}{r},\ \frac{\partial^2 r}{\partial x\partial y},\ \frac{\partial^2 r}{\partial x\partial z}\right), \quad \text{.........(42)}$$

and let $X_\nu^{(1)}$, $Y_\nu^{(1)}$, $Z_\nu^{(1)}$ be the surface tractions calculated from (u_1, v_1, w_1). We apply the reciprocal theorem to the displacements (u, v, w) and (u_1, v_1, w_1), with a boundary consisting of the surface S of the body and of the surface Σ of a small sphere surrounding (x', y', z'), and we proceed to a limit as before. The contribution of Σ can be evaluated as before by finding the work done by the unit force, acting over the displacement (u, v, w), and the same result would be arrived at analytically. If the body is subjected to body forces (X, Y, Z) as well as surface tractions X_ν, Y_ν, Z_ν, we find the formulæ*

$$(u)_0=\iiint\rho(Xu_1+Yv_1+Zw_1)\,dx\,dy\,dz$$
$$+\iint[(X_\nu u_1+Y_\nu v_1+Z_\nu w_1)-(X_\nu^{(1)}u+Y_\nu^{(1)}v+Z_\nu^{(1)}w)]\,dS, \quad \text{......(43)}$$

* The formulæ of this type are due to C. Somigliana, *Il Nuovo Cimento* (Ser. 3), tt. 17—20 (1885, 1886), and *Ann. di mat.* (Ser. 2), t. 17 (1889).

where the volume integration is to be taken (in the sense of a convergent integral) throughout the volume within S. We should find in the same way

$$(v)_0=\iiint \rho\,(Xu_2+Yv_2+Zw_2)\,dx\,dy\,dz$$
$$+\iint [(X_\nu u_2+Y_\nu v_2+Z_\nu w_2)-(X_\nu^{(2)}u+Y_\nu^{(2)}v+Z_\nu^{(2)}w)]\,dS,$$

and $$(w)_0=\iiint \rho\,(Xu_3+Yv_3+Zw_3)\,dx\,dy\,dz$$
$$+\iint [(X_\nu u_3+Y_\nu v_3+Z_\nu w_3)-(X_\nu^{(3)}u+Y_\nu^{(3)}v+Z_\nu^{(3)}w)]\,dS.$$

A method of integration similar to that of Betti has been founded upon these formulæ*. It should be noted that no displacement exists which, besides satisfying the usual conditions of continuity and the equations of equilibrium (1), gives rise to surface tractions equal to $X_\nu^{(1)}$, $Y_\nu^{(1)}$, $Z_\nu^{(1)}$, or to the similar systems of tractions $X_\nu^{(2)}$, ... and $X_\nu^{(3)}$, ..., for none of these satisfies the conditions of rigid-body-equilibrium†. When the surface tractions are given we must introduce, in addition to the unit forces at (x', y', z'), equal and opposite unit forces at a chosen point A, together with such couples at A as will, with the unit forces, yield a system in equilibrium. Let (u_1', v_1', w_1') be the displacement due to unit force parallel to x at (x', y', z') and the balancing system of force and couple at A, and let $X_\nu'^{(1)}$, $Y_\nu'^{(1)}$, $Z_\nu'^{(1)}$ be the surface tractions calculated from (u_1', v_1', w_1'). Also let (u_1'', v_1'', w_1'') be the displacement which, besides satisfying the usual conditions of continuity and the equations of equilibrium (1), gives rise to surface tractions equal to $X_\nu'^{(1)}$, $Y_\nu'^{(1)}$, $Z_\nu'^{(1)}$. We make the displacement precise by supposing that it and the corresponding rotation vanish at A. Then we have

$$(u)_0=\iiint \rho\,(Xu_1'+Yv_1'+Zw_1')\,dx\,dy\,dz$$
$$+\iint \{X_\nu(u_1'-u_1'')+Y_\nu(v_1'-v_1'')+Z_\nu(w_1'-w_1'')\}\,dS. \quad\text{......(44)}$$

The problem of determining u is reduced to that of determining (u_1'', v_1'', w_1''). The displacement $(u_1'-u_1'', v_1'-v_1'', w_1'-w_1'')$ is an analogue of the second Green's function.

If, instead of taking the displacement and rotation to vanish at A, we assign to A a series of positions very near to (x', y', z'), and proceed to a limit by moving A up to coincidence with this point, we can obtain expressions for the components of strain in terms of the given surface tractions‡. In the first place let us apply two forces, each of magnitude h^{-1}, at the point (x', y', z') and at the point $(x'+h, y', z')$, in the positive and negative directions respectively of the axis of x. In the limit when h is diminished indefinitely the displacement due to these forces is $\left(\frac{\partial u_1}{\partial x}, \frac{\partial v_1}{\partial x}, \frac{\partial w_1}{\partial x}\right)$. Let (u_{11}, v_{11}, w_{11}) be the displacement produced in the body by surface tractions equal to those calculated from the displacement $\left(\frac{\partial u_1}{\partial x}, \frac{\partial v_1}{\partial x}, \frac{\partial w_1}{\partial x}\right)$. Then the value of $(\partial u/\partial x)$ at the point (x', y', z') is given by the formula

$$\left(\frac{\partial u}{\partial x}\right)_0=-\iiint \rho\left(X\frac{\partial u_1}{\partial x}+Y\frac{\partial v_1}{\partial x}+Z\frac{\partial w_1}{\partial x}\right)dx\,dy\,dz$$
$$-\iint\left\{X_\nu\left(\frac{\partial u_1}{\partial x}-u_{11}\right)+Y_\nu\left(\frac{\partial v_1}{\partial x}-v_{11}\right)+Z_\nu\left(\frac{\partial w_1}{\partial x}-w_{11}\right)\right\}dS. \quad\text{.........(45)}$$

In like manner formulæ may be obtained for $\partial v/\partial y$ and $\partial w/\partial z$.

* G. Lauricella, *Pisa Ann.*, t. 7 (1895), attributes the method to Volterra. It was applied by C. Somigliana to the problem of the plane in *Il Nuovo Cimento* (1885, 1886).

† J. Dougall, *loc. cit.* p. 233. ‡ G. Lauricella, *loc. cit.*

Again, let us apply forces of magnitude h^{-1} in the positive directions of the axes of y and z at the origin of r, and equal forces in the negative directions of these axes at the points $(x', y', z'+h)$ and $(x', y'+h, z')$ respectively, and proceed to a limit as before. This system of forces satisfies the conditions of rigid-body-equilibrium, and the displacement due to it is

$$\left(\frac{\partial u_3}{\partial y}+\frac{\partial u_2}{\partial z},\ \frac{\partial v_3}{\partial y}+\frac{\partial v_2}{\partial z},\ \frac{\partial w_3}{\partial y}+\frac{\partial w_2}{\partial z}\right).$$

Let (u_{23}, v_{23}, w_{23}) be the displacement produced in the body by surface tractions equal to those calculated from the displacement $\left(\frac{\partial u_3}{\partial y}+\frac{\partial u_2}{\partial z}, \ldots, \ldots\right)$. Proceeding as before we obtain the equation

$$\left(\frac{\partial w}{\partial y}+\frac{\partial v}{\partial z}\right)_0 = -\iiint \rho\left\{X\left(\frac{\partial u_3}{\partial y}+\frac{\partial u_2}{\partial z}\right)+Y\left(\frac{\partial v_3}{\partial y}+\frac{\partial v_2}{\partial z}\right)+Z\left(\frac{\partial w_3}{\partial y}+\frac{\partial w_2}{\partial z}\right)\right\}dx\,dy\,dz$$

$$-\iint\left[X_\nu\left\{\left(\frac{\partial u_3}{\partial y}+\frac{\partial u_2}{\partial z}\right)-u_{23}\right\}+Y_\nu\left\{\left(\frac{\partial v_3}{\partial y}+\frac{\partial v_2}{\partial z}\right)-v_{23}\right\}+Z_\nu\left\{\left(\frac{\partial w_3}{\partial y}+\frac{\partial w_2}{\partial z}\right)-w_{23}\right\}\right]dS. \quad (46)$$

In like manner formulæ may be obtained for $\partial u/\partial z+\partial w/\partial x$ and $\partial v/\partial x+\partial u/\partial y$.

170. Outlines of various methods of integration.

One method which has been adopted sets out from the observation that, when there are no body forces, ϖ_x, ϖ_y, ϖ_z, as well as Δ, are harmonic functions within the surface of the body, and that the vector $(\varpi_x, \varpi_y, \varpi_z)$ satisfies the circuital condition

$$\frac{\partial \varpi_x}{\partial x}+\frac{\partial \varpi_y}{\partial y}+\frac{\partial \varpi_z}{\partial z}=0.$$

From this condition it appears that ϖ_x, ϖ_y, ϖ_z should be expressible in terms of two independent harmonic functions, and we may in fact write*

$$\varpi_x=\frac{\partial \phi}{\partial x}+y\frac{\partial \chi}{\partial z}-z\frac{\partial \chi}{\partial y},$$

$$\varpi_y=\frac{\partial \phi}{\partial y}+z\frac{\partial \chi}{\partial x}-x\frac{\partial \chi}{\partial z},$$

$$\varpi_z=\frac{\partial \phi}{\partial z}+x\frac{\partial \chi}{\partial y}-y\frac{\partial \chi}{\partial x},$$

where ϕ and χ are harmonic functions.

The equations of equilibrium, when there are no body forces, can be written in such forms as

$$(\lambda+2\mu)\frac{\partial \Delta}{\partial x}-2\mu\left(\frac{\partial \varpi_z}{\partial y}-\frac{\partial \varpi_y}{\partial z}\right)=0.$$

Now

$$\frac{\partial \varpi_z}{\partial y}-\frac{\partial \varpi_y}{\partial z}=-2\frac{\partial \chi}{\partial x}+x\left(\frac{\partial^2 \chi}{\partial y^2}+\frac{\partial^2 \chi}{\partial z^2}\right)-y\frac{\partial^2 \chi}{\partial x\,\partial y}-z\frac{\partial^2 \chi}{\partial x\,\partial z}$$

$$=-\left(2\frac{\partial \chi}{\partial x}+x\frac{\partial^2 \chi}{\partial x^2}+y\frac{\partial^2 \chi}{\partial x\,\partial y}+z\frac{\partial^2 \chi}{\partial x\partial z}\right)$$

$$=-\frac{\partial}{\partial x}\left(\chi+x\frac{\partial \chi}{\partial x}+y\frac{\partial \chi}{\partial y}+z\frac{\partial \chi}{\partial z}\right),$$

and it follows that

$$\Delta=-\frac{2\mu}{\lambda+2\mu}\left(\chi+x\frac{\partial \chi}{\partial x}+y\frac{\partial \chi}{\partial y}+z\frac{\partial \chi}{\partial z}\right).$$

* Cf. Lamb, *Hydrodynamics*, Chapter XI.

This expression represents, as it should, an harmonic function; and the quantitie Δ, ϖ_x, ϖ_y, ϖ_z are thus expressible in terms of two arbitrary harmonic functions ϕ and χ If now these functions can be adjusted so that the boundary conditions are satisfie Δ and (ϖ_x, ϖ_y, ϖ_z) will be determined. This method has been applied successfully to th problem of the sphere by C. W. Borchardt* and V. Cerruti†.

Another method‡ depends upon the observation that, in the notation of Article 13 $u_2=v_1$, $u_3=w_1$, $w_2=v_3$, and therefore the surface traction $X_\nu^{(1)}$ can be expressed in th form

$$X_\nu^{(1)}=l\lambda\left(\frac{\partial u_1}{\partial x}+\frac{\partial u_2}{\partial y}+\frac{\partial u_3}{\partial z}\right)+\mu\left(l\frac{\partial u_1}{\partial x}+m\frac{\partial u_1}{\partial y}+n\frac{\partial u_1}{\partial z}\right)+\mu\left(l\frac{\partial u_1}{\partial x}+m\frac{\partial u_2}{\partial x}+n\frac{\partial u_3}{\partial x}\right),$$

where l, m, n are written for $\cos(x, \nu)$, $\cos(y, \nu)$, $\cos(z, \nu)$. The surface traction $X_\nu^{(2)}$, $X_\nu^{(3)}$ can be written down by putting v and w respectively everywhere instead of in the expression for $X_\nu^{(1)}$. It follows that ($X_\nu^{(1)}$, $X_\nu^{(2)}$, $X_\nu^{(3)}$) is the *displacement* produce by certain double forces. In like manner ($Y_\nu^{(1)}$, $Y_\nu^{(2)}$, $Y_\nu^{(3)}$) and ($Z_\nu^{(1)}$, $Z_\nu^{(2)}$, $Z_\nu^{(3)}$) ar systems of displacements which satisfy the equations (1) everywhere except at the origi of r§. On this result has been founded a method (analogous to that of C. Neumann‖ i the theory of Potential) for solving the problem of given surface displacements by mean of series.

The equations of equilibrium, when there are no body forces, can also be written i the forms

$$\nabla^2\left(u+\frac{\lambda+\mu}{2\mu}x\Delta\right)=0,\quad \nabla^2\left(v+\frac{\lambda+\mu}{2\mu}y\Delta\right)=0,\quad \nabla^2\left(w+\frac{\lambda+\mu}{2\mu}z\Delta\right)=0,$$

showing that the three expressions of the type $u+\frac{1}{2}\mu^{-1}(\lambda+\mu)x\Delta$ are harmonic function These three harmonic functions must be adjusted so that the relation

$$\frac{\partial u}{\partial x}+\frac{\partial v}{\partial y}+\frac{\partial w}{\partial z}=\Delta,$$

where Δ also is an harmonic function, may be satisfied, and they must also be adjusted s as to satisfy the boundary conditions. This method has been developed by O. Tedone¶ and applied by him to the problems of a solid bounded by a plane, by two parallel plane by a sphere, by two concentric spheres, by an ellipsoid of revolution, and by a righ circular cone.

* *Berlin Monatsber.*, 1873, reprinted in C. W. Borchardt's *Ges. Werke*, Berlin, 1888, p. 245.

† *Comptes rendus de l'Association Française pour l'avancement de Science*, 1885, and *Roma, Acc Linc. Rend.* (Ser. 4), t. 2 (1886).

‡ G. Lauricella, *Pisa Ann.*, t. 7 (1895), and *Ann. di mat.* (Ser. 2), t. 23 (1895), and *Il Nuov Cimento* (Ser. 4), tt. 9, 10 (1899).

§ The result is due to C. Somigliana, *Ann. di mat.* (Ser. 2), t. 17 (1889).

‖ *Untersuchungen über das logarithmische und Newton'sche Potential*, Leipzig, 1877. C Poincaré, *loc. cit.* p. 232.

¶ *Ann. di mat.* (Ser. 3), t. 8, 1903, p. 129; (Ser. 3), t. 10, 1904, p. 13; *Roma, Acc. Linc. Rend* (Ser. 5), t. 14, 1905, pp. 76 and 316.

CHAPTER XI

THE EQUILIBRIUM OF AN ELASTIC SPHERE AND RELATED PROBLEMS

171. In this Chapter we shall consider solutions of the equations of equilibrium of an isotropic elastic solid body in terms of series involving harmonic functions, and, especially, spherical harmonics. We shall begin with some special types of solutions in terms of spherical harmonics, leading to important results in regard to the equilibrium of a solid sphere, and forming an introduction to the applications of the theory of Elasticity to Geophysics. We shall then proceed to Lord Kelvin's general solution* of the problem of the sphere, expressed in terms of spherical harmonics, regarding these functions as functions of cartesian coordinates, and dispensing with transformations to polar coordinates. After that we shall give some account of the use of series of harmonic functions, other than spherical harmonics, for the integration of the equations of equilibrium.

172. Special solutions in terms of spherical harmonics.

The equations to be solved are

$$(\lambda+\mu)\left(\frac{\partial}{\partial x}, \frac{\partial}{\partial y}, \frac{\partial}{\partial z}\right)\Delta+\mu\nabla^2(u, v, w)=0, \qquad (1)$$

where

$$\Delta=\frac{\partial u}{\partial x}+\frac{\partial v}{\partial y}+\frac{\partial w}{\partial z}. \qquad (2)$$

We know that Δ is an harmonic function, and that $\nabla^2 u$, $\nabla^2 v$, $\nabla^2 w$ also are harmonic functions. We shall consider cases in which any one of these four functions is expressed as a single term, which is a "spherical solid harmonic," that is to say a rational homogeneous function of x, y, z, of positive or negative integral degree n, satisfying Laplace's equation. Let V_n denote such a function, and let r denote the distance of the point (x, y, z) from the origin. Then V_n is of the form $r^n S_n$, where S_n is a function of the polar coordinates θ, ϕ and is independent of r. The factor S_n is described as a "spherical surface harmonic." For our purpose the most important formulæ relating to spherical harmonics are

$$\nabla^2(xV_n)=2\frac{\partial V_n}{\partial x}, \quad \nabla^2(r^m V_n)=m(m+2n+1)\,r^{m-2}V_n. \qquad (3)$$

We shall also make frequent use of the formula

$$x\frac{\partial V_n}{\partial x}+y\frac{\partial V_n}{\partial y}+z\frac{\partial V_n}{\partial z}=nV_n,$$

* See Introduction, footnote 61.

which is true for any homogeneous function, and of the identity

$$xV_n = \frac{r^2}{2n+1}\left(\frac{\partial V_n}{\partial x} - r^{2n+1}\frac{\partial}{\partial x}\frac{V_n}{r^{2n+1}}\right). \quad \text{.................(4)}$$

In the first of (3) and in (4) x may be replaced by y or z. Solutions of the three following types* are the most generally useful.

Type ω.—From (3) we see that, if ω_n is a spherical solid harmonic, $\nabla^2\left(r^2\frac{\partial\omega_n}{\partial x}\right)$ and $\nabla^2(x\omega_n)$ are spherical solid harmonics. We consider a displacement expressed by equations of the form

$$(u, v, w) = r^2\left(\frac{\partial}{\partial x}, \frac{\partial}{\partial y}, \frac{\partial}{\partial z}\right)\omega_n + \alpha_n(x, y, z)\,\omega_n, \quad \text{...........(5)}$$

where α_n is constant. These formulæ give

$$\Delta = \{2n + \alpha_n(3+n)\}\,\omega_n, \quad \text{.......................(6)}$$

and
$$\nabla^2(u, v, w) = 2(2n+1+\alpha_n)\left(\frac{\partial}{\partial x}, \frac{\partial}{\partial y}, \frac{\partial}{\partial z}\right)\omega_n,$$

and therefore equations (1) are satisfied by the forms (5) if

$$\alpha_n = -2\,\frac{n\lambda + (3n+1)\mu}{(n+3)\lambda + (n+5)\mu}. \quad \text{...................(7)}$$

Type ϕ.—We consider a displacement expressed by equations of the form

$$(u, v, w) = \left(\frac{\partial}{\partial x}, \frac{\partial}{\partial y}, \frac{\partial}{\partial z}\right)\phi_n, \quad \text{.......................(8)}$$

where ϕ_n is a spherical solid harmonic of degree n. These formulæ give $\Delta = 0$, $\nabla^2 u = 0$, ..., and the equations (1) are satisfied.

Type χ.—We consider a displacement expressed by equations of the form

$$(u, v, w) = \left(y\frac{\partial}{\partial z} - z\frac{\partial}{\partial y},\quad z\frac{\partial}{\partial x} - x\frac{\partial}{\partial z},\quad x\frac{\partial}{\partial y} - y\frac{\partial}{\partial x}\right)\chi_n, \quad \text{......(9)}$$

where χ_n is a spherical solid harmonic of degree n. These formulæ give $\Delta = 0$, $\nabla^2 u = 0$, ..., and the equations (1) are satisfied.

We shall require expressions for the tractions across any spherical surface $r = \text{const.}$ answering to these several types of displacement. The component tractions X_r, Y_r, Z_r are expressed by such formulæ as

$$X_r = \frac{x}{r}\left(\lambda\Delta + 2\mu\frac{\partial u}{\partial x}\right) + \frac{y}{r}\mu\left(\frac{\partial v}{\partial x} + \frac{\partial u}{\partial y}\right) + \frac{z}{r}\mu\left(\frac{\partial u}{\partial z} + \frac{\partial w}{\partial x}\right),$$

and these are equivalent to formulæ of the type

$$\frac{rX_r}{\mu} = \frac{\lambda}{\mu}x\Delta + \frac{\partial\zeta}{\partial x} + r\frac{\partial u}{\partial r} - u, \quad \text{...................(10)}$$

where
$$\zeta = xu + yv + zw, \quad \text{.........................(11)}$$

so that ζ/r is the radial component of the displacement.

* The notation is suggested by the analysis which will be used in the next Chapter.

In the case of type ω we have Δ given by (6) and

$$\zeta = (n + \alpha_n) r^2 \omega_n,$$

$$r\frac{\partial u}{\partial r} - u = n\left(r^2 \frac{\partial \omega_n}{\partial x} + \alpha_n x \omega_n\right),$$

and therefore

$$\frac{rX_r}{\mu} = (2n + \alpha_n) r^2 \frac{\partial \omega_n}{\partial x} + \left[2n\left(\frac{\lambda}{\mu} + 1\right) + \alpha_n\left\{(n+3)\frac{\lambda}{\mu} + (n+2)\right\}\right] x\omega_n, \quad \text{...........(12)}$$

where α_n is given by (7).

In the case of type ϕ we have $\Delta = 0$ and

$$\zeta = n\phi_n, \quad r\frac{\partial u}{\partial r} - u = (n-2)\frac{\partial \phi_n}{\partial x},$$

and therefore

$$\frac{rX_r}{\mu} = 2(n-1)\frac{\partial \phi_n}{\partial x}. \quad \text{........................(13)}$$

In the case of type χ we have $\Delta = 0$, $\zeta = 0$, and

$$\frac{rX_r}{\mu} = r\frac{\partial u}{\partial r} - u = (n-1)\left(y\frac{\partial \chi_n}{\partial z} - z\frac{\partial \chi_n}{\partial y}\right). \quad \text{..............(14)}$$

In all three types the forms of Y_r, Z_r are obtained from those of X_r by cyclical interchange of the letters x, y, z.

173. Applications of the special solutions.

(i) *Solid sphere with purely radial surface displacement.* Let a solid sphere of radius a be held strained by surface traction, so that the displacement of the boundary is purely radial, and equal to ϵS_n, where S_n denotes a spherical surface harmonic of positive integral degree n, and ϵ is a small constant. We put

$$U_n = \frac{r^n}{a^n} S_n,$$

and add solutions of the ω and ϕ types with

$$\phi_n = -a^2\omega_n, \quad \alpha_n a \omega_n = \epsilon U_n,$$

where α_n is given by (7). The surface tractions required to hold the sphere in this state are given by formulæ of the type

$$\frac{a^2 X_r}{\mu} = \frac{2+\alpha_n}{\alpha_n} a^2 \epsilon \frac{\partial U_n}{\partial x} + \left[2n\left(\frac{\lambda}{\mu}+1\right) + \alpha_n\left\{(n+3)\frac{\lambda}{\mu} + (n+2)\right\}\right]\frac{\epsilon}{\alpha_n} x U_n.$$

(ii) *Solid sphere with purely radial surface traction.* Let the boundary $r=a$ be subjected to purely normal surface traction of amount $\epsilon' S_n$, where ϵ' is constant, and let U_n be defined as in (i). We add solutions of the ω and ϕ types with

$$\phi_n = -\frac{2n+\alpha_n}{2(n-1)} a^2 \omega_n, \quad [2n(\lambda+\mu) + \{(n+3)\lambda + (n+2)\mu\}\alpha_n]\,\omega_n = \epsilon' U_n,$$

where α_n is given by (7).

From these two examples (i) and (ii) we conclude that a state of strain in a solid sphere, expressed by any linear combination of the ω and ϕ types, can be regarded as being compounded of the two states in which the sphere can be held (i) by such surface tractions as render the surface displacement purely radial, and (ii) by purely radial surface tractions.

The solution for the sphere with any given purely radial surface displacement can be obtained from (i) by expanding the surface displacement in a series of spherical surface harmonics; and the solution for the sphere with any given purely radial surface traction can be obtained from (ii) in a similar way. It should be noted that no term of the first degree can occur in the expansion of the purely radial surface traction, for radial traction expressed by the formula $Ax+By+Cz$, where A, B, C are constants, would have a resultant $\frac{4}{3}\pi a^3\sqrt{(A^2+B^2+C^2)}$ in the direction $(A:B:C)$, and could not maintain equilibrium.

(iii) *Small spherical cavity in large solid mass.* In the solutions of Article 172 n may be positive or negative, but when it is negative it is sometimes more convenient to replace ω_n, ϕ_n, χ_n by $r^{-(2n+1)}(\omega_n, \phi_n, \chi_n)$, with a positive integral n, and this procedure involves some changes of detail. Solutions in terms of solid harmonics of negative degrees are applicable to problems relating to a body in which there is a small spherical cavity. The body may be regarded as extending indefinitely in all directions.

An example of some interest is afforded by a body in which there is a distribution of shearing strain*. At a great distance from the cavity we may take the displacement to be given by the equation

$$(u, v, w)=(sy, 0, 0),$$

where s is constant. Then ω_{-3} and ϕ_{-3}, both constant multiples of $r^{-5}xy$, are the functions required, and we may transform such expressions as $x\omega_{-3}$ by means of the equation (4). It may thus be shown that a possible displacement is expressed by equations of the form

$$(u, v, w)=(sy, 0, 0)+(B+Cr^2)\left(\frac{\partial}{\partial x}, \frac{\partial}{\partial y}, \frac{\partial}{\partial z}\right)\frac{xy}{r^5}-\frac{3\lambda+8\mu}{3(\lambda+\mu)}C\left(\frac{y}{r^3}, \frac{x}{r^3}, 0\right),$$

where B and C are constants, and that the surface $r=a$ of the cavity is free from traction if

$$B=\frac{3(\lambda+\mu)}{9\lambda+14\mu}a^5s, \quad C=-\frac{3(\lambda+\mu)}{9\lambda+14\mu}a^3s.$$

The value of the shearing strain $\frac{\partial u}{\partial y}+\frac{\partial v}{\partial x}$ can be calculated. It will be found that, at the point $x=0$, $y=0$, $r=a$, it is equal to $(15\lambda+30\mu)s/(9\lambda+14\mu)$. The result shows that the shear in the neighbourhood of the cavity can be nearly equal to twice the shear at a distance from the cavity. The existence of a flaw in the form of a spherical cavity may cause a serious diminution of strength in a body subjected to shearing forces†.

(iv) *Twisted sphere.* For most of the problems that we have in view the ω and ϕ types of displacement suffice. To illustrate the χ type we may take $n=2$ and $\chi_2=A(x^2+y^2-2z^2)$, where A is constant. Then

$$(u, v, w)=A(-6yz, 6zx, 0),$$

and

$$(X_r, Y_r, Z_r)_{r=a}=A(\mu/a).(-6yz, 6zx, 0).$$

The tractions on the hemisphere $z>0$ are statically equivalent to a couple about the axis of z of moment $3\pi a^4\mu A$, and the tractions on the hemisphere $z<0$ are statically equivalent to an equal couple about the same axis in the opposite sense.

174. Sphere subjected to body force.

When a body is subjected to body force we seek in the first place a particular integral of the equations

$$(\lambda+\mu)\left(\frac{\partial}{\partial x}, \frac{\partial}{\partial y}, \frac{\partial}{\partial z}\right)\Delta+\mu\nabla^2(u, v, w)+\rho(X, Y, Z)=0, \quad \ldots(15)$$

and, when this is found, we seek, by adding to it a suitable solution of

* See *Phil. Mag.* (Ser. 5), vol. 33 (1892), p. 77.

† Cf. Article 84, *supra.*

equations (1), to obtain such a solution of equations (15) as will satisfy prescribed conditions of displacement or traction at the bounding surface of the body. The case of greatest interest is presented when the body force (X, Y, Z) is the gradient of a potential, which is expressed as a spherical solid harmonic V_n of positive integral degree n. In this case equations (15) become

$$(\lambda+\mu)\left(\frac{\partial}{\partial x}, \frac{\partial}{\partial y}, \frac{\partial}{\partial z}\right)\Delta+\mu\nabla^2(u, v, w)+\rho\left(\frac{\partial}{\partial x}, \frac{\partial}{\partial y}, \frac{\partial}{\partial z}\right)V_n=0. \quad \ldots(16)$$

A particular integral can be obtained by putting

$$(u, v, w)=\left(\frac{\partial}{\partial x}, \frac{\partial}{\partial y}, \frac{\partial}{\partial z}\right)\phi,$$

where

$$(\lambda+2\mu)\nabla^2\phi+\rho V_n=0,$$

and taking in accordance with the second of equations (3)

$$\phi=-\frac{\rho}{(\lambda+2\mu)\,2(2n+3)}r^2V_n.$$

Then we have the desired particular integral in the form

$$(u, v, w)=-\frac{\rho}{(\lambda+2\mu)\,2(2n+3)}\left(\frac{\partial}{\partial x}, \frac{\partial}{\partial y}, \frac{\partial}{\partial z}\right)(r^2V_n). \quad \ldots\ldots(17)$$

When these values for u, v, w are taken we have

$$\Delta=-\frac{\rho}{\lambda+2\mu}V_n,$$

$$\zeta=-\frac{n+2}{2(2n+3)}\frac{\rho}{\lambda+2\mu}r^2V_n,$$

$$r\frac{\partial u}{\partial r}-u=-\frac{n}{2(2n+3)}\frac{\rho}{\lambda+2\mu}\left(r^2\frac{\partial V_n}{\partial x}+2xV_n\right),$$

and the corresponding formulæ for the tractions X_r, Y_r, Z_r across any spherical surface $r=$ const. are of the type

$$\frac{rX_r}{\mu}=-\frac{\rho}{\lambda+2\mu}\left[\frac{n+1}{2n+3}r^2\frac{\partial V_n}{\partial x}+\left\{\frac{\lambda}{\mu}+\frac{2(n+1)}{2n+3}\right\}xV_n\right] \quad \ldots\ldots(18)$$

When a body bounded by the surface $r=a$ is deformed by body force as above, and the surface is free from traction, the displacement is determined by adding to the value given by (18) forms of the ω and ϕ types adjusted so that the component tractions at the boundary may vanish. We shall put

$$\omega_n=AV_n, \quad \phi_n=BV_n,$$

and determine the constants A and B.

We have at once

$$(2n+\alpha_n)a^2A+2(n-1)B=\frac{\rho}{\lambda+2\mu}\frac{n+1}{2n+3}a^2$$

and

$$\left[2n\left(\frac{\lambda}{\mu}+1\right)+\alpha_n\left\{(n+3)\frac{\lambda}{\mu}+(n+2)\right\}\right]A=\frac{\rho}{\lambda+2\mu}\left\{\frac{\lambda}{\mu}+\frac{2(n+1)}{2n+3}\right\},$$

where α_n is given by (7).

Hence we find

$$A = -\frac{\rho\{(2n+3)\lambda+(2n+2)\mu\}\{(n+3)\lambda+(n+5)\mu\}}{2(2n+3)(\lambda+2\mu)\mu\{(2n^2+4n+3)\lambda+2(n^2+n+1)\mu\}},$$

$$B = \frac{\rho n\{(n+2)\lambda+(n+1)\mu\}a^2}{2(n-1)\mu\{(2n^2+4n+3)\lambda+2(n^2+n+1)\mu\}}.$$

The radial displacement ζ/r is given by the equation

$$\zeta = \left[nB + \left\{(n+\alpha_n)A - \frac{n+2}{2(2n+3)}\frac{\rho}{\lambda+2\mu}\right\}r^2\right]V_n,$$

and this is found to be

$$\frac{\rho n[n\{(n+2)\lambda+(n+1)\mu\}a^2-(n-1)\{(n+1)\lambda+n\mu\}r^2]}{2(n-1)\mu\{(2n^2+4n+3)\lambda+2(n^2+n+1)\mu\}}V_n,$$

showing that all the spherical surfaces concentric with the boundary are strained into harmonic spheroids of the same type, but these spheroids are not similar to each other. If $n=2$ the spheroids are of ellipsoidal type, and the ellipticities* of the principal sections increase from the outermost to the centre, the ratio of the extreme values being $5\lambda+4\mu : 8\lambda+6\mu$†.

175. Generalization and Special Cases of the foregoing solution.

(i) It may be observed that, if the body force is the gradient of a potential expressed as a series ΣV_n of spherical solid harmonics, the solution is to be found by taking a sum of the solutions answering to the various values of n. Among these there cannot be a term for which $n=1$, for the corresponding body force would be a constant force in a fixed direction, and could not maintain equilibrium.

(ii) The case of an incompressible solid sphere may be noticed. It would be treated by taking Δ to tend to zero, and λ to tend to ∞, in such a way that $\lambda\Delta$ has a finite limit. The particular integral for the body force (Article 174) would contribute nothing to the displacement, but would contribute to the surface tractions on the boundary, $r=a$, a normal traction equal to $-\rho V_n$. The displacement is therefore the same as in an incompressible solid sphere strained by purely radial surface traction‡ equal to ρV_n, and can be found by the method of Article 173 (ii) by putting

$$\phi_n = -\frac{n(n+2)}{(n-1)(n+3)}a^2\omega_n, \quad \omega_n = -\frac{n+3}{2(2n^2+4n+3)}\frac{\rho V_n}{\mu}.$$

(iii) The analysis of Article 174 may be applied to find the strain produced in a solid sphere of radius a by rotation. The sphere may be taken to rotate with angular velocity ω about the axis of z. Then the equations of motion are the same as the equations of equilibrium under body force $\omega^2(x, y, 0)$, and this is the gradient of the potential $\frac{1}{2}\omega^2(x^2+y^2)$, or, as it may be written,

$$\tfrac{1}{3}\omega^2 r^2 + \tfrac{1}{6}\omega^2(x^2+y^2-2z^2).$$

The first term gives a purely radial force $\frac{2}{3}\omega^2 r$, and the corresponding displacement can be found from Article 98 (vii) by writing $\frac{2}{3}\omega^2$ instead of $-g/r_0$, and a instead of r_0.

* The ellipticity of an ellipse is the ratio of the excess of the axis major above the axis minor to the axis major.

† Kelvin and Tait, *Nat. Phil.*, Part II. p. 433.

‡ Chree, *Cambridge Phil. Soc. Trans.*, vol. 14 (1889), p. 250.

Thus this term contributes displacement expressed by

$$\frac{u}{x}=\frac{v}{y}=\frac{w}{z}=\frac{\rho a^2\omega^2}{15(\lambda+2\mu)}\left(\frac{5\lambda+6\mu}{3\lambda+2\mu}-\frac{r^2}{a^2}\right).$$

The second term in the expression for the potential is of the form V_2, and the contribution of this term to the displacement is made up of a part arising from the particular integral (17) and forms of the ω and ϕ types. The part arising from the particular integral is given by

$$(u, v, w)=-\frac{\rho\omega^2}{42(\lambda+2\mu)}\{r^2(x, y, -2z)+(x^2+y^2-2z^2)(x, y, z)\}.$$

The part arising from ω_2 is

$$-\frac{\rho\omega^2(7\lambda+6\mu)}{42(\lambda+2\mu)\mu(19\lambda+14\mu)}\{(5\lambda+7\mu)r^2(x, y, -2z)-(2\lambda+7\mu)(x^2+y^2-2z^2)(x, y, z)\},$$

and the part arising from ϕ_2 is

$$\frac{\rho\omega^2(4\lambda+3\mu)}{3\mu(19\lambda+14\mu)}a^2(x, y, -2z).$$

The complete expression of the displacement* is given by the equations

$$\frac{u}{x}=\frac{v}{y}=\frac{\rho\omega^2}{3}\left[\frac{1}{5(\lambda+2\mu)}\left(\frac{5\lambda+6\mu}{3\lambda+2\mu}a^2-r^2\right)\right.$$
$$\left.+\frac{1}{\mu(19\lambda+14\mu)}\{(4\lambda+3\mu)a^2-\tfrac{1}{2}(5\lambda+4\mu)r^2+(\lambda+\mu)(x^2+y^2-2z^2)\}\right],$$

$$\frac{w}{z}=\frac{\rho\omega^2}{3}\left[\frac{1}{5(\lambda+2\mu)}\left(\frac{5\lambda+6\mu}{3\lambda+2\mu}a^2-r^2\right)\right.$$
$$\left.+\frac{1}{\mu(19\lambda+14\mu)}\{-(8\lambda+6\mu)a^2+(5\lambda+4\mu)r^2+(\lambda+\mu)(x^2+y^2-2z^2)\}\right].$$

176. Gravitating incompressible sphere.

The chief interest of problems of the kind considered in Article 175 arises from the possibility of applying the solutions to the discussion of problems relating to the Earth. Among such problems are the question of the dependence of the ellipticity of the figure of the Earth upon the diurnal rotation, and the question of the effects produced by the disturbing attractions of the Sun and Moon. All such applications are beset by the difficulty which has been noted in Article 75, viz.: that, even when the effects of rotation and disturbing forces are left out of account, the Earth is in a condition of stress, and the internal stress is much too great to permit of the direct application of the mathematical theory of superposable small strains†. One way of evading this difficulty is to treat the material of which the Earth is composed as homogeneous and incompressible.

When the homogeneous incompressible sphere is at rest under the mutual gravitation of its parts the state of stress existing in it may be taken to be

* The complete solutions in terms of polar coordinates for a rotating sphere and spherical shell are given by Chree in the memoir cited on p. 254, and further discussed by him in *Cambridge Phil. Soc. Trans.*, vol. 14 (1889), p. 467.

† The difficulty has been emphasized by Chree, *Phil. Mag.* (Ser. 5), vol. 32 (1891).

of the nature of hydrostatic pressure*; and, if p_0 is the amount of this pressure at a distance r from the centre, the condition of equilibrium is

$$\partial p_0/\partial r = -g\rho r/a, \qquad (19)$$

where g is the acceleration due to gravity at the bounding surface $r=a$. Since p_0 vanishes at this surface, we have

$$p_0 = \tfrac{1}{2} g\rho\,(a^2 - r^2)/a. \qquad (20)$$

When the sphere is strained by the action of external forces we may measure the strain from the initial state as "unstrained" state, and we may suppose that the strain at any point is accompanied by additional stress superposed upon the initial stress p_0. We may assume further that the components of the additional stress are connected with the strain by equations of the ordinary form

$$X_x = \lambda\Delta + 2\mu e_{xx}, \ldots, \quad Y_z = \mu e_{yz}, \ldots,$$

in which we pass to a limit by taking λ to be very great compared with μ, and Δ to be very small compared with the greatest linear extension, in such a way that $\lambda\Delta$ is of the same order of magnitude as $\mu e_{xx}, \ldots$. We may put

$$\lim.\ \lambda\Delta = -p,$$

and then $p_0 + p$ is the mean pressure at any point of the body in the strained state.

Let V be the potential of the disturbing forces. The equations of equilibrium are of the type

$$\frac{\partial}{\partial x}(-p_0 + X_x) + \frac{\partial X_y}{\partial y} + \frac{\partial Z_x}{\partial z} - g\rho\frac{x}{a} + \rho\frac{\partial V}{\partial x} = 0.$$

The terms containing $-p_0$ and $-g\rho$ cancel each other, and this equation takes the form

$$-\frac{\partial p}{\partial x} + \mu\nabla^2 u + \rho\frac{\partial V}{\partial x} = 0.$$

The equations of equilibrium of the homogeneous incompressible sphere, deformed from the state of initial stress expressed by (20) by the action of external forces, are of the same form as the ordinary equations of equilibrium of a sphere subjected to disturbing forces, provided that, in the latter equations, $\lambda\Delta$ is replaced by $-p$ and $\mu\Delta$ is neglected. The existence of the initial stress p_0 has no influence on these equations, but it has an influence on the special conditions which hold at the surface. These conditions are that the *deformed* surface is free from traction. Let the equation of the deformed surface be $r = a + \epsilon S$, where ϵ is a small constant and S is some function of position on the sphere $r=a$. The "inequality" ϵS must be such that the volume is unaltered. We may calculate the traction (X_ν, Y_ν, Z_ν) across the surface $r = a + \epsilon S$. Let l', m', n' be the direction cosines of the outward drawn normal ν to this surface. Then

$$X_\nu = l'(X_x - p_0) + m' X_y + n' X_z.$$

* Cf. J. Larmor, 'On the period of the Earth's free Eulerian precession,' *Cambridge Phil. Soc. Proc.*, vol. 9 (1898), especially § 13.

In the terms X_x, X_y, X_z, which are linear in the strain-components, we may replace l', m', n' by x/a, y/a, z/a, for the true values differ from these values by quantities of the order ϵ; but we must calculate the value of the term $-l'p_0$ at the surface $r=a+\epsilon S$ correctly to the order ϵ. This is easily done because p_0 vanishes at $r=a$, and therefore at $r=a+\epsilon S$ it may be taken to be $\epsilon S\left(\frac{\partial p_0}{\partial r}\right)_{r=a}$, or $-g\rho\epsilon S$. Neglecting ϵ^2, we may write

$$-l'p_0=\frac{x}{a}g\rho\epsilon S.$$

Hence the condition that X_ν vanishes at the surface $r=a+\epsilon S$ can be written

$$(X_r)_{r=a}+\frac{x}{a}g\rho\epsilon S=0. \quad\text{.........................(21)}$$

The conditions that Y_ν, Z_ν vanish at this surface can be expressed in similar forms and the results may be interpreted in the statement:—Account can be taken of the initial stress by assuming that the mean sphere, instead of being free from traction, is subject to pressure which is equal to the weight per unit of area of the material heaped up to form the inequality*.

177. Deformation of gravitating incompressible sphere by external body force.

Let the external disturbing force be the gradient of a potential, which is expressed within the sphere as a series ΣW_n of spherical solid harmonics of positive integral degrees. The disturbing force at any point of the body is compounded of the external disturbing force and the attraction of the inequality ϵS. We may suppose ϵS to be expanded in a series $\Sigma\epsilon_n S_n$ of spherical surface harmonics. Then the attraction of the inequality is the gradient of a potential, which is expressed as a series of spherical solid harmonics by the formula

$$4\pi\gamma\rho a\,\Sigma\,(2n+1)^{-1}\,\epsilon_n\,(r/a)^n\,S_n,$$

and the potential of all the disturbing forces is expressed as a series ΣV_n of spherical solid harmonics by the formula

$$V_n=W_n+\frac{3g}{2n+1}\epsilon_n\left(\frac{r}{a}\right)^n S_n, \quad\text{...................(22)}$$

where $4\pi\gamma\rho a$ has been replaced by the equivalent $3g$.

The equations to be solved are

$$\left.\begin{aligned}-\left(\frac{\partial}{\partial x},\frac{\partial}{\partial y},\frac{\partial}{\partial z}\right)p+\mu\nabla^2(u,v,w)+\rho\left(\frac{\partial}{\partial x},\frac{\partial}{\partial y},\frac{\partial}{\partial z}\right)\Sigma V_n=0,\\ \frac{\partial u}{\partial x}+\frac{\partial v}{\partial y}+\frac{\partial w}{\partial z}=0.\end{aligned}\right\}\quad\text{...(23)}$$

* This result is often assumed without proof. It appears to involve implicitly some such argument as that given in the text.

On differentiating the left-hand members of the first three of these equations with respect to x, y, z respectively, adding, and utilising the fourth equation, it appears that $\nabla^2 p = 0$, and it is convenient then to put

$$p = \rho \Sigma V_n + \Sigma p_n, \qquad \text{.........................(24)}$$

where p_n is a spherical solid harmonic of degree n. Then equations (3) of Article 172 suggest as possible forms for u, v, w

$$(u, v, w) = \Sigma A_n r^2 \left(\frac{\partial}{\partial x}, \frac{\partial}{\partial y}, \frac{\partial}{\partial z}\right) p_n + \Sigma B_n (x, y, z) p_n,$$

where A_n and B_n are constants, and it is found that the equations (23) are satisfied by these forms if

$$\left.\begin{aligned} \mu \{2(2n+1) A_n + 2B_n\} = 1, \\ 2n A_n + (n+3) B_n = 0. \end{aligned}\right\} \qquad \text{....................(25)}$$

To these forms we may add any solutions of the equations

$$\nabla^2 (u, v, w) = 0, \qquad \frac{\partial u}{\partial x} + \frac{\partial v}{\partial y} + \frac{\partial w}{\partial z} = 0,$$

and it will be sufficient to add forms of the ϕ type, say

$$(u, v, w) = \Sigma \left(\frac{\partial}{\partial x}, \frac{\partial}{\partial y}, \frac{\partial}{\partial z}\right) \phi_n,$$

where ϕ_n is a spherical solid harmonic of degree n.

In accordance with (10) of Article 172 we calculate the traction across any surface $r = \text{const.}$ by formulæ of the type

$$\frac{rX_r}{\mu} = -\frac{xp}{\mu} + \frac{\partial \zeta}{\partial x} + r\frac{\partial u}{\partial r} - u.$$

We have p given by equation (24), and find

$$\zeta = \Sigma (nA_n + B_n) r^2 p_n + \Sigma n\phi_n, \qquad \text{....................(26)}$$

and

$$r\frac{\partial u}{\partial r} - u = \Sigma n A_n r^2 \frac{\partial p_n}{\partial x} + \Sigma n B_n x p_n + \Sigma (n-2) \frac{\partial \phi_n}{\partial x},$$

and therefore the traction calculated from the forms of u, v, w, p is expressed by equations of the type

$$\frac{rX_r}{\mu} = \Sigma \left[-\frac{x\rho V_n}{\mu} + (2nA_n + B_n) r^2 \frac{\partial p_n}{\partial x} + \left\{2nA_n + (n+2) B_n - \frac{1}{\mu}\right\} x p_n + 2(n-1) \frac{\partial \phi_n}{\partial x} \right].$$

The conditions to be satisfied at the surface $r = a$ are the kinematical condition that the radial displacement (ζ/r) is equal to $\Sigma \epsilon_n S_n$, and the conditions of the type (21). On substituting from equations (26) and (22) it is found that these conditions give

$$\left.\begin{aligned} (nA_n + B_n) a^2 p_n + n\phi_n - a\epsilon_n (r/a)^n S_n = 0, \\ (2nA_n + B_n) a^2 p_n + 2(n-1) \phi_n = 0, \\ [\mu \{2nA_n + (n+2) B_n\} - 1] p_n + g\rho \left(1 - \frac{3}{2n+1}\right) \epsilon_n \left(\frac{r}{a}\right)^n S_n = \rho W_n. \end{aligned}\right\} \text{...(27)}$$

These equations can be solved easily, and, since A_n, B_n are known from (25), we have the complete solution of the problem.

If the external disturbing potential reduces to a single term W_n the only spherical harmonics of the p_n, ϕ_n, S_n series which occur in the solution are of degree n and are simple multiples of W_n. In particular the inequality is proportional to the disturbing potential.

The most interesting cases arise when $n=2$. Then we have

$$\frac{A_2}{5}=\frac{B_2}{-4}=\frac{1}{42\mu},$$

and

$$\frac{a^2 p_2}{-2}=\frac{\phi_2}{\dfrac{8}{21\mu}}=\frac{a\epsilon_2 (r/a)^2 S_2}{\dfrac{10}{21\mu}}=\frac{\rho W_2}{\dfrac{38}{21a^2}+\dfrac{g\rho}{a}\dfrac{4}{21\mu}}.$$

Thus, in particular, the inequality* is given by the equation

$$\epsilon_2 S_2=\frac{\dfrac{5}{2}\dfrac{W_2}{g}}{1+\dfrac{19}{2}\dfrac{\mu}{g\rho a}}, \qquad \text{.........................(28)}$$

where W_2 has its value at the surface $r=a$. It follows that the inequality is less for a solid incompressible sphere of rigidity μ than it would be for an incompressible fluid sphere of the same size and mass in the ratio

$$1:1+\frac{19}{2}\frac{\mu}{g\rho a}.$$

For a sphere of the same size and mass as the Earth ($\rho=5{\cdot}527$, $a=6{\cdot}37\times 10^8$) this ratio is approximately equal to $\frac{3}{5}$ when the rigidity is the same as that of glass, and approximately equal to $\frac{1}{3}$ when the rigidity is the same as that of steel.

178. Gravitating body of nearly spherical form.

The case of a nearly spherical body of gravitating incompressible material can be included in the foregoing analysis. It is merely necessary to omit W_n from all the equations, and to suppress the kinematical condition that the value of ζ at $r=a$ is $a\Sigma\epsilon_n S_n$, thus omitting the first of equations (27).

G. H. Darwin has applied analysis of this kind, without, however, restricting it to the case of incompressible material, to the problem of determining the stresses induced in the interior of the Earth by the weight of continents†. Apart from the difficulty concerning the initial stress in a gravitating body of the size of the Earth—a difficulty which it is troublesome to avoid without treating the material as incompressible—there is another difficulty in the application of such an analysis to problems concerning compressible gravitating bodies. In the analysis we take account of the attraction of the inequality at

* Cf. Kelvin and Tait, *Nat. Phil.*, Part II. p. 436.

† *Phil. Trans. Roy. Soc.*, vol. 173 (1882), reprinted in revised form in G. H. Darwin's *Scientific Papers*, vol. 2, p. 459. Darwin's results have been discussed critically by Chree, *Cambridge Phil. Soc. Trans.*, vol. 14 (1889), and *Phil. Mag.* (Ser. 5), vol. 32 (1891).

the surface, but we neglect the inequalities of the internal attraction which arise from the changes of density in the interior; yet these inequalities of attraction are of the same order of magnitude as the attraction of the surface inequality. To illustrate this matter it will be sufficient to consider the case where the density ρ_0 in the initial state is uniform. In the strained state the density is expressed by $\rho_0(1-\Delta)$ correctly to the first order in the strains. The body force, apart from the attraction of the surface inequalities and other disturbing forces, has components per unit of mass equal to gx/a, gy/a, gz/a. Hence the expressions for $\rho X, \ldots$ in the equations of equilibrium ought to contain such terms as $g\rho_0 xa^{-1}(1-\Delta)$, and the terms of type $-g\rho_0 x\Delta/a$ are of the same order as the attractions of the surface inequalities*.

179. Rotating sphere under its own attraction.

Exactly as in Article 175 (iii) the deformation of the sphere is the same as if it were subject to the body force $\omega^2(x, y, 0)$, where ω is the angular velocity. This body force is the gradient of a potential expressed in polar coordinates by the formula $\frac{1}{3}\omega^2 r^2 - \frac{1}{3}\omega^2 r^2(\frac{3}{2}\cos^2\theta - \frac{1}{2})$, of which the first term gives rise to radial force, and the second is a spherical solid harmonic of degree 2. The radial force is of amount $\frac{2}{3}\omega^2 r$, and can be included in the term $-g\rho r/a$ of equation (19) by writing $g(1-2\omega^2 a/3g)$ instead of g. Since, in the case of the Earth, $\omega^2 a/g$ is a small fraction, equal to $\frac{1}{289}$ approximately, we may for the present purpose disregard this alteration of g. It follows from the result obtained in Article 177 that the nearly spherical figure assumed by a homogeneous incompressible solid body, of the size and mass of the Earth, under the combined influence of rotation and gravitation, is an oblate ellipsoid of revolution; and that its ellipticity is less than it would be if it were fluid in the ratio $1 : 1 + 19\mu/2g\rho a$.

The ellipticity of the figure of the Earth is about $\frac{1}{297}$. The ellipticity† of a nearly spherical spheroid of the same size and mass as the Earth, consisting of homogeneous incompressible fluid, and rotating uniformly at the rate of one revolution in 24 hours, is about $\frac{1}{230}$. The ellipticity which would be obtained by replacing the homogeneous incompressible fluid by homogeneous incompressible solid material of the rigidity of glass, to say nothing of steel, is too small; in the case of glass it would be $\frac{1}{383}$ nearly. The result that a solid of considerable rigidity takes, under the joint influence of rotation and its own gravitation, an oblate spheroidal figure appropriate to the rate of rotation, and having an ellipticity not incomparably less than if it were fluid, is important. It is difficult, however, to base an estimate of the rigidity of the Earth upon the above numerical results, because the deformation of a sphere by rotation is very greatly affected by heterogeneity of the material.

* See a paper by J. H. Jeans, *Phil. Trans. Roy. Soc.* (Ser. A), vol. 201 (1903).

† An equation of the form

$$r = a\{1 - \tfrac{2}{3}\epsilon(\tfrac{3}{2}\cos^2\theta - \tfrac{1}{2})\}$$

represents, when ϵ is small, a nearly spherical spheroid of ellipticity ϵ.

180. Tidal deformation. Tidal effective rigidity of the Earth.

The tidal disturbing forces also are derived from a potential which is a spherical solid harmonic of the second degree. The potential of the Moon at any point within the Earth can be expanded in a series of spherical solid harmonics of positive degrees. With the terms of the first degree there correspond the forces by which the relative orbital motion of the two bodies is maintained, and with the terms of higher degrees there correspond forces which produce relative displacements within the Earth. By analogy to the tidal motion of the Sea relative to the Land these displacements may be called "tides." The most important term in the disturbing potential is the term of the second degree, and it may be written $(M\gamma r^2/D^3)(\frac{3}{2}\cos^2\theta - \frac{1}{2})$, where M denotes the mass of the Moon, D the distance between the centres of the Earth and Moon, γ the constant of gravitation, and the axis from which θ is measured is the line of centres*. This is the "tide-generating potential" referred to the line of centres. When it is referred to axes fixed in the Earth, it becomes a sum of spherical harmonics of the second degree, with coefficients which are periodic functions of the time. Like statements hold with reference to the attraction of the Sun. With each term in the tide-generating potential there corresponds a deformation of the mean surface of the Sea into an harmonic spheroid of the second order, and each of these deformations is called a "tide." There are diurnal and semi-diurnal tides depending on the rotation of the Earth, fortnightly and monthly tides depending on the motion of the Moon in her orbit, annual and semi-annual tides depending on the motion of the Earth in her orbit, and a nineteen-yearly tide depending on periodic changes in the orbit of the Moon which are characterized by the revolution of the nodes in the Ecliptic.

The inequality which would be produced at the surface of a homogeneous incompressible fluid sphere, of the same size and mass as the Earth, or of an ocean covering a perfectly rigid spherical nucleus, by the force that corresponds with any term of the tide-generating potential, is called the "true equilibrium height" of the corresponding tide. From the results given in Article 184 we learn that the inequalities of the surface of a homogeneous incompressible solid sphere, of the same size and mass as the Earth and as rigid as steel, that would be produced by the same forces, would be about $\frac{1}{3}$ of the true equilibrium heights of the tides. They would be about $\frac{3}{5}$ of these heights if the rigidity were the same as that of glass. It follows that the height of the ocean tides, as measured by the rise and fall of the Sea relative to the Land, would be reduced in consequence of the elastic yielding of the solid nucleus to about $\frac{2}{3}$ of the true equilibrium height, if the rigidity were the same as that of steel, and to about $\frac{2}{5}$ of this height if the rigidity were the same as that of glass.

* See Lamb's *Hydrodynamics*, Appendix to Chapter VIII.

The name "tidal effective rigidity of the Earth" has been given by Lord Kelvin* to the rigidity which must be attributed to a homogeneous incompressible solid sphere, of the same size and mass as the Earth, in order that tides in a replica of the actual ocean resting upon it may be of the same height as the observed oceanic tides. If the tides followed the equilibrium law, the rigidity in question could be determined by observation of the actual tides and calculation of the true equilibrium height. It would be necessary to confine attention to tides of long period because those of short period are not likely to follow the equilibrium law even approximately. Of the tides of long period the nineteen-yearly tide is too minute to be detected with certainty. The annual and semi-annual tides are entirely masked by the fluctuations of ocean level that are due to the melting of ice in the polar regions. From observations of the fortnightly tides which were carried out in the Indian Ocean† it appeared that the heights of these tides are little, if anything, less than two-thirds of the true equilibrium heights. If the fortnightly tide followed the equilibrium law, we could infer that the tidal effective rigidity of the Earth is about equal to the rigidity of steel.

The fact that there are observable tides at all, and the above cited results in reference to the fortnightly tides in the Indian Ocean, have been held by Lord Kelvin to disprove the geological hypothesis that the Earth has a molten interior, upon which there rests a relatively thin solid crust, and, on this and other independent grounds, he has contended that the Earth is to be regarded as consisting mainly of solid matter of a high degree of rigidity.

The dynamical theory of the tides of long period can be worked out for an ocean of uniform depth covering the whole globe, the nucleus being treated as rigid‡. It is found that the heights of such tides, on oceans of such depths as actually exist, would be less than half of the equilibrium heights. This result was at first supposed to diminish the cogency of the tidal evidence as to the rigidity of the Earth. The dynamical reason for this result was found by H. Lamb (*Hydrodynamics*, 1895 edition). He showed that, if the oceans were symmetrical about the earth's axis, there could exist free steady motions, consisting of currents running along parallels of latitude, and that such currents would reduce the tides of long periods to amplitudes decidedly short of their equilibrium values. The actual oceans being interrupted by land barriers running north and south, it is almost certain that the tides in them are not subject to diminution from this cause§. The tidal evidence for the rigidity of the earth was thus re-habilitated.

* Sir W. Thomson, *Phil. Trans. Roy. Soc.*, vol. 153 (1863), and *Math. and Phys. Papers*, vol. 3, p. 317.

† Kelvin and Tait, *Nat. Phil.*, Part II. pp. 442—460 (contributed by G. H. Darwin).

‡ G. H. Darwin, *London Proc. Roy. Soc.*, vol. 41, 1886, p. 337, reprinted in his *Scientific Papers*, vol. 1, Cambridge, 1907, p. 366. See also Lamb, *Hydrodynamics*, Chapter VIII.

§ Lord Rayleigh, *Phil. Mag.* (Ser. 6), vol. 5, 1903, p. 136, reprinted in his *Scientific Papers*, vol. 5, Cambridge, 1912, p. 84.

Lord Kelvin's work on the solution of the equations of elastic equilibrium for an incompressible solid sphere, subject to its own gravitation and to external disturbing forces, with the application to determine the tidal effective rigidity of the Earth, has proved to be the beginning of an extensive theory. Reference has already been made to the improvement effected by J. H. Jeans*, who led the way in the direction of including the effects of compressibility, and to the application, initiated by G. H. Darwin, to the problem of determining the stresses induced in the interior of the Earth by the weight of continents and mountains. The reader, who may wish to pursue the subject, is referred to the following:—G. H. Darwin, *Scientific Papers*, especially vol. 1, pp. 389, 430, and vol. 2, p. 33, and 'The Rigidity of the Earth,' *Atti del IV Congresso...Matematici*, vol. 3, Roma, 1909; S. S. Hough, *Phil. Trans. Roy. Soc.* (Ser. A), vol. 187, 1896, p. 319; G. Herglotz, *Zeitschr. f. Math. u. Phys.*, Bd. 52, 1905, p. 275; W. Schweydar, *Beiträge zur Geophysik*, Bd. 9, 1907, p. 41; Lord Rayleigh, *London, Roy. Soc. Proc.* (Ser. A), vol. 77, 1906, p. 486, or *Scientific Papers*, vol. 5, p. 300; A. E. H. Love, *London, Roy. Soc. Proc.* (Ser. A), vol. 82, 1909, p. 73, and *Some Problems of Geodynamics*, Cambridge, 1911; J. Larmor, *London, Roy. Soc. Proc.* (Ser. A), vol. 82, p. 89; W. Schweydar, *Veröff. d. kgl. Preus. geodätischen Institutes* (Neue Folge), No. 54, 1912; K. Terazawa, *Phil. Trans. Roy. Soc.* (Ser. A), vol. 217, 1916, p. 35, and *Tokyo, J. Coll. Sci.*, vol. 37, 1916, Art. 7; H. Lamb, *London, Roy. Soc. Proc.* (Ser. A), vol. 93, 1917, p. 293; J. H. Jeans, *London, Roy. Soc. Proc.* (Ser. A), vol. 93, 1917, p. 413; L. M. Hoskins, *Amer. Math. Soc. Trans.*, vol. 21, 1920, p. 1. Other references will be found in these works.

181. A general solution of the equations of equilibrium.

The methods that have been explained in the earlier parts of this Chapter are adequate to obtain the most interesting solutions that can be expressed in terms of spherical harmonics. These solutions were originally obtained by means of a more general method†, and some account of this will now be given. We shall begin with a general solution of the equations of equilibrium of a body strained by surface tractions only, and shall then proceed to apply this solution to the equilibrium of a spherical body.

We propose to solve the equations (1) and (2) of Article 172 under the condition that u, v, w have no singularities in the neighbourhood of the origin.

Since Δ is an harmonic function, we may express it as a sum of spherical solid harmonics of positive integral degrees, which may be infinite in number. Let Δ_n be a spherical solid harmonic of positive integral degree n. We write

$$\Delta = \Sigma\Delta_n, \quad \ldots\ldots\ldots\ldots\ldots\ldots(29)$$

the summation referring to different values of n. The second of equations (3) of Article 172 gives

$$\nabla^2\left(r^2\frac{\partial\Delta_n}{\partial x}\right) = 2(2n+1)\frac{\partial\Delta_n}{\partial x},$$

with similar formulæ in which x is replaced by y or z. It follows that particular integrals of equations (1), with Δ defined by (29), could be expressed by the formula

$$(u, v, w) = -\frac{\lambda+\mu}{2\mu}r^2\Sigma\frac{1}{2n+1}\left(\frac{\partial}{\partial x}, \frac{\partial}{\partial y}, \frac{\partial}{\partial z}\right)\Delta_n,$$

* *Loc. cit. ante*, p. 260.

† Due to Lord Kelvin, see Introduction, footnote 61.

and more general integrals can be obtained by adding to these expressions for u, v, w any harmonic functions finite at the origin. Such harmonic functions must be adjusted so that the complete expressions for u, v, w shall satisfy equation (2).

The equations (1) and (2) are accordingly integrated in the form

$$(u, v, w) = -\frac{\lambda+\mu}{2\mu} r^2 \Sigma \frac{1}{2n+1} \left(\frac{\partial}{\partial x}, \frac{\partial}{\partial y}, \frac{\partial}{\partial z}\right) \Delta_n + \Sigma (U_n, V_n, W_n), \quad \text{.................(30)}$$

where U_n, V_n, W_n denote spherical solid harmonics of positive integral degree n, provided that these functions satisfy the equation

$$\Sigma \Delta_n = -\frac{\lambda+\mu}{\mu} \Sigma \frac{n}{2n+1} \Delta_n + \Sigma \left(\frac{\partial U_n}{\partial x} + \frac{\partial V_n}{\partial y} + \frac{\partial W_n}{\partial z}\right).$$

If we write

$$\psi_n = \frac{\partial U_{n+1}}{\partial x} + \frac{\partial V_{n+1}}{\partial y} + \frac{\partial W_{n+1}}{\partial z},$$

ψ_n is a spherical solid harmonic of degree n, and ψ_n and Δ_n are connected by the equation

$$\Delta_n = \frac{(2n+1)\mu}{n\lambda + (3n+1)\mu} \psi_n. \quad \text{......................(31)}$$

The formulæ (30) for u, v, w may now be expressed as sums of homogeneous functions of x, y, z in the form

$$(u, v, w) = -\Sigma M_n r^2 \left(\frac{\partial}{\partial x}, \frac{\partial}{\partial y}, \frac{\partial}{\partial z}\right) \psi_{n-1} + \Sigma (U_n, V_n, W_n), \quad \text{...(32)}$$

where U_n, V_n, W_n are spherical solid harmonics of degree n, M_n is the constant expressed by the equation

$$M_n = \frac{\lambda+\mu}{2\{(n-1)\lambda + (3n-2)\mu\}}, \quad \text{.................(33)}$$

and ψ_{n-1} is the spherical solid harmonic of degree $n-1$ expressed by the equation

$$\psi_{n-1} = \frac{\partial U_n}{\partial x} + \frac{\partial V_n}{\partial y} + \frac{\partial W_n}{\partial z}. \quad \text{..........................(34)}$$

182. Applications and extensions of the foregoing solution.

(i) The expressions (32) are general integrals of the equations of equilibrium arranged as sums of homogeneous functions of x, y, z of various degrees. By selecting a few of the lower terms, and providing them with undetermined coefficients, we may obtain solutions of a number of special problems. The displacement produced in an ellipsoid by rotation about an axis has been obtained by this method*.

(ii) It may be observed that, when n is negative, equations (32) express a solution of the equations of equilibrium, valid in a region of space from which the origin is excluded. By putting $n = -1$, $U_n = V_n = 0$, and $W_n = r^{-1}$, we obtain the solution discussed in Article 131.

* C. Chree, *Quart. J. of Math.*, vol. 23 (1888). A number of other applications of the method were made by Chree in this paper and an earlier paper in the same *Journal*, vol. 22 (1886).

(iii) When the region of space occupied by the body is bounded internally by a closed surface containing the origin, the equations can be solved in the same way as in Article 181 by the introduction of spherical solid harmonics of positive and negative integral degrees*. To illustrate the use of harmonics of negative degrees we may take the case of a cavity in an indefinitely extended body. Denoting by U_n, V_n, W_n spherical solid harmonics of positive integral degree n, we can write down a solution in the form

$$(u, v, w) = \frac{1}{r^{2n+1}}(U_n, V_n, W_n) - k_n r^2 \left(\frac{\partial}{\partial x}, \frac{\partial}{\partial y}, \frac{\partial}{\partial z}\right)\left(\frac{\psi_{n+1}}{r^{2n+3}}\right),$$

where

$$\psi_{n+1} = r^{2n+3}\left\{\frac{\partial}{\partial x}\left(\frac{U_n}{r^{2n+1}}\right) + \frac{\partial}{\partial y}\left(\frac{V_n}{r^{2n+1}}\right) + \frac{\partial}{\partial z}\left(\frac{W_n}{r^{2n+1}}\right)\right\},$$

and

$$k_n = -\frac{\lambda+\mu}{2\{(n+2)\lambda + (3n+5)\mu\}}.$$

183. The sphere with given surface displacements.

In any region of space containing the origin of coordinates, equations (32) constitute a system of integrals of the equations of equilibrium of an isotropic solid body which is free from the action of body forces. We may adapt these integrals to satisfy given conditions at the surface of a sphere of radius a. When the surface displacements are prescribed, we may suppose that the given values of u, v, w at $r = a$ are expressed as sums of surface harmonics of degree n in the forms

$$(u, v, w)_{r=a} = \Sigma(A_n, B_n, C_n). \qquad \text{.....................(35)}$$

Then $r^n A_n$, $r^n B_n$, $r^n C_n$ are given spherical solid harmonics of degree n.

Now select from (32) the terms that contain spherical surface harmonics of degree n. We see that when $r = a$ the following equations hold:

$$\left.\begin{aligned} \frac{r^n}{a^n} A_n &= -M_{n+2} a^2 \frac{\partial \psi_{n+1}}{\partial x} + U_n, \\ \frac{r^n}{a^n} B_n &= -M_{n+2} a^2 \frac{\partial \psi_{n+1}}{\partial y} + V_n, \\ \frac{r^n}{a^n} C_n &= -M_{n+2} a^2 \frac{\partial \psi_{n+1}}{\partial z} + W_n. \end{aligned}\right\} \qquad \text{..................(36)}$$

The right-hand and left-hand members of these equations are expressed as spherical solid harmonics of degree n, which are equal respectively at the surface $r = a$. It follows that they are equal for all values of x, y, z. We may accordingly use equations (36) to determine U_n, V_n, W_n in terms of A_n, B_n, C_n.

For this purpose we differentiate the left-hand and right-hand members of equations (36) with respect to x, y, z respectively and add the results. Utilizing equation (34) we find the equation

$$\psi_{n-1} = \frac{\partial}{\partial x}\left(\frac{r^n}{a^n} A_n\right) + \frac{\partial}{\partial y}\left(\frac{r^n}{a^n} B_n\right) + \frac{\partial}{\partial z}\left(\frac{r^n}{a^n} C_n\right). \qquad \text{............(37)}$$

* Lord Kelvin's solution is worked out for the case of a shell bounded by concentric spheres.

Thus all the functions ψ_n are determined in terms of the corresponding A_n, B_n, C_n, and then U_n, ... are given by such equations as

$$U_n = \frac{r_n}{a^n} A_n + M_{n+2} a^2 \frac{\partial \psi_{n+}}{\partial x}.$$

The integrals (7) may now be written in the forms

$$(u, v, w) = \Sigma \frac{r^n}{a^n}(A_n, B_n, C_n) + \Sigma M_{n+2}(a^2 - r^2)\left(\frac{\partial \psi_{n+1}}{\partial x}, \frac{\partial \psi_{n+1}}{\partial y}, \frac{\partial \psi_{n+1}}{\partial z}\right), \quad \text{...(38)}$$

in which
$$M_{n+2} = \frac{1}{2}\frac{\lambda + \mu}{(n+1)\lambda + (3n+4)\mu},$$

and
$$\psi_{n+1} = \frac{\partial}{\partial x}\left(\frac{r^{n+2}}{a^{n+2}} A_{n+2}\right) + \frac{\partial}{\partial y}\left(\frac{r^{n+2}}{a^{n+2}} B_{n+2}\right) + \frac{\partial}{\partial z}\left(\frac{r^{n+2}}{a^{n+2}} C_{n+2}\right).$$

By equations (38) the displacement at any point is expressed in terms of the prescribed displacements at the surface of the sphere.

184. Generalization of the foregoing solution.

If we omit the terms such as $A_n (r/a)^n$ from the right-hand members of equations (38) we arrive at a displacement expressed by the equation

$$(u, v, w) = (a^2 - r^2)\left(\frac{\partial}{\partial x}, \frac{\partial}{\partial y}, \frac{\partial}{\partial z}\right)\psi_{n+1}. \quad \text{......................(39)}$$

This displacement would require body force for its maintenance, and we may show easily that the requisite body force is derivable from a potential equal to

$$\frac{2}{\rho}[(n+1)\lambda + (3n+4)\mu]\psi_{n+1},$$

and that the corresponding dilatation is $-2(n+1)\psi_{n+1}$. We observe that, if λ and μ could be connected by an equation of the form

$$(n+1)\lambda + (3n+4)\mu = 0, \quad \text{..................................(40)}$$

the sphere could be held in the displaced configuration indicated by equation (39) without any body forces, and there would be no displacement of the surface. This result is in apparent contradiction with the theorem of Article 118; but it is impossible for λ and μ to be connected by such an equation as (40) for any positive integral value of n, since the strain-energy-function would not then be positive for all values of the strains.

The results just obtained have suggested the following generalization*:—Denote $(\lambda+\mu)/\mu$ by τ. Then the equations of equilibrium are of the form

$$\tau \frac{\partial \Delta}{\partial x} + \nabla^2 u = 0.$$

We may suppose that, answering to any given bounding surface, there exists a sequence of numbers, say $\tau_1, \tau_2, \ldots$, which are such that the system of equations of the type

$$\tau_\kappa \frac{\partial}{\partial x}\left(\frac{\partial U_\kappa}{\partial x} + \frac{\partial V_\kappa}{\partial y} + \frac{\partial W_\kappa}{\partial z}\right) + \nabla^2 U_\kappa = 0, \qquad (\kappa = 1, 2, \ldots)$$

* E. and F. Cosserat, *Paris, C. R.*, tt. 126 (1898), 133 (1901). The generalization here indicated is connected with researches on the problem of the sphere by E. Almansi, *Roma, Acc. Linc. Rend.* (Ser. 5), t. 6 (1897), and on the general equations by G. Lauricella, *Ann. di mat.* (Ser. 2), t. 23 (1895), and *Il nuovo Cimento* (Ser. 4), tt. 9, 10 (1899). The theory of the solution of the equations of equilibrium by this method is discussed further by I. Fredholm, *Arkiv för mat., fys. och astr.*, Bd. 2 (1905), Nr. 28, and A. Korn, *Acta Math.*, t. 32 (1909), p. 81.

possess solutions which vanish at the surface. Denote $\partial U_\kappa/\partial x+\partial V_\kappa/\partial y+\partial W_\kappa/\partial z$ by Δ_κ. Then Δ_κ is an harmonic function, and we may prove that, if κ' is different from κ,

$$\iiint \Delta_\kappa \Delta_{\kappa'}\, dx\, dy\, dz=0, \qquad \text{.................................(41)}$$

where the integration is extended through the volume within the bounding surface. We may suppose accordingly that the harmonic functions Δ_κ are such that an arbitrary harmonic function may be expressed, within the given surface, in the form of a series of the functions Δ_κ with constant coefficients, as is the case with the functions ψ_{n+1} when the surface is a sphere.

Assuming the existence of the functions $U_\kappa, \ldots$ and the corresponding numbers τ_κ, we should have the following method of solving the equations of equilibrium with prescribed displacements at the surface of the body:—Let functions u_0, v_0, w_0 be determined so as to be harmonic within the given surface and to take, at that surface, the values of the given components of displacement. The function u_0, for example, would be the analogue of $\Sigma \frac{r^n}{a^n} A_n$ in the case of a sphere. Calculate from u_0, v_0, w_0 the harmonic function Δ_0 determined by the equation

$$\Delta_0=\frac{\partial u_0}{\partial x}+\frac{\partial v_0}{\partial y}+\frac{\partial w_0}{\partial z}.$$

Assume for u, v, w within the body the expressions

$$(u, v, w)=(u_0, v_0, w_0)-\tau\Sigma\frac{A_\kappa}{\tau-\tau_\kappa}(U_\kappa, V_\kappa, W_\kappa), \qquad \text{.................(42)}$$

where the A's are constants. It may be shown easily that these expressions satisfy the equations of equilibrium provided that

$$\Sigma A_\kappa \Delta_\kappa=\Delta_0.$$

The conjugate property (41) of the functions Δ_κ enables us to express the constants A by the formula

$$A_\kappa \iiint (\Delta_\kappa)^2 dx\, dy\, dz=\iiint \Delta_0 \Delta_\kappa\, dx\, dy\, dz, \qquad \text{.....................(43)}$$

the integrations being extended through the volume of the body. The problem is therefore solved when the functions $U_\kappa, \ldots$ having the assumed properties are found*.

185. The sphere with given surface tractions.

The solution expressed by equations (32) or (38) may be adapted to satisfy the condition that the component tractions X_r, Y_r, Z_r across the surface $r=a$ may have given values. These values may be expanded in series of spherical surface harmonics. We have then to satisfy three conditions of the form

$$(X_r)_{r=a}=\Sigma X_n, \quad (Y_r)_{r=a}=\Sigma Y_n, \quad (Z_r)_{r=a}=\Sigma Z_n, \qquad \text{.........(44)}$$

where X_n, Y_n, Z_n denote spherical surface harmonics of degree n.

The component tractions X_r, Y_r, Z_r answering to the displacement expressed by (38) are to be calculated by means of the formulæ of the type (10) in Article 272, and equations (44) then yield equations determining the

* E. and F. Cosserat, *Paris, C. R.*, t. 126 (1898), have shown how to determine the functions in question when the surface is an ellipsoid. Some solutions of problems relating to ellipsoidal boundaries have been found by C. Chree, *loc. cit.* p. 264, and by D. Edwardes, *Quart. J. of Math.*, vols. 26 and 27 (1893, 1894).

surface harmonics of the type A_n in terms of the surface harmonics of the type X_n. The solution of these equations constitutes the solution of the problem.

It is convenient to re-write equations (38) in such forms as

$$u = \Sigma \left(A_n \frac{r^n}{a^n} + M_{n+2} a^2 \frac{\partial \psi_{n+1}}{\partial x} - M_n r^2 \frac{\partial \psi_{n-1}}{\partial x} \right),$$

in which all the terms under the sign of summation are homogeneous functions of x, y, z of degree n, and ψ_{n-1} is given by (37). The corresponding value of Δ is given by the equation

$$\Delta = \frac{2\mu}{\lambda + \mu} \Sigma (2n-1) M_n \psi_{n-1}. \qquad \text{(45)}$$

The expression $x\Delta$ is transformed by means of an identity of the type (4) in Article 272, so that we have

$$x\Delta = \frac{2\mu}{\lambda+\mu} r^2 \Sigma M_n \left\{ \frac{\partial \psi_{n-1}}{\partial x} - \frac{r^{2n-1}}{a^{2n-1}} \frac{\partial}{\partial x} \left(\frac{a^{2n-1}}{r^{2n-1}} \psi_{n-1} \right) \right\}.$$

Again ζ is given by the formula

$$\zeta = \Sigma \left\{ \frac{r^n}{a^n} (xA_n + yB_n + zC_n) + M_{n+2} a^2 (n+1) \psi_{n+1} - M_n r^2 (n-1) \psi_{n-1} \right\}.$$

Now by means of the identity (4) we find

$$\frac{r^n}{a^n} (xA_n + yB_n + zC_n) = \frac{r^2}{2n+1} \left(\psi_{n-1} - \frac{r^{2n+1}}{a^{2n+1}} \phi_{-n-2} \right), \qquad \text{(46)}$$

where ϕ_{-n-2} is the spherical solid harmonic of degree $-(n+2)$ determined by the equation

$$\phi_{-n-2} = \frac{\partial}{\partial x} \left(\frac{a^{n+1}}{r^{n+1}} A_n \right) + \frac{\partial}{\partial y} \left(\frac{a^{n+1}}{r^{n+1}} B_n \right) + \frac{\partial}{\partial z} \left(\frac{a^{n+1}}{r^{n+1}} C_n \right). \qquad \text{(47)}$$

It follows that ζ is given by the formula

$$\zeta = \Sigma \left[\left\{ \frac{1}{2n+1} - M_n (n-1) \right\} r^2 \psi_{n-1} + M_{n+2} (n+1) a^2 \psi_{n+1} - \frac{1}{2n+1} \frac{r^{2n+3}}{a^{2n+1}} \phi_{-n-2} \right],$$

and thence we find, on transforming $x\psi_{n-1}$ by means of an identity similar to (4),

$$\frac{\partial \zeta}{\partial x} = \Sigma \left\{ \frac{1}{2n+1} - M_n (n-1) \right\} \left[\frac{2r^2}{2n-1} \left\{ \frac{\partial \psi_{n-1}}{\partial x} - \frac{r^{2n-1}}{a^{2n-1}} \frac{\partial}{\partial x} \left(\frac{a^{2n-1}}{r^{2n-1}} \psi_{n-1} \right) \right\} + r^2 \frac{\partial \psi_{n-1}}{\partial x} \right]$$
$$+ \Sigma \left\{ M_{n+2} (n+1) a^2 \frac{\partial \psi_{n+1}}{\partial x} - \frac{1}{2n+1} \frac{\partial}{\partial x} \left(\frac{r^{2n+3}}{a^{2n+1}} \phi_{-n-2} \right) \right\}. \qquad \text{(48)}$$

Finally we have

$$r \frac{\partial u}{\partial r} - u = \Sigma \left[(n-1) \left\{ A_n \frac{r^n}{a^n} + M_{n+2} a^2 \frac{\partial \psi_{n+1}}{\partial x} - M_n r^2 \frac{\partial \psi_{n-1}}{\partial x} \right\} \right] \qquad \text{(49)}$$

On collecting the terms of (45), (48) and (49), we have the equation

$$\frac{rX_r}{\mu}=\Sigma\left[(n-1)A_n\frac{r^n}{a^n}+2nM_{n+2}a^2\frac{\partial\psi_{n+1}}{\partial x}-\frac{1}{2n+1}\frac{\partial}{\partial x}\left(\frac{r^{2n+3}}{a^{2n+1}}\phi_{-n-2}\right)\right.$$
$$+\left\{\frac{1}{2n-1}-\frac{4n}{2n-1}M_n(n-1)+\frac{2\lambda}{\lambda+\mu}M_n\right\}r^2\frac{\partial\psi_{n-1}}{\partial x}$$
$$\left.+\left\{-\frac{2}{(2n-1)(2n+1)}+\frac{2(n-1)}{2n-1}M_n-\frac{2\lambda}{\lambda+\mu}M_n\right\}r^{2n+1}\frac{\partial}{\partial x}\left(\frac{\psi_{n-1}}{r^{2n-1}}\right)\right].$$

The coefficient of $r^2\partial\psi_{n-1}/\partial x$ in the right-hand member is $-2(n-2)M_n$, and, if that of $r^{2n+1}\partial(r^{-2n+1}\psi_{n-1})/\partial x$ is denoted by $-E_n$, we find

$$E_n=\frac{1}{2n+1}\frac{\lambda(n+2)-\mu(n-3)}{\lambda(n-1)+\mu(3n-2)},\quad\text{.............}(50)$$

so that the equation becomes

$$\frac{rX_r}{\mu}=\Sigma\left[(n-1)A_n\frac{r^n}{a^n}+2nM_{n+2}a^2\frac{\partial\psi_{n+1}}{\partial x}-2(n-2)M_nr^2\frac{\partial\psi_{n-1}}{\partial x}\right.$$
$$\left.-E_nr^{2n+1}\frac{\partial}{\partial x}\left(\frac{\psi_{n-1}}{r^{2n-1}}\right)-\frac{1}{2n+1}\frac{\partial}{\partial x}\left(\frac{r^{2n+3}}{a^{2n+1}}\phi_{-n-2}\right)\right],$$

where E_n is given by (50). The terms of the sum that contain M_{n+2} and M_n as factors cancel at the surface $r=a$.

The equations (44) then yield three equations holding at the surface $r=a$ in such forms as

$$(n-1)A_n\frac{r^n}{a^n}-E_nr^{2n+1}\frac{\partial}{\partial x}\left(\frac{\psi_{n-1}}{r^{2n-1}}\right)-\frac{1}{2n+1}\frac{\partial}{\partial x}\left(\frac{r^{2n+3}}{a^{2n+1}}\phi_{-n-2}\right)=\frac{r^nX_n}{\mu a^{n-1}}.\quad\text{...}(51)$$

There are two similar equations derived from this one by replacing A_n, x, X_n successively by B_n, y, Y_n and C_n, z, Z_n.

To solve these equations for A_n, B_n, C_n we introduce two spherical solid harmonics Ψ_{n-1} and Φ_{-n-2} by the equations

$$\left.\begin{aligned}\Psi_{n-1}&=\frac{\partial}{\partial x}\left(\frac{r^n}{a^n}X_n\right)+\frac{\partial}{\partial y}\left(\frac{r^n}{a^n}Y_n\right)+\frac{\partial}{\partial z}\left(\frac{r^n}{a^n}Z_n\right),\\ \Phi_{-n-2}&=\frac{\partial}{\partial x}\left(\frac{a^{n+1}}{r^{n+1}}X_n\right)+\frac{\partial}{\partial y}\left(\frac{a^{n+1}}{r^{n+1}}Y_n\right)+\frac{\partial}{\partial z}\left(\frac{a^{n+1}}{r^{n+1}}Z_n\right).\end{aligned}\right\}\quad\text{......}(52)$$

On differentiating the left-hand and right-hand members of the equations of type (51) with respect to x, y, z and adding, we obtain the equation

$$\{n-1+n(2n+1)E_n\}\psi_{n-1}=\frac{a}{\mu}\Psi_{n-1}.\quad\text{..............}(53)$$

On multiplying the left-hand and right-hand members of the same equations by x, y, z, adding, and using (46) and (53), we obtain the equation

$$2n\phi_{-n-2}=\frac{a}{\mu}\Phi_{-n-2}.\quad\text{.........................}(54)$$

Then, ψ_{n-1} and ϕ_{-n-2} being known, the equations of type (51) determine A_n, B_n, C_n.

The prescribed surface tractions must, of course, be subject to the conditions that are necessary to secure the equilibrium of a rigid body. These conditions show immediately that there can be no constant terms in the expansions such as ΣX_n. They show also that the terms such as X_1, Y_1, Z_1 cannot be taken to be arbitrary surface harmonics of the first degree. We must have, in fact, three such equations as

$$\iint (y\Sigma Z_n - z\Sigma Y_n)\, dS = 0,$$

where the integration is extended over the surface of the sphere. Writing this equation in the form

$$\iint \left(y\Sigma \frac{r^n}{a^n} Z_n - z\Sigma \frac{r^n}{a^n} Y_n\right) dS = 0,$$

and transforming it by means of identities of the type (4), we find the equation

$$\iint \Sigma \left[\frac{\partial}{\partial y}(r^n Z_n) - \frac{\partial}{\partial z}(r^n Y_n)\right] dS - a^{2n+1} \iint \Sigma \left[\frac{\partial}{\partial y}\left(\frac{Z_n}{r^{n+1}}\right) - \frac{\partial}{\partial z}\left(\frac{Y_n}{r^{n+1}}\right)\right] dS = 0.$$

For any positive integral value of n, the subject of integration in the second of these integrals is the product of a power of r (which is equal to a) and a spherical surface harmonic, and the integral therefore vanishes, and the like statement holds concerning the first integral except in the case $n=1$. In this case we must have three such equations as

$$\frac{\partial}{\partial y}(rZ_1) = \frac{\partial}{\partial z}(rY_1),$$

and these equations show that rX_1, rY_1, rZ_1 are the partial differential coefficients with respect to x, y, z of a homogeneous quadratic function of these variables. Let $X_x^{(1)}$, ... be the stress-components that correspond with the surface tractions X_1, ... Then we have such equations as

$$rX_1 = xX_x^{(1)} + yX_y^{(1)} + zX_z^{(1)},$$
$$\dots$$

It thus appears that $X_x^{(1)}$, ... are constants, and the corresponding solution of the equations of equilibrium represents the displacement in the sphere when the material is in a state of *uniform stress*.

186. Plane strain in a circular cylinder*.

Methods entirely similar to those of Articles 183 and 185 may be applied to problems of plane strain in a circular cylinder. Taking r and θ to be polar coordinates in the plane (x, y) of the strain, we have, as plane harmonics of integral degrees, expressions of the type $r^n(\alpha_n \cos n\theta + \beta_n \sin n\theta)$, in which α_n and β_n are constants, and as analogues of surface harmonics we have the coefficients of r^n in such expressions. We may show that the analogue of the solution (38) of Article 183 is

$$(u, v) = \Sigma\left(A_n \frac{r^n}{a^n},\ B_n \frac{r^n}{a^n}\right) + \frac{\lambda+\mu}{2(\lambda+3\mu)} \Sigma \frac{a^2 - r^2}{n+1}\left(\frac{\partial \psi_{n+1}}{\partial x},\ \frac{\partial \psi_{n+1}}{\partial y}\right), \quad \dots(55)$$

in which A_n and B_n are functions of the type $\alpha_n \cos n\theta + \beta_n \sin n\theta$, and the functions ψ are plane harmonic functions expressed by equations of the form

$$\psi_{n-1} = \frac{\partial}{\partial x}\left(A_n \frac{r^n}{a^n}\right) + \frac{\partial}{\partial y}\left(B_n \frac{r^n}{a^n}\right). \quad \dots\dots\dots\dots(56)$$

* Cf. Kelvin and Tait, *Nat. Phil.*, Part II. pp. 298—300. The problem of plane *stress* in a circular cylinder was solved by Clebsch, *Elasticität*, § 42.

The equations (55) would give the displacement in a circular cylinder due to given displacements at the curved surface, when the tractions that maintain these displacements are adjusted so that there is no longitudinal displacement.

When the tractions applied to the surface are given, we may take ΣX_n, ΣY_n to be the components, parallel to the axes of x and y, of the tractions exerted across the surface $r=a$, the functions X_n, Y_n being again of the form $\alpha_n \cos n\theta + \beta_n \sin n\theta$. We write, by analogy to (47),

$$\phi_{-n-1} = \frac{\partial}{\partial x}\left(A_n \frac{a^n}{r^n}\right) + \frac{\partial}{\partial y}\left(B_n \frac{a^n}{r^n}\right), \quad \text{......(57)}$$

and we introduce functions Ψ_{n-1} and Φ_{-n-1} by the equations

$$\left.\begin{aligned}\Psi_{n-1} &= \frac{\partial}{\partial x}\left(X_n \frac{r^n}{a^n}\right) + \frac{\partial}{\partial y}\left(Y_n \frac{r^n}{a^n}\right),\\ \Phi_{-n-1} &= \frac{\partial}{\partial x}\left(X_n \frac{a^n}{r^n}\right) + \frac{\partial}{\partial y}\left(Y_n \frac{a^n}{r^n}\right).\end{aligned}\right\} \quad \text{......(58)}$$

All these functions are plane harmonics of the degrees indicated by the suffixes. The surface tractions can be calculated from equations (55). We find two equations of the type

$$(n-1)A_n \frac{r^n}{a^n} - \frac{1}{2(n-1)}\left(\frac{1}{n} + \frac{\lambda-\mu}{\lambda+3\mu}\right) r^{2n} \frac{\partial}{\partial x}\left(\frac{\psi_{n-1}}{r^{2n-2}}\right)$$
$$- \frac{1}{2n}\frac{\partial}{\partial x}\left(\frac{r^{2n+2}}{a^{2n}}\phi_{-n-1}\right) = \frac{r^n}{\mu a^{n-1}} X_n, \quad \text{......(59)}$$

from which we get

$$\left.\begin{aligned}\psi_{n-1} &= \frac{\lambda+3\mu}{2n(\lambda+\mu)}\frac{a}{\mu}\Psi_{n-1},\\ \phi_{-n-1} &= \frac{a}{2n\mu}\Phi_{-n-1},\end{aligned}\right\} \quad \text{......(60)}$$

and thus A_n, B_n can be expressed in terms of X_n, Y_n.

As examples of this method we may take the following*:

(i) $X_n = a\cos 2\theta$, $Y_n = 0$. In this case we find

$$u = \frac{a}{4\mu a}\left\{\frac{\lambda+2\mu}{\lambda+\mu}(x^2-y^2) - (x^2+y^2)\right\}, \quad v = \frac{axy}{2(\lambda+\mu)a}.$$

(ii) $X_n = a\cos 2\theta$, $Y_n = a\sin 2\theta$. In this case we find

$$u = \frac{a}{4\mu a}\left\{\frac{\lambda+3\mu}{\lambda+\mu}(x^2-y^2) - 2(x^2+y^2)\right\}, \quad v = \frac{a}{2\mu a}\frac{\lambda+3\mu}{\lambda+\mu}xy.$$

(iii) $X_n = a\cos 4\theta$, $Y_n = 0$. In this case we find

$$u = \frac{a}{4\mu a^3}\left\{\frac{\lambda+2\mu}{2(\lambda+\mu)}(x^4-6x^2y^2+y^4) - (x^4-y^4) + a^2(x^2-y^2)\right\},$$

$$v = \frac{axy}{2\mu a^3}\left\{\frac{\mu}{\lambda+\mu}(x^2-y^2) + (x^2+y^2-a^2)\right\}.$$

* The solutions in these special cases will be useful in a subsequent investigation (Chap. XVI).

187. Applications of curvilinear coordinates.

We give here some indications concerning various researches that have been made by starting from the equations of equilibrium expressed in terms of curvilinear coordinates.

(*a*) *Polar coordinates.* Lamé's original solution of the problem of the sphere and spherical shell by means of series was obtained by using the equations expressed in terms of polar coordinates*. The same equations were afterwards employed by C. W. Borchardt†, who obtained a solution of the problem of the sphere in terms of definite integrals, and by C. Chree‡, who also extended the method to problems relating to approximately spherical boundaries§, obtaining solutions in the form of series. The solutions in series can be built up by means of solid spherical harmonics (V_n) expressed in terms of polar coordinates, and related functions (U) which satisfy equations of the form $\nabla^2 U = V_n$.

(*b*) *Cylindrical coordinates.* Solutions in series have been obtained|| by observing that, if J_n is the symbol of Bessel's function of order n, $e^{kz+\iota n\theta} J_n(kr)$ is a solution of Laplace's equation. It is not difficult to deduce suitable forms for the displacements u_r, u_θ, u_z. The case in which u_θ vanishes and u_r and u_z are independent of θ will occupy us presently (Article 188). In the case of plane strain, when u_z vanishes and u_r and u_θ are independent of z, use may be made of the stress-function (cf. Article 144 *supra*); and the same method can be applied to the cases of plane stress and generalized plane stress (cf. Article 94 *supra*). The general form of this function expressed as a series proceeding by sines and cosines of multiples of θ has been given by J. H. Michell¶.

The most important problem, which has been treated by this method, is that of the stress produced in a circular ring, considered as a two-dimensional system which is subjected to forces in its plane. The ring is a thin plate, whose edges are short lengths of right circular cylinders having a common axis. The problem has been discussed by A. Timpe, *loc. cit. ante*, p. 221, afterwards by K. Wieghardt, *Wien Berichte*, Bd. 124, 1915, p. 1119, and a very complete solution has been given by L. N. G. Filon, 'The stresses in a circular ring,' *Selected Engineering papers published by the Institution of Civil Engineers*, No. 12, London, 1924.

(*c*) *Plane strain in non-circular cylinders.* When the boundaries are curves of the family $\alpha=$const., and α is the real part of a function of the complex variable $x+\iota y$, we know from Article 144 that the dilatation Δ and the rotation ϖ are such functions of x and y that $(\lambda+2\mu)\Delta+\iota 2\mu\varpi$ is a function of $x+\iota y$, and therefore also of $\alpha+\iota\beta$, where β is the function conjugate to α. For example, let the elastic solid medium be bounded internally by an elliptic cylinder. We take

$$x+\iota y = c\cosh(\alpha+\iota\beta),$$

so that the curves $\alpha=$const. are confocal ellipses, and $2c$ is the distance between the foci. Then the appropriate forms of Δ and ϖ are given by the equation

$$(\lambda+2\mu)\Delta+\iota 2\mu\varpi = \Sigma e^{-n\alpha}(A_n\cos n\beta + B_n \sin n\beta).$$

* *J. de Math.* (*Liouville*), t. 19 (1854). See also *Leçons sur les coordonnées curvilignes*, Paris, 1859. References to numerous investigations of the problem of the sphere are given by R. Marcolongo, *Teoria matematica dello equilibrio dei corpi elastici* (Milan, 1904), pp. 280, 281.

† *Loc. cit. ante*, p. 109.

‡ *Cambridge Phil. Soc. Trans.*, vol. 14 (1889).

§ *Amer. J. of Math.*, vol. 16 (1894).

|| L. Pochhammer, *J. f. Math.* (*Crelle*), Bd. 81 (1876), p. 33, and C. Chree, *Cambridge Phil. Soc. Trans.*, vol. 14 (1889).

¶ *London Math. Soc. Proc.*, vol. 31 (1900), p. 100.

If we denote by h the absolute value of the complex quantity $d(\alpha+\iota\beta)/d(x+\iota y)$, then the displacements u_α and u_β are connected with Δ and ϖ by the equations

$$\frac{\Delta}{h^2}=\frac{\partial}{\partial\alpha}\left(\frac{u_\alpha}{h}\right)+\frac{\partial}{\partial\beta}\left(\frac{u_\beta}{h}\right),\quad \frac{2\varpi}{h^2}=\frac{\partial}{\partial\alpha}\left(\frac{u_\beta}{h}\right)-\frac{\partial}{\partial\beta}\left(\frac{u_\alpha}{h}\right).$$

In the case of elliptic cylinders u_α/h and u_β/h can be expressed as series in $\cos n\beta$ and $\sin n\beta$ without much difficulty. The value of h^{-2} is $\frac{1}{2}c^2(\cosh 2\alpha-\cos 2\beta)$.

As an example* we may take the case where an elliptic cylinder of semi-axes a and b is turned about the line of centres of its normal sections through a small angle ϕ. In this case it can be shown that the displacement produced outside the cylinders is expressed by the equations

$$\frac{u_\alpha}{h}=\frac{1}{2}(a+b)^2\phi\,\frac{\mu}{\lambda+3\mu}\left(e^{-2\alpha}+\frac{\lambda+2\mu}{\mu}\,\frac{a-b}{a+b}\right)\sin 2\beta,$$

$$\frac{u_\beta}{h}=ab\,\phi+\frac{1}{2}(a+b)^2\phi\left(\frac{a-b}{a+b}-e^{-2\alpha}\right)\left\{\frac{\lambda+2\mu}{\lambda+3\mu}\,\frac{a-b}{a+b}+\frac{\mu}{\lambda+3\mu}\cos 2\beta\right\}.$$

The special solution $\Delta=A\log h$, where A is constant, and the above elliptic coordinates are employed, may be utilized to discuss the diminution in strength of a thin plate, due to a crack. The crack is identified with the line of foci, and its edges are free from traction, except, possibly, at its extremities. For this reference may be made to C. E. Inglis, *London, Inst. Naval Architects Trans.* 1913, or A. A. Griffith, *Phil. Trans. Roy. Soc.* (Ser. A), vol. 221, 1920, p. 163. Other applications of elliptic coordinates are given by S. D. Carothers, *loc. cit. ante*, p. 215; S. Yokota, *Tokyo Math. Soc. J.* (Ser. 2), vol. 8, 1915, pp. 66, 102; Th. Pöschl, *Math. Zeitschr.*, Bd. 11, 1921, p. 89.

Problems relating to two circles which are not concentric, e.g. a plate with a straight edge and a circular hole, can be treated by means of the conjugate functions that are given by the equation

$$\alpha+\iota\beta=\log\frac{x+\iota(y+a)}{x+\iota(y-a)}.$$

This system (bipolar coordinates) is discussed very fully by G. B. Jeffery, *loc. cit. ante*, p. 91, and *Brit. Assoc. Rep.* 1921, p. 356.

(*d*) *Solids of revolution.* If r, θ, z are cylindrical coordinates, and we can find α and β as conjugate functions of z and r in such a way that an equation of the form $\alpha=$const. represents the meridian curve of the surface of a body, we transform Laplace's equation $\nabla^2 V=0$ to the form

$$\frac{\partial}{\partial\alpha}\left(r\frac{\partial V}{\partial\alpha}\right)+\frac{\partial}{\partial\beta}\left(r\frac{\partial V}{\partial\beta}\right)+\frac{J^2}{r}\frac{\partial^2 V}{\partial\theta^2}=0,$$

where J denotes the absolute value of $d(z+\iota r)/d(\alpha+\iota\beta)$. If we can find solutions of this equation in the cases where V is independent of θ, or is proportional to $\sin n\theta$ or $\cos n\theta$, we can obtain expressions for the dilatation and the components of rotation as series. Wangerin† has shown how from these solutions expressions for the displacements can be deduced. The appropriate solutions of the above equation for V are known in the case of a number of solids of revolution, including ellipsoids, cones and tores.

* The problem was proposed by R. R. Webb. For a different method of obtaining the solution see D. Edwardes, *Quart. J. of Math.*, vol. 26 (1893), p. 270. The corresponding problem for a rigid ellipsoid, embedded in an elastic solid medium, and turned through a small angle about a principal axis, is discussed by E. Daniele, *Il Nuovo Cimento* (Ser. 6), t. 1, 1911.

† *Archiv f. Math.* (*Grunert*), vol. 55 (1873). The theory has been developed further by P. Jaerisch, *J. f. Math.* (*Crelle*), Bd. 104 (1889). The solution for an ellipsoid of revolution with given surface displacements has been expressed in terms of series of spheroidal harmonics by O. Tedone, *Roma, Acc. Linc. Rend.* (Ser. 5), t. 14 (1905).

188. Symmetrical strain in a solid of revolution.

When a solid of revolution is strained symmetrically by forces applied at its surface, so that the displacement is the same in all planes through the axis of revolution, we may express all the quantities that occur in terms of a single function, and reduce the equations of equilibrium of the body to a single partial differential equation. Taking r, θ, z to be cylindrical coordinates, we have the stress-equations of equilibrium in the forms

$$\frac{\partial \widehat{rr}}{\partial r}+\frac{\partial \widehat{rz}}{\partial z}+\frac{\widehat{rr}-\widehat{\theta\theta}}{r}=0,\quad \frac{\partial \widehat{rz}}{\partial r}+\frac{\partial \widehat{zz}}{\partial z}+\frac{\widehat{rz}}{r}=0. \quad \ldots\ldots\ldots\ldots\ldots(61)$$

Writing U, w for the displacements in the directions of r and z, and supposing that there is no displacement at right angles to the axial plane, we have the expressions for the strain-components

$$e_{rr}=\frac{\partial U}{\partial r},\quad e_{\theta\theta}=\frac{U}{r},\quad e_{zz}=\frac{\partial w}{\partial z},\quad e_{rz}=\frac{\partial U}{\partial z}+\frac{\partial w}{\partial r},\quad e_{r\theta}=e_{z\theta}=0. \quad \ldots(62)$$

We begin by putting, by analogy with the corresponding theory of plane strain,

$$\widehat{rz}=-\frac{\partial^2\phi}{\partial r\partial z}.$$

Then the second of equations (61) gives us

$$\widehat{zz}=\frac{\partial^2\phi}{\partial r^2}+\frac{1}{r}\frac{\partial\phi}{\partial r};$$

no arbitrary function of r need be added, for any such function can be included in ϕ. We observe that $e_{rr}=\frac{\partial}{\partial r}(re_{\theta\theta})$, and write down the equivalent equation in terms of stress-components, viz.:

$$\widehat{rr}-\sigma\,\widehat{\theta\theta}-\sigma\,\widehat{zz}=\frac{\partial}{\partial r}\{(\widehat{\theta\theta}-\sigma\,\widehat{rr}-\sigma\,\widehat{zz})\,r\},$$

and hence we obtain the equation

$$(1+\sigma)\,(\widehat{rr}-\widehat{\theta\theta})=r\frac{\partial}{\partial r}(\widehat{\theta\theta}-\sigma\,\widehat{rr}-\sigma\,\widehat{zz}).$$

We introduce a new function R by the equation

$$\widehat{rr}=\frac{\partial^2\phi}{\partial z^2}+R,$$

and then the first of equations (61) can be written

$$(1+\sigma)\frac{\partial R}{\partial r}+\frac{\partial}{\partial r}(\widehat{\theta\theta}-\sigma\,\widehat{rr}-\sigma\,\widehat{zz})=0,$$

and we may put
$$\widehat{\theta\theta}=\sigma\nabla^2\phi-R,$$

where ∇^2 denotes $\partial^2/\partial r^2+r^{-1}\partial/\partial r+\partial^2/\partial z^2$, the subjects of operation being independent of θ. No arbitrary function of z need be added, because any such function can be included in ϕ. All the stress-components have now been expressed in terms of two functions ϕ and R. The sum Θ of the principal stresses is expressed in terms of ϕ by the equation

$$\Theta=\widehat{rr}+\widehat{\theta\theta}+\widehat{zz}=(1+\sigma)\,\nabla^2\phi,$$

and, since Θ is an harmonic function, we must have $\nabla^4\phi=0$.

The functions ϕ and R are not independent of each other. To obtain the relations between them we may proceed as follows:—The equation $U/r=e_{\theta\theta}$ can be written

$$U=r(\widehat{\theta\theta}-\sigma\,\widehat{rr}-\sigma\,\widehat{zz})/E,$$

or

$$U=-(1+\sigma)\,rR/E;$$

and then the equation $\widehat{rz}=\mu e_{rz}$ can be written

$$\frac{\partial w}{\partial r}=-\frac{2(1+\sigma)}{E}\frac{\partial^2\phi}{\partial r\,\partial z}+\frac{1+\sigma}{E}r\frac{\partial R}{\partial z}.$$

Also the equation $e_{zz}=(\widehat{zz}-\sigma\,\widehat{rr}-\sigma\,\widehat{\theta\theta})/E$ can be written

$$\frac{\partial w}{\partial z}=\frac{1+\sigma}{E}\left(\frac{\partial^2\phi}{\partial r^2}+\frac{1}{r}\frac{\partial\phi}{\partial r}-\sigma\nabla^2\phi\right).$$

The equations giving $\partial w/\partial r$ and $\partial w/\partial z$ are compatible if

$$(1-\sigma)\frac{\partial}{\partial r}\nabla^2\phi+\frac{\partial^3\phi}{\partial r\,\partial z^2}=r\frac{\partial^2 R}{\partial z^2};$$

and, if we introduce a new function Ω by means of the equation

$$rR=\frac{\partial\phi}{\partial r}+\frac{\partial\Omega}{\partial r},$$

we have

$$\frac{\partial^2\Omega}{\partial z^2}=(1-\sigma)\,\nabla^2\phi,$$

where, as before, no arbitrary function of z need be added.

The stress-components are now expressed in terms of the functions ϕ and Ω which are connected by the equation last written. The equations giving $\partial w/\partial r$ and $\partial w/\partial z$ become, when Ω is introduced,

$$\frac{\partial w}{\partial r}=\frac{1+\sigma}{E}\frac{\partial}{\partial r}\left(\frac{\partial\Omega}{\partial z}-\frac{\partial\phi}{\partial z}\right),\quad \frac{\partial w}{\partial z}=\frac{1+\sigma}{E}\frac{\partial}{\partial z}\left(\frac{\partial\Omega}{\partial z}-\frac{\partial\phi}{\partial z}\right).$$

We may therefore express U and w in terms of Ω and ϕ by the formulæ

$$U=-\frac{1+\sigma}{E}\left(\frac{\partial\Omega}{\partial r}+\frac{\partial\phi}{\partial r}\right),\quad w=\frac{1+\sigma}{E}\left(\frac{\partial\Omega}{\partial z}-\frac{\partial\phi}{\partial z}\right).$$

From these formulæ we can show that Ω must be an harmonic function, for we have at the same time

$$\Delta=\frac{\partial U}{\partial r}+\frac{U}{r}+\frac{\partial w}{\partial z}=-\frac{1+\sigma}{E}\left[\nabla^2\phi+\nabla^2\Omega-2\frac{\partial^2\Omega}{\partial z^2}\right]=\frac{1+\sigma}{E}\left[(1-2\sigma)\nabla^2\phi-\nabla^2\Omega\right],$$

and

$$\Delta=\frac{1-2\sigma}{E}\Theta=\frac{1-2\sigma}{E}(1+\sigma)\,\nabla^2\phi.$$

It follows that, besides satisfying the equation $\partial^2\Omega/\partial z^2=(1-\sigma)\nabla^2\phi$, the function Ω also satisfies the equation $\nabla^2\Omega=0$.

Instead of using the two functions ϕ and Ω we may express the stress-components in terms of a single function. To this end we introduce a new function ψ by the equation $\psi=\phi+\Omega$. Then we have

$$\widehat{rr}=\frac{\partial^2\phi}{\partial z^2}+\frac{1}{r}\frac{\partial\phi}{\partial r}+\frac{1}{r}\frac{\partial\Omega}{\partial r}=\nabla^2\psi-\frac{\partial^2\phi}{\partial r^2}-\frac{\partial^2\Omega}{\partial z^2}-\frac{\partial^2\Omega}{\partial r^2}=\sigma\nabla^2\psi-\frac{\partial^2\psi}{\partial r^2},$$

and we have also

$$\widehat{\theta\theta}=\sigma\nabla^2\psi-\frac{1}{r}\frac{\partial\psi}{\partial r},\quad \widehat{zz}=(2-\sigma)\,\nabla^2\psi-\frac{\partial^2\psi}{\partial z^2}.$$

The first of equations (61) would enable us at once to express $\widehat{rz}$ in terms of a function χ such that $\psi=\partial\chi/\partial z$. We therefore drop all the subsidiary functions and retain χ only.

In accordance with the above detailed work we assume

$$\widehat{rr}=\frac{\partial}{\partial z}\left\{\sigma\nabla^2\chi-\frac{\partial^2\chi}{\partial r^2}\right\},\quad \widehat{\theta\theta}=\frac{\partial}{\partial z}\left\{\sigma\nabla^2\chi-\frac{1}{r}\frac{\partial\chi}{\partial r}\right\},$$

$$\widehat{zz}=\frac{\partial}{\partial z}\left\{(2-\sigma)\nabla^2\chi-\frac{\partial^2\chi}{\partial z^2}\right\}. \quad\text{..........(63)}$$

Then the first of equations (61) gives us

$$\widehat{rz}=\frac{\partial}{\partial r}\left\{(1-\sigma)\nabla^2\chi-\frac{\partial^2\chi}{\partial z^2}\right\}, \quad\text{..................(64)}$$

and the second is satisfied by this value of $\widehat{rz}$ if

$$\nabla^4\chi=0. \quad\text{..............................(65)}$$

The stress-components are now expressed in terms of a single function χ which satisfies equation (65)*.

The corresponding displacements are easily found from the stress-strain relations in the forms

$$U=-\frac{1+\sigma}{E}\frac{\partial^2\chi}{\partial r\partial z},\quad w=\frac{1+\sigma}{E}\left\{(1-2\sigma)\nabla^2\chi+\frac{\partial^2\chi}{\partial r^2}+\frac{1}{r}\frac{\partial\chi}{\partial r}\right\}. \quad\text{...(66)}$$

189. Symmetrical strain in a cylinder.

When the body is a circular cylinder with plane ends at right angles to its axis, the function χ will have to satisfy conditions at a cylindrical surface $r=a$, and at two plane surfaces $z=$const. It must also satisfy equation (65). Solutions of this equation in terms of r and z can be found by various methods.

The equation is satisfied by any solid zonal harmonic, i.e. by any function of the form $(r^2+z^2)^{n+\frac{1}{2}}\frac{\partial^n}{\partial z^n}(r^2+z^2)^{-\frac{1}{2}}$, and also by the product of such a function and (r^2+z^2). All these functions are rational integral functions of r and z, which contain even powers of r only. Any sum of these functions each multiplied by a constant is a possible form for χ.

The equation (65) is satisfied also by any harmonic function of the form $e^{\pm kz}J_0(kr)$, where k is any constant, real or imaginary, and $J_0(x)$ stands for Bessel's function of zero order. It is also satisfied by any function of the form $e^{\pm kz}r\frac{d}{dr}J_0(kr)$, for we have

$$\nabla^2\left\{e^{\pm kz}r\frac{d}{dr}J_0(kr)\right\}=-(2k^2e^{\pm kz}J_0(kr).$$

When k is imaginary we may write these solutions in the form

$$J_0(\iota\kappa r)(A\cos\kappa z+B\sin\kappa z)+r\frac{d}{dr}J_0(\iota\kappa r)(C\cos\kappa z+D\sin\kappa z), \quad\text{...........(67)}$$

in which κ is real and A, B, C, D are real constants. Any sum of such expressions, with different values for κ, and different constants A, B, C, D, is a possible form for χ.

The formulæ for the displacements U, w that would be found by each of these methods have been obtained otherwise by C. Chree†. They have been applied to the problem of

* A method of expressing all the quantities in terms of a single function, which satisfies a partial differential equation of the fourth order different from (65), has been given by J. H. Michell, *London Math. Soc. Proc.*, vol. 31 (1900), pp. 144—146.

† *Cambridge Phil. Soc. Trans.*, vol. 14 (1889), p. 250.

a cylinder pressed between two planes, which are in contact with its plane ends, by L. N. G. Filon*. Of the solutions which are rational and integral in r and z, he keeps those which could be obtained by the above method by taking χ to contain no terms of degree higher than the seventh, and to contain uneven powers of z only. Of the solutions that could be obtained by taking χ to be a series of terms of type (67), he keeps those which result from putting $\kappa = n\pi/c$, where n is an integer and $2c$ is the length of the cylinder, and omits the cosines. He finds that these solutions are sufficiently general to admit of the satisfaction of the following conditions:

(i) the cylindrical boundary $r=a$ is free from traction;

(ii) the ends remain plane, or w=const. when $z = \pm c$;

(iii) the ends do not expand at the perimeter, or $U=0$ when $r=a$ and $z=\pm c$;

(iv) the ends are subjected to a given resultant pressure.

He shows how a correction may be made when, instead of condition (iii), it is assumed that the ends expand by a given amount. The results are applied to the explanation of certain discrepancies in estimates of the strength of short cylinders to resist crushing loads, the discrepancies arising from the employment of different kinds of tests; and they are applied also to explain the observation that, when cylinders (or spheres) are compressed between parallel planes, pieces of an approximately conical shape are sometimes cut out at the parts subjected to pressure.

Instead of taking the second solution of equation (65) in terms of Bessel's functions to be expressed by $e^{\pm kz} r \dfrac{d}{dr} \{J_0(kr)\}$, we may take it to have the form $ze^{\pm kz} J_0(kr)$. The expressions, which would thus be obtained for the displacements U, w, have been utilized by F. Purser, *loc. cit. ante*, p. 147.

* *Phil. Trans. Roy. Soc.* (Ser. A), vol. 198 (1902). Filon gives in the same paper the solutions of other problems relating to symmetrical strain in a cylinder.

CHAPTER XII

VIBRATIONS OF SPHERES AND CYLINDERS

190. In this Chapter we shall illustrate the method explained in Article 126 for the solution of the problem of free vibrations of a solid body. The free vibrations of an isotropic elastic sphere have been worked out in detail by various writers*. In discussing this problem we shall use the method of Lamb and record some of his results.

When the motion of every particle of a body is simple harmonic and of period $2\pi/p$, the displacement is expressed by formulæ of the type

$$u = Au' \cos(pt + \epsilon), \quad v = Av' \cos(pt + \epsilon), \quad w = Aw' \cos(pt + \epsilon), \quad \text{...(1)}$$

in which u', v', w' are functions of x, y, z, and A is an arbitrary small constant expressing the amplitude of the vibratory motion. When the body is vibrating freely, the equations of motion and boundary conditions can be satisfied only if p is one of the roots of the "frequency equation," and u', v', w' are "normal functions." In general we shall suppress the accents on u', v', w', and treat these quantities as components of displacement. At any stage we may restore the amplitude-factor A and the time-factor $\cos(pt+\epsilon)$ so as to obtain complete expressions for the displacements.

The equations of small motion of the body are

$$(\lambda + \mu)\left(\frac{\partial \Delta}{\partial x}, \frac{\partial \Delta}{\partial y}, \frac{\partial \Delta}{\partial z}\right) + \mu\nabla^2(u, v, w) = \rho\left(\frac{\partial^2 u}{\partial t^2}, \frac{\partial^2 v}{\partial t^2}, \frac{\partial^2 w}{\partial t^2}\right), \quad \text{......(2)}$$

where

$$\Delta = \frac{\partial u}{\partial x} + \frac{\partial v}{\partial y} + \frac{\partial w}{\partial z}. \quad \text{......(3)}$$

When u, v, w are proportional to $\cos(pt + \epsilon)$ we obtain the equations

$$(\lambda + \mu)\left(\frac{\partial \Delta}{\partial x}, \frac{\partial \Delta}{\partial y}, \frac{\partial \Delta}{\partial z}\right) + \mu\nabla^2(u, v, w) + \rho p^2(u, v, w) = 0. \quad \text{......(4)}$$

Differentiating the left-hand members of these equations with respect to x, y, z respectively, and adding the results, we obtain an equation which may be written

$$(\nabla^2 + h^2)\Delta = 0, \quad \text{......(5)}$$

where

$$h^2 = p^2\rho/(\lambda + 2\mu). \quad \text{......(6)}$$

Again, if we write

$$\kappa^2 = p^2\rho/\mu, \quad \text{......(7)}$$

equations (4) take the form

$$(\nabla^2 + \kappa^2)(u, v, w) = \left(1 - \frac{\kappa^2}{h^2}\right)\left(\frac{\partial \Delta}{\partial x}, \frac{\partial \Delta}{\partial y}, \frac{\partial \Delta}{\partial z}\right).$$

* Reference may be made to P. Jaerisch, *J. f. Math.* (*Crelle*), Bd. 88 (1880); H. Lamb, *London Math. Soc. Proc.*, vol. 13 (1882); C. Chree, *Cambridge Phil. Soc. Trans.*, vol. 14 (1889).

We may suppose that Δ is determined so as to satisfy equation (5), then one solution (u_1, v_1, w_1) of the equations last written is

$$(u_1, v_1, w_1) = -\frac{1}{h^2}\left(\frac{\partial\Delta}{\partial x}, \frac{\partial\Delta}{\partial y}, \frac{\partial\Delta}{\partial z}\right),$$

and a more complete solution is obtained by adding to these values for u_1, v_1, w_1, complementary solutions (u_2, v_2, w_2) of the system of equations

$$(\nabla^2 + \kappa^2)\, u_2 = 0,\ (\nabla^2 + \kappa^2)\, v_2 = 0,\ (\nabla^2 + \kappa^2)\, w_2 = 0, \quad \text{........(8)}$$

and

$$\frac{\partial u_2}{\partial x} + \frac{\partial v_2}{\partial y} + \frac{\partial w_2}{\partial z} = 0. \quad \text{..............................(9)}$$

When these functions are determined the displacement can be written in the form

$$(u, v, w) = A\,(u_1 + u_2,\ v_1 + v_2,\ w_1 + w_2)\cos(pt + \epsilon). \quad \text{.........(10)}$$

191. Solution by means of spherical harmonics.

A solution of the equation $(\nabla^2 + h^2)\,\Delta = 0$ can be obtained by supposing that Δ is of the form $f(r)\,S_n$, where $r^2 = x^2 + y^2 + z^2$, and S_n is a spherical surface harmonic of degree n. We write R_n instead of $f(r)$. Then rR_n is a solution of Riccati's equation

$$\left(\frac{\partial^2}{\partial r^2} + h^2 - \frac{n(n+1)}{r^2}\right)(rR_n) = 0,$$

of which the complete primitive is expressible in the form

$$rR_n = r^{n+1}\left(\frac{1}{r}\frac{\partial}{\partial r}\right)^n \frac{A_n \sin hr + B_n \cos hr}{r},$$

A_n and B_n being arbitrary constants. The function $r^n S_n$ is a spherical solid harmonic of degree n. When the region of space within which Δ is to be determined contains the origin, so that the function Δ has no singularities in the neighbourhood of the origin, we take for Δ the formula

$$\Delta = \Sigma\omega_n \psi_n(hr), \quad \text{..........................(11)}$$

where ω_n is a spherical solid harmonic of positive degree n, the summation refers to different values of n, and $\psi_n(x)$ is the function determined by the equation

$$\psi_n(x) = \left(\frac{1}{x}\frac{d}{dx}\right)^n \left(\frac{\sin x}{x}\right). \quad \text{.......................(12)}$$

The function $\psi_n(x)$ is expressible as a power series, viz.:

$$\psi_n(x) = \frac{(-)^n}{1.3.5\ldots(2n+1)}\left\{1 - \frac{x^2}{2(2n+3)} + \frac{x^4}{2.4.(2n+3)(2n+5)} - \ldots\right\}, \quad \text{...(13)}$$

which is convergent for all finite values of x. It is an "integral function." It may be expressed in terms of a Bessel's function by the formula

$$\psi_n(x) = (-)^n \tfrac{1}{2}\sqrt{(2\pi)}\, x^{-(n+\frac{1}{2})} J_{n+\frac{1}{2}}(x). \quad \text{.......................(14)}$$

It satisfies the differential equation

$$\left(\frac{d^2}{dx^2} + \frac{2(n+1)}{x}\frac{d}{dx} + 1\right)\psi_n(x) = 0. \quad \text{..........................(15)}$$

The functions $\psi_n(x)$ for consecutive values of n are connected by the equations

$$x\frac{d\psi_{n-1}(x)}{dx}=x^2\psi_n(x)=-\psi_{n-2}(x)-(2n-1)\psi_{n-1}(x).\quad\text{..............(16)}$$

The function $\Psi_n(x)$ determined by the equation

$$\Psi_n(x)=\left(\frac{1}{x}\frac{d}{dx}\right)^n\left(\frac{\cos x}{x}\right),$$

which has a pole of order $2n+1$ at the origin, and is expressible by means of a Bessel's function of order $-(n+\frac{1}{2})$, satisfies equations (15) and (16).

In like manner solutions of equations (8) and (9) which are free from singularities in the neighbourhood of the origin can be expressed in the forms

$$u_2=U_n\psi_n(\kappa r),\quad v_2=V_n\psi_n(\kappa r),\quad w_2=W_n\psi_n(\kappa r),\quad\text{.........(17)}$$

where U_n, V_n, W_n are spherical solid harmonics of degree n, provided that these harmonics are so related that

$$\frac{\partial u_2}{\partial x}+\frac{\partial v_2}{\partial y}+\frac{\partial w_2}{\partial z}=0.\quad\text{.......................(9 \textit{bis})}$$

One way of satisfying this equation is to take U_n, V_n, W_n to have the forms

$$U_n=y\frac{\partial\chi_n}{\partial z}-z\frac{\partial\chi_n}{\partial y},\quad V_n=z\frac{\partial\chi_n}{\partial x}-x\frac{\partial\chi_n}{\partial z},\quad W_n=x\frac{\partial\chi_n}{\partial y}-y\frac{\partial\chi_n}{\partial x},\quad\text{......(18)}$$

where χ_n is a spherical solid harmonic of degree n; for with these forms we have

$$\frac{\partial U_n}{\partial x}+\frac{\partial V_n}{\partial y}+\frac{\partial W_n}{\partial z}=0;\quad\text{and}\quad xU_n+yV_n+zW_n=0.$$

A second way of satisfying equation (9 *bis*) results from the observation that curl (u_2, v_2, w_2) satisfies the same system of equations (8) and (9) as (u_2, v_2, w_2). If we take u_2', v_2', w_2' to be given by the equations

$$(u_2', v_2', w_2')=\psi_n(\kappa r)\left(y\frac{\partial\chi_n}{\partial z}-z\frac{\partial\chi_n}{\partial y},\ z\frac{\partial\chi_n}{\partial x}-x\frac{\partial\chi_n}{\partial z},\ x\frac{\partial\chi_n}{\partial y}-y\frac{\partial\chi_n}{\partial x}\right),$$

we find such formulæ as

$$\frac{\partial w_2'}{\partial y}-\frac{\partial v_2'}{\partial z}=\kappa\psi_n'(\kappa r)\left(n\frac{x}{r}\chi_n-r\frac{\partial\chi_n}{\partial x}\right)-(n+1)\psi_n(\kappa r)\frac{\partial\psi_n}{\partial x},$$

where $\psi_n'(\kappa r)$ means $d\psi_n(\kappa r)/d(\kappa r)$. By means of the identity

$$x\chi_n=\frac{r^2}{2n+1}\left\{\frac{\partial\chi_n}{\partial x}-r^{2n+1}\frac{\partial}{\partial x}\left(\frac{\chi_n}{r^{2n+1}}\right)\right\}\quad\text{..............(19)}$$

and the relations between ψ functions with consecutive suffixes, the above formula is reduced to the following:

$$\frac{\partial w_2'}{\partial y}-\frac{\partial v_2'}{\partial z}=\frac{n+1}{2n+1}\psi_{n-1}(\kappa r)\frac{\partial\chi_n}{\partial x}-\frac{n}{2n+1}\psi_{n+1}(\kappa r)\kappa^2r^{2n+3}\frac{\partial}{\partial x}\left(\frac{\chi_n}{r^{2n+1}}\right),$$

of which each term is of the form $U_n\psi_n(\kappa r)$. In like manner the other components of curl (u_2', v_2', w_2') can be formed.

Hence, taking χ_n and ϕ_{n+1} to be any two solid harmonics of degrees indicated by their suffixes, we have solutions of the equations (8) and (9) in such forms as

$$u_2 = \Sigma \left[\psi_n(\kappa r)\left(y\frac{\partial \chi_n}{\partial z} - z\frac{\partial \chi_n}{\partial y} + \frac{\partial \phi_{n+1}}{\partial x}\right) - \frac{n+1}{n+2}\psi_{n+2}(\kappa r)\,\kappa^2 r^{2n+5}\frac{\partial}{\partial x}\left(\frac{\phi_{n+1}}{r^{2n+3}}\right)\right]. \quad \text{.........(20)}$$

The corresponding forms of v_2 and w_2 are obtained from this by cyclical interchange of the letters x, y, z.

192. Formation of the boundary conditions for a vibrating sphere.

We have now to apply this analysis to the problem of the free vibrations of a solid sphere. For this purpose we must calculate the traction across a spherical surface with its centre at the origin. The components X_r, Y_r, Z_r of this traction are expressed, as in Article 172, by formulæ of the type

$$\frac{rX_r}{\mu} = \frac{\lambda}{\mu}x\Delta + \frac{\partial}{\partial x}(ux + vy + wz) + r\frac{\partial u}{\partial r} - u. \quad \text{...........(21)}$$

In this formula Δ has the form given in (11), viz.: $\Sigma\omega_n\psi_n(hr)$, and u, v, w have such forms as

$$u = -\frac{1}{h^2}\frac{\partial \Delta}{\partial x} + \Sigma\left[\psi_n(\kappa r)\left(y\frac{\partial \chi_n}{\partial z} - z\frac{\partial \chi_n}{\partial y} + \frac{\partial \phi_{n+1}}{\partial x}\right) - \frac{n+1}{n+2}\psi_{n+2}(\kappa r)\,\kappa^2 r^{2n+5}\frac{\partial}{\partial x}\left(\frac{\phi_{n+1}}{r^{2n+3}}\right)\right]. \quad \text{...........(22)}$$

We find

$$ux + vy + wz = -\frac{r}{h^2}\frac{\partial \Delta}{\partial r} + \Sigma(n+1)\{\psi_n(\kappa r) + \kappa^2 r^2\psi_{n+2}(\kappa r)\}\,\phi_{n+1},$$

or

$$ux+vy+wz = -\Sigma\left[-\frac{1}{h^2}\{n\psi_n(hr) + hr\psi_n'(hr)\}\,\omega_n - (n+1)(2n+3)\psi_{n+1}(\kappa r)\phi_{n+1}\right]. \quad \text{...............(23)}$$

This formula gives us an expression for the radial displacement

$$(ux + vy + wz)/r.$$

In forming the typical terms of $x\Delta$, $\dfrac{\partial}{\partial x}(ux + vy + wz)$, $r\dfrac{\partial u}{\partial r} - u$ we make continual use of identities of the type (19) and of the equations satisfied by the ψ functions. We shall obtain in succession the contributions of the several harmonic functions ω_n, ϕ_n, χ_n to each of the above expressions.

The function ω_n contributes to $x\Delta$ the terms

$$\frac{1}{2n+1}\psi_n(hr)\left\{r^2\frac{\partial \omega_n}{\partial x} - r^{2n+3}\frac{\partial}{\partial x}\left(\frac{\omega_n}{r^{2n+1}}\right)\right\}, \quad \text{..............(24)}$$

and the functions ϕ_n, χ_n contribute nothing to $x\Delta$.

The function ω_n contributes to $\partial(ux+vy+wz)/\partial x$ the terms

$$-\frac{1}{h^2}\{n\psi_n(hr)+hr\psi_n'(hr)\}\frac{\partial\omega_n}{\partial x}$$

$$-\frac{1}{h^2}\{(n+1)\,hr\psi_n'(hr)+h^2r^2\psi_n''(hr)\}\frac{1}{2n+1}\left\{\frac{\partial\omega_n}{\partial x}-r^{2n+1}\frac{\partial}{\partial x}\left(\frac{\omega_n}{r^{2n+1}}\right)\right\},$$

which reduce to

$$-\frac{1}{h^2}\left\{\left(n-\frac{h^2r^2}{2n+1}\right)\psi_n(hr)+\frac{n}{2n+1}hr\psi_n'(hr)\right\}\frac{\partial\omega_n}{\partial x}$$

$$-\left\{\psi_n(hr)+\frac{n+1}{hr}\psi_n'(hr)\right\}\frac{r^{2n+3}}{2n+1}\frac{\partial}{\partial x}\left(\frac{\omega_n}{r^{2n+1}}\right). \qquad \text{...............(25)}$$

The function ϕ_n contributes to $\partial(ux+vy+wz)/\partial x$ the terms

$$-n\{(2n+1)\,\psi_n(\kappa r)+\kappa r\psi_n'(\kappa r)\}\frac{\partial\phi_n}{\partial x}+n\kappa\psi_n'(\kappa r)\,r^{2n+2}\frac{\partial}{\partial x}\left(\frac{\phi_n}{r^{2n+1}}\right). \qquad \text{...(26)}$$

The function χ_n contributes nothing to this expression.

The function ω_n contributes to u the terms

$$-\frac{1}{h^2}\left[\left\{\psi_n(hr)+\frac{1}{2n+1}hr\psi_n'(hr)\right\}\frac{\partial\omega_n}{\partial x}-\frac{1}{2n+1}hr\psi_n'(hr)\,r^{2n+1}\frac{\partial}{\partial x}\left(\frac{\omega_n}{r^{2n+1}}\right)\right], \qquad \text{............(27)}$$

and it contributes to $r\dfrac{\partial u}{\partial r}-u$ the terms

$$-\frac{n-2}{h^2}\left[\left\{\psi_n(hr)+\frac{1}{2n+1}hr\psi_n'(hr)\right\}\frac{\partial\omega_n}{\partial x}-\frac{1}{2n+1}hr\psi_n'(hr)\,r^{2n+1}\frac{\partial}{\partial x}\left(\frac{\omega_n}{r^{2n+1}}\right)\right]$$

$$-\frac{1}{h^2}\left\{\frac{2(n+1)}{2n+1}hr\psi_n'(hr)+\frac{h^2r^2}{2n+1}\psi_n''(hr)\right\}\frac{\partial\omega_n}{\partial x}$$

$$+\frac{1}{(2n+1)\,h^2}\{hr\psi_n'(hr)+h^2r^2\psi_n''(hr)\}\,r^{2n+1}\frac{\partial}{\partial x}\left(\frac{\omega_n}{r^{2n+1}}\right),$$

which reduce to

$$-\frac{1}{h^2}\left[\left\{(n-2)-\frac{h^2r^2}{2n+1}\right\}\psi_n(hr)+\frac{n-2}{2n+1}hr\psi_n'(hr)\right]\frac{\partial\omega_n}{\partial x}$$

$$-\left\{\psi_n(hr)+\frac{n+3}{hr}\psi_n'(hr)\right\}\frac{r^{2n+3}}{2n+1}\frac{\partial}{\partial x}\left(\frac{\omega_n}{r^{2n+1}}\right). \qquad \text{..................(28)}$$

The function ϕ_n contributes to $r\partial u/\partial r-u$ the terms

$$\{(n-2)\,\psi_{n-1}(\kappa r)+\kappa r\psi'_{n-1}(\kappa r)\}\frac{\partial\phi_n}{\partial x}$$

$$-\frac{n}{n+1}\kappa^2\{n\psi_{n+1}(\kappa r)+\kappa r\psi'_{n+1}(\kappa r)\}\,r^{2n+3}\frac{\partial}{\partial x}\left(\frac{\phi_n}{r^{2n+1}}\right). \qquad \text{......(29)}$$

The function χ_n contributes to the same expression the terms

$$\{(n-1)\,\psi_n(\kappa r)+\kappa r\psi_n'(\kappa r)\}\left(y\frac{\partial\chi_n}{\partial z}-z\frac{\partial\chi_n}{\partial y}\right). \qquad \text{.........(30)}$$

Complete expressions for the tractions X_r, Y_r, Z_r can now be written down in accordance with (21), and we may express the conditions that these tractions vanish at the surface of a sphere $r=a$ in forms of which the type is

$$\Sigma\left[p_n\left(y\frac{\partial\chi_n}{\partial z}-z\frac{\partial\chi_n}{\partial y}\right)+a_n\frac{\partial\omega_n}{\partial x}+b_n r^{2n+3}\frac{\partial}{\partial x}\left(\frac{\omega_n}{r^{2n+1}}\right)\right.$$
$$\left.+c_n\frac{\partial\phi_n}{\partial x}+d_n r^{2n+3}\frac{\partial}{\partial x}\left(\frac{\phi_n}{r^{2n+1}}\right)\right]=0, \qquad \text{.........(31)}$$

where p_n, a_n, b_n, c_n, d_n are constants. The values of these constants can be found from the above analysis. When we write κ^2/h^2-2 for λ/μ, and use the equations satisfied by the ψ functions, we find the following expressions for the constants

$$\left.\begin{aligned}
p_n&=(n-1)\psi_n(\kappa a)+\kappa a\psi_n'(\kappa a),\\
a_n&=\frac{1}{(2n+1)h^2}\{\kappa^2a^2\psi_n(ha)+2(n-1)\psi_{n-1}(ha)\},\\
b_n&=-\frac{1}{2n+1}\left\{\frac{\kappa^2}{h^2}\psi_n(ha)+\frac{2(n+2)}{ha}\psi_n'(ha)\right\},\\
c_n&=\kappa^2a^2\psi_n(\kappa a)+2(n-1)\psi_{n-1}(\kappa a),\\
d_n&=\kappa^2\frac{n}{n+1}\left\{\psi_n(\kappa a)+\frac{2(n+2)}{\kappa a}\psi_n'(\kappa a)\right\}.
\end{aligned}\right\} \qquad \text{...........(32)}$$

There are two additional equations of the type (31) which are to be obtained from the one written down by cyclical interchange of the letters x, y, z. These equations hold at the surface $r=a$.

193. Incompressible material.

In the case of incompressible material we have to take $\Delta=0$ and to replace $\lambda\Delta$ by $-\Pi$, where Π denotes a finite pressure. The equations of motion become three of the type

$$-\frac{\partial\Pi}{\partial x}+\mu\nabla^2u=\rho\frac{\partial^2u}{\partial t^2},$$

in which $\partial u/\partial x+\partial v/\partial y+\partial w/\partial z=0$. We find at once that Π must be an harmonic function, and we may put

$$\Pi=-\mu\Sigma\omega_n,$$

in which ω_n is a spherical solid harmonic of degree n. When u, v, w are simple harmonic functions of t with period $2\pi/p$, the equations of motion become three equations of the type

$$(\nabla^2+\kappa^2)u-\mu^{-1}\partial\Pi/\partial x=0,$$

and the integrals can be found in such forms as

$$u=-\frac{1}{\kappa^2}\Sigma\frac{\partial\omega_n}{\partial x}+u_2,$$

where u_2 is given by (20). The formula for rX_r/μ now becomes

$$\frac{rX_r}{\mu}=-\frac{x\Pi}{\mu}+\frac{\partial}{\partial x}(ux+vy+wz)+r\frac{\partial u}{\partial r}-u,$$

and the terms contributed to the right-hand member by ω_n are

$$\left(\frac{r^2}{2n+1}-\frac{2(n-1)}{\kappa^2}\right)\frac{\partial\omega_n}{\partial x}-\frac{r^{2n+3}}{2n+1}\frac{\partial}{\partial x}\left(\frac{\omega_n}{r^{2n+1}}\right),$$

while the terms contributed by ϕ_n and χ_n are the same as before. The result of assuming incompressibility of the material is therefore to change a_n into $\frac{a^2}{2n+1} - \frac{2(n-1)}{\kappa^2}$ and b_n into $-\frac{1}{2n+1}$, without altering the remaining coefficients in the left-hand member of (31).

194. Frequency equations for vibrating sphere.

The left-hand members of the equations of type (31) are sums of spherical solid harmonics of positive degrees, and they vanish at the surface $r=a$. It follows that they vanish everywhere. If we differentiate the left-hand members of these equations with respect to x, y, z respectively and add the results we obtain the equation

$$b_n\omega_n + d_n\phi_n = 0. \qquad \text{.................(33)}$$

If we multiply the left-hand members of the equations of type (31) by x, y, z respectively and add the results, we find, after simplification by means of (33), the equation

$$a_n\omega_n + c_n\phi_n = 0. \qquad \text{.................(34)}$$

The equations of type (31) then show that we must have

$$p_n\left(y\frac{\partial\chi_n}{\partial z} - z\frac{\partial\chi_n}{\partial y}\right) = 0, \quad p_n\left(z\frac{\partial\chi_n}{\partial x} - x\frac{\partial\chi_n}{\partial z}\right) = 0, \quad p_n\left(x\frac{\partial\chi_n}{\partial y} - y\frac{\partial\chi_n}{\partial x}\right) = 0.$$

It follows that the vibrations fall into two classes. In the first class ω_n and ϕ_n vanish and the frequency is given by the equation

$$p_n = 0, \qquad \text{.................(35)}$$

where p_n is given by the first of (32). In the second class χ_n vanishes and the frequency is given by the equation

$$a_nd_n - b_nc_n = 0, \qquad \text{.................(36)}$$

where a_n, b_n, c_n, d_n are given by (32). In the vibrations of this class ω_n and ϕ_n are connected with each other by the compatible equations (33) and (34).

195. Vibrations of the first class*.

When the vibration is of the first class the displacement is of the form

$$(u, v, w) = A\cos(pt+\epsilon)\,\psi_n(\kappa r)\left(y\frac{\partial\chi_n}{\partial z} - z\frac{\partial\chi_n}{\partial y},\quad z\frac{\partial\chi_n}{\partial x} - x\frac{\partial\chi_n}{\partial z},\quad x\frac{\partial\chi_n}{\partial y} - y\frac{\partial\chi_n}{\partial x}\right), \text{...(37)}$$

where $\kappa^2 = p^2\rho/\mu$; and the possible values of p are determined by the equation

$$(n-1)\,\psi_n(\kappa a) + \kappa a\,\psi_n'(\kappa a) = 0. \qquad \text{.................(38)}$$

The dilatation vanishes. The radial displacement also vanishes, so that the displacement at any point is directed at right angles to the radius drawn from the centre of the sphere. It is also directed at right angles to the normal to that surface of the family $\chi_n=\text{const.}$ which passes through the point. The spherical surfaces determined by the equation $\psi_n(\kappa r)=0$ are "nodal," that is to say the displacement vanishes at these surfaces. The spherical surfaces determined by the equation

$$(n-1)\,\psi_n(\kappa r) + \kappa r\,\psi_n'(\kappa r) = 0,$$

* The results stated in this Article and the following are due to H. Lamb, *loc. cit.* p. 278.

in which κ is a root of (38), are "anti-nodal," that is to say there is no traction across these surfaces. If $\kappa_1, \kappa_2, \ldots$ are the values of κ in ascending order which satisfy (38), the anti-nodal surfaces corresponding with the vibration of frequency $(2\pi)^{-1}\sqrt{(\mu/\rho)}\,\kappa_s$ have radii equal to $\kappa_1 a/\kappa_s, \kappa_2 a/\kappa_s, \ldots \kappa_{s-1} a/\kappa_s$.

If $n=1$ we have *rotatory vibrations**. Taking the axis of z to be the axis of the harmonic χ_1, the displacement is

$$(u, v, w) = A\cos(pt+\epsilon)\,\psi_1(\kappa r)\,(y, -x, 0),$$

so that every spherical surface concentric with the boundary turns round the axis of z through a small angle proportional to $\psi_1(\kappa r)$, or to $(\kappa r)^{-2}\cos\kappa r - (\kappa r)^{-3}\sin\kappa r$. The possible values of κ are the roots of the equation $\psi_1'(\kappa a)=0$, or

$$\tan\kappa a = 3\kappa a/(3-\kappa^2 a^2).$$

The lowest roots of this equation are

$$\frac{\kappa a}{\pi} = 1{\cdot}8346,\quad 2{\cdot}8950,\quad 3{\cdot}9225,\quad 4{\cdot}9385,\quad 5{\cdot}9489,\quad 6{\cdot}9563,\ \ldots.$$

The number $\pi/\kappa a$ is the ratio of the period of oscillation to the time taken by a wave of distortion† to travel over a distance equal to the diameter of the sphere. The nodal surfaces are given by the equation $\tan\kappa r = \kappa r$, of which the roots are

$$\frac{\kappa r}{\pi} = 1{\cdot}4303,\quad 2{\cdot}4590,\quad 3{\cdot}4709,\quad 4{\cdot}4774,\quad 5{\cdot}4818,\quad 6{\cdot}4844,\ \ldots.$$

196. Vibrations of the second class.

When the vibration is of the second class the components of displacement are expressed by equations of the type

$$u = A\cos(pt+\epsilon)\left[-\frac{1}{h^2}\left\{\psi_n(hr)+\frac{hr}{2n+1}\psi_n'(hr)\right\}\frac{\partial\omega_n}{\partial x}+\frac{1}{(2n+1)h}\psi_n'(hr)\,r^{2n+2}\frac{\partial}{\partial x}\left(\frac{\omega_n}{r^{2n+1}}\right)\right.$$
$$\left.+\psi_{n-1}(\kappa r)\frac{\partial\phi_n}{\partial x}-\frac{n}{n+1}\psi_{n+1}(\kappa r)\,\kappa^2 r^{2n+3}\frac{\partial}{\partial x}\left(\frac{\phi_n}{r^{2n+1}}\right)\right]. \quad \ldots(39)$$

The displacement has, in general, both transverse and radial components, but the rotation has no radial component. The frequency equation (36) cannot be solved numerically until the ratio κ/h is known. We shall consider chiefly incompressible material, for which $h/\kappa=0$, and material fulfilling Poisson's condition ($\lambda=\mu$), for which $\kappa/h=\sqrt{3}$.

Radial vibrations.

When $n=0$ we have radial vibrations. The normal functions are of the form

$$u=\frac{x}{r}\psi_0'(hr),\quad v=\frac{y}{r}\psi_0'(hr),\quad w=\frac{z}{r}\psi_0'(hr), \quad \ldots\ldots(40)$$

and the frequency equation is $b_0=0$, or

$$\psi_0(ha)+\frac{4}{\kappa^2 a^2}ha\,\psi_0'(ha)=0, \quad \ldots\ldots(41)$$

which is

$$\frac{\tan ha}{ha}=\frac{1}{1-\frac{1}{4}(\kappa^2/h^2)\,h^2a^2}.$$

There are, of course, no radial vibrations when the material is incompressible. When $\kappa^2/h^2=3$, the six lowest roots of the frequency equation are given by

$$\frac{ha}{\pi} = {\cdot}8160,\quad 1{\cdot}9285,\quad 2{\cdot}9359,\quad 3{\cdot}9658,\quad 4{\cdot}9728,\quad 5{\cdot}9774.$$

* Modes of vibration analogous to the rotatory vibrations of the sphere have been found for any solid of revolution by P. Jaerisch, *J. f. Math.* (*Crelle*), Bd. 104 (1889).

† The velocity of waves of distortion is $(\mu/\rho)^{\frac{1}{2}}$. See Chapter XIII.

The number π/ha is the ratio of the period of oscillation to the time taken by a wave of dilatation* to travel over a distance equal to the diameter of the sphere.

Spheroidal vibrations.

When $n=2$ and ω_2 and ϕ_2 are zonal harmonics we have what may be called *spheroidal vibrations*, in which the sphere is distorted into an ellipsoid of revolution becoming alternately prolate and oblate according to the phase of the motion. Vibrations of this type would tend to be forced by forces of appropriate period and of the same type as tidal disturbing forces. It is found that the lowest root of the frequency equation for free vibrations of this type is given by $\kappa a/\pi = \cdot 848$ when the material is incompressible, and by $\kappa a/\pi = \cdot 840$ when the material fulfils Poisson's condition. For a sphere of the same size and mass as the Earth, supposed to be incompressible and as rigid as steel, the period of the gravest free vibration of the type here described is about 66 minutes.

197. Further investigations on the vibrations of spheres.

The vibrations of a sphere that would be forced by surface tractions proportional to simple harmonic functions of the time have been investigated by Chree†. Free vibrations of a shell bounded by concentric spherical surfaces have been discussed by Lamb‡, with special reference to the case in which the shell is thin. The influence of gravity on the free vibrations of an incompressible sphere has been considered by Bromwich§. He found, in particular, that the period of the "spheroidal" vibrations of a sphere of the same size and mass as the Earth and as rigid as steel would be diminished from 66 to 55 minutes by the mutual gravitation of the parts of the sphere. A more general discussion of the effects of gravitation in a sphere of which the material is not incompressible has been given by Jeans‖. It has been proved that, when both gravity and compressibility are taken into account, the period of spheroidal vibrations of a sphere of the same size and mass as the Earth, as rigid as steel, and having a Poisson's ratio equal to $\frac{1}{4}$, would be almost exactly one hour¶.

It is a matter of some interest to determine the number of modes of vibration of a body which have frequencies not exceeding some assigned (high) frequency. The question arises in the Thermodynamic theory of specific heats, and for that theory it is important that the vibrations of the body should be executed in such ways that no work is done by the surface tractions. This condition is satisfied if the surface is free, and it is also satisfied if the surface is fixed, so that the values of the components of displacement vanish at the surface. The vibrations of a homogeneous isotropic body with a fixed spherical boundary have been worked out by P. Debye**, and the number of modes counted.

198. Radial vibrations of a hollow sphere††.

The radial vibrations of a sphere or a spherical shell may be investigated very simply in terms of polar coordinates. In the notation of Article 98 we should find that the radial displacement U satisfies the equation

$$\frac{\partial^2 U}{\partial r^2} + \frac{2}{r}\frac{\partial U}{\partial r} - \frac{2}{r^2}U + h^2 U = 0,$$

* The velocity of waves of dilatation is $\{(\lambda+2\mu)/\rho\}^{\frac{1}{2}}$. See Chapter XIII.

† *Loc. cit.* p. 278.

‡ *London Math. Soc. Proc.*, vol. 14 (1883).

§ *London Math. Soc. Proc.*, vol. 30 (1899).

‖ *Phil. Trans. Roy. Soc.* (Ser. A), vol. 201 (1903).

¶ A. E. H. Love, *Some Problems of Geodynamics.*

** *Ann. d. Phys.* (Ser. 4), Bd. 39, 1912, p. 789.

†† The problem of the radial vibrations of a solid sphere was one of those discussed by Poisson in his memoir of 1828. See Introduction, footnote 36.

and that the radial traction $\widehat{rr}$ across a sphere of radius r is

$$(\lambda+2\mu)\frac{\partial U}{\partial r}+2\lambda\frac{U}{r}.$$

The primitive of the differential equation for U may be written

$$U=\frac{d}{d(hr)}\left(\frac{A\sin hr+B\cos hr}{hr}\right);$$

and the condition that the traction $\widehat{rr}$ vanishes at a spherical surface of radius r is

$$[(\lambda+2\mu)\{(2-h^2r^2)\sin hr-2hr\cos hr\}+2\lambda(hr\cos hr-\sin hr)]A$$
$$+[(\lambda+2\mu)\{(2-h^2r^2)\cos hr+2hr\sin hr\}-2\lambda(hr\sin hr+\cos hr)]B=0.$$

When the sphere is complete up to the centre we must put $B=0$, and the condition for the vanishing of the traction at $r=a$ is the frequency equation which we found before. In the case of a spherical shell the frequency equation is found by eliminating the ratio $A:B$ from the conditions which express the vanishing of $\widehat{rr}$ at $r=a$ and at $r=b$. We write

$$4h^2/\kappa^2=\nu,$$

so that $2\lambda/(\lambda+2\mu)=2-\nu$, and then the equation is

$$\frac{\nu ha+(h^2a^2-\nu)\tan ha}{(h^2a^2-\nu)-\nu ha\tan ha}=\frac{\nu hb+(h^2b^2-\nu)\tan hb}{(h^2b^2-\nu)-\nu hb\tan hb}.$$

In the particular case of a very thin spherical shell this equation may be replaced by

$$\frac{\partial}{\partial a}\frac{\nu ha+(h^2a^2-\nu)\tan ha}{(h^2a^2-\nu)-\nu ha\tan ha}=0,$$

which is

$$h^2a^2\sec^2 ha\,\{h^2a^2-\nu(3-\nu)\}=0,$$

and we have therefore

$$ha=\sqrt{\{\nu(3-\nu)\}}.$$

In terms of Poisson's ratio σ the period is

$$\pi a\sqrt{\left(\frac{\rho}{\mu}\frac{1-\sigma}{1+\sigma}\right)}.$$

199. Vibrations of a circular cylinder.

We shall investigate certain modes of vibration of an isotropic circular cylinder, the curved surface of which is free from traction, on the assumption that, if the axis of z coincides with the axis of the cylinder, the displacement is a simple harmonic function of z as well as of t*. Vibrations of these types would result, in an unlimited cylinder, from the superposition of two trains of waves travelling along the cylinder in opposite directions. When the cylinder is of finite length the frequency of free vibration would be determined by the conditions that the plane ends are free from traction. We shall find that, in general, these conditions are not satisfied exactly by modes of vibration of the kind described, but that, when the radius of the cylinder is small compared with its length, they are satisfied approximately.

* The theory is effectively due to L. Pochhammer, *J. f. Math.* (*Crelle*), Bd. 81 (1876), p. 324. It has been discussed also by C. Chree, *loc. cit.* p. 278.

We use the equations of vibration referred to cylindrical coordinates r, θ, z. The equations are

$$\left.\begin{aligned} \rho\frac{\partial^2 u_r}{\partial t^2} &= (\lambda+2\mu)\frac{\partial\Delta}{\partial r} - \frac{2\mu}{r}\frac{\partial\varpi_z}{\partial\theta} + 2\mu\frac{\partial\varpi_\theta}{\partial z},\\ \rho\frac{\partial^2 u_\theta}{\partial t^2} &= (\lambda+2\mu)\frac{1}{r}\frac{\partial\Delta}{\partial\theta} - 2\mu\frac{\partial\varpi_r}{\partial z} + 2\mu\frac{\partial\varpi_z}{\partial r},\\ \rho\frac{\partial^2 u_z}{\partial t^2} &= (\lambda+2\mu)\frac{\partial\Delta}{\partial z} - \frac{2\mu}{r}\frac{\partial}{\partial r}(r\varpi_\theta) + \frac{2\mu}{r}\frac{\partial\varpi_r}{\partial\theta}, \end{aligned}\right\} \quad \text{............(42)}$$

in which

$$\Delta = \frac{1}{r}\frac{\partial(ru_r)}{\partial r} + \frac{1}{r}\frac{\partial u_\theta}{\partial\theta} + \frac{\partial u_z}{\partial z}, \quad \text{.....................(43)}$$

and

$$2\varpi_r = \frac{1}{r}\frac{\partial u_z}{\partial\theta} - \frac{\partial u_\theta}{\partial z},\quad 2\varpi_\theta = \frac{\partial u_r}{\partial z} - \frac{\partial u_z}{\partial r},\quad 2\varpi_z = \frac{1}{r}\left(\frac{\partial(ru_\theta)}{\partial r} - \frac{\partial u_r}{\partial\theta}\right), \quad \text{......(44)}$$

so that ϖ_r, ϖ_θ, ϖ_z satisfy the identical relation

$$\frac{1}{r}\frac{\partial(r\varpi_r)}{\partial r} + \frac{1}{r}\frac{\partial\varpi_\theta}{\partial\theta} + \frac{\partial\varpi_z}{\partial z} = 0. \quad \text{.....................(45)}$$

The stress-components $\widehat{rr}$, $\widehat{r\theta}$, $\widehat{rz}$ vanish at the surface of the cylinder $r=a$. These stress-components are expressed by the formulæ

$$\widehat{rr} = \lambda\Delta + 2\mu\frac{\partial u_r}{\partial r},\quad \widehat{r\theta} = \mu\left\{\frac{1}{r}\frac{\partial u_r}{\partial\theta} + r\frac{\partial}{\partial r}\left(\frac{u_\theta}{r}\right)\right\},\quad \widehat{rz} = \mu\left(\frac{\partial u_r}{\partial z} + \frac{\partial u_z}{\partial r}\right). \quad \text{...(46)}$$

In accordance with what has been said above we shall take u_r, u_θ, u_z to be of the forms

$$u_r = Ue^{\iota(\gamma z+pt)},\quad u_\theta = Ve^{\iota(\gamma z+pt)},\quad u_z = We^{\iota(\gamma z+pt)}, \quad \text{.........(47)}$$

in which U, V, W are functions of r, θ.

200. Torsional vibrations.

We can obtain a solution in which U and W vanish and V is independent of θ. The first and third of equations (42) are satisfied identically, and the second of these equations becomes

$$\frac{\partial^2 V}{\partial r^2} + \frac{1}{r}\frac{\partial V}{\partial r} - \frac{1}{r^2}V + \kappa'^2 V = 0, \quad \text{.....................(48)}$$

where $\kappa'^2 = p^2\rho/\mu - \gamma^2$. Hence V is of the form $BJ_1(\kappa' r)$, where B is a constant, and J_1 denotes Bessel's function of order unity. The conditions at the surface $r=a$ are satisfied if κ' is a root of the equation

$$\frac{\partial}{\partial a}\left\{\frac{J_1(\kappa' a)}{a}\right\} = 0.$$

One solution of the equation is $\kappa'=0$, and the corresponding form of V given by equation (48) is $V = Br$, where B is a constant.

We have therefore found a simple harmonic wave-motion of the type

$$u_r = 0,\quad u_\theta = Bre^{\iota(\gamma z+pt)},\quad u_z = 0, \quad \text{..................(49)}$$

in which $\gamma^2 = p^2\rho/\mu$. Such waves are waves of torsion, and they are propagated along the cylinder with velocity $\sqrt{(\mu/\rho)}$*.

The traction across a normal section $z = \text{const.}$ vanishes if $\partial u_\theta/\partial z$ vanishes; and we can have, therefore, free torsional vibrations of a circular cylinder of length l, in which the displacement is expressed by the formula

$$\frac{u_\theta}{r} = \cos\frac{n\pi z}{l} B_n \cos\left(\frac{n\pi t}{l}\sqrt{\frac{\mu}{\rho}} + \epsilon\right), \quad \text{.................(50)}$$

n being any integer, and the origin being at one end.

201. Longitudinal vibrations.

We can obtain a solution in which V vanishes and U and W are independent of θ. The second of equations (42) is then satisfied identically, and from the first and third of these equations we find

$$\left.\begin{aligned} &\frac{\partial^2\Delta}{\partial r^2} + \frac{1}{r}\frac{\partial\Delta}{\partial r} + h'^2\Delta = 0, \\ &\frac{\partial^2\varpi_\theta}{\partial r^2} + \frac{1}{r}\frac{\partial\varpi_\theta}{\partial r} - \frac{\varpi_\theta}{r^2} + \kappa'^2\varpi_\theta = 0, \end{aligned}\right\} \quad \text{....................(51)}$$

where $$h'^2 = p^2\rho/(\lambda + 2\mu) - \gamma^2, \quad \kappa'^2 = p^2\rho/\mu - \gamma^2. \quad \text{..............(52)}$$

We must therefore take Δ and ϖ_θ, as functions of r, to be proportional to $J_0(h'r)$ and $J_1(\kappa'r)$. Then to satisfy the equations

$$\Delta = \left(\frac{\partial U}{\partial r} + \frac{U}{r} + \iota\gamma W\right)e^{\iota(\gamma z + pt)}, \quad 2\varpi_\theta = \left(\iota\gamma U - \frac{\partial W}{\partial r}\right)e^{\iota(\gamma z + pt)}$$

we have to take U and W to be of the forms

$$\left.\begin{aligned} U &= A\frac{\partial}{\partial r}J_0(h'r) + C\gamma J_1(\kappa'r), \\ W &= A\iota\gamma J_0(h'r) + \frac{\iota C}{r}\frac{\partial}{\partial r}\{rJ_1(\kappa'r)\}, \end{aligned}\right\} \quad \text{..............(53)}$$

where A and C are constants.

The traction across the cylindrical surface $r = a$ vanishes if A and C are connected by the equations

$$\left.\begin{aligned} &A\left[2\mu\frac{\partial^2 J_0(h'a)}{\partial a^2} - \frac{p^2\rho\lambda}{\lambda + 2\mu}J_0(h'a)\right] + 2\mu C\gamma\frac{\partial J_1(\kappa'a)}{\partial a} = 0, \\ &2A\gamma\frac{\partial J_0(h'a)}{\partial a} + C\left(2\gamma^2 - \frac{p^2\rho}{\mu}\right)J_1(\kappa'a) = 0. \end{aligned}\right\} \text{...(54)}$$

On eliminating the ratio $A : C$ we obtain the frequency equation.

When the radius of the cylinder is small we may approximate to the frequency by expanding the Bessel's functions. On putting

$$J_0(h'a) = 1 - \tfrac{1}{4}h'^2a^2 + \tfrac{1}{64}h'^4a^4, \quad J_1(\kappa'a) = \tfrac{1}{2}(\kappa'a - \tfrac{1}{8}\kappa'^3a^3),$$

* Cf. Lord Rayleigh, *Theory of Sound*, Chapter VII.

the frequency equation becomes

$$\left(\frac{p^2\rho}{\mu} - 2\gamma^2\right)\kappa' a\left(1 - \frac{\kappa'^2 a^2}{8}\right)\left[h'^2(1 - \tfrac{3}{8}a^2h'^2) + \frac{\lambda}{\mu}\frac{p^2\rho}{\lambda + 2\mu}(1 - \tfrac{1}{4}a^2h'^2)\right]$$
$$+ 2\gamma^2\kappa'(1 - \tfrac{3}{8}a^2\kappa'^2)\, ah'^2(1 - \tfrac{1}{8}a^2h'^2) = 0.$$

It is easily seen that no wave-motion of the type in question can be found by putting $\kappa' = 0$. Omitting the factor $\kappa' a$ and the terms of order a^2, we find a first approximation to the value of p in terms of γ in the form

$$p = \gamma\sqrt{(E/\rho)}, \qquad \text{.............................(55)}$$

where $E, = \mu(3\lambda + 2\mu)/(\lambda + \mu)$, is Young's modulus. The waves thus found are "longitudinal" and the velocity with which they are propagated along the cylinder is $\sqrt{(E/\rho)}$ approximately*.

When we retain terms in a^2, we find a second approximation† to the velocity in the form

$$p = \gamma\sqrt{(E/\rho)}\,(1 - \tfrac{1}{4}\sigma^2\gamma^2 a^2), \qquad \text{...................(56)}$$

where $\sigma, = \frac{1}{2}\lambda/(\lambda + \mu)$, is Poisson's ratio.

When the cylinder is terminated by two plane sections $z = 0$ and $z = l$, and these sections are free from traction, $\widehat{zz}$ and $\widehat{zr}$ must vanish at $z = 0$ and $z = l$. We find for the values of $\widehat{zz}$ and $\widehat{zr}$ at any section the expressions

$$\widehat{zz} = -\left[A\left(p^2\rho\frac{\lambda}{\lambda + 2\mu} + 2\mu\gamma^2\right)J_0(h'r) + 2\mu\iota\gamma C\left\{\frac{\partial J_1(\kappa' r)}{\partial r} + \frac{J_1(\kappa' r)}{r}\right\}\right]e^{\iota(\gamma z + pt)},$$

$$\widehat{zr} = \mu\iota\left[2A\gamma\frac{\partial J_0(h'r)}{\partial r} + C\left(2\gamma^2 - \frac{p^2\rho}{\mu}\right)J_1(\kappa' r)\right]e^{\iota(\gamma z + pt)}.$$

Now we can have a solution of the form

$$\left.\begin{aligned} u_r &= \left[A_n\frac{\partial J_0(h'r)}{\partial r} + \frac{n\pi}{l}C_nJ_1(\kappa' r)\right]\sin\frac{n\pi z}{l}\cos(p_nt + \epsilon), \\ u_z &= \left[\frac{n\pi}{l}A_nJ_0(h'r) + C_n\left\{\frac{\partial J_1(\kappa' r)}{\partial r} + \frac{J_1(\kappa' r)}{r}\right\}\right]\cos\frac{n\pi z}{l}\cos(p_nt + \epsilon), \end{aligned}\right\} \text{...(57)}$$

in which the ratio $A_n : C_n$ is known from the conditions which hold at $r = a$, γ has been replaced by $n\pi/l$, and p_n is approximately equal to $(n\pi/l)\sqrt{(E/\rho)}$ when a is small compared with l. This solution satisfies the condition $\widehat{zz} = 0$ at $z = 0$ and at $z = l$, but it does not satisfy the condition $\widehat{zr} = 0$ at these surfaces. Since, however, $\widehat{zr} = 0$ at the surface $r = a$ for all values of z, the traction $\widehat{zr}$ is very small at all points on the terminal sections $z = 0$ and $z = l$ when a is small compared with l.

* Cf. Lord Rayleigh, *Theory of Sound*, Chapter VII.

† The result is due to L. Pochhammer, *loc. cit.* p. 287. It was found independently by C. Chree, *Quart. J. of Math.*, vol. 21 (1886), and extended by him, *Quart. J. of Math.*, vol. 24 (1890), to cases in which the normal section of the cylinder is not circular and the material is not isotropic; in these cases the term $\frac{1}{4}\sigma^2\gamma^2 a^2$ of the above expression (56) is replaced by $\frac{1}{2}\sigma^2\gamma^2\kappa^2$, where κ is the radius of gyration of the cylinder about the line of centres of the normal sections.

If we take u_r to contain $\cos(n\pi z/l)$, and u_z to contain $-\sin(n\pi z/l)$, the other factors being the same as before, we have a solution of the problem of longitudinal vibrations in a cylinder of which the centres of both ends are fixed.

202. Transverse vibrations.

Another interesting solution of equations (42) can be obtained by taking u_r and u_z to be proportional to $\cos\theta$, and u_θ to be proportional to $\sin\theta$. Modifying the notation of (47) in Article 199, we may write

$$u_r = U\cos\theta\, e^{\iota(\gamma z+pt)},\quad u_\theta = V\sin\theta\, e^{\iota(\gamma z+pt)},\quad u_z = W\cos\theta\, e^{\iota(\gamma z+pt)}, \quad\ldots(58)$$

where U, V, W are functions of r. Then we have

$$\left.\begin{aligned}
\Delta &= \cos\theta\, e^{\iota(\gamma z+pt)}\left(\frac{\partial U}{\partial r}+\frac{U}{r}+\frac{V}{r}+\iota\gamma W\right),\\
2\varpi_r &= -\sin\theta\, e^{\iota(\gamma z+pt)}\left(\frac{W}{r}+\iota\gamma V\right),\\
2\varpi_\theta &= \cos\theta\, e^{\iota(\gamma z+pt)}\left(\iota\gamma U-\frac{\partial W}{\partial r}\right),\\
2\varpi_z &= \sin\theta\, e^{\iota(\gamma z+pt)}\left(\frac{\partial V}{\partial r}+\frac{V}{r}+\frac{U}{r}\right).
\end{aligned}\right\} \quad\ldots\ldots\ldots\ldots(59)$$

From equations (42) we may form the equation

$$\frac{\partial^2\Delta}{\partial r^2}+\frac{1}{r}\frac{\partial\Delta}{\partial r}-\frac{\Delta}{r^2}+h'^2\Delta=0, \quad\ldots\ldots\ldots\ldots\ldots\ldots(60)$$

where h'^2 is given by the first of equations (52); and it follows that Δ can be written in the form

$$\Delta = -\frac{p^2\rho}{\lambda+2\mu}AJ_1(h'r)\cos\theta\, e^{\iota(\gamma z+pt)}, \quad\ldots\ldots\ldots\ldots\ldots\ldots(61)$$

where A is a constant.

Again, we may form the equation

$$-\frac{p^2\rho}{\mu}\varpi_z = \frac{1}{r}\frac{\partial}{\partial r}\left(r\frac{\partial\varpi_z}{\partial r}\right)-\frac{\varpi_z}{r^2}-\frac{\partial}{\partial z}\left\{\frac{1}{r}\frac{\partial}{\partial r}(r\varpi_r)+\frac{1}{r}\frac{\partial\varpi_\theta}{\partial\theta}\right\},$$

which, in virtue of (45), is the same as

$$\frac{\partial^2\varpi_z}{\partial r^2}+\frac{1}{r}\frac{\partial\varpi_z}{\partial r}-\frac{\varpi_z}{r^2}+\kappa'^2\varpi_z=0, \quad\ldots\ldots\ldots\ldots\ldots\ldots(62)$$

where κ'^2 is given by the second of equations (52). It follows that $2\varpi_z$ can be written in the form

$$2\varpi_z = \kappa'^2 CJ_1(\kappa' r)\sin\theta\, e^{\iota(\gamma z+pt)}, \quad\ldots\ldots\ldots\ldots\ldots\ldots(63)$$

where C is a constant.

We may form also the equation

$$-\frac{p^2\rho}{\mu}\varpi_r = -\frac{\varpi_r}{r^2}-\gamma^2\varpi_r-\frac{1}{r^2}\frac{\partial}{\partial r}\left(r\frac{\partial\varpi_\theta}{\partial\theta}\right)-\frac{\partial}{\partial r}\frac{\partial\varpi_z}{\partial z},$$

which, in virtue of (45), is the same as

$$\frac{1}{r^2}\frac{\partial}{\partial r}\left\{r\frac{\partial}{\partial r}(r\varpi_r)\right\}-\frac{\varpi_r}{r^2}+\kappa'^2\varpi_r+\frac{2}{r}\iota\gamma\varpi_z=0. \qquad \text{............(64)}$$

In this equation $2\varpi_z$ has the value given in (63), and it follows that $2\varpi_r$ can be written in the form

$$2\varpi_r=\left\{\iota\gamma C\frac{\partial J_1(\kappa' r)}{\partial r}+\iota B\frac{p^2\rho}{\mu}\frac{J_1(\kappa' r)}{r}\right\}\sin\theta e^{\iota(\gamma z+pt)}, \qquad \text{......(65)}$$

where B is a constant. The equations connecting the quantities U, V, W with Δ, ϖ_r, ϖ_z can then be satisfied by putting

$$\left.\begin{aligned} U &= A\frac{\partial J_1(h' r)}{\partial r}+B\gamma\frac{\partial J_1(\kappa' r)}{\partial r}+C\frac{J_1(\kappa' r)}{r},\\ V &= -A\frac{J_1(h' r)}{r}-B\gamma\frac{J_1(\kappa' r)}{r}-C\frac{\partial J_1(\kappa' r)}{\partial r},\\ W &= \iota A\gamma J_1(h' r)-\iota B\kappa'^2 J_1(\kappa' r). \end{aligned}\right\} \qquad \text{.........(66)}$$

When these forms for U, V, W are substituted in (58) we have a solution of equations (42). Since $u_r\sin\theta+u_\theta\cos\theta$ vanishes when $r=0$, the motion of points on the axis of the cylinder takes place in the plane containing the unstrained position of that axis and the line from which θ is measured; and, since u_z vanishes when $r=0$, the motion of these points is at right angles to the axis of the cylinder. Hence the vibrations are of a "transverse" or "flexural" type.

We could form the conditions that the cylindrical surface is free from traction. These conditions are very complicated, but it may be shown by expanding the Bessel's functions in series that, when the radius a of the cylinder is very small, the quantities p and γ are connected by the approximate equation *

$$p^2=\tfrac{1}{4}a^2\gamma^4(E/\rho), \qquad \text{..................................(67)}$$

where E is Young's modulus. This is the well-known equation for the frequency $p/2\pi$ of flexural waves of length $2\pi/\gamma$ travelling along a cylindrical bar. The ratios of the constants A, B, C which correspond with any value of γ are determined by the conditions at the cylindrical surface.

When the cylinder is terminated by two normal sections $z=0$ and $z=l$, we write m/l for the real positive fourth root of $4p^2\rho/a^2E$. We can obtain four forms of solution by substituting for $\iota\gamma$ in (52), (58), (66) the four quantities $\pm m/l$ and $\pm\iota m/l$ successively. With the same value of p we should have four sets of constants A, B, C, but the ratios $A:B:C$ in each set would be known. The conditions that the stress-components $\widehat{zz}$, $\widehat{z\theta}$ vanish at the ends of the cylinder would yield sufficient equations to enable us to eliminate the constants of the types A, B, C and obtain an equation for p. The condition that the stress-component $\widehat{zr}$ vanishes at the ends cannot be satisfied exactly; but, as in the problem of longitudinal vibrations, it is satisfied approximately when the cylinder is thin.

* Cf. Lord Rayleigh, *Theory of Sound*, Chapter VIII.

CHAPTER XIII

THE PROPAGATION OF WAVES IN ELASTIC SOLID MEDIA

203. THE solution of the equations of free vibration of a body of given form can be adapted to satisfy any given initial conditions, when the frequency equation has been solved and the normal functions determined; but the account that would in this way be given of the motion that ensues upon some local disturbance originated within a body, all points (or some points) of the boundary being at considerable distances from the initially disturbed portion, would be difficult to interpret. In the beginning of the motion the parts of the body that are near to the boundary are not disturbed, and the motion is the same as it would be if the body were of unlimited extent. We accordingly consider such states of small motion in an elastic solid medium, extending indefinitely in all (or in some) directions, as are at some time restricted to a limited portion of the medium, the remainder of the medium being at rest in the unstressed state. We begin with the case of an isotropic medium.

204. Waves of dilatation and waves of distortion.

The equations of motion of the medium may be written

$$(\lambda+\mu)\left(\frac{\partial\Delta}{\partial x},\ \frac{\partial\Delta}{\partial y},\ \frac{\partial\Delta}{\partial z}\right)+\mu\nabla^2(u,v,w)=\rho\left(\frac{\partial^2 u}{\partial t^2},\ \frac{\partial^2 v}{\partial t^2},\ \frac{\partial^2 w}{\partial t^2}\right). \quad \ldots(1)$$

If we differentiate the left-hand and right-hand members of these three equations with respect to x, y, z respectively and add the results, we obtain the equation

$$(\lambda+2\mu)\nabla^2\Delta=\rho\frac{\partial^2\Delta}{\partial t^2}\,. \quad \ldots\ldots(2)$$

If we eliminate Δ from the equations (1) by performing the operation *curl* upon the left-hand and right-hand members we obtain the equations

$$\mu\nabla^2(\varpi_x,\varpi_y,\varpi_z)=\rho\frac{\partial^2}{\partial t^2}(\varpi_x,\varpi_y,\varpi_z). \quad \ldots\ldots(3)$$

If Δ vanishes the equations of motion become

$$\mu\nabla^2(u,v,w)=\rho\frac{\partial^2}{\partial t^2}(u,v,w). \quad \ldots\ldots(4)$$

If ϖ_x, ϖ_y, ϖ_z vanish, so that (u, v, w) is the gradient of a potential ϕ, we may put $\nabla^2\phi$ for Δ, and then we have

$$\left(\frac{\partial\Delta}{\partial x},\ \frac{\partial\Delta}{\partial y},\ \frac{\partial\Delta}{\partial z}\right)=\nabla^2(u,v,w).$$

In this case the equations of motion become

$$(\lambda + 2\mu)\nabla^2(u, v, w) = \rho\frac{\partial^2}{\partial t^2}(u, v, w). \quad \text{.................(5)}$$

Equations (2), (3), (4), (5) are of the form

$$\frac{\partial^2\phi}{\partial t^2} = c^2\nabla^2\phi\,; \quad \text{..............................(6)}$$

for Δ, c^2 has the value $(\lambda + 2\mu)/\rho$; for ϖ_x, ... it has the value μ/ρ. The equation (6) will be called the "characteristic equation."

If ϕ is a function of t and of one coordinate only, say of x, the equation (6) becomes

$$\frac{\partial^2\phi}{\partial t^2} = c^2\frac{\partial^2\phi}{\partial x^2},$$

which may be integrated in the form

$$\phi = f(x - ct) + F(x + ct),$$

f and F denoting arbitrary functions, and the solution represents plane waves propagated with velocity c. If ϕ is a function of t and r only, r denoting the radius vector from a fixed point, the equation takes the form

$$\frac{\partial^2\phi}{\partial t^2} = \frac{c^2}{r}\frac{\partial^2}{\partial r^2}(r\phi),$$

which can be integrated in the form

$$\phi = \frac{f(r - ct)}{r} + \frac{F(r + ct)}{r},$$

and again the solution represents waves propagated with velocity c. A function of the form $r^{-1}f(r - ct)$ represents spherical waves diverging from a source at the origin of r.

We learn that waves of dilatation involving no rotation travel through the medium with velocity $\{(\lambda + 2\mu)/\rho\}^{\frac{1}{2}}$, and that waves of distortion involving rotation without dilatation travel with velocity $\{\mu/\rho\}^{\frac{1}{2}}$. Waves of these two types are sometimes described as "irrotational" and "equivoluminal" respectively*.

If plane waves of any type are propagated through the medium with any velocity c we may take u, v, w to be functions of

$$lx + my + nz - ct,$$

in which l, m, n are the direction-cosines of the normal to the plane of the waves. The equations of motion then give rise to three equations of the type

$$\rho c^2 u'' = (\lambda + \mu)\, l\,(lu'' + mv'' + nw'') + \mu\,(l^2 + m^2 + n^2)\, u'',$$

where the accents denote differentiation of the functions with respect to their argument. On elimination of u'', v'', w'' we obtain an equation for c, viz.:

$$(\lambda + 2\mu - \rho c^2)(\mu - \rho c^2)^2 = 0, \quad \text{....................(7)}$$

showing that all plane waves travel with one or other of the velocities found above.

* Lord Kelvin, *Phil. Mag.* (Ser. 5), vol. 47 (1899). The result that in an isotropic solid there are two types of waves propagated with different velocities is due to Poisson. The recognition of the irrotational and equivoluminal characters of the two types of waves is due to Stokes. See Introduction.

205. Motion of a surface of discontinuity. Kinematical conditions.

If an arbitrary small disturbance is originated within a restricted portion of an elastic solid medium, neighbouring portions will soon be set in motion and thrown into states of strain. The portion of the medium which is disturbed at a subsequent instant will not be the same as that which was disturbed initially. We may suppose that the disturbed portion at any instant is bounded by a surface S. If the medium is isotropic, and the propagated disturbance involves dilatation without rotation, we may expect that the surface S will move normally to itself with velocity $\{(\lambda+2\mu)/\rho\}^{\frac{1}{2}}$; if it involves rotation without dilatation, we may expect the velocity of the surface to be $\{\mu/\rho\}^{\frac{1}{2}}$. We assume that the surface moves normally to itself with velocity c, and seek the conditions that must be satisfied at the moving surface.

On one side of the surface S at time t the medium is disturbed so that there is displacement (u, v, w); on the other side there is no displacement. We take the velocity c to be directed from the first side towards the second, so that the disturbance spreads into parts of the medium which previously were undisturbed. The displacement (u, v, w) is necessarily continuous in crossing S, and it therefore vanishes at this moving surface. Let the normal to S in the direction in which c is estimated be denoted by ν; and let s denote any direction in the tangent plane at a point of S, so that s and ν are at right angles to each other. Since u vanishes at every point of S, the equation

$$\frac{\partial u}{\partial x}\cos(x, s)+\frac{\partial u}{\partial y}\cos(y, s)+\frac{\partial u}{\partial z}\cos(z, s)=0$$

holds for all directions s which satisfy the equation

$$\cos(x, s)\cos(x, \nu)+\cos(y, s)\cos(y, \nu)+\cos(z, s)\cos(z, \nu)=0.$$

It follows that, at all points of S,

$$\frac{\partial u/\partial x}{\cos(x, \nu)}=\frac{\partial u/\partial y}{\cos(y, \nu)}=\frac{\partial u/\partial z}{\cos(z, \nu)}=\frac{\partial u}{\partial \nu}\quad\text{..................(8)}$$

Again $u=0$ is an equation which holds at the moving surface S, and this equation must be satisfied to the first order in δt when for x, y, z, t we substitute

$$x+c\cos(x, \nu)\,\delta t,\quad y+c\cos(y, \nu)\,\delta t,\quad z+c\cos(z, \nu)\,\delta t,\quad t+\delta t.$$

It follows that at every point of S we must have

$$\frac{\partial u}{\partial t}+c\left\{\cos(x, \nu)\frac{\partial u}{\partial x}+\cos(y, \nu)\frac{\partial u}{\partial y}+\cos(z, \nu)\frac{\partial u}{\partial z}\right\}=0.\quad\text{......(9)}$$

On combining the equations (8) and (9) we find that the following equations must hold at all points of S:

$$\frac{\partial u/\partial x}{\cos(x, \nu)}=\frac{\partial u/\partial y}{\cos(y, \nu)}=\frac{\partial u/\partial z}{\cos(z, \nu)}=\frac{\partial u}{\partial \nu}=-\frac{1}{c}\frac{\partial u}{\partial t}\quad\text{.........(10)}$$

Exactly similar equations hold with v and w in place of u. In these equations the differential coefficients of u, ... are, of course, to be calculated from the expressions for u, ... on that side of S on which there is disturbance at time t.

206. Motion of a surface of discontinuity. Dynamical conditions.

The dynamical conditions which hold at the surface S are found by considering the changes of momentum of a thin slice of the medium in the immediate neighbourhood of S. We mark out a small area δS of S, and consider the prismatic element of the medium which is bounded by S, by the normals to S at the edge of δS and by a surface parallel to S at a distance $c\,\delta t$ from it. In the short time δt, this element passes from a state of rest without strain to a state of motion and strain corresponding with the displacement (u, v, w). The change is effected by the resultant traction across the boundaries of the elements, that is by the traction across δS, and the change of momentum is equal to the time-integral of this traction. The traction in question acts across the surface normal to ν upon the matter on that side of the surface towards which ν is drawn, so that its components per unit of area are $-X_\nu$, $-Y_\nu$, $-Z_\nu$. The resultants are obtained by multiplying these by δS, and their impulses by multiplying by δt. The equation of momentum is therefore

$$\rho\delta S\,.\,c\delta t\left(\frac{\partial u}{\partial t},\ \frac{\partial v}{\partial t},\ \frac{\partial w}{\partial t}\right) = -(X_\nu,\ Y_\nu,\ Z_\nu)\,\delta S\,\delta t,$$

from which we have the equations

$$\rho c\left(\frac{\partial u}{\partial t},\ \frac{\partial v}{\partial t},\ \frac{\partial w}{\partial t}\right) = -(X_\nu,\ Y_\nu,\ Z_\nu). \quad\text{.................(11)}$$

In these equations $\partial u/\partial t$, ... and X_ν, ... are to be calculated from the values of u, ... on that side of S on which there is disturbance; and the equations hold at all points of S.

In the case where there is motion and strain on both sides of the surface S, but the displacements on the two sides of S are expressed by different formulæ, we may denote them by (u_1, v_1, w_1) and (u_2, v_2, w_2). At all points of S the displacement must be the same whether it is calculated from the expressions for u_1, ... or from those for u_2, ... We may prove that the values at S of the differential coefficients of u_1, ... are connected by equations of the type

$$\frac{\dfrac{\partial u_1}{\partial x}-\dfrac{\partial u_2}{\partial x}}{\cos(x,\nu)} = \frac{\dfrac{\partial u_1}{\partial y}-\dfrac{\partial u_2}{\partial y}}{\cos(y,\nu)} = \frac{\dfrac{\partial u_1}{\partial z}-\dfrac{\partial u_2}{\partial z}}{\cos(z,\nu)} = \frac{\partial u_1}{\partial \nu}-\frac{\partial u_2}{\partial \nu} = -\frac{1}{c}\left(\frac{\partial u_1}{\partial t}-\frac{\partial u_2}{\partial t}\right),$$

with similar equations in which u is replaced by v or by w. If we denote the tractions calculated from (u_1, v_1, w_1) by $X_x^{(1)}$, ... and those calculated from (u_2, v_2, w_2) by $X_x^{(2)}$, ... we may show that the values at S of these quantities and of $\partial u_1/\partial t$, ... are connected by the equations

$$\rho c\left(\frac{\partial u_1}{\partial t}-\frac{\partial u_2}{\partial t},\ \frac{\partial v_1}{\partial t}-\frac{\partial v_2}{\partial t},\ \frac{\partial w_1}{\partial t}-\frac{\partial w_2}{\partial t}\right) = (X_\nu^{(2)}-X_\nu^{(1)},\ Y_\nu^{(2)}-Y_\nu^{(1)},\ Z_\nu^{(2)}-Z_\nu^{(1)}).$$

207. Velocity of waves in isotropic medium.

If we write l, m, n for the direction-cosines of ν, the equations (11) become three equations of the type

$$-\rho c\frac{\partial u}{\partial t}=\left\{(\lambda+\mu)\,l\frac{\partial u}{\partial x}+\mu\left(l\frac{\partial u}{\partial x}+m\frac{\partial u}{\partial y}+n\frac{\partial u}{\partial z}\right)\right.$$
$$\left.+\left(\lambda l\frac{\partial v}{\partial y}+\mu m\frac{\partial v}{\partial x}\right)+\left(\lambda l\frac{\partial w}{\partial z}+\mu m\frac{\partial w}{\partial x}\right)\right\},\quad\ldots\ldots\ldots(12)$$

of which the right-hand member may also be written in the form

$$(\lambda+2\mu)\,l\left(\frac{\partial u}{\partial x}+\frac{\partial v}{\partial y}+\frac{\partial w}{\partial z}\right)+\mu\left\{m\frac{\partial u}{\partial y}+m\frac{\partial v}{\partial x}-2l\frac{\partial v}{\partial y}\right\}$$
$$+\mu\left\{n\frac{\partial u}{\partial z}+n\frac{\partial w}{\partial x}-2l\frac{\partial w}{\partial z}\right\}\ldots\ldots\ldots\ldots\ldots\ldots\ldots\ldots(13)$$

These equations hold at the surface S, at which also we have nine equations of the type

$$\frac{\partial u}{\partial x}=-\frac{1}{c}\,l\frac{\partial u}{\partial t},\ \ldots\ldots\ldots\ldots\ldots\ldots\ldots\ldots\ldots\ldots(14)$$

so that, for example,

$$l\frac{\partial v}{\partial y}=m\frac{\partial v}{\partial x}=-\frac{lm}{c}\frac{\partial v}{\partial t}.$$

On substituting for $\partial u/\partial x$, ... from (14) in (12), we obtain the equation

$$\rho c^2\frac{\partial u}{\partial t}=\{(\lambda+\mu)\,l^2+\mu\}\frac{\partial u}{\partial t}+(\lambda+\mu)\left(lm\frac{\partial v}{\partial t}+ln\frac{\partial w}{\partial t}\right);\ \ \ldots\ldots(15)$$

and, on eliminating $\partial u/\partial t$, $\partial v/\partial t$, $\partial w/\partial t$ from this and the two similar equations, we obtain the equation (7) of Article 204. The form (13) and the equations of type (14) show that equation (12) may also be written

$$-\rho c\frac{\partial u}{\partial t}=(\lambda+2\mu)\,l\left(\frac{\partial u}{\partial x}+\frac{\partial v}{\partial y}+\frac{\partial w}{\partial z}\right)-\mu m\left(\frac{\partial v}{\partial x}-\frac{\partial u}{\partial y}\right)+\mu n\left(\frac{\partial u}{\partial z}-\frac{\partial w}{\partial x}\right).\ (16)$$

Hence it follows that, when the rotation vanishes, we have three equations of the type

$$\rho c^2\frac{\partial u}{\partial t}=(\lambda+2\mu)\left(l^2\frac{\partial u}{\partial t}+lm\frac{\partial v}{\partial t}+ln\frac{\partial w}{\partial t}\right),$$

from which we should find that $\rho c^2=\lambda+2\mu$; and, when the dilatation vanishes, we have three equations of the type

$$\rho c^2\frac{\partial u}{\partial t}=\mu\left\{(m^2+n^2)\frac{\partial u}{\partial t}-lm\frac{\partial v}{\partial t}-ln\frac{\partial w}{\partial t}\right\},$$

from which we should find that $\rho c^2=\mu$.

These results show that the surface of discontinuity advances with a velocity which is either $\{(\lambda+2\mu)/\rho\}$ or $(\mu/\rho)^{\frac{1}{2}}$, and that, if there is no rotation, the velocity is necessarily $\{(\lambda+2\mu)/\rho\}^{\frac{1}{2}}$, and, if there is no dilatation, the velocity is necessarily $(\mu/\rho)^{\frac{1}{2}}$.

208. Velocity of waves in æolotropic solid medium.

Equations of the types (10) and (11) hold whether the solid is isotropic or not. The former give the six equations

$$\left.\begin{aligned} e_{xx} &= -l\frac{\dot{u}}{c}, & e_{yy} &= -m\frac{\dot{v}}{c}, & e_{zz} &= -n\frac{\dot{w}}{c}, \\ e_{yz} &= -\left(m\frac{\dot{w}}{c}+n\frac{\dot{v}}{c}\right), & e_{zx} &= -\left(n\frac{\dot{u}}{c}+l\frac{\dot{w}}{c}\right), & e_{xy} &= -\left(l\frac{\dot{v}}{c}+m\frac{\dot{u}}{c}\right) \end{aligned}\right\} \quad (17)$$

in which the dots denote differentiation with respect to t, and l, m, n are written for $\cos(x, \nu)$, ... The equations (11) can be written in such forms as

$$-\rho c\dot{u} = l\frac{\partial W}{\partial e_{xx}} + m\frac{\partial W}{\partial e_{xy}} + n\frac{\partial W}{\partial e_{zx}}, \quad \text{..................(18)}$$

where W denotes the strain-energy-function expressed in terms of the components of strain.

Now let ξ, η, ζ stand for $\dot{u}/c$, $\dot{v}/c$, $\dot{w}/c$. Equations (17) are a linear substitution expressing e_{xx}, ... in terms of ξ, η, ζ. When this substitution is carried out W becomes a homogeneous quadratic function of ξ, η, ζ. Denote this function by Π. We observe that, since e_{yy}, e_{zz}, e_{yz} are independent of ξ, we have the equation

$$\frac{\partial \Pi}{\partial \xi} = -l\frac{\partial W}{\partial e_{xx}} - m\frac{\partial W}{\partial e_{xy}} - n\frac{\partial W}{\partial e_{zx}},$$

and we have similar equations for $\partial\Pi/\partial\eta$ and $\partial\Pi/\partial\zeta$. Hence the equations of type (18) can be written

$$\rho c^2\xi = \frac{\partial \Pi}{\partial \xi}, \quad \rho c^2\eta = \frac{\partial \Pi}{\partial \eta}, \quad \rho c^2\zeta = \frac{\partial \Pi}{\partial \zeta}. \quad \text{..................(19)}$$

Now suppose that Π is given by the equation

$$\Pi = \tfrac{1}{2}[\lambda_{11}\xi^2 + \lambda_{22}\eta^2 + \lambda_{33}\zeta^2 + 2\lambda_{23}\eta\zeta + 2\lambda_{31}\zeta\xi + 2\lambda_{12}\xi\eta], \quad \text{......(20)}$$

then the equations (19) show that c^2 satisfies the equation

$$\begin{vmatrix} \lambda_{11} - \rho c^2, & \lambda_{12}, & \lambda_{31} \\ \lambda_{12}, & \lambda_{22} - \rho c^2, & \lambda_{23} \\ \lambda_{31}, & \lambda_{23}, & \lambda_{33} - \rho c^2 \end{vmatrix} = 0. \quad \text{..............(21)}$$

Since ξ, η, ζ are connected with e_{xx}, ... by a real linear substitution, the homogeneous quadratic function Π is necessarily positive, and therefore equation (21) yields three real positive values for c^2. The coefficients of this equation depend upon the direction (l, m, n). There are accordingly three real wave-velocities answering to any direction of propagation of waves*.

* For a general discussion of the three types of waves we may refer to Lord Kelvin, *Baltimore Lectures*, London 1904.

The above investigation is effectively due to E. B. Christoffel*, who has given the following method for the formation of the function Π:—Let the six components of strain $e_{xx}, e_{yy}, \ldots, e_{xy}$ be denoted by $x_1, x_2, \ldots x_6$; and let c_x denote the form

$$c_1 x_1 + c_2 x_2 + \ldots + c_6 x_6,$$

in which $c_1, c_2, \ldots$ have no quantitative meaning, but $c_1{}^2$ is to be replaced by c_{11}, $c_1 c_2$ by c_{12} and so on, $c_{11}, c_{12}, \ldots$ being the coefficients in the strain-energy-function. Then we may write

$$2W = (c_x)^2.$$

Again, let $\lambda_1, \lambda_2, \lambda_3$ be defined by the symbolical equations

$$\lambda_1 = c_1 l + c_6 m + c_5 n, \quad \lambda_2 = c_6 l + c_2 m + c_4 n, \quad \lambda_3 = c_5 l + c_4 m + c_3 n,$$

then we have
$$-c_x = \lambda_1 \xi + \lambda_2 \eta + \lambda_3 \zeta, \quad 2W = (\lambda_1 \xi + \lambda_2 \eta + \lambda_3 \zeta)^2,$$

and therefore the coefficients $\lambda_{11}, \ldots$ in the function Π are to be obtained by squaring the form $\lambda_1 \xi + \lambda_2 \eta + \lambda_3 \zeta$, or we have

$$\lambda_{11} = c_{11} l^2 + c_{66} m^2 + c_{55} n^2 + 2c_{56} mn + 2c_{15} nl + 2c_{16} lm,$$

$$\lambda_{12} = c_{16} l^2 + c_{26} m^2 + c_{45} n^2 + (c_{46} + c_{25}) mn + (c_{14} + c_{56}) nl + (c_{12} + c_{66}) lm,$$

....

209. Wave-surfaces.

The envelope of the plane

$$lx + my + nz = c \quad \text{.......................................(22)}$$

in which c is the velocity of propagation of waves in the direction (l, m, n) is the "wave-surface" belonging to the medium. It is the surface bounding the disturbed portion of the medium after the lapse of one unit of time, beginning at an instant when the disturbance is confined to the immediate neighbourhood of the origin. In the case of isotropy, c is independent of l, m, n, and is given by the equation (7); in the case of æolotropy c is a function of l, m, n given by the equation (21). In the general case the wave-surface is clearly a surface of three sheets, corresponding with the three values of c^2 which are roots of (21). In the case of isotropy two of the sheets are coincident, and all the sheets are concentric spheres.

Green† observed that, in the general case of æolotropy, the three possible directions of displacement answering to the three velocities of propagation of plane waves with a given wave-normal, are parallel to the principal axes of a certain ellipsoid, and are, therefore, at right angles to each other. The ellipsoid would be expressed in our notation by the equation $(\lambda_{11}, \lambda_{22}, \ldots \lambda_{12})(x, y, z)^2 = \text{const.}$ He showed that, when W has the form

$$\tfrac{1}{2} A (e_{xx} + e_{yy} + e_{zz})^2 + \tfrac{1}{2} L (e_{yz}{}^2 - 4e_{yy} e_{zz}) + \tfrac{1}{2} M (e_{zx}{}^2 - 4e_{zz} e_{xx}) + \tfrac{1}{2} N (e_{xy}{}^2 - 4e_{xx} e_{yy}), \quad (23)$$

the wave-surface is made up of a sphere, corresponding with the propagation of waves of irrotational dilatation, and Fresnel's wave-surface, viz.: the envelope of the plane (22) subject to the condition

$$\frac{l^2}{c^2 - L/\rho} + \frac{m^2}{c^2 - M/\rho} + \frac{n^2}{c^2 - N/\rho} = 0. \quad \text{..............................(24)}$$

The two sheets of this surface correspond with the propagation of waves of equivoluminal distortion. Green arrived at the above expression for W as the most general which would allow of the propagation of purely transverse plane waves, i.e. of waves with displacement parallel to the wave-fronts.

* *Ann. di Mat.* (Ser. 2), t. 8 (1877), reprinted in E. B. Christoffel, *Ges. math. Abhandlungen*, Bd. 2, Leipzig 1910, p. 81.

† 'On the propagation of light in crystallized media,' *Cambridge Phil. Soc. Trans.*, vol. 7 (1839), or *Mathematical Papers*, London 1871, p. 293.

Green's formula (23) for W is included in the formula (15) of Article 110, viz.:

$$2W=(A, B, C, F, G, H)(e_{xx}, e_{yy}, e_{zz})^2+Le_{yz}^2+Me_{zx}^2+Ne_{xy}^2,$$

which characterizes elastic solid media having three orthogonal planes of symmetry. To obtain Green's formula we have to put

$$A=B=C, \quad F=A-2L, \quad G=A-2M, \quad H=A-2N.$$

It is noteworthy that these relations are not satisfied in cubic crystals.

Green's formula for the strain-energy-function contains the strain-components only; the notion of a medium for which

$$W=2(L\varpi_x^2+M\varpi_y^2+N\varpi_z^2) \quad\text{.................................(25)}$$

was introduced by MacCullagh*. The wave-surface is Fresnel's wave-surface.

Lord Rayleigh †, following out a suggestion of Rankine's, has discussed the propagation of waves in a medium in which the kinetic energy has the form

$$\iiint \frac{1}{2}\left[\rho_1\left(\frac{\partial u}{\partial t}\right)^2+\rho_2\left(\frac{\partial v}{\partial t}\right)^2+\rho_3\left(\frac{\partial w}{\partial t}\right)^2\right]dx\,dy\,dz, \quad\text{..................(26)}$$

while the strain-energy-function has the form appropriate to an isotropic elastic solid. Such a medium is said to exhibit "æolotropy of inertia." When the medium is incompressible the wave-surface is the envelope of the plane (22) subject to the condition

$$\frac{l^2}{c^2\rho_1-\mu}+\frac{m^2}{c^2\rho_2-\mu}+\frac{n^2}{c^2\rho_3-\mu}=0; \quad\text{..............................(27)}$$

it is the first negative pedal of Fresnel's wave-surface with respect to its centre.

The case where the energy-function of the medium is a function of the components of rotation as well as of the strain-components, so that it is a homogeneous quadratic function of the nine quantities $\frac{\partial u}{\partial x}, \frac{\partial u}{\partial y}, \frac{\partial u}{\partial z}, \ldots$, has been discussed by H. M. Macdonald ‡. The most general form which is admissible if transverse waves are to be propagated independently of waves of dilatation is shown to lead to Fresnel's wave-surface for the transverse waves.

The still more general case in which there is æolotropy of inertia as well as of elastic quality has been investigated by T. J. I'A. Bromwich §. It appears that, in this case, the requirement that two of the waves shall be purely transverse does not lead to the same result as the requirement that they shall be purely rotational, although the two requirements do lead to the same result when the æolotropy does not affect the inertia. The wave-surface for the rotational waves is derived from Fresnel's wave-surface by a homogeneous strain.

210. Motion determined by the characteristic equation.

It appears that, even in the case of an isotropic solid, much complexity is introduced into the question of the propagation of disturbances through the solid by the possible co-existence of two types of waves propagated with different velocities. It will be well in the first instance to confine our attention to waves of a single type—irrotational or equivoluminal. The motion is then determined by the characteristic equation (6) of Article 204, viz.

$$\partial^2\phi/\partial t^2 = c^2\nabla^2\phi.$$

* 'An essay towards a dynamical theory of crystalline reflexion and refraction,' *Dublin, Trans. Roy. Irish Acad.*, vol. 21 (1839), or *Collected Works of James MacCullagh*, Dublin 1880, p. 145.

† 'On Double Refraction,' *Phil. Mag.* (Ser. 4), vol. 41 (1871), or *Scientific Papers*, vol. 1, Cambridge 1899.

‡ *London Math. Soc. Proc.*, vol. 32 (1900), p. 311.

§ *London Math. Soc. Proc.*, vol. 34 (1902), p. 307.

This equation was solved by Poisson* in a form in which the value of ϕ at any place and time is expressed in terms of the initial values of ϕ and $\partial\phi/\partial t$. Poisson's result can be stated as follows: Let ϕ_0 and $\dot{\phi}_0$ denote the initial values of ϕ and $\partial\phi/\partial t$. With any point (x, y, z) as centre describe a sphere of radius ct, and let $\bar{\phi}_0$ and $\bar{\dot{\phi}}_0$ denote the mean values of ϕ_0 and $\dot{\phi}_0$ on this sphere. Then the value of ϕ at the point (x, y, z) at the instant t is expressed by the equation

$$\phi = \frac{d}{dt}(t\bar{\phi}_0) + t\bar{\dot{\phi}}_0. \qquad \text{.........................(28)}$$

If the initial disturbance is confined to the region of space within a closed surface Σ_0, then ϕ_0 and $\dot{\phi}_0$ have values different from zero at points within Σ_0, and vanish outside Σ_0. Taking any point within or on Σ_0 as centre, we may describe a sphere of radius ct; then the disturbance at time t is confined to the aggregate of points which are on the surfaces of these spheres. This aggregate is, in general, bounded by a surface of two sheets—an inner and an outer. When the outer sheet reaches any point, the portion of the medium which is close to the point takes suddenly the small strain and velocity implied by the values of ϕ and $\partial\phi/\partial t$; and after the inner sheet passes the point, the same portion of the medium returns to rest without strain†.

The characteristic equation was solved in a more general manner by Kirchhoff‡. Instead of a sphere he took any surface S, and instead of the initial values of ϕ and $\partial\phi/\partial t$ on S he took the values of ϕ and its first derivative at points on S, and at certain instants previous to the instant t. If Q is any point on S, and r is the distance of Q from the point (x, y, z), the values of ϕ and its first derivatives are estimated for the point Q at the instant $t - r/c$. Let $[\phi]$, ... denote the values of ϕ, ... estimated as stated. Then the value of ϕ at the point (x, y, z) at the instant t is expressed by the equation

$$\phi = \frac{1}{4\pi}\iint\left\{[\phi]\frac{\partial r^{-1}}{\partial \nu} - r^{-1}\left[\frac{\partial\phi}{\partial\nu}\right] - \frac{1}{cr}\frac{\partial r}{\partial\nu}\left[\frac{\partial\phi}{\partial t}\right]\right\} dS, \qquad \text{.........(29)}$$

where ν denotes the direction of the normal to S drawn towards that side on which (x, y, z) is situated.

Kirchhoff's formula (29) may be obtained very simply§, by substituting $t - r/c$ for t in $\phi(x, y, z, t)$, where r now denotes the distance of (x, y, z) from the origin. Denoting the

* *Paris, Mém. de l'Institut*, t. 3 (1820). A simple proof was given by Liouville, *J. de Math. (Liouville)*, t. 1 (1856). A symbolical proof is given by Lord Rayleigh, *Theory of Sound*, Chapter XIV.

† Cf. Stokes, 'Dynamical theory of Diffraction,' *Cambridge Phil. Soc. Trans.*, vol. 9 (1849), or *Math. and Phys. Papers*, vol. 2, p. 243.

‡ *Ann. Phys. Chem. (Wiedemann)*, Bd. 18 (1883). See also Kirchhoff, *Vorlesungen über math. Physik, Optik*, Leipzig, 1891.

§ Cf. Beltrami, *Roma, Acc. Linc. Rend.* (Ser. 5), t. 4 (1895).

function $\phi(x, y, z, t-r/c)$ by $\psi(x, y, z, t)$, we may show that when $\phi(x, y, z, t)$ satisfies the characteristic equation (6), ψ satisfies the equation

$$\frac{1}{r}\nabla^2\psi+\frac{2}{c}\left[\frac{\partial}{\partial x}\left(\frac{x}{r^2}\frac{\partial\psi}{\partial t}\right)+\frac{\partial}{\partial y}\left(\frac{y}{r^2}\frac{\partial\psi}{\partial t}\right)+\frac{\partial}{\partial z}\left(\frac{z}{r^2}\frac{\partial\psi}{\partial t}\right)\right]=0. \quad \text{..............(30)}$$

If this equation holds throughout the region within a closed surface S which does not contain the origin, we integrate the left-hand member of this equation through the volume within S and transform the volume integral into a surface integral, thus obtaining the equation

$$\iint\left(\psi\frac{\partial r^{-1}}{\partial\nu}-\frac{1}{r}\frac{\partial\psi}{\partial\nu}-\frac{2}{cr}\frac{\partial r}{\partial\nu}\frac{\partial\psi}{\partial t}\right)dS=0.$$

If now $[\phi]$, ... denote the values of ϕ, ... at the instant $t-r/c$, this equation is the same as

$$\iint\left\{[\phi]\frac{\partial r^{-1}}{\partial\nu}-\frac{1}{r}\left[\frac{\partial\phi}{\partial\nu}\right]-\frac{1}{cr}\frac{\partial r}{\partial\nu}\left[\frac{\partial\phi}{\partial t}\right]\right\}dS=0,$$

since, as is easily proved,

$$\frac{\partial\psi}{\partial\nu}=\left[\frac{\partial\phi}{\partial\nu}\right]-\frac{1}{c}\frac{\partial r}{\partial\nu}\left[\frac{\partial\phi}{\partial t}\right].$$

When the origin is within the surface S we integrate the left-hand member of (30) through the volume contained between S and a small sphere Σ with its centre at the origin, and pass to a limit by contracting the radius of Σ indefinitely. We thus find for the value of ϕ at the origin the formula (29), and the same formula gives the value of ϕ at any point and instant. The formula holds for a region of space bounded internally or externally by a closed surface S, provided that, at all instants which come into consideration, ϕ and its first derivatives are continuous, and its second derivatives are finite and are connected by equation (6), at all points of the region*. In case the region is outside S, ϕ must tend to zero at infinite distances in the order r^{-1} at least. These conditions may be expressed by saying that all the sources of disturbance are on the side of S remote from (x, y, z).

Kirchhoff's formula (29) can be shown to include Poisson's†. The formula may also be written in the form

$$\phi=\frac{1}{4\pi}\iint\left\{\frac{\partial}{\partial\nu}\left(\frac{[\phi]}{r}\right)-r^{-1}\left[\frac{\partial\phi}{\partial\nu}\right]\right\}dS, \quad \text{..........................(31)}$$

where $\dfrac{\partial}{\partial\nu}\left(\dfrac{[\phi]}{r}\right)$ is to be formed by first substituting $t-r/c$ for t in ϕ and then differentiating as if r were the only variable quantity in $[\phi]/r$. The formula (31) is an analogue of Green's formula (7) of Article 158. It can be interpreted in the statement that the value of ϕ at any point outside a closed surface (which encloses all the sources of disturbance) is the same as that due to a certain distribution of fictitious sources and double sources on the surface. It is easy to prove, in the manner of Article 124, that the motion inside or outside S, that is due to given initial conditions, is uniquely determined by the values of either ϕ or $\partial\phi/\partial\nu$ at S. The theorem expressed by equation (31) can be deduced from the properties of superficial distributions of sources and double sources and the theorem of uniqueness of solution‡.

211. Arbitrary initial conditions.

When the initial conditions are not such that the disturbance is entirely irrotational or equivoluminal, the results are more complicated. Expressions for the components of the displacement which arises, at any place and time,

* For the case where there is a moving surface of discontinuity outside S, see a paper by the Author, *London Math. Soc. Proc.* (Ser. 2), vol. 1 (1904), p. 37.

† See my paper just cited.

‡ Cf. J. Larmor, *London Math. Soc. Proc.* (Ser. 2), vol. 1 (1904).

from a given initial distribution of displacement and velocity, have been obtained*, and the result may be stated in the following form:

Let (u_0, v_0, w_0) be the initial displacement, supposed to be given throughout a region of space T and to vanish on the boundary of T and outside T, and let $(\dot{u}_0, \dot{v}_0, \dot{w}_0)$ be the initial velocity supposed also to be given throughout T and to vanish outside T. Let a and b denote the velocities of irrotational and equivoluminal waves. Let S_1 denote a sphere of radius at having its centre at the point (x, y, z), and S_2 a sphere of radius bt having its centre at the same point. Let V denote that part of the volume contained between these spheres which is within T. Let r denote the distance of any point (x', y', z') within V, or on the parts of S_1 and S_2 that are within T, from the point (x, y, z), and let q_0 denote the initial displacement at (x', y', z'), and $\dot{q}_0$ the initial velocity at the same point, each projected upon the radius vector r, supposed drawn from (x, y, z). Then the displacement u at (x, y, z) at the instant t can be written

$$u = \frac{1}{4\pi}\iiint\left\{(t\dot{u}_0 + u_0)\frac{\partial^2 r^{-1}}{\partial x^2} + (t\dot{v}_0 + v_0)\frac{\partial^2 r^{-1}}{\partial x \partial y} + (t\dot{w}_0 + w_0)\frac{\partial^2 r^{-1}}{\partial x \partial z}\right\} dV$$
$$+ \frac{1}{4\pi}\iint\left\{r\left(u_0\frac{\partial^2 r^{-1}}{\partial x^2} + v_0\frac{\partial^2 r^{-1}}{\partial x \partial y} + w_0\frac{\partial^2 r^{-1}}{\partial x \partial z}\right) + \frac{\partial r^{-1}}{\partial x}\left(t\dot{q}_0 + q_0 + r\frac{\partial q_0}{\partial r}\right)\right\} dS_1$$
$$- \frac{1}{4\pi}\iint\left\{r\left(u_0\frac{\partial^2 r^{-1}}{\partial x^2} + v_0\frac{\partial^2 r^{-1}}{\partial x \partial y} + w_0\frac{\partial^2 r^{-1}}{\partial x \partial z}\right) + \frac{\partial r^{-1}}{\partial x}\left(t\dot{q}_0 + q_0 + r\frac{\partial q_0}{\partial r}\right)\right.$$
$$\left. - \frac{1}{r^2}\left(t\dot{u}_0 + u_0 + r\frac{\partial u_0}{\partial r}\right)\right\} dS_2, \quad \text{.................................(32)}$$

and similar expressions for v and w can be written down. The surface-integrations extend over the parts of S_1 and S_2 that are within T.

The dilatation and the rotation can be calculated from these formulæ, and it can be shown that the dilatation is entirely confined to a wave of dilatation propagated with velocity a, and the rotation to a wave of rotation propagated with velocity b. If r_1 and r_2 are the greatest and least distances of any point O of the medium from the boundary of T, the motion at O begins at the instant $t = r_2/a$, the wave of dilatation ends at the instant $t = r_1/a$, the wave of rotation begins at the instant $t = r_2/b$, and the motion ceases at the instant $t = r_1/b$. If the wave of dilatation ends before the wave of rotation begins, the motion between the two waves is of the character of irrotational motion in an incompressible fluid†; at a distance from T which is great compared with any linear dimension of T this motion is relatively feeble.

The problem of the integration of the equations of small motion of an isotropic elastic solid has been the subject of very numerous researches. Reference may be made to the ollowing memoirs in addition to those already cited:—V. Cerruti, 'Sulle vibrazioni dei

* For references see Introduction, p. 18. Reference may also be made to a paper by the Author in *London Math. Soc. Proc.* (Ser. 2), vol. 1 (1904), p. 291.

† Cf. Stokes, *loc. cit.* p. 301.

corpi elastici isotropi,' *Roma, Acc. Linc.*, *Mem. fis. mat.*, 1880; V. Volterra, 'Sur les vibrations des corps élastiques isotropes,' *Acta Math.*, t. 18 (1894); G. Lauricella, 'Sulle equazioni del moto dei corpi elastici,' *Torino Mem.* (Ser. 2), t. 45 (1895); O. Tedone, 'Sulle vibrazioni dei corpi solidi omogenei ed isotropi,' *Torino Mem.* (Ser. 2), t. 47 (1897), and 'S. alcune formole...d. dinamica d. mezzi,' *Torino Atti*, t. 42 (1907); J. Coulon, 'Sur l'intégration des équations aux dérivées partielles du second ordre par la méthode des caractéristiques,' Paris (*Thèse*) 1902. Hadamard's treatise, *Leçons sur la propagation des ondes*, Paris 1903, also may be consulted.

212. Motion due to body forces.

Exactly as in Article 130 we express the body forces in the form

$$(X, Y, Z) = \text{gradient of } \Phi + \text{curl } (L, M, N),$$

and the displacement in the form

$$(u, v, w) = \text{gradient of } \phi + \text{curl } (F, G, H).$$

Then the equations of motion of the type

$$(\lambda+\mu)\frac{\partial\Delta}{\partial x} + \mu\nabla^2 u + \rho X = \rho\,\frac{\partial^2 u}{\partial t^2}$$

can be satisfied if ϕ, F, G, H satisfy the equations

$$\frac{\partial^2\phi}{\partial t^2} - a^2\nabla^2\phi = \Phi\,, \qquad \frac{\partial^2 F}{\partial t^2} - b^2\nabla^2 F = L\,, \ldots$$

and particular solutions can be expressed in the forms*

$$\left.\begin{aligned} \phi &= \frac{1}{4\pi a^2}\iiint \frac{1}{r}\,\Phi'\left(t-\frac{r}{a}\right) dx'\,dy'\,dz'\,, \\ F &= \frac{1}{4\pi b^2}\iiint \frac{1}{r}\,L'\left(t-\frac{r}{b}\right) dx'\,dy'\,dz'\,, \\ &\ldots\ldots\ldots\ldots\ldots\ldots\ldots\ldots\ldots\ldots\ldots\ldots \end{aligned}\right\} \qquad \ldots\ldots\ldots\ldots\ldots(33)$$

The values of Φ, L, ... are given in terms of X, Y, Z by the equations (7) of Article 130, and the integrations expressed in (33) can be performed.

Taking the case of a single force of magnitude $\chi(t)$, acting at the origin in the direction of the axis of x, we have, as in Article 130,

$$\Phi'\left(t-\frac{r}{a}\right) = -\frac{1}{4\pi\rho}\,\chi\left(t-\frac{r}{a}\right)\frac{\partial R^{-1}}{\partial x'}\,, \qquad L' = 0\,,$$

$$M'\left(t-\frac{r}{b}\right) = \frac{1}{4\pi\rho}\,\chi\left(t-\frac{r}{b}\right)\frac{\partial R^{-1}}{\partial z'}\,, \quad N'\left(t-\frac{r}{b}\right) = -\frac{1}{4\pi\rho}\,\chi\left(t-\frac{r}{b}\right)\frac{\partial R^{-1}}{\partial y'}\,,$$

where R denotes the distance of (x', y', z') from the origin. We may partition space around the point (x, y, z) into thin sheets by means of spherical surfaces having that point as centre, and thus we may express the integrations in (33) in such forms as

$$\iiint \frac{1}{r}\,\Phi'\left(t-\frac{r}{a}\right) dx'\,dy'\,dz' = \int_0^\infty -\frac{1}{4\pi\rho}\,\chi\left(t-\frac{r}{a}\right)\frac{dr}{r}\iint \frac{\partial R^{-1}}{\partial x'}\,dS\,,$$

* Cf. L. Lorenz, *J. f. Math.* (*Crelle*), Bd. 58 (1861), or *Œuvres Scientifiques*, t. 2, Copenhagen 1899, p. 1. See also Lord Rayleigh, *Theory of Sound*, vol. 2, § 276.

where dS denotes an element of surface of a sphere with centre at (x, y, z) and radius equal to r. Now $\iint(\partial R^{-1}/\partial x')\,dS$ is equal to zero when the origin is inside S, and to $4\pi r^2(\partial r_0^{-1}/\partial x)$ when the origin is outside S, r_0 denoting the distance of (x, y, z) from the origin. In the former case $r_0 < r$, and in the latter $r_0 > r$. We may therefore replace the upper limit of integration with respect to r by r_0, and find

$$\phi = -\frac{1}{4\pi a^2\rho}\frac{\partial r_0^{-1}}{\partial x}\int_0^{r_0} r\chi\left(t-\frac{r}{a}\right)dr.$$

Having found ϕ we have no further use for the r that appears in the process, and we may write r instead of r_0, so that r now denotes the distance of (x, y, z) from the origin. Then we have

$$\phi = -\frac{1}{4\pi\rho}\frac{\partial r^{-1}}{\partial x}\int_0^{r/a} t'\chi(t-t')\,dt'. \quad \text{.................(34)}$$

In like manner we should find

$$\left.\begin{aligned} F=0,\quad G&=\frac{1}{4\pi\rho}\frac{\partial r^{-1}}{\partial z}\int_0^{r/b} t'\chi(t-t')\,dt',\\ H&=-\frac{1}{4\pi\rho}\frac{\partial r^{-1}}{\partial y}\int_0^{r/b} t'\chi(t-t')\,dt'.\end{aligned}\right\} \quad \text{..............(35)}$$

The displacement due to the force $\chi(t)$ is given by the equations*

$$\left.\begin{aligned} u&=\frac{1}{4\pi\rho}\frac{\partial^2 r^{-1}}{\partial x^2}\int_{r/a}^{r/b} t'\chi(t-t')\,dt' + \frac{1}{4\pi\rho r}\left(\frac{\partial r}{\partial x}\right)^2\left\{\frac{1}{a^2}\chi\left(t-\frac{r}{a}\right)-\frac{1}{b^2}\chi\left(t-\frac{r}{b}\right)\right\}\\ &\quad+\frac{1}{4\pi\rho b^2 r}\chi\left(t-\frac{r}{b}\right),\\ v&=\frac{1}{4\pi\rho}\frac{\partial^2 r^{-1}}{\partial x\partial y}\int_{r/a}^{r/b} t'\chi(t-t')\,dt' + \frac{1}{4\pi\rho r}\frac{\partial r}{\partial x}\frac{\partial r}{\partial y}\left\{\frac{1}{a^2}\chi\left(t-\frac{r}{a}\right)-\frac{1}{b^2}\chi\left(t-\frac{r}{b}\right)\right\},\\ w&=\frac{1}{4\pi\rho}\frac{\partial^2 r^{-1}}{\partial x\partial z}\int_{r/a}^{r/b} t'\chi(t-t')\,dt' + \frac{1}{4\pi\rho r}\frac{\partial r}{\partial x}\frac{\partial r}{\partial z}\left\{\frac{1}{a^2}\chi\left(t-\frac{r}{a}\right)-\frac{1}{b^2}\chi\left(t-\frac{r}{b}\right)\right\}.\end{aligned}\right\}(36)$$

213. Additional results relating to motion due to body forces.

(i) The dilatation and rotation calculated from (36) are given by the equations

$$\Delta=\frac{1}{4\pi a^2\rho}\frac{\partial}{\partial x}\left\{\frac{1}{r}\chi\left(t-\frac{r}{a}\right)\right\},\quad \varpi_x=0,\quad 2\varpi_y=\frac{1}{4\pi b^2\rho}\frac{\partial}{\partial z}\left\{\frac{1}{r}\chi\left(t-\frac{r}{b}\right)\right\},$$

$$2\varpi_z=-\frac{1}{4\pi b^2\rho}\frac{\partial}{\partial y}\left\{\frac{1}{r}\chi\left(t-\frac{r}{b}\right)\right\}. \quad \text{......(37)}$$

(ii) The expressions (36) reduce to (11) of Article 130 when $\chi(t)$ is replaced by a constant.

(iii) The tractions over a spherical cavity required to maintain the displacement expressed by (36) are statically equivalent to a single force parallel to the axis of x. When the radius of the cavity is diminished indefinitely, the magnitude of the force is $\chi(t)$.

* Formulæ equivalent to (36) were obtained by Stokes, *loc. cit.* p. 301.

(iv) As in Article 132, we may find the effects of various nuclei of strain*. In the case of a "centre of compression" we have, omitting a constant factor,

$$(u, v, w) = \left(\frac{\partial}{\partial x}, \frac{\partial}{\partial y}, \frac{\partial}{\partial z}\right)\left\{\frac{1}{r}\chi\left(t-\frac{r}{a}\right)\right\}, \qquad \text{.........................(38)}$$

representing irrotational waves of a well-known type. In the case of a "centre of rotation about the axis of z" we have, omitting a factor,

$$(u, v, w) = \left(\frac{\partial}{\partial y}, -\frac{\partial}{\partial x}, 0\right)\left\{\frac{1}{r}\chi\left(t-\frac{r}{b}\right)\right\}, \qquad \text{.........................(39)}$$

representing equivoluminal waves of a well-known type.

(v) If we combine two centres of compression of opposite signs, in the same way as two forces are combined to make a "double force without moment," we obtain irrotational waves of the type expressed by the equation

$$(u, v, w) = \left(\frac{\partial^2}{\partial x \partial z}, \frac{\partial^2}{\partial y \partial z}, \frac{\partial^2}{\partial z^2}\right)\left\{\frac{1}{r}\chi\left(t-\frac{r}{a}\right)\right\}. \qquad \text{.....................(40)}$$

If we combine two pairs of centres of rotation about the axes of x and y and about parallel axes, in the same way as two pairs of forces are combined to make a centre of rotation, we obtain equivoluminal waves of the type

$$(u, v, w) = \left(\frac{\partial^2}{\partial x \partial z}, \frac{\partial^2}{\partial y \partial z}, -\frac{\partial^2}{\partial x^2} - \frac{\partial^2}{\partial y^2}\right)\left\{\frac{1}{r}\chi\left(t-\frac{r}{b}\right)\right\}, \qquad \text{..............(41)}$$

in which the displacement is expressed by the same formulæ as the electric force in the field around Hertz's† oscillator. Lord Kelvin‡ has shown that by superposing solutions of the types (40) and (41) we may obtain the effect of an oscillating rigid sphere close to the origin.

(vi) When $\chi(t)$ is a simple harmonic function of the time, say $\chi(t) = A \cos pt$, we find

$$\int_{r/a}^{r/b} t'\chi(t-t')\,dt' = \frac{A}{p^2}\left\{\cos p\left(t-\frac{r}{b}\right) - \cos p\left(t-\frac{r}{a}\right) - \frac{pr}{b}\sin p\left(t-\frac{r}{b}\right) + \frac{pr}{a}\sin p\left(t-\frac{r}{a}\right)\right\},$$

and complete expressions for the effects of the forces can be written down by (36)§. In this case we may regard the whole phenomenon as consisting in the propagation of two trains of simple harmonic waves with velocities respectively equal to a and b; but the formulæ (36) show that, in more general cases, the effect produced at the instant t at a point distant r from the point of application of the forces does not depend on the magnitude of the force at the two instants $t - r/a$ and $t - r/b$ only, but also on the magnitude of the force at intermediate instants. It is as if certain effects were propagated with velocities intermediate between a and b, as well as the definite effects (dilatation and rotation) that are propagated with these velocities||.

* For a more detailed discussion, see my paper cited on p. 303.

† Hertz, *Electric Waves*, English edition, p. 137. For the discussion in regard to the result see W. König, *Ann. Phys. Chem.* (*Wiedemann*), Bd. 37 (1889), and Lord Rayleigh, *Phil. Mag.* (Ser. 6), vol. 6 (1903), p. 385, reprinted in his *Scientific Papers*, vol. 5, p. 142.

‡ *Phil. Mag.* (Ser. 5), vols. 47 and 48 (1899).

§ For the effects of forces which are simple harmonic functions of the time, see Lord Rayleigh, *Theory of Sound*, vol. 2, pp. 418 *et seq.* The theory of waves due to forces of damped harmonic type, and the subsidence of vibrations caused by their communication to a surrounding elastic solid medium, have been discussed by E. Laura, *Torino Mem.* (Ser. 2), t. 60 (1910), *Torino Atti*, t. 46 (1911), and *Roma, Acc. Linc. Rend.* (Ser. 5), t. 21 (1 Sem.), 1912, and by O. Tedone, *Roma, Acc. Linc. Rend.* (Ser. 5), t. 22 (1 Sem.), 1913.

|| Cf. my paper cited on p. 303, and Stokes's result recorded on p. 303.

(vii) Particular integrals of the equations of motion under body forces which are proportional to a simple harmonic function of the time (written $e^{\iota pt}$) can be expressed in the forms

$$\phi = \frac{e^{\iota pt}}{4\pi a^2}\iiint \Phi' \frac{e^{-\iota pr/a}}{r} dx'dy'dz',$$

$$F = \frac{e^{\iota pt}}{4\pi b^2}\iiint L' \frac{e^{-\iota pr/b}}{r} dx'dy'dz',$$

....

where

$$\Phi = -\frac{1}{4\pi}\iiint\left(X'\frac{\partial r^{-1}}{\partial x} + Y'\frac{\partial r^{-1}}{\partial y} + Z'\frac{\partial r^{-1}}{\partial z}\right)dx'dy'dz',$$

$$L = \frac{1}{4\pi}\iiint\left(Z'\frac{\partial r^{-1}}{\partial y} - Y'\frac{\partial r^{-1}}{\partial z}\right)dx'dy'dz',$$

....

214. Waves propagated over the surface of an isotropic elastic solid body*.

Among periodic motions special importance attaches to those plane waves of simple harmonic type, propagated over the bounding surface of a solid body, which involve a disturbance that penetrates but a little distance into the interior of the body. We shall take the body to be bounded by the plane $z = 0$, and shall suppose that the positive sense of the axis of z is directed towards the interior of the body. Then the waves in question are characterized by the occurrence, in the expressions for the quantities defining the motion, of factors of the form e^{-rz} and e^{-sz}, where r and s are real and positive.

Let the direction of propagation of the waves be the axis of x, and let the dilatation Δ be expressed by the formula

$$\Delta = Pe^{-rz}e^{\iota(pt-fx)}, \qquad (42)$$

where P is constant. Then p/f is the velocity of propagation. Denoting $p^2\rho/(\lambda+2\mu)$ by h^2, as in Article 190, and remembering that Δ satisfies the equation $(\nabla^2+h^2)\Delta=0$, we see that

$$r^2 = f^2 - h^2. \qquad (43)$$

A displacement answering to (42) is given by the equations

$$(u_1, v_1, w_1) = (\iota f, 0, r)\, h^{-2}Pe^{-rz+\iota(pt-fx)}, \qquad (44)$$

and with this we may compound any displacement (u_2, v_2, w_2) which satisfies $\text{div}\,(u_2, v_2, w_2) = 0$, $(\nabla^2+\kappa^2)(u_2, v_2, w_2) = 0$, where, as in Article 190, κ^2 is written for $p^2\rho/\mu$. We write

$$(u_2, v_2, w_2) = (\iota s, \beta, f)\,\kappa^{-2}Qe^{-sz+\iota(pt-fx)}, \qquad (45)$$

where β is constant, and

$$s^2 = f^2 - \kappa^2. \qquad (46)$$

The surface $z = 0$ being free from traction, the equations

$$\frac{\partial u}{\partial z}+\frac{\partial w}{\partial x}=0, \quad \frac{\partial v}{\partial z}+\frac{\partial w}{\partial y}=0, \quad \lambda\Delta+2\mu\frac{\partial w}{\partial z}=0, \qquad (47)$$

* Cf. Lord Rayleigh, *London Math. Soc. Proc.*, vol. 17 (1887), or *Scientific Papers*, vol. 2, p. 441.

in which $(u, v, w) = (u_1 + u_2, v_1 + v_2, w_1 + w_2)$, must hold at that surface. These equations give

$$2rf\,P/h^2 + (s^2 + f^2)\,Q/\kappa^2 = 0,$$
$$\beta = 0,\ (\kappa^2 - 2h^2)\,P/h^2 - 2r^2P/h^2 - 2sf\,Q/\kappa^2 = 0, \quad \text{......(48)}$$

where $\kappa^2/h^2 - 2$ has been written for λ/μ.

The equation $\beta = 0$ shows that the motion is two-dimensional. There is no displacement in a direction parallel to the plane boundary and transverse to the direction of propagation.

The elimination of P and Q from the remaining equations of (48) gives

$$\left(\frac{\kappa^2}{f^2} - 2\right)^2 - 4\frac{rs}{f^2} = 0, \quad \text{..........................(49)}$$

or by (43) and (46)

$$\left(\frac{\kappa^2}{f^2} - 2\right)^4 = 16\left(1 - \frac{h^2}{f^2}\right)\left(1 - \frac{\kappa^2}{f^2}\right).$$

If we write κ'^2 for κ^2/f^2 and h'^2 for h^2/f^2, this equation becomes

$$\kappa'^8 - 8\kappa'^6 + 24\kappa'^4 - 16(1 + h'^2)\,\kappa'^2 + 16h'^2 = 0. \quad \text{...........(50)}$$

When the material is incompressible, so that $h'^2/\kappa'^2 = 0$, equation (50) becomes a cubic for κ'^2, viz.

$$\kappa'^6 - 8\kappa'^4 + 24\kappa'^2 - 16 = 0,$$

which has one real positive root $\kappa'^2 = 0{\cdot}91262...$ and two complex roots $3{\cdot}5436... \pm \iota\,(2{\cdot}2301...)$. Since κ'^2 is finite and h'^2/κ'^2 is zero, equation (43) shows that r^2 is real, and equation (49) shows that, for the complex values of κ'^2,

$$4rs/f^2 = -(2{\cdot}5904...) \pm \iota\,(6{\cdot}8852...).$$

Since the real part of s, given by this equation, has the opposite sign to r, there are no waves of the required type answering to the complex values of κ'^2. The real value $\kappa'^2 = 0{\cdot}91262...$ gives

$$r^2 = f^2,\quad s^2 = (0{\cdot}08737...)\,f^2,$$

so that there is a wave-motion of the required type. The velocity of propagation is given by the equation

$$p/f = (0{\cdot}9553...)\,\sqrt{(\mu/\rho)}.$$

When the material fulfils Poisson's condition $(\lambda = \mu)$, so that $\kappa'^2/h'^2 = 3$, equation (50) becomes

$$(\kappa'^2 - 4)(3\kappa'^4 - 12\kappa'^2 + 8) = 0.$$

The roots $\kappa'^2 = 4$ and $\kappa'^2 = 2 + \frac{2}{3}\sqrt{3}$ are irrelevant, since they make $h'^2 > 1$ and r a pure imaginary. The remaining root $\kappa'^2 = 0{\cdot}8453...$ gives

$$r^2 = (0{\cdot}7182...)\,f^2,\quad s^2 = (0{\cdot}1546...)\,f^2,$$

and the velocity of propagation is now given by the equation

$$p/f = (0{\cdot}9194...)\,\sqrt{(\mu/\rho)}.$$

In both cases the waves travel over the surface with a velocity, which is independent of the wave-length $2\pi/f$, and slightly less than the velocity of equivoluminal waves propagated through the body. Waves of this kind are often called "Rayleigh-waves."

Concerning the above type of waves Lord Rayleigh (*loc. cit.*) remarked: "It is not improbable that the surface waves here investigated play an important part in earthquakes, and in the collision of elastic solids. Diverging in two dimensions only, they must acquire at a great distance from the source a continually increasing preponderance." The subject has been investigated further by T. J. I'A. Bromwich* and H. Lamb†. The former showed that, when gravity is taken into account, the results obtained by Lord Rayleigh are not essentially altered. The latter has discussed the effect of a limited initial disturbance at or near the surface of a solid body. He showed that, at a distance from the source, the disturbance begins after an interval answering to the propagation of a wave of irrotational dilatation; a second stage of the motion begins after an interval answering to the propagation of a wave of equivoluminal distortion, and a disturbance of much greater amplitude begins to be received after an interval answering to the propagation of waves of the type investigated by Lord Rayleigh. The expectation that the theory of Rayleigh waves would throw light on seismic phenomena has been realized‡.

The theory of surface waves has been extended by H. Lamb§ to the case of a solid body bounded by two parallel planes.

* *London Math. Soc. Proc.*, vol. 30 (1899).

† *Phil. Trans. Roy. Soc.* (Ser. A), vol. 203 (1904).

‡ See the Author's Essay *Some Problems of Geodynamics*, or G. W. Walker, *Modern Seismology*, London 1913. For a more extended discussion of the mathematical theory of earthquake waves reference may be made to J. H. Jeans, *London, Roy. Soc. Proc.* (Ser. A), vol. 102, 1923, p. 554.

§ *London, Roy. Soc. Proc.* (Ser. A), vol. 93, 1917, p. 114.

CHAPTER XIV

TORSION

215. Stress and strain in a twisted prism.

In Article 86 (*d*) we found a stress-system which could be maintained in a cylinder, of circular section, by terminal couples about the axis of the cylinder. The cylinder is twisted by the couples, so that any cross-section is turned, relatively to any other, through an angle proportional to the distance between the planes of section. The traction on any cross-section at any point is tangential to the section, and is at right angles to the plane containing the axis of the cylinder and the point; the magnitude of this traction at any point is proportional to the distance of the point from the axis.

When the section of the cylinder or prism is not circular, the above stress-system does not satisfy the condition that the cylindrical boundary is free from traction. We seek to modify it in such a way that all the conditions may be satisfied. Since the tractions applied at the ends of the prism are statically equivalent to couples in the planes of the ends, and the portion of the prism contained between any cross-section and an end is kept in equilibrium by the tractions across this section and the couple at the end, the tractions in question must be equivalent to a couple in the plane of the cross-section, and the moment of this couple must be the same for all cross-sections. A suitable distribution of tangential traction on the cross-sections must be the essential feature of the stress-system of which we are in search. Accordingly, we seek to satisfy all the conditions by means of a distribution of *shearing stress*, made up of suitably directed tangential tractions on the elements of the cross-sections, combined, as they must be, with equal tangential tractions on elements of properly chosen longitudinal sections.

We shall find that a system of this kind is adequate; and we can foresee, to some extent, the character of the strain and displacement within the prism. For the strain corresponding with the shearing stress, which we have described, is shearing strain which involves, in general, two simple shears at each point. One of these simple shears consists of a relative sliding in a transverse direction of elements of different cross-sections; this is the type of strain which occurred in the circular cylinder. The other simple shear consists of a relative sliding, parallel to the length of the prism, of different longitudinal linear elements. By this shear the cross-sections become distorted into curved surfaces. The shape into which any cross-section is distorted is determined by the displacement in the direction of the length of the prism.

216. The torsion problem*.

We shall take the generators of the surface of the prism to be parallel to the axis of z, and shall suppose that the material is isotropic. The discussion in the last Article leads us to assume for the displacement the formulæ

$$u = -\tau yz, \quad v = \tau zx, \quad w = \tau\phi, \quad \text{.....................(1)}$$

where ϕ is a function of x and y, and τ is the twist. We work out the consequences of this assumption.

The strain-components that do not vanish are e_{zx} and e_{yz}, and these are given by the equations

$$e_{zx} = \tau\left(\frac{\partial\phi}{\partial x} - y\right), \quad e_{yz} = \tau\left(\frac{\partial\phi}{\partial y} + x\right). \quad \text{..............(2)}$$

The stress-components that do not vanish are X_z and Y_z, and they are given by the equations

$$X_z = \mu\tau\left(\frac{\partial\phi}{\partial x} - y\right), \quad Y_z = \mu\tau\left(\frac{\partial\phi}{\partial y} + x\right). \quad \text{..............(3)}$$

The equations of equilibrium, when there are no body forces, are satisfied if the equation

$$\frac{\partial^2\phi}{\partial x^2} + \frac{\partial^2\phi}{\partial y^2} = 0 \quad \text{....................................(4)}$$

holds at all points of any cross-section. The condition that the cylindrical bounding surface of the prism is free from traction is satisfied if the equation

$$\frac{\partial\phi}{\partial\nu} = y\cos(x, \nu) - x\cos(y, \nu) \quad \text{.....................(5)}$$

holds at all points of the bounding curve of any cross-section. Here $d\nu$ denotes the element of the outward-drawn normal to this curve. The compatibility of the boundary-condition (5) with the differential equation (4) is shown by integrating the left-hand and right-hand members of (5) round the boundary, and transforming the line-integrals into surface-integrals taken over the area of the cross-section. The integral of the left-hand member of (5) taken round the boundary is equivalent to the integral of the left-hand member of (4) taken over the area of the cross-section; it therefore vanishes. The integral of the right-hand member of (5) taken round the boundary also vanishes.

The tractions on any cross-section are, of course, statically equivalent to a single force (which may be zero) at the origin of (x, y) and a couple. We show that they are equivalent to a couple only. The axis of the couple is

* The theory is due to Saint-Venant. See Introduction, footnote 50 and p. 19.

clearly parallel to the generators of the surface of the prism. We have to show that

$$\iint X_z dx dy = 0, \quad \iint Y_z dx dy = 0.$$

Now

$$\iint X_z dx dy = \mu\tau \iint \left(\frac{\partial \phi}{\partial x} - y\right) dx dy,$$

and this may be replaced by

$$\mu\tau \iint \left[\frac{\partial}{\partial x}\left\{x\left(\frac{\partial \phi}{\partial x} - y\right)\right\} + \frac{\partial}{\partial y}\left\{x\left(\frac{\partial \phi}{\partial y} + x\right)\right\}\right] dx dy,$$

by the help of the differential equation (4). The expression last written may be transformed into an integral taken round the bounding curve, viz.

$$\mu\tau \int x \left\{\frac{\partial \phi}{\partial \nu} - y \cos(x, \nu) + x \cos(y, \nu)\right\} ds,$$

where ds is the element of arc of the bounding curve. This integral vanishes in consequence of the boundary-condition (5). We have thus proved that $\iint X_z dx dy = 0$, and in a similar way we may prove that $\iint Y_z dx dy = 0$. It follows that the tractions on a cross-section are statically equivalent to a couple about the axis of z of moment

$$\mu\tau \iint \left(x^2 + y^2 + x\frac{\partial \phi}{\partial y} - y\frac{\partial \phi}{\partial x}\right) dx dy. \quad \text{.................(6)}$$

We have now proved that the prism can be held in the displaced position given by equations (1) by means of couples applied at its ends, the axes of the couples being parallel to the central-line of the prism. The moment of the couple when the twist is τ is a quantity $C\tau$, where

$$C = \mu \iint \left(x^2 + y^2 + x\frac{\partial \phi}{\partial y} - y\frac{\partial \phi}{\partial x}\right) dx dy. \quad \text{.................(7)}$$

The quantity C is the product of the rigidity of the material and a quantity of the fourth degree in the linear dimensions of the cross-section. C is sometimes called the "torsional rigidity" of the prism.

The complete solution of the problem of torsion, for a prism of any form of section, is effected when ϕ is determined so as to satisfy the equation (4) and the boundary-condition (5). The problem of determining ϕ for a given boundary is sometimes called the "torsion problem" for that boundary. The function ϕ is sometimes called the "torsion-function" for the boundary.

In the above solution the twisting couple is applied by means of tractions X_z, Y_z, which are expressed by (3). The practical utility of the solution is not confined to the case where the couple is applied in this way. When the length of the prism is great compared with the linear dimensions of its cross-section, the solution will represent the state of the prism everywhere except in comparatively small parts near the ends, whether the twisting couple is applied in the specified way or not. [Cf. Article 89.]

The potential energy per unit of length of the twisted prism is

$$\tfrac{1}{2}\mu\tau^2 \iint \left\{\left(\frac{\partial\phi}{\partial x} - y\right)^2 + \left(\frac{\partial\phi}{\partial y} + x\right)^2\right\} dx\,dy,$$

and this is equal to

$$\tfrac{1}{2}C\tau^2 + \tfrac{1}{2}\mu\tau^2 \iint \left\{x\frac{\partial\phi}{\partial y} - y\frac{\partial\phi}{\partial x} + \left(\frac{\partial\phi}{\partial x}\right)^2 + \left(\frac{\partial\phi}{\partial y}\right)^2\right\} dx\,dy.$$

Now
$$\iint \left\{\left(\frac{\partial\phi}{\partial x}\right)^2 + \left(\frac{\partial\phi}{\partial y}\right)^2\right\} dx\,dy = \int \phi \frac{\partial\phi}{\partial\nu}\,ds$$
$$= \int \phi \{y \cos(x, \nu) - x \cos(y, \nu)\}\,ds$$
$$= \iint \left(y\frac{\partial\phi}{\partial x} - x\frac{\partial\phi}{\partial y}\right) dx\,dy.$$

It follows that the potential energy per unit of length is $\frac{1}{2}C\tau^2$.

217. Method of solution of the torsion problem.

Since ϕ is a plane harmonic function, there exists a conjugate function ψ which is such that $\phi + \iota\psi$ is a function of the complex variable $x + \iota y$; and, if ψ can be found, ϕ can be written down by means of the equations

$$\frac{\partial\phi}{\partial x} = \frac{\partial\psi}{\partial y}, \quad \frac{\partial\phi}{\partial y} = -\frac{\partial\psi}{\partial x}.$$

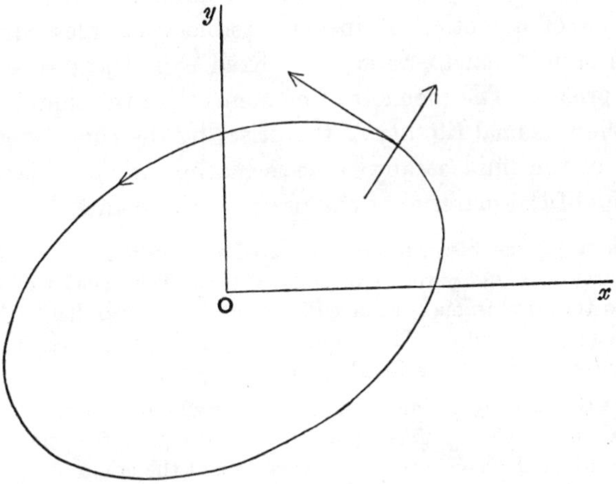

Fig. 21.

The function ψ satisfies the equation $\dfrac{\partial^2\psi}{\partial x^2} + \dfrac{\partial^2\psi}{\partial y^2} = 0$, at all points within the bounding curve of the cross-section, and a certain condition at this boundary. We proceed to find the boundary-condition for ψ.

Taking ds for the element of arc of the bounding curve, and observing that, when the senses of s and ν are those indicated by arrows in Fig. 21, $\cos(x, \nu) = dy/ds$, $\cos(y, \nu) = -dx/ds$, we may write the condition (5)

$$\frac{\partial\psi}{\partial y}\frac{dy}{ds} + \frac{\partial\psi}{\partial x}\frac{dx}{ds} = y\frac{dy}{ds} + x\frac{dx}{ds},$$

and it follows that at the boundary,

$$\psi - \tfrac{1}{2}(x^2 + y^2) = \text{const.} \qquad \text{........................(8)}$$

The problem is thus reduced to that of finding a plane harmonic function which satisfies this condition. Apart from additive constants the functions ϕ and ψ are uniquely determinate*.

218. Analogies with Hydrodynamics.

(*a*) The functions ϕ and ψ are mathematically identical with the velocity-potential and stream-function of a certain irrotational motion of incompressible frictionless fluid, contained in a vessel of the same shape as the prism†. This motion is that which would be set up by rotating the vessel about its axis with angular velocity equal to -1.

(*b*) The function $\psi - \frac{1}{2}(x^2 + y^2)$ is mathematically identical with the velocity in a certain laminar motion of viscous fluid. The fluid flows under pressure through a pipe, and the section of the pipe is the same as that of the prism‡.

(*c*) The function $\psi - \frac{1}{2}(x^2 + y^2)$ is also mathematically identical with the stream-function of a motion of incompressible frictionless fluid circulating with uniform spin, equal to unity, in a fixed cylindrical vessel of the same shape as the prism§. The moment of momentum of the liquid is equal to the quotient of the torsional rigidity of the prism by the rigidity of the material. The velocity of the fluid at any point is mathematically identical with the shearing strain of the material of the prism at the point.

In the analogy (*a*) the vessel rotates as stated relatively to some frame regarded as fixed, and the axes of x and y rotate with the vessel. The velocity of a particle of the fluid relative to the fixed frame is resolved into components parallel to the instantaneous positions of the axes of x and y. These components are $\partial\phi/\partial x$ and $\partial\phi/\partial y$. The velocity of the fluid relative to the vessel is utilized in the analogy (*c*).

We may use the analogy in the form (*a*) to determine the effect of twisting the prism about an axis when the effect of twisting about any parallel axis is known. Let ϕ_0 be the torsion-function when the axis meets a cross-section at the origin of (x, y); and let ϕ' be the torsion-function when the prism is twisted about an axis parallel to the first, and meeting the section at a point (x', y'). Rotation of the vessel about the second axis is equivalent at any instant to rotation about the first axis combined with a certain motion of translation, which is the same for all points of the vessel. This instantaneous motion of translation is the motion of the first axis produced by rotation about the second; and the

* The functions are determined for a number of forms of boundary in Articles 221, 222 *infra*. For the special condition, necessary to secure uniqueness in the case of a hollow shaft, see Article 222 (iii).

† Kelvin and Tait, *Nat. Phil.*, Part II., pp. 242 *et seq.* The velocity-potential is here defined by the convention that the velocity of the fluid in the positive sense of the axis of x is $\partial\phi/\partial x$, not $-\partial\phi/\partial x$.

‡ J. Boussinesq, *J. de math.* (*Liouville*), (Sér. 2), t. 16 (1871).

§ A. G. Greenhill, Article 'Hydromechanics,' *Ency. Brit.*, 9th edition.

component velocities in the directions of the axes are $-y'$ and x', since the angular velocity of the vessel is -1. It follows that we must have $\phi' = \phi_0 - xy' + yx'$. The component displacements are therefore given by the equations

$$u = -\tau(y-y')z, \quad v = \tau(x-x')z, \quad w = \tau\phi';$$

and the stress is the same as in the case where the axis of rotation passes through the origin. The torsional couple and the potential energy also are the same in the two cases.

219. Distribution of shearing stress.

The stress at any point consists of two superposed stress-systems. In one system we have shearing stresses X_z and Y_z of amounts $-\mu\tau y$ and $\mu\tau x$ respectively. In this system the tangential traction per unit of area on the plane $z =$ const. is directed, at each point, along the tangent to a circle, having its centre at the origin and passing through the point. There must be equal tangential traction per unit of area on a plane passing through the axis of this circle, and this traction is directed parallel to the axis of z. In the second system we have shearing stresses X_z and Y_z of amounts $\mu\tau\partial\phi/\partial x$ and $\mu\tau\partial\phi/\partial y$. The corresponding tangential traction per unit of area on the plane $z =$ const. is directed at each point along the normal to that curve of the family $\phi =$ const. which passes through the point, and its amount is proportional to the gradient of ϕ. There must be equal tangential traction per unit of area on a cylindrical surface standing on that curve of the family $\phi =$ const. which passes through the point, and the direction of this traction is that of the axis of z. These statements concerning the stress are independent of the choice of axes of x and y in the plane of the cross-section, so long as the origin remains the same.

The resultant of the two stress-systems consists of shearing stress with components X_z and Y_z, which are given by the equations (3). If we put

$$\psi - \tfrac{1}{2}(x^2+y^2) = \Psi, \qquad \text{.........................(9)}$$

the direction of the tangential traction (X_z, Y_z) across the normal section at any point is the tangent to that curve of the family $\Psi =$ const. which passes through the point, and the magnitude of this traction is $\mu\tau\partial\Psi/\partial\nu$, where $d\nu$ is the element of the normal to the curve. The curves $\Psi =$ const. may be called "lines of shearing stress."

The magnitude of the resultant tangential traction may also be expressed by the formula

$$\mu\tau\left\{\left(\frac{\partial\phi}{\partial x} - y\right)^2 + \left(\frac{\partial\phi}{\partial y} + x\right)^2\right\}^{\frac{1}{2}}, \qquad \text{....................(10)}$$

and this result is independent of the directions of the axes of x and y. If we choose for the axis of x a line parallel to the direction of the tangential traction at one point P, the shearing stress at P will be equal to the value at P of the function $\mu\tau(\partial\phi/\partial x - y)$, and the x-component of the traction at any other point Q will be equal to the value of the same function at Q. Now this function, being harmonic, cannot have a maximum or a minimum value at P; there is therefore some point, Q, in the neighbourhood of P, at which it has a greater value than it has at P. Thus the x-component of the traction at some point Q near to P is greater than the traction at P; and the traction at Q must therefore be greater than that at P. It follows that the shearing stress cannot be a maximum at any point within the prism; and therefore the greatest value of the shearing stress is found on the cylindrical boundary*.

220. Strength to resist torsion.

The resultant shearing strain is proportional to the resultant shearing stress, and the extension and contraction along the principal axes of the strain at any point are each equal to half the shearing strain at the point; and thus the strength of the prism to resist torsion depends on the maximum shearing stress. Practical rules for the limit of safe loading must express the condition that this maximum is not to exceed a certain value.

Some results of practical importance can be deduced from the form of hydrodynamical analogy [Article 218 (c)] in which use is made of a circulating motion with uniform spin. Suppose a shaft transmitting a couple to contain a cylindrical flaw of circular section with its axis parallel to that of the shaft. If the diameter of the cavity is small compared with that of the shaft, and the cavity is at a distance from the surface great compared with its diameter, the problem is very nearly the same as that of liquid streaming past a cylinder. Now we know that the velocity of liquid streaming past a circular cylinder has a maximum value equal to twice the velocity of the stream, and we may infer that, in the case of the shaft, the shear near the cavity is twice as great as that at a distance. If the cavity is a good deal nearer to the surface than to the axis, or if there is a semicircular groove on the surface, the shear in the neighbourhood of the cavity (or the groove) may be nearly twice the maximum shear that would exist if there were no cavity (or groove)†.

If the boundary has anywhere a sharp corner projecting outwards, the velocity of the fluid at the corner vanishes, and therefore the shear in the torsion problem is zero at such a corner. If the boundary has a sharp corner projecting inwards, the velocity is theoretically infinite, and the torsion of a prism with such a section will be accompanied by *set* in the neighbourhood of the corner.

Saint-Venant in his memoir of 1855 called attention to the inefficiency of corners projecting outwards, and gave several numerical illustrations of the

* Thi theorem was first stated by J. Boussinesq, *loc. cit.* The proof in the text will be found in a paper by L. N. G. Filon, *Phil. Trans. Roy. Soc.* (Ser. A), vol. 193 (1900). Boussinesq had supposed that the points of maximum shearing stress must be those points of the contour which are nearest to the axis; but Filon showed that this is not necessarily the case.

† Cf. J. Larmor, *Phil. Mag.* (Ser. 5), vol. 33 (1892).

diminution of torsional rigidity in prisms having such corners as compared with circular cylinders of the same sectional area.

221. Solution of the torsion problem for certain boundaries.

We shall now show how to find the function ϕ from the equation (4) and the condition (5) when the boundary of the section of the prism has one or other of certain special forms. The arbitrary constant which may be added to ϕ will in general be adjusted so that ϕ shall vanish at the origin.

(*a*) *The circle.*

If the cylinder of circular section is twisted about its axis of figure, ϕ vanishes, and we have the solution already given in Article 86 (*d*). If it is twisted about any parallel axis ϕ does not vanish, but can be determined by the method explained in Article 218. In the latter case the cross-sections are not distorted, but are displaced so as to make an angle differing slightly from a right angle with the axis.

(*b*) *The ellipse.*

The function ψ is a plane harmonic function which satisfies the condition $\psi - \frac{1}{2}(x^2+y^2) = \text{const.}$ at the boundary $x^2/a^2 + y^2/b^2 = 1$. If we assume for ψ a form $A\,(x^2-y^2)$, we find the equation

$$(\tfrac{1}{2} - A)\,a^2 = (\tfrac{1}{2} + A)\,b^2. \qquad \text{.......................(11)}$$

It follows that we must have

$$\psi = \frac{1}{2}\frac{a^2-b^2}{a^2+b^2}(x^2-y^2), \qquad \phi = -\frac{a^2-b^2}{a^2+b^2}xy. \qquad \text{...........(12)}$$

It is clear that this solution is applicable to the case of a boundary consisting of two concentric similar and similarly situated ellipses. The prism is then a hollow elliptic tube.

(*c*) *The rectangle**.

The boundaries are given by the equations $x = \pm a$, $y = \pm b$. The function ψ differs by a constant from $\frac{1}{2}(y^2+a^2)$ when $x = \pm a$ and $b > y > -b$; it differs by the same constant from $\frac{1}{2}(x^2+b^2)$ when $y = \pm b$ and $a > x > -a$. We introduce a new function ψ' by means of the equation

$$\psi' = \psi - \tfrac{1}{2}(x^2 - y^2) - \tfrac{1}{2}b^2.$$

Then ψ' is a plane harmonic function within the rectangle; and we may take ψ' to vanish on the sides $y = \pm b$, and to be equal to $y^2 - b^2$ on the sides $x = \pm a$. Since the boundary-conditions are not altered when we change x into $-x$ or y into $-y$, we seek to satisfy all the conditions by assuming for ψ' a formula of the type $\Sigma A_m \cosh mx \cos my$. The conditions which hold at the boundaries $y = \pm b$ require that m should be $\frac{1}{2}(2n+1)\pi/b$, where n is an

* The corresponding hydrodynamical problem was solved by Stokes, *Cambridge Phil. Soc. Trans.*, vol. 8 (1843), reprinted in his *Math. and Phys. Papers*, vol. 1, p. 16.

integer. If we assume that, when $b > y > -b$, the function $y^2 - b^2$ can be expanded in a series according to the formula

$$y^2 - b^2 = \Sigma A_{2n+1} \cosh \frac{(2n+1)\pi a}{2b} \cos \frac{(2n+1)\pi y}{2b},$$

we may determine the coefficients by multiplying both members of this equation by $\cos\{(2n+1)\pi y/2b\}$, and integrating both members with respect to y between the extreme values $-b$ and b. We should thus find

$$A_{2n+1} \cosh \frac{(2n+1)\pi a}{2b} = (-)^{n+1} 4b^2 \frac{2^3}{(2n+1)^3 \pi^3}.$$

This process suggests that when $b > y > -b$, the sum of the series

$$\sum_{n=0}^{\infty} 4b^2 \left(\frac{2}{\pi}\right)^3 \frac{(-)^{n+1}}{(2n+1)^3} \cos \frac{(2n+1)\pi y}{2b} \quad \text{...............(13)}$$

is $y^2 - b^2$. We cannot at once conclude that this result is proved by Fourier's theorem*, because a Fourier's series of cosines of multiples of $\pi y/2b$ represents a function in an interval given by the inequalities $2b > y > -2b$, and the value $y^2 - b^2$ of the function to be expanded is given only in the interval $b > y > -b$. If the Fourier's series of cosines contains uneven multiples of $\pi y/2b$ only, the sign of every term of it is changed when for y we put $2b - y$; it follows that, if the series (13) is a Fourier's series of which the sum is $y^2 - b^2$ when $b > y > 0$, the sum of the series when $2b > y > b$ is $b^2 - (2b - y)^2$. Now we may show that the Fourier's series for an even function of y, which has the value $y^2 - b^2$ when $b > y > 0$, and the value $b^2 - (2b - y)^2$ when $2b > y > b$, is in fact the series (13). We may conclude that the form of ψ is

$$\tfrac{1}{2}b^2 + \tfrac{1}{2}(x^2 - y^2) - 4b^2 \left(\frac{2}{\pi}\right)^3 \sum_{n=0}^{\infty} \frac{(-)^n}{(2n+1)^3} \frac{\cosh \dfrac{(2n+1)\pi x}{2b}}{\cosh \dfrac{(2n+1)\pi a}{2b}} \cos \frac{(2n+1)\pi y}{2b},$$

and hence that

$$\phi = -xy + 4b^2 \left(\frac{2}{\pi}\right)^3 \sum_{n=0}^{\infty} \frac{(-)^n}{(2n+1)^3} \frac{\sinh \dfrac{(2n+1)\pi x}{2b}}{\cosh \dfrac{(2n+1)\pi a}{2b}} \sin \frac{(2n+1)\pi y}{2b} \dagger. \quad \text{...(14)}$$

222. Additional results.

The torsion problem has been solved for many forms of boundary. One method is to assume a plane harmonic function as the function ψ, and determine possible boundaries from the equation $\psi - \frac{1}{2}(x^2 + y^2) = \text{const.}$ As an example of this method we may take ψ

* Observe, for example, that the Fourier's series of cosines of multiples of $\pi y/2b$ which has the sum $y^2 - b^2$ throughout the interval $2b > y > -2b$ is

$$\tfrac{1}{3}b^2 + \frac{16b^2}{\pi^2} \sum_{n=1}^{\infty} \frac{(-)^n}{n^2} \cos \frac{n\pi y}{2b}.$$

† The expression for ϕ must be unaltered when x and y, a and b, are interchanged. For an account of the identities which arise from this observation the reader is referred to a paper by F. Purser, *Messenger of Math.*, vol. 11 (1882).

to be $A(x^3-3xy^2)$; if we put $A=-1/6a$, the boundary can be the equilateral triangle*, of altitude $3a$, of which the sides are given by the equation

$$(x-a)(x-y\sqrt{3}+2a)(x+y\sqrt{3}+2a)=0.$$

Other examples of this method have been discussed by Saint-Venant.

Another method is to use conjugate functions ξ, η such that $\xi+\iota\eta$ is a function of $x+\iota y$. If these functions can be chosen so that the boundary is made up of curves along which either ξ or η has a constant value, then ψ is the real part of a function of $\xi+\iota\eta$, which has a given value at the boundary; and the problem is of the same kind as the torsion problem for the rectangle. We give some examples of this method:

(i) A sector of a circle†, boundaries given by $r=0$, $r=a$, $\theta=\pm\beta$.—We find

$$\psi=\tfrac{1}{2}r^2\frac{\cos 2\theta}{\cos 2\beta}+a^2\sum_0^\infty\left[A_{2n+1}\left(\frac{r}{a}\right)^{(2n+1)\frac{\pi}{2\beta}}\cos\left\{(2n+1)\frac{\pi\theta}{2\beta}\right\}\right],$$

where
$$A_{2n+1}=(-)^{n+1}\left[\frac{1}{(2n+1)\pi-4\beta}-\frac{2}{(2n+1)\pi}+\frac{1}{(2n+1)\pi+4\beta}\right].$$

If we write $re^{\iota\theta}=ax$, then

$$\psi-\iota\phi=\tfrac{1}{2}a^2\frac{x^2}{\cos 2\beta}-\frac{a^2}{2\beta}\left\{x^2\int_0^x\frac{x^{\frac{\pi}{2\beta}-3}}{1+x^{\frac{\pi}{\beta}}}dx-\frac{4\beta}{\pi}\tan^{-1}x^{\pi/2\beta}+\frac{1}{x^2}\int_0^x\frac{x^{\frac{\pi}{2\beta}+1}}{1+x^{\frac{\pi}{\beta}}}dx\right\},$$

where $|x|\leqslant 1$, and $\tan^{-1}x^{\pi/2\beta}$ denotes that branch of the function which vanishes with x.

In case $\pi/2\beta$ is an integer greater than 2 the integrations can be performed, but when $\pi/2\beta=2$ the first two terms become infinite, and their sum has a finite limit, and we find for a quadrantal cylinder

$$\psi-\iota\phi=\frac{2a^2}{\pi}\left[-x^2\log x+\tan^{-1}x^2+\tfrac{1}{4}\left(x^2-\frac{1}{x^2}\right)\log(1+x^4)\right].$$

For a semicircular cylinder

$$\psi-\iota\phi=\frac{a^2}{\pi}\left[\tfrac{1}{2}\pi x^2-i\left(x+\frac{1}{x}\right)+\tfrac{1}{2}\iota\left(x^2+\frac{1}{x^2}-2\right)\log\frac{1+x}{1-x}\right].$$

(ii) For a curvilinear rectangle bounded by two concentric circular arcs and two radii, we use conjugate functions α and β, which are given by the equation

$$x+\iota y=ce^{\alpha+\iota\beta};$$

we take the outer radius, a to be ce^{α_0} and the inner, b to be $ce^{-\alpha_0}$ (so that c is the geometrical mean of the radii), and we take the bounding radii to be given by the equations $\beta=\pm\beta_0$. We find

$$\phi=-\tfrac{1}{2}abe^{2\alpha}\frac{\sin 2\beta}{\cos 2\beta_0}+2^5ab\beta_0^2\sum_0^\infty A_n\Phi_n,$$

where
$$\Phi_n=\left\{\cosh 2\alpha_0\frac{\sinh\dfrac{(2n+1)\pi\alpha}{2\beta_0}}{\cosh\dfrac{(2n+1)\pi\alpha_0}{2\beta_0}}+\sinh 2\alpha_0\frac{\cosh\dfrac{(2n+1)\pi\alpha}{2\beta_0}}{\sinh\dfrac{(2n+1)\pi\alpha_0}{2\beta_0}}\right\},$$

and
$$A_n=\frac{(-)^n\sin\dfrac{(2n+1)\pi\beta}{2\beta_0}}{\{(2n+1)\pi-4\beta_0\}(2n+1)\pi\{(2n+1)\pi+4\beta_0\}}.$$

(iii) When the twisted prism is a hollow shaft, the inner and outer boundaries being circles which are not concentric, we may use the conjugate functions ξ, η determined by the equation

$$x+\iota y=c\tan\tfrac{1}{2}(\xi+\iota\eta);$$

* See Figures 23 and 24 in Article 223.

† See A. G. Greenhill, *Messenger of Math.*, vol. 8 (1878), p. 89, and vol. 10 (1880), p. 83.

and, if $\eta=\alpha$ represents the outer boundary, and $\eta=\beta$ the inner, we may prove* that

$$\psi=2c^2\sum_{n=1}^{\infty}(-)^n\frac{e^{-n\beta}\coth\beta\sinh n(\eta-\alpha)+e^{-n\alpha}\coth\alpha\sinh n(\beta-\eta)}{\sinh n(\beta-\alpha)}\cos n\xi.$$

In this example the differential equation and boundary-condition for ψ would still be satisfied if a term of the form $A\eta$ were added to the expression given for ψ. The conjugate function ϕ would then contain a term of the form $A\xi$, and the displacement w, or $\tau\phi$, would then be many-valued. To secure a one-valued expression for w it would be necessary to put $A=0$. A similar result holds for any hollow shaft.

(iv) When the boundaries are confocal ellipses and hyperbolas we may use the conjugate functions ξ, η determined by the equation

$$x+\iota y=c\cosh(\xi+\iota\eta).$$

In the case of a hollow tube, of which the section is bounded by two confocal ellipses ξ_0 and ξ_1, we may prove† that

$$\psi=\tfrac{1}{4}c^2\frac{\sinh 2(\xi_0-\xi)+\sinh 2(\xi-\xi_1)}{\sinh 2(\xi_0-\xi_1)}\cos 2\eta.$$

223. Graphic expression of the results.

(a) *Distortion of the cross-sections.*

The curves $\phi=$const. are the contour lines of the surface into which any cross-section of the prism is distorted. These curves were traced by Saint-Venant for a number of forms of the boundary. Two of the results are shown in Fig. 22 and Fig. 23. In both

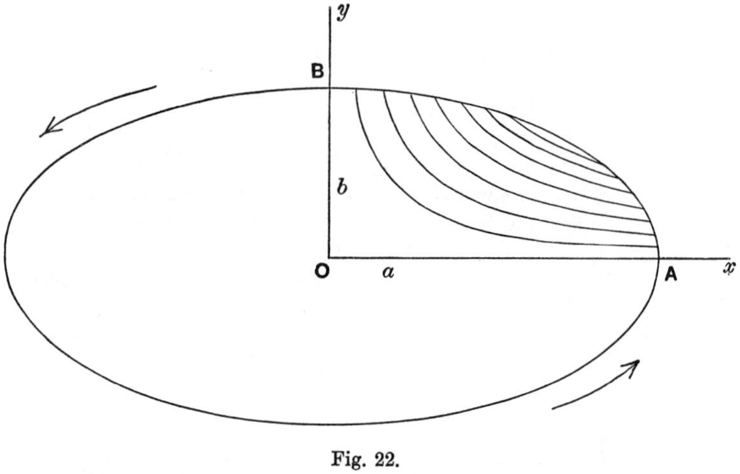

Fig. 22.

cases the cross-section is divided into a number of compartments, 4 in Fig. 22, 6 in Fig. 23, and ϕ changes sign as we pass from any compartment to an adjacent

* H. M. Macdonald, *Cambridge Phil. Soc. Proc.*, vol. 8 (1893).

† Cf. A. G. Greenhill, *Quart. J. of Math.*, vol. 16 (1879). Other examples of elliptic and hyperbolic boundaries are worked out by Filon, *loc. cit.*, p. 316 with special reference to the effect of key-ways, an effect further investigated by T. H. Gronwall, *Amer. Math. Soc. Trans.*, vol. 20 (1919), p. 234, who treats the case of an indentation in the form of a circular arc in the circular section of a shaft. The torsion of a shaft whose cross-section is bounded by a polygon is discussed by the method of conformal representation by E. Trefftz, *Math. Ann.*, Bd. 82 (1921). The special case of a right-angled triangle is treated by a simple method by C. Kolossoff, *Paris C. R.*, t. 178 (1924), p. 2057.

compartment, but the forms of the curves $\phi=$const. are unaltered. If we think of the axis of the prism as vertical, then the curved surface into which any cross-section is strained lies above its initial position in one compartment and below it in the adjacent compartments. Saint-Venant showed that the sections of a square prism are divided in this way into 8 compartments by the diagonals and the lines drawn parallel to the sides through the centroid. When the prism is a rectangle, of which one pair of opposite sides is much longer than the other pair, there are only 4 compartments separated by the lines drawn parallel to the sides through the centroid. The limiting case between rectangles which are divided into 4 compartments and others which are divided into 8 compartments occurs when the ratio of adjacent sides is 1·4513. The study of the figures has promoted comprehension of the result that the cross-sections of a twisted prism, of non-circular section, do not remain plane.

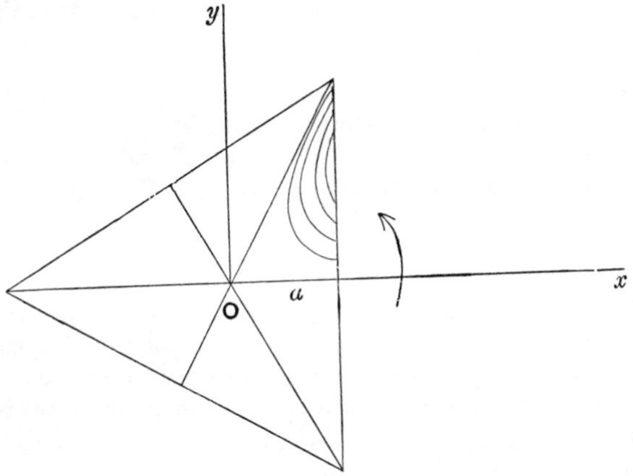

Fig. 23.

(*b*) *Lines of shearing stress.*

The distribution of tangential traction on the cross-sections of a twisted prism can be represented graphically by means of the lines of shearing stress. These lines are determined by the equation

$$\psi-\tfrac{1}{2}(x^2+y^2)=c.$$

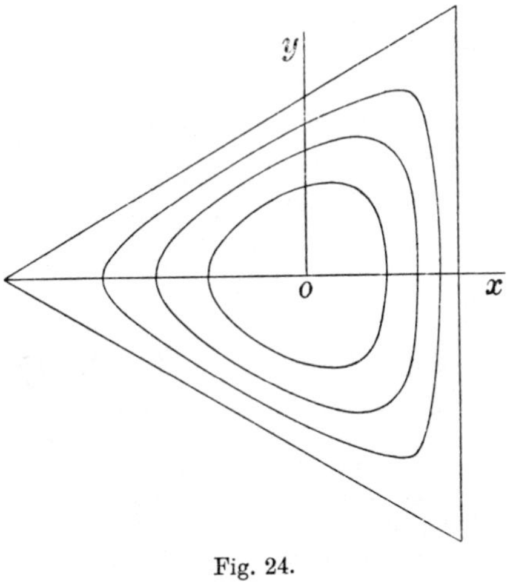

Fig. 24.

They have the property that the tangential traction on the cross-section is directed at any point along the tangent to that curve of the family which passes through the point. If the curves are traced for equidifferent values of c, the tangential traction at any point is measured by the closeness of consecutive curves.

In the case of the prism of elliptic section

$$\psi - \tfrac{1}{2}(x^2+y^2) = -(x^2b^2+y^2a^2)/(a^2+b^2),$$

and the lines of shearing stress are therefore concentric similar and similarly situated ellipses. In the case of the equilateral triangle

$$\psi - \tfrac{1}{2}(x^2+y^2) = -\tfrac{1}{6}a^{-1}[x^3-3xy^2+3ax^2+3ay^2],$$

and the lines of shearing stress are of the forms shown in Fig. 24.

224. Analogy to the form of a stretched membrane loaded uniformly*.

Let a homogeneous membrane be stretched with uniform tension T and fixed at its edge. Let the edge be a given curve in the plane of x, y. When the membrane is subjected to pressure, of amount p per unit of area, it will undergo a small displacement z, and z is a function of x and y which vanishes at the edge. The equation of equilibrium of the membrane is

$$T\left(\frac{\partial^2 z}{\partial x^2}+\frac{\partial^2 z}{\partial y^2}\right)+p=0.$$

The function $2Tz/p$ is determined by the same conditions as the function Ψ of Article 219, provided that the edge of the membrane is the same as the bounding curve of the cross-section of the twisted prism. It follows that the contour lines of the loaded membrane are identical with the lines of shearing stress in the cross-section of the prism.

Further the torsional rigidity of the prism can be represented by the volume contained between the surface of the loaded membrane and the plane of its edge. We have seen already in Article 216 that the torsional rigidity is given by the equation

$$C=\mu\iint\left\{\left(\frac{\partial\phi}{\partial x}-y\right)^2+\left(\frac{\partial\phi}{\partial y}+x\right)^2\right\}dx\,dy,$$

or, in terms of Ψ, we have

$$\begin{aligned} C&=\mu\iint\left\{\left(\frac{\partial\Psi}{\partial y}\right)^2+\left(\frac{\partial\Psi}{\partial x}\right)^2\right\}dx\,dy\\ &=\mu\int\Psi\frac{\partial\Psi}{\partial\nu}ds-\mu\iint\Psi\left(\frac{\partial^2\Psi}{\partial x^2}+\frac{\partial^2\Psi}{\partial y^2}\right)dx\,dy\\ &=2\mu\iint\Psi\,dx\,dy,\end{aligned}$$

since Ψ vanishes at the edge and $\dfrac{\partial^2\Psi}{\partial x^2}+\dfrac{\partial^2\Psi}{\partial y^2}+2=0$. It follows that the volume in question is $(p/4\mu T)\,C$.

225. Twisting couple.

The couple can be evaluated from (6) of Article 216 when the function ϕ is known. We shall record the results in certain cases.

* The analogy here described was pointed out by L. Prandtl, *Phys. Zeitschr.*, Bd. 4 (1903), it affords a means of exhibiting to the eye the distribution of stress in a twisted prism. The method is further developed by A. A. Griffith and G. I. Taylor, *Engineering, London*, vol. 104 (1917), pp. 655, 699, or *London Inst. Mech. Engineers, Proc.*, 1917, p. 755.

(*a*) *The circle.*

If a is the radius of the circle the twisting couple is

$$\tfrac{1}{2}\mu\tau\pi a^4. \qquad \text{.......(15)}$$

(*b*) *The ellipse.*

From the value of ϕ in Article 221 (*b*) we find that the twisting couple is

$$\mu\tau\pi a^3b^3/(a^2+b^2). \qquad \text{.......(16)}$$

(*c*) *The rectangle.*

From the result of Article 221 (*c*) we find for the twisting couple the formula

$$\mu\tau\,\tfrac{4}{3}ab\,(a^2+b^2)-\mu\tau\,\tfrac{4}{3}ab\,(a^2-b^2)+4\mu\tau\,b^2\left(\frac{2}{\pi}\right)^3\iint\left\{x\frac{\partial\Phi}{\partial y}-y\frac{\partial\Phi}{\partial x}\right\}dx\,dy,$$

where Φ stands for the series

$$\sum_{n=0}^{\infty}\frac{(-)^n}{(2n+1)^3}\frac{\sinh\dfrac{(2n+1)\pi x}{2b}\sin\dfrac{(2n+1)\pi y}{2b}}{\cosh\dfrac{(2n+1)\pi a}{2b}}.$$

Taking one term of the series, we have a term of the integral, viz.:

$$\frac{(-)^n}{(2n+1)^2\cosh\{(2n+1)\pi a/2b\}}\frac{\pi}{2b}\iint\left\{x\sinh\frac{(2n+1)\pi x}{2b}\cos\frac{(2n+1)\pi y}{2b}\right.$$
$$\left.-y\cosh\frac{(2n+1)\pi x}{2b}\sin\frac{(2n+1)\pi y}{2b}\right\}dx\,dy.$$

Now

$$\int_{-a}^{a}x\sinh\frac{(2n+1)\pi x}{2b}dx=\frac{2b}{(2n+1)\pi}\left[2a\cosh\frac{(2n+1)\pi a}{2b}-\frac{2b}{(2n+1)\pi}2\sinh\frac{(2n+1)\pi a}{2b}\right],$$

$$\int_{-a}^{a}\cosh\frac{(2n+1)\pi x}{2b}dx=\frac{2b}{(2n+1)\pi}2\sinh\frac{(2n+1)\pi a}{2b},$$

$$\int_{-b}^{b}\cos\frac{(2n+1)\pi y}{2b}dy=\frac{2b}{(2n+1)\pi}2(-1)^n,$$

$$\int_{-b}^{b}y\sin\frac{(2n+1)\pi y}{2b}dy=\frac{8b^2}{(2n+1)^2\pi^2}(-1)^n.$$

Hence the twisting couple is equal to

$$\tfrac{8}{3}\mu\tau ab^3+\left(\frac{4}{\pi}\right)^4\mu\tau ab^3\sum_{n=0}^{\infty}\frac{1}{(2n+1)^4}-\mu\tau b^4\left(\frac{4}{\pi}\right)^5\sum_{n=0}^{\infty}\frac{1}{(2n+1)^5}\tanh\frac{(2n+1)\pi a}{2b}.$$

Since $\sum\limits_{n=0}^{\infty}(2n+1)^{-4}$ is $\pi^4/96$, we may write down the value of the twisting couple in the form

$$\tfrac{16}{3}\mu\tau ab^3-\mu\tau b^4\left(\frac{4}{\pi}\right)^5\sum_{n=0}^{\infty}\frac{1}{(2n+1)^5}\tanh\frac{(2n+1)\pi a}{2b}\ \text{.........(17)}$$

The series in (17) has been evaluated by Saint-Venant for numerous values of the ratio $a:b$. When $a>3b$ it is very nearly constant, and the value of the twisting couple is nearly equal to $\mu\tau ab^3\left[\frac{16}{3}-\frac{b}{a}(3\cdot361)\right]$. For a square the couple is $(2\cdot2492)\,\mu\tau a^4$.

The twisting couple was also calculated by Saint-Venant for a number of other forms of section. He found that the resistance of a prism to torsion is often very well expressed by replacing the section of the prism by an ellipse of the same area and the same moment of inertia*. The formula for the twisting couple in the case of an ellipse of area A and moment of inertia I is $\mu\tau A^4/4\pi^2 I$.

226. Torsion of æolotropic prism.

The theory which has been explained in Article 216 can be extended to a prism of æolotropic material when the normal section is a plane of symmetry of structure. Taking the axis of z to be parallel to the generators of the bounding surface, we have the strain-energy-function expressed in the form belonging to crystalline materials that correspond with the group C_2 (Article 109). The displacement being expressed by the formulæ (1), the stress-components that do not vanish are X_z and Y_z, and these are given by the equations

$$X_z=\tau\left[c_{55}\left(\frac{\partial\phi}{\partial x}-y\right)+c_{45}\left(\frac{\partial\phi}{\partial y}+x\right)\right],\quad Y_z=\tau\left[c_{44}\left(\frac{\partial\phi}{\partial y}+x\right)+c_{45}\left(\frac{\partial\phi}{\partial x}-y\right)\right].$$

The equations of equilibrium are equivalent to the equation

$$c_{55}\frac{\partial^2\phi}{\partial x^2}+c_{44}\frac{\partial^2\phi}{\partial y^2}+2c_{45}\frac{\partial^2\phi}{\partial x\,\partial y}=0,$$

which must hold over the area of the cross-section; and the condition that the bounding surface may be free from traction is satisfied if the equation

$$c_{55}\frac{\partial\phi}{\partial x}\cos(x,\nu)+c_{44}\frac{\partial\phi}{\partial y}\cos(y,\nu)+c_{45}\left\{\frac{\partial\phi}{\partial y}\cos(x,\nu)+\frac{\partial\phi}{\partial x}\cos(y,\nu)\right\}$$
$$=c_{55}y\cos(x,\nu)-c_{44}x\cos(y,\nu)-c_{45}\{x\cos(x,\nu)-y\cos(y,\nu)\}$$

holds at all points of the bounding curve. Exactly in the same way as in the case of isotropy, we may prove that the differential equation and the boundary-condition are compatible, and that the tractions across a normal section are equivalent to a couple of moment

$$\tau\iint\left\{c_{44}x^2+c_{55}y^2-2c_{45}xy+c_{44}x\frac{\partial\phi}{\partial y}-c_{55}y\frac{\partial\phi}{\partial x}+c_{45}\left(x\frac{\partial\phi}{\partial x}-y\frac{\partial\phi}{\partial y}\right)\right\}dx\,dy.$$

The analysis is simplified considerably in case $c_{45}=0$. If we put L for c_{44} and M for c_{55}, the differential equation may be written

$$M\frac{\partial^2\phi}{\partial x^2}+L\frac{\partial^2\phi}{\partial y^2}=0;$$

and, if $f(x,y)=0$ is the equation of the bounding curve, the boundary-condition may be written

$$M\frac{\partial f}{\partial x}\frac{\partial\phi}{\partial x}+L\frac{\partial f}{\partial y}\frac{\partial\phi}{\partial y}=My\frac{\partial f}{\partial x}-Lx\frac{\partial f}{\partial y}.$$

We change the variables by putting

$$x'=x\sqrt{\frac{L+M}{2M}},\quad y'=y\sqrt{\frac{L+M}{2L}},\quad \phi'=\phi\frac{L+M}{2\sqrt{(LM)}}.$$

Then ϕ' satisfies the equation

$$\frac{\partial^2\phi'}{\partial x'^2}+\frac{\partial^2\phi'}{\partial y'^2}=0.$$

* Saint-Venant, *Paris, C. R.*, t. 88 (1879).

The equation $f(x, y)=0$ becomes $F(x', y')=0$, where

$$F(x', y') \equiv f\left(x' \sqrt{\frac{2M}{L+M}},\ y' \sqrt{\frac{2L}{L+M}}\right),$$

so that

$$\frac{\partial F}{\partial x'}=\frac{\partial f}{\partial x} \sqrt{\frac{2M}{L+M}}, \quad \frac{\partial F}{\partial y'}=\frac{\partial f}{\partial y} \sqrt{\frac{2L}{L+M}};$$

and the boundary-condition is transformed into

$$\frac{\partial F}{\partial x'}\frac{\partial \phi'}{\partial x'}+\frac{\partial F}{\partial y'}\frac{\partial \phi'}{\partial y'}=y'\frac{\partial F}{\partial x'}-x'\frac{\partial F}{\partial y'}$$

which is

$$\frac{\partial \phi'}{\partial \nu'}=y' \cos(x', \nu')-x' \cos(y', \nu'),$$

if $d\nu'$ is the element of the normal to the transformed boundary. Thus ϕ can be found for any boundary if ϕ' can be found for an orthographic projection of that boundary; and the problem of finding ϕ' is the simple torsion problem which we considered before.

As an example we may take a rectangular prism with boundaries given by $x=\pm a$, $y=\pm b$. We should find that the formula for ϕ is

$$\phi=-xy+\sqrt{\frac{M}{L}}\frac{2^5 b^2}{\pi^3}\sum_{n=0}^{\infty}\frac{(-)^n}{(2n+1)^3}\frac{\sinh\dfrac{(2n+1)\pi x\sqrt{L}}{2b\sqrt{M}}}{\cosh\dfrac{(2n+1)\pi a\sqrt{L}}{2b\sqrt{M}}}\sin\frac{(2n+1)\pi y}{2b},$$

and that the twisting couple is expressed by the formula

$$M\tau ab^3\left\{\frac{16}{3}-\frac{b\sqrt{M}}{a\sqrt{L}}\left(\frac{4}{\pi}\right)^5\sum_{n=0}^{\infty}\frac{1}{(2n+1)^5}\tanh\frac{(2n+1)\pi a\sqrt{L}}{2b\sqrt{M}}\right\}.$$

This formula has been used by W. Voigt in his researches on the elastic constants of crystals. [See Article 113.]

226 A. Bar of varying circular section.

When the twisted bar is isotropic and of circular section, but the radius of the circle is a function of the position of its centre on the axis of the bar, the displacement of any point is directed at right angles to the axial plane passing through the point, just as in the case of a bar of uniform circular section. Let v denote this displacement. Then, using cylindrical polar coordinates r, θ, z, with an axis of z coinciding with the axis of the bar, we have the components of strain and stress expressed by the equations

$$e_{rr}=0,\quad e_{\theta\theta}=0,\quad e_{zz}=0,\quad e_{\theta z}=\frac{\partial v}{\partial z},\quad e_{zr}=0,\quad e_{r\theta}=\frac{\partial v}{\partial r}-\frac{v}{r},$$

$$\widehat{rr}=0,\quad \widehat{\theta\theta}=0,\quad \widehat{zz}=0,\quad \widehat{\theta z}=\mu\frac{\partial v}{\partial z},\quad \widehat{zr}=0,\quad \widehat{r\theta}=\mu\left(\frac{\partial v}{\partial r}-\frac{v}{r}\right),$$

for v is a function of z and r, but is independent of θ.

The equations of equilibrium [Article 59 (i)] reduce to the single equation

$$\frac{\partial^2 v}{\partial r^2}+\frac{1}{r}\frac{\partial v}{\partial r}-\frac{v}{r^2}+\frac{\partial^2 v}{\partial z^2}=0.$$

This equation may be written

$$\frac{\partial}{\partial r}\left\{r^3\frac{\partial}{\partial r}\left(\frac{v}{r}\right)\right\}+\frac{\partial}{\partial z}\left\{r^3\frac{\partial}{\partial z}\left(\frac{v}{r}\right)\right\}=0,$$

showing that there exists a function ψ which has the properties expressed by the equations

$$r^3 \frac{\partial}{\partial r}\left(\frac{v}{r}\right) = -\frac{\partial \psi}{\partial z},$$

$$r^3 \frac{\partial}{\partial z}\left(\frac{v}{r}\right) = \frac{\partial \psi}{\partial r}.$$

The function ψ satisfies the differential equation obtained by eliminating v/r from these equations, viz.:

$$\frac{\partial^2 \psi}{\partial r^2} - \frac{3}{r}\frac{\partial \psi}{\partial r} + \frac{\partial^2 \psi}{\partial z^2} = 0.$$

The stress-components, which do not vanish, are expressed by the equations

$$\widehat{\theta z} = \frac{\mu}{r^2}\frac{\partial \psi}{\partial r}, \quad \widehat{r\theta} = -\frac{\mu}{r^2}\frac{\partial \psi}{\partial z},$$

and the condition that the bounding surface is free from traction takes the form

$$\psi = \text{const. at the boundary.}$$

The above theory is due to J. H. Michell*. It was re-discovered by A. Föppl†, and further developed by F. A. Willers‡, who investigated, in particular, an approximate solution for a bar consisting of two portions, each portion being a circular cylinder, and the two portions having the same axis but different radii. Accounts of the theory and various special solutions of the analytical problem arising from it are given by E. T. Stegmann§ and Th. Pöschl||.

An obvious particular solution of the equation for ψ is $\psi = Ar^4$, where A is constant. By this solution the displacement and stress in a bar of uniform circular section are expressed in terms of ψ.

One method of obtaining particular solutions of the equation for ψ is to transform it to spherical polar coordinates (r', θ', ϕ'), by putting

$$z = r'\cos\theta', \quad r = r'\sin\theta', \quad \theta = \phi'.$$

The equation becomes
$$\frac{\partial^2 \psi}{\partial r'^2} - \frac{2}{r'}\frac{\partial \psi}{\partial r'} - \frac{3\cot\theta'}{r'^2}\frac{\partial \psi}{\partial \theta'} + \frac{1}{r'^2}\frac{\partial^2 \psi}{\partial \theta'^2} = 0.$$

If we assume for ψ an expression of the form

$$\psi = r'^n \psi_n,$$

where ψ_n is a function of θ', we find that ψ_n must satisfy the equation

$$\frac{d^2\psi_n}{d\theta'^2} - 3\cot\theta' \frac{d\psi_n}{d\theta'} + n(n-3)\psi_n = 0;$$

and if we then put
$$\psi_n = \sin^2\theta' . \chi_n,$$
and write μ' for $\cos\theta'$, this equation becomes

$$\frac{d}{d\mu'}\left\{(1-\mu'^2)\frac{d\chi_n}{d\mu'}\right\} + \left\{(n-2)(n-1) - \frac{4}{1-\mu'^2}\right\}\chi_n = 0,$$

and a solution is
$$\chi_n = (1-\mu'^2)\frac{d^2}{d\mu'^2}\{P_{n-2}(\mu')\},$$
where P_{n-2} denotes the zonal surface harmonic (Legendre's coefficient) of degree $n-2$. Thus ψ can be of the form
$$Ar'^n (1-\mu'^2)^2 \frac{d^2}{d\mu'^2}\{P_{n-2}(\mu')\},$$

* *London, Math. Soc. Proc.*, vol. 31, 1900, pp. 140, 141.

† *München, Akad. d. Wiss. Sitzungsber.*, Bd. 35, 1905, pp. 249, 504.

‡ *Zeitschr. f. Math. u. Phys.*, Bd. 55, 1907, p. 225.

§ *South Africa Roy. Soc. Trans.*, vol. 7 (1919), p. 147.

|| *Zeitschr. f. angewandte Math. u. Mech.*, Bd. 2 (1921), p. 137.

where A is a constant. The case where ψ is of the form Ar^4 is included in this formula by putting $n=4$. In all the solutions of this type ψ is a rational function of z and r.

Another method of obtaining particular solutions of the equation for ψ is to assume that ψ is of the form $e^{\pm kz}\,.\,R$, where R is a function of r. It then appears that R satisfies the equation

$$\left(\frac{d^2}{dr^2}+\frac{1}{r}\frac{d}{dr}+k^2-\frac{4}{r^2}\right)\left(\frac{R}{r^2}\right)=0,$$

so that we may write
$$\psi=Ae^{\pm kx}\,.\,r^2 J_2(kr),$$

where A is a constant, and $J_2(kr)$ denotes Bessel's function of order 2.

226 B. Distribution of traction over terminal section.

In the theory of torsion, developed in this Chapter, the twisting couple is supposed to be applied by means of tangential tractions exerted upon the terminal sections, and these tractions are supposed to be distributed over the sections according to determinate laws. When the external forces, whose resultant is the twisting couple, are distributed in some other way over the terminal sections, or the neighbouring portions of the cylindrical boundary, the theory avails for the determination of the stress in all parts of the twisted bar except those near to the ends; but near the ends there are "local perturbations." (Cf. Articles 89 and 133.)

The nature of the local perturbations may be illustrated by means of the analysis in Article 226 A. It will be sufficient to examine the case of a circular cylinder of radius a, twisted by tractions of the type $\widehat{\theta z}$ distributed over the terminal section $z=0$. We shall suppose that z is positive within the cylinder. Then a solution of the equation for ψ can be written

$$\psi=\tfrac{1}{4}\tau r^4+\sum_{n=1}^{\infty} A_n r^2 e^{-k_n z} J_2(k_n r),$$

where τ, A_1, A_2, ... are constants, and k_1, k_2, ... are the roots, in order of increasing magnitude of the equation $J_2(ka)=0$. The corresponding value of $\widehat{\theta z}$ at the section $z=0$ is given by the equation

$$(\widehat{\theta z})_{z=0}=\mu\left\{\tau r+\sum_{n=1}^{\infty} A_n k_n J_1(k_n r)\right\},$$

for
$$\frac{1}{r^2}\frac{d}{dr}\{r^2 J_2(kr)\}=k\left\{J_2'(kr)+\frac{2}{kr}J_2(kr)\right\}=k\,J_1(kr),$$

where the accent denotes differentiation of the function $J_2(kr)$ with respect to its argument kr, and $J_1(kr)$ denotes Bessel's function of order 1.

The equation
$$J_2(kr)=-J_1'(kr)+\frac{1}{kr}J_1(kr)$$

shows that k_1, k_2, ... are the roots of the equation

$$J_1'(ka)=\frac{1}{ka}J_1(ka),$$

and the equation $$\left(\frac{d^2}{dr^2}+\frac{1}{r}\frac{d}{dr}+k^2-\frac{1}{r^2}\right)J_1(kr)=0$$
shows that
$$\int_0^a r^2 J_1(kr)\,dr = -\frac{1}{k^2}\int_0^a \left(r^2\frac{d^2}{dr^2}+r\frac{d}{dr}-1\right)J_1(kr)\,dr$$
$$= -\frac{1}{k^2}\int_0^a \frac{d}{dr}\left\{r^2\frac{dJ_1(kr)}{dr}-rJ_1(kr)\right\}dr$$
$$= -\frac{a^2}{k}\left\{J_1'(ka)-\frac{1}{ka}J_1(ka)\right\}.$$
Hence the twisting couple, which is
$$\int_0^a r\,(\widehat{\theta z})_{z=0}\,2\pi r\,dr,$$
is $\frac{1}{2}\mu\pi a^4\tau$, and the terms in $J_2(k_n r)$ contribute nothing to this couple for any of the values of k which can occur.

It is known* that an arbitrary function of r can be expanded, within the interval $a > r > 0$, in a series of the form
$$\Sigma\, a_n J_1(k_n r),$$
where the k's are roots of the equation
$$J_1'(ka)/J_1(ka) = 1/ka.$$
Thus we see that the assumed formula for ψ can represent the effect of any forces of the type $\widehat{\theta z}$ which are statically equivalent to the couple $\frac{1}{2}\mu\pi a^4\tau$. The occurrence of the factors $e^{-k_n z}$ shows that the effects due to the distribution of the forces constituting the couple, as distinguished from their resultant moment, diminish exponentially as the distance from the terminal section increases.

The analysis of this Article was given effectively by F. Purser, *Dublin, Roy. Irish Acad. Proc.*, vol. 26, Sect. A, 1906, p. 54, afterwards in a more general form by O. Tedone, *Roma, Acc. Linc. Rend.* (Ser. 5), t. 20, (Sem. 2), 1911, p. 617. The corresponding theory for twisting couple applied by means of tractions, exerted upon a portion of the cylindrical boundary, can be worked out by means of solutions of the equation for ψ of the form
$$(A\cos kz + B\sin kz)\,r^2 J_2(ikr).$$

This theory was obtained effectively by another method by L. N. G. Filon, *Phil. Trans. Roy. Soc.* (Ser. A), vol. 198, 1902, p. 147, afterwards more completely by A. Timpe, *Math. Ann.*, Bd. 71, 1912, p. 480.

The effect of various methods of applying torsional couple to a circular cylinder is discussed by K. Wolf, *Wien Ber.*, Bd. 125 (1916), p. 1149. The torsion of a rectangular prism, one of whose cross-sections is constrained to remain plane, is considered by S. Timoschenko, *London Math. Soc. Proc.* (Ser. 2), vol. 20 (1922), p. 389.

* See Lord Rayleigh, *Theory of Sound*, vol. 1, § 203, and G. N. Watson, *Theory of Bessel Functions*, Cambridge, 1922, Ch. 18.

CHAPTER XV

THE BENDING OF A BEAM BY TERMINAL TRANSVERSE LOAD

227. Stress in a bent beam.

In Article 87 we described the state of stress in a cylinder or prism of any form of section held bent by terminal couples. The stress at a point consisted of longitudinal tension, or pressure, expressed by the formula

$$\text{tension} = -Mx/I,$$

where M is the bending moment, the plane of (y, z) contains the central-line, the axis of x is directed towards the centre of curvature, and I is the moment of inertia of the cross-section about an axis through its centroid at right angles to the plane of bending. In Article 95 we showed how an extension of this theory could be made to the problem of the bending of a rectangular beam, of small breadth, by terminal transverse load. We found that the requisite stress-system involved tangential traction on the cross-sections as well as longitudinal tensions and pressures, but that the requisite tension, or pressure, was determined in terms of the bending moment by the same formula as in the case of bending by terminal couples. This theory will now be generalized for a beam of any form of section*. Tangential tractions on the elements of the cross-sections imply equal tangential tractions, acting in the direction of the central-line, on elements of properly chosen longitudinal sections, the two tangential tractions at each point constituting a *shearing stress.* It is natural to expect that the stress-system which we seek to determine consists of longitudinal tensions, and pressures, determined as above, together with shearing stress, involving suitably directed tangential tractions on the elements of the cross-sections. We shall verify this anticipation, and shall show that there is one, and only one, distribution of shearing stress by means of which the problem can be solved.

228. Statement of the problem.

To fix ideas we take the central-line of the beam to be horizontal, and one end of it to be fixed, and we suppose that forces are applied to the cross-section through this end so as to keep the beam in a nearly horizontal position, and that forces are applied to the cross-section containing the other end in such a way as to be statically equivalent to a vertical load W acting in a line through the centroid of the section. We take the origin at the fixed end, and the axis of z along the central-line, and we draw the axis of x vertically downwards. Further we suppose that the axes of x and y are parallel to the

* The theory is due to Saint-Venant. See Introduction, footnote 50, and p. 20.

principal axes of inertia of the cross-sections at their centroids. We denote the length of the beam by l, and suppose the material to be isotropic. We consider the case in which there are no body forces and no tractions on the cylindrical bounding surface.

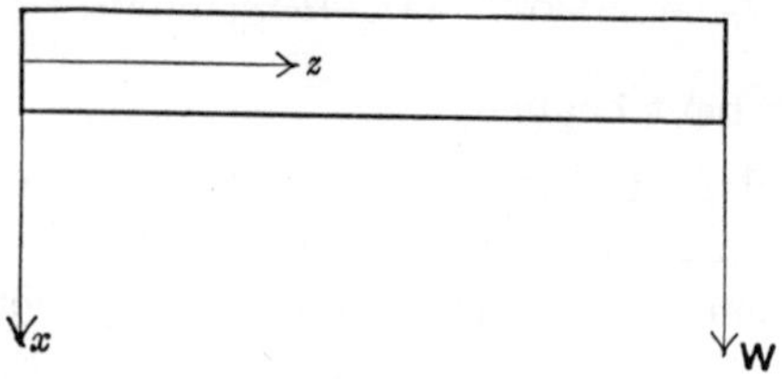

Fig. 25.

The bending moment at the cross-section distant z from the fixed end is $W(l-z)$. We assume that the tension on any element of this section is given by the equation

$$Z_z = -W(l-z)\,x/I, \quad \text{..........................(1)}$$

where I stands for the integral $\iint x^2\,dx\,dy$ taken over the area of the cross-section. We assume that the stress consists of this tension Z_z and shearing stress having components X_z and Y_z, so that the stress-components X_x, Y_y, X_y vanish; and we seek to determine the components of shearing stress X_z and Y_z.

Two of the equations of equilibrium become $\partial X_z/\partial z = 0$, $\partial Y_z/\partial z = 0$, and it follows that X_z and Y_z must be independent of z. The third of the equations of equilibrium becomes

$$\frac{\partial X_z}{\partial x} + \frac{\partial Y_z}{\partial y} + \frac{Wx}{I} = 0. \quad \text{..........................(2)}$$

The condition that the cylindrical bounding surface is free from traction is

$$X_z \cos(x, \nu) + Y_z \cos(y, \nu) = 0. \quad \text{.....................(3)}$$

The problem before us is to determine X_z and Y_z as functions of x and y in accordance with the following conditions:

(i) The differential equation (2) is satisfied at all points of the cross-section of the beam.

(ii) The condition (3) is satisfied at all points of the bounding curve of this section.

(iii) The tractions on the elements of area of the terminal cross-section ($z = l$) are statically equivalent to a force W, directed parallel to the axis of x, and acting at the centroid of the section.

(iv) The stress-system in which $X_x = Y_y = X_y = 0$, Z_z is given by (1), and X_z, Y_z satisfy the conditions already stated, is such that the conditions of compatibility of strain-components (Article 17) are satisfied.

229. Necessary type of shearing stress.

The assumed stress-system satisfies the equations

$$X_x = Y_y = X_y = 0,\ Z_z = -W(l-z)\,x/I,\ \frac{\partial X_z}{\partial z} = \frac{\partial Y_z}{\partial z} = 0,$$

and consequently the strain-components satisfy the equations

$$e_{zz} = -\frac{W(l-z)\,x}{EI},\ e_{xx} = e_{yy} = -\sigma e_{zz},\ e_{xy} = 0,\ \frac{\partial e_{zx}}{\partial z} = \frac{\partial e_{yz}}{\partial z} = 0,$$

where E and σ denote the Young's modulus and Poisson's ratio of the material.

The equations of compatibility of the type

$$\frac{\partial^2 e_{yy}}{\partial z^2} + \frac{\partial^2 e_{zz}}{\partial y^2} = \frac{\partial^2 e_{yz}}{\partial y\,\partial z}$$

are satisfied identically, as also is the equation

$$2\frac{\partial^2 e_{zz}}{\partial x \partial y} = \frac{\partial}{\partial z}\left(\frac{\partial e_{yz}}{\partial x} + \frac{\partial e_{zx}}{\partial y} - \frac{\partial e_{xy}}{\partial z}\right).$$

The remaining equations of compatibility of this type become

$$\frac{\partial}{\partial x}\left(\frac{\partial e_{yz}}{\partial x} - \frac{\partial e_{zx}}{\partial y}\right) = 0,\quad \frac{\partial}{\partial y}\left(\frac{\partial e_{yz}}{\partial x} - \frac{\partial e_{zx}}{\partial y}\right) = -\frac{2\sigma W}{EI}.$$

From these equations we deduce the equation

$$\frac{\partial e_{yz}}{\partial x} - \frac{\partial e_{zx}}{\partial y} = 2\tau - \frac{2\sigma W}{EI}\,y,$$

where 2τ is a constant of integration; and from this equation it follows that e_{yz} and e_{zx} can be expressed in the forms

$$e_{yz} = \tau x + \frac{\partial \phi_0}{\partial y},\quad e_{zx} = -\tau y + \frac{\partial \phi_0}{\partial x} + \frac{\sigma W}{EI}\,y^2, \quad \text{..............(4)}$$

where ϕ_0 is a function of x and y.

On substituting from these equations in the formulæ $X_z = \mu e_{zx}$ and $Y_z = \mu e_{yz}$, and using the relation $\mu = \frac{1}{2}E/(1+\sigma)$, we see that equation (2) takes the form

$$\frac{\partial^2 \phi_0}{\partial x^2} + \frac{\partial^2 \phi_0}{\partial y^2} + \frac{2(1+\sigma)\,W}{EI}\,x = 0,$$

and condition (3) takes the form

$$\frac{\partial \phi_0}{\partial \nu} = \tau\,\{y \cos(x, \nu) - x \cos(y, \nu)\} - \frac{\sigma W}{EI}\,y^2 \cos(x, \nu).$$

These relations are simplified by putting

$$\phi_0 = \tau\phi - \frac{W}{EI}\{\chi + \tfrac{1}{6}\sigma x^3 + (1 + \tfrac{1}{2}\sigma)\,xy^2\}. \quad \text{..............(5)}$$

Then ϕ is the torsion function for the section (Article 216), and χ is a function which satisfies the equation

$$\frac{\partial^2 \chi}{\partial x^2} + \frac{\partial^2 \chi}{\partial y^2} = 0 \quad \text{..................................(6)}$$

at all points of a cross-section, and the condition

$$\frac{\partial \chi}{\partial \nu} = -\left\{\tfrac{1}{2}\sigma x^2 + \left(1 - \tfrac{1}{2}\sigma\right) y^2\right\} \cos(x, \nu) - (2+\sigma)\, xy \cos(y, \nu) \quad \ldots\ldots(7)$$

at all points of the bounding curve. The compatibility of the differential equation (6) and the boundary-condition (7) is shown by observing that, since the integral $\iint x\,dx\,dy$ taken over the cross-section vanishes, the integral of the right-hand member of (7) taken round the boundary vanishes. The problem of determining the function χ from equation (6) and condition (7) may be called the "flexure problem" for the section.

When the functions ϕ and χ are known the shearing stresses X_z and Y_z are known in the forms

$$\left.\begin{aligned} X_z &= \mu\tau\left(\frac{\partial \phi}{\partial x} - y\right) - \frac{W}{2(1+\sigma) I}\left\{\frac{\partial \chi}{\partial x} + \tfrac{1}{2}\sigma x^2 + \left(1 - \tfrac{1}{2}\sigma\right) y^2\right\}, \\ Y_z &= \mu\tau\left(\frac{\partial \phi}{\partial y} + x\right) - \frac{W}{2(1+\sigma) I}\left\{\frac{\partial \chi}{\partial y} + (2+\sigma)\, xy\right\}. \end{aligned}\right\} \quad \ldots(8)$$

The terms that contain τ are of the same form as the tractions in the torsion problem; and they express a system of tractions on the elements of area of the cross-section, which are statically equivalent to a couple about the axis z of moment

$$\mu\tau \iint \left(x^2 + y^2 + x\frac{\partial \phi}{\partial y} - y\frac{\partial \phi}{\partial x}\right) dx\,dy.$$

The terms which contain W would give rise to a couple about the same axis of moment

$$\frac{W}{2(1+\sigma) I}\iint \left\{y\frac{\partial \chi}{\partial x} - x\frac{\partial \chi}{\partial y} + \left(1 - \tfrac{1}{2}\sigma\right) y^3 - \left(2 + \tfrac{1}{2}\sigma\right) x^2 y\right\} dx\,dy.$$

We adjust τ so that the sum of these couples vanishes.

The tractions on the elements of area of a cross-section are statically equivalent to a certain force at the centroid of the section and a certain couple. We show that the force is of magnitude W and is directed parallel to the axis of x, and that the couple is of moment $W(l-z)$ and has its axis parallel to the axis of y. These statements are equivalent to the equations

$$\iint X_z\,dx\,dy = W, \quad \iint Y_z\,dx\,dy = 0, \quad \iint Z_z\,dx\,dy = 0, \quad \ldots\ldots\ldots(9)$$

and

$$\iint y\, Z_z\,dx\,dy = 0, \quad \iint - x Z_z\,dx\,dy = W(l-z), \quad \iint (xY_z - yX_z)\,dx\,dy = 0. \ldots(10)$$

Now by (2) and (3) we may write down the equations

$$\begin{aligned} \iint X_z\,dx\,dy &= \iint \left\{X_z + x\left(\frac{\partial X_z}{\partial x} + \frac{\partial Y_z}{\partial y}\right) + \frac{Wx^2}{I}\right\} dx\,dy \\ &= W + \int x\left\{X_z \cos(x, \nu) + Y_z \cos(y, \nu)\right\} ds \\ &= W. \end{aligned}$$

In like manner, observing that $\iint xy\,dx\,dy$ vanishes, we may prove the second of equations (9). The third of these equations and the first two of equations (10) follow at once from the formula (1) for Z_z, and the constant τ has already been adjusted so that the third of equations (10) shall be satisfied.

The functions ϕ and χ are each determinate, except for an additive constant which does not affect the stress. In the case of a hollow shaft it is necessary to impose the condition that ϕ and χ must be one-valued. Cf. Article 222 (iii) *supra*. We have therefore shown that the problem stated in Article 228 admits of one, and only one, solution.

230. Formulæ for the displacement.

The displacement can be deduced from the strain without determining the forms of ϕ and χ. The details of the work are as follows:

We have the equation

$$\frac{\partial w}{\partial z} = -\frac{W(l-z)x}{EI},$$

from which we deduce the equation

$$w = -\frac{Wl}{EI}xz + \frac{1}{2}\frac{W}{EI}xz^2 + \phi', \qquad \text{.............................(11)}$$

where ϕ' is a function of x and y. Again, we have the equations

$$\left.\begin{aligned} \frac{\partial u}{\partial x} &= \sigma\frac{Wl}{EI}x - \sigma\frac{W}{EI}zx, \\ \frac{\partial u}{\partial z} &= \frac{Wl}{EI}z - \frac{1}{2}\frac{W}{EI}z^2 - \tau y + \frac{\sigma W}{EI}y^2 + \frac{\partial \phi_0}{\partial x} - \frac{\partial \phi'}{\partial x}, \end{aligned}\right\}$$

of which the second is obtained from (11) and the second of (4). These two equations are compatible if

$$\frac{\partial^2(\phi_0 - \phi')}{\partial x^2} + \sigma\frac{W}{EI}x = 0.$$

Again, we have the equations

$$\left.\begin{aligned} \frac{\partial v}{\partial y} &= \sigma\frac{Wl}{EI}x - \sigma\frac{W}{EI}zx, \\ \frac{\partial v}{\partial z} &= \tau x + \frac{\partial \phi_0}{\partial y} - \frac{\partial \phi'}{\partial y}; \end{aligned}\right\}$$

and these are compatible if

$$\frac{\partial^2(\phi_0 - \phi')}{\partial y^2} + \sigma\frac{W}{EI}x = 0.$$

Further, by differentiating the left-hand member of the equation $\frac{\partial u}{\partial y} + \frac{\partial v}{\partial x} = 0$ with respect to z, we obtain the equation

$$\frac{\partial^2(\phi_0 - \phi')}{\partial x \partial y} + \sigma\frac{W}{EI}y = 0.$$

The three equations for $\phi_0 - \phi'$ show that we must have

$$\phi' = \phi_0 + \sigma\frac{W}{EI}\left(\tfrac{1}{6}x^3 + \tfrac{1}{2}xy^2\right) - \beta x + \alpha y + \gamma',$$

where α, β, γ' are constants. When we substitute for ϕ_0 from (5) we find the following expression for ϕ':

$$\phi' = \tau\phi - \frac{W}{EI}(\chi + xy^2) - \beta x + \alpha y + \gamma'.$$

The displacement w is now determined. When we substitute for ϕ' in the equations for $\partial u/\partial z$ and $\partial v/\partial z$, we obtain the equations

$$\frac{\partial u}{\partial z} = -\tau y + \frac{W}{EI}\{lz - \tfrac{1}{2}z^2 - \tfrac{1}{2}\sigma(x^2 - y^2)\} + \beta,$$

$$\frac{\partial v}{\partial z} = \tau x - \sigma\frac{W}{EI}xy - \alpha.$$

From the equations for $\partial u/\partial x$ and $\partial u/\partial z$ we obtain the following form for u:

$$u = -\tau yz + \frac{W}{EI}[\tfrac{1}{2}l(z^2 + \sigma x^2) - \tfrac{1}{2}z\sigma(x^2 - y^2) - \tfrac{1}{6}z^3] + \beta z + F_1(y),$$

where $F_1(y)$ is an unknown function of y. In like manner we find the following form for v:

$$v = \tau zx + \frac{W}{EI}\sigma(l - z)xy - \alpha z + F_2(x),$$

where $F_2(x)$ is an unknown function of x. Since $\partial u/\partial y + \partial v/\partial x = 0$, the functions F_1, F_2 satisfy the equation

$$\frac{\partial F_1}{\partial y} + \frac{\partial F_2}{\partial x} + \sigma\frac{W}{EI}ly = 0;$$

and we must have

$$F_1(y) = -\tfrac{1}{2}\sigma\frac{W}{EI}ly^2 - \gamma y + \alpha', \quad F_2(x) = \gamma x + \beta',$$

where α', β', γ are constants of integration.

We have now found the displacement in the form

$$\left.\begin{aligned} u &= -\tau yz + \frac{W}{EI}[\tfrac{1}{2}(l - z)\sigma(x^2 - y^2) + \tfrac{1}{2}lz^2 - \tfrac{1}{6}z^3] - \gamma y + \beta z + \alpha', \\ v &= \tau zx + \frac{W}{EI}\sigma(l - z)xy + \gamma x - \alpha z + \beta', \\ w &= \tau\phi - \frac{W}{EI}[x(lz - \tfrac{1}{2}z^2) + \chi + xy^2] - \beta x + \alpha y + \gamma', \end{aligned}\right\} \quad \ldots(12)$$

in which α, β, γ, α', β', γ' are constants of integration. These equations give the most general possible form for the displacement (u, v, w) when the stress is determined by the conditions stated in Article 228.

The terms of (12) that contain α, β, γ, α', β', γ' represent a displacement which would be possible in a rigid body, and these constants are to be determined by imposing some conditions of fixity at the origin. (Cf. Article 18.)

We have supposed that the origin is fixed, and we must therefore have $\alpha' = 0$, $\beta' = 0$. We shall, in general, suppose that the additive constants in the expressions for ϕ and χ are determined so that these functions vanish at the origin. Then we must also have $\gamma' = 0$.

Besides fixing a point, we may fix a line through the point. We shall suppose that the linear element which, in the unstressed state, lies along the axis of y retains its primitive direction. Then we must have $\alpha = 0$, $\gamma = 0$.

Besides fixing a point, and a linear element through the point, we may fix a surface element through the line. The value of the constant β depends upon the choice of this element. If we choose the element of the cross-section, we must have $\partial w/\partial x = 0$ at the origin. If we choose the element of the neutral plane (i.e. the plane $x=0$), we must have $\partial u/\partial z = 0$ at the origin. In the former case the central element of the cross-section at the fixed end remains vertical; in the latter case the element of the central-line at the fixed end remains horizontal. There is no reason for assuming that in all practical cases either of these conditions holds; most probably different values of β fit the circumstances of different particular cases.

231. Solution of the problem of flexure for certain boundaries.

We shall now show how to find the function χ from the equation (6) and the condition (7) when the boundary of the section of the beam has one or other of certain special forms. The constant which may be added to χ will generally be chosen so that χ vanishes at the origin.

(a) *The circle.*

The equation of the bounding curve is $x^2 + y^2 = a^2$. In terms of polar coordinates (r, θ) the boundary condition at the curve $r = a$ is

$$\frac{\partial \chi}{\partial r} = -a^2 \cos\theta \{\tfrac{1}{2}\sigma \cos^2\theta + (1 - \tfrac{1}{2}\sigma)\sin^2\theta\} - a^2 \sin\theta \{(2+\sigma)\sin\theta\cos\theta\},$$

or $$\frac{\partial \chi}{\partial r} = -(\tfrac{3}{4} + \tfrac{1}{2}\sigma)\, a^2 \cos\theta + \tfrac{3}{4} a^2 \cos 3\theta.$$

Since χ is a plane harmonic function within the circle $r = a$, we must have

$$\chi = -(\tfrac{3}{4} + \tfrac{1}{2}\sigma)\, a^2 r \cos\theta + \tfrac{1}{4} r^3 \cos 3\theta,$$

or $$\chi = -(\tfrac{3}{4} + \tfrac{1}{2}\sigma)\, a^2 x + \tfrac{1}{4}(x^3 - 3xy^2). \qquad \text{..................(13)}$$

(b) *Concentric circles.*

The beam has the form of a hollow tube. If a_0 is the radius of the outer circle, and a_1 that of the inner, we may prove that χ is of the form

$$\chi = -(\tfrac{3}{4} + \tfrac{1}{2}\sigma)\left\{(a_0^2 + a_1^2)\, r + \frac{a_0^2 a_1^2}{r}\right\}\cos\theta + \tfrac{1}{4} r^3 \cos 3\theta + \text{const.} \qquad \text{........(14)}$$

In this case we cannot adjust the additive constant so as to make χ vanish at the origin, but the origin is in the cavity of the tube.

(c) *The ellipse.*

The equation of the bounding curve is $x^2/a^2 + y^2/b^2 = 1$. We introduce conjugate functions ξ, η by means of the relation

$$x + \iota y = (a^2 - b^2)^{\frac{1}{2}} \cosh(\xi + \iota\eta),$$

and denote $\left|\dfrac{d(\xi + \iota\eta)}{d(x + \iota y)}\right|$ by h. The value of h at a point on the boundary is

p/ab, where p is the central perpendicular on the tangent at the point. The boundary-condition may be written

$$h\frac{\partial\chi}{\partial\xi}=-\frac{px}{a^2}\{\tfrac{1}{2}\sigma x^2+(1-\tfrac{1}{2}\sigma)y^2\}-\frac{py}{b^2}(2+\sigma)xy,$$

or

$$\frac{\partial\chi}{\partial\xi}=-b\cos\eta\{\tfrac{1}{2}\sigma a^2\cos^2\eta+(1-\tfrac{1}{2}\sigma)b^2\sin^2\eta\}-a\sin\eta(2+\sigma)ab\sin\eta\cos\eta;$$

and this is the same as

$$\frac{\partial\chi}{\partial\xi}=-[(\tfrac{1}{2}+\tfrac{5}{8}\sigma)a^2b+(\tfrac{1}{4}-\tfrac{1}{8}\sigma)b^3]\cos\eta+[(\tfrac{1}{2}+\tfrac{1}{8}\sigma)a^2b+(\tfrac{1}{4}-\tfrac{1}{8}\sigma)b^3]\cos 3\eta.$$

Hence we must have

$$\chi=-[(\tfrac{1}{2}+\tfrac{5}{8}\sigma)a^2b+(\tfrac{1}{4}-\tfrac{1}{8}\sigma)b^3]\frac{\cosh\xi}{\sinh\xi_0}\cos\eta$$
$$+\tfrac{1}{3}[(\tfrac{1}{2}+\tfrac{1}{8}\sigma)a^2b+(\tfrac{1}{4}-\tfrac{1}{8}\sigma)b^3]\frac{\cosh 3\xi}{\sinh 3\xi_0}\cos 3\eta,$$

where ξ_0 denotes the value of ξ at the boundary, so that

$$(a^2-b^2)^{\frac{1}{2}}\cosh\xi_0=a,\quad (a^2-b^2)^{\frac{1}{2}}\sinh\xi_0=b.$$

Now we have

$$(x+\iota y)^3=(a^2-b^2)^{\frac{3}{2}}\tfrac{1}{4}\{\cosh 3(\xi+\iota\eta)+3\cosh(\xi+\iota\eta)\},$$

so that

$$4\frac{x^3-3xy^2}{(a^2-b^2)^{\frac{3}{2}}}-3\frac{x}{(a^2-b^2)^{\frac{1}{2}}}=\cosh 3\xi\cos 3\eta.$$

Also we have

$$\sinh 3\xi_0=4\sinh^3\xi_0+3\sinh\xi_0.$$

Hence we find

$$\chi=-[(\tfrac{1}{2}+\tfrac{5}{8}\sigma)a^2+(\tfrac{1}{4}-\tfrac{1}{8}\sigma)b^2]x$$
$$+\tfrac{1}{3}[(\tfrac{1}{2}+\tfrac{1}{8}\sigma)a^2+(\tfrac{1}{4}-\tfrac{1}{8}\sigma)b^2]\frac{4(x^3-3xy^2)-3x(a^2-b^2)}{3a^2+b^2},$$

or

$$\chi=-\frac{a^2\{2(1+\sigma)a^2+b^2\}}{3a^2+b^2}x+\frac{1}{3}\frac{2a^2+b^2+\frac{1}{2}\sigma(a^2-b^2)}{3a^2+b^2}(x^3-3xy^2).\quad\ldots(15)$$

In the above analysis we have proceeded as if a were greater than b, but it is easy to verify that the final result holds also when $b>a$. In case $b=a$ this result reduces to that already found for the circle.

(*d*) *Confocal ellipses.*

By an analysis similar to the above the problem might be solved for a section bounded by two confocal ellipses. The result could not be expressed rationally in terms of x and y. Taking ξ_0 and ξ_1 to be the values of ξ which correspond with the outer and inner boundaries, and writing c for $(a^2-b^2)^{\frac{1}{2}}$, we may show that

$$\chi=c^3\cos\eta[(\tfrac{1}{4}-\tfrac{1}{8}\sigma)\cosh\xi-(\tfrac{3}{4}+\tfrac{1}{2}\sigma)\{\cosh\xi_0\cosh\xi_1\cosh(\xi_0+\xi_1)\cosh\xi$$
$$-\sinh\xi_0\sinh\xi_1\sinh(\xi_0+\xi_1)\sinh\xi\}]$$
$$+c^3\cos 3\eta\left[\tfrac{1}{16}\cosh 3\xi-(\tfrac{5}{16}+\tfrac{1}{8}\sigma)\frac{\sinh\xi_0\cosh 3(\xi-\xi_1)-\sinh\xi_1\cosh 3(\xi_0-\xi)}{3\sinh 3(\xi_0-\xi_1)}\right].\quad(16)$$

(*e*) *The rectangle.*

The equations of the boundaries are $x = \pm a$, $y = \pm b$. The boundary-condition at $x = \pm a$ is

$$\frac{\partial \chi}{\partial x} = -\left\{\tfrac{1}{2}\sigma a^2 + (1 - \tfrac{1}{2}\sigma)\, y^2\right\}, \quad (b > y > -b).$$

The boundary-condition at $y = \pm b$ is

$$\frac{\partial \chi}{\partial y} = \mp (2 + \sigma)\, bx, \quad (a > x > -a).$$

We introduce a new function χ' by the equation

$$\chi' = \chi - \tfrac{1}{6}(2 + \sigma)(x^3 - 3xy^2). \quad \text{......................(17)}$$

Then χ' is a plane harmonic function within the rectangle, $\partial\chi'/\partial y$ vanishes at $y = \pm b$, and the condition at $x = \pm a$ becomes

$$\frac{\partial \chi'}{\partial x} = -(1 + \sigma)\, a^2 + \sigma y^2.$$

Now when $b > y > -b$ the function y^2 can be expanded in a Fourier's series as follows:

$$y^2 = \frac{b^2}{3} + \frac{4b^2}{\pi^2} \sum_{n=1}^{\infty} \frac{(-)^n}{n^2} \cos\frac{n\pi y}{b}.$$

Hence χ' can be expressed in the form

$$\chi' = \left\{-(1 + \sigma)\, a^2 + \tfrac{1}{3}\sigma b^2\right\} x + \sigma \frac{4b^3}{\pi^3} \sum_{n=1}^{\infty} \frac{(-)^n}{n^3} \frac{\sinh \dfrac{n\pi x}{b}}{\cosh \dfrac{n\pi a}{b}} \cos\frac{n\pi y}{b}, \text{...(18)}$$

and, by means of this and (17), χ can be written down.

(*f*) *Additional results.*

The results for the circle and ellipse are included in the formula

$$\chi = Ax + B(x^3 - 3xy^2);$$

the solution for the ellipse was first found by adjusting the constants A and B of this formula, and several other examples of the same method were discussed by Saint-Venant. Among sections for which the problem is solved by this formula we may note the curve of which the ordinate is given by the equation

$$y = \pm b \,|\, (1 - x^2/a^2)^\sigma \,|, \quad (a > x > -a).$$

The corresponding function χ is

$$\chi = -a^2 x + \tfrac{1}{3}(1 - \tfrac{1}{2}\sigma)(x^3 - 3xy^2).$$

When $\sigma = \frac{1}{4}$ the above equation becomes $x^2/a^2 + y^4/b^4 = 1$. The curve is shown in Fig. 26 for the case where $a = 2b$.

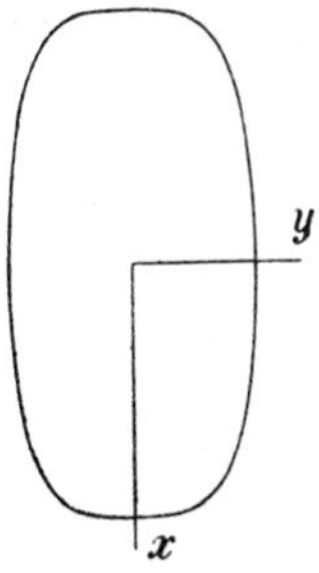

Fig. 26.

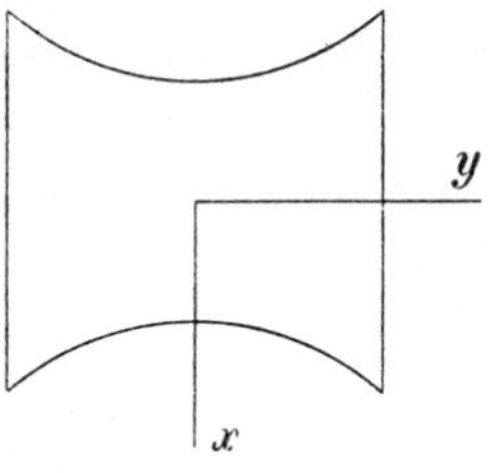

Fig. 27.

As another example we may observe that the formula*

$$\chi = -a^2x + \tfrac{1}{6}(2+\sigma)(x^3 - 3xy^2)$$

solves the problem for a section bounded by two arcs of the hyperbola $x^2(1+\sigma) - y^2\sigma = a^2$ and two straight lines $y = \pm a$. The section is shown in Fig. 27, σ being taken to be $\frac{1}{4}$.

232. Analysis of the displacement.

(a) *Curvature of the strained central-line.*

The central-line of the beam is bent into a curve of which the curvatures in the planes (x, z) and (y, z) are expressed with sufficient approximation by the values of $\partial^2 u/\partial z^2$ and $\partial^2 v/\partial z^2$ when x and y vanish. These quantities can be calculated from the expressions for the components of strain by means of the formulæ

$$\frac{\partial^2 u}{\partial z^2} = \frac{\partial e_{zx}}{\partial z} - \frac{\partial e_{zz}}{\partial x}, \quad \frac{\partial^2 v}{\partial z^2} = \frac{\partial e_{yz}}{\partial z} - \frac{\partial e_{zz}}{\partial y},$$

or they may be calculated from equations (12). We find

$$\frac{\partial^2 u}{\partial z^2} = \frac{W(l-z)}{EI}, \quad \frac{\partial^2 v}{\partial z^2} = 0.$$

It follows that the plane of the curve into which the central-line is bent is the plane of (x, z), and that its radius of curvature R at any point is equal to $EI/W(l-z)$. The denominator of this expression is the bending moment, M say; and therefore the curvature $1/R$ of the central-line is connected with the bending moment M by the equation

$$M = EI/R, \quad \text{..............................(19)}$$

and the curvature at any point is the same as it would be if the beam were bent by terminal couples equal to the value of M at the point.

(b) *Neutral plane.*

The extension of any longitudinal filament is given by the equation

$$e_{zz} = -x/R. \quad \text{..............................(20)}$$

It follows that filaments which lie in the plane $x = 0$ suffer no extension or contraction; in other words, this plane is a "neutral plane." The extension, or contraction, of any longitudinal linear element is determined by its distance from the neutral plane and the curvature of the central-line, by exactly the same rule as holds in the case of bending by terminal couples.

(c) *Obliquity of the strained cross-sections.*

The strained central-line is not at right angles to the strained cross-sections, but the cosine of the angle at which they cut is the value, at any point of the central-line, of the strain-component e_{zx}. We shall denote it by s_0. Then we have

$$s_0 = \frac{\text{shearing stress at centroid}}{\text{rigidity of material}}, \quad \text{.................(21)}$$

* Grashof, *Elasticität und Festigkeit*, p. 246.

and we may calculate s_0 by the formula

$$s_0 = -(W/EI)(\partial\chi/\partial x)_0, \quad \text{......................(22)}$$

where the suffix 0 indicates that zero is to be substituted for x and y after the differentiation has been performed.

The quantity s_0 is a small constant, so that all the strained cross-sections cut the strained central-line at the same angle $\frac{1}{2}\pi - s_0$. The relative situation of the strained central-line and an initially vertical filament is illustrated by Fig. 14 in Article 95.

If the element of the strained cross-section at the centroid of the fixed end is vertical, the constant β in the displacement, as given by (12), is equal to s_0*.

When the bounding curve is the ellipse $x^2/a^2+y^2/b^2=1$, we find

$$s_0 = \frac{4W}{E\pi ab}\frac{2a^2(1+\sigma)+b^2}{3a^2+b^2}.$$

If in (21) the shearing stress at the centroid were replaced by the average shearing stress $(W/\pi ab)$, the estimated value of s_0 would be too small, in a ratio varying from $\frac{3}{4}$, when a is large compared with b, to $\frac{5}{8}$ when b is large compared with a†.

When the boundary is a rectangle we find

$$s_0 = \frac{3W(1+\sigma)}{4Eab}\left[1 - \frac{\sigma}{1+\sigma}\frac{b^2}{a^2}\left\{\frac{1}{3} + \frac{4}{\pi^2}\sum_{n=1}^{\infty}\frac{(-1)^n}{n^2\cosh\frac{n\pi a}{b}}\right\}\right]. \quad \text{...............(23)}$$

The expression in square brackets was tabulated by Saint-Venant, σ being taken to be $\frac{1}{4}$, with the following results:

a/b	·25	·5	·75	1	1·25	1·5	2	2·5	3
value of expression	·676	·849	·907	·94	·962	·971	·983	·989	·993

(*d*) *Deflexion.*

The deflexion of the beam is the displacement of a point on the central-line in the direction of the load; it is the value of u when $x = y = 0$. If we denote it by ξ we have

$$\xi = \frac{W}{EI}\left(\tfrac{1}{2}z^2 l - \tfrac{1}{6}z^3\right) + \beta z. \quad \text{......................(24)}$$

The equation

$$EI\frac{d^2\xi}{dz^2} = W(l-z), \quad \text{........................(25)}$$

which expresses the proportionality of the bending moment to the curvature, would suffice to determine the deflexion if the direction of the strained central-line at the origin were known. Equation (24) is the primitive of (25) when the condition that ξ vanishes with z is imposed. The term βz in (24) depends

* In Saint-Venant's memoir β is identified with s_0.

† In obtaining these numbers σ is put equal to $\frac{1}{4}$.

on the mode of fixing, as has been explained at the end of Article 230; the other term depends on the bending moment.

(*e*) *Twist.*

The terms of (11) which contain the constant τ indicate that the beam twists under the load. The amount of the twist cannot be determined until the functions ϕ and χ have been found. In each of the particular cases that we have solved τ vanishes. This is due to the symmetry of the sections. An example of an unsymmetrical form of section for which the analysis could be worked out is shown in Fig. 28, which represents the cross-section of a hollow tube with a cavity placed excentrically. (Cf. Article 222, Result iii.) The case of a cantilever whose cross-section is a sector of a circle, or is bounded by two concentric circles and two radii, the load-plane being at right angles to the axes of symmetry, is discussed in detail by M. Seegar and K. Pearson*. The case where the section is an isosceles triangle is treated by S. Timoschenko. (See Article 234C, *infra.*)

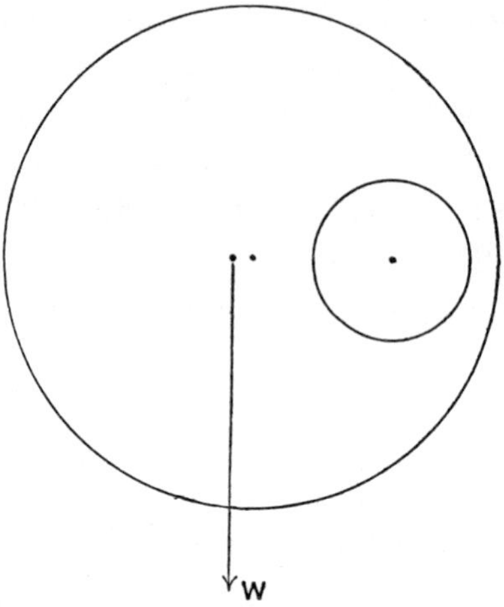

Fig. 28.

(*f*) *Anticlastic curvature.*

The terms of u, v, as given by (12), which depend on x, y, but not on τ, represent changes of shape of the cross-sections in their own planes. These changes are of the same kind as those described in Article 88. It follows that the neutral plane is deformed into an anticlastic surface. The strained central-line is one of the lines of curvature of this surface; the corresponding centres of curvature are below the neutral plane, and the corresponding radii of curvature are expressed by the formula $EI/W(l-z)$. The other centre of curvature of the surface, at any point of the central-line, is above the neutral plane; and the corresponding radii of curvature are expressed by the formula $EI/\sigma W(l-z)$.

(*g*) *Distortion of the cross-sections into curved surfaces.*

The expression for w may be written

$$w = \tau\phi - \frac{W}{EI}x(lz - \tfrac{1}{2}z^2) - \beta x + s_0 x - \frac{W}{EI}\left[\chi - x\left(\frac{\partial\chi}{\partial x}\right)_0 + xy^2\right]. \quad ..(26)$$

The term $\tau\phi$ corresponds with the twisting of the beam by the load, and we know that it represents a distortion of the cross-sections into curved surfaces. The terms $-x\{W(lz-\frac{1}{2}z^2)/EI+\beta\}$ represent a displacement by which the

* *London, Roy. Soc. Proc.* (Ser. A), vol. 96 (1920), p. 211.

cross-sections become at right angles to the strained central-line. The term $s_0 x$ represents a displacement by which each cross-section is turned back, towards the central-line, through an angle s_0, as explained in (c) above. The remaining terms in W/EI represent a distortion of the cross-sections into curved surfaces, independent of that which depends upon $\tau\phi$. If we construct the surface which is given by the equation

$$z = -\frac{W}{EI}\left\{\chi - x\left(\frac{\partial \chi}{\partial x}\right)_0 + xy^2\right\} + \tau\phi, \quad \text{.................(27)}$$

and suppose it to be placed so that its tangent plane at the origin coincides with the tangent plane of a strained cross-section at its centroid, the strained cross-section will coincide with this surface.

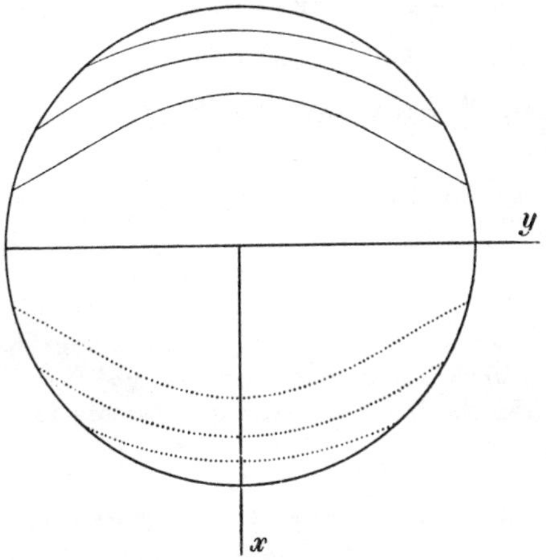

Fig. 29.

In the case of a circular boundary the value of the right-hand member of (27) is

$$-(W/E\pi a^4)\, x\,(x^2+y^2),$$

and the contour lines of the strained cross-section are found by equating this expression to a constant. Some of these lines are traced in Fig. 29.

233. Distribution of shearing stress.

The importance of the transverse component Y_z of the tangential traction on the cross-sections may be seen in the case of the elliptic boundary. When a is large compared with b, the maximum value of Y_z is small compared with that of X_z; as the ratio of b to a increases, the ratio of the maximum of Y_z to that of X_z increases; and, when b is large compared with a, the maximum of Y_z is large compared with that of X_z. Thus the importance of Y_z increases as the shape of the beam approaches to that of a plank.

We may illustrate graphically the distribution of tangential traction on the cross-sections by tracing curves, which are such that the tangent to any one of them at any point is in the direction of the line of action of the tangential traction at the point. As in Article 219, these curves may be called "lines of shearing stress." The differential equation of the family of curves is

$$dx/X_z = dy/Y_z, \quad \text{.............................(28)}$$

or
$$\left\{\frac{\partial\chi}{\partial y} + (2+\sigma)\,xy\right\}dx - \left\{\frac{\partial\chi}{\partial x} + \tfrac{1}{2}\sigma x^2 + (1-\tfrac{1}{2}\sigma)\,y^2\right\}dy = 0.$$

Since $\partial X_z/\partial x + \partial Y_z/\partial y$ is not equal to zero, the magnitude of the shearing stress is *not* measured by the closeness of neighbouring curves of the family.

As an example we may consider the case of the elliptic boundary. The differential equation is

$$xy\,dx\left[\frac{(4+\sigma)\,a^2+(2-\sigma)\,b^2}{3a^2+b^2} - (2+\sigma)\right]$$
$$=\left[\frac{a^2}{3a^2+b^2}\{2a^2(1+\sigma)+b^2\} - \frac{x^2-y^2}{3a^2+b^2}\{(2+\tfrac{1}{2}\sigma)\,a^2+(1-\tfrac{1}{2}\sigma)\,b^2\} - \tfrac{1}{2}\sigma(x^2-y^2) - y^2\right]dy,$$

and this may be expressed in the form

$$2x\frac{dx}{dy}\{(1+\sigma)\,a^2+\sigma b^2\} - \frac{x^2}{y}\{2(1+\sigma)\,a^2+b^2\} + \frac{a^2}{y}\{2(1+\sigma)\,a^2+b^2\} - y(1-2\sigma)\,a^2 = 0.$$

This equation has an integrating factor $y^{-\frac{2(1+\sigma)a^2+b^2}{(1+\sigma)a^2+\sigma b^2}}$, and the complete primitive may be expressed in the form

$$1 - \frac{x^2}{a^2} - \frac{y^2}{b^2} = Cy^{\frac{2(1+\sigma)a^2+b^2}{(1+\sigma)a^2+\sigma b^2}},$$

where C is an arbitrary constant. Since $\sigma < \frac{1}{2}$ all the curves of the family touch the elliptic boundary at the highest and lowest points $(\pm a, 0)$. The case of a circular boundary is included, and the lines of shearing stress are in this case given by the equation

$$a^2 - x^2 - y^2 = Cy^{\frac{3+2\sigma}{1+2\sigma}}.$$

Some of these curves are traced in Fig. 30, σ being taken to be $\frac{1}{4}$.

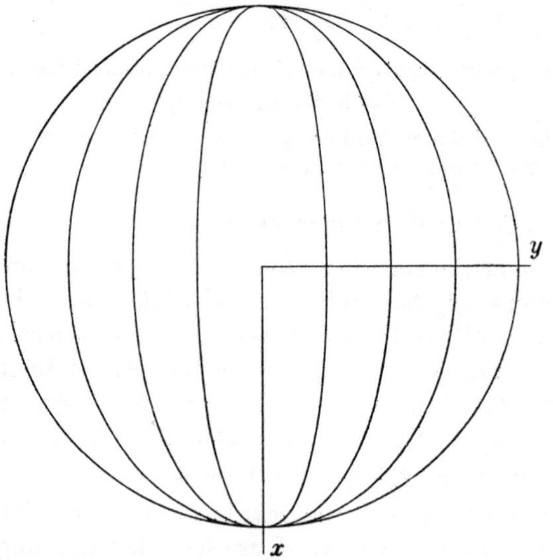

Fig. 30.

234. Generalizations of the preceding theory.

(a) *Asymmetric loading.*

When the load, W' say, is directed parallel to the axis of y instead of the axis of x, the requisite stress-components are, as before, X_z, Y_z, Z_z, given by the equations

$$X_z=\mu\tau\left(\frac{\partial\phi}{\partial x}-y\right)-\frac{W'}{2(1+\sigma)I'}\left\{\frac{\partial\chi'}{\partial x}+(2+\sigma)xy\right\},$$

$$Y_z=\mu\tau\left(\frac{\partial\phi}{\partial y}+x\right)-\frac{W'}{2(1+\sigma)I'}\left\{\frac{\partial\chi'}{\partial y}+\tfrac{1}{2}\sigma y^2+(1-\tfrac{1}{2}\sigma)x^2\right\},$$

$$Z_z=-\frac{W'(l-z)y}{I'},$$

where I' denotes the integral $\iint y^2\,dx\,dy$ taken over the area of the cross-section, and χ' is a plane harmonic function which satisfies the boundary-condition

$$\frac{\partial\chi'}{\partial\nu}=-(2+\sigma)xy\cos(x,\nu)-\{\tfrac{1}{2}\sigma y^2+(1-\tfrac{1}{2}\sigma)x^2\}\cos(y,\nu). \quad\text{............(29)}$$

The constant τ is adjusted, as before, so that the tractions on a cross-section may not yield any couple about the axis of z. Apart from a displacement which would be possible in a rigid body, the displacement is given by the equations

$$\left.\begin{aligned}u&=-\tau yz+\frac{W'}{EI'}\sigma(l-z)xy,\\ v&=\tau zx+\frac{W'}{EI'}\{\tfrac{1}{2}(l-z)\sigma(y^2-x^2)+\tfrac{1}{2}lz^2-\tfrac{1}{6}z^3\},\\ w&=\tau\phi-\frac{W'}{EI'}\{y(lz-\tfrac{1}{2}z^2)+\chi'+yx^2\}.\end{aligned}\right\}\quad\text{..................(30)}$$

When the direction of the load is not that of one of the principal axes of the cross-sections at their centroids, we may resolve the load, P say, into components W and W' parallel to the axes of x and y. The solution is to be obtained by combining the solutions given in Articles 229, 230 with that given here. Omitting displacements which would be possible in a rigid body we deduce from the expressions (12) and (30) the equations of the strained central-line in the form

$$x=\frac{W}{EI}(\tfrac{1}{2}lz^2-\tfrac{1}{6}z^3),\qquad y=\frac{W'}{EI'}(\tfrac{1}{2}lz^2-\tfrac{1}{6}z^3),$$

and this line is therefore a plane curve in the plane

$$W'x/I'=Wy/I.$$

The neutral plane is determined by the equation $e_{zz}=0$, and, since

$$e_{zz}=-\frac{W}{EI}(l-z)x-\frac{W'}{EI'}(l-z)y,$$

this is the plane

$$Wx/I+W'y/I'=0.$$

The neutral plane is therefore at right angles to the plane of bending. The load plane is given by the equation $y/x=W'/W$. Since I and I' are respectively the moments of inertia of the cross-section about the axes of y and x, the result may be expressed in the form:—The traces of the load plane and the neutral plane on the cross-section are conjugate diameters of the ellipse of inertia of the cross-section at its centroid*.

(b) *Combined strain.*

We may write down the solution of the problem of a beam held bent by terminal couple about any axis in the plane of its cross-section, by means of the results given in

* The result was given by Saint-Venant in the memoir on torsion of 1855.

Article 87; we have merely to combine the results for two component couples about the principal axes of the cross-section at its centroid. By combining the solution of the problems of extension by terminal tractive load [Articles 69 and 70 (*h*)], of torsion (Chapter XIV), of bending by couples, and of bending by terminal transverse load, we may obtain the state of stress or strain in a beam deformed by forces applied at its ends alone in such a way as to be statically equivalent to any given resultant and resultant moment. In all these solutions the stress-components denoted by X_x, Y_y, X_y vanish.

As regards the strength of a beam to resist bending we may remark that, when the linear dimensions of the cross-section are small compared with the length, the most important of the stress-components is the longitudinal tension, and the most important of the strain-components is the longitudinal extension, and the greatest values are found in each case in the sections at which the bending moment is greatest, and at the points of these sections which are furthest from the neutral plane. The condition of safety for a bent beam can be expressed in the form:—The maximum bending moment must not exceed a certain limiting value.

The condition of safety of a twisted prism was considered in Article 220. The quantity which must not, in this case, exceed a certain limiting value is the shear; and this is generally greatest at those points of the boundary which are nearest to the central-line. When the beam is at the same time bent and twisted, the components of stress which are different from zero are the longitudinal tension Z_z due to bending and the shearing stresses X_z and Y_z. If the length of the beam is great compared with the linear dimensions of the cross-section the values of Z_z near the section $z=0$ and the terms of X_z and Y_z that depend upon twisting can be comparable with each other, and they are large compared with the terms of X_z and Y_z that are due to bending. For the purpose of an estimate of strength we might omit the shearing stresses and shearing strains that are due to bending, and take account of those only which are due to twisting.

In any case in which the stress-components X_z, Y_z, Z_z are different from zero and X_x, Y_y, X_y vanish, the principal stress-components can be found by observing that the stress-quadric is of the form

$$z(2X_z x + 2Y_z y + Z_z z) = \text{const.},$$

and therefore one principal plane of stress at any point is the plane drawn parallel to the central-line to contain the direction of the resultant, at the point, of the tangential tractions on the cross-section. The normal traction on this plane vanishes, and the values of the two principal stresses which do not vanish are

$$\tfrac{1}{2}Z_z \pm \tfrac{1}{2}[Z_z^2 + 4(X_z^2 + Y_z^2)]^{\frac{1}{2}}. \qquad \text{.............................(31)}$$

In any such case the strain-quadric is of the form

$$\frac{1}{E}[-\sigma Z_z(x^2+y^2+z^2) + (1+\sigma)\,z\,(2X_z x + 2Y_z y + Z_z z)] = \text{const.},$$

and the principal extensions are equal to

$$-\frac{\sigma Z_z}{E},\quad \frac{(1-\sigma)Z_z}{2E} \pm \frac{1+\sigma}{2E}[Z_z^2 + 4(X_z^2 + Y_z^2)]^{\frac{1}{2}}, \qquad \text{.................(32)}$$

the first of these being the extension of a line at right angles to that principal plane of stress on which the normal traction vanishes.

(*c*) *Æolotropic material.*

The complexity of the problem of Article 228 is not essentially increased if the material of the beam is taken to be æolotropic, provided that the planes through any point, which are parallel to the principal planes, are planes of symmetry of structure. We suppose the axes of x, y, z to be chosen in the same way as in Article 228, and assume that the strain-energy-function has the form

$$\tfrac{1}{2}(A, B, C, F, G, H)(e_{xx}, e_{yy}, e_{zz})^2+\tfrac{1}{2}(Le_{yz}^2+Me_{zx}^2+Ne_{xy}^2).$$

We denote the Young's modulus of the material for tension in the direction of the axis of z by E, and we denote the Poisson's ratios which correspond respectively with contractions parallel to the axes of x and y and tension in the direction of the axis of z, by σ_1 and σ_2. We assume a stress-system restricted by the equations

$$X_x=Y_y=X_y=0, \quad Z_z=-\frac{W}{I}(l-z)\,x. \qquad (33)$$

Then we may show that X_z and Y_z necessarily have the forms:

$$\left.\begin{aligned} X_z&=M\tau\left(\frac{\partial\phi}{\partial x}-y\right)-\frac{MW}{EI}\left[\frac{\partial\chi}{\partial x}+\tfrac{1}{2}\sigma_1x^2+\frac{E-M\sigma_1-2L\sigma_2}{2L}y^2\right],\\ Y_z&=L\tau\left(\frac{\partial\phi}{\partial y}+x\right)-\frac{LW}{EI}\left[\frac{\partial\chi}{\partial y}+\frac{E-M\sigma_1}{L}xy\right],\end{aligned}\right\} \qquad (34)$$

where ϕ and χ are solutions of the same partial differential equation

$$\left(M\frac{\partial^2}{\partial x^2}+L\frac{\partial^2}{\partial y^2}\right)_{\chi}^{\phi}=0,$$

which respectively satisfy the following boundary-conditions:

$$\cos(x,\nu)\,M\frac{\partial\phi}{\partial x}+\cos(y,\nu)\,L\frac{\partial\phi}{\partial y}=\cos(x,\nu)\,My-\cos(y,\nu)\,Lx,$$

$$\cos(x,\nu)\,M\frac{\partial\chi}{\partial x}+\cos(y,\nu)\,L\frac{\partial\chi}{\partial y}=-\cos(x,\nu)\,M\left(\tfrac{1}{2}\sigma_1x^2+\frac{E-M\sigma_1-2L\sigma_2}{2L}y^2\right)$$
$$-\cos(y,\nu)(E-M\sigma_1)\,xy.$$

Further we may show that the displacement corresponding with the stress-system expressed by (33) and (34) necessarily has the form:

$$\left.\begin{aligned} u&=-\tau yz+\frac{W}{EI}\left[\tfrac{1}{2}(l-z)(\sigma_1x^2-\sigma_2y^2)+\tfrac{1}{2}lz^2-\tfrac{1}{6}z^3\right]-\gamma y+\beta z+\alpha',\\ v&=\tau zx+\frac{W}{EI}(l-z)\,\sigma_2xy+\gamma x-\alpha z+\beta',\\ w&=\tau\phi-\frac{W}{EI}\left[x(lz-\tfrac{1}{2}z^2)+\chi+\frac{E-M\sigma_1-L\sigma_2}{2L}xy^2\right]-\beta x+\alpha y+\gamma'.\end{aligned}\right\} \qquad (35)$$

As in Article 230, we may take $\alpha'=\beta'=\gamma'=0$ and $\alpha=\gamma=0$. The constant of integration τ can be adjusted so that the traction at the loaded end may be statically equivalent to a single force, W, acting at the centroid of the terminal section in the direction of the axis of x. The results may be interpreted in the same way as in Article 232.

234 c. Analogy to the form of a stretched membrane under varying pressure*.

The equations of Articles 228, 229 can be solved by putting

$$X_z=\frac{\partial U}{\partial y}-\frac{Wx^2}{2I}+f(y), \quad Y_z=-\frac{\partial U}{\partial x},$$

where $f(y)$ is a function of y only, provided that U satisfies the equation

$$\frac{\partial^2U}{\partial x^2}+\frac{\partial^2U}{\partial y^2}=\frac{\sigma}{1+\sigma}\frac{Wy}{I}-f'(y)+c,$$

where c is a constant, at all points within the bounding curve of the cross-section, and also satisfies the condition

$$\frac{\partial U}{\partial s}=\left\{\frac{Wx^2}{2I}-f(y)\right\}\frac{\partial y}{\partial s}$$

* S. Timoschenko, *London Math. Soc. Proc.* (Ser. 2), vol. 20, 1922, p. 398.

at all points of this curve, ds denoting the element of arc of this curve. The differential equation for U is the same as would determine the normal displacement of a membrane, stretched by uniform tension, and subject to pressure which varies with y. If the boundary is such that the right-hand member of the expression for $\partial U/\partial s$ vanishes at the boundary, the edge of the membrane is fixed. The constant c must be adjusted so as to satisfy the condition that there is no couple about the axis of z, just as τ was adjusted in Article 229.

It has been shown that this method leads to some interesting exact solutions, including those for the circle, ellipse, and rectangle, and also to some interesting approximate solutions, including that for an isosceles triangle, the plane of flexure being at right angles to the lines of symmetry of the cross-sections.

235. Criticisms of certain methods.

(a) In many treatises on Applied Mechanics* the shearing stress is calculated from the stress-equations of equilibrium, without reference to the conditions of compatibility of strain-components, by the aid of certain assumptions as to the distribution of tangential traction on the cross-section. In particular, when the section is a rectangle, and the load is a force W parallel to the axis of x, it is assumed (i) that Y_z is zero, (ii) that X_z is independent of y. Conditions (i) and (ii) of Article 228, combined with these assumptions, lead to the following stress-system:

$$X_x = Y_y = X_y = Y_z = 0, \quad X_z = \frac{W}{2I}\left(3\frac{I}{\omega} - x^2\right), \quad Z_z = -\frac{W}{I}(l-z)\,x, \quad \text{.........(36)}$$

in which ω is the area of the cross-section, and I is the moment of inertia previously so denoted. The resultant traction $\iint X_z dx\,dy$ is equal to W.

If this stress-system could be correct, there would exist functions u, v, w which would be such that

$$\frac{\partial v}{\partial y} = \frac{\sigma W}{EI}(l-z)\,x, \quad \frac{\partial u}{\partial z} + \frac{\partial w}{\partial x} = \frac{W}{2\mu I}\left(3\frac{I}{\omega} - x^2\right), \quad \frac{\partial w}{\partial y} + \frac{\partial v}{\partial z} = \frac{\partial v}{\partial x} + \frac{\partial u}{\partial y} = 0.$$

Now we have the identical equation

$$2\frac{\partial^3 v}{\partial x\,\partial y\,\partial z} = \frac{\partial^2}{\partial x\,\partial y}\left(\frac{\partial w}{\partial y} + \frac{\partial v}{\partial z}\right) - \frac{\partial^2}{\partial y^2}\left(\frac{\partial u}{\partial z} + \frac{\partial w}{\partial x}\right) + \frac{\partial^2}{\partial y\,\partial z}\left(\frac{\partial v}{\partial x} + \frac{\partial u}{\partial y}\right);$$

but this equation is not consistent with the above values for $\partial v/\partial y, \ldots$; for, when these values are substituted, the left-hand member is equal to $-2\sigma W/EI$, and the right-hand member is equal to zero. It follows that the stress-system expressed by (36) is not possible in an isotropic solid body.

We know already from Article 95 that the stress-system (36) gives correctly the *average stress* across the breadth of the section, and therefore gives a good approximation to the actual stress when the breadth is small compared with the depth. The extent to which it is inadequate may be estimated by means of the table in Article 232 (c); for it would give for s_0 the factor outside the square bracket in the right-hand member of (23). It fails also to give correctly the direction of the tangential traction on the cross-sections, for it makes this traction everywhere vertical, whereas near the top and bottom bounding lines it is nearly horizontal.

(b) In the extension of this method to sections which are not rectangular it is recognized† that the component Y_z of shearing stress must exist as well as X_z. The case

* See for example the treatises of Rankine and Grashof quoted in the Introduction, footnotes 94 and 95, and those of Ewing, Bach and Föppl quoted in the footnote on p. 112.

† See, in particular, the treatise of Grashof already cited.

selected for discussion is that in which the cross-section is symmetrical with respect to a vertical axis. The following assumptions are made:

(i) X_z is independent of y, (ii) the resultants of X_z and Y_z at all points P' which have a given x meet in a point on the axis of x. To satisfy the boundary-condition (3) this point must be that marked T in Fig. 31, viz. the point where the tangent at P to the bounding curve of the section meets this axis.

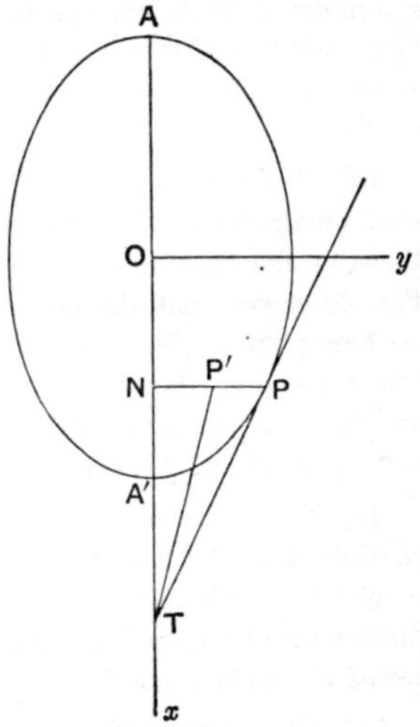

Fig. 31.

To express the assumption (ii) analytically, let η be the ordinate (NP) of P and y that of P', then

$$Y_z = \frac{y}{\eta}\frac{d\eta}{dx} X_z. \quad \text{.................(37)}$$

Equation (2) then becomes

$$\frac{\partial X_z}{\partial x} + \frac{1}{\eta}\frac{\partial \eta}{\partial x} X_z + \frac{Wx}{I} = 0,$$

and the solution which makes X_z vanish at the highest point ($x = -a$) is

$$\eta X_z = -\frac{W}{I}\int_{-a}^{x} x\eta\, dx,$$

and it is easy to see that this solution also makes X_z vanish at the lowest point.

The stress-system obtained by these assumptions is expressed by the equations

$$X_x = Y_y = X_y = 0, \quad X_z = -\frac{W}{\eta I}\int_{-a}^{x} x\eta\, dx, \quad Y_z = -\frac{Wy}{\eta^2 I}\frac{d\eta}{dx}\int_{-a}^{x} x\eta\, dx, \quad Z_z = -\frac{Wx(l-z)}{I}; \quad \text{.....................(38)}$$

it satisfies the equations of equilibrium and the boundary-condition, and it gives the right value W for the resultant of the tangential tractions on the section. But, in general, it is not a possible stress-system, for the same reason as in the case of the rectangle, viz. the conditions of compatibility of strain-components cannot be satisfied.

(c) These conditions may be shown easily to lead to the following equation:

$$\frac{d}{dx}\left\{\frac{1}{\eta^2}\frac{d\eta}{dx}\int_{-a}^{x} x\eta\, dx\right\} = \frac{\sigma}{1+\sigma}, \quad \text{...............................(39)}$$

which determines η as a function of x, and therewith determines those forms of section for which the stress-system (38) is a possible one. To integrate (39) we put

$$\int_{-a}^{x} x\eta\, dx = \xi, \quad \text{...(40)}$$

and then ξ satisfies the equation

$$\frac{d}{dx}\left(x\frac{\xi\xi''}{\xi'^2} - \frac{\xi}{\xi'}\right) = \frac{\sigma}{1+\sigma},$$

where ξ', ξ'' mean $d\xi/dx$, $d^2\xi/dx^2$. The complete primitive can be shown to be

$$\xi = C\left\{(a'-x)^{\frac{2a'}{a+a'}}(x+a)^{\frac{2a}{a+a'}}\right\}^{1+\sigma},$$

where C, a and a' are arbitrary constants. On eliminating ξ by means of the relation (40) we see that the equation of the bounding curve must have the form

$$\eta = \frac{C}{x}\frac{d}{dx}\left[(a'-x)^{\frac{2a'}{a+a'}}(x+a)^{\frac{2a}{a+a'}}\right]^{1+\sigma} \quad \text{.........................(41)}$$

The constants a and a' express the height of the highest point of the curve, and the depth of its lowest point, measured from the centroid.

Unless the bounding curve of the section has one of the forms included in equation (41) the stress is not correctly given by (38). It may be observed that, if the section is symmetrical with respect to the axis of y, so that $a'=a$, the equation (41) is of the form $(\eta/b)^{1/\sigma}+x^2/a^2=1$. We saw in Article 231 (f) that the problem of flexure could be solved for this section, and the curve was traced in Fig. 26 for the case where $\sigma=\frac{1}{4}$ and $a=2b$.

(d) We may observe that in the case of the elliptic (or circular) boundary this method would make the lines of shearing stress ellipses, having their axes in the same directions as those of the bounding curve and touching this curve at the highest and lowest points. Fig. 30 shows that the correct curves are flatter than these ellipses in the neighbourhood of these points. In regard to the obliquity of the strained cross-sections, the method would give for s_0 the value $8W(1+\sigma)/3E\pi ab$, which is nearly correct when the breadth is small, or b is small compared with a, but is too small by about 5 per cent. in the case of the circle, and by nearly 20 per cent. when b is large compared with a.

(e) The existence of a term of the form βz in the expression for the deflexion [Article 232 (d)] has been recognized by writers of technical treatises. The term was named by Rankine (*loc. cit.*) "the additional deflexion due to shearing." In view of the discussion at the end of Article 230 concerning the meaning of the constant β, the name seems not to be a good one.

(f) The theorem of Article 120 is sometimes used to determine the additional deflexion*. The theorem yields the equation

$$\tfrac{1}{2}\iint (X_z u+Y_z v+Z_z w)_{z=l}\,dx\,dy-\tfrac{1}{2}\iint (X_z u+Y_z v+Z_z w)_{z=0}\,dx\,dy$$
$$=\tfrac{1}{2}\iiint [\{X_x^2+Y_y^2+Z_z^2-2\sigma(Y_yZ_z+\ldots)\}/E+(X_z^2+Y_z^2+X_y^2)/\mu]\,dx\,dy\,dz. \quad \ldots(42)$$

When the tractions over the ends are assigned in a special manner in accordance with the formulæ (1) and (8), so that the displacement is given by (12), the first term of the left-hand member of (42) becomes $\frac{1}{6}W^2l^3/EI+\frac{1}{2}W\beta l$, and the second term becomes

$$-\tfrac{1}{2}W\beta l-\tfrac{1}{2}\iint [(X_z u+Y_z v)_{z=0}-(Wlx/I)\{\sigma\phi-W(\chi+xy^2)/EI\}]\,dx\,dy,$$

where the expression under the sign of integration is independent of β. The right-hand member of (42) becomes $\frac{1}{6}W^2l^3/EI+\frac{1}{2}l\mu^{-1}\iint(X_z^2+Y_z^2)\,dx\,dy$, which also is independent of β. Thus, in this case, equation (42) fails to determine the additional deflexion. When the tractions over the ends are not distributed exactly in accordance with (1) and (8), the displacement is practically of the form given by (12) in the greater part of the beam, but must be subject to local irregularity near the ends. The left-hand member of (42) is approximately equal to $\frac{1}{2}W\delta$, where δ is the deflexion at the loaded end, and the right-hand member is approximately equal to $\frac{1}{6}W^2l^3/EI$; but, for a closer approximation we should require a knowledge not only of X_z and Y_z in the greater part of the beam, but also of the terminal irregularity.

* See e.g. W. J. M. Rankine, *loc. cit.*, or J. Perry, *Applied Mechanics* (London, 1899), p. 461.

CHAPTER XVI

THE BENDING OF A BEAM LOADED UNIFORMLY ALONG ITS LENGTH

236. IN this Chapter we shall discuss some problems of the equilibrium of an isotropic body of cylindrical form, by imposing particular restrictions on the character of the stress. Measuring the coordinate z along the length of the cylinder, we shall in the first place suppose that the stress is independent of z, then that it is expressed by linear functions of z, and finally that it is expressed by quadratic functions of z. We shall find that the first two restrictions lead to solutions which have been obtained in previous Chapters*, but that the assumption of quadratic functions of z enables us to solve the problem of the bending of a beam by a load distributed uniformly along its length.

237. Stress uniform along the beam.

We take the axis of z to be the central-line of the beam, and the axes of x and y to be parallel to the principal axes of the cross-sections at their centroids. We suppose that there are no body forces, and that the cylindrical bounding surface is free from traction. We investigate those states of stress in which the stress-components are independent of z.

The equations of equilibrium take the form

$$\frac{\partial X_x}{\partial x}+\frac{\partial X_y}{\partial y}=0,\quad \frac{\partial X_y}{\partial x}+\frac{\partial Y_y}{\partial y}=0,\quad \frac{\partial X_z}{\partial x}+\frac{\partial Y_z}{\partial y}=0, \qquad \text{............(1)}$$

and the conditions which hold at the cylindrical boundary are

$$\cos(x, \nu) X_x+\cos(y, \nu) X_y=0,\quad \cos(x, \nu) X_y+\cos(y, \nu) Y_y=0,$$
$$\cos(x, \nu) X_z+\cos(y, \nu) Y_z=0. \qquad \text{...(2)}$$

The conditions of compatibility of strain-components take the forms

$$\frac{\partial^2 e_{zz}}{\partial y^2}=0,\quad \frac{\partial^2 e_{zz}}{\partial x^2}=0,\quad \frac{\partial^2 e_{zz}}{\partial x \partial y}=0, \qquad \text{.....................(3)}$$

with

$$\frac{\partial}{\partial x}\left(\frac{\partial e_{yz}}{\partial x}-\frac{\partial e_{zx}}{\partial y}\right)=0,\quad \frac{\partial}{\partial y}\left(\frac{\partial e_{yz}}{\partial x}-\frac{\partial e_{zx}}{\partial y}\right)=0, \qquad \text{..............(4)}$$

and

$$\frac{\partial^2 e_{yy}}{\partial x^2}+\frac{\partial^2 e_{xx}}{\partial y^2}-\frac{\partial^2 e_{xy}}{\partial x \partial y}=0. \qquad \text{.........................(5)}$$

The equations (3) show that e_{zz} is a linear function of x and y, say

$$e_{zz}=\epsilon-\kappa x-\kappa' y, \qquad \text{..........................(6)}$$

where ϵ, κ, κ' are constants. Whenever this is the case equations (1) and conditions (2) lead to the conclusion that X_x, Y_y, X_y vanish.

* Cf. W. Voigt, *Göttingen Abhandlungen*, Bd. 34 (1887).

To prove this we observe that, if u', v' are any functions of x and y, these equations and conditions require that

$$\iint\left\{X_x\frac{\partial u'}{\partial x}+Y_y\frac{\partial v'}{\partial y}+X_y\left(\frac{\partial v'}{\partial x}+\frac{\partial u'}{\partial y}\right)\right\}dx\,dy=0, \quad\text{.....................(7)}$$

the integration being taken over the cross-section; for the left-hand member is at once transformable into

$$\int[\{X_x\cos(x,\nu)+X_y\cos(y,\nu)\}u'+\{X_y\cos(x,\nu)+Y_y\cos(y,\nu)\}v']\,ds$$
$$-\iint\left\{\left(\frac{\partial X_x}{\partial x}+\frac{\partial X_y}{\partial y}\right)u'+\left(\frac{\partial X_y}{\partial x}+\frac{\partial Y_y}{\partial y}\right)v'\right\}dx\,dy,$$

where ds is an element of arc of the bounding curve of the cross-section. Now in equation (7) put

(i) $u'=x,\ v'=0$, we find $\iint X_x\,dx\,dy=0$,

(ii) $u'=x^2,\ v'=0$, we find $\iint xX_x\,dx\,dy=0$,

(iii) $u'=xy,\ v'=-\frac{1}{2}x^2$, we find $\iint yX_x\,dx\,dy=0$;

and in like manner we may prove that

$$\iint Y_y\,dx\,dy=0,\quad \iint xY_y\,dx\,dy=0,\quad \iint yY_y\,dx\,dy=0.$$

It follows from these results and (6) that

$$\iint X_x e_{zz}\,dx\,dy=0,\quad \iint Y_y e_{zz}\,dx\,dy=0.$$

Again, in equation (7) let u', v' be the components parallel to the axes of x and y of the displacement which corresponds with the stress X_x, ..., then this equation becomes

$$\iint(X_xe_{xx}+Y_ye_{yy}+X_ye_{xy})\,dx\,dy=0. \quad\text{..........................(8)}$$

But we have

$$X_xe_{xx}+Y_ye_{yy}=-\sigma(X_x+Y_y)e_{zz}+E^{-1}(1+\sigma)\{(1-\sigma)(X_x^2+Y_y^2)-2\sigma X_xY_y\}.$$

The integral of the term $-\sigma(X_x+Y_y)e_{zz}$ vanishes, and the quadratic form

$$(1-\sigma)(X_x^2+Y_y^2)-2\sigma X_xY_y$$

is definite and positive, since $\sigma<\frac{1}{2}$; also we have $X_ye_{xy}=\mu^{-1}X_y^2$. Hence the integral of the expression $X_xe_{xx}+Y_ye_{yy}+X_ye_{xy}$ is necessarily positive, and equation (8) cannot be satisfied unless X_x, Y_y, X_y vanish identically.

It follows that we must have

$$e_{xx}=-\sigma e_{zz},\quad e_{yy}=-\sigma e_{zz},\quad e_{xy}=0, \quad\text{..................(9)}$$

where e_{zz} is given by (6); and then equation (5) is satisfied identically.

The remaining equations and conditions are the third of the equations (1), the third of the conditions (2), equations (4), and the relations $X_z=\eta e_{zx}$, $Y_z=\mu e_{yz}$. From these we find, as in Article 229, that the most general forms for e_{zx}, e_{yz} are

$$e_{zx}=\tau\left(\frac{\partial\phi}{\partial x}-y\right),\quad e_{yz}=\tau\left(\frac{\partial\phi}{\partial y}+x\right), \quad\text{..................(10)}$$

where τ is a constant of integration, and ϕ is the torsion function for the cross-section (Article 216).

The strain is expressed by equations (6), (9), (10), and it follows that the most general state of strain which is consistent with the conditions (i) that the stress is uniform along the beam, (ii) that no forces are applied to the beam except at the ends, consists of the strain associated with simple longitudinal tension (cf. Article 69), two simple flexures involving curvatures κ and κ' in the planes of (x, z) and (y, z) [cf. Article 87], and torsion τ as in Chapter XIV.

The theorem proved in this Article for isotropic solids, viz., that, if e_{zz} is linear in x and y, and if there are no body forces and no surface tractions on the cylindrical boundary, the stress-components X_x, Y_y, X_y must vanish, is true also for æolotropic materials, provided that the plane of (x, y) is a plane of symmetry*.

238. Stress varying uniformly along the beam.

We take the axes of x, y, z in the same way as before, and retain the suppositions that there are no body forces and that the cylindrical bounding surface of the beam is free from traction; and we investigate those states of stress in which the stress-components, and strain-components, are linear functions of z. We write the stress-components and strain-components in such forms as

$$X_x = X_x^{(1)} z + X_x^{(0)}, \quad e_{xx} = e_{xx}^{(1)} z + e_{xx}^{(0)}. \quad \text{..............(11)}$$

The equations of equilibrium take such forms as

$$z\left(\frac{\partial X_x^{(1)}}{\partial x} + \frac{\partial X_y^{(1)}}{\partial y}\right) + \frac{\partial X_x^{(0)}}{\partial x} + \frac{\partial X_y^{(0)}}{\partial y} + X_z^{(1)} = 0, \quad \text{...........(12)}$$

and the conditions at the cylindrical boundary take such forms as

$$z\{\cos(x, \nu) X_x^{(1)} + \cos(y, \nu) X_y^{(1)}\} + \cos(x, \nu) X_x^{(0)} + \cos(y, \nu) X_y^{(0)} = 0. \quad \text{..(13)}$$

The conditions of compatibility of strain-components are

$$\left.\begin{aligned} & z\frac{\partial^2 e_{zz}^{(1)}}{\partial x^2} + \frac{\partial^2 e_{zz}^{(0)}}{\partial x^2} - \frac{\partial e_{zx}^{(1)}}{\partial x} = 0, \quad z\frac{\partial^2 e_{zz}^{(1)}}{\partial y^2} + \frac{\partial^2 e_{zz}^{(0)}}{\partial y^2} - \frac{\partial e_{yz}^{(1)}}{\partial y} = 0, \\ & 2z\frac{\partial^2 e_{zz}^{(1)}}{\partial x \partial y} + 2\frac{\partial^2 e_{zz}^{(0)}}{\partial x \partial y} - \frac{\partial e_{yz}^{(1)}}{\partial x} - \frac{\partial e_{zx}^{(1)}}{\partial y} = 0, \end{aligned}\right\} \quad \text{...(14)}$$

with

$$\left.\begin{aligned} & z\frac{\partial}{\partial x}\left(\frac{\partial e_{yz}^{(1)}}{\partial x} - \frac{\partial e_{zx}^{(1)}}{\partial y}\right) + \frac{\partial}{\partial x}\left(\frac{\partial e_{yz}^{(0)}}{\partial x} - \frac{\partial e_{zx}^{(0)}}{\partial y}\right) + 2\frac{\partial e_{xx}^{(1)}}{\partial y} - \frac{\partial e_{xy}^{(1)}}{\partial x} = 0, \\ & z\frac{\partial}{\partial y}\left(\frac{\partial e_{yz}^{(1)}}{\partial x} - \frac{\partial e_{zx}^{(1)}}{\partial y}\right) + \frac{\partial}{\partial y}\left(\frac{\partial e_{yz}^{(0)}}{\partial x} - \frac{\partial e_{zx}^{(0)}}{\partial y}\right) - 2\frac{\partial e_{yy}^{(1)}}{\partial x} + \frac{\partial e_{xy}^{(1)}}{\partial y} = 0, \end{aligned}\right\} \quad (15)$$

and

$$z\left(\frac{\partial^2 e_{yy}^{(1)}}{\partial x^2} + \frac{\partial^2 e_{xx}^{(1)}}{\partial y^2} - \frac{\partial^2 e_{xy}^{(1)}}{\partial x \partial y}\right) + \frac{\partial^2 e_{yy}^{(0)}}{\partial x^2} + \frac{\partial^2 e_{xx}^{(0)}}{\partial y^2} - \frac{\partial^2 e_{xy}^{(0)}}{\partial x \partial y} = 0. \quad \text{...(16)}$$

* J. Boussinesq, *J. de Math. (Liouville)*, (Sér. 2), t. 16 (1871).

In all these equations the terms containing z and the terms independent of z must vanish separately. The relations between components of stress and components of strain take such forms as

$$E(e_{xx}^{(1)}z + e_{xx}^{(0)}) = X_x^{(1)}z + X_x^{(0)} - \sigma(Y_y^{(1)}z + Y_y^{(0)} + Z_z^{(1)}z + Z_z^{(0)}),$$

in which the terms that contain z, and those which are independent of z, on the two sides of the equations must be equated severally.

Selecting first the terms in z, we observe that all the letters with index (1) satisfy the same equations as are satisfied by the same letters in Article 237, and it follows that we may put

$$\left.\begin{aligned} e_{zz}^{(1)} &= \epsilon_1 - \kappa_1 x - \kappa_1' y, \\ e_{xx}^{(1)} &= e_{yy}^{(1)} = -\sigma e_{zz}^{(1)}, \quad e_{xy}^{(1)} = 0, \\ e_{xz}^{(1)} &= \tau_1\left(\frac{\partial\phi}{\partial x} - y\right), \quad e_{yz}^{(1)} = \tau_1\left(\frac{\partial\phi}{\partial y} + x\right), \end{aligned}\right\} \quad \text{............(17)}$$

in which ϵ_1, κ_1, κ_1', τ_1 are constants, and ϕ is the torsion function for the cross-section.

Again, selecting the terms independent of z, we find from the first two of equations (12)

$$\iint\{xY_z^{(1)} - yX_z^{(1)}\}\,dx\,dy = \iint\left\{y\left(\frac{\partial X_x^{(0)}}{\partial x} + \frac{\partial X_y^{(0)}}{\partial y}\right) - x\left(\frac{\partial X_y^{(0)}}{\partial x} + \frac{\partial Y_y^{(0)}}{\partial y}\right)\right\}dx\,dy$$

$$= \int y\{\cos(x,\nu)\,X_x^{(0)} + \cos(y,\nu)X_y^{(0)}\} - x\{\cos(x,\nu)\,X_y^{(0)} + \cos(y,\nu)\,Y_y^{(0)}\}\,ds,$$

which vanishes by the first two of equations (13). Also we have by (17)

$$\iint\{xY_z^{(1)} - yX_z^{(1)}\}\,dx\,dy = \mu\tau_1\iint\left\{x^2 + y^2 + x\frac{\partial\phi}{\partial y} - y\frac{\partial\phi}{\partial x}\right\}dx\,dy,$$

where the integral on the right is the coefficient of μ in the expression for the torsional rigidity of the beam. It follows that τ_1 must vanish, and hence that $X_z^{(1)}$ and $Y_z^{(1)}$ vanish.

This conclusion is otherwise evident; for if τ_1 did not vanish we should have twist of variable amount $\tau_1 z$ maintained by tractions at the ends. The torsional couples at different sections could not then balance.

By selecting the terms independent of z in the third of equations (12) and conditions (13) we find the differential equation

$$\frac{\partial X_z^{(0)}}{\partial x} + \frac{\partial Y_z^{(0)}}{\partial y} + Z_z^{(1)} = 0$$

and the boundary-condition

$$X_z^{(0)}\cos(x,\nu) + Y_z^{(0)}\cos(y,\nu) = 0,$$

which are inconsistent unless

$$\iint Z_z^{(1)}\,dx\,dy = 0.$$

Since $Z_z^{(1)} = E(\epsilon_1 - \kappa_1 x - \kappa_1' y)$, this equation requires ϵ_1 to vanish.

We may now rewrite equations (17) in the form

$$e_{zz}^{(1)} = -\kappa_1 x - \kappa_1' y,\quad e_{xx}^{(1)} = e_{yy}^{(1)} = -\sigma e_{zz}^{(1)},\quad e_{yz}^{(1)} = e_{zx}^{(1)} = e_{xy}^{(1)} = 0. \quad \ldots(18)$$

Since $X_z^{(1)}$ and $Y_z^{(1)}$ vanish, we find, by selecting the terms independent of z in the first two of equations (12) and conditions (13), that $X_x^{(0)}$, $Y_y^{(0)}$, $X_y^{(0)}$ vanish and that $e_{zz}^{(0)}$ is a linear function of x and y. We may therefore put

$$e_{zz}^{(0)} = \epsilon_0 - \kappa_0 x - \kappa_0' y,\quad e_{xx}^{(0)} = e_{yy}^{(0)} = -\sigma e_{zz}^{(0)},\quad e_{xy}^{(0)} = 0, \quad \ldots\ldots(19)$$

where ϵ_0, κ_0, κ_0' are constants. Equation (16) is satisfied identically.

Further, by selecting the terms independent of z in the third of equations (12), and the third of conditions (13), and in equations (15), we find, as in Articles 229 and 234 (*a*), that $e_{zx}^{(0)}$ and $e_{yz}^{(0)}$ must have the forms

$$\left.\begin{aligned} e_{zx}^{(0)} &= \tau_0\left(\frac{\partial\phi}{\partial x} - y\right) + \kappa_1\left\{\frac{\partial\chi}{\partial x} + \tfrac{1}{2}\sigma x^2 + (1-\tfrac{1}{2}\sigma)\,y^2\right\} + \kappa_1'\left\{\frac{\partial\chi'}{\partial x} + (2+\sigma)\,xy\right\},\\ e_{yz}^{(0)} &= \tau_0\left(\frac{\partial\phi}{\partial y} + x\right) + \kappa_1\left\{\frac{\partial\chi}{\partial y} + (2+\sigma)\,xy\right\} + \kappa_1'\left\{\frac{\partial\chi'}{\partial y} + \tfrac{1}{2}\sigma y^2 + (1-\tfrac{1}{2}\sigma)\,x^2\right\},\end{aligned}\right\} \quad (20)$$

where χ and χ' are the flexure functions for the cross-section, corresponding with bending in the planes of (x, z) and (y, z), and τ_0 is a constant.

We have shown that, in the body with a cylindrical boundary, the most general state of stress consistent with the conditions that no forces are applied except at the ends, and that the stress-components are linear functions of z, has the properties (i) that X_z and Y_z are independent of z, (ii) that X_x, Y_y, X_y vanish. Thus the only stress-component that depends upon z is Z_z which is a linear function of z. Conversely, if there are no body forces and X_x, Y_y, X_y all vanish, the equations of equilibrium become

$$\frac{\partial X_z}{\partial z} = 0,\quad \frac{\partial Y_z}{\partial z} = 0,\quad \frac{\partial X_z}{\partial x} + \frac{\partial Y_z}{\partial y} + \frac{\partial Z_z}{\partial z} = 0,$$

and it follows from these that X_z and Y_z are independent of z and that Z_z is a linear function of z. Thus the condition that the stress varies uniformly along the beam is the same as the conditions that X_x, Y_y, X_y vanish*.

The most general state of strain which is consistent with the conditions (i) that the stress varies uniformly along the beam, (ii) that no forces are applied to the beam except at the ends, consists of extension due to terminal tractive load, bending by transverse forces, and by couples, applied at the terminal sections, and torsion produced by couples applied to the same sections about axes coinciding with the central-line. The resultant force at any section has components parallel to the axes of x, y, z which are equal to

$$-EI\kappa_1,\quad -EI'\kappa_1',\quad E\epsilon_0,$$

where $I = \iint x^2\,dx\,dy$ and $I' = \iint y^2\,dx\,dy$; and the resultant couple at any section has components about axes parallel to the axes of x, y which are equal to

$$-EI'(\kappa_0' + \kappa_1' z),\quad EI(\kappa_0 + \kappa_1 z),$$

* For the importance of these results in connexion with the historical development of the theory, see Introduction, p. 21.

and a component about the axis of z which is equal to

$$\mu\tau_0\iint\left(x^2+y^2+x\frac{\partial\phi}{\partial y}-y\frac{\partial\phi}{\partial y}\right)dx\,dy$$
$$+\mu\kappa_1\iint\left\{x\frac{\partial\chi}{\partial y}-y\frac{\partial\chi}{\partial x}+(2+\tfrac{1}{2}\sigma)x^2y-(1-\tfrac{1}{2}\sigma)y^3\right\}dx\,dy$$
$$+\mu\kappa_1'\iint\left\{x\frac{\partial\chi'}{\partial y}-y\frac{\partial\chi'}{\partial x}-(2+\tfrac{1}{2}\sigma)xy^2+(1-\tfrac{1}{2}\sigma)x^3\right\}dx\,dy.$$

The solutions of the problems thus presented have been discussed in previous Chapters.

239. Uniformly loaded beam. Reduction of the problem to one of plane strain*.

Taking the axes in the same way as before, we shall now suppose that all the components of stress and strain are expressed by quadratic functions of z so that for example

$$X_x=X_x^{(2)}z^2+X_x^{(1)}z+X_x^{(0)},\quad e_{xx}=e_{xx}^{(2)}z^2+e_{xx}^{(1)}z+e_{xx}^{(0)}.\quad\ldots\ldots(21)$$
$$\ldots\qquad\qquad\ldots$$

We shall suppose also that there is body force, specified by components X, Y parallel to the axes of x, y, and surface traction on the cylindrical boundary, specified similarly by X_ν, Y_ν, these quantities being independent of z. Then in the equations of equilibrium, the boundary-conditions, the equations of compatibility of strain-components, and the stress-strain relations, the terms of the second, first and zero degrees in z may be taken separately.

Selecting first the terms that contain z^2, we find, exactly as in Article 238, that we may put

$$\left.\begin{aligned}&e_{zz}^{(2)}=\epsilon_2-\kappa_2x-\kappa_2'y,\\&e_{xx}^{(2)}=e_{yy}^{(2)}=-\sigma e_{zz}^{(2)},\quad e_{xy}^{(2)}=0,\\&e_{zx}^{(2)}=\tau_2\left(\frac{\partial\phi}{\partial x}-y\right),\quad e_{yz}^{(2)}=\tau_2\left(\frac{\partial\phi}{\partial y}+x\right),\end{aligned}\right\}\quad\ldots\ldots\ldots(22)$$

where ϵ_2, κ_2, κ_2', τ_2 are constants, and ϕ is the torsion function for the section.

Again, selecting the terms that contain z, we may show that τ_2 and ϵ_2 must vanish, and that we may put

$$\left.\begin{aligned}&e_{zz}^{(1)}=\epsilon_1-\kappa_1x-\kappa_1'y,\\&e_{xx}^{(1)}=e_{yy}^{(1)}=-\sigma e_{zz}^{(1)},\quad e_{xy}^{(1)}=0,\\&e_{zx}^{(1)}=\tau_1\left(\frac{\partial\phi}{\partial x}-y\right)+2\kappa_2\left\{\frac{\partial\chi}{\partial x}+\tfrac{1}{2}\sigma x^2+(1-\tfrac{1}{2}\sigma)y^2\right\}+2\kappa_2'\left\{\frac{\partial\chi'}{\partial x}+(2+\sigma)xy\right\},\\&e_{yz}^{(1)}=\tau_1\left(\frac{\partial\phi}{\partial y}+x\right)+2\kappa_2\left\{\frac{\partial\chi}{\partial y}+(2+\sigma)xy\right\}+2\kappa_2'\left\{\frac{\partial\chi'}{\partial y}+\tfrac{1}{2}\sigma y^2+(1-\tfrac{1}{2}\sigma)x^2\right\},\end{aligned}\right\}$$
$$\ldots\ldots\ldots(23)$$

* The theory is due to J. H. Michell, *Quart. J. of Math.*, vol. 32 (1901).

where ϵ_1, κ_1, κ_1', τ_1 are constants, and χ and χ' are the two flexure functions for the section.

For the determination of $X_x^{(0)}$, ... we have the equations of equilibrium

$$\left.\begin{aligned} \frac{\partial X_x^{(0)}}{\partial x} + \frac{\partial X_y^{(0)}}{\partial y} + X_z^{(1)} + \rho X &= 0, \\ \frac{\partial X_y^{(0)}}{\partial x} + \frac{\partial Y_y^{(0)}}{\partial y} + Y_z^{(1)} + \rho Y &= 0, \\ \frac{\partial X_z^{(0)}}{\partial x} + \frac{\partial Y_z^{(0)}}{\partial y} + Z_z^{(1)} \qquad &= 0, \end{aligned}\right\} \quad \text{..................(24)}$$

and the boundary-conditions

$$\left.\begin{aligned} X_x^{(0)} \cos(x, \nu) + X_y^{(0)} \cos(y, \nu) - X_\nu &= 0, \\ X_y^{(0)} \cos(x, \nu) + Y_y^{(0)} \cos(y, \nu) - Y_\nu &= 0, \\ X_z^{(0)} \cos(x, \nu) + Y_z^{(0)} \cos(y, \nu) \qquad &= 0. \end{aligned}\right\} \quad \text{...........(25)}$$

The third of equations (24) and of conditions (25) are incompatible unless the constant ϵ_1 of (23) vanishes.

Further we have $e_{xx}^{(0)}$, ... and $X_x^{(0)}$, ... connected by the ordinary stress-strain relations, and we have the equations of compatibility of strain-components in the forms

$$\left.\begin{aligned} \frac{\partial^2 e_{zz}^{(0)}}{\partial x^2} + 2\sigma(\kappa_2 x + \kappa_2' y) &= \frac{\partial e_{zx}^{(1)}}{\partial x}, \\ \frac{\partial^2 e_{zz}^{(0)}}{\partial y^2} + 2\sigma(\kappa_2 x + \kappa_2' y) &= \frac{\partial e_{yz}^{(1)}}{\partial y}, \\ 2\frac{\partial^2 e_{zz}^{(0)}}{\partial x \partial y} &= \frac{\partial e_{yz}^{(1)}}{\partial x} + \frac{\partial e_{zx}^{(1)}}{\partial y}, \end{aligned}\right\} \quad \text{..................(26)}$$

with

$$\left.\begin{aligned} \frac{\partial}{\partial x}\left(\frac{\partial e_{yz}^{(0)}}{\partial x} - \frac{\partial e_{zx}^{(0)}}{\partial y}\right) + 2\sigma\kappa_1 &= 0, \\ \frac{\partial}{\partial y}\left(\frac{\partial e_{yz}^{(0)}}{\partial x} - \frac{\partial e_{zx}^{(0)}}{\partial y}\right) - 2\sigma\kappa_1 &= 0, \end{aligned}\right\} \quad \text{..................(27)}$$

and

$$\frac{\partial^2 e_{xx}^{(0)}}{\partial y^2} + \frac{\partial^2 e_{yy}^{(0)}}{\partial x^2} = \frac{\partial^2 e_{xy}^{(0)}}{\partial x \partial y}. \quad \text{.....................(28)}$$

Equations (26) give us the form of $e_{zz}^{(0)}$, viz.,

$$e_{zz}^{(0)} = \epsilon_0 - \kappa_0 x - \kappa_0' y + 2\kappa_2(\chi + xy^2) + 2\kappa_2'(\chi' + x^2 y) + \tau_1\phi; \quad \text{...(29)}$$

and, by a similar process to that in Article 238, we find

$$\left.\begin{aligned} e_{zx}^{(0)} &= \tau_0\left(\frac{\partial\phi}{\partial x} - y\right) + \kappa_1\left\{\frac{\partial\chi}{\partial x} + \tfrac{1}{2}\sigma x^2 + (1 - \tfrac{1}{2}\sigma)y^2\right\} + \kappa_1'\left\{\frac{\partial\chi'}{\partial x} + (2+\sigma)xy\right\}, \\ e_{yz}^{(0)} &= \tau_0\left(\frac{\partial\phi}{\partial y} + x\right) + \kappa_1\left\{\frac{\partial\chi}{\partial y} + (2+\sigma)xy\right\} + \kappa_1'\left\{\frac{\partial\chi'}{\partial y} + \tfrac{1}{2}\sigma y^2 + (1 - \tfrac{1}{2}\sigma)x^2\right\}, \end{aligned}\right\} \quad (30)$$

wherein ϵ_0, κ_0, κ_0', τ_0 are constants, and ϕ, χ, χ' are the functions previously so denoted.

It remains to determine $X_x^{(0)}$, $Y_y^{(0)}$, $X_y^{(0)}$ from the first two of (24), the first two of (25), the appropriate stress-strain relations and the equation (28). This determination requires in effect the solution of a problem of plane strain. If we put

$$X_x^{(0)} = \lambda e_{zz}^{(0)} + X_x', \quad Y_y^{(0)} = \lambda e_{zz}^{(0)} + Y_y', \quad \text{..............(31)}$$

then the equations of the problem of plane strain are

$$\left.\begin{aligned} \frac{\partial X_x'}{\partial x} + \frac{\partial X_y^{(0)}}{\partial y} + \left[\rho X + X_z^{(1)} + \lambda \frac{\partial e_{zz}^{(0)}}{\partial x}\right] = 0, \\ \frac{\partial X_y^{(0)}}{\partial x} + \frac{\partial Y_y'}{\partial y} + \left[\rho Y + Y_z^{(1)} + \lambda \frac{\partial e_{zz}^{(0)}}{\partial y}\right] = 0, \end{aligned}\right\} \quad \text{............(32)}$$

together with equation (28), the equations

$$X_x' = \lambda e_{yy}^{(0)} + (\lambda + 2\mu)\, e_{xx}^{(0)}, \quad Y_y' = \lambda e_{xx}^{(0)} + (\lambda + 2\mu)\, e_{yy}^{(0)}, \quad X_y^{(0)} = \mu e_{xy}^{(0)}, \quad \text{.........(33)}$$

and the boundary-conditions

$$\left.\begin{aligned} X_x' \cos(x, \nu) + X_y^{(0)} \cos(y, \nu) = [X_\nu - \lambda e_{zz}^{(0)} \cos(x, \nu)], \\ X_y^{(0)} \cos(x, \nu) + Y_y' \cos(y, \nu) = [Y_\nu - \lambda e_{zz}^{(0)} \cos(y, \nu)]. \end{aligned}\right\} \quad \text{......(34)}$$

The expressions in square brackets in (32) and (34) may be regarded as known.

The theory here explained admits of extension to any case in which the forces applied to the beam along its length have longitudinal components as well as transverse components, provided that all these components are independent of z*. This restriction may be removed, and the theory extended further to any case in which all the forces applied to the beam along its length are represented by rational integral functions of z†.

240. The constants of the solution.

Let W, W' denote the components parallel to the axes of x and y of the uniform load, so that we have

$$W = \iint \rho X dx dy + \int X_\nu dS$$

with a similar formula for W'. From equations (32) and (34) we find

$$W = -\iint X_z^{(1)} dx dy, \quad W' = -\iint Y_z^{(1)} dx dy. \quad \text{..............(35)}$$

Now we may write down the equations

$$\begin{aligned} \iint X_z\, dx dy &= \iint \left\{\frac{\partial}{\partial x}(x X_z) + \frac{\partial}{\partial y}(x Y_z) - x\left(\frac{\partial X_z}{\partial x} + \frac{\partial Y_z}{\partial y}\right)\right\} dx dy \\ &= \int x \{X_z \cos(x, \nu) + Y_z \cos(y, \nu)\}\, ds + \iint x \{Z_z^{(1)} + 2z Z_z^{(2)}\}\, dx dy \\ &= -EI(\kappa_1 + 2z\kappa_2), \end{aligned}$$

with similar equations for $\iint Y_z\, dx dy$. Hence we find

$$2EI\kappa_2 = W, \quad 2EI'\kappa_2' = W'. \quad \text{....................(36)}$$

Thus the constants κ_2, κ_2' are determined in terms of the load per unit of length.

* J. H. Michell, *loc. cit.*, p. 354.

† E. Almansi, *Roma, Acc. Linc. Rend.* (Ser. 6), t. 10 (1901).

If the body forces and the surface tractions on the cylindrical bounding surface give rise to a couple about the axis of z, the moment of this couple is

$$\iint \rho\,(xY - yX)\,dx\,dy + \int (xY_\nu - yX_\nu)\,ds.$$

and from equations (32) and (34) we find that this expression is equal to

$$-\iint \{xY_z^{(1)} - yX_z^{(1)}\}\,dx\,dy.$$

On substituting $\mu e_{zx}^{(1)}$ for $X_z^{(1)}$ and $\mu e_{yz}^{(1)}$ for $Y_z^{(1)}$, and using the expressions given in (23) for $e_{zx}^{(1)}$ and $e_{yz}^{(1)}$, we have an equation to determine τ_1. When no twisting couple is applied along the length of the beam, and the section is symmetrical with respect to the axes of x and y, τ_1 vanishes.

The constants κ_2, κ_2', τ_1 depend, therefore, on the force- and couple-resultants of the load per unit of length. The terms of the solution which contain the remaining constants ϵ_0, κ_0, κ_0', κ_1, κ_1', τ_0 are the same as the terms of the complete solution of the problem of Article 238. These constants depend therefore on the force- and couple-resultants of the tractions applied to the terminal sections of the beam. Since the terms containing κ_2, κ_2', τ_1 alone would involve the existence of tractions on the normal sections, the force- and couple-resultants on a terminal section must be expressed by adding the contributions due to the terms in κ_2, κ_2', τ_1 to the contributions evaluated at the end of Article 238. The remaining constants ϵ_0, ... are then expressed in terms of the load per unit of length and the terminal forces and couples.

When the functions ϕ, χ, χ' are known and the problem of plane strain is solved, we know the state of stress and strain in the beam bent by uniform load, distributed in any assigned way, and by terminal forces and couples. As in Chapters XIV and XV, the terminal forces and couples may be of any assigned amounts, but the tractions of which they are the statical equivalents must be distributed in certain definite ways.

241. Strain and stress in the elements of the beam.

Three of the components of strain are determined without solving the problem of plane strain. These are e_{zz}, e_{zx}, e_{yz}. We have

$$\left.\begin{aligned}
e_{zz} &= \epsilon_0 - (\kappa_0 + \kappa_1 z + \kappa_2 z^2)\,x - (\kappa_0' + \kappa_1' z + \kappa_2' z^2)\,y + 2\kappa_2(\chi + xy^2) \\
&\qquad + 2\kappa_2'(\chi' + x^2 y) + \tau_1\phi, \\
e_{zx} &= (\tau_0 + \tau_1 z)\left(\frac{\partial\phi}{\partial x} - y\right) + (\kappa_1 + 2\kappa_2 z)\left\{\frac{\partial\chi}{\partial x} + \tfrac{1}{2}\sigma x^2 + (1 - \tfrac{1}{2}\sigma)\,y^2\right\} \\
&\qquad + (\kappa_1' + 2\kappa_2' z)\left\{\frac{\partial\chi'}{\partial x} + (2 + \sigma)\,xy\right\}, \\
e_{yz} &= (\tau_0 + \tau_1 z)\left(\frac{\partial\phi}{\partial y} + x\right) + (\kappa_1 + 2\kappa_2 z)\left\{\frac{\partial\chi}{\partial y} + (2 + \sigma)\,xy\right\} \\
&\qquad + (\kappa_1' + 2\kappa_2' z)\left\{\frac{\partial\chi'}{\partial y} + (1 - \tfrac{1}{2}\sigma)\,x^2 + \tfrac{1}{2}\sigma y^2\right\}.
\end{aligned}\right\} \quad \text{...(37)}$$

The constant ϵ_0 is the extension of the central-line. We shall see presently that, in general, it is not proportional to the resultant longitudinal tension. The constants τ_0 and τ_1 are interpreted by the observation that $\tau_0 + \tau_1 z$ is the twist of the beam.

To interpret the constants denoted by $\kappa_0, \ldots$, we observe that the curvature of the central-line in the plane of (x, z) is the value of $\partial^2 u/\partial z^2$ when $x = y = 0$. Now we have

$$\frac{\partial^2 u}{\partial z^2} = \frac{\partial e_{zx}}{\partial z} - \frac{\partial e_{zz}}{\partial x}$$

$$= (\kappa_0 + \kappa_1 z + \kappa_2 z^2) - \tau_1 y + \kappa_2 \sigma (x^2 - y^2) + 2\kappa_2' \sigma xy, \qquad \text{.........(38)}$$

and therefore the curvature in question is $\kappa_0 + \kappa_1 z + \kappa_2 z^2$. In like manner we should find that the curvature of the central-line in the plane of (y, z), estimated as the value of $\partial^2 v/\partial z^2$ when $x = y = 0$, is $\kappa_0' + \kappa_1' z + \kappa_2' z^2$.

The presence of the terms

$$\epsilon_0 + 2\kappa_2 (\chi + xy^2) + 2\kappa_2' (\chi' + x^2 y) + \tau_1 \phi$$

in the expression for e_{zz} shows that the simple relation of the extension of the longitudinal filaments to the curvature of the central-line, which we noticed in the case of bending by terminal forces [Article 232 (*b*)], does not hold in the present problem.

Of the stress-components two only, X_z and Y_z, are determined without solving the problem of plane strain. The resultants of these for a cross-section are respectively $-EI(\kappa_1 + 2\kappa_2 z)$ and $-EI'(\kappa_1' + 2\kappa_2' z)$. The distribution over the cross-section of the tangential tractions X_z and Y_z which are statically equivalent to these resultants is the same as in Saint-Venant's solutions (Chapter XV). When there is a twist $\tau_0 + \tau_1 z$, the tractions X_z and Y_z which accompany the twist are distributed over the cross-sections in the same way as in the torsion problem (Chapter XIV).

The stress-component Z_z is not equal to Ee_{zz} because the stress-components X_x, Y_y are not zero, but the force- and couple-resultants of the tractions Z_z on the elements of a cross-section can be expressed in terms of the constants of the solution without solving the problem of plane strain. The resultant of the tractions Z_z is the resultant longitudinal tension. The moments of the tractions Z_z about axes drawn through the centroid of a cross-section parallel to the axes of y and x are the components about these axes of the *bending moment* at the section.

To express the resultant longitudinal tension we observe that

$$\iint Z_z dx dy = \iint Z_z^{(0)} dx dy = \iint [Ee_{zz}^{(0)} + \sigma (X_x^{(0)} + Y_y^{(0)})] dx dy.$$

Now we may write down the equations

$$\iint X_x^{(0)} dx dy = \iint \left\{ \frac{\partial}{\partial x} (x X_x^{(0)}) + \frac{\partial}{\partial y} (x X_y^{(0)}) - x \left(\frac{\partial X_x^{(0)}}{\partial x} + \frac{\partial X_y^{(0)}}{\partial y} \right) \right\} dx dy$$

$$= \int x \{ X_x^{(0)} \cos (x, \nu) + X_y^{(0)} \cos (y, \nu) \} ds + \iint x (X_z^{(1)} + \rho X) dx dy.$$

The integral $\iint Y_y^{(0)}\,dx\,dy$ may be transformed in the same way, and hence we find the formula

$$\iint Z_z\,dx\,dy = \iint [Ee_{zz}^{(0)} + \sigma x(X_z^{(1)} + \rho X) + \sigma y(Y_z^{(1)} + \rho Y)]\,dx\,dy$$
$$+ \sigma \int (xX_\nu + yY_\nu)\,ds. \quad \text{.......(39)}$$

Since the resultant longitudinal tension is the same at all sections, and is equal to the prescribed terminal tension, this equation determines the constant ϵ_0.

To express the bending moments, let M be the bending moment in the plane of (x, z). Then

$$M = -\iint xZ_z\,dx\,dy, \quad \text{.......(40)}$$

and therefore we have

$$\frac{\partial M}{\partial z} = -\iint x(Z_z^{(1)} + 2zZ_z^{(2)})\,dx\,dy = EI(\kappa_1 + 2z\kappa_2).$$

This equation shows that M is expressible in the form

$$M = EI(\kappa_0 + \kappa_1 z + \kappa_2 z^2) + \text{const.} \quad \text{.......(41)}$$

In like manner we may show that the bending moment in the plane of (y, z) is expressible in the form

$$EI'(\kappa_0' + \kappa_1' z + \kappa_2' z^2) + \text{const.}$$

We shall show immediately how the constants may be determined.

242. Relation between the curvature and the bending moment.

We shall consider the case in which one end $z = 0$ is held fixed, the other end $z = l$ is free from traction, and the load is statically equivalent to a force W per unit of length acting at the centroid of the cross-section in the direction of the axis of x*. The bending moment M is given by the equation

$$M = \tfrac{1}{2}W(l - z)^2, \quad \text{.......(42)}$$

and the comparison of this equation with (41) gives the equations

$$\kappa_1 = -Wl/EI, \quad \kappa_2 = \tfrac{1}{2}W/EI. \quad \text{.......(43)}$$

We observe that, if the constant added to the right-hand member of (41) were zero, the relation between the bending moment and the curvature would be the same as in uniform bending by terminal couples and in bending

* The important case of a beam supported at the ends, and carrying a load W per unit of length, can be treated by compounding the solution for a beam with one end free, bent by the uniform load, with that for a beam bent by a terminal transverse load equal to $-\tfrac{1}{2}Wl$.

by terminal load. The constant in question does not in general vanish. To determine it we observe that the value of M at $z=0$ is

$$-\iint x\left[Ee_{zz}^{(0)}+\sigma\left(X_x^{(0)}+Y_y^{(0)}\right)\right]dx\,dy,$$

and therefore

$$M-EI\left(\kappa_0+\kappa_1 z+\kappa_2 z^2\right)=\iint -x\left[E\left(e_{zz}^{(0)}+\kappa_0 x\right)+\sigma\left(X_x^{(0)}+Y_y^{(0)}\right)\right]dx\,dy. \quad \text{.........(44)}$$

Now we may write down the equations

$$\iint x\left(X_x^{(0)}+Y_y^{(0)}\right)dx\,dy$$

$$=\iint\left[\frac{\partial}{\partial x}\left\{\tfrac{1}{2}(x^2-y^2)X_x^{(0)}+xyX_y^{(0)}\right\}+\frac{\partial}{\partial y}\left\{\tfrac{1}{2}(x^2-y^2)X_y^{(0)}+xyY_y^{(0)}\right\}\right.$$

$$\left.-\left\{\tfrac{1}{2}(x^2-y^2)\left(\frac{\partial X_x^{(0)}}{\partial x}+\frac{\partial X_y^{(0)}}{\partial y}\right)+xy\left(\frac{\partial X_y^{(0)}}{\partial x}+\frac{\partial Y_y^{(0)}}{\partial y}\right)\right\}\right]dx\,dy$$

$$=\int\left[\tfrac{1}{2}(x^2-y^2)X_\nu+xyY_\nu\right]ds+\iint\left[\tfrac{1}{2}(x^2-y^2)\left(\rho X+X_z^{(1)}\right)+xy\left(\rho Y+Y_z^{(1)}\right)\right]dx\,dy.$$

Hence we have the result

$$M-EI\left(\kappa_0+\kappa_1 z+\kappa_2 z^2\right)$$

$$=-\iint Ex\left(e_{zz}^{(0)}+\kappa_0 x\right)dx\,dy-\sigma\int\left[\tfrac{1}{2}(x^2-y^2)X_\nu+xyY_\nu\right]ds$$

$$-\sigma\iint\left[\tfrac{1}{2}(x^2-y^2)\left(\rho X+X_z^{(1)}\right)+xy\left(\rho Y+Y_z^{(1)}\right)\right]dx\,dy. \quad \text{......(45)}$$

Since M is given by (42) this equation determines the constant κ_0. The right-hand member of (45) is the value of the added constant in the right-hand member of (41).

The result that the bending moment is not proportional to the curvature*, when load is applied along the beam, may be illustrated by reference to cases in which curvature is produced without any bending moment. One such case is afforded by the results of Article 87, if we simply interchange the axes of y and z. It then appears that a stress-system in which all the stress-components except Y_y vanish, while Y_y has the form Eax, can be maintained by surface tractions of amount $Eax\cos(y,\nu)$ parallel to the axis of y. These tractions are self-equilibrating on every section, and there is no bending moment. The corresponding displacement is given by the equations

$$u=-\tfrac{1}{2}a\left(\sigma x^2+y^2-\sigma z^2\right), \quad v=axy, \quad w=-\sigma axz,$$

so that the central-line ($x=0$, $y=0$) is bent to curvature σa.

Another case is afforded by the state of stress expressed by the equations

$$X_x=Eax, \quad Y_y=Eax, \quad X_y=-Eay, \quad X_z=Y_z=Z_z=0,$$

which can be maintained by surface tractions of amounts

$$Ea\{x\cos(x,\nu)-y\cos(y,\nu)\}, \quad Ea\{x\cos(y,\nu)-y\cos(x,\nu)\}$$

parallel to the axes of x and y. These tractions are self-equilibrating on every section,

* The result was obtained first by K. Pearson. See Introduction, footnote 92. The formula (45) is due to J. H. Michell, *loc. cit.*, p. 354. The amount of the extra curvature in some special cases is calculated in Article 244.

and there is no bending moment. The corresponding displacement is given by the equations

$$u=a\{\tfrac{1}{2}(1-\sigma)x^2-\tfrac{1}{2}(3+\sigma)y^2+\sigma z^2\},\quad v=a(1-\sigma)xy,\quad w=-2a\sigma xz,$$

and the curvature of the central-line is $2\sigma a$.

If we consider a slice of the beam between two normal sections as made up of filaments having a direction transverse to that of the beam, and regard these filaments as bent by forces applied at their ends, it is clear that the central-line of the beam must receive a curvature, arising from the contractions and extensions of the longitudinal filaments, in exactly the same way as transverse filaments of a beam bent by terminal load receive a curvature. The tendency to anticlastic curvature which we remarked in the case of a beam bent by terminal loads affords an explanation of the production, by distributed loads, of some curvature over and above that which is related in the ordinary way to the bending moment. This explanation suggests that the effect here discussed is likely to be most important in such structures as suspension bridges, where a load carried along the middle of the roadway is supported by tensions in rods attached at the sides.

243. Extension of the central-line.

The fact that the central-line of a beam bent by transverse load is, in general, extended or contracted was noted long ago as a result of experiment*, and it is not difficult to see beforehand that such a result must be true. Consider, for example, the case of a beam of rectangular section loaded along the top. There must be pressure on any horizontal section increasing from zero at the lower surface to a finite value at the top. With this pressure there must be associated a contraction of the vertical filaments and an extension of the horizontal filaments. The value of the extension of the horizontal central-line is determined by means of the formula (39). Since the stress is not expressed completely by the vertical pressure, this extension is not expressed so simply as the above argument might lead us to infer.

The result that $\epsilon_0 \neq 0$ may be otherwise expressed by saying that the neutral plane, if there is one, does not contain the central-line. In general the locus of the points at which e_{zz} vanishes, or there is no longitudinal extension, might be called the "neutral-surface." If it is plane it is the neutral plane.

244. Illustrations of the theory.

(*a*) *Form of the solution of the problem of plane strain.* When the body force is the weight of the beam, and there are no surface tractions, we may make some progress with the solution of the problem of plane strain (Article 239) without finding χ. In this case, putting $X=g$, $Y=0$, we see that the solution of the stress-equations (32) can be expressed in the form

$$\left.\begin{aligned} X_x' &= \frac{\partial^2\Omega}{\partial y^2} - \lambda e_{zz}{}^{(0)} - g\rho x - 2\kappa_2\mu\,[\chi+\tfrac{1}{6}\sigma x^3+(1-\tfrac{1}{2}\sigma)\,xy^2],\\ Y_y' &= \frac{\partial^2\Omega}{\partial x^2} - \lambda e_{zz}{}^{(0)} \qquad\quad - 2\kappa_2\mu\,[\chi+(1+\tfrac{1}{2}\sigma)\,xy^2],\\ X_y{}^{(0)} &= -\frac{\partial^2\Omega}{\partial x\partial y}, \end{aligned}\right\} \quad\text{..............(46)}$$

where Ω must be adjusted so that the equation of compatibility (28) is satisfied. We may show that this equation leads to the following equation for Ω:

$$\nabla_1{}^4\Omega = 2\mu\kappa_2(2+\sigma)\,x. \quad\text{.................................(47)}$$

If we take the particular solution

$$\Omega=\frac{\mu\kappa_2(2+\sigma)}{96}\,x\,(x^2+y^2)^2, \quad\text{.................................(48)}$$

* Fabré, *Paris*, *C. R.*, t. 46 (1858).

we find for X_x', ... a set of values involving surface traction, and an additional stress-system must be superposed so as to annul this surface traction without involving any body force; in other words a complementary solution of $\nabla_1^4\Omega=0$ must be added to the value of Ω given in (48), and this solution must be adjusted so that the boundary-conditions are satisfied.

(b) *Solution of the problem of plane strain for a beam of circular section bent by its own weight.* When the boundary is a circle $x^2+y^2=a^2$, we have

$$\chi=-(\tfrac{3}{4}+\tfrac{1}{2}\sigma)\,a^2x+\tfrac{1}{4}(x^3-3xy^2); \quad \text{......(49)}$$

and the surface values of the stress-components given by (46), when Ω is given by (48), can be simplified by observing that, in accordance with (36), $g\rho=\mu\kappa_2a^2(1+\sigma)$. It will be found that these values are given by the equations

$$\left.\begin{aligned} X_x'&=\mu\kappa_2\frac{2+\sigma}{24}(x^3+3xy^2)-\lambda e_{zz}^{(0)}-\tfrac{1}{3}\mu\sigma\kappa_2(x^3-3xy^2),\\ Y_y'&=\mu\kappa_2\frac{2+\sigma}{24}(5x^3+3xy^2)-\lambda e_{zz}^{(0)}+\mu\kappa_2(1+\tfrac{3}{4}\sigma)\,a^2x+\tfrac{1}{4}\mu\sigma\kappa_2(x^3-3xy^2),\\ X_y^{(0)}&=-\mu\kappa_2\frac{2+\sigma}{24}(y^3+3yx^2). \end{aligned}\right\} \quad \text{......(50)}$$

The surface tractions arising from the terms in $\mu\kappa_2\dfrac{2+\sigma}{24}$ can be annulled by superposing the stress-system*

$$X_x'=-\frac{2+\sigma}{24}\mu\kappa_2a^2x, \quad Y_y'=-\frac{2+\sigma}{8}\mu\kappa_2a^2x, \quad X_y^{(0)}=\frac{2+\sigma}{24}\mu\kappa_2a^2y. \quad \text{......(51)}$$

The surface tractions arising from the terms in $\mu\kappa_2a^2x$ can be annulled by superposing the stress-system

$$X_x'=0, \quad Y_y'=-\mu\kappa_2(1+\tfrac{3}{4}\sigma)\,a^2x, \quad X_y^{(0)}=0. \quad \text{......(52)}$$

The surface tractions arising from the terms in $\mu\sigma\kappa_2(x^3-3xy^2)$ can be annulled by superposing the stress-system

$$X_x'=\mu\sigma\kappa_2x(\tfrac{1}{8}x^2-\tfrac{5}{8}y^2+\tfrac{5}{24}a^2), \quad Y_y'=\mu\sigma\kappa_2x(-\tfrac{1}{24}x^2+\tfrac{3}{8}y^2+\tfrac{3}{8}a^2),$$
$$X_y^{(0)}=\mu\sigma\kappa_2y\{-\tfrac{3}{8}x^2+\tfrac{5}{24}(y^2-a^2)\}. \quad \text{......(53)}$$

The stress-components X_x', Y_y', $X_y^{(0)}$ are therefore determined, and thus the problem of plane strain is solved for a circular boundary.

I find the following expressions for the stress-components in a circular cylinder bent by its own weight:

$$X_x=\frac{\mu\kappa_2x}{12}[(5+2\sigma)(a^2-x^2)-3(1-2\sigma)y^2], \quad Y_y=\frac{\mu\kappa_2x}{12}[3(1+2\sigma)(a^2-y^2)-(1-2\sigma)x^2],$$

$$X_y=\frac{\mu\kappa_2y}{12}[(1-2\sigma)(a^2-y^2)-3(1+2\sigma)x^2],$$

$$X_z=\mu(\kappa_1+2\kappa_2z)[-(\tfrac{3}{4}+\tfrac{1}{2}\sigma)(a^2-x^2)+(\tfrac{1}{4}-\tfrac{1}{2}\sigma)y^2], \quad Y_z=\mu(\kappa_1+2\kappa_2z)(\tfrac{1}{2}+\sigma)\,xy,$$
$$Z_z=-E(\kappa_0+\kappa_1z+\kappa_2z^2)\,x-\mu\kappa_2x[\tfrac{1}{3}(9+13\sigma+4\sigma^2)\,a^2-(1+\tfrac{1}{2}\sigma)(x^2+y^2)].$$

The constant κ_2 is given by the equation

$$\kappa_2=g\rho/\mu a^2(1+\sigma).$$

When the beam, of length l, is fixed horizontally at $z=0$, and the end $z=l$ is unloaded,

$$\kappa_1=-2\kappa_2l, \quad \kappa_0=\kappa_2\left[l^2-a^2\frac{7+12\sigma+4\sigma^2}{6(1+\sigma)}\right].$$

* Some of the solutions of the problem of plane strain in a circular cylinder which are required here were given in Article 186.

When the beam, of length $2l$, is supported at the ends $z=l$ and $z=-l$, these ends being at the same level,

$$\kappa_1=0, \quad \kappa_0=-\kappa_2\left[l^2+a^2\frac{7+12\sigma+4\sigma^2}{6(1+\sigma)}\right].$$

An independent calculation of the displacement kindly sent to me by Mr G. C. Calliphronas confirms these results.

(c) *Correction of the curvature in this case.* In the case of a beam of circular section bent by its own weight we may show that $\epsilon_0=0$, or the central-line is unextended, and that

$$\kappa_0=\frac{2g\rho}{E}\frac{l^2}{a^2}\left(1-\frac{7+12\sigma+4\sigma^2}{6(1+\sigma)}\frac{a^2}{l^2}\right). \qquad \text{.........................(54)}$$

If the curvature were calculated from the bending moment by the ordinary rule the second term in the bracket would be absent. Thus the correction to the curvature arising from the distribution of the load is small of the order

$$\left[\frac{\text{linear dimension of cross-section}}{\text{length of beam}}\right]^2.$$

A consideration of the form of (45) would show that this result holds in general for a beam bent by its own weight*.

(d) *Narrow rectangular beam loaded along the top.*

The theory may be illustrated further by the case of a beam of rectangular section and small breadth loaded uniformly along its upper surface†. We shall treat the problem as one of generalized plane stress‡, and we shall neglect the weight of the beam. Let $2a$ be the depth of the beam, $2b$ the breadth, and l the length. Take the axis of z along the horizontal central-line, and the axis of x vertically downwards at the fixed end, $z=0$. Let W denote the load per unit of length. The average stress-components $\bar{X}_x$, $\bar{Z}_z$, $\bar{X}_z$ can be expressed in the forms

$$\left.\begin{aligned}\bar{X}_x&=-\frac{W}{4b}+E\kappa_2(a^2x-\tfrac{1}{3}x^3),\\ \bar{Z}_z&=-EAx+\tfrac{2}{3}E\kappa_2x^3-E(\kappa_1z+\kappa_2z^2)x,\\ \bar{X}_z&=-\tfrac{1}{2}E(a^2-x^2)(\kappa_1+2\kappa_2z),\end{aligned}\right\} \qquad \text{.......................(55)}$$

where, in order to satisfy equation (42), we must have

$$\kappa_2=\frac{3W}{8Ea^3b}, \quad \kappa_1=-\frac{3Wl}{4Ea^3b}, \quad A=\frac{3Wl^2}{8Ea^3b}\left(1+\frac{2}{5}\frac{a^2}{l^2}\right). \qquad \text{...............(56)}$$

The curvature of the central-line can be shown to be

$$A-(2+\sigma)\kappa_2a^2+\kappa_1z+\kappa_2z^2,$$

which is equal to

$$\frac{3W}{8Ea^3b}\left[(l-z)^2-(\tfrac{8}{5}+\sigma)a^2\right].$$

The term containing $(\frac{8}{5}+\sigma)a^2$ gives the correction of the curvature that would be calculated by the ordinary rule.

* Solutions of the problem of the bending of a circular or elliptic cylinder by loads distributed in certain special ways have been given by Pearson, *Quart. J. of Math.*, vol. 24 (1889), and by Pearson and Filon, *Quart. J. of Math.*, vol. 31 (1900).

† Another extreme case of rectangular section, viz., that where the beam is of small depth, is treated as an example of the theory of plates by C. A. Garabedian, *Paris, C. R.*, t. 179 (1924), p. 381.

‡ The problem has been discussed by J. H. Michell, *Quart. J. of Math.*, vol. 31 (1900), and also by L. N. G. Filon, *Phil. Trans. Roy. Soc.* (Ser. A), vol. 201 (1903), and *London, Roy. Soc. Proc.*, vol. 72 (1904).

The extension of the central-line can be shown to be $\sigma W/4bE$; it is just half as great as the extension of the beam when free at the ends, supported along the base, and carrying the same load along the top. The neutral surface is given by the equation

$$x\left[3\frac{(l-z)^2}{a^2}+3\left(\tfrac{2}{5}+\sigma\right)-(2+\sigma)\frac{x^2}{a^2}\right]=2\sigma a.$$

At a considerable distance from the free end the depth of this surface below the central-line is nearly equal to $\frac{2}{3}\sigma a^3/(l-z)^2$. The result that the neutral surface is on the side of the central-line towards the centres of curvature has been verified experimentally*.

(*e*) *Doubly supported beam.* If we superpose on the stress-system found in (55) that due to a load $-\frac{1}{2}Wl$ at the end $z=l$, we shall obtain the solution for a narrow rectangular beam bent by uniform load W per unit of length and supported at both ends. The additional stress-system is given, in accordance with the results of Article 95, by the equations

$$\overline{X}_x=0,\quad \overline{Z}_z=\frac{3}{8}\frac{Wl}{a^3b}(l-z)\,x,\quad \overline{X}_z=-\frac{3}{16}\frac{Wl}{a^3b}(a^2-x^2),$$

and the average stress in the beam is expressed by the formulæ

$$\left.\begin{aligned}\overline{X}_x&=-\frac{1}{8}\frac{W}{a^3b}(a-x)^2(2a+x),\\ \overline{Z}_z&=\frac{3}{8}\frac{W}{a^3b}\left[\tfrac{2}{3}x^3-\tfrac{2}{5}a^2x+xz(l-z)\right],\\ \overline{X}_z&=-\frac{3}{8}\frac{W}{a^3b}(a^2-x^2)\left(z-\tfrac{1}{2}l\right).\end{aligned}\right\}\qquad\qquad(57)$$

* See a paper by E. G. Coker, *Edinburgh, Roy. Soc. Trans.*, vol. 41 (1904), p. 229.

CHAPTER XVII

THE THEORY OF CONTINUOUS BEAMS

245. Extension of the theory of the bending of beams.

In previous Chapters we have discussed certain exact solutions of the problem of the bending of beams by loads which are applied in special ways. In the problem of the beam bent by a load concentrated at one end (Chapter XV) we found that the "Bernoulli-Eulerian" theorem of the proportionality of the curvature to the bending moment is verified. In the problem of the beam bent by a load distributed uniformly along its length (Chapter XVI) we found that this theorem is not verified, but that, over and above the curvature that would present itself if this theorem were true, there is an additional constant curvature, the amount of which depends upon the distribution over the cross-section of the forces constituting the load. We appear to be justified in concluding from these results that, in a beam slightly bent by any forces, the law of proportionality of the bending moment to the curvature is sufficiently exact at sections which are at a considerable distance from any place of loading or of support, but that, in the neighbourhood of such a place, there may be an additional local curvature. We endeavoured to trace the circumstances in which the additional curvature can become very important, and we solved some problems in which we found it to be unimportant. From the results that we obtained we appear to be justified in concluding that, in most practical problems relating to long beams, the additional curvature is not of very much importance.

The state of stress and strain that is produced in the interior of a beam, slightly bent by any forces, may be taken to be given with sufficient approximation by Saint-Venant's solution (Chapter XV) at all points which are at a considerable distance from any place of loading or of support*; and again, at a place near the middle of a considerable length over which the load is distributed uniformly or nearly uniformly, they may be taken to be given with sufficient approximation by Michell's solution (Chapter XVI). But we have not so detailed information in regard to the state of stress or strain near to a place of concentrated load or to a place of support. Near to such a place the actual distribution of the forces applied to the beam must be very influential. Attempts have been made to study the state of strain at such places experimentally. In the research of Carus Wilson† a beam of

* This view is confirmed by L. Pochhammer's investigation of the strain in a circular cylinder deformed by given forces. See his *Untersuchungen über das Gleichgewicht des elastischen Stabes*, Kiel, 1879.

† *Phil. Mag.* (Ser. 5), vol. 32 (1891).

glass of rectangular section, supported symmetrically on two rollers B, C, was bent by means of a third roller A above its middle, and the state of strain in the line AD (Fig. 32) was examined by means of polarized light transmitted horizontally through the beam. The results of the research were explained by Stokes* by the aid of certain empirical assumptions. Stokes pointed out that, if the problem is taken to be a two-dimensional one, the pressure W at A could be balanced by applying to the side BC of the beam pressures distributed according to the law of a simple radial distribution of pressure

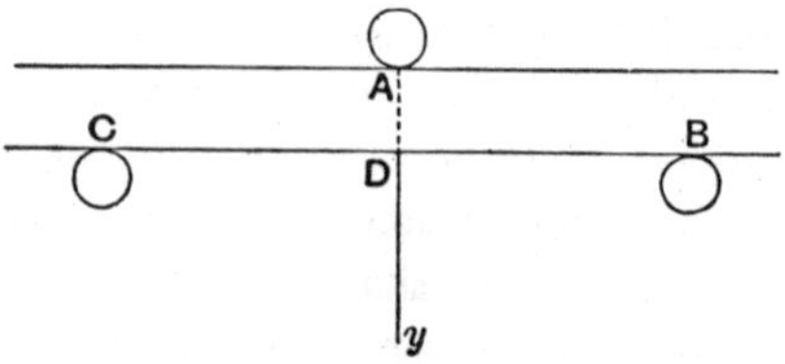

Fig. 32.

(Article 149) directed towards A. In like manner the pressures $\frac{1}{2}W$ at B and C, together with radial tension directed from A, and applied along the side BC according to the same law as before, would be a system of forces in statical equilibrium. By superposing these two systems of forces we obtain a system in which the only forces are those actually applied to the beam. The state of stress produced by the forces of the first system is that which we found in Article 150. The state of stress produced by the forces of the second system cannot be determined theoretically, but, at any point of AD, it must consist of a certain vertical pressure and a certain horizontal tension. Stokes assumed that each of these stress-components varies uniformly along the length of AD. The vertical pressure calculated from the two systems vanishes at D, and that calculated from the second system vanishes at A; these conditions together with the knowledge of the resultant, and resultant moment about A, of the horizontal tensions, are sufficient, when the above assumption is made, to determine the stress at any point of AD. Taking A as origin, and AD as axis of y, we find by this method the following values for the stress-components at any point of AD:

$$\text{horizontal tension, } X_x, = \frac{W}{b}\left(\frac{4}{\pi} - \frac{3a}{b}\right) + \frac{6W}{b^2}\left(\frac{a}{b} - \frac{1}{\pi}\right)y,$$

$$\text{vertical pressure, } -Y_y, = \frac{2W}{\pi}\left(\frac{1}{y} - \frac{y}{b^2}\right),$$

where b is the depth of the beam, and $2a$ is the span BC. The stress is equivalent to mean tension unaccompanied by shearing stress at those points at which $X_x = Y_y$. In order that these points may be real we must have $6a/b > 40/\pi$, or (span/depth) $> 4{\cdot}25$ nearly. When this condition is satisfied

* Stokes's work is published in Carus Wilson's paper; it is reprinted in Stokes's *Math. and Phys. Papers*, vol. 5, p. 238.

there are two such points. The positions of these points can be determined experimentally, since they are characterized by the absence of any doubly refractive property of the glass, and the actual and calculated positions were found to agree very closely.

A general theory of two-dimensional problems of this character has been given by L. N. G. Filon*. Among the problems solved by him is included that of a beam of infinite length to one side of which pressure is applied at one point. The components of displacement and of stress were expressed by means of definite integrals, and the results are rather difficult to interpret. It is clear that, if the solution of this special problem could be obtained in a manageable form, the solution of such questions as that discussed by Stokes could be obtained by synthesis. Filon concluded from his work that Stokes's value for the horizontal tension requires correction, more especially in the lower half of the beam, but that his value for the vertical pressure is a good approximation. As regards the question of the relation between the curvature and the bending moment, Filon concluded that the Bernoulli-Eulerian theorem is approximately verified, but that, in applying it to determine the deflexion due to a concentrated load, account ought to be taken of a term of the same kind as the so-called "additional deflexion due to shearing" [Article 235 (*e*)]. Consider for example a beam *BC* supported at both ends and carrying a concentrated load *W* at the middle point *A* (Fig. 33). Either part, *AC* or

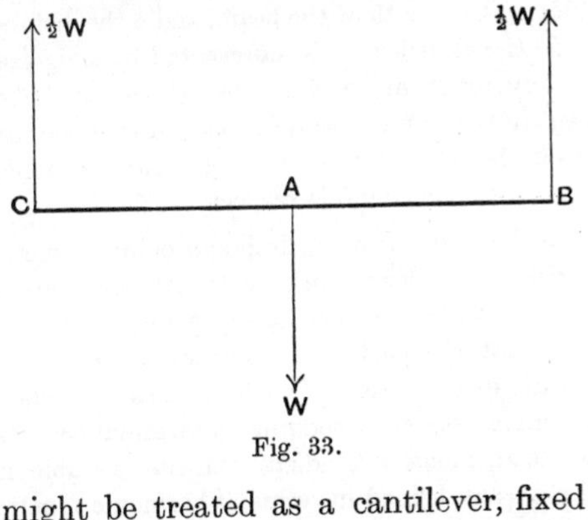

Fig. 33.

AB, of the beam might be treated as a cantilever, fixed at *A* and bent by terminal load $\frac{1}{2}W$ acting upwards at the other end; but Saint-Venant's solution would not be strictly applicable to the parts *AB* or *AC*, for the cross-sections are distorted into curved surfaces which would not fit together at *A*. In Saint-Venant's solution of the cantilever problem the central part of the cross-section at *A* is vertical, and the tangent to the central-line at *A* makes with the horizontal a certain small angle s_0. [Article 232 (*c*).] Filon concluded from his solution that the deflexion of the centrally loaded beam may be

* *Phil. Trans. Roy. Soc.* (Ser. A), vol. 201 (1903). Reference may also be made to a thesis by C. Ribière, *Sur divers cas de la flexion des prismes rectangles*, Bordeaux, 1888.

determined approximately by the double cantilever method, provided that the central-line at the point of loading A is taken to be bent through a small angle, so that AB and AC are inclined upwards at the same small angle to the horizontal. He estimated this small angle as about $\frac{3}{4}s_0$.

The correction of the central deflexion which would be obtained in this way would be equivalent, in the case of a narrow rectangular beam, to increasing it by the fraction $45d^2/16l^2$ of itself, where l is the length of the span, and d is the depth of the beam. The correction is therefore not very important in a long beam.

It must be understood that the theory here cited does not state that the central-line is bent through a small angle at the point immediately under the concentrated load. The exact expression for the displacement shows in fact that the direction is continuous at this point. What the theory states is that we may make a good approximation to the deflexion by assuming the Bernoulli-Eulerian curvature-theorem—which is not exactly true—and at the same time assuming a discontinuity of direction of the central-line—which does not really occur.

245 A. Further investigations.

Filon* has verified his theory experimentally by means of polarized light.

The subject has been investigated in a simpler way by H. Lamb†. He treats the problem as one of generalized plane stress (Article 94), and considers the case of a series of equal loads applied at a series of points, situated at regular intervals along the length of an infinite beam. He finds an expression for the deflexion consisting of three terms. The first term is identical with the deflexion given by the Bernoulli-Eulerian theory. The additional deflexion expressed by the second term is of the order d^2/a^2 as compared with that expressed by the first term, d denoting the depth of the beam, and a the distance between consecutive load-points; and this additional deflexion is represented by a zig-zag line whose successive straight portions make very obtuse angles with one another at the load-points. The third term is very small except in the immediate neighbourhood of the load-points, where it has the effect of rounding off the angles of the zig-zag. Lamb concludes that the Bernoulli-Eulerian theory is "entitled to considerable respect."

The matter has been discussed from a different point of view by J. Dougall‡. He considers an infinite circular cylinder to which external forces are applied in any manner, and finds the solution for concentrated force at any point, either within the cylinder or on the surface. He shows that the particular solutions of which this general solution is composed fall into two distinct classes. The first class consists of Saint-Venant's six solutions answering to simple extension, bending by terminal couples, torsion, and bending by terminal transverse load, along with displacements possible in a rigid body. The solutions of the second class are defined in terms of harmonic functions of the type

$$e^{\beta z/a} J_n(\beta r/a) \cos n(\theta - \theta_0),$$

where a is the radius of the cylinder, r, θ, z are cylindrical coordinates referred to the axis of the cylinder as axis of z, β is a root of a certain transcendental equation independent of a, n is an integer, and J_n the symbol of a Bessel's function of order n. The modes of equilibrium expressed by the solutions of the first class are described as "permanent free modes," those expressed by solutions of the second class as "transitory free modes." The distinction between permanent and transitory modes had been arrived at by Dougall in an

* *Phil. Mag.* (Ser. 6), vol. 23, 1912, p. 63.

† *Atti d. IV congr. internazionale d. matematici*, t. 3, Rome 1909, p. 12.

‡ *Edinburgh, Roy. Soc. Trans.*, vol. 49, 1914, p. 895.

investigation concerning the theory of elastic plates, cited in Article 313 *infra*, and a general account of them was given by him in *Proc. of the fifth international Congress of Mathematicians*, Cambridge 1913, p. 328. The occurrence of the factor $e^{\beta z/a}$ in the solutions expressing transitory modes indicates the nature of these modes as local perturbations. (Cf. Article 226 B *supra.*) The permanent modes answering to displacements possible in a rigid body are required for fitting together the solutions on the two sides of a section to which forces are applied. The general conclusion to be drawn from Dougall's work is favourable to the Bernoulli-Eulerian theory. Dougall indicates the extension of his methods to cylinders of sections other than circular.

The analysis for a circular cylinder has also been discussed by O. Tedone, *Roma, Acc. Linc. Rend.* (Ser. 5), t. 13 (Sem. 1), 1904, p. 232, and t. 21 (Sem. 1), 1912, p. 384.

246. The problem of continuous beams*.

In what follows we shall develop the consequences of assuming the Bernoulli-Eulerian curvature-theorem to hold in the case of a long beam, of small depth and breadth, resting on two or more supports at the same level, and bent by transverse loads distributed in various ways. We shall take the beam to be slightly bent in a principal plane. We take an origin anywhere in the line of the supports, and draw the axis of x horizontally to the right through the supports, and the axis of y vertically downwards. The curvature is expressed with sufficient approximation by d^2y/dx^2. The tractions exerted across a normal section of the beam, by the parts for which x is greater than it is at the section upon the parts for which x is less, are statically equivalent to a shearing force N, directed parallel to the axis of y, and a couple $\mathbf{G}$ in the plane of (x, y). The conditions of rigid-body equilibrium of a short length Δx of the beam between two normal sections yield the equation

$$\frac{d\mathbf{G}}{dx} + N = 0. \quad \text{.................................(1)}$$

The couple $\mathbf{G}$ is taken to be expressed by the equation

$$\mathbf{G} = \mathbf{B}\frac{d^2y}{dx^2}, \quad \text{.................................(2)}$$

where $\mathbf{B}$ is the product of Young's modulus for the material and the moment of inertia of a normal section about an axis through its centroid at right angles to the plane of (x, y)†. The senses of the force and couple, estimated as above, are indicated in Fig. 34. Except in estimating $\mathbf{B}$ no account is taken of the breadth or depth of the beam.

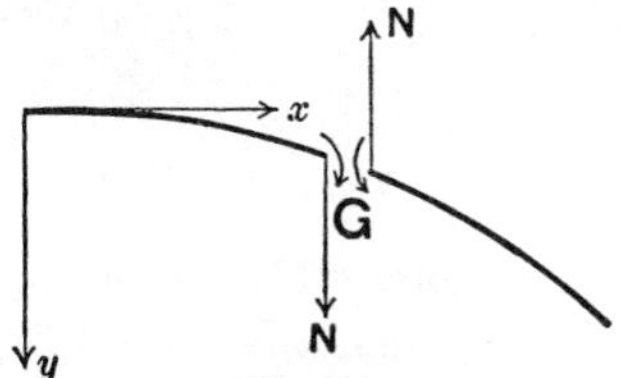

Fig. 34.

* The theory was initiated by Navier. See Introduction, p. 22. Special cases have been discussed by many writers, among whom we may mention Weyrauch, *Aufgaben zur Theorie elastischer Körper*, Leipzig, 1885.

† **B** is often called the "flexural rigidity."

In the problems that we shall consider the points of support will be taken to be at the same level. At these points the condition $y=0$ must be satisfied. At a free end of the beam the conditions $N=0$, $\mathbf{G}=0$ must be satisfied. At an end which rests freely on a support (or a "supported" end) the conditions are $y=0$, $\mathbf{G}=0$. At an end which is "built-in" (*encastré*) the direction of the central-line may be taken to be prescribed*. In the problems that we shall solve it will be taken to be horizontal. The displacement y is to be determined by equating the flexural couple $\mathbf{G}$ at any section, of which the centroid is P, to the sum of the moments about P of all the forces which act upon any portion of the beam, terminated towards the left at the section†. This method yields a differential equation for y, and the constants of integration are to be determined by the above special conditions. The expressions for y as a function of x are not the same in the two portions of the beam separated by a point at which there is a concentrated load, or by a point of support, but these expressions must have the same value at the point; in other words, the displacement y is continuous in passing through the point. We shall assume also that the direction of the central-line, or dy/dx, is continuous in passing through such a point. Equations (1) and (2) show that the curvature, estimated as d^2y/dx^2, is continuous in passing through the point. The difference of the shearing forces N calculated from the displacements on the two sides of the point must balance the concentrated load, or the pressure of the support; and thus the shearing force, and therefore also d^3y/dx^3, is discontinuous at such a point.

247. Single span.

We consider first a number of cases in which there are two points of support situated at the ends of the beam. In all these cases we denote the length of the span between the supports by l.

(*a*) *Terminal forces and couples.*

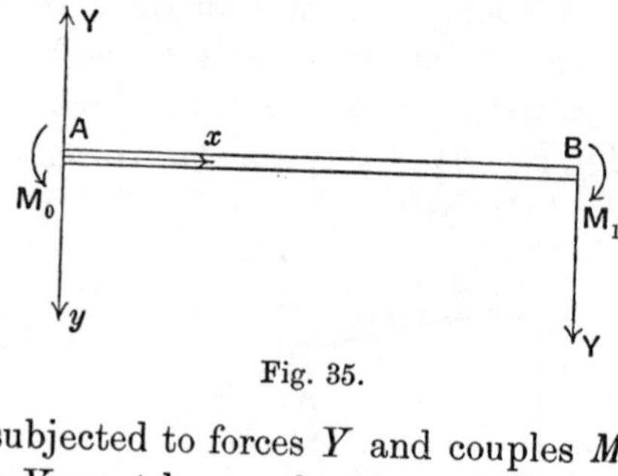

Fig. 35.

Let the beam be subjected to forces Y and couples M_0 and M_1 at the ends A and B. The forces Y must be equal and opposite, and, when the senses are

* Such an end is often described as "clamped."

† This is, of course, the same as the sum of the moments, with reversed signs, of all the forces which act upon any portion of the beam terminated towards the right at the section.

those indicated in Fig. 35, they must be expressible in terms of M_1 and M_0 by the equation

$$lY = M_0 - M_1.$$

The bending moment at any section x is $(l-x)Y + M_1$, or

$$M_0(l-x)/l + M_1 x/l.$$

The equation of equilibrium is accordingly

$$\mathbf{B}\frac{d^2y}{dx^2} = M_0\frac{l-x}{l} + M_1\frac{x}{l}.$$

Integrating this equation, and determining the constants of integration so that y may vanish at $x=0$ and at $x=l$, we find that the deflexion is given by the following equation:

$$\mathbf{B}y = -\tfrac{1}{6}l^{-1}x(l-x)\{M_0(2l-x) + M_1(l+x)\}. \quad \text{...........(3)}$$

The deflexion given by this equation may be described as "due to the couples at the ends of the span."

(*b*) *Uniform load. Supported ends.*

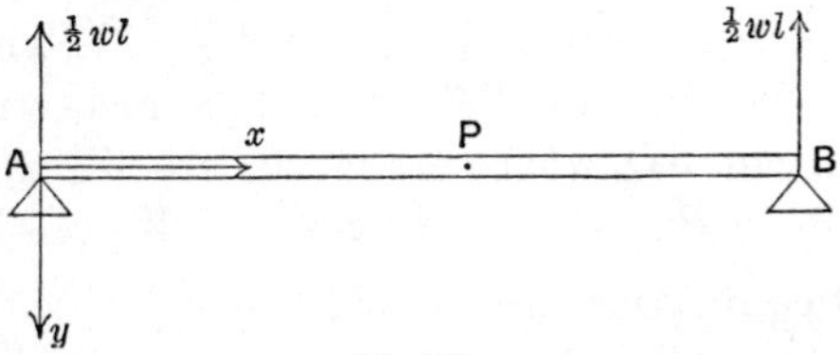

Fig. 36.

Taking w to be the weight per unit of length of the beam, we observe that the pressures on the supports are each of them equal to $\tfrac{1}{2}wl$. The moment about any point P of the weight of the part BP of the beam is $\tfrac{1}{2}w(l-x)^2$, and therefore the bending moment at P, estimated in the sense already explained, is the sum of this moment and $-\tfrac{1}{2}wl(l-x)$, or it is

$$-\tfrac{1}{2}wx(l-x).$$

The equation of equilibrium is accordingly

$$\mathbf{B}\frac{d^2y}{dx^2} = -\tfrac{1}{2}wx(l-x).$$

Integrating this equation, and determining the constants of integration so that y may vanish at $x=0$ and at $x=l$, we find the equation

$$\mathbf{B}y = \tfrac{1}{24}wx(l-x)\{l^2 + x(l-x)\}. \quad \text{....................(4)}$$

If we refer to the middle point of the span as origin, by putting $x = \tfrac{1}{2}l + x'$, we find

$$\mathbf{B}y = \tfrac{1}{24}w(\tfrac{1}{4}l^2 - x'^2)(\tfrac{5}{4}l^2 - x'^2).$$

(*c*) *Uniform load. Built-in ends.*

The solution is to be obtained by adding to the solution in case (*b*) a solution of case (*a*) adjusted so that dy/dx may vanish at $x=0$ and $x=l$. It is clear from symmetry that $M_1 = M_0$ and $Y=0$. We have therefore

$$\mathbf{B}y = \tfrac{1}{24}wx(l-x)(l^2 + lx - x^2) - \tfrac{1}{2}Mx(l-x),$$

where M is written for M_0 or M_1. The terminal conditions give

$$M = \tfrac{1}{12} wl^2,$$

and the equation for the deflexion becomes

$$\mathbf{B}y = \tfrac{1}{24} wx^2 (l-x)^2,$$

or, referred to the middle point of the span as origin of x', it becomes

$$\mathbf{B}y = \tfrac{1}{24} w (\tfrac{1}{4} l^2 - x'^2)^2.$$

(*d*) *Concentrated load. Supported ends.*

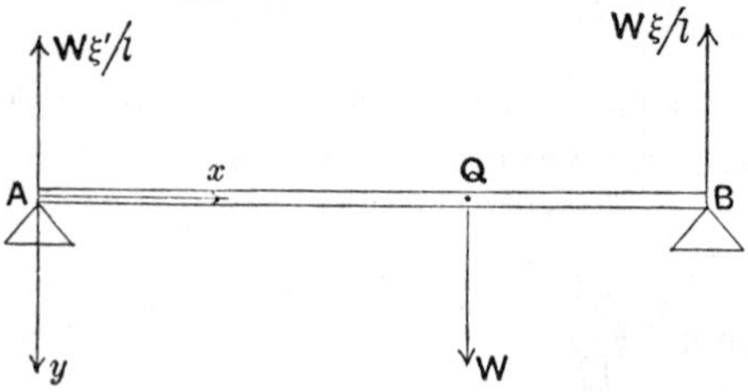

Fig 37.

Let a load W be concentrated at a point Q in AB, at which $x = \xi$. We shall write ξ' for $l - \xi$, so that $AQ = \xi$ and $BQ = \xi'$. The pressures on the supports A and B are equal to $W\xi'/l$ and $W\xi/l$ respectively. The bending moment at any point in AQ, where $\xi > x > 0$, is $-W\xi' x/l$; and the bending moment at any point in BQ, where $l > x > \xi$ is $-W\xi(l-x)/l$.

The equations of equilibrium are accordingly

$$\text{in AQ} \quad \mathbf{B}\frac{d^2y}{dx^2} = -\frac{W\xi'}{l} x,$$

$$\text{in BQ} \quad \mathbf{B}\frac{d^2y}{dx^2} = -\frac{W\xi}{l}(l-x).$$

We integrate these in the forms

$$\mathbf{B}(y - x \tan \alpha) = -\tfrac{1}{6} l^{-1} W\xi' x^3,$$

$$\mathbf{B}\{y - (l-x)\tan\beta\} = -\tfrac{1}{6} l^{-1} W\xi (l-x)^3,$$

where $\tan\alpha$ and $\tan\beta$ are the downward slopes of the central-line at the points A and B. The conditions of continuity of y and dy/dx at Q are

$$\mathbf{B}\xi \tan\alpha - \tfrac{1}{6} l^{-1} W\xi'\xi^3 = \mathbf{B}\xi' \tan\beta - \tfrac{1}{6} l^{-1} W\xi\xi'^3,$$

$$\mathbf{B}\tan\alpha - \tfrac{1}{2} l^{-1} W\xi'\xi^2 = -\mathbf{B}\tan\beta + \tfrac{1}{2} l^{-1} W\xi\xi'^2.$$

These equations give

$$\mathbf{B}\tan\alpha = \tfrac{1}{6} l^{-1} W\xi\xi'(\xi + 2\xi'), \quad \mathbf{B}\tan\beta = \tfrac{1}{6} l^{-1} W\xi\xi'(2\xi + \xi').$$

Hence in AQ, where $\xi > x > 0$, we have

$$\mathbf{B}y = \tfrac{1}{6} l^{-1} W\xi' \{\xi(\xi + 2\xi') x - x^3\}, \quad \text{.....................(5)}$$

and in BQ, where $l > x > \xi$, we have

$$\mathbf{B}y = \tfrac{1}{6} l^{-1} W\xi \{\xi'(2\xi + \xi')(l-x) - (l-x)^3\}. \quad \text{...........(6)}$$

We observe that the deflexion at any point P when the load is at Q is equal to the deflexion at Q when the same load is at P.

The central deflexion due to the weight of the beam, as determined by the solution of case (*b*), is the same as that due to $\frac{5}{8}$ of the weight concentrated at the middle of the span.

(*e*) *Concentrated load. Built-in ends.*

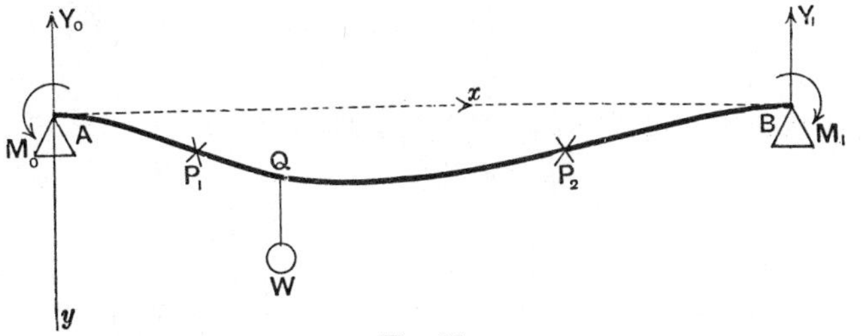

Fig. 38.

To the values of $\mathbf{B}y$ given in (5) and (6) we have to add the value of $\mathbf{B}y$ given in (3), and determine the constants M_0 and M_1 by the conditions that dy/dx vanishes at $x=0$ and at $x=l$. We find

$$W\xi'\xi(\xi+2\xi')-(2M_0+M_1)l^2=0,$$
$$W\xi'\xi(2\xi+\xi')-(M_0+2M_1)l^2=0,$$

from which

$$M_0=W\xi\xi'^2/l^2, \quad M_1=W\xi^2\xi'/l^2$$

Hence in AQ, where $\xi>x>0$, we have

$$\mathbf{B}y=\tfrac{1}{6}l^{-3}W\xi'^2x^2\{3\xi(l-x)-\xi'x\},$$

and in BQ, where $l>x>\xi$, we have

$$\mathbf{B}y=\tfrac{1}{6}l^{-3}W\xi^2(l-x)^2\{3\xi'x-\xi(l-x)\}.$$

We notice that the deflexion at P when the load is at Q is the same as the deflexion at Q when the same load is at P.

The points of inflexion are given by $d^2y/dx^2=0$, and we find that there is an inflexion at P_1 in AQ where

$$AP_1=AQ\,.\,AB/(3AQ+BQ).$$

In like manner there is an inflexion at P_2 in BQ where

$$BP_2=BQ\,.\,AB/(3BQ+AQ).$$

The point where the central-line is horizontal is given by $dy/dx=0$. If such a point is in AQ it must be at a distance from A equal to twice AP_1, and for this to happen AQ must be $>BQ$. Conversely, if $AQ<BQ$, the point is in BQ at a distance from B equal to twice BP_2.

The forces Y_0 and Y_1 at the supports are given by the equations

$$Y_0=W\xi'^2(3\xi+\xi')/l^3, \quad Y_1=W\xi^2(\xi+3\xi')/l^3.$$

248. The theorem of three moments*.

Let A, B, C be three consecutive supports of a continuous beam resting on any number of supports at the same level, and let M_A, M_B, M_C denote the

* The theorem is due to Clapeyron. See Introduction, p. 22. Generalizations have been given by various writers among whom may be mentioned M. Levy, *Statique graphique*, t. 2, Paris 1886, who treats the case where the supports are not all in the same level; R. R. Webb, *Cambridge Phil. Soc. Proc.*, vol. 6 (1886), who treats the case of variable flexural rigidity; K. Pearson, *Messenger of Math.*, vol. 19 (1890), who treats the case in which the supports are slightly compressible. The extension of the theory to loads, which are not directed at right angles to the undisturbed central-line of the beam, is considered by H. Zimmermann, *Berlin Sitzungsberichte*, Bd. 44 (1905), and by W. L. Cowley and H. Levy, *London, Roy. Soc. Proc.* (Ser. A), vol. 94 (1918).

bending moments at A, B, C. Denote the shearing forces on the two sides o the support B by B_0 and B_1, with a similar notation for the others. The pressure on the support B is B_0+B_1. Now B_0 is determined by taking

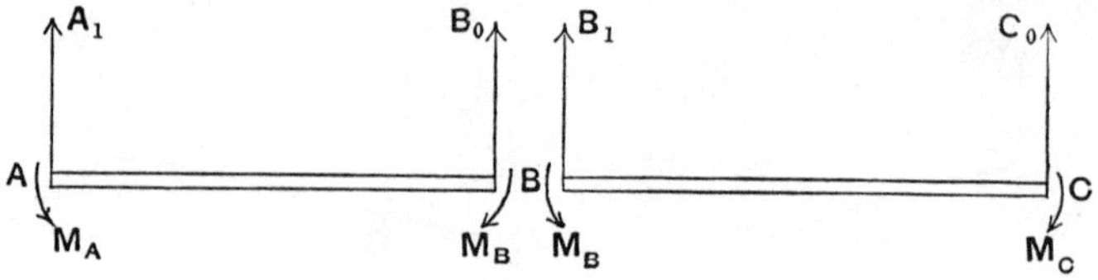

Fig. 39.

moments about A for the equilibrium of the span AB, and B_1 is determined by taking moments about C for the equilibrium of the span BC. Hence the pressure B_0+B_1 can be expressed in terms of the bending moments at A, B, C when the manner of loading of the spans is known. Again, the deflexion in the span AB may be obtained by adding the deflexion due to the load on this span when its ends are supported to that due to the bending moments at the ends. [Article 247 (a).] The deflexion in the span BC may be determined by the same method. The condition of continuity of direction of the central-line at B becomes then a relation connecting the bending moments at A, B, C. A similar relation holds for any three consecutive supports. This relation is the theorem of three moments. By means of this relation, combined with the special conditions which hold at the first and last supports, the bending moments at all the supports can be calculated.

To express this theory analytically, we take the origin anywhere in the line of the supports, and draw the axis of x horizontally to the right, and the axis of y vertically downwards. We take the points of support to be at $x=a, b, c, \ldots$. The lengths of the spans, $b-a$, $c-b$, ..., will be denoted by $l_{AB}, l_{BC}, \ldots$. We investigate a series of cases.

(a) *Uniform load.*

Let w be the load per unit of length. The deflexion in AB is given, in accordance with the results of Article 247 (a) and (b), by the equation

$$\mathbf{B}y=\tfrac{1}{24}w(x-a)(b-x)\{(b-a)^2+(x-a)(b-x)\}$$
$$-\tfrac{1}{6}(x-a)(b-x)\{M_B(b+x-2a)+M_A(2b-x-a)\}/(b-a).$$

A similar equation may be written down for the deflexion in BC. The condition that the two values of dy/dx at $x=b$ are equal is

$$-\tfrac{1}{24}w(b-a)^3+\tfrac{1}{6}(2M_B+M_A)(b-a)=\tfrac{1}{24}w(c-b)^3-\tfrac{1}{6}(2M_B+M_C)(c-b),$$

and the equation of three moments is therefore

$$l_{AB}(M_A+2M_B)+l_{BC}(2M_B+M_C)=\tfrac{1}{4}w(l_{AB}{}^3+l_{BC}{}^3). \quad \ldots\ldots\ldots(7)$$

To determine the pressure on the support B we form the equations of moments for AB about A, and for BC about C. We have

$$B_0 l_{AB}-\tfrac{1}{2}wl_{AB}{}^2-M_B+M_A=0,$$
$$B_1 l_{BC}-\tfrac{1}{2}wl_{BC}{}^2-M_B+M_C=0.$$

These equations give B_0 and B_1, and the pressure on the support B is B_0+B_1. In this way the pressures on all the supports may be calculated.

(*b*) *Equal spans.*

When the spans are equal, equation (7) may be written as a linear difference equation of the second order in the form

$$M_{n-1}+4M_n+M_{n+1}=\tfrac{1}{2}wl^2,$$

and the solution is of the form

$$M_n=\tfrac{1}{12}wl^2+A\alpha^n+B\beta^n,$$

where A and B are constants, and α and β are the roots of the quadratic $x^2+4x+1=0$, or we have

$$\alpha=-2+\sqrt{3},\quad \beta=-2-\sqrt{3}.$$

The constants A and B are to be determined from the values of M at the first and last supports.

(*c*) *Uniform load on each span.*

Let w_{AB} denote the load per unit of length on the span AB, and w_{BC} that on BC. Then we find, in the same way as in case (*a*), the equation of three moments in the form

$$l_{AB}(M_A+2M_B)+l_{BC}(2M_B+M_C)=\tfrac{1}{4}w_{AB}l_{AB}^3+\tfrac{1}{4}w_{BC}l_{BC}^3.$$

(*d*) *Concentrated load on one span.*

Let a load W be concentrated at a point Q in BC given by $x=\xi$. The deflexion in AB is given, in accordance with the results of Article 247 (*a*), by the equation

$$\mathbf{B}y=-\tfrac{1}{6}(x-a)(b-x)\{M_A(2b-x-a)+M_B(b+x-2a)\}/(b-a),$$

and that in BQ is given by

$$\mathbf{B}y=\tfrac{1}{6}W[(\xi-b)(c-\xi)(2c-b-\xi)(x-b)-(c-\xi)(x-b)^3]/(c-b)$$
$$-\tfrac{1}{6}(x-b)(c-x)\{M_B(2c-x-b)+M_C(c+x-2b)\}/(c-b).$$

The condition of continuity of dy/dx at $x=b$ is

$$\tfrac{1}{6}(M_A+2M_B)(b-a)=\tfrac{1}{6}W(\xi-b)(c-\xi)(2c-b-\xi)/(c-b)-\tfrac{1}{6}(2M_B+M_C)(c-b),$$

and the equation of three moments for A, B, C is therefore

$$l_{AB}(M_A+2M_B)+l_{BC}(2M_B+M_C)=Wl_{BQ}l_{QC}(1+l_{QC}/l_{BC}), \quad\text{......(8)}$$

where l_{BQ} and l_{QC} are the distances of Q from B and C. In like manner if D is the next support beyond C, the equation of three moments for B, C, D is

$$l_{BC}(M_B+2M_C)+l_{CD}(2M_C+M_D)=Wl_{BQ}l_{QC}(1+l_{BQ}/l_{BC}). \quad\text{......(9)}$$

249. Graphic method of solution of the problem of continuous beams*.

The equation of equilibrium (2), viz. $\mathbf{B}\dfrac{d^2y}{dx^2}=\mathbf{G}$, is of the same form as the equation determining the curve assumed by a loaded string or chain, when the load per unit length of the horizontal projection is proportional to $-\mathbf{G}$. For, if T denotes the tension of the string, m the load per unit length of the

* The method is due to Mohr. See Introduction, footnote 99.

horizontal projection, and ds the element of arc of the catenary curve, the equations of equilibrium, referred to axes drawn in the same way as in Article 246, are

$$T\frac{dx}{ds} = \text{const.} = \tau \text{ say}, \quad \frac{d}{ds}\left(T\frac{dy}{ds}\right) + m\frac{dx}{ds} = 0,$$

and these lead, by elimination of T, to the equation

$$\tau\frac{d^2y}{dx^2} + m = 0.$$

It follows that the form of the curve assumed by the central-line of the beam in any span is the same as that of a catenary or funicular curve determined by forces proportional to $\mathbf{G}\delta x$ on any length δx of the span, provided that the funicular is made to pass through the ends of the span. The forces $\mathbf{G}\delta x$ are to be directed upwards or downwards according as $\mathbf{G}$ is positive or negative.

The tangents of such a funicular at the ends of a span can be determined without finding the funicular, for they depend only on the statical resultant and moment of the fictitious forces $\mathbf{G}\delta x$. To see this we take the ends of the span to be $x=0$ and $x=l$, and integrate the equation (2) in the forms

$$x\frac{dy}{dx} - y = \int_0^x x\frac{\mathbf{G}}{\mathbf{B}}dx, \quad (l-x)\frac{dy}{dx} + y = -\int_x^l (l-x)\frac{\mathbf{G}}{\mathbf{B}}dx,$$

and hence we obtain the equation

$$l\frac{dy}{dx} = \int_0^x x\frac{\mathbf{G}}{\mathbf{B}}dx - \int_x^l (l-x)\frac{\mathbf{G}}{\mathbf{B}}dx,$$

from which it follows that

$$\left(\frac{dy}{dx}\right)_0 = -\int_0^l \frac{(l-x)\mathbf{G}}{l\mathbf{B}}dx, \quad \left(\frac{dy}{dx}\right)_l = \int_0^l \frac{x\mathbf{G}}{l\mathbf{B}}dx.$$

These values depend only on the resultant and resultant moment of the forces $\mathbf{G}\delta x$, and therefore the direction of the central-line of the beam at the ends of the span would be determined by drawing the funicular, not for the forces $\mathbf{G}\delta x$, but for a statically equivalent system of forces.

The flexural couple $\mathbf{G}$ at any point of a span AB may be found by adding the couple calculated from the bending moments at the ends, when there is no load on the span, to the couple calculated from the load on the span, when the ends are "supported." The bending moment due to the couples at the ends of the span is represented graphically by the ordinates of the line $A'B'$ in Fig. 40, where AA' and BB' represent on any suitable scale the bending moments at A and B. The bending moment due to uniform load on the span is equal to $-\frac{1}{2}wx(l-x)$, as in Article 247 (b), and it may be represented by the ordinates of a parabola as in Fig. 41. The bending moment due to a concentrated load is equal to $-Wx(l-\xi)/l$, when $\xi > x > 0$, and to $-W(l-x)\xi/l$, when $l > x > \xi$, as in Article 247 (*d*); and it

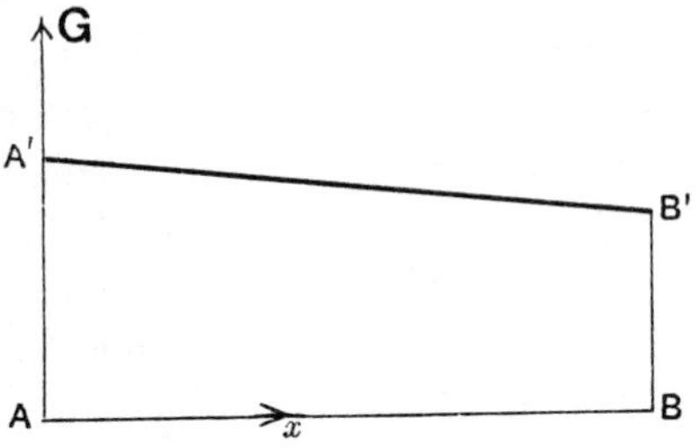

Fig. 40.

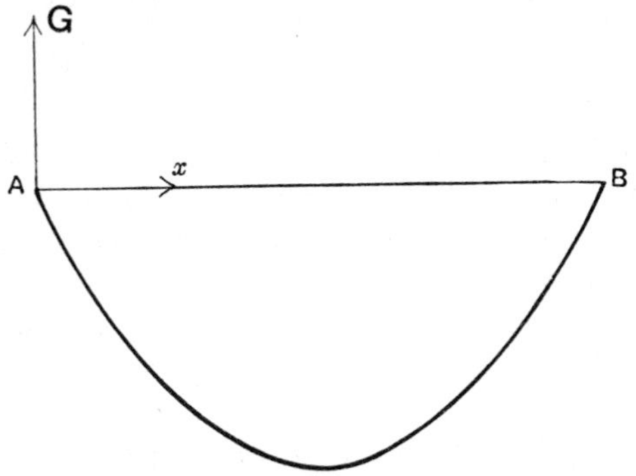

Fig. 41.

may be represented by the ordinate of a broken line as in Fig. 42. The bending moment due to the load on the span may be represented in a general way by the ordinate of the thick line in Fig. 43.

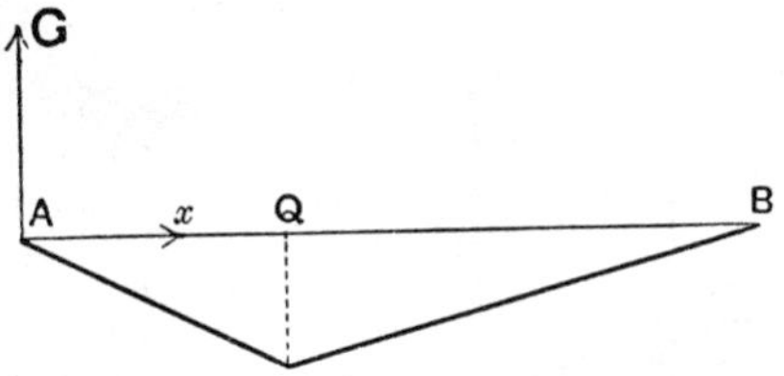

Fig. 42.

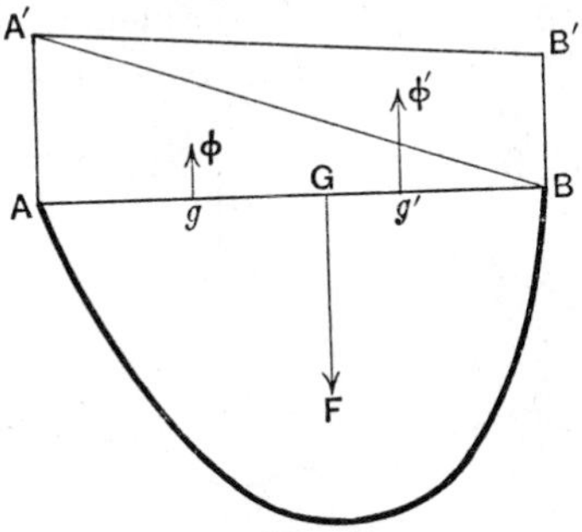

Fig. 43.

The fictitious forces $\mathbf{G}\delta x$ are statically equivalent to the following:—(i) a force ϕ represented by the area of the triangle $AA'B$, acting upwards through that point of trisection g of AB which is nearer to A, (ii) a force ϕ', represented by the area of the triangle $A'BB'$, acting upwards through the other point of trisection g' of AB, (iii) a force F, represented by the area contained between AB and the thick line in Fig. 43, acting downwards through the centroid of this area. We take the line of action of F to meet AB in the point G. When the load on the span is uniform, $F = \frac{1}{6}wl^3$, and G is at the middle point of AB. When there is an isolated load, $F = \frac{1}{2}W\xi(l-\xi)$, and G is at a distance from A equal to $\frac{1}{3}(l+\xi)$.

The forces F and the points G are known for each span, and the points g, g' are known also. The forces ϕ, ϕ' are unknown, since they are proportional to the bending moments at the supports, but these forces are connected by certain relations. Let $A_0, A_1, \ldots$ denote the supports in order, let ϕ_1, ϕ_1', F_1 denote the equivalent system of forces for the first span A_0A_1, and so on.

Let M_0, M_1, M_2, ... denote the bending moments at the supports. Then we observe, for example, that $\phi_1' : \phi_2 = M_1 . A_0A_1 : M_1 . A_1A_2$, and therefore the ratio $\phi_1' : \phi_2$ is known. Similarly the ratio $\phi_2' : \phi_3$ is known, and so on.

If the forces ϕ, ϕ', as well as F, were known for any span, we could construct a funicular polygon for them of which the extreme sides could be made to pass through the ends of the span. Since the direction of the central-line of the beam is continuous at the points of support, the extreme sides of the funiculars which pass through the common extremity of two consecutive spans are in the same straight line. The various funicular polygons belonging to the different spans form therefore a single funicular polygon for the system of forces consisting of all the forces ϕ, ϕ', F.

250. Development of the graphic method.

The above results enable us to construct the funicular just described, and to determine the forces ϕ, or the bending moments at the supports, when the bending moments at the first and last supports are given. We consider the case where these two bending moments are zero*, or the ends of the beam are "supported." We denote the sides of the funicular by 1, 2, 3, ... so that the sides 1, 3, 6, ... pass through the supports A_0, A_1, A_2, ...

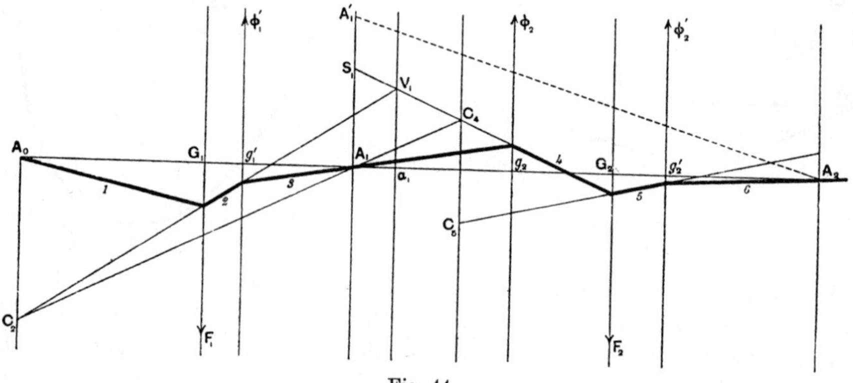

Fig. 44.

We consider the triangle formed by the sides 2, 3, 4. Two of its vertices lie on fixed lines, viz.: the verticals through g_1' and g_2. The third vertex V_1 also lies on a fixed line. For the side 3 could be kept in equilibrium by the forces ϕ_1' and ϕ_2 and the tensions in the sides 2, 4, and therefore V_1 is on the line of action of the resultant of ϕ_1' and ϕ_2; but this line is the vertical through the point α_1, where $\alpha_1 g_2 = A_1 g_1'$ and $\alpha_1 g_1' = A_1 g_2$, for $\phi_1' : \phi_2 = A_1 g_1' : A_1 g_2$. Again, the point C_2 where the side 2 meets the vertical through A_0 is

* The sketch of the graphic method given in the text is not intended to be complete. For further details the reader is referred to M. Lévy, *loc. cit.*, p. 373. A paper by Perry and Ayrton in *London, Roy. Soc. Proc.*, vol. 29 (1879), may also be consulted. The memoir by Canevazzi cited in the Introduction, footnote 99, contains a very luminous account of the theory.

determined by the condition that the triangle formed by the sides 1 and 2 and the line A_0C_2 is a triangle of forces for the point of intersection of the sides 1 and 2, and A_0C_2 represents the known force F_1 on the scale on which we represent forces by lines. Since the vertices of the triangle formed by the sides 2, 3, 4 lie on three fixed parallel lines, and the sides 2 and 3 pass through the fixed points C_2 and A_1, the side 4 passes through a fixed point C_4, which can be constructed by drawing any two triangles to satisfy the stated conditions.

In the above the point C_2 may be taken arbitrarily, but, when it is chosen, A_0G_1 represents the constant horizontal component of the tension in the sides of the funicular on the same scale as that on which A_0C_2 represents the force F_1.

We may show in the same way that the vertices of the triangle formed by the sides 5, 6, 7 lie on three fixed vertical lines, and that its sides pass through three fixed points. The vertical on which the intersection V_2 of the lines 5 and 7 lies passes through the point α_2, where $\alpha_2 g_3 = A_2 g_2'$ and $\alpha_2 g_2' = A_2 g_3$. The fixed point C_5, through which the side 5 passes, is on the vertical through C_4, and at such a distance from C_4 that this vertical and the sides 4 and 5 make up a triangle of forces for the point of intersection of the sides 4 and 5. The line C_4C_5 then represents the force F_2 on a certain scale, which is not the same as the scale on which A_0C_2 represents F_1, for the horizontal projection of G_2C_4 represents the constant horizontal component tension in the funicular on the scale on which C_4C_5 represents F_2. Since C_4 is known, the ratio of scales in question is determined, and C_5 is therefore determined. The side 6 passes through the fixed point A_2, and the fixed point C_7 through which the side 7 passes can be constructed in the same way as C_4 was constructed.

In this way we construct two series of points $C_2, C_5, \ldots C_{3k-1}, \ldots$ and $C_4, C_7, \ldots C_{3k+1}, \ldots$. We construct also the series of points $\alpha_1, \alpha_2, \ldots \alpha_k, \ldots$, where $\alpha_k g_k' = A_k g_{k+1}$ and $\alpha_k g_{k+1} = A_k g_k'$. By aid of these series of points we may construct the required funicular.

Consider the case of n spans, the end A_n, as well as A_0, being simply supported. The line joining C_{3n-1} to A_n is the last side $(3n-1)$ of the funicular, since the force ϕ_n', like ϕ_1, is zero. The side $(3n-2)$ meets the side $(3n-1)$ on the line of action of F_n, and passes through the point C_{3n-2}. Let this side $(3n-2)$ meet the vertical through α_{n-1} in V_{n-1}. Then the line $V_{n-1}C_{3n-4}$ is the side $(3n-4)$. The side $(3n-3)$ is determined by joining the point where the side $(3n-2)$ meets the vertical through g_n to the point where the side $(3n-4)$ meets the vertical through g'_{n-1}. This side $(3n-3)$ necessarily passes through A_{n-1} in consequence of the mode of construction of the points C. Proceeding in this way we can construct the funicular.

When the funicular is constructed we may determine the bending moments at the supports by measurement upon the figure. For example, let the side 4 meet the vertical through A_1 in S_1. Then A_1S_1 and the sides 3 and 4 make up a triangle of forces for the point of intersection of 3 and 4. The horizontal projection of either of the sides of this triangle which are not vertical is $\frac{1}{3} A_1A_2$. Hence A_1S_1 represents the force ϕ_2 on the same scale as $\frac{1}{3} A_1A_2$ represents the horizontal tension in the sides of the funicular. Thus A_1S_1/A_1A_2 represents the force ϕ_2 on a constant scale. But ϕ_2 represents the product of M_1 and A_1A_2 also on a constant scale. Hence $A_1S_1/A_1A_2^2$ represents the bending moment at A_1 on a constant scale. In like manner, if the side $3k+1$ meets the vertical through A_k in the point S_k, then $A_kS_k/A_kA_{k+1}^2$ represents the bending moment at A_k.

CHAPTER XVIII

GENERAL THEORY OF THE BENDING AND TWISTING OF THIN RODS

251. BESIDES the problem of continuous beams there are many physical and technical problems which can be treated as problems concerning long thin rods, and, on this understanding, are capable of approximate solution. In this Chapter we shall consider the general theory of the behaviour of such bodies, reserving the applications of the theory for subsequent Chapters. The special circumstance of which the theory must take account is the possibility that the relative displacements of the parts of a long thin rod may be by no means small, and yet the strains which occur in any part of the rod may be small enough to satisfy the requirements of the mathematical theory. This possibility renders necessary some special kinematical investigations, subsidiary to the general analysis of strain considered in Chapter I.

252. Kinematics of thin rods*.

In the unstressed state the rod is taken to be cylindrical or prismatic, so that homologous lines in different cross-sections are parallel to each other. If the rod is simply twisted, without being bent, linear elements of different cross-sections which are parallel in the unstressed state become inclined to each other. We select one set of linear elements, which in the unstressed state are parallel to each other and lie along principal axes of the cross-sections at their centroids. Let δf be the angle in the strained state between the directions of two such elements which lie in cross-sections at a distance δs apart. Then $\lim_{\delta s=0} \delta f/\delta s$ measures the *twist*.

When the rod is bent, the twist cannot be estimated quite so simply. We shall suppose that the central-line becomes a tortuous curve of curvature $1/\rho$ and measure of tortuosity $1/\Sigma$. We take a system of fixed axes of x, y, z of which the axis of z is parallel to the central-line in the unstressed state, and the axes of x, y are parallel in the same state to principal axes of the cross-sections at their centroids. Let P be any point of the central-line, and, in the unstressed state, let three linear elements of the rod issue from P in the directions of the axes of x, y, z. When the rod is deformed these linear elements do not in general continue to be at right angles to each other, but by means of them we can construct a system of orthogonal axes of x, y, z. The origin of this sytem is the displaced position P_1 of P, the axis of z is the

* Cf. Kelvin and Tait, *Nat. Phil.*, Part I, pp. 94 *et seq.*, and Kirchhoff, *J. f. Math.* (*Crelle*), Bd. 56 (1859), or *Ges. Abhandlungen* (Leipzig 1882), p. 285, or *Vorlesungen über math. Physik, Mechanik*, Vorlesung 28.

tangent at P_1 to the strained central-line, and the plane (x, z) contains the linear element which, in the unstressed state, issues from P in the direction of the axis of x. The plane of (x, z) is a "principal plane" of the rod. The sense of the axis of x is chosen arbitrarily. The sense of the axis of z is chosen to be that in which the arc s of the central-line, measured from some assigned point of it, increases; and then the sense of the axis of y is determined by the condition that the axes of x, y, z in this order are a right-handed system. The system of axes constructed as above for any point on the strained central-line will be called the "principal torsion-flexure axes" of the rod at the point.

Let P' be a point of the central-line near to P, and let P_1' be the displaced position of P'. The length δs_1 of the arc P_1P_1' of the strained central-line may differ slightly from the length δs of PP'. If ϵ is the *extension* of the central-line at P_1 we have

$$\lim_{\delta s=0} (\delta s_1/\delta s) = (1+\epsilon). \qquad \text{.........................(1)}$$

The extension ϵ may be zero. For any application of the mathematical theory of Elasticity to be possible, it must be a small quantity of the order of the strains contemplated in the theory.

Suppose the origin of a frame of three orthogonal axes of x, y, z to move along the strained central-line of the rod with unit velocity, and the three axes to be directed always along the principal torsion-flexure axes of the rod at the origin of the frame. We may resolve the angular velocity with which the frame rotates into components directed along the instantaneous positions of the axes. We shall denote these components by κ, κ', τ. Then κ and κ' are the *components of curvature* of the strained central-line at P_1, and τ is the *twist* of the rod at P_1.

These statements may be regarded as definitions of the twist and components of curvature. It is clear that the new definition of the twist coincides with that which was given above in the case of a rod which is not bent, and that κ, κ' are the curvatures, as defined geometrically, of the projections of the strained central-line on the planes of (y, z) and (x, z), and therefore the resultant of κ and κ' is a vector directed along the binormal of the strained central-line and equal to the curvature $1/\rho$ of this curve.

253. Kinematical formulæ.

We investigate in the first place the relation between the twist of the rod and the measure of tortuosity of its strained central-line. Let l, m, n denote the direction-cosines of the binormal of this curve at P_1 referred to the principal torsion-flexure axes at P_1, and let l', m', n' denote the direction-cosines of the binormal at P_1' referred to the principal torsion-flexure axes at P_1'. Then the limits such as $\lim_{\delta s_1=0} (l'-l)/\delta s_1$ are denoted by $dl/ds_1, \dots$. Again let

$l+\delta l, \ldots$ denote the direction-cosines of the binormal at P_1' referred to the principal torsion-flexure axes at P_1. We have the formulæ*

$$\lim_{\delta s_1=0} \delta l/\delta s_1 = dl/ds_1 - m\tau + n\kappa',$$

$$\lim_{\delta s_1=0} \delta m/\delta s_1 = dm/ds_1 - n\kappa + l\tau,$$

$$\lim_{\delta s_1=0} \delta n/\delta s_1 = dn/ds_1 - l\kappa' + m\kappa.$$

The measure of tortuosity $1/\Sigma$ of the strained central-line is given by the formula

$$1/\Sigma^2 = \lim_{\delta s_1=0} [(\delta l)^2 + (\delta m)^2 + (\delta n)^2]/(\delta s_1)^2,$$

and the sign of Σ is determined by choosing the senses in which the principal normal, binormal and tangent of the curve are drawn. We suppose the prin-

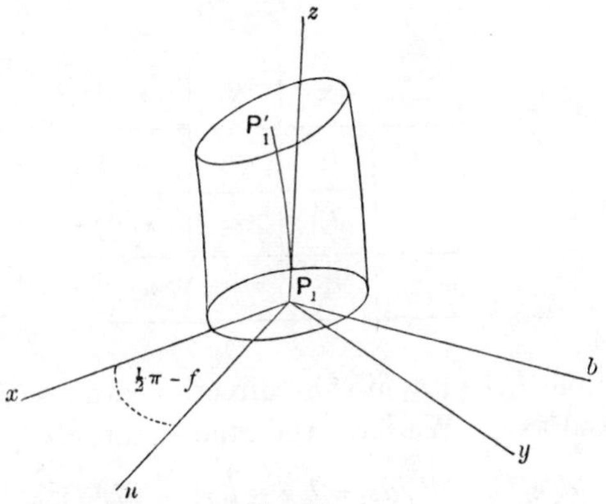

Fig. 45.

cipal normal (marked n in Fig. 45) to be drawn towards the centre of curvature, and the tangent to be drawn in the sense in which s_1 increases, and we choose the sense in which the binormal (marked b in the figure) is drawn in such a way that the principal normal, the binormal and the tangent, taken in this order, are parallel to the axes of a right-handed system. Now we may put

$$l = \kappa\rho = -\cos f, \quad m = \kappa'\rho = \sin f, \quad n = 0,$$

where ρ is the radius of curvature; and then $\frac{1}{2}\pi - f$ is the angle between the principal plane (x, z) of the rod and the principal normal of the strained central-line. On substituting in the expression for $1/\Sigma^2$, and making use of the above convention, we find the equation

$$\tau = \frac{df}{ds_1} + \frac{1}{\Sigma}, \quad \text{.............................(2)}$$

in which

$$\tan f = -(\kappa'/\kappa). \quad \text{.............................(3)}$$

* Cf. E. J. Routh, *Dynamics of a system of rigid bodies* (London 1884), Part II, Chapter I.

The necessity of introducing such an angle as f into the theory was noted by Saint-Venant*. The case in which f vanishes or is constant was the only one considered by the earlier writers on the subject. The linear elements of the deformed rod which issue from the strained central-line in the direction of the principal normals of this curve are, in the unstressed state, very nearly coincident with a family of lines at right angles to the central-line. If f vanishes or is constant these lines are parallel in the unstressed state. We may describe a state of the bent and twisted rod in which f vanishes or is constant as such that the rod, if simply unbent, would be prismatic. When f is variable the rod, if simply unbent, would be a twisted prism, and the twist would be df/ds_1.

With a view to the calculation of κ, κ', τ we take the axes of x, y, z at P_1 to be connected with *any* system of fixed axes of x, y, z by the orthogonal scheme

	x	y	z
x	l_1	m_1	n_1
y	l_2	m_2	n_2
z	l_3	m_3	n_3

, ...(4)

in which, for example, l_1, m_1, n_1 are the direction-cosines of the axis of x at P_1 referred to the fixed axes. We have the nine equations

$$\left.\begin{aligned} dl_1/ds_1 &= l_2\tau - l_3\kappa', & dl_2/ds_1 &= l_3\kappa - l_1\tau, & dl_3/ds_1 &= l_1\kappa' - l_2\kappa, \\ dm_1/ds_1 &= m_2\tau - m_3\kappa', & dm_2/ds_1 &= m_3\kappa - m_1\tau, & dm_3/ds_1 &= m_1\kappa' - m_2\kappa, \\ dn_1/ds_1 &= n_2\tau - n_3\kappa', & dn_2/ds_1 &= n_3\kappa - n_1\tau, & dn_3/ds_1 &= n_1\kappa' - n_2\kappa, \end{aligned}\right\} \quad \text{...(5)}$$

which express the conditions that the axes of x, y, z are fixed, while those of x, y, z are moving with the angular velocity (κ, κ', τ)†. From these we obtain such equations as

$$\kappa = l_3 \frac{dl_2}{ds_1} + m_3 \frac{dm_2}{ds_1} + n_3 \frac{dn_2}{ds_1}.$$

The differentiations with respect to s_1 may, since ϵ is small, be replaced by differentiations with respect to s, provided that the left-hand members of the equations are multiplied by $1+\epsilon$. If κ, κ', τ are themselves small, and quantities of the order $\epsilon\kappa$ are neglected, the factor $1+\epsilon$ may be replaced by unity. If κ, κ', τ are not regarded as small quantities, a first approximation to their values can be obtained by replacing $1+\epsilon$ by unity. To estimate the

* *Paris, C. R.*, t. 17 (1843).

† Cf. E. J. Routh, *loc. cit.*, p. 383.

quantities κ, κ', τ we may therefore ignore the distinction between ds_1 and ds and write our formulæ

$$\left.\begin{aligned}\kappa &= l_3\frac{dl_2}{ds} + m_3\frac{dm_2}{ds} + n_3\frac{dn_2}{ds},\\ \kappa' &= l_1\frac{dl_3}{ds} + m_1\frac{dm_3}{ds} + n_1\frac{dn_3}{ds},\\ \tau &= l_2\frac{dl_1}{ds} + m_2\frac{dm_1}{ds} + n_2\frac{dn_1}{ds}.\end{aligned}\right\} \quad \text{.....................(6)}$$

The direction-cosines $l_1, \ldots$ can be expressed in terms of three angles θ, ψ, ϕ, as is usual in the theory of the motion of a rigid body. Let θ be the angle which the axis of z at P_1 makes with the fixed axis of z, ψ the angle which a plane parallel to these axes makes with the fixed plane of (x, z), ϕ the angle which the principal plane (x, z) of the rod at P_1 makes with the plane zP_1z. Then the direction-cosines in question are expressed by the equations

$$\left.\begin{aligned}&l_1 = -\sin\psi\sin\phi + \cos\psi\cos\phi\cos\theta, && m_1 = \cos\psi\sin\phi + \sin\psi\cos\phi\cos\theta, && n_1 = -\sin\theta\cos\phi,\\ &l_2 = -\sin\psi\cos\phi - \cos\psi\sin\phi\cos\theta, && m_2 = \cos\psi\cos\phi - \sin\psi\sin\phi\cos\theta, && n_2 = \sin\theta\sin\phi,\\ &l_3 = \sin\theta\cos\psi, && m_3 = \sin\theta\sin\psi, && n_3 = \cos\theta.\end{aligned}\right\}$$

.........(7)

The relations connecting $d\theta/ds$, $d\psi/ds$, $d\phi/ds$ with κ, κ', τ are obtained at once from Fig. 46 by observing that κ, κ', τ are the projections on the principal torsion-flexure axes at P_1 of a vector which is equivalent to vectors $d\theta/ds$, $d\psi/ds$, $d\phi/ds$ localized in certain lines. The line $P_1\xi$ in which $d\theta/ds$ is

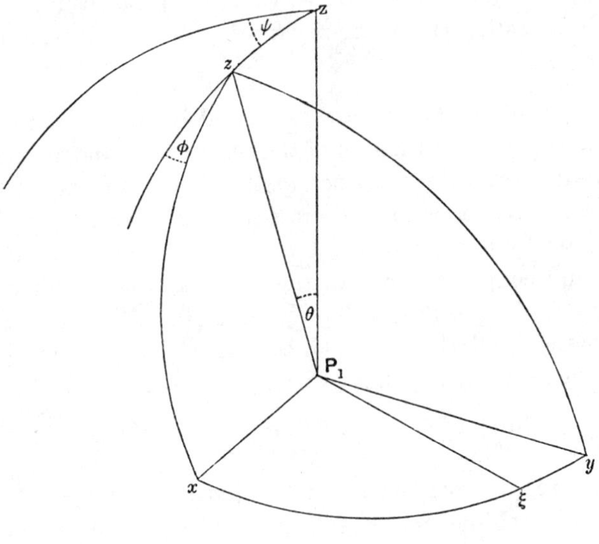

Fig. 46.

localized is at right angles to the plane zP_1z, and $d\psi/ds$ and $d\phi/ds$ are localized in the lines P_1z and P_1z. We have therefore the equations

$$\kappa = \frac{d\theta}{ds}\sin\phi - \frac{d\psi}{ds}\sin\theta\cos\phi, \quad \kappa' = \frac{d\theta}{ds}\cos\phi + \frac{d\psi}{ds}\sin\theta\sin\phi,$$

$$\tau = \frac{d\phi}{ds} + \frac{d\psi}{ds}\cos\theta. \quad \text{.........................(8)}$$

254. Equations of equilibrium.

When the rod is deformed the action of the part of it that is on one side of a cross-section upon the part on the other side is expressed, in the usual way, by means of tractions estimated per unit of area of the section. These tractions are statically equivalent to a force acting at the centroid of the section and a couple. The axis of z being directed along the tangent to the central-line at this centroid, the tractions on the section are denoted by X_z, Y_z, Z_z. The components parallel to the axes of x, y, z of the force- and couple-resultants of these tractions are N, N', T and G, G', H, where

$$\left.\begin{aligned} N = \iint X_z\,dx\,dy, \quad N' = \iint Y_z\,dx\,dy, \quad T = \iint Z_z\,dx\,dy, \\ G = \iint yZ_z\,dx\,dy, \quad G' = \iint -xZ_z\,dx\,dy, \quad H = \iint (xY_z - yX_z)\,dx\,dy, \end{aligned}\right\} \quad (9)$$

the integrations being taken over the area of the section. The forces N, N' are "shearing-forces," the force T is the "tension," the couples G, G' are "flexural couples," the couple H is the "torsional couple." The forces N, N', T will be called the *stress-resultants*, and the couples G, G', H the *stress-couples.*

The forces applied to the rod are estimated by means of their force- and couple-resultants per unit of length of the central-line, and, in thus estimating them, we may disregard the extension of this line. Let the forces applied to the portion of the rod between the cross-sections drawn through P_1 and P_1' be reduced statically to a force at P_1 and a couple; and let the components of this force and couple, referred to the principal torsion-flexure axes at P_1, be denoted by $[X]$, $[Y]$, $[Z]$, and $[K]$, $[K']$, $[\Theta]$. When P_1' is brought to coincidence with P_1 all these quantities vanish, but the quotients such as $[X]/\delta s$ can have finite limits. Let us write

$$\lim_{\delta s=0} [X]/\delta s = X, \ldots, \lim_{\delta s=0} [K]/\delta s = K, \ldots;$$

then X, Y, Z are the components of the force-resultant at P_1 per unit of length of the central-line, and K, K', Θ are the components of the couple-resultant.

Now the forces applied to the portion of the rod contained between two cross-sections balance the resultant and resultant moment of the tractions across these sections. Let δ denote the excess of the value of any quantity belonging to the section through P_1' above the value that belongs to the section through P_1; also let x, y, z denote the coordinates of P_1 referred to fixed axes, and x′, y′, z′ those of any point on the central-line between P_1 and P_1'. Using the scheme (4), we can at once write down the equations of equilibrium of the portion in such forms as

$$\delta(l_1 N + l_2 N' + l_3 T) + \int_s^{s+\delta s} (l_1 X + l_2 Y + l_3 Z)\, ds = 0,$$

and
$$\delta(l_1 G + l_2 G' + l_3 H) + \delta y \{(n_1 N + n_2 N' + n_3 T) + \delta(n_1 N + n_2 N' + n_3 T)\}$$
$$- \delta z \{(m_1 N + m_2 N' + m_3 T) + \delta(m_1 N + m_2 N' + m_3 T)\}$$
$$+ \int_s^{s+\delta s} \{(\mathrm{y}' - \mathrm{y})(n_1 X + n_2 Y + n_3 Z) - (\mathrm{z}' - \mathrm{z})(m_1 X + m_2 Y + m_3 Z)\}\, ds$$
$$+ \int_s^{s+\delta s} (l_1 K + l_2 K' + l_3 \Theta)\, ds = 0.$$

We divide the left-hand members of these equations by δs, and pass to a limit by diminishing δs indefinitely. This operation requires the performance of certain differentiations. The results of differentiating $l_1, \ldots$ are expressed by equations (5), since the extension of the central-line may be disregarded. We choose the fixed axes of x, y, z to coincide with the principal torsion-flexure axes of the rod at P_1. Then, after the differentiations are performed, we may put $l_1 = 1$, $m_1 = 0$, and so on. The limits of $\delta x/\delta s$, $\delta y/\delta s$, $\delta z/\delta s$ are 0, 0, 1. The limits of such quantities as

$$(\delta s)^{-1} \int_s^{s+\delta s} (l_1 X + l_2 Y + l_3 Z)\, ds, \quad (\delta s)^{-1} \int_s^{s+\delta s} (l_1 K + l_2 K' + l_3 \Theta)\, ds$$

are X, Y, Z and K, K', Θ. The limits of such quantities as

$$(\delta s)^{-1} \int_s^{s+\delta s} (\mathrm{y}' - \mathrm{y})(n_1 X + n_2 Y + n_3 Z)\, ds$$

are zero. We have, therefore, the following forms for the equations of equilibrium*:

$$\left.\begin{aligned} \frac{dN}{ds} - N'\tau + T\kappa' + X &= 0, \\ \frac{dN'}{ds} - T\kappa + N\tau + Y &= 0, \\ \frac{dT}{ds} - N\kappa' + N'\kappa + Z &= 0, \end{aligned}\right\} \qquad \text{......................(10)}$$

* The equations were given by Clebsch, *Elasticität*, § 50, but they were effectively contained in the work of Kirchhoff, *loc. cit.*, p. 381.

and

$$\left.\begin{aligned}\frac{dG}{ds}-G'\tau+H\kappa'-N'+K=0,\\ \frac{dG'}{ds}-H\kappa+G\tau+N+K'=0,\\ \frac{dH}{ds}-G\kappa'+G'\kappa+\Theta=0.\end{aligned}\right\}\qquad(11)$$

In addition to these equations there will in general be certain special conditions which hold at the ends of the rod. These may be conditions of fixity, or the forces and couples applied at the ends may be given. In the latter case the terminal values of the stress-resultants and stress-couples are prescribed. These special conditions may be used to determine the constants that are introduced in the process of integrating the equations of equilibrium.

255. The ordinary approximate theory.

The equations of equilibrium contain nine unknown quantities: N, N', T, G, G', H, κ, κ', τ. It is clear that, if three additional equations connecting these quantities could be found, there would be sufficient equations to determine the curvature and twist of the rod and the stress-resultants and stress-couples. The ordinary approximate theory—a generalization of the "Bernoulli-Eulerian" theory—consists in assuming that the stress-couples are connected with the curvature and twist of the rod by equations of the form

$$G=A\kappa,\quad G'=B\kappa',\quad H=C\tau,\qquad(12)$$

where A, B, C are constants depending on the elastic quality of the material and the shape and dimensions of the cross-section. The nature of this dependence is known from the results obtained in comparatively simple cases. For isotropic material we should have

$$A=E\omega k^2,\quad B=E\omega k'^2,$$

where E is Young's modulus for the material, ω is the area of the cross-section, and k and k' are the radii of gyration of the cross-section about the axes of x and y, which are principal axes at its centroid. In the same case C would be the torsional rigidity considered in Chapter XIV. If the cross-section of the rod has kinetic symmetry, so that $A=B$, the flexural couples G, G', as expressed in the formulæ (12), are equivalent to a single couple, of which the axis is the binormal of the strained central-line, and the magnitude is B/ρ, where ρ is the radius of curvature of this curve.

The theory is obviously incomplete until it is shown that the formulæ (12) are, at least approximately, correct. An investigation of this question, based partly on the work of Kirchhoff and Clebsch*, will now be given.

* See Introduction, pp. 23 and 24.

256. Nature of the strain in a bent and twisted rod.

In Kirchhoff's theory of thin rods much importance attaches to certain kinematical equations. These equations are not free from difficulty, and the following investigation, which is direct if a little tedious, is offered as a substitute for the kinematical part of Kirchhoff's theory. We suppose that a thin rod is actually bent, so that the central-line has a certain curvature, and twisted, so that the "twist" has a certain value, and we seek to ascertain the restrictions, if any, which are thereby imposed upon the strain in the rod. For the sake of greater generality we shall suppose also that the central-line undergoes a certain small extension.

Now we can certainly imagine a state of the rod in which the cross-sections remain plane, and at right angles to the central-line, and suffer no strain in their planes; and we may suppose that each such section is so oriented in the normal plane of the strained central-line that the twist, as already defined, has the prescribed value. To express this state of the rod we denote by x, y the coordinates of any point Q, lying in the cross-section of which the centroid is P, referred to the principal axes at P of this cross-section. When the section is displaced bodily, as explained above, the point P moves to P_1 and the coordinates of P_1, referred to any fixed axes, may be taken to be $\mathrm{x}, \mathrm{y}, \mathrm{z}$. The principal axes at P of the cross-section through P are moved into the positions of the axes of x, y at P_1 defined in Article 252. The state of the rod described above is therefore such that the coordinates, referred to the fixed axes, of the point Q_1, to which Q is displaced, are

$$\mathrm{x} + l_1 x + l_2 y, \quad \mathrm{y} + m_1 x + m_2 y, \quad \mathrm{z} + n_1 x + n_2 y,$$

where $l_1, \ldots$ are the direction-cosines defined by the scheme (4).

Any state of the rod, which involves the right extension and curvature of the central-line and the right twist, may be derived from the state just described by a displacement which, in the case of a thin rod, must be small, for one point in each cross-section and one plane element drawn through each tangent of the central-line are not displaced. Let ξ, η, ζ be the components of this additional displacement for the point Q, referred to the axes of x, y, z at the point P_1. The coordinates, referred to the fixed axes, of the final position of Q are

$$\mathrm{x} + l_1(x+\xi) + l_2(y+\eta) + l_3\zeta, \quad \mathrm{y} + m_1(x+\xi) + m_2(y+\eta) + m_3\zeta,$$
$$\mathrm{z} + n_1(x+\xi) + n_2(y+\eta) + n_3\zeta. \quad \ldots\ldots\ldots\ldots\ldots\ldots(13)$$

To estimate the strain in the rod we take a point Q' near to Q. In the unstrained state Q' will, in general, be in a normal section different from that drawn through P. We take it to be in the normal section drawn through P', so that the arc $PP' = \delta s$. We take the coordinates of Q' referred to the principal axes at P' of the cross-section drawn through P' to be $x + \delta x$, $y + \delta y$.

Then δx, δy, δs are the projections on the fixed axes of the linear element QQ'. We take r to be the length of this element, and write

$$\delta x = lr, \quad \delta y = mr, \quad \delta s = nr,$$

so that l, m, n are the direction-cosines, referred to the fixed axes, of the line QQ'. We can write down expressions like those in (13) for the coordinates of the final position of Q', and we can therefore express the length r_1 of the line joining the final positions of QQ' in terms of r and l, m, n. Since the direction l, m, n is arbitrary, the result gives us the six components of strain.

In obtaining the length r_1 we must express all the quantities which involve r correctly to the first order, but powers of r above the first may be neglected. To obtain the expressions for the coordinates of the final position of Q' we note the changes that must be made in the several terms of (13). The quantities x, y, z, l_1, ... are functions of s only, but the quantities ξ, η, ζ are functions of x, y, s. We must therefore in (13) replace

$$\mathrm{x} \text{ by } \mathrm{x} + \frac{\partial \mathrm{x}}{\partial s} nr, \quad \mathrm{y} \text{ by } \mathrm{y} + \frac{\partial \mathrm{y}}{\partial s} nr, \quad \mathrm{z} \text{ by } \mathrm{z} + \frac{\partial \mathrm{z}}{\partial s} nr,$$

$$l_1 \text{ by } l_1 + \frac{\partial l_1}{\partial s} nr, \ldots$$

$$\ldots$$

$$x \text{ by } x + lr, \quad y \text{ by } y + mr,$$

$$\xi \text{ by } \xi + \frac{\partial \xi}{\partial x} lr + \frac{\partial \xi}{\partial y} mr + \frac{\partial \xi}{\partial s} nr, \ldots.$$

Further the quantities $\partial\mathrm{x}/\partial s$, ... are given by the equations

$$\frac{\partial \mathrm{x}}{\partial s} = (1+\epsilon)\, l_3, \quad \frac{\partial \mathrm{y}}{\partial s} = (1+\epsilon)\, m_3, \quad \frac{\partial \mathrm{z}}{\partial s} = (1+\epsilon)\, n_3,$$

and the quantities $\partial l_1/\partial s$, ... are given by the equations

$$\frac{\partial l_1}{\partial s} = (1+\epsilon)(l_2\tau - l_3\kappa'), \ldots$$

$$\ldots$$

where the coefficients of $(1+\epsilon)$ are the right-hand members of equations (5).

It follows that the difference of the x-coordinates of the final positions of Q and Q' is

$$\begin{aligned} r\Bigg[(1+\epsilon)\, l_3 n + l_1 \left\{\left(1+\frac{\partial \xi}{\partial x}\right) l + \frac{\partial \xi}{\partial y} m + \frac{\partial \xi}{\partial s} n\right\} + (1+\epsilon)(l_2\tau - l_3\kappa')\, n\, (x+\xi) \\ + l_2 \left\{\frac{\partial \eta}{\partial x} l + \left(1+\frac{\partial \eta}{\partial y}\right) m + \frac{\partial \eta}{\partial s} n\right\} + (1+\epsilon)(l_3\kappa - l_1\tau)\, n\, (y+\eta) \\ + l_3 \left\{\frac{\partial \zeta}{\partial x} l + \frac{\partial \zeta}{\partial y} m + \frac{\partial \zeta}{\partial s} n\right\} + (1+\epsilon)(l_1\kappa' - l_2\kappa)\, n\zeta\Bigg]. \end{aligned}$$

For the differences of the y- and z-coordinates we have similar expressions with m_1, m_2, m_3 and n_1, n_2, n_3 respectively in place of l_1, l_2, l_3. Since the scheme (4) is orthogonal, the result of squaring and adding these expressions is

$$r^2\left[\left(1+\frac{\partial\xi}{\partial x}\right)l+\frac{\partial\xi}{\partial y}m+\frac{\partial\xi}{\partial s}n+(1+\epsilon)\,n\,\{\kappa'\zeta-\tau(y+\eta)\}\right]^2$$
$$+r^2\left[\frac{\partial\eta}{\partial x}l+\left(1+\frac{\partial\eta}{\partial y}\right)m+\frac{\partial\eta}{\partial s}n+(1+\epsilon)\,n\,\{\tau(x+\xi)-\kappa\zeta\}\right]^2$$
$$+r^2\left[\frac{\partial\zeta}{\partial x}l+\frac{\partial\zeta}{\partial y}m+\frac{\partial\zeta}{\partial s}n+(1+\epsilon)\,n\,\{1+\kappa(y+\eta)-\kappa'(x+\xi)\}\right]^2, \quad\text{...(14)}$$

and this is r_1^2. We have therefore expressed r_1^2 in the form of a homogeneous quadratic function of l, m, n.

Now, the strains being small, r_1 is nearly equal to r, and we can write

$$r_1^2=r^2(1+2e),$$

where e is the extension in the direction l, m, n. Further we shall have

$$e=e_{xx}l^2+e_{yy}m^2+e_{zz}n^2+e_{yz}mn+e_{zx}nl+e_{xy}lm,$$

where the quantities e_{xx}, ... are the six components of strain. The coefficient of l in the first line of the expression (14) must be nearly equal to unity, and the coefficients of m and n in this line must be nearly zero. Similar statements *mutatis mutandis* hold with regard to the coefficients of l, m, n in the remaining lines. We therefore obtain the following expressions for the components of strain:

$$e_{xx}=\frac{\partial\xi}{\partial x},\quad e_{yy}=\frac{\partial\eta}{\partial y},\quad e_{xy}=\frac{\partial\xi}{\partial y}+\frac{\partial\eta}{\partial x},\quad\text{..................(15)}$$

and

$$\left.\begin{aligned}e_{zx}&=\frac{\partial\zeta}{\partial x}+\frac{\partial\xi}{\partial s}+(1+\epsilon)\{\kappa'\zeta-\tau(y+\eta)\},\\ e_{yz}&=\frac{\partial\zeta}{\partial y}+\frac{\partial\eta}{\partial s}+(1+\epsilon)\{\tau(x+\xi)-\kappa\zeta\},\\ e_{zz}&=\epsilon+\frac{\partial\zeta}{\partial s}+(1+\epsilon)\{\kappa(y+\eta)-\kappa'(x+\xi)\}.\end{aligned}\right\}\quad\text{...........(16)}$$

In obtaining the formulæ (15) and (16) we have not introduced any approximations except such as arise from the consideration that the strains are "small," and, in particular, that ϵ, being the extension of the central-line, must be small. But we can see, without introducing any other considerations, that the terms of (16), as they stand, are not all of the same order of magnitude. In the first place it is clear that the terms $-\tau y$, τx, κy, $-\kappa' x$ must be small; in other words, the linear dimensions of the cross-section must be small compared with the radius of curvature of the central-line, or with the reciprocal of the twist. Such terms as $\kappa'\zeta$, $\tau\eta$, ... are small also. We may therefore omit the products of ϵ and these small quantities, and rewrite equations (16) in the forms

$$\left.\begin{aligned} e_{zx} &= \frac{\partial \zeta}{\partial x} - \tau y + \frac{\partial \xi}{\partial s} - \tau \eta + \kappa' \zeta, \\ e_{yz} &= \frac{\partial \zeta}{\partial y} + \tau x + \frac{\partial \eta}{\partial s} - \kappa \zeta + \tau \xi, \\ e_{zz} &= \epsilon - \kappa' x + \kappa y + \frac{\partial \zeta}{\partial s} - \kappa' \xi + \kappa \eta. \end{aligned}\right\} \qquad \text{.................(17)}$$

Now the position of the origin of x, y, and that of the principal plane of (x, z), are unaffected by the displacement (ξ, η, ζ), and therefore this displacement is subject to the restrictions:

(i) ξ, η, ζ vanish with x and y for all values of s,

(ii) $\partial\eta/\partial x$ vanishes with x and y for all values of s.

We conclude that, provided that the strain in the rod is everywhere small, the necessary forms of the strain-components are given by equations (15) and (17), where the functions ξ, η, ζ are subject to the restrictions (i) and (ii).

257. Approximate formulæ for the strain.

We have now to introduce the simplifications which arise from the consideration that the rod is "thin." The quantities ξ, η, ζ may be expanded as power series in x and y, the coefficients in the expansions being functions of s; and the expansions must be valid for sufficiently small values of x and y, that is to say in a portion of the rod near to the central-line*. There are no constant terms in these expansions because ξ, η, ζ vanish with x and y. Further $\partial\xi/\partial x$ and $\partial\xi/\partial y$ must be small quantities of the order of admissible strains, and therefore the coefficients of those terms of ξ which are linear in x and y must be small of this order. It follows that ξ itself must be small of a higher order, viz., that of the product of the small quantity $\partial\xi/\partial x$ and the small coordinate x. Similar considerations apply to η and ζ. As a first step in the simplification of (17) we may therefore omit such terms as $-\tau\eta$, $\kappa'\zeta$. When this is done we have the formulæ†

$$\epsilon_{zx} = \frac{\partial \zeta}{\partial x} - \tau y + \frac{\partial \xi}{\partial s}, \quad e_{yz} = \frac{\partial \zeta}{\partial y} + \tau x + \frac{\partial \eta}{\partial s}, \quad e_{zz} = \epsilon - \kappa' x + \kappa y + \frac{\partial \zeta}{\partial s}, \text{...(18)}$$

and these with (15) are approximate expressions for the strain-components.

* The expansions may not be valid over the whole of a cross-section. The failure of Cauchy's theory of the torsion of a prism of rectangular cross-section (Introduction, footnote 85) sufficiently illustrates this point. But the argument in the text as to the relative order of magnitude of such terms as τy and such terms as $\tau\eta$ could hardly be affected by the restricted range of validity of the expansions.

† It may be observed that Saint-Venant's formulæ for the torsion of a prism are included in

Again we may observe that similar considerations to those just adduced in the case of ξ apply also in the case of $\partial\xi/\partial s$; this quantity must be of the order of the product of the small quantity $\partial^2\xi/\partial x\partial s$ and the small coordinate x, which is the same as the order of the product of the small quantity $\partial\xi/\partial x$ and the small fraction x/l, where l is a length comparable with (or equal to) the length of the rod. Thus, in general, $\partial\xi/\partial s$ is small compared with $\partial\xi/\partial x$. Similar considerations apply to $\partial\eta/\partial s$ and $\partial\zeta/\partial s$*. As a second step in the simplification of (17) we may omit $\partial\xi/\partial s$, $\partial\eta/\partial s$, $\partial\zeta/\partial s$ and obtain the formulæ†

$$e_{zx}=\frac{\partial\zeta}{\partial x}-\tau y,\quad e_{yz}=\frac{\partial\zeta}{\partial y}+\tau x,\quad e_{zz}=\epsilon-\kappa' x+\kappa y. \qquad\text{.........(19)}$$

Again we may observe that in Saint-Venant's solutions already cited ϵ vanishes, and in some solutions obtained in Chapter XVI ϵ is small compared with $\kappa' x$. In many important problems ϵ is small compared with such quantities as τx or $\kappa' x$. Whenever this is the case we may make a third step in the simplification of the formulæ (17) by omitting ϵ. They would then read

$$e_{zx}=\frac{\partial\zeta}{\partial x}-\tau y,\quad e_{yz}=\frac{\partial\zeta}{\partial y}+\tau x,\quad e_{zz}=-\kappa' x+\kappa y. \qquad\text{.........(20)}$$

With these we must associate the formulæ (15), and in the set of formulæ we may suppose, as has been explained, that ξ, η, ζ are approximately independent of s.

It appears therefore that the most important strains in a bent and twisted rod are (i) extension of the longitudinal filaments related to the curvature of the central-line in the manner noted in Article 232 (*b*), (ii) shearing strains of the same kind as those which occur in the torsion problem discussed in Chapter XIV, (iii) relative displacement of elements of any cross-section parallel to the plane of the section. The last of these strains is approximately the same for different cross-sections provided that they are near together.

258. Discussion of the ordinary approximate theory.

To determine the stress-resultants and stress-couples we require the values of the stress-components X_z, Y_z, Z_z. Since

$$Z_z=\frac{E}{(1+\sigma)(1-2\sigma)}\{\sigma(e_{xx}+e_{yy})+(1-\sigma)e_{zz}\},$$

the formulæ (15) and (18) by putting $\xi=\eta=0$; and his formulæ for bending by terminal load are included by putting

$$\xi=-\sigma\kappa xy+\tfrac{1}{2}\sigma\kappa'(x^2-y^2),\quad \eta=\sigma\kappa' xy+\tfrac{1}{2}\sigma\kappa(x^2-y^2).$$

In each case ζ must be determined appropriately.

* The result, so far as $\partial\xi/\partial s$ and $\partial\eta/\partial s$ are concerned, is exemplified by Saint-Venant's formulæ just cited. In Saint-Venant's solutions ζ is

$$\tau\phi-\frac{d\kappa'}{ds}(\chi+xy^2)+\frac{d\kappa}{ds}(\chi'+x^2y),$$

where χ and χ' are the flexure functions, and ϕ is the torsion function, for the cross-section. The functions χ and χ' are small of the order a^2x, where a is an appropriate linear dimension of the cross-section. In this case ζ is actually independent of s.

† These are Kirchhoff's formulæ.

where E is Young's modulus and σ is Poisson's ratio for the material, the expression for this stress-component cannot be obtained without finding the lateral extensions e_{xx}, e_{yy} given by the formulæ (15), as well as the longitudinal extension e_{zz} given by the third of (17), (18), (19) or (20). To express the stress-components completely we require values for ξ, η, ζ, and these cannot be found except by solving the equations of equilibrium subject to conditions which hold at the cylindrical or prismatic bounding surface of any small portion of the rod. If the rod is vibrating, the equations of small motion ought to be solved. We may, however, approximate to the stress-resultants and stress-couples by retracing the steps of the argument in the last Article.

When there are no body forces or kinetic reactions, and the initially cylindrical bounding surface of the rod is free from traction, the portion between any two neighbouring cross-sections is held in equilibrium by the tractions on its ends. According to our final approximation, expressed by equations (15) and (20), ξ, η, ζ are independent of s, and, in the portion of the rod considered, κ, κ', τ also may be regarded as independent of s. This portion of the rod may therefore be regarded as a prism held strained by tractions on its ends in such a way that the strain, and therefore also the stress, are the same at corresponding points in the intermediate cross-sections. The theorem of Article 237 shows that, in such a prism, the stress-components X_x, Y_y, X_y must vanish, and, since e_{zz} is given by the third of (20), we must have

$$\frac{\partial \xi}{\partial x} = \frac{\partial \eta}{\partial y} = \sigma(\kappa' x - \kappa y), \quad \frac{\partial \xi}{\partial y} + \frac{\partial \eta}{\partial x} = 0. \quad \text{..............(21)}$$

Further the stress-components X_z, Y_z, Z_z must be given by Saint-Venant's formulæ

$$X_z = \mu\tau\left(\frac{\partial \phi}{\partial x} - y\right), \quad Y_z = \mu\tau\left(\frac{\partial \phi}{\partial y} + x\right), \quad Z_z = -E(\kappa' x - \kappa y), \text{ ...(22)}$$

where ϕ is the torsion function for the section (Article 216). The stress-couples are then given by the formulæ (12) of Article 255. To this order of approximation the stress-resultants vanish.

When we retain ϵ, as in the formulæ (19), no modification is made in the formulæ for the stress-couples, and the shearing forces still vanish. To the expression $\sigma(\kappa' x - \kappa y)$ in the right-hand member of (21) we must add the term $-\sigma\epsilon$, and the tension is given by the formula

$$T = E\omega\epsilon, \quad \text{..............................(23)}$$

where ω is the area of the cross-section.

When we abandon the supposition that ξ, η, ζ are independent of s, we may obtain a closer approximation by assuming that the strains, instead of being uniform along the length of a small portion of the rod, vary uniformly along this length. When there are no body forces, and the initially cylindrical boundary is free from traction, the theorem of Article 238 shows that the only possible solutions are Saint-Venant's. The stress-couples and the tension are given by the same formulæ as before, but the shearing forces do not vanish.

In the general case, in which forces are applied to parts of the rod other than the ends, we ought to retain the formulæ (17) for the strains, and the formulæ (21) do not hold. We know from the investigations of Chapter XVI that the formulæ (12) and (23) are not exact, although they may be approximately correct. The corrections that ought to be made in them depend upon the distribution of the applied forces over the cross-sections.

From this discussion we may conclude that the formulæ (12) and (23) yield good approximations to the values of the stress-couples and the tension in parts of the rod which are at a distance from any place of loading or support, but that, in the neighbourhood of such places, they are of doubtful validity.

Since the equations (10) and (11) combined with the formulæ (12) determine all the stress-resultants as well as the curvature and twist, the formula (23) determines the extension ϵ.

In ordinary circumstances ϵ is small in comparison with such quantities as κx, which represent the extensions produced in non-central longitudinal filaments by bending. This may be seen as follows:—the order of magnitude of T is, in general, the same as that of N, or N', and this order is, by equations (11), that of $\partial G/\partial s$. Hence the order of ϵ is that of $(E\omega)^{-1}(\partial G/\partial s)$. Now κ is of the order $G/E\omega a^2$, where a is an appropriate linear dimension of the cross-sections, and the order of κx is therefore that of $(E\omega)^{-1}(G/a)$. Thus κx is, in general, a very much larger quantity than ϵ.

In any problem in which bending, or twisting, is an important feature we may, for a first approximation, regard the central-line as unextended.

The potential energy per unit of length of the rod is easily found from equations (21) and (22) in the form

$$\tfrac{1}{2}(A\kappa^2 + B\kappa'^2 + C\tau^2). \qquad \text{.........(24)}$$

If there is no curvature or twist the potential energy is

$$\tfrac{1}{2}E\omega\epsilon^2.$$

258 A. Small displacement.

When the rod is but slightly deformed we resolve the displacement of a point on the central-line in fixed directions. Let the axes of x, y, z used in Article 253 be so chosen that the axis of z is along the unstrained central-line, and the axes of x and y are parallel to principal axes of a cross-section at its centroid. Let the displacement of a point in the central-line resolved in the directions of these fixed axes be u, v, w. Further let β denote the cosine of the angle between the axes of x and y. Then the coordinates of the displaced positions of two points, initially at a distance δs apart, differ by the quantities

$$\frac{du}{ds}\delta s, \quad \frac{dv}{ds}\delta s, \quad \left(1+\frac{dw}{ds}\right)\delta s.$$

If quantities of the second order in u, v, w, β are neglected, the extension ϵ of the central-line is given by

$$\epsilon=\frac{dw}{ds}.$$

The coefficients of the orthogonal scheme (4) of Article 253 are given to the same order by the equations

$$l_1=1,\quad m_1=\beta,\quad n_1=-\frac{du}{ds},$$

$$l_2=-\beta,\quad m_2=1,\quad n_2=-\frac{dv}{ds},$$

$$l_3=\frac{du}{ds},\quad m_3=\frac{dv}{ds},\quad n_3=1.$$

The component curvatures κ, κ' and the twist τ are given by the formulæ (6) of Article 253, and, to the same order, we have

$$\kappa=-\frac{d^2v}{ds^2},\quad \kappa'=\frac{d^2u}{ds^2},\quad \tau=\frac{d\beta}{ds}.$$

It appears that all the quantities required to express the deformed state of the rod are expressible in terms of u, v, w and β. The quantity β is, to the first order, identical with that which in the notation of Article 253 would be denoted by $\phi+\psi$, or it is the angle through which a plane section is rotated around the central-line.

With the above values of κ, κ', τ, the stress-couples are expressed in terms of the displacement by the aid of equations (12) of Article 255; and, with the above value of ϵ, the tension is expressed in terms of the displacement by the aid of equation (23) of Article 258. Equations (11) of Article 254 become, on omission of terms of the second order in the displacement,

$$\frac{dG}{ds}-N'+K=0,\quad \frac{dG'}{ds}+N+K'=0,\quad \frac{dH}{ds}+\Theta=0,$$

and the first two of these show that N and N' are in general of the first order in the displacement. Equations (10) of Article 254 become, on omission of terms of the second order,

$$\frac{dN}{ds}+X=0,\quad \frac{dN'}{ds}+Y=0,\quad \frac{dT}{ds}+Z=0.$$

It will be observed that the last of these equations determines T, and thence ϵ and w, while the remaining equations determine u, v and β.

259. Rods naturally curved*.

The rod in the unstressed state may possess both curvature and twist, the central-line being a tortuous curve, and the principal axes of the cross-sections at their centroids making with the principal normals of this curve angles which vary from point to point of the curve. The principal axes of a cross-section at its centroid and the tangent of the central-line at this point form a triad of orthogonal axes of x_0, y_0, z_0, the axis of z_0 being directed along the tangent. We suppose the origin of this triad of axes to move along the curve with unit velocity. The components of the angular velocity of the moving triad of axes, referred to the instantaneous positions of the axes, will be denoted by

* The theory is substantially due to Clebsch, *Elasticität*, § 55. It had been indicated in outline by Kirchhoff, *loc. cit.*, p. 381.

$\kappa_0, \kappa_0', \tau_0$. Then κ_0, κ_0' are the components of the initial curvature, and τ_0 is the initial twist. If $1/\Sigma_0$ is the measure of tortuosity of the central-line at any point, and $\frac{1}{2}\pi - f_0$ is the angle which the principal plane of (x_0, z_0) at the point makes with the principal normal of the central-line, we have the formulæ

$$\tan f_0 = -\kappa_0'/\kappa_0, \quad \tau_0 = 1/\Sigma_0 + df_0/ds, \quad \text{..............(25)}$$

which are analogous to (2) and (3) in Article 253.

When the rod is further bent and twisted, we may construct at each point on the strained central-line a system of "principal torsion-flexure axes," in the same way as in Article 252, so that the axis of z is the tangent of the strained central-line at the point, and the plane of (x, z) contains the linear element which, in the unstressed state, issues from the point and lies along the axis of x_0. By means of this system of axes we determine, in the same way as before, the components of curvature of the strained central-line and the twist of the rod. We shall denote the components of curvature by κ_1, κ_1', and the twist by τ_1.

The equations of equilibrium can be written down, by the method of Article 254, in the forms

$$\left.\begin{aligned} \frac{dN}{ds} - N'\tau_1 + T\kappa_1' + X = 0, \\ \frac{dN'}{ds} - T\kappa_1 + N\tau_1 + Y = 0, \\ \frac{dT}{ds} - N\kappa_1' + N'\kappa_1 + Z = 0, \end{aligned}\right\} \quad \text{....................(26)}$$

and

$$\left.\begin{aligned} \frac{dG}{ds} - G'\tau_1 + H\kappa_1' - N' + K = 0, \\ \frac{dG'}{ds} - H\kappa_1 + G\tau_1 + N + K' = 0, \\ \frac{dH}{ds} - G\kappa_1' + G'\kappa_1 + \Theta = 0. \end{aligned}\right\} \quad \text{..................(27)}$$

The rod could be held straight and prismatic by suitable forces, and, according to the ordinary approximation (Article 255), the stress-couples at any cross-section would be $-A\kappa_0, -B\kappa_0', -C\tau_0$. The straight prismatic rod could be bent and twisted to the state expressed by $\kappa_1, \kappa_1', \tau_1$ and then, according to the same approximation, there would be additional couples $A\kappa_1, B\kappa_1', C\tau_1$. The stress-couples in the rod when bent and twisted from the state expressed by $\kappa_0, \kappa_0', \tau_0$ to that expressed by $\kappa_1, \kappa_1', \tau_1$ would then be given by the formulæ*

$$G = A(\kappa_1 - \kappa_0), \quad G' = B(\kappa_1' - \kappa_0'), \quad H = C(\tau_1 - \tau_0). \quad \text{......(28)}$$

* These formulæ, due to Clebsch, were obtained also, by a totally different process, by A. B. Basset, *Amer. J. of Math.*, vol. 17 (1895).

It is clear from the discussion in Article 258 that these formulæ can be used with greater certainty if the rod is subjected to terminal forces and couples only than if forces are applied to it along its length.

It may be noted that, even when the cross-section of the rod has kinetic symmetry, so that $A=B$, the flexural couples are not equivalent to a single couple about the binormal of the strained central-line unless $\kappa_1'/\kappa_0'=\kappa_1/\kappa_0$. When this condition is satisfied the flexural couple is of amount $B(1/\rho_1-1/\rho_0)$, where ρ_1 and ρ_0 are the radii of curvature of the central-line in the stressed and unstressed states.

The above method of calculating the stress-couples requires the ratios of the thickness of the rod to the radius of curvature and to the reciprocal of the twist to be small of the order of small strains contemplated in the mathematical theory of Elasticity. Unless this condition is satisfied the rod cannot be held straight and untwisted without producing in it strains which exceed this order. It is, however, not necessary to assume that this condition is satisfied in order to obtain the formulæ (28) as approximately correct formulæ for the stress-couples. We may apply to the question the method of Article 256, and take account of the initial curvature and twist by means of the equations

$$lr=\delta x-y\tau_0\,\delta s,\quad mr=\delta y+x\tau_0\,\delta s,\quad nr=\delta s\,(1-\kappa_0'x+\kappa_0 y),$$

or

$$\delta x=r\left(l+n\frac{\tau_0 y}{1+\gamma}\right),\quad \delta y=r\left(m-n\frac{\tau_0 x}{1+\gamma}\right),\quad \delta s=\frac{rn}{1+\gamma},$$

where γ stands for $\kappa_0 y-\kappa_0' x$. We should then find instead of (14)

$$\begin{aligned}r_1^2=r^2&\left[\left(1+\frac{\partial\xi}{\partial x}\right)l+\frac{\partial\xi}{\partial y}m+\frac{n}{1+\gamma}\left\{\frac{\partial\xi}{\partial s}+\tau_0\left(y\frac{\partial\xi}{\partial x}-x\frac{\partial\xi}{\partial y}\right)\right\}+\frac{(1+\epsilon)\,n}{1+\gamma}\{-(\tau_1-\tau_0)\,y-\tau_1\eta+\kappa_1'\zeta\}\right]^2\\&+r^2\left[\frac{\partial\eta}{\partial x}l+\left(1+\frac{\partial\eta}{\partial y}\right)m+\frac{n}{1+\gamma}\left\{\frac{\partial\eta}{\partial s}+\tau_0\left(y\frac{\partial\eta}{\partial x}-x\frac{\partial\eta}{\partial y}\right)\right\}+\frac{(1+\epsilon)\,n}{1+\gamma}\{(\tau_1-\tau_0)\,x-\kappa_1\zeta+\tau_1\xi\}\right]^2\\&+r^2\left[\frac{\partial\zeta}{\partial x}l+\frac{\partial\zeta}{\partial y}m+(1+\epsilon)\,n+\frac{n}{1+\gamma}\left\{\frac{\partial\zeta}{\partial s}+\tau_0\left(y\frac{\partial\zeta}{\partial x}-x\frac{\partial\zeta}{\partial y}\right)\right\}+\frac{(1+\epsilon)\,n}{1+\gamma}\{(\kappa_1-\kappa_0)\,y-(\kappa_1'-\kappa_0')\,x\right.\\&\left.\qquad-\kappa_1'\xi+\kappa_1\eta\}\right]^2.\end{aligned}$$

In deducing approximate expressions for the strain-components we denote by $[\gamma]$ any quantity of the order of the ratio (thickness)/(radius of curvature) or (thickness)/(reciprocal of twist), whether initial or final, and by $[e]$ any quantity of the order of the strain. Thus, $\tau_0 y$ and $\tau_1 y$ are of the order $[\gamma]$; $\partial\xi/\partial x$ and $(\kappa_1-\kappa_0)\,y$ are of the order $[e]$. If, in the above expression for r_1^2, we reject all terms of the order of the product $[\gamma]\,[e]$ as well as all terms of the order $[e]^2$, we find instead of (19) the formulæ

$$e_{zx}=\frac{\partial\zeta}{\partial x}-(\tau_1-\tau_0)\,y,\quad e_{yz}=\frac{\partial\zeta}{\partial y}+(\tau_1-\tau_0)\,x,\quad e_{zz}=\epsilon+(\kappa_1-\kappa_0)\,y-(\kappa_1'-\kappa_0')\,x.$$

From these we could deduce the formulæ (28) in the same way as (12) are deduced from (19), and they would be subject to the same limitations.

CHAPTER XIX

PROBLEMS CONCERNING THE EQUILIBRIUM OF THIN RODS

260. Kirchhoff's kinetic analogue.

We shall begin our study of the applications of the theory of the last Chapter with a proof of Kirchhoff's theorem*, according to which the equations of equilibrium of a thin rod, straight and prismatic when unstressed, and held bent and twisted by forces and couples applied at its ends alone, can be identified with the equations of motion of a heavy rigid body turning about a fixed point.

No forces or couples being applied to the rod except at the ends, the quantities X, Y, Z and K, K', Θ in equations (10) and (11) of Article 254 vanish. Equations (10) of that Article become

$$\frac{dN}{ds} - N'\tau + T\kappa' = 0, \quad \frac{dN'}{ds} - T\kappa + N\tau = 0, \quad \frac{dT}{ds} - N\kappa' + N'\kappa = 0, \ldots\ldots(1)$$

which express the constancy, as regards magnitude and direction, of the resultant of N, N', T; and, in fact, this resultant has the same magnitude, direction and sense as the force applied to that end of the rod towards which s is measured. We denote this force by R.

Equations (11) of Article 254 become, on substitution from (12) of Article 255, and omission of K, K', Θ,

$$A\frac{d\kappa}{ds} - (B-C)\,\kappa'\tau = N', \quad B\frac{d\kappa'}{ds} - (C-A)\,\tau\kappa = -N, \quad C\frac{d\tau}{ds} - (A-B)\,\kappa\kappa' = 0.$$
$$\ldots\ldots\ldots(2)$$

The terms on the right-hand side are equal to the moments about the axes of x, y, z of a force equal and opposite to R applied at the point (0, 0, 1). We may therefore interpret equations (2) as the equations of motion of a top, that is to say of a heavy rigid body turning about a fixed point. In this analogy the line of action of the force R (applied at that end of the rod towards which s is measured) represents the vertical drawn upwards, s represents the time, the magnitude of R represents the weight of the body, A, B, C represent the moments of inertia of the body about principal axes at the fixed point, (κ, κ', τ) represents the angular velocity of the body referred to the instantaneous position of this triad of axes. The centre of gravity of the body is on the C-axis at unit distance from the fixed point; and this axis, drawn from the fixed point to the centre of gravity at the instant s, is identical, in direction and sense, with the tangent of the central-line of the rod, drawn in the sense in which s increases, at that point P_1 of this line

* G. Kirchhoff, *loc. cit.*, p. 381.

which is at an arc-distance s from one end. The body moves so that its principal axes at the fixed point are parallel at the instant s to the principal torsion-flexure axes of the rod at P_1.

On eliminating N and N' from the third of equations (1) by the aid of equations (2), we find the equation

$$\frac{dT}{ds} + A\kappa\frac{d\kappa}{ds} + B\kappa'\frac{d\kappa'}{ds} + (A - B)\,\tau\kappa\kappa' = 0,$$

or, by the third of (2),

$$\frac{d}{ds}\{T + \tfrac{1}{2}(A\kappa^2 + B\kappa'^2 + C\tau^2)\} = 0,$$

giving the equation $\quad T + \tfrac{1}{2}(A\kappa^2 + B\kappa'^2 + C\tau^2) = \text{const.}$ ....(3)

This equation is equivalent to the energy-integral of the equations of motion of the kinetic analogue.

261. Extension of the theorem of the kinetic analogue to rods naturally curved*.

The theorem may be extended to rods which in the unstressed state have curvature and twist, provided that the components of initial curvature κ_0, κ_0' and the initial twist τ_0, defined as in Article 259, are constants. This is the case if, in the unstressed state, the rod is straight but not prismatic, in such a way that homologous transverse lines in different cross-sections lie on a right helicoid; or if the central-line is an arc of a circle, and the rod free from twist; or if the central-line is a portion of a helix, and the rod has such an initial twist that, if simply unbent, it would be prismatic.

When the rod is bent and twisted by forces and couples applied at its ends only, so that the components of curvature and the twist, as defined in Article 259, become κ_1, κ_1', τ_1, the stress-resultants N, N', T satisfy the equations

$$\frac{dN}{ds} - N'\tau_1 + T\kappa_1' = 0, \quad \frac{dN'}{ds} - T\kappa_1 + N\tau_1 = 0, \quad \frac{dT}{ds} - N\kappa_1' + N'\kappa_1 = 0. \quad \text{.........(4)}$$

These equations express the result that N, N', T are the components, parallel to the principal torsion-flexure axes at any section, of a force which is constant in magnitude and direction. We denote this force, as before, by R. Since the stress-couples at any section are $A(\kappa_1 - \kappa_0)$, $B(\kappa_1' - \kappa_0')$, $C(\tau_1 - \tau_0)$ we have the equations

$$\left.\begin{aligned} A\frac{d\kappa_1}{ds} - B(\kappa_1' - \kappa_0')\tau_1 + C(\tau_1 - \tau_0)\kappa_1' &= N', \\ B\frac{d\kappa_1'}{ds} - C(\tau_1 - \tau_0)\kappa_1 + A(\kappa_1 - \kappa_0)\tau_1 &= -N, \\ C\frac{d\tau_1}{ds} - A(\kappa_1 - \kappa_0)\kappa_1' + B(\kappa_1' - \kappa_0')\kappa_1 &= 0. \end{aligned}\right\} \quad \text{.......................(5)}$$

The kinetic analogue is a rigid body turning about a fixed point and carrying a flywheel or gyrostat rotating about an axis fixed in the body. The centre of gravity of the flywheel is at the fixed point. The direction-cosines l, m, n of the axis of the flywheel, referred to the principal axes of the body at the point, and the moment of momentum h of the flywheel about this axis, are given by the equations

$$-A\kappa_0 = hl, \quad -B\kappa_0' = hm, \quad -C\tau_0 = hn. \quad \text{..........................(6)}$$

The angular velocity of the rigid body referred to principal axes at the fixed point is $(\kappa_1, \kappa_1', \tau_1)$ and the interpretation of the remaining symbols is the same as before.

* J. Larmor, *London Math. Soc. Proc.*, vol. 15 (1884).

262. The problem of the elastica*.

As a first application of the theorem of Article 260 we take the problem of determining the forms in which a thin rod, straight and prismatic in the unstressed state, can be held by forces and couples applied at its ends only, when the rod is bent in a principal plane, so that the central-line becomes a plane curve, and there is no twist. The kinetic analogue is then a rigid pendulum of weight R, turning about a fixed horizontal axis. The motion of the pendulum is determined completely by the energy-equation and the initial conditions. In like manner the figure of the central-line of the rod is determined completely by the appropriate form of equation (3) and the terminal conditions.

We take the plane of bending to be that for which the flexural rigidity is B. Then κ and τ vanish, and the stress-couple is a flexural couple G', $= B\kappa'$, in the plane of bending. The stress-resultants are a tension T and a shearing force N, the latter directed towards the centre of curvature. Let θ be the angle which the tangent of the central-line at any point, drawn in the sense in which s increases, makes with the line of action of the force R applied at the end from which s is measured (see Fig. 47). Then we have $T = -R\cos\theta$, and $\kappa' = -d\theta/ds$, and the equation (3) becomes

$$-R\cos\theta + \tfrac{1}{2}B\,(d\theta/ds)^2 = \text{const.} \quad \ldots\ldots(7)$$

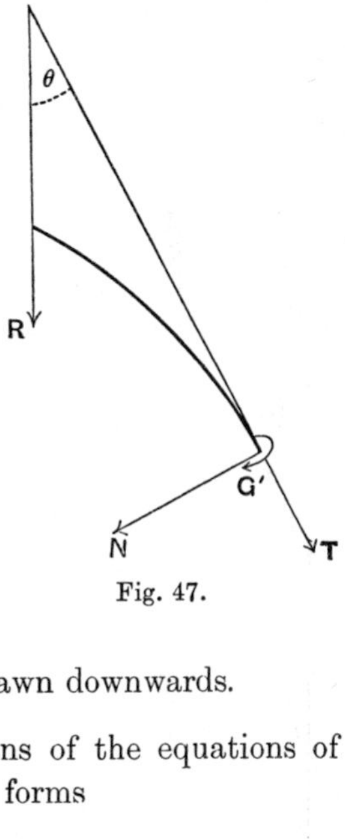

Fig. 47.

In the kinetic analogue B is the moment of inertia of the pendulum about the axis of suspension, and the centre of gravity is at unit distance from the axis. The line drawn from the centre of suspension to the centre of gravity at the instant s makes an angle θ with the vertical drawn downwards.

Equation (7) can be obtained very simply by means of the equations of equilibrium. These equations can be expressed in the forms

$$T = -R\cos\theta, \quad N = -R\sin\theta, \quad \frac{dG'}{ds} + N = 0,$$

from which, by putting $G' = -B\,(d\theta/ds)$, we obtain the equation

$$B\,(d^2\theta/ds^2) + R\sin\theta = 0, \quad \ldots\ldots\ldots\ldots\ldots\ldots\ldots\ldots(8)$$

and equation (7) is the first integral of this equation.

* The problem of the *elastica* was first solved by Euler. See Introduction, p. 3. The systematic application of the theorem of the kinetic analogue to the problem was worked out by W. Hess, *Math. Ann.*, Bd. 25 (1885). Numerous special cases were discussed by L. Saalschütz, *Der belastete Stab*, Leipzig, 1880.

The shape of the curve, called the *elastica*, into which the central-line is bent, is to be determined by means of equation (7). The results take different forms according as there are, or are not, inflexions. At an inflexion $d\theta/ds$ vanishes, and the flexural couple vanishes, so that the rod can be held in the form of an *inflexional elastica* by terminal force alone, without couple. The end points are then inflexions, and it is clear that all the inflexions lie on the line of action of the terminal force R—the *line of thrust*. The kinetic analogue of an inflexional elastica is an *oscillating pendulum*. Since the interval of time between two instants when the pendulum is momentarily at rest is a constant, equal to half the period of oscillation, the inflexions are spaced equally along the central-line of the rod. To hold the rod with its central-line in the form of a *non-inflexional elastica* terminal couples are required as well as terminal forces. The kinetic analogue is a *revolving pendulum*. In the particular case where there are no terminal forces the rod is bent into an arc of a circle. The kinetic analogue in this case is a rigid body revolving about a horizontal axis which passes through its centre of gravity.

If the central-line of the rod, in the unstressed state, is a circle, and there is no initial twist, the kinetic analogue (Article 261) is a pendulum on the axis of which a flywheel is symmetrically mounted. The motion of the pendulum is independent of that of the flywheel, and in like manner the possible figures of the central-line of the rod when further bent by terminal forces and couples are the same as for a naturally straight rod. The magnitude of the terminal couple alone is altered owing to the initial curvature.

263. Classification of the forms of the elastica.

(*a*) *Inflexional elastica.*

Let s be measured from an inflexion, and let a be the value of θ at the inflexion $s=0$. We write equation (7) in the form

$$\tfrac{1}{2}B\left(\frac{d\theta}{ds}\right)^2+R(\cos a-\cos\theta)=0. \qquad\text{.............................(9)}$$

To integrate it we introduce Jacobian elliptic functions of an argument u with a modulus k which are given by the equations

$$u=s\sqrt{(R/B)},\quad k=\sin\tfrac{1}{2}a. \qquad\text{.................................(10)}$$

Then we have

$$\frac{d\theta}{du}=2k\,\mathrm{cn}\,(u+K),\quad \sin\tfrac{1}{2}\theta=k\,\mathrm{sn}\,(u+K), \qquad\text{........................(11)}$$

where K is the real quarter period of the elliptic functions. To determine the shape of the curve, let x, y be the coordinates of a point referred to fixed axes, of which the axis of x coincides with the line of thrust. Then we have the equations

$$d\mathrm{x}/ds=\cos\theta,\quad d\mathrm{y}/ds=\sin\theta,$$

and these equations give

$$\left.\begin{aligned}\mathrm{x}&=\sqrt{\left(\frac{B}{R}\right)}\left[-u+2\{E\,\mathrm{am}\,(u+K)-E\,\mathrm{am}\,K\}\right],\\ \mathrm{y}&=-2k\sqrt{\left(\frac{B}{R}\right)}\,\mathrm{cn}\,(u+K),\end{aligned}\right\} \qquad\text{..................(12)}$$

where $E\,\mathrm{am}\,u$ denotes the elliptic integral of the second kind expressed by the formula

$$E\,\mathrm{am}\,u=\int_0^u \mathrm{dn}^2 u\,du,$$

and the constants of integration have been determined so that x and y may vanish with s. The inflexions are given by $\cos\theta=\cos\alpha$, or $\mathrm{sn}^2(u+K)=1$, and therefore the arc between two consecutive inflexions is $2\sqrt{(B/R)}\,.\,K$, and the inflexions are spaced equally along the axis of x at intervals

$$2\sqrt{(B/R)}\,(2E\,\mathrm{am}\,K-K).$$

The points at which the tangents are parallel to the line of thrust are given by $\sin\theta=0$, or $\mathrm{sn}(u+K)\,\mathrm{dn}(u+K)=0$, so that u is an uneven multiple of K. It follows that the curve forms a series of *bays*, separated by points of inflexion and divided into equal *half-bays* by the points at which the tangents are parallel to the line of thrust.

The change of the form of the curve as the angle α increases is shown by Figs. 48—55 overleaf. When $\alpha>\frac{1}{2}\pi$, x is negative for small values of u, and has its numerically greatest negative value when u has the smallest positive value which satisfies the equation $\mathrm{dn}^2(u+K)=\frac{1}{2}$. Let u_1 denote this value. The value of u for which x vanishes is given by the equation $u=2\{E\,\mathrm{am}(u+K)-E\,\mathrm{am}\,K\}$. When u exceeds this value, x is positive, and x has a maximum value when $u=2K-u_1$. Figs. 50—52 illustrate cases in which x_K is respectively greater than, equal to, and less than $|\mathrm{x}_{u_1}|$. Fig. 53 shows the case in which $\mathrm{x}_K=0$ or $2E\,\mathrm{am}\,K=K$. This happens when $\alpha=130°$ approximately. In this case all the double points and inflexions coincide at the origin, and the curve may consist of several exactly equal and similar pieces lying one over another. Fig. 54 shows a case in which $2E\,\mathrm{am}\,K<K$, or $\mathrm{x}_K<0$; the curve proceeds in the negative direction of the axis of x. The limiting case of this, when $\alpha=\pi$, is shown in Fig. 55, in which the rod (of infinite length) forms a single loop, and the pendulum of the kinetic analogue starts close to the position of unstable equilibrium and just makes one complete revolution.

(b) *Non-inflexional elastica.*

When there are no inflexions we write equation (7) in the form

$$\tfrac{1}{2}B\left(\frac{d\theta}{ds}\right)^2=R\cos\theta+R\left(1+2\frac{1-k^2}{k^2}\right), \quad\text{.......................(13)}$$

where k is less than unity, and we introduce Jacobian elliptic functions of modulus k and argument u, where

$$u=k^{-1}s\sqrt{(R/B)}. \quad\text{.......................................(14)}$$

We measure s from a point at which θ vanishes. Then we have

$$\frac{d\theta}{ds}=\frac{2}{k}\sqrt{\left(\frac{R}{B}\right)}\,\mathrm{dn}\,u,\quad \sin\tfrac{1}{2}\theta=\mathrm{sn}\,u, \quad\text{..........................(15)}$$

and the coordinates x and y are expressed in terms of u by the equations

$$\left.\begin{aligned}\mathrm{x}&=k\sqrt{\left(\frac{B}{R}\right)}\left[\left(1-\frac{2}{k^2}\right)u+\frac{2}{k^2}E\,\mathrm{am}\,u\right],\\ \mathrm{y}&=-\frac{2}{k}\sqrt{\left(\frac{B}{R}\right)}\,\mathrm{dn}\,u,\end{aligned}\right\}\quad\text{.......................(16)}$$

in which the constants of integration are chosen so that x vanishes with s, and the axis of x is parallel to the line of action of R, and at such a distance from it that the force R and

Fig. 48.

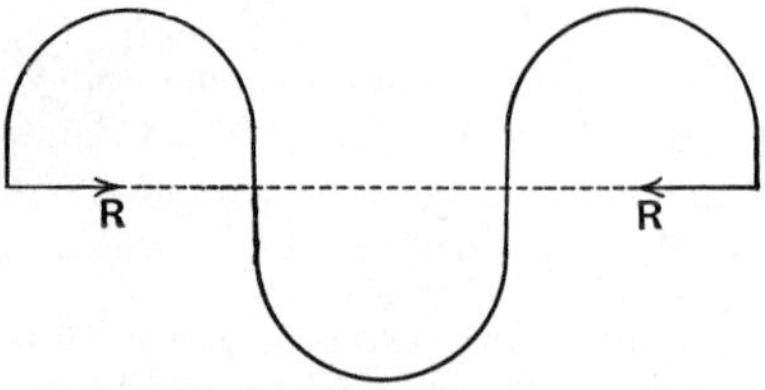

Fig. 49.

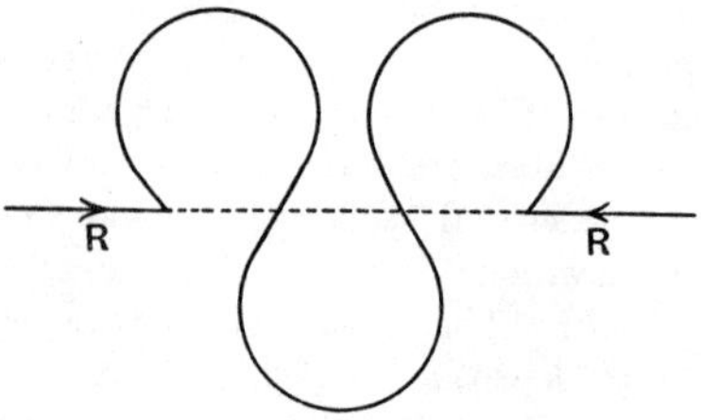

Fig. 50.

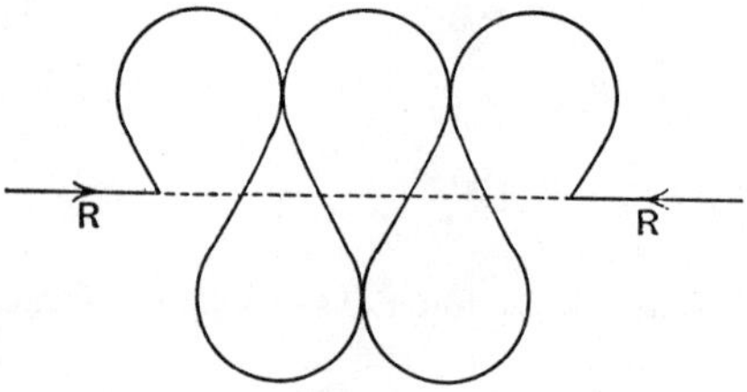

Fig. 51.

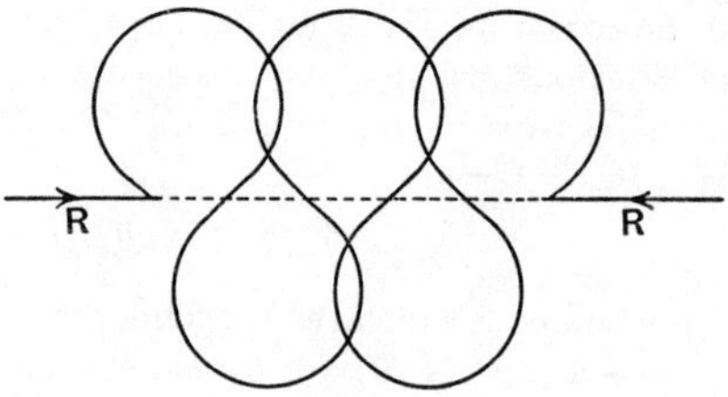

Fig. 52.

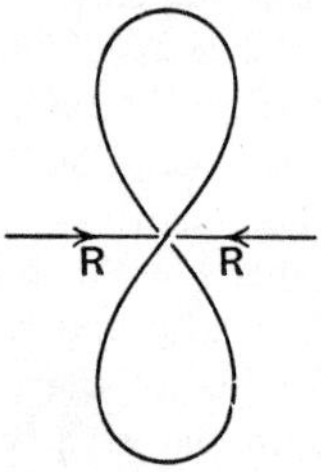

Fig. 53.

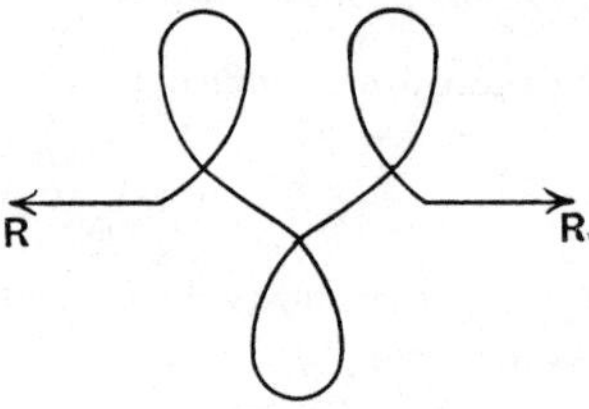

Fig. 54.

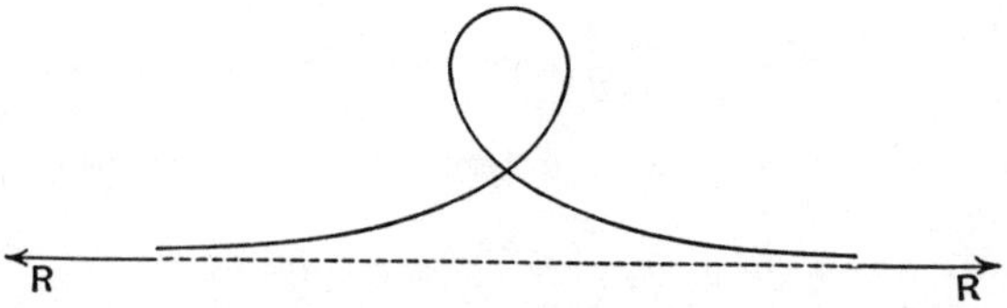

Fig. 55.

the couple $-B(d\theta/ds)$ which must be applied at the ends of the rod are statically equivalent to a force R acting along the axis of x. The curve consists of a series of loops lying altogether on one side of this axis. The form of the curve is shown in Fig. 56.

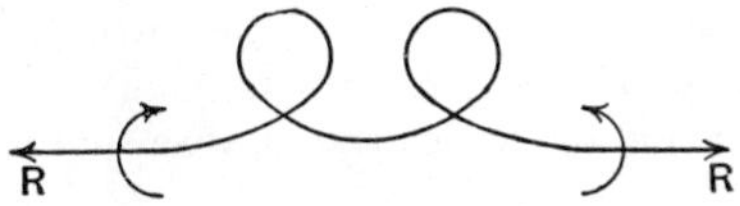

Fig. 56.

264. Buckling of long thin strut under thrust*.

The limiting form of the *elastica* when α is very small is obtained by writing θ for $\sin\theta$ in equation (8). We have then, as first approximations,

$$\theta = \alpha \cos\{s\sqrt{(R/B)}\}, \quad x = s, \quad y = \alpha\sqrt{(B/R)}\sin\{x\sqrt{(R/B)}\}, \quad \text{...(17)}$$

so that the curve is approximately a curve of sines of small amplitude. The distance between two consecutive inflexions is $\pi\sqrt{(B/R)}$. It appears therefore that a long straight rod can be bent by forces applied at its ends in a direction parallel to that of the rod when unstressed, provided that the length l and the force R are connected by the inequality

$$l^2 R > \pi^2 B. \quad \text{.................................(18)}$$

If the direction of the rod at one end is constrained to be the same as that of the force, the length is half that between consecutive inflexions, and the inequality (18) becomes

$$l^2 R > \tfrac{1}{4}\pi^2 B. \quad \text{.............................(19)}$$

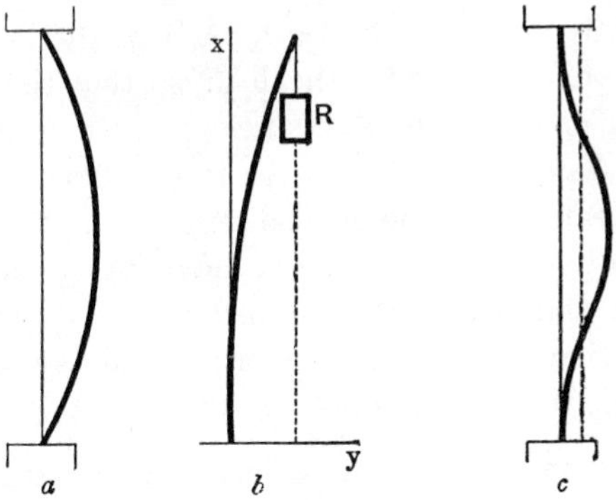

Fig. 57.

If the ends of the rod are constrained to remain in the same straight line, the length is twice that between consecutive inflexions, and the inequality (18) becomes

$$l^2 R > 4\pi^2 B. \quad \text{.................................(20)}$$

These three cases are illustrated in Fig. 57.

* The theory was initiated by Euler. See Introduction, p. 3.

Any of these results can be obtained very easily without having recourse to the general theory of the *elastica*. We take the second case, and suppose that a long thin rod is set up vertically and loaded at the top with a weight R, while the lower end is constrained to remain vertical*. Let the axes of x and y be the vertical line drawn upwards through the lowest point and a horizontal line drawn through the same point in the plane of bending, as shown in Fig. 57 *b*. If the rod is very slightly bent, the equation of equilibrium of the portion between any section and the loaded end is, with sufficient approximation,

$$-B\frac{d^2y}{dx^2}+R(y_1-y)=0,$$

where y_1 is the displacement of the loaded end. The solution of this equation which satisfies the conditions that y vanishes with x, and that $y=y_1$ when $x=l$, is

$$y=y_1\left[1-\frac{\sin\{(l-x)\sqrt{(R/B)}\}}{\sin\{l\sqrt{(R/B)}\}}\right],$$

and this solution makes dy/dx vanish with x if $\cos\{l\sqrt{(R/B)}\}=0$. Hence the least value of l by which the conditions can be satisfied is $\frac{1}{2}\pi\sqrt{(B/R)}$.

It should be noted that, in the approximate theory here explained, there occurs an indeterminate quantity, a or y_1, and the approximate theory cannot be made to yield the value of this quantity. For example it cannot be made to determine the terminal deflexion in the problem illustrated in Fig. 57 *b*†. The theory of the *elastica* leads easily to the result that, when this deflexion is small compared with l, its amount is

$$4\left\{\frac{2l}{\pi}-\left(\frac{B}{R}\right)^{\frac{1}{2}}\right\}^{\frac{1}{2}}\left(\frac{B}{R}\right)^{\frac{1}{4}}.$$

This remark does not invalidate the statement that, when a is small, the *elastica* is nearly identical with a curve of sines. As a matter of fact, if the distance between consecutive inflexions and the maximum ordinates of a curve of sines and an *elastica* are the same, and the maximum ordinate is small compared with the distance between consecutive inflexions, the curves coincide to a high order of approximation.

From the above we conclude that, in the case represented by Fig. 57 *b*, if the length is slightly greater than $\frac{1}{2}\pi\sqrt{(B/R)}$, or the load is slightly greater than $\frac{1}{4}\pi^2B/l^2$, the rod bends under the load, so that the central-line assumes the form of one half-bay of a curve of sines of small amplitude. If the length of the rod is less than the critical length it simply contracts under the load. If the length is greater than the critical length, and the load is truly central while the rod is truly cylindrical, the rod may simply contract; but the equilibrium of the rod thus contracted is *unstable*. To verify this it is merely necessary to show that the potential energy of the system in a bent state is less than that in the contracted state.

265. Computation of the strain-energy of the strut.

Let the length l be slightly greater than $\frac{1}{2}\pi\sqrt{(B/R)}$. Let ω denote the area of the cross-section of the rod, and E the Young's modulus of the material. If the rod simply contracts, the amount of the contraction is $R/E\omega$, the loaded end descends through a distance $Rl/E\omega$, and the loss of potential energy on this account is $R^2l/E\omega$. The potential energy of contraction is $\frac{1}{2}R^2l/E\omega$. The potential energy lost in the passage from the unstressed state to the simply contracted state is, therefore, $\frac{1}{2}R^2l/E\omega$.

* We neglect the weight of the rod. The problem of the bending of a vertical rod under its own weight will be considered in Article 276.

† Cf. R. W. Burgess, *Phys. Rev.*, March, 1917.

If the rod is of sufficient length to be deformed into one half-bay of a curve of the *elastica* family we may show that the loss of energy incurred in passing from the unstressed state to the bent state exceeds that incurred in passing from the unstressed state to the simply contracted state. The deformed rod is, of course, contracted as well as bent, and the amount of the contraction at any point is $(R\cos\theta)/E\omega$. The length of the deformed rod being denoted by l', we have

$$l'=\int_0^{l'} ds, \qquad l=\int_0^{l'}\left(1+\frac{R\cos\theta}{E\omega}\right)ds,$$

so that

$$l'=K\sqrt{\left(\frac{B}{R}\right)}, \qquad l=l'\left[1+\frac{R}{E\omega}\left\{\frac{2E\,\mathrm{am}\,K}{K}-1\right\}\right]. \quad\text{...............(21)}$$

Here K is the real quarter-period of elliptic functions of modulus $\sin\frac{1}{2}a$, $(=k)$, and a is the small angle which the central-line of the rod at the loaded end makes with the line of action of the load.

The potential energy lost through the descent of the load is $R\left(l-\int_0^{l'}\cos\theta\,ds\right)$. The potential energy of bending is $\frac{1}{2}B\int_0^{l'}(d\theta/ds)^2\,ds$, or $R\int_0^{l'}(\cos\theta-\cos a)\,ds$. The potential energy of contraction is $\frac{1}{2}E\omega\int_0^{l'}(R\cos\theta/E\omega)^2\,ds$ or $\frac{1}{2}(R^2/E\omega)\left(l'-\int_0^{l'}\sin^2\theta\,ds\right)$. Hence the loss of potential energy incurred in passing from the unstressed state to the bent state is

$$R\left\{l+l'\cos a-2\int_0^{l'}\cos\theta\,ds\right\}-\frac{1}{2}\frac{R^2}{E\omega}\left\{l'-\int_0^{l'}\sin^2\theta\,ds\right\},$$

and the excess of the potential energy in the simply contracted state above that in the bent state is

$$R\left\{l+l'\cos a-2\int_0^{l'}\cos\theta\,ds\right\}-\frac{1}{2}\frac{R^2}{E\omega}\left\{l+l'-\int_0^{l'}\sin^2\theta\,ds\right\}.$$

In the terms of this expression which contain the factor $R^2/E\omega$, we may identify l with l', because these terms are already small of the second order in the strain-components. Hence the expression may be written

$$R\left(l+l'\cos a-2\int_0^{l'}\cos\theta\,ds\right)-\frac{R^2}{E\omega}\left(l'-\frac{1}{2}\int_0^{l'}\sin^2\theta\,ds\right). \quad\text{...............(22)}$$

To evaluate this expression we have the results expressed by (21) and the result

$$\int_0^{l'}\cos\theta\,ds=l'\left(\frac{2E\,\mathrm{am}\,K}{K}-1\right),$$

and we require the value of $\int_0^{l'}\sin^2\theta\,ds$.

Now $$\sin^2\theta=4k^2\,\mathrm{sn}^2(u+K)\,\mathrm{dn}^2(u+K)=4k^2k'^2(\mathrm{cn}^2u/\mathrm{dn}^4u),$$

and $$\int_0^{l'}\sin^2\theta\,ds=4\sqrt{\left(\frac{B}{R}\right)}\int_0^K\left(\frac{k'^2}{\mathrm{dn}^2u}-\frac{k'^4}{\mathrm{dn}^4u}\right)du.$$

Also $$\int\frac{du}{\mathrm{dn}^4u}=-\frac{k^2}{3k'^2}\frac{\mathrm{sn}\,u\,\mathrm{cn}\,u}{\mathrm{dn}^3u}+\frac{2(1+k'^2)}{3k'^2}\int\frac{du}{\mathrm{dn}^2u}-\frac{u}{3k'^2},$$

and $$\int\frac{du}{\mathrm{dn}^2u}=-\frac{k^2}{k'^2}\frac{\mathrm{sn}\,u\,\mathrm{cn}\,u}{\mathrm{dn}\,u}+\frac{1}{k'^2}\int\mathrm{dn}^2u\,.\,du.$$

Hence $$\int_0^{l'}\sin^2\theta\,ds=\tfrac{4}{3}l'\{1-k^2-(1-2k^2)(E\,\mathrm{am}\,K)/K\}.$$

The expression (22) can now be evaluated in the form

$$Rl'\left\{1+\frac{R}{E\omega}\left(\frac{2E\,\mathrm{am}\,K}{K}-1\right)+1-2k^2-2\left(\frac{2E\,\mathrm{am}\,K}{K}-1\right)\right\}$$
$$-\frac{R^2l'}{E\omega}\left[1-\tfrac{2}{3}\left\{1-k^2-(1-2k^2)\frac{E\,\mathrm{am}\,K}{K}\right\}\right].$$

To determine the sign of this expression we expand the functions of k which occur as far as terms in k^4. We have

$$K=\tfrac{1}{2}\pi(1+\tfrac{1}{4}k^2+\tfrac{9}{64}k^4),\quad E\,\mathrm{am}\,K=\tfrac{1}{2}\pi(1-\tfrac{1}{4}k^2-\tfrac{3}{64}k^4),\quad (E\,\mathrm{am}\,K)/K=1-\tfrac{1}{2}k^2-\tfrac{1}{16}k^4,$$

and the expression becomes

$$\tfrac{1}{4}Rl'k^4(1-3R/E\omega),$$

which is certainly positive for any feasible value of $R/E\omega$*.

It will be observed that, if the rod is but slightly bent, l' is nearly equal to $l(1-R/E\omega)$, and the condition for the existence of an *elastica* satisfying the terminal conditions is

$$l'>\tfrac{1}{2}\pi\sqrt{(B/R)},$$

so that, in strictness, the condition (19) of Article 264 should be replaced by

$$l^2R>\tfrac{1}{4}\pi^2B(1+2R/E\omega),$$

l being the unstrained length of the strut. Conditions (18) and (20) should be modified in the same way. The correction is of no practical importance.

266. Resistance to buckling.

The strains developed in the rod, whether it is short and simply contracts or is long and bends, are supposed to be elastic strains, that is to say such as disappear on the removal of the load. For Euler's theory of the buckling of a long thin strut, explained in Article 264, to have any practical bearing, it is of course necessary that the load required, in accordance with inequalities such as (19), to produce bending should be less than that which would produce set by crushing. This condition is not satisfied unless the length of the strut is great compared with the linear dimensions of the cross-section. In view of the lack of precise information as to the conditions of safety in general (Chapter IV) and of failure by crushing (Article 189), a precise estimate of the smallest ratio of length to diameter for which this condition would be satisfied is not to be expected.

The practical question of the conditions of failure by buckling of a rod or strut under thrust involves some other considerations. When the thrust is not truly central, or its direction not precisely that of the rod, the longitudinal thrust is accompanied by a bending couple or a transverse load. The contraction produced by the thrust R is $R/E\omega$. When the thrust is not truly central, the bending moment is of the order Rc, where c is some linear dimension of the cross-section, and the extension of a longitudinal filament due to the bending moment is of the order Rc^2/B, which may easily be two or three times as great, numerically, as the contraction $R/E\omega$. The bending moment may, therefore, produce failure by buckling under a load less than the crushing load. Again, when the line of thrust makes a small angle β with the central-line, the transverse load $R\sin\beta$ yields, at a distance comparable with the length l of the rod, a bending moment comparable with $lR\sin\beta$; and the

* For a correction of the analysis of this Article, as it appeared in the second edition, the Author is indebted to S. Timoschenko, 'Sur la stabilité des systèmes élastiques,' *Paris, Ann. des ponts et chaussées*, 1913, p. 17.

extension of a longitudinal filament due to this bending moment is comparable with $lRc \sin \beta/B$. Thus even a slight deviation of the direction of the load from the central-line may produce failure by buckling in a fairly long strut. Such causes of failure as are here considered can best be discussed by means of Saint-Venant's theory of bending (Chapter XV); but, for a reason already mentioned, a precise account of the conditions of failure owing to such causes is hardly to be expected.

It is clear that such considerations as are here advanced will be applicable to other cases of buckling besides that of the buckling of a rod under thrust. The necessity for them was emphasized by E. Lamarle*. His work has been discussed critically and appreciatively by K. Pearson†. In recent years the conditions of buckling have been the subject of considerable discussion‡.

267. Elastic stability.

The possibility of a straight form and a bent form with the same terminal load is not in conflict with the theorem of Article 118, because the thin rod can, without undergoing strains greater than are contemplated in the mathematical theory of Elasticity, be deformed in such a way that the relative displacements of its parts are not small§.

The theory of the stability of elastic systems, exemplified in the discussion in Articles 264, 265, may be brought into connexion with Poincaré's theory of "equilibrium of bifurcation‖." The form of the rod is determined by the extension ϵ at the loaded end and the total curvature α; and these quantities depend upon the load R, the length l and flexural rigidity B being regarded as constants. We might represent the state of the rod by a point, determined by the coordinates ϵ and α, and, as R varies, the point would describe a curve. When R is smaller than the critical load, α vanishes, and the equilibrium state, defined by ϵ as a function of R, is stable. When R exceeds the critical value, a possible state of equilibrium would still be given by $\alpha=0$; but there is another possible state of equilibrium in which α does not vanish, and in this state α and ϵ are determinate functions of R, so that the equilibrium states for varying values of R are represented by points of a certain curve. This curve issues from that point of the line $\alpha=0$ which represents the extension, or rather contraction, under the critical load. Poincaré describes such a point

* 'Mém. sur la flexion du bois,' *Ann. des travaux publics de Belgique*, t. 4 (1846).

† Todhunter and Pearson's *History*, vol. 1, pp. 678 *et seq.*

‡ Reference may be made to the writings of J. Kübler, C. J. Kriemler, L. Prandtl in *Zeitschr. d. Deutschen Ingenieure*, Bd. 44 (1900), of Kübler and Kriemler in *Zeitschr. f. Math. u. Phys.*, Bde. 45–47 (1900–1902), and the dissertation by Kriemler, 'Labile u. stabile Gleichgewichtsfiguren...auf Biegung beanspruchter Stäbe...' (Karlsruhe, 1902), also to the paper by Timoschenko cited in Article 265, to that by Southwell to be cited in Article 267 A, and to two papers by H. Zimmermann, *Berlin Sitzungsberichte*, 1921, pp. 775 and 884.

§ Cf. G. H. Bryan, *Cambridge Phil. Soc. Proc.*, vol. 6 (1888).

‖ *Acta Mathematica*, t. 7 (1885).

as a "point of bifurcation," and he shows that, in general, there is an "exchange of stabilities" at such a point, that is to say, in the present example, the states represented by points on the line $\alpha = 0$, at which ϵ numerically exceeds the extension under the critical load, are unstable, and the stability is transferred to states represented by points on the curve in which $\alpha \neq 0$.

267 A. Southwell's method.

Another method of investigating problems of elastic stability has been proposed by R. V. Southwell*. We may most conveniently explain this method in its application to the problem of Article 264, and especially the case illustrated in Fig. 57 *b*. Similar principles are involved in any other application of the method, and other examples will be found in Chapters XXIV and XXIV A.

We consider the series of configurations in which the rod can be held by gradually increasing R. For very small values of R the rod is simply contracted. We suppose the contracted rod with given R to suffer a very small displacement, by which it becomes slightly bent. If the value of R is such that the slightly bent state can be maintained without altering R, the equilibrium in the contracted state is critical, and any further increase in R results in buckling. The point emphasized by Southwell is that the superior limit to the values of R consistent with stability, and the accompanying contraction, are relatively considerable. It follows that the simplified methods of Article 258 A do not avail without modification to determine the small transverse displacement which can occur if R slightly exceeds this limit. The necessary modification will appear in what follows.

Let s_1 denote the contracted length of a portion of the rod measured from the lower end, and, as in Article 258 A, let u, v, w, β specify the displacement of the rod from the simply contracted state. Let T_0 denote the tension in the simply contracted state, and let the value of T in the bent state be expressed as $T_0 + T'$. Then the component curvatures and the twist in this state are given by the equations

$$\kappa = -\frac{d^2v}{ds_1^2}, \quad \kappa' = \frac{d^2u}{ds_1^2}, \quad \tau = \frac{d\beta}{ds_1}. \qquad \text{..................(23)}$$

We omit terms of the second order in u, v, w, β. Then equations (11) of Article 254 become

$$-A\frac{d^3v}{ds_1^3} - N' = 0, \quad B\frac{d^3u}{ds_1^3} + N = 0, \quad C\frac{d^2\beta}{ds_1^2} = 0,$$

and equations (10) of the same Article become

$$-B\frac{d^4u}{ds_1^4} + T_0\frac{d^2u}{ds_1^2} = 0, \quad -A\frac{d^4v}{ds_1^4} + T_0\frac{d^2v}{ds_1^2} = 0, \quad \frac{dT'}{ds} = 0.$$

* 'On the general theory of elastic stability,' *Phil. Trans. Roy. Soc.* (Ser. A), vol. 213 (1913), p. 187.

The terminal conditions at the lower end ($s_1=0$) are

$$u=0,\quad v=0,\quad \beta=0,\quad \frac{du}{ds_1}=0,\quad \frac{dv}{ds_1}=0.$$

The terminal conditions at the upper end ($s_1=l_1$) are

$$G=0,\quad G'=0,\quad H=0,\quad N-T_0\frac{du}{ds_1}=0,\quad N'-T_0\frac{dv}{ds_1}=0,\quad T_0+T'=-R.$$

Now $T_0=-R$, and we have therefore $T'=0$. Also we see that we must have $\beta=0$. The most general possible form for u is

$$A_1\cos\{\sqrt{(R/B)}\,s_1\}+B_1\sin\{\sqrt{(R/B)}\,s_1\}+C_1 s_1+D_1,$$

where A_1, B_1, C_1, D_1 are constants. The terminal conditions require

$$B_1=0,\quad C_1=0,\quad D_1=-A_1,\quad \cos\{\sqrt{(R/B)}\,l_1\}=0.$$

Similar considerations apply to v, and the condition that the equilibrium may be critical is the same as that previously obtained.

268. Stability of inflexional elastica.

When the lower end of the loaded rod is constrained to remain vertical, and the length l slightly exceeds $\frac{3}{2}\pi\sqrt{(B/R)}$, a possible form of the central-line is a curve of sines of small amplitude having two inflexions, as in Fig. 58 *b* overleaf. Another possible form is an *elastica* illustrated in Fig. 58 *c*. In general, if n is an integer such that

$$\tfrac{1}{2}(2n+1)\pi>l\sqrt{(R/B)}>\tfrac{1}{2}(2n-1)\pi, \quad\text{.........................(24)}$$

n forms besides the unstable straight form are possible, and they consist respectively of 1, 3, ... $2n-1$ half-bays of different curves of the *elastica* family. The forms of these curves are given respectively by the equations

$$K=l\sqrt{(R/B)}\times[1,\ \tfrac{1}{3},\ \ldots,\ 1/(2n-1)]. \quad\text{...........................(25)}$$

We shall show that all these forms except that with the greatest K, that is the smallest number of inflexions, are unstable*.

Omitting the practically unimportant potential energy due to extension or contraction of the central-line, we may estimate the loss of potential energy in passing from the unstressed state to the bent state in which there are $r+1$ inflexions, in the same way as in Article 265, as

$$R\left[l(1+\cos\alpha)-2\int_0^l\cos\theta\,ds\right], \quad\text{...............................(26)}$$

and this is $$(2r+1)\sqrt{(BR)}\,(4K_r-4E_r-2K_rk_r^2), \quad\text{..........................(27)}$$

where E_r is written for $E\,\mathrm{am}\,K_r$, and the suffix r indicates the number $(r+1)$ of inflexions. We compare the potential energies of the forms with $r+1$ and $s+1$ inflexions, s being greater than r. Since

$$(2r+1)K_r=(2s+1)K_s, \quad\text{...................................(28)}$$

the potential energy in the form with $s+1$ inflexions is the greater if

$$(2s+1)(2E_s+K_sk_s^2)>(2r+1)(2E_r+K_rk_r^2).$$

* The result is opposed to that of L. Saalschütz, *Der belastete Stab* (Leipzig, 1880), but I do not think that his argument is quite convincing. The result stated in the text agrees with that obtained by a different method by J. Larmor, *loc. cit.*, p. 400. It is supported also by the investigation of M. Born, 'Untersuchungen ü. d. Stabilität d. elastischen Linie in Ebene u. Raum, unter verschiedenen Grenzbedingungen' (*Diss.*), Göttingen, 1906.

Since
$$E \operatorname{am} K = (1-k^2)\left(K + k\frac{dK}{dk}\right),$$
this condition is
$$(1-k_s^2)\left(1+\frac{2k_s}{K_s}\frac{dK_s}{dk_s}\right) > (1-k_r^2)\left(1+\frac{2k_r}{K_r}\frac{dK_r}{dk_r}\right). \quad \text{.................(29)}$$
But, since
$$\frac{d}{dk}\left\{(1-k^2)\left(1+\frac{2k}{K}\frac{dK}{dk}\right)\right\} = -\frac{2k(1-k^2)}{K}\left(\frac{dK}{dk}\right)^2,$$
it follows that $(1-k^2)\left(1+\frac{2k}{K}\frac{dK}{dk}\right)$ diminishes as k increases. Now when $s>r$, $K_s<K_r$, and $k_s<k_r$; and therefore the inequality (29) is satisfied.

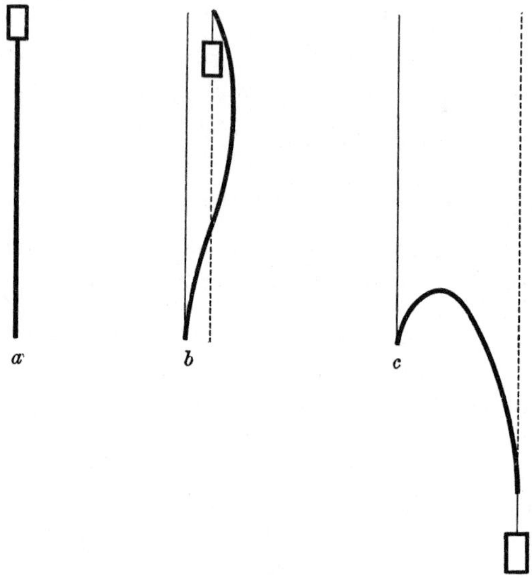

Fig. 58.

In the case illustrated in Fig. 58 the three possible forms are (*a*) the unstable straight form, (*b*) the slightly bent form with two inflexions, (*c*) the bent form with one inflexion. The angle a for the form (*c*) is given by $K=\frac{3}{2}\pi$, and it lies between 175° and 176°.

It may be observed that the conclusion that the stable form is that with a single inflexion is not in conflict with Poincaré's theory of the exchange of stabilities at a point of bifurcation, because the loci, in the domain of ϵ and a, which represent forms with two or more inflexions, do not issue from the locus which represents forms with one inflexion, but from the locus $a=0$, which represents straight forms.

The instability of forms of the elastica with more than the smallest possible number of inflexions between the ends is well known as an experimental fact. Any particular case can be investigated in the same way as the special case discussed above, in which the tangent at one end is, owing to constraint, parallel to the line of thrust. An investigation of this kind cannot, however, decide the question whether any particular form is stable or unstable for displacements in which the central-line is moved out of its plane. This question has not been solved completely. One special case of it will be considered in Article 272 (*e*). Other cases are considered by M. Born, *loc. cit.*, p. 411.

269. Rod bent and twisted by terminal forces and couples.

We resume now the general problem of Article 260, and express the directions of the principal torsion-flexure axes at any point P_1 on the strained central-line by means of the angles θ, ψ, ϕ defined in Article 253. We choose as the fixed direction $P_1 z$ in Fig. 46 of that Article the direction of the force applied to the rod at the end towards which s is measured. The stress-resultants N, N', T are equivalent to a force R in this direction, and therefore

$$(N, N', T) = R(-\sin\theta\cos\phi,\ \sin\theta\sin\phi,\ \cos\theta). \quad\text{.........(30)}$$

Equation (3) of Article 260 becomes

$$\tfrac{1}{2}(A\kappa^2 + B\kappa'^2 + C\tau^2) + R\cos\theta = \text{const.} \quad\text{..............(31)}$$

Since the forces applied at the ends of the rod have no moment about the line $P_1 z$, the sum of the components of the stress-couples about a line drawn through the centroid of any section parallel to this line is equal to the corresponding sum for that terminal section towards which s is measured. We have therefore the equation

$$-A\kappa\sin\theta\cos\phi + B\kappa'\sin\theta\sin\phi + C\tau\cos\theta = \text{const.} \quad\text{......(32)}$$

The analogue of this equation in the problem of the top expresses the constancy of the moment of momentum of the top about a vertical axis drawn through the fixed point.

The equations (31) and (32) are two integrals of the equations (2) of Article 260, and, if a third integral could be obtained, $d\theta/ds$, $d\psi/ds$, $d\phi/ds$ would be expressible in terms of θ, ψ, ϕ, and the possible forms in which the rod could be held might be found. In the general case no third integral is known; but, when the two flexural rigidities A and B are equal, the third of these equations yields at once the integral

$$\tau = \text{const.} \quad\text{..............................(33)}$$

The quantities κ, κ', τ are expressed in terms of θ, ψ, ϕ, $d\theta/ds, \ldots$ by equations (8) of Article 253, and the equations (31), (32), (33) can be integrated* so as to express θ, ψ, ϕ as functions of s, and then the form of the central-line is to be determined by means of the equations

$$\frac{dx}{ds} = \sin\theta\cos\psi, \quad \frac{dy}{ds} = \sin\theta\sin\psi, \quad \frac{dz}{ds} = \cos\theta,$$

where x, y, z are coordinates referred to fixed axes.

We shall not proceed with this general theory, but shall consider some important special cases.

* See F. Klein u. A. Sommerfeld, *Theorie des Kreisels*, Heft 2, Leipzig, 1898, or E. T. Whittaker, *Analytical Dynamics*, Cambridge, 1904.

270. Rod bent to helical form*

The *steady motion* of a symmetrical top, with its axis of figure inclined at a constant angle $\frac{1}{2}\pi - \alpha$ to the vertical drawn upwards, is the analogue of a certain configuration of a bent and twisted rod for which $A = B$. Putting $\theta = \frac{1}{2}\pi - \alpha$, and $d\theta/ds = 0$, we have, by (8) of Article 253,

$$\kappa = -\frac{d\psi}{ds}\cos\alpha\cos\phi, \quad \kappa' = \frac{d\psi}{ds}\cos\alpha\sin\phi, \quad \tau = \frac{d\phi}{ds} + \sin\alpha\frac{d\psi}{ds},$$

and, by (31), (32), (33) of Article 269,

$$\tau = \text{const.}, \quad \kappa^2 + \kappa'^2 = \text{const.}, \quad d\psi/ds = \text{const.}$$

The curvature of the central-line is constant and equal to $\cos\alpha\,(d\psi/ds)$, and the binormal of this curve lies in the plane of (x, y) and makes an angle ϕ with the axis of x reversed. It follows that ϕ is identical with the angle denoted by f in Article 253, and that the measure of tortuosity of the curve is $\sin\alpha\,(d\psi/ds)$. Since the central-line is a curve of constant curvature and tortuosity, it is a *helix traced on a right circular cylinder*. The axis of the helix is parallel to the line of action of R, and α is the angle which the tangent at any point of the helix makes with a plane at right angles to this axis.

Let r be the radius of the cylinder on which the helix lies. Then the curvature $1/\rho$ and the measure of tortuosity $1/\Sigma$ are given by the equations

$$1/\rho = \cos^2\alpha/r, \quad 1/\Sigma = \sin\alpha\cos\alpha/r, \quad \text{..................(34)}$$

and we may write

$$\kappa = -\cos\phi\cos^2\alpha/r, \quad \kappa' = \sin\phi\cos^2\alpha/r, \quad d\psi/ds = \cos\alpha/r, \quad d\phi/ds = \tau - \sin\alpha\cos\alpha/r. \quad \text{.........(35)}$$

From equations (2) of Article 260 we find

$$(N, N') = (-\cos\phi, \sin\phi)\,[C\tau\cos^2\alpha/r - B\sin\alpha\cos^3\alpha/r^2],$$

and then from equations (30) we find

$$R = C\tau\cos\alpha/r - B\sin\alpha\cos^2\alpha/r^2. \quad \text{.........(36)}$$

The terminal force is of the nature of tension or pressure according as the right-hand member of (36) is positive or negative. (See Fig. 59.) For the force to be of the nature of tension, τ must exceed $B\sin\alpha\cos\alpha/Cr$.

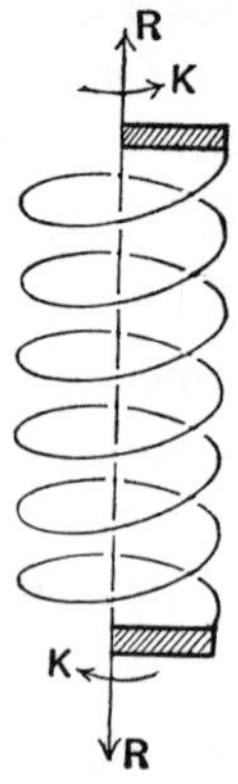

Fig. 59.

The axis of the terminal couple lies in the tangent plane of the cylinder at the end of the central-line, and the components of this couple about the binormal and tangent of the helix at this point are $B\cos^2\alpha/r$ and $C\tau$. The components of the same couple about the tangent of the circular section and the generator of the cylinder at the same point are, therefore, Rr and K, where K is given by the equation

$$K = C\tau\sin\alpha + B\cos^3\alpha/r. \quad \text{.....................(37)}$$

* Cf. Kirchhoff, *loc. cit.*, p. 381.

It follows that the rod can be held so that it has a given twist, and its central-line forms a given helix, by a wrench of which the force R and the couple K are given by equations (36) and (37), and the axis of the wrench is the axis of the helix. The force and couple of the wrench are applied to rigid pieces to which the ends of the rod are attached.

The helical form can be maintained by terminal force alone, without any couple; and then the force is of magnitude $B\cos^2\alpha/r^2\sin\alpha$, and acts as thrust along the axis of the helix. In this case there must be twist of amount $-B\cos^3\alpha/Cr\sin\alpha$. The form can be maintained also by terminal couple alone, without any force; and then the couple is of magnitude $B\cos\alpha/r$, and its axis is parallel to the axis of the helix. In this case there must be twist of amount $B\sin\alpha\cos\alpha/Cr$.

When the state of the rod is such that, if simply unbent, it would be prismatic, $d\phi/ds$ vanishes, and the twist of the rod is equal to the measure of tortuosity of the central-line (cf. Article 253). To hold the rod so that it has this twist, and the central-line is a given helix, a wrench about the axis of the helix is required; and the force R and couple K of the wrench are given by the equations

$$R=-(B-C)\sin\alpha\cos^2\alpha/r^2,\quad K=(B\cos^2\alpha+C\sin^2\alpha)\cos\alpha/r.$$

271. Theory of spiral springs*.

When the sections of the rod have kinetic symmetry, so that $A=B$, and the unstressed rod is helical with such initial twist that, if simply unbent, it would be prismatic, we may express the initial state by the formulæ

$$\kappa_0=0,\quad \kappa_0'=\cos^2\alpha/r,\quad \tau_0=\sin\alpha\cos\alpha/r. \quad \text{...........(38)}$$

By suitable terminal forces and couples the rod can be held in the state expressed by the formulæ

$$\kappa_1=0,\quad \kappa_1'=\cos^2\alpha_1/r_1,\quad \tau_1=\sin\alpha_1\cos\alpha_1/r_1, \quad \text{...........(39)}$$

where r_1, α_1 are the radius and angle of a new helix. The stress-couples at any section are then given by the equations

$$G=0,\quad G'=B\left(\frac{\cos^2\alpha_1}{r_1}-\frac{\cos^2\alpha}{r}\right),\quad H=C\left(\frac{\sin\alpha_1\cos\alpha_1}{r_1}-\frac{\sin\alpha\cos\alpha}{r}\right),$$

and the stress-resultants are given by the equations

$$N=0,\quad T=N'\tan\alpha_1,$$

$$N'=C\frac{\cos^2\alpha_1}{r_1}\left(\frac{\sin\alpha_1\cos\alpha_1}{r_1}-\frac{\sin\alpha\cos\alpha}{r}\right)-B\frac{\sin\alpha_1\cos\alpha_1}{r_1}\left(\frac{\cos^2\alpha_1}{r_1}-\frac{\cos^2\alpha}{r}\right).$$

All the equations of Article 259 are satisfied. The new configuration can be maintained by a wrench of which the axis is the axis of the helix, and the force R and couple K are given by the equations

$$\left.\begin{aligned}R&=C\frac{\cos\alpha_1}{r_1}\left(\frac{\sin\alpha_1\cos\alpha_1}{r_1}-\frac{\sin\alpha\cos\alpha}{r}\right)-B\frac{\sin\alpha_1}{r_1}\left(\frac{\cos^2\alpha_1}{r_1}-\frac{\cos^2\alpha}{r}\right),\\ K&=C\sin\alpha_1\left(\frac{\sin\alpha_1\cos\alpha_1}{r_1}-\frac{\sin\alpha\cos\alpha}{r}\right)+B\cos\alpha_1\left(\frac{\cos^2\alpha_1}{r_1}-\frac{\cos^2\alpha}{r}\right).\end{aligned}\right\}\ (40)$$

* Cf. Kelvin and Tait, *Nat. Phil.*, Part II., pp. 139 *et seq.*

The theory of spiral springs is founded on this result. We take the spring in the unstressed state to be determined by the equations (38), so that the central-line is a helix of angle α traced on a cylinder of radius r, and the principal normals and binormals in the various cross-sections are homologous lines of these sections. We take l to be the length of the spring, and h to be the length of its projection on the axis of the helix, then the cylindrical coordinates r, θ, z of one end being $r, 0, 0$, those of the other end are r, χ, h, where

$$\chi = (l\cos\alpha)/r, \quad h = l\sin\alpha. \quad \text{.....................(41)}$$

We suppose the spring to be deformed by a wrench about the axis of the helix, and take the force R and couple K of the wrench to be given. We shall suppose that the central-line of the strained spring becomes a helix of angle α_1 on a cylinder of radius r_1, and that the principal normals and binormals continue to be homologous lines in the cross-sections. Then R and K are expressed in terms of α_1 and r_1 by the equations (40). When the deformation is small we may write $r+\delta r$ and $\alpha+\delta\alpha$ for r_1 and α_1, and suppose that small changes $\delta\chi$ and δh are made in χ and h. We have

$$\delta h = (l\cos\alpha)\,\delta\alpha, \quad \delta\chi = -[(l\sin\alpha)/r]\,\delta\alpha - [(l\cos\alpha)/r^2]\,\delta r,$$

from which

$$\delta\alpha = (\delta h)/(l\cos\alpha), \quad \delta r/r^2 = -(\sin\alpha\,.\,\delta h + r\cos\alpha\,.\,\delta\chi)/(lr\cos^2\alpha).$$

Hence
$$\delta\frac{\sin\alpha\cos\alpha}{r} = -\sin\alpha\cos\alpha\frac{\delta r}{r^2} + \frac{\cos 2\alpha}{r}\delta\alpha$$
$$= \cos\alpha\frac{\delta h}{lr} + \sin\alpha\frac{\delta\chi}{l},$$

and
$$\delta\frac{\cos^2\alpha}{r} = -\cos^2\alpha\frac{\delta r}{r^2} - 2\sin\alpha\cos\alpha\frac{\delta\alpha}{r}$$
$$= \frac{\cos\alpha}{l}\delta\chi - \frac{\sin\alpha}{lr}\delta h.$$

It follows that the force R and the couple K are expressed in terms of $l, r, \alpha, \delta h, \delta\chi$ by the equations

$$\left.\begin{aligned} R &= \frac{1}{lr^2}[(C\cos^2\alpha + B\sin^2\alpha)\,\delta h + (C-B)\sin\alpha\cos\alpha\,.\,r\delta\chi], \\ K &= \frac{1}{lr}[(C-B)\sin\alpha\cos\alpha\,.\,\delta h + (C\sin^2\alpha + B\cos^2\alpha)\,r\delta\chi]. \end{aligned}\right\} \quad \text{...(42)}$$

If the spring is deformed by axial force alone*, without couple, the axial displacement δh and the angular displacement $\delta\chi$ are given by the equations

$$\delta h = lr^2\left(\frac{\sin^2\alpha}{B} + \frac{\cos^2\alpha}{C}\right)R, \quad \delta\chi = lr\sin\alpha\cos\alpha\left(\frac{1}{C} - \frac{1}{B}\right)R.$$

* The results for this case were found by Saint-Venant, *Paris, C. R.*, t. 17 (1843). A number of special cases are worked out by Kelvin and Tait, *loc. cit.*, and also by J. Perry, *Applied Mechanics* (London, 1899). The theory has been verified experimentally by J. W. Miller, *Phys. Rev.*, vol. 14 (1902). The vibrations of a spiral spring, supporting a weight so great that the inertia of the spring may be neglected, have been worked out in accordance with the above theory by L. R. Wilberforce, *Phil. Mag.* (Ser. 5), vol. 38 (1894).

If the cross-section of the spring is a circle of radius a, $1/C-1/B$ is $4\sigma/E\pi a^4$, where σ is Poisson's ratio and E is Young's modulus for the material. Hence both δh and $\delta\chi$ are positive. In the same case δr is negative, so that the spring is coiled more closely as it stretches.

272. Additional results.

(*a*) *Rod subjected to terminal couples.*

When a rod which is straight and prismatic in the unstressed state is held bent and twisted by terminal couples, the kinetic analogue is a rigid body moving under no forces. The analogue has been worked out in detail by W. Hess*. When the cross-section has kinetic symmetry so that $A=B$, the equations of equilibrium show that the twist τ and the curvature $(\kappa^2+\kappa'^2)^{\frac{1}{2}}$ are constants, and that, if we put as in Article 253

$$\tan f = -\kappa'/\kappa,$$

then

$$B\,(df/ds)=(B-C)\,\tau.$$

It follows that the measure of tortuosity of the central-line is $C\tau/B$, and, therefore, that this line is a helix traced on a circular cylinder. If we use Euler's angles θ, ψ, ϕ as in Article 253, and take the axis of the helix to be parallel to the axis of z in Fig. 46 of that Article, θ is constant, and $\frac{1}{2}\pi-\theta$ is the angle α of the helix. The axis of the terminal couple is the axis of the helix, and the magnitude of the couple is $B\cos\alpha/r$, as we found before, r being the radius of the cylinder on which the helix lies.

(*b*) *Straight rod with initial twist.*

When the rod in the unstressed state has twist τ_0 and no curvature, and the cross-section has kinetic symmetry so that $A=B$, the rod can be held bent so that its central-line has the form of a helix (α, r), and twisted so that the twist is τ_1, by a wrench about the axis of the helix; and the force R and couple K of the wrench are found by writing $\tau_1-\tau_0$ for τ in equations (36) and (37) of Article 270.

(*c*) *Rod bent into circular hoop and twisted uniformly.*

When the rod in the unstressed state is straight and prismatic, and the cross-section has kinetic symmetry, one of the forms in which it can be held by terminal forces and couples is that in which the central-line is a circle, and the twist is uniform along the length. The tension vanishes, and the shearing force at any section is directed towards the centre of the circle, and its amount is $C\tau/r$, where r is the radius of the circle.

(*d*) *Stability of rod subjected to twisting couple and thrust.*

When the rod, supposed to be straight and prismatic in the unstressed state, is held twisted, but without curvature, by terminal couples, these couples may be of such an amount as could hold the rod bent and twisted. If $A=B$ the central-line, if it is bent, must be a helix. When the couple K is just great enough to hold the rod bent without displacement of the ends, the central-line just forms one complete turn of the helix, the radius r of the helix is very small, and the angle α of the helix is very nearly equal to $\frac{1}{2}\pi$. We have the equations

$$K=C\tau=Br^{-1}\cos\alpha, \quad l\cos\alpha=2\pi r,$$

where τ is the twist, and l the length of the rod. Hence this configuration can be maintained if $2\pi/l=K/B$. We infer that, under a twisting couple which exceeds $2\pi B/l$, the straight twisted rod is unstable.

* *Math. Ann.*, Bd. 23 (1884).

This question of stability may be investigated in a more general manner by supposing that the rod is held by terminal thrust R and twisting couple K in a form in which the central-line is very nearly straight. The kinetic analogue is a symmetrical top which moves so that its axis remains nearly upright. The problem admits of a simple solution by the use of fixed axes of x, y, z, the axis of z coinciding with the axes of the applied couples and with the line of thrust. The central-line is near to this axis, and meets it at the ends. The twist τ is constant, and the torsional couple $C\tau$ can be equated to K with sufficient approximation. The flexural couple is of amount B/ρ, where ρ is the radius of curvature of the central-line, and its axis is the binormal of this curve. The direction-cosines of this binormal can be expressed in such forms as

$$\rho\left(\frac{dy}{ds}\frac{d^2z}{ds^2}-\frac{dz}{ds}\frac{d^2y}{ds^2}\right),$$

and therefore the components of the flexural couple at any section about axes parallel to the axes of x and y can be expressed with sufficient approximation in the forms

$$-B\frac{d^2y}{ds^2},\quad B\frac{d^2x}{ds^2}.$$

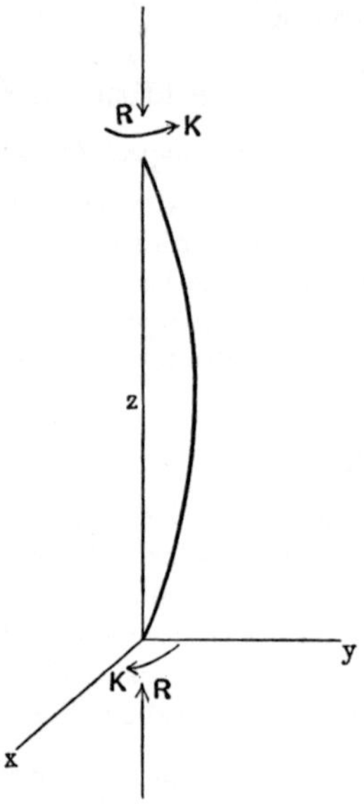

Fig. 60.

For the equilibrium of the part of the rod contained between this section and one end we take moments about axes drawn through the centroid of the section parallel to the axes of x and y, and we thus obtain the equations

$$\left.\begin{aligned}-B\frac{d^2y}{ds^2}+K\frac{dx}{ds}-yR=0,\\ B\frac{d^2x}{ds^2}+K\frac{dy}{ds}+xR=0.\end{aligned}\right\}\quad\text{.............................(43)}$$

The complete primitives are

$$x=L_1\sin(q_1s+\epsilon_1)+L_2\sin(q_2s+\epsilon_2),$$
$$y=L_1\cos(q_1s+\epsilon_1)+L_2\cos(q_2s+\epsilon_2),$$

where L_1, L_2, ϵ_1, ϵ_2 are arbitrary constants, and q_1, q_2 are the roots of the equation

$$Bq^2+Kq-R=0.$$

The terminal conditions are (i) that the coordinates x and y vanish at the ends $s=0$ and $s=l$, (ii) that the axis of the terminal couple coincides with the axis of z. The equations (43) show that the second set of conditions are satisfied if the first set are satisfied. We have therefore the equations

$$L_1\sin\epsilon_1+L_2\sin\epsilon_2=0,\qquad L_1\cos\epsilon_1+L_2\cos\epsilon_2=0,$$

and

$$L_1\sin(q_1l+\epsilon_1)+L_2\sin(q_2l+\epsilon_2)=0,\quad L_1\cos(q_1l+\epsilon_1)+L_2\cos(q_2l+\epsilon_2)=0.$$

On substituting for $L_2\cos\epsilon_2$ and $L_2\sin\epsilon_2$ from the first pair in the second pair, we find the equations

$$L_1\{\sin(q_1l+\epsilon_1)-\sin(q_2l+\epsilon_1)\}=0,\quad L_1\{\cos(q_1l+\epsilon_1)-\cos(q_2l+\epsilon_1)\}=0,$$

from which it follows that q_1l and q_2l differ by a multiple of 2π. The least length l by which the conditions can be satisfied is given by the equation

$$2\pi/l=|q_1-q_2|,$$

or

$$\frac{\pi^2}{l^2}=\frac{K^2}{4B^2}+\frac{R}{B}.$$

The rod subjected to thrust R and twisting couple K is therefore unstable if

$$\frac{\pi^2}{l^2} < \frac{K^2}{4B^2} + \frac{R}{B} \quad\text{.......................................(44)}$$

This condition* includes that obtained above for the case where there is no thrust, and also that obtained in (18) of Article 264 for the case where there is no couple. If the rod is subjected to tension instead of thrust, R is negative, and thus a sufficient tension will render the straight form stable in spite of a large twisting couple.

(e) *Stability of flat blade bent in its plane*†.

Let the section of the rod be such that the flexural rigidity B, for bending in one principal plane, is large compared with either the flexural rigidity A, for bending in the perpendicular plane, or with the torsional rigidity C. This would be the case if, for example, the cross-section were a rectangle of which one pair of sides is much longer than

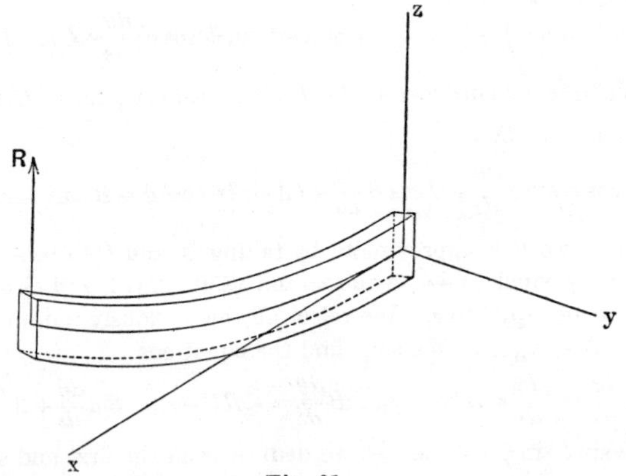

Fig. 61.

the other pair. Let the rod, built in at one end so as to be horizontal, be bent by a vertical transverse load R applied at the other end in the plane of greatest flexural rigidity. We shall use the notation of Article 253, and suppose, as in Article 270, that the line of action of the load R has the direction and sense of the line P_1z, and we shall take the plane of (z, x) to be parallel to the vertical plane containing the central-line in the unstressed state. If the length l, or the load R, is not too great, while the flexural rigidity B is large, the rod will be slightly bent in this plane, in the manner discussed in Chapter XV. But, when the length, or load, exceed certain limits, the rod can be held by the terminal force, directed as above stated, in a form in which the central-line is bent out of the plane (x, z), and then the rod will also be twisted. It will appear that the defect of torsional rigidity is quite as influential as that of flexural rigidity in rendering possible this kind of buckling.

Let s be measured from the fixed end of the central-line, and let x_1, y_1, z_1 be the coordinates of the loaded end of this line. Let x, y, z be the coordinates of any point P_1 on the strained central-line. For the equilibrium of the part of the rod contained between the section drawn through P_1 and the loaded end we take moments about axes drawn

* The result is due to A. G. Greenhill, *Inst. Mech. Engineers, Proc.*, 1883.

† Cf. A. G. M. Michell, *Phil. Mag.* (Ser. 5), vol. 48 (1899), and L. Prandtl, 'Kipperscheinungen' (*Diss.*), Nürnberg, 1899. The problem here solved and other problems, concerning the stability of a flat blade under various conditions of loading and support, are considered by various writers, among whom may be mentioned S. Timoschenko, *loc. cit.*, p. 408 and *Phil. Mag.* (Ser. 6), vol. 43 1922), p. 1023, M. K. Grober, *Phys. Zeitschr.*, Bd. 15 (1914), pp. 460 and 889, and J. Prescott, *Phil. Mag.* (Ser. 6), vol. 36 (1918), p. 297 and vol. 39 (1920), p. 194.

through P_1 parallel to the fixed axes. Using the direction-cosines defined by the scheme (4) of Article 253, we have the equations

$$\left.\begin{aligned} -(A\kappa l_1+B\kappa' l_2+C\tau l_3)+(\mathrm{y}_1-\mathrm{y})\,R&=0,\\ -(A\kappa m_1+B\kappa' m_2+C\tau m_3)-(\mathrm{x}_1-\mathrm{x})\,R&=0,\\ A\kappa n_1+B\kappa' n_2+C\tau n_3\qquad\qquad&=0.\end{aligned}\right\}\qquad(45)$$

When we substitute for κ, κ', τ from equations (8) of Article 253, and for l_1, ... from equations (7) of the same Article, we have

$$A\kappa l_1+B\kappa' l_2+C\tau l_3$$
$$=[-(A\sin^2\phi+B\cos^2\phi)\sin\psi+(A-B)\sin\phi\cos\phi\cos\psi\cos\theta]\frac{d\theta}{ds}+C\cos\psi\sin\theta\frac{d\phi}{ds}$$
$$+[-(A\cos^2\phi+B\sin^2\phi)\cos\psi\sin\theta\cos\theta+(A-B)\sin\phi\cos\phi\sin\psi\sin\theta+C\cos\psi\sin\theta\cos\theta]\frac{d\psi}{ds},$$
$$A\kappa m_1+B\kappa' m_2+C\tau m_3$$
$$=[(A\sin^2\phi+B\cos^2\phi)\cos\psi+(A-B)\sin\phi\cos\phi\sin\psi\cos\theta]\frac{d\theta}{ds}+C\sin\psi\sin\theta\frac{d\phi}{ds}$$
$$-[(A\cos^2\phi+B\sin^2\phi)\sin\psi\sin\theta\cos\theta+(A-B)\sin\phi\cos\phi\cos\psi\sin\theta-C\sin\psi\sin\theta\cos\theta]\frac{d\psi}{ds},$$
$$A\kappa n_1+B\kappa' n_2+C\tau n_3$$
$$=-(A-B)\sin\phi\cos\phi\sin\theta\frac{d\theta}{ds}+C\cos\theta\frac{d\phi}{ds}+(A\sin^2\theta\cos^2\phi+B\sin^2\theta\sin^2\phi+C\cos^2\theta)\frac{d\psi}{ds}.$$

In equations (45) we now approximate by taking A and C to be small compared with B, and θ to be nearly equal to $\frac{1}{2}\pi$, while ϕ and ψ are small, and also by taking x_1 to be equal to l and x to be equal to s. We reject all the obviously unimportant terms in the expressions for $(A\kappa l_1+\ldots)$, ... We thus find the equations

$$-B\psi\frac{d\theta}{ds}+C\frac{d\phi}{ds}=R(\mathrm{y}_1-\mathrm{y}),\quad B\frac{d\theta}{ds}=-R(l-s),\quad B\phi\frac{d\theta}{ds}+A\frac{d\psi}{ds}=0.$$

Since $dy/ds=m_3=\sin\theta\sin\psi=\psi$ nearly, we deduce from the first and second equations of this set the equation

$$C\frac{d^2\phi}{ds^2}+\frac{d}{ds}\{R(l-s)\psi\}=-R\psi,$$

and from the second and third equations of the same set we deduce the equation

$$A\frac{d\psi}{ds}=R(l-s)\phi;$$

and, on eliminating $d\psi/ds$ between the two equations last written, we find the equation

$$C\frac{d^2\phi}{ds^2}+\frac{R^2}{A}(l-s)^2\phi=0.\qquad(46)$$

This equation can be transformed into Bessel's equation by the substitutions

$$\xi=\tfrac{1}{2}(l-s)^2R/\sqrt{(AC)},\quad \phi=\eta(l-s)^{\frac{1}{2}}.\qquad(47)$$

It becomes

$$\frac{d^2\eta}{d\xi^2}+\frac{1}{\xi}\frac{d\eta}{d\xi}+\left(1-\frac{1}{16\xi^2}\right)\eta=0;$$

and the primitive is of the form

$$\phi=[A'J_{\frac{1}{4}}(\xi)+B'J_{-\frac{1}{4}}(\xi)](l-s)^{\frac{1}{2}},\qquad(48)$$

where A' and B' are constants.

Now when $s=l$, $d\psi/ds$ vanishes, and the twisting couple $C\tau$ vanishes; hence $d\phi/ds$ vanishes. This condition requires that A' should vanish. Further, ϕ vanishes when $s=0$, and thus the critical length is given by the equation $J_{-\frac{1}{4}}(\xi)=0$ at $\xi=\frac{1}{2}l^2R/\sqrt{(AC)}$, or

$$1-\frac{1}{2.6}\frac{R^2l^4}{AC}+\ldots+(-)^n\frac{1}{2.4\ldots(2n).6.14\ldots(8n-2)}\frac{R^{2n}l^{4n}}{A^nC^n}+\ldots=0.$$

The lowest root of this equation for $R^2 l^4/AC$ is 16 nearly, and we infer that the rod bent by terminal transverse load in the plane of greatest flexural rigidity is unstable if $l > \gamma (AC)^{\frac{1}{4}}/R^{\frac{1}{2}}$, where γ is a number very nearly equal to 2.

The result has been verified experimentally by A. G. M. Michell and L. Prandtl. It should be observed that the rod, if of such a length as that found, will be bent a good deal by the load R, unless B is large compared with A and C, and thus the above method is not applicable to the general problem of the stability of the elastica for displacements out of its plane.

273. Rod bent by forces applied along its length.

When forces and couples are applied to the rod at other points, as well as at the ends, and the stress-couples are assumed to be given by the ordinary approximations (Article 255), forms are possible in which the rod could not be held by terminal forces and couples only. When there are no couples except at the ends, the third of equations (11) of Article 254 becomes

$$C \frac{d\tau}{ds} - (A - B)\, \kappa\kappa' = 0,$$

and this equation shows that to hold the rod bent to a given curvature without applying couples along its length, a certain rate of variation of the twist along the length is requisite. In other words a certain twist, indeterminate to a constant *près*, is requisite.

When there are no applied couples except at the ends, and the curvature is given, while the twist has the required rate of variation, N and N' are given by the first two of equations (2) of Article 260. The requisite forces X, Y, Z of Article 254 and the tension T are then connected by the three equations (10) of that Article. We may therefore impose one additional condition upon these quantities. For example, we may take Z to be zero, and then we learn that a given rod can be held with its central-line in the form of a given curve by forces which at each point are directed along a normal to the curve, provided that the rod has a suitable twist.

Similar statements are applicable to the case in which the rod, in the unstressed state, has a given curvature and twist.

As an example* of the application of these remarks we may take the case of a rod which in the unstressed state forms a circular hoop of radius r_0, with one principal axis of each cross-section inclined to the plane of the hoop at an angle f_0, the same for all cross-sections. We denote by B the flexural rigidity corresponding with this axis. The initial state is expressed by the equations

$$\kappa_0 = -r_0^{-1} \cos f_0, \quad \kappa_0' = r_0^{-1} \sin f_0, \quad \tau_0 = 0.$$

Let the rod be bent into a circular hoop of radius r_1, with one principal axis of each cross-section inclined to the plane of the hoop at an angle f_1, the same for all cross-sections. The state of the rod is then expressed by the equations

$$\kappa_1 = -r_1^{-1} \cos f_1, \quad \kappa_1' = r_1^{-1} \sin f_1, \quad \tau_1 = 0.$$

* Cf. Kelvin and Tait, *Nat. Phil.*, Part II., pp. 166 *et seq.*

To hold the rod in this state forces must be applied to each section so as to be equivalent to a couple about the central-line; the amount of this couple per unit of length is

$$\frac{1}{r_0 r_1}(A\sin f_1\cos f_0 - B\cos f_1\sin f_0) - \frac{1}{r_1^2}(A-B)\sin f_1\cos f_1.$$

273 A. Influence of stiffness on the form of a suspended wire.

As another example of the equilibrium of a thin rod under forces applied along its length, we consider the problem of a wire suspended from two fixed points at the same level*. We shall suppose that the wire is stretched taut under a high terminal tension, so that its central-line at any point is but slightly inclined to the horizontal, and denote the inclination of the tangent to the horizontal by θ. Then in the equations (10) and (11) of Article 254 and (12) of Article 255 we have to put

$$\kappa=\tau=0,\quad \kappa'=\frac{d\theta}{ds},$$

$$G=H=0,\quad G'=B\frac{d\theta}{ds},$$

$$K=K'=\Theta=0,\quad X=-w\cos\theta,\quad Z=-w\sin\theta,\quad Y=0,$$

where w is the weight of the wire per unit of length. The equations become

$$B\frac{d^2\theta}{ds^2}+N=0,$$

$$\frac{dN}{ds}+T\frac{d\theta}{ds}-w\cos\theta=0,$$

$$\frac{dT}{ds}-N\frac{d\theta}{ds}-w\sin\theta=0.$$

Elimination of T and N yields the equation

$$B\left\{\frac{d}{ds}\left(\frac{d^3\theta}{ds^3}\Big/\frac{d\theta}{ds}\right)+\frac{d\theta}{ds}\frac{d^2\theta}{ds^2}\right\}-w\left\{2\sin\theta+\left(\frac{d^2\theta}{ds^2}\cos\theta\right)\Big/\left(\frac{d\theta}{ds}\right)^2\right\}=0,$$

which can be integrated in the form

$$B\left\{\left(\frac{d^3\theta}{ds^3}\cos\theta\right)\Big/\frac{d\theta}{ds}+\frac{d^2\theta}{ds^2}\sin\theta\right\}+(w\cos^2\theta)\Big/\frac{d\theta}{ds}=a,$$

where a is a constant of integration. On putting $\theta=0$, we see that a is the value of the tension T at a point where $\theta=0$, so we shall put T_0 for a. The equation can be integrated again in the form

$$B\frac{d^2\theta}{ds^2}\sec\theta+ws=T_0\tan\theta,$$

where no constant need be added if s is measured from a point where $\theta=0$.

If, as was supposed, θ is everywhere small, this equation may be replaced by the simpler equation

$$B\frac{d^2\theta}{ds^2}-T_0\,.\,\theta=-ws,$$

* A. E. Young, *Phil. Mag.* (Ser. 6), vol. 29, 1915, p. 96.

and integrated in the form

$$\theta = \alpha \cosh \lambda s + \beta \sinh \lambda s + \frac{w}{T_0} s,$$

where λ is written for $\sqrt{(T_0/B)}$, and α and β are arbitrary constants, and then α must be put equal to zero because θ vanishes with s.

If the ends of the wire at the supports are constrained to be horizontal, and the length of the wire between the supports is l, we have $\theta = 0$ when $s = \pm \frac{1}{2} l$, and then

$$\beta = -\frac{w}{T_0} \frac{\frac{1}{2} l}{\sinh \frac{1}{2} \lambda l}.$$

The length of the wire between the supports exceeds the distance between the supports by

$$2 \int_0^{\frac{1}{2} l} (1 - \cos \theta)\, ds,$$

or approximately

$$\int_0^{\frac{1}{2} l} \left(\frac{w}{T_0}\right)^2 \left(s - \tfrac{1}{2} l \frac{\sinh \lambda s}{\sinh \frac{1}{2} \lambda l}\right)^2 ds,$$

and this is

$$\frac{w^2}{T_0^2} \left(\frac{l^3}{24} + \frac{l}{\lambda^2} - \frac{3l^2}{8\lambda \tanh \frac{1}{2} \lambda l} - \frac{l^3}{16 \sinh^2 \frac{1}{2} \lambda l}\right).$$

The first term in this expression gives the excess length calculated by neglecting the stiffness, and the remaining terms give the correction for stiffness.

274. Rod bent in one plane by uniform normal pressure.

We consider next the problem of a rod held bent in a principal plane by normal pressure which is uniform along its length. The quantity X of Article 254 expresses the magnitude of this pressure per unit of length.

Let F denote the resultant of the shearing force N and the tension T at any cross-section, F_{x}, F_{y} its components parallel to fixed axes of x and y in the plane of the bent central-line. We may obtain two equations of equilibrium by resolving all the forces which act upon any portion of the rod parallel to the fixed axes. These equations are

$$\frac{d}{ds} F_{\mathrm{x}} + X \frac{d\mathrm{y}}{ds} = 0, \quad \frac{d}{ds} F_{\mathrm{y}} - X \frac{d\mathrm{x}}{ds} = 0.$$

It follows that the origin O can be chosen so that we have

$$F_{\mathrm{x}} = -\mathrm{y} X, \quad F_{\mathrm{y}} = \mathrm{x} X;$$

and therefore the magnitude of F at any point P of the strained central-line is rX, where r is the distance OP, and the direction of F is at right angles to OP. This result can be expressed in the following form:—Let P_1 and P_2 be any two points of the strained central-line, and let F_1 and F_2 be the resultants of the shearing force and tension on the cross-sections through P_1 and P_2, the senses of F_1 and F_2 being such that these forces arise from the action of the rest of the rod on the portions between P_1 and P_2. From P_1, P_2 draw lines P_1O, P_2O at right angles to the directions of F_1, F_2. We may regard the arc P_1P_2 as the limit of a polygon of a large number of sides, and this polygon as in equilibrium under the flexural couples at its ends, the forces F_1, F_2, and a force $X\delta s$ directed at right angles to any side of the polygon of which the length is δs. The forces are at right angles to the sides of the figure formed by OP_1, OP_2 and this polygon, and are proportional to them; and the lengths of OP_1 and OP_2 are F_1/X and F_2/X. The senses in which the lines must be drawn are indicated in Fig. 62, where in the right-hand figure OP_1P_2 is shown as a force-polygon *.

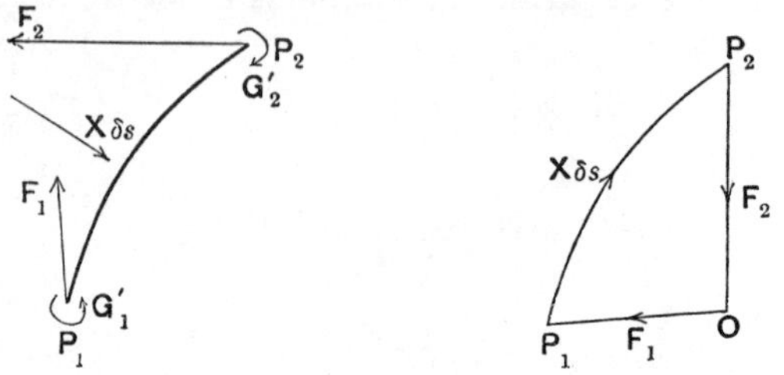

Fig. 62.

Let r denote the distance OP. Then

$$N = -F\frac{dr}{ds} = -rX\frac{dr}{ds}.$$

The stress-couple G' satisfies the equation

$$\frac{dG'}{ds} = -N = rX\frac{dr}{ds}.$$

Hence we have

$$G' = \tfrac{1}{2}Xr^2 + \text{const.}$$

In the particular case where the central-line in the unstressed state is a straight line or a circle, the curvature $1/\rho$ of the curve into which it is bent is given by the equation

$$B/\rho = \tfrac{1}{2}Xr^2 + \text{const.} \quad \text{.........................(49)}$$

The possible forms of the central-line can be determined from this equation †.

275. Stability of circular ring under normal pressure.

When the central-line in the unstressed state is a circle of radius a, and the rod is very slightly bent, equation (49) can be written in the approximate form

$$\frac{d^2u}{d\theta^2} + u = c + \frac{X}{2Bu^2},$$

* The theory is due to M. Lévy, *J. de Math.* (*Liouville*), (Sér. 3), t. 10 (1884).

† The complete integration of equation (49) by means of elliptic functions was effected by G. H. Halphen, *Paris, C. R.*, t. 98 (1884). See also his *Traité des fonctions elliptiques*, Partie 2, Ch. 5 (Paris, 1888). The subject has been investigated further by A. G. Greenhill, *Math. Ann.*, Bd. 52 (1899).

where $1/u$ and θ are the polar coordinates of a point on the central-line referred to O as origin, and c is a constant. The value of u differs very little from $1/a$, and we may therefore put $u=1/a+\xi$, where ξ is small, and obtain the approximate equation

$$\frac{d^2\xi}{d\theta^2}+\xi=-\frac{X}{B}a^3\xi.$$

Hence ξ is of the form $\xi_0\cos(n\theta+\gamma)$, where ξ_0 and γ are constants, and n is given by the equation

$$n^2=1+Xa^3/B.$$

Now the function ξ must be periodic in θ with period 2π, for, otherwise, the rod would not continue to form a complete ring. Hence n must be an integer. If n were 1, the circle would be displaced without deformation. The least value of the pressure X by which any deformation of the circular form can be produced is obtained by putting $n=2$. We infer that, if $X<3B/a^3$, the ring simply contracts under the pressure, but the ring tends to collapse if

$$X>3B/a^3. \qquad\qquad(50)^*$$

276. Height consistent with stability †.

As a further example of the equilibrium of a rod under forces applied along its length, we consider the problem of a vertical column, of uniform material and cross-section, bent by its own weight. Let a long thin rod be set up in a vertical plane so that the lower end is constrained to remain vertical, and suppose the length to be so great that the rod bends. Take the origin of fixed axes of x and y at the lower end, draw the axis of x vertically upwards and the axis of y horizontally in the plane of bending. (See Fig. 63.) For the equilibrium of the portion of the rod contained between any section and the free end, we resolve along the normal to the central-line, and then, since the central-line is nearly coincident with the axis of x, we find the equation

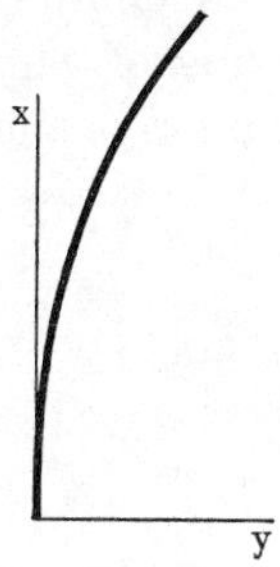

Fig. 63.

$$N=W\frac{l-\mathrm{x}}{l}\frac{d\mathrm{y}}{d\mathrm{x}},$$

where W is the weight of the rod. The equation of equilibrium $dG/ds+N=0$ can, therefore, be replaced by the approximate equation

$$B\frac{d^2p}{d\mathrm{x}^2}+W\frac{l-\mathrm{x}}{l}p=0, \qquad\qquad(51)$$

where p is written for $d\mathrm{y}/d\mathrm{x}$. The terminal conditions are that $dp/d\mathrm{x}$ vanishes at $\mathrm{x}=l$, and y and p vanish at $\mathrm{x}=0$.

Equation (51) can be transformed into Bessel's equation by the substitutions

$$\xi=\frac{2}{3}\sqrt{\left(\frac{W}{lB}\right)}(l-\mathrm{x})^{\frac{3}{2}},\quad p=\eta\,(l-\mathrm{x})^{\frac{1}{2}}. \qquad\qquad(52)$$

* The result is due to M. Lévy, *loc. cit.*

† The theory is due to A. G. Greenhill, *Cambridge Phil. Soc. Proc.*, vol. 4 (1881). It has been discussed critically by C. Chree, *Cambridge Phil. Soc. Proc.*, vol. 7 (1892).

It becomes $$\frac{d^2\eta}{d\xi^2}+\frac{1}{\xi}\frac{d\eta}{d\xi}+\left(1-\frac{1}{9\xi^2}\right)\eta=0,$$

and the primitive is of the form

$$p=[A'J_{\frac{1}{3}}(\xi)+B'J_{-\frac{1}{3}}(\xi)](l-\text{x})^{\frac{1}{2}},$$

where A' and B' are constants.

To make $dp/d\text{x}$ vanish at $\text{x}=l$ we must have $A'=0$, and to make p vanish at $\text{x}=0$ we must have $J_{-\frac{1}{3}}(\xi)=0$ at $\xi=\frac{2}{3}l(W/B)^{\frac{1}{2}}$. Hence the critical length is given by the equation

$$1-\frac{1}{3.2}\frac{l^2W}{B}+\ldots+(-)^n\frac{1}{3.6\ldots(3n).2.5\ldots(3n-1)}\frac{l^{2n}W^n}{B^n}+\ldots=0.$$

The lowest root of this equation for l^2W/B is $7.84\ldots$, and we infer that the rod will be bent by its own weight if the length exceeds $(2.80\ldots)\sqrt{(B/W)}$. The numerical value agrees with that obtained by a different method by S. Timoschenko, *loc. cit.*, p. 408.

Greenhill (*loc. cit.*, p. 425) has worked out a number of cases in which the rod is of varying section, and has applied his results to the explanation of the forms and growth of trees.

CHAPTER XX

VIBRATIONS OF RODS. PROBLEMS OF DYNAMICAL RESISTANCE

277. THE vibrations of thin rods or bars, straight and prismatic when unstressed, fall naturally into three classes: longitudinal, torsional, lateral. The "longitudinal" vibrations are characterized by the periodic extension and contraction of elements of the central-line, and, for this reason, they will sometimes be described as "extensional." The "lateral" vibrations are characterized by the periodic bending and straightening of portions of the central-line, as points of this line move to and fro at right angles to its unstrained direction; for this reason they will sometimes be described as "flexural." In Chapter XII we investigated certain modes of vibration of a circular cylinder. Of these modes one class are of strictly torsional type, and other classes are effectively of extensional and flexural types when the length of the cylinder is large compared with the radius of its cross-section. We have now to explain how the theory of such vibrations for a thin rod of any form of cross-section can be deduced from the theory of Chapter XVIII.

In order to apply this theory it is necessary to assume that the ordinary approximations described in Articles 255 and 258 hold when the rod is vibrating. This assumption may be partially justified by the observation that the equations of motion are the same as equations of equilibrium under certain body forces—the reversed kinetic reactions. It then amounts to assuming that the mode of distribution of these forces is not such as to invalidate seriously the approximate equations (21), (22), (23) of Article 258. The assumption may be put in another form in the statement that, when the rod vibrates, the internal strain in the portion between two neighbouring cross-sections is the same as it would be if that portion were in equilibrium under tractions on its ends, which produce in it the instantaneous extension, twist and curvature. No complete justification of this assumption has been given, but it is supported by the results, already cited, which are obtained in the case of a circular cylinder. It seems to be legitimate to state that the assumption gives a better approximation in the case of the graver modes of vibration, which are the most important, than in the case of the modes of greater frequency, and that, for the former, the approximation is quite sufficient.

The various modes of vibration have been investigated so fully by Lord Rayleigh* that it will be unnecessary here to do more than obtain the equations of vibration. After forming these equations we shall apply them to the discussion of some problems of dynamical resistance.

* *Theory of Sound*, Chapters VII and VIII.

278. Extensional vibrations.

Let w be the displacement, parallel to the central-line, of the centroid of that cross-section which, in the equilibrium state, is at a distance s from some chosen point of the line. Then the extension is $\partial w/\partial s$, and the tension is $E\omega\,(\partial w/\partial s)$, where E is Young's modulus, and ω the area of a cross-section. The kinetic reaction, estimated per unit of length of the rod, is $\rho\omega\,(\partial^2 w/\partial t^2)$, where ρ is the density of the material. The equation of motion, formed in the same way as the equations of equilibrium in Article 254, is

$$\rho\frac{\partial^2 w}{\partial t^2}=E\frac{\partial^2 w}{\partial s^2}. \qquad \text{.............................(1)}$$

The condition to be satisfied at a free end is $\partial w/\partial s=0$; at a fixed end w vanishes.

If we form the equation of motion by the energy-method (Article 115) we may take account of the inertia of the lateral motion* by which the cross-sections are extended or contracted in their own planes. If x and y are the coordinates of any point in a cross-section, referred to axes drawn through its centroid, the lateral displacements are

$$-\sigma x\,(\partial w/\partial s), \quad -\sigma y\,(\partial w/\partial s),$$

where σ is Poisson's ratio. Hence the kinetic energy per unit of length is

$$\tfrac{1}{2}\rho\omega\left\{\left(\frac{\partial w}{\partial t}\right)^2+\sigma^2K^2\left(\frac{\partial^2 w}{\partial s\,\partial t}\right)^2\right\},$$

where K is the radius of gyration of a cross-section about the central-line. The potential energy per unit of length is

$$\tfrac{1}{2}E\omega\left(\frac{\partial w}{\partial s}\right)^2,$$

and, therefore, the variational equation of motion is

$$\delta\int dt\int\left[\tfrac{1}{2}\rho\omega\left\{\left(\frac{\partial w}{\partial t}\right)^2+\sigma^2K^2\left(\frac{\partial^2 w}{\partial s\,\partial t}\right)^2\right\}-\tfrac{1}{2}E\omega\left(\frac{\partial w}{\partial s}\right)^2\right]ds=0,$$

where the integration with respect to s is taken along the rod. In forming the variations we use the identities

$$\frac{\partial w}{\partial t}\frac{\partial\,\delta w}{\partial t}+\frac{\partial^2 w}{\partial t^2}\delta w=\frac{\partial}{\partial t}\left(\frac{\partial w}{\partial t}\delta w\right), \qquad \frac{\partial w}{\partial s}\frac{\partial\,\delta w}{\partial s}+\frac{\partial^2 w}{\partial s^2}\delta w=\frac{\partial}{\partial s}\left(\frac{\partial w}{\partial s}\delta w\right),$$

$$2\left(\frac{\partial^2 w}{\partial s\,\partial t}\frac{\partial^2\,\delta w}{\partial s\,\partial t}-\frac{\partial^4 w}{\partial s^2\partial t^2}\delta w\right)=\frac{\partial}{\partial s}\left(\frac{\partial^2 w}{\partial s\,\partial t}\frac{\partial\,\delta w}{\partial t}-\frac{\partial^3 w}{\partial s\,\partial t^2}\delta w\right)+\frac{\partial}{\partial t}\left(\frac{\partial^2 w}{\partial s\,\partial t}\frac{\partial\,\delta w}{\partial s}-\frac{\partial^3 w}{\partial s^2\partial t}\delta w\right);$$

and, on integrating by parts, and equating to zero the coefficient of δw under the sign of double integration, we obtain the equation

$$\rho\left(\frac{\partial^2 w}{\partial t^2}-\sigma^2K^2\frac{\partial^4 w}{\partial s^2\partial t^2}\right)=E\frac{\partial^2 w}{\partial s^2}. \qquad \text{.............................(2)}$$

By retaining the term $\rho\sigma^2K^2\partial^4 w/\partial s^2\partial t^2$ we should obtain the correction of the velocity of wave-propagation which was found by Pochhammer and Chree (Article 201), or the correction of the frequency of free vibration which was calculated by Lord Rayleigh†.

* The lateral *strain* is already taken into account when the tension is expressed as the product of E and $\omega\,(\partial w/\partial s)$. If the longitudinal strain alone were considered the constant that enters into the expression for the tension would not be E but $\lambda+2\mu$.

† *Theory of Sound*, § 157.

279. Torsional vibrations.

Let ψ denote the relative angular displacement of two cross-sections, so that $\partial\psi/\partial s$ is the twist of the rod. The centroids of the sections are not displaced, but the component displacements of a point in a cross-section parallel to axes of x and y, chosen as before, are $-\psi y$ and ψx. The torsional couple is $C(\partial\psi/\partial s)$, where C is the torsional rigidity. The moment of the kinetic reactions about the central-line, estimated per unit of length of the rod, is $\rho\omega K^2(\partial^2\psi/\partial t^2)$. The equation of motion, formed in the same way as the third of the equations of equilibrium (11) of Article 254, is

$$\rho\omega K^2\frac{\partial^2\psi}{\partial t^2}=C\frac{\partial^2\psi}{\partial s^2}\ \ldots\ldots\ldots\ldots\ldots\ldots\ldots\ldots(3)$$

The condition to be satisfied at a free end is $\partial\psi/\partial s=0$; at a fixed end ψ vanishes.

When we apply the energy-method, we may take account of the inertia of the motion by which the cross-sections are deformed into curved surfaces. Let ϕ be the torsion-function for the section (Article 216). Then the longitudinal displacement is $\phi(\partial\psi/\partial s)$, and the kinetic energy of the rod per unit of length is

$$\tfrac{1}{2}\rho\left[\omega K^2\left(\frac{\partial\psi}{\partial t}\right)^2+\left(\frac{\partial^2\psi}{\partial s\partial t}\right)^2\int\phi^2 d\omega\right].$$

The potential energy is $\frac{1}{2}C(\partial\psi/\partial s)^2$, and the equation of vibration, formed as before, is

$$\rho\omega K^2\frac{\partial^2\psi}{\partial t^2}-\rho\left(\int\phi^2 d\omega\right)\frac{\partial^4\psi}{\partial s^2\partial t^2}=C\frac{\partial^2\psi}{\partial s^2}.$$

By inserting in this equation the values of C and $\int\phi^2 d\omega$ that belong to the section, we could obtain an equation of motion of the same form as (2) and could work out a correction for the velocity of wave-propagation and the frequency of any mode of vibration. In the case of a circular cylinder there is no correction and the velocity of propagation is that found in Article 200.

280. Flexural vibrations.

Let the rod vibrate in a principal plane, which we take to be that of (x, z) as defined in Article 252. Let u denote the displacement of the centroid of any section at right angles to the unstrained central-line. We may take the angle between this line and the tangent of the strained central-line to be $\partial u/\partial s$, and the curvature to be $\partial^2 u/\partial s^2$. The flexural couple G' is $B\partial^2 u/\partial s^2$, where $B=E\omega k'^2$, k' being the radius of gyration of the cross-section about an axis through its centroid at right angles to the plane of bending. The magnitude of the kinetic reaction, estimated per unit of length, is, for a first approximation, $\rho\omega(\partial^2 u/\partial t^2)$, and its direction is that of the displacement u. The longitudinal displacement of any point is $-x(\partial u/\partial s)$; and therefore the moment of the kinetic reactions, estimated per unit of length, about an axis perpendicular to the plane of bending is $\rho\omega k'^2(\partial^3 u/\partial s\partial t^2)$. The equations of vibration formed in the same way as the first of the set of equations (10) and the second of the set of equations (11) of Article 254 are

$$\frac{\partial N}{\partial s} = \rho\omega \frac{\partial^2 u}{\partial t^2}, \quad E\omega k'^2 \frac{\partial^3 u}{\partial s^3} + N = \rho\omega k'^2 \frac{\partial^3 u}{\partial s \partial t^2}, \quad \text{..............(4)}$$

and, on eliminating N, we have the equation of vibration

$$\rho\left(\frac{\partial^2 u}{\partial t^2} - k'^2 \frac{\partial^4 u}{\partial s^2 \partial t^2}\right) = -Ek'^2 \frac{\partial^4 u}{\partial s^4}. \quad \text{....................(5)}$$

If "rotatory inertia" is neglected we have the approximate equation

$$\rho \frac{\partial^2 u}{\partial t^2} = -Ek'^2 \frac{\partial^4 u}{\partial s^4}, \quad \text{..........................(6)}$$

and the shearing force N at any section is $-E\omega k'^2 \partial^3 u/\partial s^3$. At a free end $\partial^2 u/\partial s^2$ and $\partial^3 u/\partial s^3$ vanish, at a clamped end u and $\partial u/\partial s$ vanish, at a "supported" end u and $\partial^2 u/\partial s^2$ vanish.

By retaining the term representing the effect of rotatory inertia we could obtain a correction of the velocity of wave-propagation, or of the frequency of vibration, of the same kind as those previously mentioned*. Another correction, which may be of the same degree of importance as this when the section of the rod does not possess kinetic symmetry, may be obtained by the energy-method, by taking account of the inertia of the motion by which the cross-sections are distorted in their own planes†. The components of displacement parallel to axes of x and y in the plane of the cross-section, the axis of x being in the plane of bending, are

$$u + \tfrac{1}{2}\sigma \frac{\partial^2 u}{\partial s^2}(x^2 - y^2), \quad \sigma \frac{\partial^2 u}{\partial s^2} xy;$$

and the kinetic energy per unit of length is expressed correctly to terms of the fourth order in the linear dimensions of the cross-section by the formula

$$\tfrac{1}{2}\rho\omega \left\{\left(\frac{\partial u}{\partial t}\right)^2 + \sigma(k'^2 - k^2)\frac{\partial u}{\partial t}\frac{\partial^3 u}{\partial s^2 \partial t} + k'^2\left(\frac{\partial^2 u}{\partial s \partial t}\right)^2\right\},$$

where k is the radius of gyration of the cross-section about an axis through its centroid drawn in the plane of bending. The term in $\sigma(k'^2 - k^2)$ depends on the inertia of the motion by which the cross-sections are distorted in their planes, and the term in k'^2 depends on the rotatory inertia. The potential energy is expressed by the formula

$$\tfrac{1}{2} E\omega k'^2 \left(\frac{\partial^2 u}{\partial s^2}\right)^2.$$

The variational equation of motion is

$$\delta \int dt \int ds \left[\left\{\rho\left(\frac{\partial u}{\partial t}\right)^2 + \sigma(k'^2 - k^2)\frac{\partial u}{\partial t}\frac{\partial^3 u}{\partial s^2 \partial t} + k'^2\left(\frac{\partial^2 u}{\partial s \partial t}\right)^2\right\} - Ek'^2\left(\frac{\partial^2 u}{\partial s^2}\right)^2\right] = 0.$$

In forming the variations we use the identities

$$\frac{\partial^2 u}{\partial s^2}\frac{\partial^2 \delta u}{\partial s^2} - \frac{\partial^4 u}{\partial s^4}\delta u = \frac{\partial}{\partial s}\left(\frac{\partial^2 u}{\partial s^2}\frac{\partial \delta u}{\partial s} - \frac{\partial^3 u}{\partial s^3}\delta u\right),$$

$$\frac{\partial \delta u}{\partial t}\frac{\partial^3 u}{\partial s^2 \partial t} + \frac{\partial u}{\partial t}\frac{\partial^3 \delta u}{\partial s^2 \partial t} + 2\delta u \frac{\partial^4 u}{\partial s^2 \partial t^2} = \frac{\partial}{\partial t}\left(\delta u \frac{\partial^3 u}{\partial s^2 \partial t} + \frac{\partial u}{\partial t}\frac{\partial^2 \delta u}{\partial s^2}\right) + \frac{\partial}{\partial s}\left(\delta u \frac{\partial^3 u}{\partial s \partial t^2} - \frac{\partial \delta u}{\partial s}\frac{\partial^2 u}{\partial t^2}\right)$$

* Cf. Lord Rayleigh, *Theory of Sound*, § 186.

† The cross-sections are distorted into curved surfaces and inclined obliquely to the strained central-line, but the inertia of these motions would give a much smaller correction. It is shown, however, by S. Timoschenko, *Phil. Mag.* (Ser. 6), vol. 41, p. 744 and vol. 43, p. 125, to be at least as important as the correction for rotatory inertia.

as well as identities of the types used in Article 278. The resulting equation of motion is

$$\rho\left[\frac{\partial^2 u}{\partial t^2} - \{k'^2(1-\sigma)+k^2\sigma\}\frac{\partial^4 u}{\partial s^2 \partial t^2}\right] = -Ek'^2\frac{\partial^4 u}{\partial s^4}. \quad \text{......................(7)}$$

Corrections of the energy such as that considered here will, of course, affect the terminal conditions at a free, or supported end, as well as the differential equation of vibration. Since they rest on the assumption that the internal strain in any small portion of the vibrating rod contained between neighbouring cross-sections is the same as in a prism in which the right extension, or twist, or curvature is produced by forces applied at the ends and holding the prism in equilibrium, they cannot be regarded as very rigorously established. Lord Rayleigh (*loc. cit.*) calls attention to the increase of importance of such corrections with the frequency of the vibration. We have already remarked that the validity of the fundamental assumption diminishes as the frequency rises.

281. Rod fixed at one end and struck longitudinally at the other*.

We shall illustrate the application of the theory of vibrations to problems of dynamical resistance by solving some problems in which a long thin rod is thrown into extensional vibration by shocks or moving loads.

We take first the problem of a rod fixed at one end and struck at the other by a massive body moving in the direction of the length of the rod. We measure t from the instant of impact and s from the fixed end, and we denote by l the length of the rod, by m the ratio of the mass of the striking body to that of the rod, by V the velocity of the body at the instant of impact, by w the longitudinal displacement, and by a the velocity of propagation of extensional waves in the rod.

The differential equation of extensional vibration is

$$\frac{\partial^2 w}{\partial t^2} = a^2\frac{\partial^2 w}{\partial s^2}. \quad \text{................................(8)}$$

The terminal condition at $s=0$ is $w=0$. The terminal condition at $s=l$ is the equation of motion of the striking body, or it is

$$ml\frac{\partial^2 w}{\partial t^2} = -a^2\frac{\partial w}{\partial s}, \quad \text{............................(9)}$$

since the pressure at the end is, in the notation of Article 278, $-E\omega(\partial w/\partial s)$, and $E\omega/a^2$ is equal to the mass of the rod per unit of length. The initial condition is that, when $t=0$, $w=0$ for all values of s between 0 and l, but at $s=l$

$$\lim_{t=+0}(\partial w/\partial t) = -V, \quad \text{..........................(10)}$$

since the velocity of the struck end becomes, at the instant of impact, the same as that of the striking body.

* Cf. J. Boussinesq, *Applications des potentiels...*, pp. 508 *et seq.*, or Saint-Venant in the 'Annotated Clebsch,' *Note finale du* § 60 and *Changements et additions*. A new and powerful method of solving problems of the kind here discussed has been devised by T. J. I'A. Bromwich, *London, Math. Soc. Proc.* (Ser. 2), vol. 15 (1916), p. 401, and further developed by him in *Phil. Mag.* (Ser. 6), vol. 37 (1919), p. 407.

We have to determine w for positive values of t, and for all values of s between 0 and l, by means of these equations and conditions. The first step is to express the solution of the differential equation (8) in the form

$$w = f(at - s) + F(at + s), \quad \text{.......................(11)}$$

where f and F denote arbitrary functions.

The second step is to use the terminal condition at $s = 0$ to eliminate one of the arbitrary functions. This condition gives in fact

$$f(at) + F(at) = 0,$$

and we may, therefore, write the solution of equation (8) in the form

$$w = f(at - s) - f(at + s). \quad \text{.......................(12)}$$

The third step is to use the initial conditions to determine the function f in a certain interval. We think of f as a function of an argument ζ, which may be put equal to $at - s$ or $at + s$ when required. Since $\partial w/\partial s$ and $\partial w/\partial t$ vanish with t for all values of s between 0 and l we have,

$$\text{when} \quad l > \zeta > 0, \quad -f'(-\zeta) - f'(\zeta) = 0, \quad f'(-\zeta) - f'(\zeta) = 0.$$

Hence it follows that, when $l > \zeta > -l$, $f'(\zeta)$ vanishes and $f(\zeta)$ is a constant which can be taken to be zero; or we have the result

$$\text{when} \quad l > \zeta > -l, \quad f(\zeta) = 0. \quad \text{....................(13)}$$

The fourth step is to use the terminal condition (9) at $s = l$ to form an equation by means of which the value of $f(\zeta)$ as a function of ζ can be determined outside the interval $l > \zeta > -l$. The required equation, called the "continuing equation*," is

$$ml\,[f''(at - l) - f''(at + l)] = f'(at - l) + f'(at + l),$$

or, as it may be written,

$$f''(\zeta) + (1/ml)f'(\zeta) = f''(\zeta - 2l) - (1/ml)f'(\zeta - 2l). \quad \text{......(14)}$$

We regard this equation in the first instance as an equation to determine $f'(\zeta)$. The right-hand member is known, it has in fact been shown to be zero, in the interval $3l > \zeta > l$. We may therefore determine the form of $f'(\zeta)$ in this interval by integrating the equation (14). The constant of integration is to be determined by means of the condition (10). The function $f'(\zeta)$ will then be known in the interval $3l > \zeta > l$, and therefore the right-hand member of (14) is known in the interval $5l > \zeta > 3l$. We determine the form of $f'(\zeta)$ in this interval by integrating the equation (14), and we determine the constant of integration by the condition that there is no discontinuity in the velocity at $s = l$ after the initial instant. The function $f'(\zeta)$ will then be known in the interval $5l > \zeta > 3l$. By proceeding in this way we can determine $f'(\zeta)$ for all values of ζ which exceed $-l$.

* *Équation promotrice* of Saint-Venant.

The integral of (14) is always of the form

$$f'(\zeta) = Ce^{-\zeta/ml} + e^{-\zeta/ml}\int e^{\zeta/ml}\{f''(\zeta-2l) - \frac{1}{ml}f'(\zeta-2l)\}\,d\zeta, \quad \text{...(15)}$$

where C is a constant of integration. When $3l > \zeta > l$ the expression under the sign of integration vanishes, and $f'(\zeta)$ is of the form $Ce^{-\zeta/ml}$. Now the condition (10) gives

$$a[f'(-l+0) - f'(l+0)] = -V, \text{ or } f'(l+0) = V/a.$$

Hence $Ce^{-1/m} = V/a$, and we have the result

$$\text{when } 3l > \zeta > l, \quad f'(\zeta) = \frac{V}{a}e^{-(\zeta-l)/ml}. \quad \text{...............(16)}$$

We observe that $f'(\zeta)$ is discontinuous at $\zeta = l$.

When $5l > \zeta > 3l$ we have

$$f''(\zeta-2l) - (1/ml)f'(\zeta-2l) = -2(V/mla)e^{-(\zeta-3l)/ml},$$

and equation (15) can be written

$$f'(\zeta) = Ce^{-\zeta/ml} - 2(V/mla)(\zeta-3l)e^{-(\zeta-3l)/ml}.$$

The condition of continuity of velocity at $s = l$ at the instant $t = 2l/a$ gives

$$f'(l-0) - f'(3l-0) = f'(l+0) - f'(3l+0),$$

or

$$-\frac{V}{a}e^{-2/m} = \frac{V}{a} - Ce^{-3/m},$$

giving

$$C = (V/a)(e^{1/m} + e^{3/m}).$$

Hence, when $5l > \zeta > 3l$,

$$f'(\zeta) = \frac{V}{a}e^{-(\zeta-l)/ml} + \frac{V}{a}\left\{1 - \frac{2}{ml}(\zeta-3l)\right\}e^{-(\zeta-3l)/ml}. \quad \text{.........(17)}$$

When $7l > \zeta > 5l$ we have

$$f''(\zeta-2l) - \frac{1}{ml}f'(\zeta-2l) = -\frac{2V}{mla}[e^{-(\zeta-3l)/ml} + 2e^{-(\zeta-5l)/ml}] + \frac{4V}{m^2l^2a}(\zeta-5l)e^{-(\zeta-5l)/ml},$$

and equation (15) can be written

$$f'(\zeta) = Ce^{-\zeta/ml} - \frac{2V}{mla}(\zeta-5l)[e^{-(\zeta-3l)/ml} + 2e^{-(\zeta-5l)/ml}] + \frac{2V}{m^2l^2a}(\zeta-5l)^2e^{-(\zeta-5l)/ml}$$

The condition of continuity of velocity at $s = l$ at the instant $t = 4l/a$ gives

$$f'(3l-0) - f'(5l-0) = f'(3l+0) - f'(5l+0),$$

or

$$\frac{V}{a}e^{-2/m} - \frac{V}{a}(e^{-4/m} + e^{-2/m}) + \frac{4V}{ma}e^{-2/m} = \frac{V}{a}(e^{-2/m} + 1) - Ce^{-5/m},$$

giving $C = \frac{V}{a}\left\{e^{1/m} + \left(1 - \frac{4}{m}\right)e^{3/m} + e^{5/m}\right\}$. Hence, when $7l > \zeta > 5l$,

$$f'(\zeta) = \frac{V}{a}e^{-(\zeta-l)/ml} + \frac{V}{a}\left\{1 - \frac{2}{ml}(\zeta-3l)\right\}e^{-(\zeta-3l)/ml} + \frac{V}{a}\left\{1 - \frac{4}{ml}(\zeta-5l) + \frac{2}{m^2l^2}(\zeta-5l)^2\right\}e^{-(\zeta-5l)/ml}. \quad \text{...(18)}$$

The function $f(\zeta)$ can be determined by integrating $f'(\zeta)$, and the constant of integration is to be determined by the condition that there is no sudden change in the displacement at $s=l$. This condition gives, by putting $t=0$, $2l/a$, ... such equations as

$$0=f(-l+0)-f(l+0),$$

$$f(l-0)-f(3l-0)=f(l+0)-f(3l+0),$$

from which, since $f(-l+0)$ and $f(l-0)$ vanish, we find

$$f(l+0)=0=f(l-0),\quad f(3l+0)=f(3l-0),\ \ldots.$$

Hence there is no discontinuity in $f(\zeta)$, as is otherwise evident, since $f'(\zeta)$ possesses only finite discontinuities separated by intervals in which it is continuous. We have therefore merely to integrate $f'(\zeta)$ in each of the intervals $3l>\zeta>l$, $5l>\zeta>3l$, ... and determine the constants of integration so that $f(l)=0$ and $f(\zeta)$ is continuous. We find the following results:

$$\left.\begin{aligned}
&\text{when } 3l>\zeta>l,\\
&\qquad f(\zeta)=(mlV/a)\{1-e^{-(\zeta-l)/ml}\};\\
&\text{when } 5l>\zeta>3l,\\
&\qquad f(\zeta)=-\frac{mlV}{a}e^{-(\zeta-l)/ml}+\frac{mlV}{a}\left\{1+\frac{2}{ml}(\zeta-3l)\right\}e^{-(\zeta-3l)/ml};\\
&\text{when } 7l>\zeta>5l,\\
&\qquad f(\zeta)=\frac{mlV}{a}\{1-e^{-(\zeta-l)/ml}\}+\frac{mlV}{a}\left\{1+\frac{2}{ml}(\zeta-3l)\right\}e^{-(\zeta-3l)/ml}\\
&\qquad\qquad -\frac{mlV}{a}\left\{1+\frac{2}{m^2l^2}(\zeta-5l)^2\right\}e^{-(\zeta-5l)/ml};\\
&\qquad\ldots\ldots\ldots\ldots
\end{aligned}\right\}\quad\ldots(19)$$

The solution expresses the result that, at the instant of impact, a wave of compression sets out from the struck end, and travels towards the fixed end, where it is reflected. The motion of the striking body generates a continuous series of such waves, which advance towards the fixed end, and are reflected there.

In the above solution we have proceeded as if the striking body became attached to the rod, so that the condition (9) holds for all positive values of t; but, if the bodies remain detached, the solution continues to hold so long only as there is positive pressure between the rod and the striking body. When, in the above solution, the pressure at $s=l$ becomes negative, the impact ceases. This happens when $f'(at-l)+f'(at+l)$ becomes negative. So long as $2l>at>0$ this expression is equal to $(V/a)e^{-at/ml}$, which is positive. When $4l>at>2l$, it is

$$\frac{V}{a}e^{-at/ml}\left[1+2e^{2/m}\left(1-\frac{at-2l}{ml}\right)\right],$$

which vanishes when $2at/ml=4/m+2+e^{-2/m}$, and this equation can have a root in the interval $4l>at>2l$ if $2+e^{-2/m}<4/m$. Now the equation $2+e^{-2/m}=4/m$ has a root lying between $m=1$ and $m=2$, viz.: $m=1{\cdot}73\ldots$. Hence, if $m<1{\cdot}73$, the impact ceases at an instant in the interval $4l/a>t>2l/a$, and this instant is given by the equation

$$t=\frac{l}{a}(2+m+\tfrac{1}{2}me^{-2/m}).$$

If $m>1{\cdot}73$ we may in like manner determine whether or no the impact ceases at an instant in the interval $6l/a>t>4l/a$, and so on. It may be shown also that the greatest compression of the rod occurs at the fixed end, and that, if $m<5$, its value is $2(1+e^{-2/m})V/a$, but, if $m>5$, its value is approximately equal to $(1+\sqrt{m})V/a$. If the problem were treated as a statical problem by neglecting the inertia of the rod, the greatest compression would be $\sqrt{m}(V/a)$. For further details in regard to this problem reference may be made to the authorities cited on p. 431.

282. Rod free at one end and struck longitudinally at the other*.

When the end $s=0$ is free, $\partial w/\partial s$ vanishes at this end for all values of t, or we have $-f'(at)+F'(at)=0$. Hence we may put $F(\zeta)=f(\zeta)$ and write instead of (12),

$$w=f(at-s)+f(at+s),$$

and, as before, we find that $f(\zeta)$ vanishes in the interval $l>\zeta>-l$.

The continuing equation is now

$$f''(\zeta)+(1/ml)f'(\zeta)=-f''(\zeta-2l)+(1/ml)f'(\zeta-2l)$$

and the discontinuity of $f'(\zeta)$ at $\zeta=l$ is determined by the equation

$$a[f'(-l+0)+f'(l+0)]=-V, \quad\text{or}\quad f'(l+0)=-V/a.$$

Hence we find the results:

when $3l>\zeta>l$,

$$f'(\zeta)=-\frac{V}{a}e^{-(\zeta-l)/ml}, \text{ and } f(\zeta)=-\frac{Vml}{a}\{1-e^{-(\zeta-l)/ml}\};$$

when $5l>\zeta>3l$,

$$f'(\zeta)=-\frac{V}{a}e^{-(\zeta-l)/ml}+\frac{V}{a}\left\{1-\frac{2}{ml}(\zeta-3l)\right\}e^{-(\zeta-3l)/ml}.$$

Now the extension at $s=l$ is $f'(at+l)-f'(at-l)$, and, until $t=2l/a$, this is

$$-(V/a)\,e^{-at/ml},$$

which is negative, so that the pressure remains positive until the instant $t=2l/a$; but, immediately after this instant, the extension becomes $(V/a)(2-e^{-2/m})$, which is positive, so that the pressure vanishes and the impact ceases at the instant $t=2l/a$, that is to say after the time taken by a wave of extension to travel over twice the length of the rod. The wave generated at the struck end at the instant of impact is a wave of compression; it is reflected at the free end as a wave of extension. The impact ceases when this reflected wave reaches the end in contact with the striking body. The state of the rod and the velocity of the striking body at this instant are determined by the above formulæ. The body moves with velocity $Ve^{-2/m}$ in the same direction as before the impact; and the rod moves in the same direction, the velocity of its centre of mass being $mV(1-e^{-2/m})$. The velocity at any point of the rod is $2Ve^{-1/m}\cosh(s/ml)$, and the extension at any point of it is $2(V/a)e^{-1/m}\sinh(s/ml)$, so that the rod rebounds vibrating.

* Cf. J. Boussinesq, *loc. cit.*, p. 431.

283. Rod loaded suddenly.

Let a massive body be suddenly attached without velocity to the lower end of a rod, which is hanging vertically with its upper end fixed. With a notation similar to that in Article 281, we can write down the equation of vibration in the form

$$\frac{\partial^2 w}{\partial t^2} = a^2 \frac{\partial^2 w}{\partial s^2} + g, \quad \text{.........................(20)}$$

and the value of w in the equilibrium state is $\frac{1}{2} gs(2l - s)/a^2$. Hence we write

$$w = \tfrac{1}{2} gs(2l - s)/a^2 + w', \quad \text{.......................(21)}$$

and then w' must be of the form

$$w' = \phi(at - s) - \phi(at + s), \quad \text{....................(22)}$$

and, as before, we find that, in the interval $l > \zeta > -l$, $\phi(\zeta)$ vanishes.

The equation of motion of the attached mass is

$$\left(\frac{\partial^2 w'}{\partial t^2}\right)_{s=l} = g - \frac{a^2}{ml}\left(\frac{\partial w'}{\partial s}\right)_{s=l}, \quad \text{....................(23)}$$

which gives the continuing equation

$$\phi''(\zeta) + \frac{1}{ml}\phi'(\zeta) = \phi''(\zeta - 2l) - \frac{1}{ml}\phi'(\zeta - 2l) - \frac{g}{a^2}, \quad \text{........(24)}$$

and the constants of integration are to be determined so that there is no discontinuity of velocity or of displacement. We find the following results: when $3l > \zeta > l$,

$$\left.\begin{aligned} \phi'(\zeta) &= -\frac{g}{a^2} ml \{1 - e^{-(\zeta - l)/ml}\}, \\ \phi(\zeta) &= -\frac{g}{a^2} m^2 l^2 \left\{\frac{\zeta - l}{ml} - 1 + e^{-(\zeta - l)/ml}\right\}. \end{aligned}\right\} \quad \text{........(25)}$$

Further the equations by which $\phi'(\zeta)$ is determined in this problem can be identified with those by which $f(\zeta)$ was determined in Article 281 by writing $-g/a$ for V. The solution is not restricted to the range of values of t within which the tension at the lower end remains one-signed.

The expression for the extension at any point is

$$g(l - s)/a^2 - \phi'(at - s) - \phi'(at + s),$$

and, at the fixed end, this is equal to

$$lg/a^2 - 2\phi'(at), \text{ or } lg/a^2 + 2(g/aV) f(at),$$

where f is the function so denoted in Article 281. The maximum value occurs when $f'(at) = 0$.

Taking $m = 1$, so that the attached mass is equal to the mass of the rod, we find from (16) that $f'(at)$ does not vanish before $t = 3l/a$, but from (17) that it vanishes between $t = 3l/a$ and $t = 5l/a$ if the equation

$$1 + e^2\{1 - 2(\zeta - 3l)/l\} = 0$$

has a root in the interval $5l > \zeta > 3l$. The root is $\zeta = l\{3 + \frac{1}{2}(1 + 1/e^2)\}$, or $\zeta = l\,(3\cdot568)$, which is in this interval. The greatest extension at the fixed end is

$$\frac{lg}{a^2}\{1 + 2e^{-2\cdot568}[-1 + e^2\{1 + 2\,(0\cdot568)\}]\},$$

or $(lg/a^2)(1 + 4e^{-0\cdot568})$, or $(3\cdot27)\,lg/a^2$. The statical strain at the fixed end, when the rod supports the attached mass in equilibrium, is $2lg/a^2$, and the ratio of the maximum dynamical strain to this is 1·63 : 1. This strain occurs at the instant $t = (3\cdot568)\,l/a$.

Taking $m = 2$, so that the attached mass is twice the mass of the rod, we find from (16) that $f'(at)$ does not vanish before $t = 3l/a$, but from (17) that it vanishes between $t = 3l/a$ and $t = 5l/a$ if the equation

$$1 + e\{1 - (\zeta - 3l)/l\} = 0$$

has a root in the interval $5l > \zeta > 3l$. The root is $\zeta = l\,(4 + 1/e)$, or $\zeta = l\,(4\cdot368)$, which is in this interval. The greatest extension at the fixed end is

$$\frac{lg}{a^2}\{1 + 4e^{-\frac{1}{2}(3\cdot368)}[-1 + (1 + 1\cdot368)\,e]\},$$

or $lg/a^2(1 + 8e^{-0\cdot684})$ or $(5\cdot04)\,lg/a^2$. The statical strain in this case is $3lg/a^2$, and the ratio of the maximum dynamical strain to the statical strain is 1·68 : 1. This strain occurs at the instant $t = (4\cdot368)\,l/a$.

Taking $m = 4$, so that the attached mass is four times the mass of the rod, we find from (17) that $f'(at)$ does not vanish before $t = 5l/a$, but from (18) that it vanishes between $t = 5l/a$ and $t = 7l/a$ if the equation

$$1 - \tfrac{1}{2}\{(\zeta - 5l)/l\}\,e^{\frac{1}{2}} + [1 - (\zeta - 5l)/l + \tfrac{1}{8}(\zeta - 5l)^2/l^2]\,e = 0$$

has a root in the interval $7l > \zeta > 5l$. The smaller root is $\zeta = l\,(6\cdot183)$, which is in this interval. The greatest extension at the fixed end is

$$\frac{lg}{a^2}\left[1 + 8 - 8e^{-(\zeta - l)/4l}\left\{1 - \left(2 + \frac{1}{2}\frac{\zeta - 5l}{l}\right)e^{\frac{1}{2}} + \left(1 + \frac{1}{8}\frac{(\zeta - 5l)^2}{l^2}\right)e\right\}\right],$$

where ζ is given by the above equation. The extension in question is therefore

$$\frac{lg}{a^2}[9 + 8e^{-\frac{1}{4}(1\cdot183)}\{2e^{-\frac{1}{2}} - (1\cdot183)\}],$$

which is found to be $(9\cdot18)\,(lg/a^2)$. The statical strain in this case is $5\,(lg/a^2)$, and the ratio of the maximum dynamical strain to the statical strain is 1·84 nearly. This strain occurs at the instant $t = (6\cdot183)\,l/a$.

The noteworthy result is that, even when the attached mass is not a large multiple of the mass of the rod, the greatest strain due to sudden loading does not fall far short of the theoretical limit, viz. twice the statical strain. (Cf. Article 84.) The principles to be applied to problems involving sudden changes of longitudinal motion have been perhaps sufficiently exemplified in this Article and the two preceding. An example of practical importance is solved in a paper by J. Perry "Winding ropes in mines," *Phil. Mag.* (Ser. 6), vol. 11 (1906), p. 107.

284. Longitudinal impact of rods.

The problem of the longitudinal impact of two rods or bars has been solved by means of analysis of the same kind as that in Article 281*. It is slightly more complicated, because different undetermined functions are required to express the states of the two bars; but it is simpler because these functions are themselves simple. The problem can be solved also by

* Saint-Venant, *J. de Math. (Liouville)*, (Sér. 2), t. 12 (1867).

considering the propagation of waves along the two rods*. The extension ϵ and velocity v at the front of an extensional wave travelling along a rod are connected by the equation $\epsilon = -v/a$. (Cf. Article 205.) The same relation holds at any point of a wave of compression travelling entirely in one direction, as is obvious from the formula $w = f(at - s)$ which characterizes such a wave. When a wave of compression travelling along the rod reaches a free end, it is reflected; and the nature of the motion and strain in the reflected wave is most simply investigated by regarding the rod as produced indefinitely, and supposing a wave to travel in the opposite direction along the continuation of the rod in such a way that, when the two waves are superposed, there is no compression at the end section. It is clear that the velocity propagated with the "image" wave in the continuation of the rod must be the same as that propagated with the original wave, and that the extension propagated with the "image" wave must be equal numerically to the compression in the original wave†.

Now let l, l' be the lengths of the rods, supposed to be of the same material and cross-section‡, and let V, V' be their velocities, supposed to be in the same sense. We shall take $l > l'$. When the rods come into contact the ends at the junction take a common velocity, which is determined by the condition that the system consisting of two very small contiguous portions of the rods, which have their motions changed in the same very short time, does not, in that time, lose or gain momentum. The common velocity must therefore be $\frac{1}{2}(V + V')$. Waves set out from the junction and travel along both rods, and the velocity of each element of either rod, relative to the rod as a whole, when the wave reaches it, is $\frac{1}{2}(V \sim V')$, so that the waves are waves of compression, and the compression is $\frac{1}{2}(V \sim V')/a$.

To trace the subsequent state of the shorter rod l', we think of this rod as continued indefinitely beyond the free end, and we reduce it to rest by impressing on the whole system a velocity equal and opposite to V'. At the instant of impact a positive wave§ starts from the junction and travels along the rod; the velocity and compression in this wave are $\frac{1}{2}(V \sim V')$ and $\frac{1}{2}(V \sim V')/a$. At the same instant a negative "image" wave starts from the section distant $2l'$ from the junction in the fictitious continuation of the rod; the velocity and extension in this "image" wave are $\frac{1}{2}(V \sim V')$ and $\frac{1}{2}(V \sim V')/a$. After a time l'/a from the instant of impact both these waves reach the free end, and they are then superposed. Any part of the actual rod in which they are superposed becomes unstrained and takes the velocity $V \sim V'$. When the reflected wave

* Cf. Kelvin and Tait, *Nat. Phil.*, Part I., pp. 280, 281.

† Cf. Lord Rayleigh, *Theory of Sound*, vol. 2, § 257.

‡ Saint-Venant, *loc. cit.*, discusses the case of different materials or sections as well.

§ An extensional wave is "positive" or "negative" according as the velocity of the material is in the same sense as the velocity of propagation or in the opposite sense.

reaches the junction, that is to say after a time $2l'/a$ from the instant of impact, the whole of the rod l' is moving with the velocity $V \sim V'$, and is unstrained. Hence, superposing the original velocity V', we have the result that, after the time taken by an extensional wave to travel over twice the length of the shorter rod, this rod is unstrained and is moving with the velocity V originally possessed by the longer rod.

To trace the state of the longer rod l from the beginning of the impact, we think of this rod as continued indefinitely beyond its free end, and we reduce it to rest by impressing on the whole system a velocity equal and opposite to V. At the instant of impact a positive wave starts from the junction and travels along the rod; the velocity and compression in this wave are $\frac{1}{2}(V \sim V')$ and $\frac{1}{2}(V \sim V')/a$. At the same instant a negative "image" wave starts from the section distant $2l$ from the junction in the fictitious continuation of the rod; the velocity and extension in this "image" wave are $\frac{1}{2}(V \sim V')$ and $\frac{1}{2}(V \sim V')/a$. After a time $2l'/a$ from the instant of impact the junction end becomes free from pressure, and a rear surface of the actual wave is formed. Hence, the rod being regarded as continued indefinitely, the wave of compression and the "image" wave of extension are both of length $2l'$. Immediately after the instant $2l'/a$ the junction end becomes unstrained and takes zero velocity. Hence, superposing the original velocity V, we see that this end takes actually the velocity V, so that the junction ends of the two rods remain in contact but without pressure.

The state of the longer rod l between the instants $2l'/a$ and $2l/a$ is determined by superposing the waves of length $2l'$, which started out at the instant of impact from the junction end and the section distant $2l$ from it in the fictitious continuation of the rod. After a time greater than l/a these waves are superposed over a finite length of the rod, terminated at the free end, and this part becomes unstrained and takes a velocity $V \sim V'$, the velocity $-V$ being supposed, as before, to be impressed on the system. The state of the rod at the instant $2l/a$ in the case where $l > 2l'$ is different from the state at the same instant in the case where $l < 2l'$. If $l > 2l'$ the wave of compression has passed out of the rod, and the wave of extension occupies a length $2l'$ terminated at the junction. The strain in this portion is extension equal to $\frac{1}{2}(V \sim V')/a$ and the velocity in the portion is $\frac{1}{2}(V \sim V')$, the velocity $-V$ being impressed as before. The remainder of the rod is unstrained and has the velocity zero. Hence, superposing the original velocity V, we see that a length $l - 2l'$ terminated at the free end has at this instant the velocity V and no strain, and the remainder has the velocity $\frac{1}{2}(V + V')$ and extension $\frac{1}{2}(V \sim V')/a$. The wave in the rod is now reflected at the junction, so that it becomes a wave of compression travelling away from the junction, the compression is $\frac{1}{2}(V \sim V')/a$ and the velocity of the junction end becomes V'. The ends that came into contact have now exchanged velocities, and the rods separate.

If $l < 2l'$ the waves of compression and extension are, at the instant $2l/a$, superposed over a length equal to $2l' - l$ terminated at the free end, and the rest of the rod is occupied by the wave of extension. The velocity $-V$ being impressed as before, the portion of length $2l' - l$ terminated at the free end is unstrained and has the velocity $V \sim V'$, and the remaining portion has extension $\frac{1}{2}(V \sim V')/a$ and velocity $\frac{1}{2}(V \sim V')$. Hence, superposing the original velocity V, we see that a length $2l' - l$ terminated at the free end has at the instant the velocity V' and no strain, and the remainder has the velocity $\frac{1}{2}(V + V')$ and the extension $\frac{1}{2}(V \sim V')/a$. The wave is reflected at the junction, as in the other case, and the junction end takes the velocity V'.

In both cases the rods separate after an interval equal to the time taken by a wave of extension to travel over twice the length of the longer rod. The shorter rod takes the original velocity of the longer, and rebounds without strain; while the longer rebounds in a state of vibration. The centres of mass of the two rods move after impact in the same way as if there were a "coefficient of restitution" equal to the ratio $l' : l$.

284 A. Impact and vibrations.

Reference has already been made in the Introduction (pp. 25, 26) to the suggestion that the phenomena of impact, and, in particular, the existence of the Newtonian "coefficient of restitution" might be traced to the presence after impact of some energy existing in the form of vibrations of the bodies which have come into collision*. The result which has just been obtained appeared, at first sight, to corroborate this suggestion; but the difficulty arose that the result is not verified by experiment. This difficulty led Voigt† to imagine that some special conditions must hold near the ends of two rods which impinge longitudinally, or, in other words, that the rods should be thought of as separated by a layer of transition, in which the determining circumstance is the geometrical character of the terminal surfaces. This matter has been further investigated by J. E. Sears‡. He made an elaborate series of experiments on the longitudinal impact of metal rods with rounded ends, and constructed a theory, according to which the state of a small portion of either rod near the ends that come into contact is determined by Hertz's theory of impact (Chapter VIII, *supra*), while the state of the remaining portions is determined by Saint-Venant's theory, described in Article 284. Sears' theory was confirmed by experiment. Further experiments are described by J. E. P. Wagstaff, *London, Roy. Soc. Proc.* (Ser. A), vol. 105 (1924), p. 544.

In regard to the general question of vibrations set up in bodies by impact reference may be made to Lord Rayleigh, *Phil. Mag.* (Ser. 6), vol. 11, 1916,

* See Kelvin and Tait, *Nat. Phil.*, Part I., §§ 302—304.

† See Introduction, footnote 113.

‡ *Cambridge Phil. Soc. Proc.*, vol. 14, 1908, p. 257, and *Cambridge Phil. Soc. Trans.*, vol. 21, 1912, p. 49.

p. 283, or *Scientific Papers,* vol. 4, p. 292. Further experiments on impact are described by B. Hopkinson, *loc. cit. ante,* p. 117.

285. Problems of dynamical resistance involving transverse vibration.

The results obtained in Articles 281—284 illustrate the general character of dynamical resistances. Similar methods to those used in these Articles cannot be employed in problems that involve transverse vibration for lack of a general functional solution of the equation (6) of Article 280*. In such problems the best procedure seems to be to express the displacement as the sum of a series of normal functions, and to adjust the constant coefficients of the terms of the series so as to satisfy the initial conditions. For examples of the application of this method reference may be made to Lord Rayleigh† and Saint-Venant‡.

A simplified method of obtaining an approximate solution can sometimes be employed. For example, suppose that the problem is that of a rod "supported" at both ends and struck by a massive body moving with a given velocity. After the impact let the striking body become attached to the rod. At any instant after the instant of impact we may, for an approximation, regard the rod as at rest and bent by a certain transverse load applied at the point of impact. It will have, at the point, a certain deflexion, which is determined in terms of the load by the result of Article 247 (*d*). The load is equal to the pressure between the rod and the striking body, and the deflexion of the rod at the point of impact is equal to the displacement of the striking body from its position at the instant of impact. The equation of motion of the striking body, supposed subjected to a force equal and opposite to this transverse load, combined with the conditions that, at the instant of impact, the body has the prescribed velocity, and is instantaneously at the point of impact, are sufficient conditions to determine the displacement of the striking body and the pressure between it and the rod at any subsequent instant. In this method, sometimes described as Cox's method§, the deflexion of the rod by the striking body is regarded as a statical effect, and thus this method is in a sense an anticipation of Hertz's theory of impact (Article 139). It has already been pointed out that a similar method was used also by Willis and Stokes in their treatment of the problem of the travelling load||.

A somewhat similar method has been employed by Lord Rayleigh¶ for an approximate determination of the frequency of the gravest mode of transverse vibration of a rod. He set out from a general theorem to the effect that the frequency of any dynamical system, that would be found by assuming the displacement to be of a specified type, cannot be less than the frequency of the gravest mode of vibration of the system. For a rod clamped at one end and free at the other, he showed that a good approximation to the frequency may be made by assuming the displacement of the rod to be of the same type as if it were deflected statically by a transverse load, concentrated at a distance from the free end

* Fourier's solution by means of definite integrals, given in the *Bulletin des Sciences à la Société philomatique*, 1818 (cf. Lord Rayleigh, *Theory of Sound*, vol. 1, § 192), is applied to problems of dynamical resistance by J. Boussinesq, *Applications des Potentiels*, pp. 456 *et seq.*

† *Theory of Sound*, vol. 1, § 168.

‡ See the 'Annotated Clebsch,' *Note du* § 61.

§ H. Cox, *Cambridge Phil. Soc. Trans.*, vol. 9 (1850). Cf. Todhunter and Pearson's *History*, vol. 1, Article 1435.

|| See Introduction, p. 26.

¶ *Theory of Sound*, vol. 1, § 182.

equal to one quarter of the length. This method has been the subject of some discussion*. It has been shown to be applicable to the determination of the frequency of the gravest mode of transverse vibration of a rod of variable cross-section†. It has been shown also that a method of successive approximation to the various normal functions for such a rod, and their frequencies, can be founded upon such solutions as Lord Rayleigh's when these solutions are regarded as first approximations‡.

286. The whirling of shafts§.

A long shaft rotating between bearings remains straight at low speeds, but when the speed is high enough the shaft can rotate steadily in a form in which the central-line is bent. The shaft is then said to "whirl." Let u be the transverse displacement of a point on the central-line, Ω the angular velocity with which the shaft rotates. When the motion is steady the equation of motion, formed in the same way as equation (6) in Article 280, is

$$-\rho\Omega^2 u = -Ek'^2 \frac{d^4 u}{ds^4}, \quad\text{.........................(26)}$$

and the solution of this equation must be adjusted to satisfy appropriate conditions at the ends of the shaft. We shall consider the case in which the ends $s=0$ and $s=l$ are "supported." The equation is the same as that for a rod executing simple harmonic vibrations of period $2\pi/\Omega$. In order that the equation

$$Ek'^2 \frac{d^4 u}{ds^4} = \rho\Omega^2 u \quad\text{.............................(27)}$$

may have a solution which makes u and d^2u/ds^2 vanish at $s=0$ and at $s=l$, the speed of rotation Ω must be such that $\Omega/2\pi$ is equal to the frequency of a normal mode of flexural vibration of the doubly-supported shaft. Thus the lowest speed at which whirling takes place is such that $\Omega/2\pi$ is equal to the frequency of the gravest mode of flexural vibration of such a shaft. If we write

$$\rho\Omega^2/Ek'^2 = m^4,$$

* C. A. B. Garrett, *Phil. Mag.* (Ser. 6), vol. 8 (1904), and C. Chree, *Phil. Mag.* (Ser. 6), vol. 9 (1905).

† J. Morrow, *Phil. Mag.* (Ser. 6), vol. 10 (1905). Some special cases of the vibrations of a rod of variable section, in which the exact forms of the normal functions can be determined in terms of Bessel's functions, were discussed by Kirchhoff, *Berlin Monatsberichte*, 1879, or *Ges. Abhandlungen*, p. 339. Other calculable cases of the vibrations of rods of variable section are discussed by P. F. Ward, *Phil. Mag.* (Ser. 6), vol. 25 (1913), p. 85, J. W. Nicholson, *London, Roy. Soc. Proc.* (Ser. A), vol. 93 (1917), p. 506 and vol. 97 (1920), p. 172, and D. M. Wrinch, *London, Roy. Soc. Proc.* (Ser. A), vol. 101 (1922), p. 493 and *Phil. Mag.* (Ser. 6), vol. 46 (1923), p. 273. Nicholson points out that the problem may have some biological interest. It has also an interest in its connexion with the "whirling" of shafts, considered in Article 286 *infra*.

‡ A. Davidoglou, 'Sur l'équation des vibrations transversales des verges élastiques,' Paris (*Thèse*), 1900.

§ Cf. A. G. Greenhill, *Inst. Mech. Engineers, Proc.*, 1883.

the possible values of m are given by the equation $\sin ml = 0$, and the smallest value of Ω for which whirling can take place is

$$(\pi^2 k'/l^2) \sqrt{(E/\rho)}.$$

The above is merely an outline of the explanation of the important phenomenon of whirling, in regard to the possibility of which reference may be made to W. J. M. Rankine, *The Engineer*, vol. 27, 1869, p. 249. The same simple theory for an unloaded shaft under various terminal conditions is developed by A. G. Greenhill (*loc. cit.*). An investigation of the nature of the displacement in the rotating and vibrating shaft, combining the method of Southwell (*loc. cit.*, p. 410) and that of Pochhammer (*loc. cit.*, p. 287), has been given by F. B. Pidduck, *London, Math. Soc. Proc.* (Ser. 2), vol. 18 (1920), p. 393. The important technical problem of a shaft carrying loads, pulleys for example, has been discussed theoretically and experimentally by S. Dunkerley, *Phil. Trans. Roy. Soc.* (Ser. A), vol. 185 (1894) and C. Chree, *Phil. Mag.* (Ser. 6), vol. 7 (1904). It clearly involves the problem of determining the frequency of the gravest mode of transverse vibration of the shaft that is consistent with the terminal conditions. For further developments in regard to the theory reference may be made to R. V. Southwell, *Phil. Mag.* (Ser. 6), vol. 41 (1921), p. 419 and W. L. Cowley and H. Levy, same vol., p. 584. Special cases of loading are treated by H. H. Jeffcott, *Phil. Mag.* (Ser. 6), vol. 37 (1919), p. 304 and vol. 42 (1921), p. 635, also *London, Roy. Soc. Proc.* (Ser. A), vol. 95 (1919), p. 106, S. Lees, *Phil. Mag.* (Ser. 6), vol. 37 (1919), p. 515 and vol. 45 (1923), p. 689 (with a note by W. McF. Orr at p. 708), and E. H. Darnley, *Phil. Mag.* (Ser. A), vol. 41 (1921), p. 81. The vibrations of continuous beams are considered by W. L. Cowley and H. Levy, *London, Roy. Soc. Proc.* (Ser. A), vol. 95 (1919), p. 440, and the stability of a rotating shaft under end thrust and twisting couple by R. V. Southwell, *Brit. Assoc. Rep.* 1921, p. 345.

CHAPTER XXI

SMALL DEFORMATION OF NATURALLY CURVED RODS

287. In the investigations of Chapters XVIII and XIX we have given prominence to the consideration of modes of deformation of a thin rod which involve large displacements of the central-line and twist that is not small, and we have regarded cases in which the displacement of the central-line and the twist are small as limiting cases. This was the method followed, for example, in the theory of spiral springs (Article 271). In such cases the formulæ for the components of curvature and twist may be calculated, as has been explained, by treating the central-line as unextended. We can give a systematic account of such modes of deformation as involve small displacements only by introducing quantities to denote the components of the displacement of points on the central-line, and subjecting these quantities to a condition which expresses that the central-line is not extended*.

288. Specification of the displacement.

The small deformation of naturally straight rods has been sufficiently investigated already, and we shall therefore suppose that, in the unstressed state, the rod has curvature and twist. As in Article 259, we shall use a system of axes of x_0, y_0, z_0, the origin of which moves along the unstrained central-line with unit velocity, the axis of z_0 being always directed along the tangent to this line, and the axes of x_0 and y_0 being directed along the principal axes of the cross-sections at their centroids. We have denoted by $\frac{1}{2}\pi - f_0$ the angle which the axis of x_0 at any point makes with the principal normal of the unstrained central-line at the point, and by κ_0, κ_0', τ_0 the components of initial curvature and the initial twist. We have the formula

$$\kappa_0'/\kappa_0 = -\tan f_0.$$

The curvature $1/\rho_0$ and the tortuosity $1/\Sigma_0$ of the central-line are given by the formulæ

$$(1/\rho_0)^2 = \kappa_0^2 + \kappa_0'^2, \quad 1/\Sigma_0 = \tau_0 - df_0/ds,$$

in which s denotes the arc of the central-line measured from some chosen point of it.

When the rod is slightly deformed, any particle of the central-line undergoes a small displacement, the components of which, referred to the axes of x_0, y_0, z_0, with origin at the unstrained position P of the particle, will be

* The theory was partially worked out by Saint-Venant in a series of papers in *Paris, C. R.*, t. 17 (1843), and more fully by J. H. Michell, *Messenger of Math.*, vol. 19 (1890). The latter has also obtained some exact solutions of the equations of equilibrium of an elastic solid body bounded by an incomplete tore, and these solutions are confirmatory of the theory when the tore is thin. See *London Math. Soc. Proc.*, vol. 31 (1900), p. 130.

denoted by u, v, w. The rod will receive a new curvature and twist, defined, as in Articles 252 and 259, by means of a moving system of "principal torsion-flexure axes." We recall the conventions that the axis of z in this system is directed along the tangent of the strained central-line at the point P_1 to which P is displaced, and that the plane of (x, z) is the tangent plane at P_1 of the surface made up of the aggregate of particles which, in the unstressed state, lie in the plane of (x_0, z_0) at P. We have denoted the components of curvature and the twist of the strained central-line at P_1 by $\kappa_1, \kappa_1', \tau_1$. When the displacement (u, v, w) of any point of the central-line is known, the tangent of the strained central-line at any point is known, and it is clear that one additional quantity will suffice to determine the orientation of the axes of (x, y, z) at P_1 relative to the axes of (x_0, y_0, z_0) at P. We shall take this quantity to be the cosine of the angle between the axis of x at P_1 and the axis of y_0 at P, and shall denote it by β. The relative orientation of the two sets of axes may be determined by the orthogonal scheme of transformation

	x_0	y_0	z_0
x	L_1	M_1	N_1
y	L_2	M_2	N_2
z	L_3	M_3	N_3

..............................(1)

in which, for example, L_1 is the cosine of the angle between the axis of x at P_1 and the axis of x_0 at P. We shall express the cosines $L_1, \ldots$, the components of curvature κ_1, κ_1' and the twist τ_1 in terms of u, v, w, β.

289. Orientation of the principal torsion-flexure axes.

The direction-cosines L_3, M_3, N_3 are those of the tangent at P_1 to the strained central-line referred to the axes of x_0, y_0, z_0 at P. Now the coordinates of P_1 referred to these axes are identical with the components of displacement u, v, w. Let P' be a point of the unstrained central-line near to P, let δs be the arc PP', and let $\delta x_0, \delta y_0, \delta z_0$ be the coordinates of P' referred to the axes of x_0, y_0, z_0 at P, also let ξ, η, ζ be the coordinates of P_1', the displaced position of P', referred to the same axes. The limits such as $\lim_{\delta s=0} (\xi - u)/\delta s$ are the direction-cosines $L_3, \ldots$. Let (u', v', w') be the displacement of P' referred to the axes of x_0, y_0, z_0 at P', and (U', V', W') the same displacement referred to the axes of x_0, y_0, z_0 at P. Then

$$(\xi, \eta, \zeta) = (\delta x_0 + U', \delta y_0 + V', \delta z_0 + W').$$

The limits of $\delta x_0/\delta s, \delta y_0/\delta s, \delta z_0/\delta s$ are 0, 0, 1. The limits of $(u' - u)/\delta s, \ldots$ are $du/ds, \ldots$ and we have the usual formulæ connected with moving axes in such forms as

$$\lim_{\delta s=0} \frac{U' - u}{\delta s} = \frac{du}{ds} - v\tau_0 + w\kappa_0'.$$

Hence we obtain the equations

$$L_3=\frac{du}{ds}-v\tau_0+w\kappa_0',\quad M_3=\frac{dv}{ds}-w\kappa_0+u\tau_0,\quad N_3=1+\frac{dw}{ds}-u\kappa_0'+v\kappa_0. \quad \text{...(2)}$$

The equation $L_3^2+M_3^2+N_3^2=1$ leads, when we neglect squares and products of u, v, w, to the equation

$$\frac{dw}{ds}-u\kappa_0'+v\kappa_0=0, \quad \text{.............................(3)}$$

which expresses the condition that the central-line is unextended. In consequence of this equation we have $N_3=1$.

The direction-cosines of the axes of x, y at P_1, referred to the axes of x_0, y_0, z_0 at P, are determined by the conditions that M_1 is β and that the scheme of transformation (1) is orthogonal and its determinant is 1. These conditions give us

$$\left.\begin{array}{lll} L_1=1, & M_1=\beta, & N_1=-L_3, \\ L_2=-\beta, & M_2=1, & N_2=-M_3. \end{array}\right\} \quad \text{.....................(4)}$$

These equations might be found otherwise from the formulæ (7) of Article 253 by writing $L_1, \ldots$ instead of $l_1, \ldots$, taking θ to be small, and putting β for $\phi+\psi$. They are, of course, correct to the first order in the small quantities u, v, w, β.

290. Curvature and twist.

For the calculation of the components of curvature and the twist we have the formulæ (6) of Article 253, in which $\kappa_1, \ldots$ are written for $\kappa, \ldots$. In those formulæ $l_1, \ldots$ denoted direction-cosines of the axes of x, y, z referred to fixed axes. Here we have taken $L_1, \ldots$ to denote the direction-cosines of the axes of x, y, z at P_1 referred to the axes of x_0, y_0, z_0 at P. If P' is a point near to P, so that the arc $PP'=\delta s$, and P_1' is the displaced position of P', we may denote by $L_1', \ldots$ the direction-cosines of the axes of x, y, z at P_1' referred to the axes of x_0, y_0, z_0 at P', and then the limits such as $\lim_{\delta s=0}(L_1'-L_1)/\delta s$ are the differential coefficients such as dL_1/ds. Let the fixed axes of reference for $l_1, \ldots$ be the axes of x_0, y_0, z_0 at P, and let $l_1+\delta l_1, \ldots$ denote the direction-cosines of the axes of x, y, z at P_1' referred to these fixed axes. Then the limits such as $\lim_{\delta s=0}\delta l_1/\delta s$ are the differential coefficients such as dl_1/ds. It is clear that, at P, $l_1=L_1, \ldots$ but that $dl_1/ds \neq dL_1/ds, \ldots$. We have in fact the usual formulæ connected with moving axes, viz.:

$$dl_1/ds=dL_1/ds-M_1\tau_0+N_1\kappa_0',$$

$$dm_1/ds=dM_1/ds-N_1\kappa_0+L_1\tau_0,$$

$$dn_1/ds=dN_1/ds-L_1\kappa_0'+M_1\kappa_0,$$

with similar formulæ for $dl_2/ds, \ldots$ and $dl_3/ds, \ldots$.

In the formulæ (6) of Article 253 we write $\kappa_1, \ldots$ for $\kappa, \ldots$, put $n_3 = N_3 = 1$, replace $l_1, \ldots$ by the values found for $L_1, \ldots$ in (2) and (4), and substitute the values just found for $dl_1/ds, \ldots$. Rejecting terms of the second order in the small quantities u, v, w, β, we obtain the equations

$$\left.\begin{aligned} \kappa_1 &= \kappa_0 + \beta\kappa_0' - \frac{dM_3}{ds} - \tau_0 L_3, \\ \kappa_1' &= \kappa_0' - \beta\kappa_0 + \frac{dL_3}{ds} - \tau_0 M_3, \\ \tau_1 &= \tau_0 + \frac{d\beta}{ds} + \kappa_0 L_3 + \kappa_0' M_3, \end{aligned}\right\} \qquad \text{.....(5)}$$

in which L_3 and M_3 are given by the first two of equations (2).

291. Simplified formulæ.

The formulæ are simplified in the case where $f_0 = \frac{1}{2}\pi$. In this case the axis of x_0, which is a principal axis of a cross-section at a point of the unstrained central-line, coincides with the principal normal of this curve at the point. When this is the case we have

$$\left.\begin{aligned} &\kappa_0 = 0, \quad \kappa_0' = 1/\rho_0, \quad \tau_0 = 1/\Sigma_0, \\ &L_3 = \frac{du}{ds} - \frac{v}{\Sigma_0} + \frac{w}{\rho_0}, \quad M_3 = \frac{dv}{ds} + \frac{u}{\Sigma_0}, \quad N_3 = 1, \\ &\kappa_1 = \frac{\beta}{\rho_0} - \frac{d}{ds}\left(\frac{dv}{ds} + \frac{u}{\Sigma_0}\right) - \frac{1}{\Sigma_0}\left(\frac{du}{ds} - \frac{v}{\Sigma_0} + \frac{w}{\rho_0}\right), \\ &\kappa_1' = \frac{1}{\rho_0} + \frac{d}{ds}\left(\frac{du}{ds} - \frac{v}{\Sigma_0} + \frac{w}{\rho_0}\right) - \frac{1}{\Sigma_0}\left(\frac{dv}{ds} + \frac{u}{\Sigma_0}\right), \\ &\tau_1 = \frac{1}{\Sigma_0} + \frac{d\beta}{ds} + \frac{1}{\rho_0}\left(\frac{dv}{ds} + \frac{u}{\Sigma_0}\right). \end{aligned}\right\} \qquad \text{.....(6)}$$

The condition that the central-line is unextended is

$$\frac{dw}{ds} = \frac{u}{\rho_0}. \qquad \text{.....(7)}$$

The measures of curvature and tortuosity and the direction-cosines of the principal normal and binormal can be calculated from these formulæ or from the more general formulæ of Article 290.

292. Problems of equilibrium.

The theory is applicable to such problems as the deformation of the links of chains* by the pressure of adjacent links, and it may be used also to give an account of the behaviour of arches†, the link or the arch being treated as a

* E. Winkler, *Der Civilingenieur*, Bd. 4 (1858). Winkler's memoir is described at length and corrected in detail in Todhunter and Pearson's *History*, vol. 2, pp. 422 *et seq.*

† M. Bresse, *Recherches analytiques sur la flexion et la résistance des pièces courbes*, Paris 1854. An account of this treatise also is given in Todhunter and Pearson's *History*, vol. 2, pp. 352 *et seq.* H. T. Eddy, *Amer. J. of Math.*, vol. 1 (1878), has proposed a graphical method of treatment of the problem of arches.

thin curved rod. The equations of equilibrium have been given in Article 259, and we have found in preceding Articles of this chapter expressions for all the quantities that occur in terms of the displacement (u, v, w) and the angular displacement β, the quantities u, v, w being themselves connected by an equation (3) or (7). Naturally any special problem, such as those mentioned, is of a very technical character, and we shall content ourselves here with a slight study of some cases of the bending of a rod in the form of an incomplete circular ring.

(a) *Incomplete circular ring bent in its plane.*

Let the unstrained central-line be a circle of radius a, and let θ be the angle between the radius drawn from the centre of the circle to any point on it and a chosen radius, then

$$\rho_0 = ds/d\theta = a.$$

The displacement u is directed along the radius drawn inwards, and the displacement w is directed along the tangent of the circle in the sense in which θ increases. We shall suppose that the plane of the circle is a principal plane of the rod at any point, and that the flexural rigidity for bending in this plane is B. Then v, β and $1/\Sigma_0$ vanish, and the condition that the central-line is unextended is

$$\frac{dw}{d\theta} = u. \quad \text{......................................(8)}$$

The flexural couple G' in the plane of the circle is

$$G' = \frac{B}{a^2}\left(\frac{d^3w}{d\theta^3} + \frac{dw}{d\theta}\right); \quad \text{..........................(9)}$$

the other flexural couple and the torsional couple vanish.

Let the rod be bent by forces having components X, Z per unit of length directed along the radius and tangent at any point. The equations of equilibrium obtained from (26) and (27) of Article 259 are

$$\frac{dN}{d\theta} + T + Xa = 0, \quad \frac{dT}{d\theta} - N + Za = 0, \quad \frac{dG'}{d\theta} + Na = 0. \quad \text{......(10)}$$

Hence we find that the shearing force N and the tension T are expressed in terms of w by the equations

$$N = -\frac{B}{a^3}\left(\frac{d^4w}{d\theta^4} + \frac{d^2w}{d\theta^2}\right), \quad T = -Xa + \frac{B}{a^3}\left(\frac{d^5w}{d\theta^5} + \frac{d^3w}{d\theta^3}\right), \quad \text{......(11)}$$

and that w satisfies the equation *

$$\frac{B}{a^3}\left(\frac{d^6w}{d\theta^6} + 2\frac{d^4w}{d\theta^4} + \frac{d^2w}{d\theta^2}\right) = a\left(\frac{dX}{d\theta} - Z\right). \quad \text{..............(12)}$$

* Cf. H. Lamb, *London Math. Soc. Proc.*, vol. 19 (1888), p. 365. The results given in the text under the numbers (i)—(v) are taken from this paper. For further investigations concerning the incomplete circular ring reference may be made to R. Mayer, *Zeitschr. f. Math. u. Phys.*, Bd. 61 (1913), p. 246, H. Hencky, *Zeitschr. f. angewandte Math. u. Mech.*, Bd. 2 (1921), p. 292, and S. Timoschenko, same Journal, Bd. 3 (1922), p. 358.

We note the following results:

(i) When the rod is slightly bent by couples equal to K applied at its ends in its plane, the central-line remains circular, but its radius is reduced by the fraction Ka/B of itself.

(ii) When the ends of the rod are given by $\theta = \pm\alpha$, so that the line joining them subtends an angle 2α at the centre, and the rod is slightly bent by forces equal to R acting as tension along this line as in Fig. 64, the displacement is given by the equations

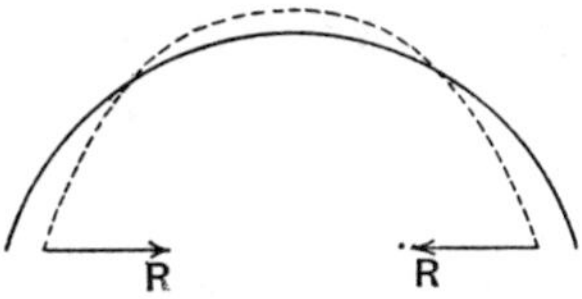

Fig. 64.

$$w = -(a^3R/B)\,\theta\,(\cos\alpha + \tfrac{1}{2}\cos\theta), \quad u = \partial w/\partial\theta.$$

If, as in Fig. 64, the ends of the rod move along the line of action of the forces R, an additional displacement, which would be possible in a rigid body, must be superposed on this displacement.

(iii) When the rod is slightly bent by forces equal to S, applied as shown in Fig. 65 to rigid pieces attached to its ends and extending across the chord of the incomplete ring, the displacement is given by the equations

$$w = -\tfrac{1}{2}(a^3S/B)\,\theta\sin\theta, \quad u = \partial w/\partial\theta.$$

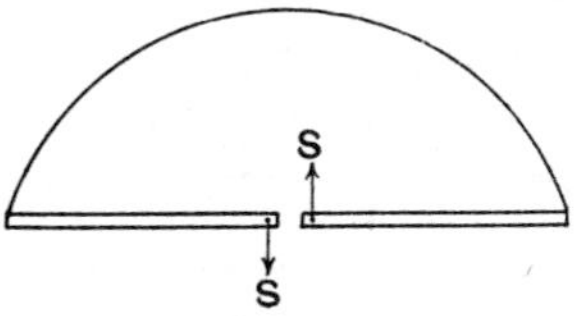

Fig. 65.

(iv) When the rod forms a complete circular ring, and is slightly bent by normal pressures equal to X_1 applied at the opposite ends of a diameter, we measure θ from this diameter as shown in Fig. 66, and find for the displacement w at a point on that side of this diameter in which $\pi > \theta > 0$

$$w = -X_1(a^3/B)\,[\theta/\pi - \tfrac{1}{2}(1 - \cos\theta - \tfrac{1}{2}\theta\sin\theta)], \quad u = \partial w/\partial\theta.$$

The displacements are clearly the same at any two points symmetrically situated on opposite sides of this diameter.

We may deduce the value of u at any point, and we may prove that the diameter which coincides with the line of thrust is shortened by $\{(\pi^2-8)/4\pi\}(X_1a^3/B)$, while the perpendicular diameter is lengthened by

$$\{(4-\pi)/2\pi\}(X_1a^3/B)^*.$$

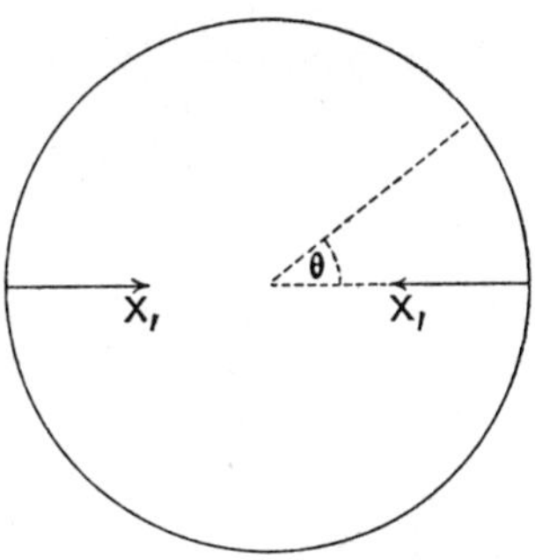

Fig. 66.

(v) When the rod forms a complete circular ring of weight W, which is suspended from a point in its circumference, we measure θ from the highest point, and find for the displacement w at a point for which $\pi > \theta > 0$ the value

$$w = -W(a^3/B)(8\pi)^{-1}\{(\theta-\pi)^2\sin\theta - 4(\theta-\pi)(1-\cos\theta) - \pi^2\sin\theta\};$$

the displacement is the same at the corresponding point in the other half of the ring.

In this case we may prove that the amounts by which the vertical diameter is lengthened and the horizontal diameter shortened are the halves of what they would be if the weight W were concentrated at the lowest point.

(vi) When the rod forms a complete circular ring which rotates with angular velocity ω about one diameter†, taken as axis of y, its central-line describes a surface of revolution of which the meridian curve is given by the equations

$$x = a\sin\theta + \tfrac{1}{12}(m\omega^2a^5/B)\sin^3\theta,$$
$$y = a\cos\theta + \tfrac{1}{12}(m\omega^2a^5/B)(1-\cos^3\theta),$$

* These results are due to Saint-Venant, *Paris, C. R.*, t. 17 (1843).

† G. A. V. Peschka, *Zeitschr. f. Math. u. Phys.* (*Schlömilch*), Bd. 13 (1868).

where m denotes the mass of the ring per unit of length, and θ is measured from the diameter about which the ring rotates. This diameter is shortened and the perpendicular diameter lengthened by the same amount $\frac{1}{6}(m\omega^2 a^5/B)$.

(b) *Incomplete circular ring bent out of its plane.*

As before we take a for the radius of the circle, and specify a point on it by an angle θ; and we take the plane of the circle to be that principal plane of the rod for which the flexural rigidity is B. We consider the case where the rod is bent by a load W, applied at the end $\theta=\alpha$ in a direction at right angles to this plane, and is fixed at the end $\theta=0$, so that the tangent at this point is fixed in direction, and the transverse linear element which, in the unstressed state, is directed towards the centre of the circle is also fixed in direction*. Then u, v, w, β, $du/d\theta$, $dv/d\theta$ vanish with θ.

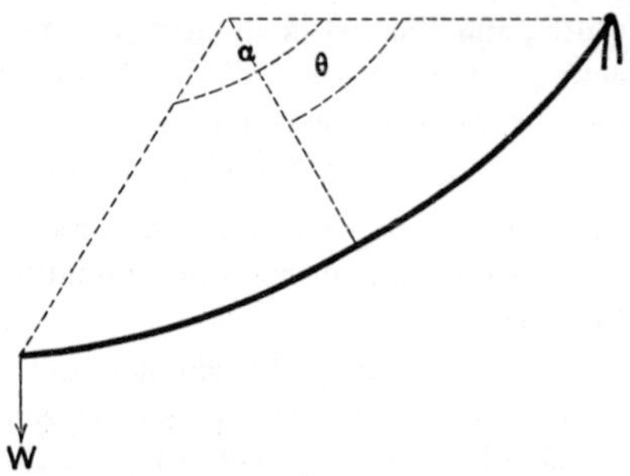

Fig. 67.

The stress-resultants N, N', T at any section are statically equivalent to the force W, of which the direction is parallel to that of the axis of y_0 at any section, and we have, therefore,

$$N=\beta W, \quad N'=W, \quad T=(W/a).(dv/d\theta). \quad \text{............(13)}$$

The equations of moments are, therefore,

$$\frac{dG}{d\theta}+H=aW, \quad \frac{dG'}{d\theta}=-a\beta W, \quad \frac{dH}{d\theta}-G=0. \quad \text{............(14)}$$

From the first and third of these, combined with the conditions that G and H vanish when $\theta=\alpha$, we find

$$G=-aW\sin(\alpha-\theta), \quad H=aW\{1-\cos(\alpha-\theta)\}. \quad \text{.........(15)}$$

Now we have

$$G=-\frac{A}{a^2}\left(\frac{d^2v}{d\theta^2}-a\beta\right), \quad H=\frac{C}{a^2}\frac{d}{d\theta}(v+a\beta), \quad \text{............(16)}$$

and from these equations and the terminal conditions at $\theta=0$ we can obtain the equations

$$\left.\begin{aligned} v+a\beta &= \frac{Wa^3}{C}\{\theta-\sin\alpha+\sin(\alpha-\theta)\}, \\ v &= \frac{Wa^3}{C}\{(\theta-\sin\theta)-\sin\alpha(1-\cos\theta)\} \\ &\quad +\tfrac{1}{2}Wa^3\left(\frac{1}{C}+\frac{1}{A}\right)\{\theta\cos(\alpha-\theta)-\sin\theta\cos\alpha\}. \end{aligned}\right\} \quad \text{...(17)}$$

We may prove also that u and w are small of the order v^2.

* The problem has been discussed by Saint-Venant, *Paris, C. R.*, t. 17 (1843), and by H. Resal, *J. de Math.* (*Liouville*), (Sér. 3), t. 3 (1877). The treatment of the incomplete circular ring as a thin rod is a first approximation to a theory of the bending of curved beams. For a discussion of curved beams reference may be made to J. J. Guest, *London, Roy. Soc. Proc.* (Ser. A), vol. 95, 1918, p. 1.

293. Vibrations of a circular ring.

We shall illustrate the application of the theory to vibrations by considering the free vibrations of a rod which, in the unstressed state, forms a circular ring or a portion of such a ring, and we shall restrict our work to the case where the cross-section of the ring also is circular. We denote the radius of the cross-section by c, and that of the circle formed by the central-line by a, and we take the displacement u to be directed along the radius drawn towards the centre of the latter circle. The equations of motion, formed as in Articles 278—280, are

$$\frac{\partial N}{\partial \theta} + T = ma\frac{\partial^2 u}{\partial t^2}, \quad \frac{\partial N'}{\partial \theta} = ma\frac{\partial^2 v}{\partial t^2}, \quad \frac{\partial T}{\partial \theta} - N = ma\frac{\partial^2 w}{\partial t^2}, \quad \text{......(18)}$$

and

$$\left.\begin{aligned} &\frac{\partial G}{\partial \theta} + H - N'a = -\tfrac{1}{4}c^2 m\frac{\partial^3 v}{\partial t^2 \partial \theta}, \\ &\frac{\partial G'}{\partial \theta} + Na = \tfrac{1}{4}c^2 m\frac{\partial^2}{\partial t^2}\left(\frac{\partial u}{\partial \theta} + w\right), \\ &\frac{\partial H}{\partial \theta} - G = \tfrac{1}{2}c^2 ma\frac{\partial^2 \beta}{\partial t^2}, \end{aligned}\right\} \quad \text{.....................(19)}$$

in which m is the mass of the ring per unit of length, and

$$G = \tfrac{1}{4}E\pi\frac{c^4}{a^2}\left(a\beta - \frac{\partial^2 v}{\partial \theta^2}\right), \quad G' = \tfrac{1}{4}E\pi\frac{c^4}{a^2}\left(\frac{\partial^2 u}{\partial \theta^2} + \frac{\partial w}{\partial \theta}\right), \quad H = \tfrac{1}{2}\mu\pi\frac{c^4}{a^2}\left(\frac{\partial v}{\partial \theta} + a\frac{\partial \beta}{\partial \theta}\right), \quad \text{...........(20)}$$

E being the Young's modulus and μ the rigidity of the material of the ring.

The above equations with the condition

$$\frac{\partial w}{\partial \theta} = u \quad \text{..............................(8 } bis\text{)}$$

yield the equations of motion.

It is clear that the above system of equations falls into two sets. In the first set v and β vanish, and the motion is specified by the displacement u or w, these variables being connected by equation (8); in this case we have flexural vibrations of the ring in its plane. In the second set u and w vanish, and the motion is specified by v or β, so that we have flexural vibrations involving both displacement at right angles to the plane of the ring and twist.

It may be shown in the same way that the vibrations of a curved rod fall into two such classes whenever the central-line of the unstressed rod is a plane curve, and its plane is a principal plane of the rod at each point. In case the central-line is a curve of double curvature there is no such separation of the modes of vibration into two classes, and the problem becomes extremely complicated*.

* The vibrations of a rod of which the natural form is helical have been investigated by J. H. Michell, *loc. cit.*, p. 444, and also by the present writer, *Cambridge Phil. Soc. Trans.*, vol. 18 (1899).

(a) *Flexural vibrations in the plane of the ring.*

We shall simplify the question by neglecting the "rotatory inertia." This amounts to omitting the right-hand member of the second of equations (19). We have then

$$N = -\frac{E\pi c^4}{4a^3}\left(\frac{\partial^4 w}{\partial \theta^4} + \frac{\partial^2 w}{\partial \theta^2}\right), \quad T = ma\frac{\partial^3 w}{\partial t^2 \partial \theta} - \frac{\partial N}{\partial \theta},$$

and

$$\frac{E\pi c^4}{4a^3}\left(\frac{\partial^6 w}{\partial \theta^6} + 2\frac{\partial^4 w}{\partial \theta^4} + \frac{\partial^2 w}{\partial \theta^2}\right) = ma\frac{\partial^2}{\partial t^2}\left(w - \frac{\partial^2 w}{\partial \theta^2}\right).$$

The normal functions for free vibration are determined by taking w to be of the form $W\cos(pt+\epsilon)$, where W is a function of θ. We then have the equation

$$\frac{\partial^6 W}{\partial \theta^6} + 2\frac{\partial^4 W}{\partial \theta^4} + \frac{\partial^2 W}{\partial \theta^2}\left(1 - \frac{4ma^4p^2}{E\pi c^4}\right) + \frac{4ma^4p^2}{E\pi c^4}W = 0.$$

The complete primitive is of the form

$$W = \sum_{\kappa=1}^{\kappa=3}(A_\kappa \cos n_\kappa \theta + B_\kappa \sin n_\kappa \theta),$$

where n_1, n_2, n_3 are the roots of the equation

$$n^2(n^2-1)^2 = (n^2+1)(4ma^4p^2/E\pi c^4).$$

If the ring is complete n must be an integer, and there are vibrations with n wave-lengths to the circumference, n being any integer greater than unity. The frequency is then given by the equation*

$$p^2 = \frac{E\pi c^4}{4ma^4}\frac{n^2(n^2-1)^2}{n^2+1}. \qquad \text{.........................(21)}$$

When the ring is incomplete the frequency equation is to be obtained by forming the conditions that N, T, G' vanish at the ends. The result is difficult to interpret except in the case where the initial curvature is very slight, or the radius of the central-line is large compared with its length. The pitch is then slightly lower than for a straight bar of the same length, material and cross-section†.

(b) *Flexural vibrations at right angles to the plane of the ring.*

We shall simplify the problem by neglecting the "rotatory inertia," that is to say we shall omit the right-hand members of the first and third of equations (19); we shall also suppose that the ring is complete. We may then write

$$v = V\cos(n\theta+\alpha)\cos(pt+\epsilon), \quad \beta = B'\cos(n\theta+\alpha)\cos(pt+\epsilon),$$

* The result is due to R. Hoppe, *J. f. Math.* (*Crelle*), Bd. 73 (1871).

† The question has been discussed very fully by H. Lamb, *loc. cit.*, p. 448.

where V, B', α, ϵ are constants, and n is an integer. From the first and third of equations (19) and the second of equations (18) we find the equations

$$n^2(aB'+n^2V)+\frac{2\mu}{E}n^2(aB'+V)=\frac{4ma^4p^2}{E\pi c^4}V,$$

$$\frac{2\mu}{E}n^2(aB'+V)+(aB'+n^2V)=0,$$

from which we obtain the frequency equation*

$$p^2=\frac{E\pi c^4}{4ma^4}\frac{n^2(n^2-1)^2}{n^2+1+\sigma}, \qquad (22)$$

where σ is Poisson's ratio for the material, and we have used the relation $E=2\mu(1+\sigma)$. It is noteworthy that, even in the gravest mode ($n=2$), the frequency differs extremely little from that given by equation (21) for the corresponding mode involving flexure in the plane of the ring.

(c) *Torsional and extensional vibrations.*

A curved rod possesses also modes of free vibration analogous to the torsional and extensional vibrations of a straight rod. For the torsional vibrations of a circular ring we take u and w to vanish, and suppose that v is small in comparison with $a\beta$, then the second of equations (18) and the first of equations (19) are satisfied approximately, and the third of equations (19) becomes approximately

$$\frac{\mu\pi c^4}{2a^2}\frac{\partial^2(a\beta)}{\partial\theta^2}-\frac{E\pi c^4}{4a^2}a\beta=\tfrac{1}{2}mc^2\frac{\partial^2(a\beta)}{\partial t^2}.$$

For a complete circular ring there are vibrations of this type with n wave-lengths to the circumference, and the frequency $p/2\pi$ is given by the equation

$$p^2=\frac{\mu\pi c^2}{ma^2}(1+\sigma+n^2). \qquad (23)$$

When $n=0$, the equations of motion can be satisfied exactly by putting $v=0$ and taking β to be independent of θ. The characteristic feature of this mode of vibration is that each circular cross-section of the circular ring is turned in its own plane through the same small angle β about the central-line, while this line is not displaced†.

For the extensional modes of vibration of a circular ring we take v and β to vanish, and suppose that equation (8) does not hold. Then the extension of the central-line is $a^{-1}(\partial w/\partial\theta-u)$, and the tension T is $E\pi c^2a^{-1}(\partial w/\partial\theta-u)$. The couples G, H and the shearing force N' vanish. The expressions for the couple G' and the shearing force N contain c^4 as a factor, while the expression for T contains c^2 as a factor. We may, therefore, for an approximation, omit G' and N, and neglect the rotatory inertia which gives rise to the right-hand member of the second of equations (19). The equations to be satisfied by u and w are then the first and third of equations (18), viz.:

$$ma\frac{\partial^2u}{\partial t^2}=\frac{E\pi c^2}{a}\left(\frac{\partial w}{\partial\theta}-u\right),\quad ma\frac{\partial^2w}{\partial t^2}=\frac{E\pi c^2}{a}\left(\frac{\partial^2w}{\partial\theta^2}-\frac{\partial u}{\partial\theta}\right).$$

* The result is due to J. H. Michell, *loc. cit.*, p. 444.

† The result that the modes of vibration involving displacements v and β are of two type was recognized by A. B. Basset, *London Math. Soc. Proc.*, vol. 23 (1892), and the frequency of the torsional vibrations was found by him.

The displacement in free vibrations of frequency $p/2\pi$ is given by equations of the form

$$u=(A\sin n\theta+B\cos n\theta)\cos(pt+\epsilon),$$

$$w=n(A\cos n\theta-B\sin n\theta)\cos(pt+\epsilon),$$

where

$$p^2=\frac{E\pi c^2}{ma^2}(1+n^2). \qquad \text{.................................(24)}$$

When $n=0$, w vanishes and u is independent of θ, and the equations of motion are satisfied exactly. The ring vibrates radially, so that the central-line forms a circle of periodically variable radius, and the cross-sections move without rotation.

The modes of vibration considered in (*c*) of this Article are of much higher pitch than those considered in (*a*) and (*b*), and they would probably be difficult to excite.

CHAPTER XXII

THE STRETCHING AND BENDING OF PLATES

294. Specification of stress in a plate.

The internal actions between the parts of a thin plate are most appropriately expressed in terms of stress-resultants and stress-couples reckoned across the whole thickness. We take the plate to be of thickness $2h$, and on the plane midway between the faces, called the "middle plane," we choose an origin and rectangular axes of x and y, and we draw the axis of z at right angles to this plane so that the axes of x, y, z are a right-handed system. We draw any cylindrical surface C to cut the middle plane in a curve s. The edge of the plate is such a surface as C, and the corresponding curve is the "edge-line." We draw the normal ν to s in a chosen sense, and choose the sense of s so that ν, s, z are parallel to the directions of a right-handed system of axes. We consider the action exerted by the part of the plate lying on that side of C towards which ν is drawn upon the part lying on the other side. Let δs be a short length of the curve s, and let two generating lines of C be drawn through the extremities of δs to mark out on C an area A. The tractions on the area A are statically equivalent to a force at the centroid of A and a couple. We resolve this force and couple into components directed along ν, s, z. Let $[T]$, $[S]$, $[N]$ denote the components of the force, $[H]$, $[G]$, $[K]$ those of the couple. When δs is diminished indefinitely these quantities have zero limits, and the limit of $[K]/\delta s$ also is zero, but $[T]/\delta s, \ldots [G]/\delta s$ may be finite. We denote the limits of $[T]/\delta s, \ldots$ by $T, \ldots$. Then T, S, N are the components of the *stress-resultant* belonging to the line s, and H, G are the components of the *stress-couple* belonging to the same line. T is a tension, S and N are shearing forces tangential and normal to the middle plane, G is a flexural couple, and H a torsional couple. When the normal ν to s is parallel to the axis of x, s is parallel to the axis of y. In this case we give a suffix 1 to $T, \ldots$. When the normal ν is parallel to the axis of y, s is parallel to the negative direction of the axis of x. In this case we give a suffix 2 to $T, \ldots$. The conventions in regard to the senses of these forces and couples are illustrated in Fig. 68.

For the expression of $T, \ldots$ we take temporary axes of x', y', z which are parallel to the directions of ν, s, z, and denote by $X'_{x'}, \ldots$ the stress-components referred to these axes. Then we have the formulæ*

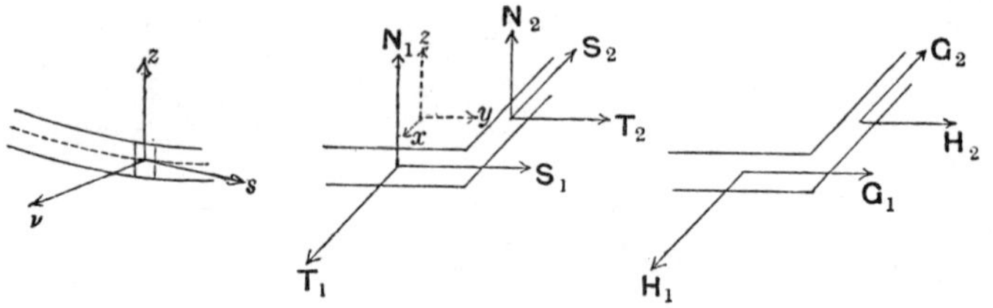

Fig. 68.

$$T = \int_{-h}^{h} X'_{x'} dz, \quad S = \int_{-h}^{h} X'_{y'} dz, \quad N = \int_{-h}^{h} X'_z dz,$$

$$H = \int_{-h}^{h} -zX'_{y'} dz, \quad G = \int_{-h}^{h} zX'_{x'} dz;$$

and, in the two particular cases in which ν is parallel respectively to the axes of x and y, these formulæ become

$$\left.\begin{array}{l} T_1 = \int_{-h}^{h} X_x dz, \quad S_1 = \int_{-h}^{h} X_y dz, \quad N_1 = \int_{-h}^{h} X_z dz, \\ H_1 = \int_{-h}^{h} -zX_y dz, \quad G_1 = \int_{-h}^{h} zX_x dz, \end{array}\right\} \quad \ldots\ldots\ldots(1)$$

and

$$\left.\begin{array}{l} S_2 = \int_{-h}^{h} -X_y dz, \quad T_2 = \int_{-h}^{h} Y_y dz, \quad N_2 = \int_{-h}^{h} Y_z dz, \\ G_2 = \int_{-h}^{h} zY_y dz, \quad H_2 = \int_{-h}^{h} zX_y dz. \end{array}\right\} \quad \ldots\ldots\ldots(2)$$

We observe that in accordance with these formulæ

$$S_2 = -S_1, \quad H_2 = -H_1. \quad \ldots\ldots\ldots(3)$$

295. Transformation of stress-resultants and stress-couples.

When the normal ν to the curve s makes angles θ and $\frac{1}{2}\pi - \theta$ with the axes of x and y, $T, S, \ldots$ are to be calculated from such formulæ as

$$T = \int_{-h}^{h} X'_{x'} dz,$$

in which the stress-components $X'_{x'}, \ldots$ are to be found from the formulæ (9) of Article 49 by putting

$$l_1 = \cos\theta, \; m_1 = \sin\theta, \; l_2 = -\sin\theta, \; m_2 = \cos\theta, \; n_1 = n_2 = l_3 = m_3 = 0, \; n_3 = 1.$$

* It is assumed that the plate is but slightly bent. Cf. Article 328 in Chapter XXIV.

We find

$$\left.\begin{aligned} T &= T_1 \cos^2\theta + T_2 \sin^2\theta + S_1 \sin 2\theta, \\ S &= \tfrac{1}{2}(T_2 - T_1)\sin 2\theta + S_1 \cos 2\theta, \\ N &= N_1 \cos\theta + N_2 \sin\theta, \\ G &= G_1 \cos^2\theta + G_2 \sin^2\theta - H_1 \sin 2\theta, \\ H &= \tfrac{1}{2}(G_1 - G_2)\sin 2\theta + H_1 \cos 2\theta. \end{aligned}\right\} \qquad \text{.............(4)}$$

Instead of resolving the stress-resultants and stress-couples belonging to the line s in the directions ν, s, z we might resolve them in the directions x, y, z. The components of the stress-resultant would be:

$$\left.\begin{aligned} &\text{parallel to } x,\ T\cos\theta - S\sin\theta, \text{ or } T_1\cos\theta + S_1\sin\theta, \\ &\text{parallel to } y,\ T\sin\theta + S\cos\theta, \text{ or } T_2\sin\theta + S_1\cos\theta, \\ &\text{parallel to } z,\ N_1\cos\theta + N_2\sin\theta; \end{aligned}\right\} \qquad \text{.........(5)}$$

and those of the couple would be:

$$\left.\begin{aligned} &\text{about an axis parallel to } x,\ H\cos\theta - G\sin\theta, \text{ or } H_1\cos\theta - G_2\sin\theta, \\ &\text{about an axis parallel to } y,\ H\sin\theta + G\cos\theta, \text{ or } G_1\cos\theta - H_1\sin\theta. \end{aligned}\right\} \qquad \text{......(6)}$$

296. Equations of equilibrium.

Let C denote, as before, a cylindrical surface cutting the middle plane at right angles in a curve s, which we take to be a simple closed contour. The external forces applied to the portion of the plate within C may consist of body forces and of surface tractions on the faces ($z = h$ and $z = -h$) of the plate. These external forces are statically equivalent to a single force, acting at the centroid P of the volume within C, and a couple. Let $[X']$, $[Y']$, $[Z']$ denote the components of the force parallel to the axes of x, y, z, and $[L']$, $[M']$, $[N']$ the components of the couple about the same axes. When the area ω within the curve s is diminished indefinitely by contracting s towards P, the limits of $[X']$, ... $[L']$, ... are zero and the limit of $[N']/\omega$ also is zero, but the limits of $[X']/\omega$, ... may be finite. We denote the limits of $[X']/\omega$, ... by X', ... Then X', Y', Z' are the components of the force-resultant of the external forces estimated per unit of area of the middle plane, and L', M' are the components of the couple-resultant of the same forces estimated in the same way.

The body force per unit of mass is denoted, as usual, by (X, Y, Z), and the density of the material by ρ. The definitions of X', Y', Z', L', M' are expressed analytically by the formulæ

$$\left.\begin{aligned} X' &= \int_{-h}^{h} \rho X dz + (X_z)_{z=h} - (X_z)_{z=-h}, \\ Y' &= \int_{-h}^{h} \rho Y dz + (Y_z)_{z=h} - (Y_z)_{z=-h}, \\ Z' &= \int_{-h}^{h} \rho Z dz + (Z_z)_{z=h} - (Z_z)_{z=-h}, \end{aligned}\right\} \qquad \text{...................(7)}$$

and

$$\left.\begin{aligned} L' &= \int_{-h}^{h} -z\rho Y dz - h\{(Y_z)_{z=h} + (Y_z)_{z=-h}\},\\ M' &= \int_{-h}^{h} z\rho X dz \quad + h\{(X_z)_{z=h} + (X_z)_{z=-h}\}.\end{aligned}\right\} \quad \text{...............(8)}$$

We equate to zero the force- and couple-resultants of all the forces acting on the portion of the plate within the cylindrical surface C. From the formulæ (5) we have the equations

$$\left.\begin{aligned} &\int (T_1 \cos\theta + S_1 \sin\theta)\, ds + \iint X' dx\, dy = 0,\\ &\int (T_2 \sin\theta + S_1 \cos\theta)\, ds + \iint Y' dx\, dy = 0,\\ &\int (N_1 \cos\theta + N_2 \sin\theta)\, ds + \iint Z' dx\, dy = 0,\end{aligned}\right\} \quad \text{...............(9)}$$

where the surface-integrals are taken over the area within s, and the line-integrals are taken round this curve. From the formulæ (5) and (6) we have the equations

$$\left.\begin{aligned} &\int \{(H_1 \cos\theta - G_2 \sin\theta) + y(N_1 \cos\theta + N_2 \sin\theta)\}\, ds + \iint (L' + yZ')\, dx\, dy = 0,\\ &\int \{(G_1 \cos\theta - H_1 \sin\theta) - x(N_1 \cos\theta + N_2 \sin\theta)\}\, ds + \iint (M' - xZ')\, dx\, dy = 0,\\ &\int \{x(T_2 \sin\theta + S_1 \cos\theta) - y(T_1 \cos\theta + S_1 \sin\theta)\}\, ds + \iint (xY' - yX')\, dx\, dy = 0.\end{aligned}\right\}$$

.........(10)

Since $\cos\theta$ and $\sin\theta$ are the direction-cosines of the normal to s referred to the axes of x and y, we may transform the line-integrals into surface-integrals. We thus find from (9) three equations which hold at every point of the middle plane, viz.

$$\frac{\partial T_1}{\partial x} + \frac{\partial S_1}{\partial y} + X' = 0, \quad \frac{\partial S_1}{\partial x} + \frac{\partial T_2}{\partial y} + Y' = 0, \quad \frac{\partial N_1}{\partial x} + \frac{\partial N_2}{\partial y} + Z' = 0. \quad \text{...(11)}$$

We transform the equations (10) in the same way and simplify the results by using equations (11). The third equation is identically satisfied. We thus find two equations which hold at every point of the middle plane, viz.

$$\frac{\partial H_1}{\partial x} - \frac{\partial G_2}{\partial y} + N_2 + L' = 0, \quad \frac{\partial G_1}{\partial x} - \frac{\partial H_1}{\partial y} - N_1 + M' = 0. \quad \text{.........(12)}$$

Equations (11) and (12) are the equations of equilibrium of the plate.

297. Boundary-conditions.

In a thick plate subjected to given forces the tractions specified by X_ν, Y_ν, Z_ν, where ν denotes the normal to the edge, have prescribed values at every point of the edge. When the plate is thin, the actual distribution of the tractions applied to the edge, regarded as a cylindrical surface, is of no practical importance. We represent therefore the tractions applied to the edge by their force- and couple-resultants, estimated per unit of length of the edge-line, i.e. the curve in which the edge cuts the middle surface. It follows from Saint-Venant's principle (Article 89) that the effects produced at a distance from the edge by two systems of tractions which give rise to the same force- and couple-resultants, estimated as above, are practically the same. Let these resultants be specified by components T, S, N and H, G in the senses previously assigned for T, S, N and H, G, the normal to the edge-line being drawn outwards. Let the stress-resultants and stress-couples belonging to a curve parallel to the edge-line, and not very near to it, be calculated in accordance with the previously stated conventions, the normal to this curve being drawn towards the edge-line; and let limiting values of these quantities be found by bringing the parallel curve to coincidence with the edge-line. Let these limiting values be denoted by $\bar{T}$, $\bar{S}$, $\bar{N}$ and $\bar{H}$, $\bar{G}$. It is most necessary to observe that the statical equivalence of the applied tractions and the stress-resultants and stress-couples at the edge does *not* require the satisfaction of all the equations

$$\bar{T} = \mathrm{T}, \quad \bar{S} = \mathrm{S}, \quad \bar{N} = \mathrm{N}, \quad \bar{H} = \mathrm{H}, \quad \bar{G} = \mathrm{G}.$$

These five equations are equivalent to the boundary-conditions adopted by Poisson*. A system of four boundary-conditions was afterwards obtained by Kirchhoff†, who set out from a special assumption as to the nature of the strain within the plate, and proceeded by the method of variation of the energy-function. The meaning of the reduction of the number of conditions from five to four was first pointed out by Kelvin and Tait‡. It lies in the circumstance that the actual distribution of tractions on the edge which give rise to the torsional couple is immaterial. The couple on any finite length might be applied by means of tractions directed at right angles to the middle plane, and these, when reduced to force- and couple-resultants, estimated per unit of length of the edge-line, would be equivalent to a distribution of shearing force of the type N instead of torsional couple of the type H. The required shearing force is easily found to be $-\partial \mathrm{H}/\partial s$. This result is obtained by means of the following theorem of Statics: A line-distribution of couple of amount H per unit of length of a plane closed curve s, the axis of the couple at any point being normal to the curve, is statically equivalent to a line-distribution of force of amount $-\partial H/\partial s$, the direction of the force at any point being at right angles to the plane of the curve.

* See Introduction, footnote 36. Poisson's solutions of special problems are not invalidated, because in all of them $\bar{H}$ vanishes.

† See Introduction, footnote 125.

‡ *Nat. Phil.* first edition, 1867. The same explanation was given by J. Boussinesq in 1871. See Introduction, footnote 128.

The theorem is proved at once by forming the force- and couple-resultants of the line-distribution of force $-\partial H/\partial s$. The axis of z being at right angles to the plane of the curve, the force at any point is directed parallel to the axis of z, and the force-resultant is expressed by the integral $\int -\frac{\partial H}{\partial s} ds$ taken round the closed curve. This integral vanishes. The components of the couple-resultant about the axes of x and y are expressed by the integrals $\int -y\frac{\partial H}{\partial s} ds$ and $\int x\frac{\partial H}{\partial s} ds$ taken round the curve. If ν denotes the direction of the normal to the curve, we have

$$\int -y\frac{\partial H}{\partial s} ds = \int H\frac{\partial y}{\partial s} ds = \int H\cos(x, \nu)\, ds,$$

and

$$\int x\frac{\partial H}{\partial s} ds = \int -H\frac{\partial x}{\partial s} ds = \int H\cos(y, \nu)\, ds,$$

the integrations being taken round the curve. The expressions $\int H\cos(x, \nu)\, ds$ and $\int H\cos(y, \nu)\, ds$ are the values of the components of the couple-resultant of the line-distribution of couple H.

The theorem may be illustrated by a figure. We may think of the curve s as a polygon of a large number of sides. The couple $H\delta s$, belonging to any side of length δs, is statically equivalent to two forces each of magnitude H, directed at right angles to the plane of the curve in opposite senses, and acting at the ends of the side. The couples belonging to the adjacent sides may similarly be replaced by pairs of forces of magnitude $H+\delta H$ or $H-\delta H$ as shown in Fig. 69, where δH means $(\partial H/\partial s)\,\delta s$. In the end we are left with a force $-\delta H$ at one end of any side of length δs, or, in the limit, with a line-distribution of force $-\partial H/\partial s$.

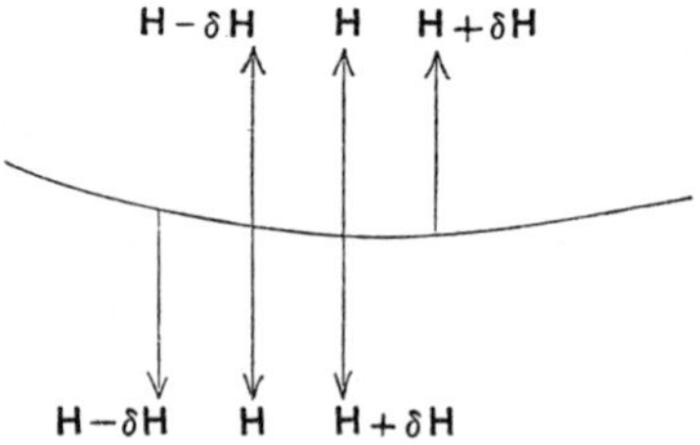

Fig. 69.

From this theorem it follows that, for the purpose of forming the equations of equilibrium of any portion of the plate contained within a cylindrical surface C, which cuts the middle surface at right angles in a curve s, the torsional couple H may be omitted, provided that the shearing stress-resultant N is replaced by $N-\partial H/\partial s$*. Now the boundary-conditions are limiting forms of the equations of equilibrium for certain short narrow strips of the plate; the contour in which the boundary of any one of these strips cuts the middle plane consists of a short arc of the edge-line, the two normals to this curve at the ends of the arc, and the arc of a curve parallel to the edge-line intercepted between these normals. The limit is taken by first bringing the parallel curve to coincidence with the edge-line, and then diminishing the length of the arc of the edge-line indefinitely. In accordance with the above

* This result might be used in forming the equations of equilibrium (11) and (12). The line-integrals in the third of equations (9) and the first two of equations (10) would be written

$$\int\left(N-\frac{\partial H}{\partial s}\right) ds, \quad \int\left\{-G\sin\theta+y\left(N-\frac{\partial H}{\partial s}\right)\right\} ds, \quad \int\left\{G\cos\theta-x\left(N-\frac{\partial H}{\partial s}\right)\right\} ds,$$

and these can be transformed easily into the forms given in (9) and (10).

theorem we are to form these equations by omitting $\overline{H}$ and H, and replacing $\overline{N}$ and N by $\overline{N}-\partial H/\partial s$ and $\mathrm{N}-\partial \mathrm{H}/\partial s$. The boundary-conditions are thus found to be

$$\overline{T}=\mathrm{T},\quad \overline{S}=\mathrm{S},\quad \overline{N}-\partial\overline{H}/\partial s=\mathrm{N}-\partial\mathrm{H}/\partial s,\quad \overline{G}=\mathrm{G}.$$

These four equations are equivalent to the boundary-conditions adopted by Kirchhoff.

In investigating the boundary-conditions by the process just sketched we observe that the terms contributed to the equations of equilibrium by the body forces and the tractions on the faces of the plate do not merely vanish in the limit, but the quotients of them by the length of the short arc of the edge-line which is part of the contour of the strip also vanish in the limit when this length is diminished indefinitely. If this arc is denoted by δs we have such equations as

$$\lim_{\delta s=0}(\delta s)^{-1}\iint X'\,dx\,dy=0,\qquad \lim_{\delta s=0}(\delta s)^{-1}\iint (L'+yZ')\,dx\,dy=0,$$

the integration being taken over the area within the contour of the strip. The equations of equilibrium of the strip lead therefore to the equations

$$\left.\begin{aligned}&\lim_{\delta s=0}(\delta s)^{-1}\int(T\cos\theta-S\sin\theta)\,ds=0,\quad \lim_{\delta s=0}(\delta s)^{-1}\int(T\sin\theta+S\cos\theta)\,ds=0,\\ &\lim_{\delta s=0}(\delta s)^{-1}\int\left(N-\frac{\partial H}{\partial s}\right)ds=0,\quad \lim_{\delta s=0}(\delta s)^{-1}\int\left\{-G\sin\theta+y\left(N-\frac{\partial H}{\partial s}\right)\right\}ds=0,\\ &\lim_{\delta s=0}(\delta s)^{-1}\int\left\{G\cos\theta-x\left(N-\frac{\partial H}{\partial s}\right)\right\}ds=0,\end{aligned}\right\}\quad\ldots(13)$$

in which the integrations are taken all round the contour of the strip, and T, ... denote the force- and couple-resultants of the tractions on the edges of the strip, estimated in accordance with the conventions laid down in Article 294. We evaluate the contributions made to the various line-integrals by the four lines in which the edges of the strip cut the middle plane. Since the parallel curve is brought to coincidence with the edge-line, the contributions of the short lengths of the two normals to this curve have zero limits; and we have to evaluate the contributions of the arcs of the edge-line and of the parallel curve. Let ν_0 denote the direction of the normal to the edge-line drawn outwards. The contributions of this arc may be estimated as

$$\{\mathrm{T}\cos(x,\nu_0)-\mathrm{S}\cos(y,\nu_0)\}\,\delta s,\quad \{\mathrm{T}\cos(y,\nu_0)+\mathrm{S}\cos(x,\nu_0)\}\,\delta s,\quad \left\{\mathrm{N}-\frac{\partial\mathrm{H}}{\partial s}\right\}\delta s,$$

and
$$\left\{-\mathrm{G}\cos(y,\nu_0)+y\left(\mathrm{N}-\frac{\partial\mathrm{H}}{\partial s}\right)\right\}\delta s,\quad \left\{\mathrm{G}\cos(x,\nu_0)-x\left(\mathrm{N}-\frac{\partial\mathrm{H}}{\partial s}\right)\right\}\delta s.$$

In evaluating the contributions of the arc of the parallel curve, we observe that the conventions, in accordance with which the T, ... belonging to this curve are estimated, require the normal to the curve to be drawn in the opposite sense to ν_0, and the curve to be described in the opposite sense to the edge-line, but the arc of the curve over which we integrate has the same length δs as the arc of the edge-line. In the limit when the parallel curve is brought to coincidence with the edge-line we have, in accordance with these conventions,

$$T=\overline{T},\quad S=\overline{S},\quad N=-\overline{N},\quad G=\overline{G},\quad H=\overline{H},\quad \partial H/\partial s=-\partial\overline{H}/\partial s,$$

and
$$\cos\theta=-\cos(x,\nu_0),\quad \sin\theta=-\cos(y,\nu_0).$$

Hence the contributions of the arc of the parallel curve may be estimated as

$$\{-\bar{T}\cos(x, \nu_0)+\bar{S}\cos(y, \nu_0)\}\,\delta s, \quad \{-\bar{T}\cos(y, \nu_0)-\bar{S}\cos(x, \nu_0)\}\,\delta s, \quad \left\{-\bar{N}+\frac{\partial \bar{H}}{\partial s}\right\}\delta s,$$

and

$$\left\{\bar{G}\cos(y, \nu_0)+y\left(-\bar{N}+\frac{\partial \bar{H}}{\partial s}\right)\right\}\delta s, \quad \left\{-\bar{G}\cos(x, \nu_0)-x\left(-\bar{N}+\frac{\partial \bar{H}}{\partial s}\right)\right\}\delta s.$$

On adding the contributions of the two arcs, dividing by δs, and equating the resulting expressions to zero, we have the boundary-conditions in the forms previously stated.

In general we shall omit the bars over the letters T, ..., and write the boundary-conditions at an edge to which given forces are applied in the form

$$T=\mathrm{T}, \quad S=\mathrm{S}, \quad N-\frac{\partial H}{\partial s}=\mathrm{N}-\frac{\partial \mathrm{H}}{\partial s}, \quad G=\mathrm{G}. \qquad \text{............(14)}$$

At a free edge T, S, $N-\partial H/\partial s$, G vanish. At a "supported" edge the displacement w of a point on the middle plane at right angles to this plane vanishes, and T, S, G also vanish. At a clamped edge, where the inclination of the middle plane is not permitted to vary, the displacement (u, v, w) of a point on the middle plane vanishes, and $\partial \mathrm{w}/\partial \nu$ also vanishes, ν denoting the direction of the normal to the edge-line.

The effect of the mode of application of the torsional couple may be illustrated further by an exact solution of the equations of equilibrium of isotropic solids*. Let the edge-line be the rectangle given by $x=\pm a$, $y=\pm b$. The plate is then an extreme example of a flat rectangular bar. When such a bar is twisted by opposing couples about the axis of x, so that the twist produced is τ, we know from Article 221 (c) that the displacement is given by

$$u=-\tau yz+\tau\frac{2^5h^2}{\pi^3}\sum_{n=0}^{\infty}\frac{(-)^n}{(2n+1)^3}\frac{\sinh\dfrac{(2n+1)\pi y}{2h}\sin\dfrac{(2n+1)\pi z}{2h}}{\cosh\dfrac{(2n+1)\pi b}{2h}}, \quad v=-\tau xz, \quad w=\tau xy,$$

provided that the tractions by which the torsional couple is produced are expressed by the formulæ

$$X_y=-2\mu\tau z+\mu\tau\frac{2^4h}{\pi^2}\sum_{n=0}^{\infty}\frac{(-)^n}{(2n+1)^2}\frac{\cosh\dfrac{(2n+1)\pi y}{2h}\sin\dfrac{(2n+1)\pi z}{2h}}{\cosh\dfrac{(2n+1)\pi b}{2h}},$$

$$X_z=\mu\tau\frac{2^4h}{\pi^2}\sum_{n=0}^{\infty}\frac{(-)^n}{(2n+1)^2}\frac{\sinh\dfrac{(2n+1)\pi y}{2h}\cos\dfrac{(2n+1)\pi z}{2h}}{\cosh\dfrac{(2n+1)\pi b}{2h}}.$$

There are no tractions on the faces $z=\pm h$ or on the edges $y=\pm b$. The total torsional couple on the edge $x=a$ is

$$\tfrac{16}{3}\mu\tau h^3 b-\mu\tau h^4\left(\frac{4}{\pi}\right)^5\sum_{n=0}^{\infty}\frac{1}{(2n+1)^5}\tanh\frac{(2n+1)\pi b}{2h};$$

and of this one-half is contributed by the tractions X_y directed parallel to the middle plane, and the other half by the tractions X_z directed at right angles to the middle plane.

* Kelvin and Tait, *Nat. Phil.*, Part II., pp. 267 *et seq.*

When the plate is very thin the total torsional couple is approximately equal to $\frac{16}{3}\mu\tau h^3 b$, so that the average torsional couple per unit of length of the edge-lines $x = \pm a$ is approximately equal to $\frac{8}{3}\mu\tau h^3$. At any point which is not near an edge $y = \pm b$, the state of the plate is expressed approximately by the equations

$$u = -\tau yz, \quad v = -\tau zx, \quad w = \tau xy.$$

The traction X_y is nearly equal to $-2\mu\tau z$ at all points which are not very near to the edges $y = \pm b$, and the traction X_z is very small at all such points. The distribution of traction on the edge $x = a$ is very nearly equivalent to a constant torsional couple such as would be denoted by H_1, of amount $\frac{4}{3}\mu\tau h^3$, combined with shearing stress-resultants such as would be denoted by N_1, having values which differ appreciably from zero only near the corners ($x = a$, $y = \pm b$), and equivalent to forces at the corners of amount $\frac{4}{3}\mu\tau h^3$. At a distance from the free edges $y = \pm b$ which exceeds three or four times the thickness, the stress is practically expressed by giving the value $-2\mu\tau z$ to the stress-component X_y and zero values to the remaining stress-components. The greater part of the plate is in practically the same state as it would be if there were torsional couples, specified by $H_1 = \frac{4}{3}\mu\tau h^3$ at all points of the edges $x = \pm a$, and $H_2 = -\frac{4}{3}\mu\tau h^3$ at all points of the edges $y = \pm b$. Thus the forces at the corners may be replaced by a statically equivalent distribution of torsional couple on the free edges, without sensibly altering the state of the plate, except in a narrow region near these edges.

Within this region the value of the torsional couple H_2, belonging to any line $y = \text{const.}$, which would be calculated from the exact solution, diminishes rapidly, from $-\frac{4}{3}\mu\tau h^3$ to zero, as the edge is approached. The rapid diminution of H_2 is accompanied, as we should expect from the second of equations (12), by large values of N_1. If we integrate N_1 across the region, that is to say, if we form the integral $\int N_1 dy$, taken over a length, equal to three or four times the thickness, along any line drawn at right angles to an edge $y = b$ or $y = -b$ and terminated at that edge, we find the value of the integral to be very nearly equal to $\pm\frac{4}{3}\mu\tau h^3$.

This remark enables us to understand why, in the investigation of equations (14), the third of equations (13), viz. $\lim_{\delta s=0} (\delta s)^{-1} \int \left(N - \frac{\partial H}{\partial s}\right) ds = 0$, where the integration is taken round the contour of a "strip," as was explained, should not be replaced by the equation $\lim_{\delta s=0} (\delta s)^{-1} \int N ds = 0$, and also why the latter equation does not lead to the result $\overline{N} = \text{N}$. When $\overline{N}$, $\overline{H}$ are calculated from the state of strain which holds at a distance from the edge, and equations (14) are established by the method employed above, it is implied that no substantial difference will be made in the results if the linear dimensions of the strip, instead of being diminished indefinitely, are not reduced below lengths equal to three or four times the thickness. When the dimensions of the strip are of this order, the contributions made to the integral $\int N ds$ by those parts of the contour which are normal to the edge-line may not always be negligible; but, if not, they will be practically balanced by the contributions made to $\int -(\partial H/\partial s)\, ds$ by the same parts of the contour*.

298. Relation between the flexural couples and the curvature.

In Article 90 we found a particular solution of the equations of equilibrium of an isotropic elastic solid body, which represents the deformation of a plate

* Cf. H. Lamb, *London Math. Soc. Proc.*, vol. 21 (1891), p. 70.

slightly bent by couples applied at its edges. To express the result which we then found in the notation of Article 294 we proceed as follows:—On the surface into which the middle plane is bent we draw the principal tangents at any point. We denote by s_1, s_2 the directions of these lines on the unstrained middle plane, by R_1, R_2 the radii of curvature of the normal sections of the surface drawn through them respectively, by G_1', G_2' the flexural couples belonging to plane sections of the plate which are normal to the middle surface and to the lines s_1, s_2 respectively. We determine the senses of these couples by the conventions stated in Article 294 in the same way as if s_1, s_2, z were parallel to the axes of a right-handed system. Then, according to Article 90, when the plate is bent so that R_1, R_2 are constants, and the directions s_1, s_2 are fixed, the stress-resultants and the torsional couples belonging to the principal planes of section vanish, and the flexural couples G_1', G_2' belonging to these planes are given by the equations

$$G_1' = -D(1/R_1 + \sigma/R_2), \quad G_2' = -D(1/R_2 + \sigma/R_1), \qquad \text{.........(15)}$$

where, with the usual notation for elastic constants,

$$D = \tfrac{2}{3}Eh^3/(1-\sigma^2) = \tfrac{8}{3}\mu h^3(\lambda+\mu)/(\lambda+2\mu). \qquad \text{...............(16)}$$

The constant D will be called the "flexural rigidity" of the plate.

Now let the direction s_1 make angles ϕ and $\frac{1}{2}\pi - \phi$ with the axes of x and y. Then, according to (4), G_1, G_2, H_1 are given by the equations

$$G_1 \cos^2\phi + G_2 \sin^2\phi - H_1 \sin 2\phi = -D(1/R_1 + \sigma/R_2),$$
$$G_1 \sin^2\phi + G_2 \cos^2\phi + H_1 \sin 2\phi = -D(1/R_2 + \sigma/R_1),$$
$$\tfrac{1}{2}(G_1 - G_2)\sin 2\phi + H_1 \cos 2\phi = 0,$$

from which we find

$$G_1 = -D\left[\frac{\cos^2\phi}{R_1} + \frac{\sin^2\phi}{R_2} + \sigma\left(\frac{\sin^2\phi}{R_1} + \frac{\cos^2\phi}{R_2}\right)\right],$$
$$G_2 = -D\left[\frac{\sin^2\phi}{R_1} + \frac{\cos^2\phi}{R_2} + \sigma\left(\frac{\cos^2\phi}{R_1} + \frac{\sin^2\phi}{R_2}\right)\right],$$
$$H_1 = \tfrac{1}{2}D(1-\sigma)\sin 2\phi\left(\frac{1}{R_1} - \frac{1}{R_2}\right).$$

Again, let w be the displacement of a point on the middle plane in the direction of the normal to this plane, and write

$$\kappa_1 = \frac{\partial^2 \mathrm{w}}{\partial x^2}, \quad \kappa_2 = \frac{\partial^2 \mathrm{w}}{\partial y^2}, \quad \tau = \frac{\partial^2 \mathrm{w}}{\partial x \partial y}. \qquad \text{..................(17)}$$

Then the indicatrix of the surface into which the middle plane is bent is given, with sufficient approximation, by the equation

$$\kappa_1 x^2 + \kappa_2 y^2 + 2\tau xy = \text{const.};$$

and, when the form on the left is transformed to coordinates ξ, η, of which the axes coincide in direction with the lines s_1, s_2, it becomes

$$\xi^2/R_1 + \eta^2/R_2.$$

Hence we have the equations

$$\kappa_1 = \frac{\cos^2\phi}{R_1} + \frac{\sin^2\phi}{R_2}, \quad \kappa_2 = \frac{\sin^2\phi}{R_1} + \frac{\cos^2\phi}{R_2}, \quad 2\tau = \sin 2\phi\left(\frac{1}{R_1} - \frac{1}{R_2}\right),$$

and the formulæ for G_1, G_2, H_1 become

$$G_1 = -D(\kappa_1 + \sigma\kappa_2), \quad G_2 = -D(\kappa_2 + \sigma\kappa_1), \quad H_1 = D(1-\sigma)\tau. \ldots(18)$$

We shall show that the formulæ (18), in which κ_1, κ_2, τ are given by (17), and D by (16), are either correct or approximately correct values of the stress-couples in a very wide class of problems. We observe here that they are equivalent to the statements that the flexural couples belonging to the two principal planes of section at any point are given, in terms of the principal radii of curvature at the point, by the formulæ (15), and that the torsional couples belonging to these two principal planes vanish.

If s denotes the direction of the tangent to any curve drawn on the middle plane, and ν the direction of the normal to this curve, and if θ denotes the angle between the directions ν, x, we find, by substituting from (17) and (18) in (4), the equations

$$G = -D\left[\cos^2\theta\left(\frac{\partial^2 w}{\partial x^2} + \sigma\frac{\partial^2 w}{\partial y^2}\right) + \sin^2\theta\left(\frac{\partial^2 w}{\partial y^2} + \sigma\frac{\partial^2 w}{\partial x^2}\right) + (1-\sigma)\sin 2\theta\frac{\partial^2 w}{\partial x\partial y}\right],$$

$$H = D(1-\sigma)\left[\sin\theta\cos\theta\left(\frac{\partial^2 w}{\partial y^2} - \frac{\partial^2 w}{\partial x^2}\right) + (\cos^2\theta - \sin^2\theta)\frac{\partial^2 w}{\partial x\partial y}\right].$$

We may transform these equations, so as to avoid the reference to fixed axes of x and y*, by means of the formulæ

$$\frac{\partial}{\partial s} = \cos\theta\frac{\partial}{\partial y} - \sin\theta\frac{\partial}{\partial x}, \quad \frac{\partial}{\partial \nu} = \cos\theta\frac{\partial}{\partial x} + \sin\theta\frac{\partial}{\partial y}, \quad \frac{\partial\theta}{\partial\nu} = 0, \quad \frac{\partial\theta}{\partial s} = \frac{1}{\rho'}, \ldots(19)$$

where ρ' is the radius of curvature of the curve in question. We find

$$G = -D\left\{\frac{\partial^2 w}{\partial\nu^2} + \sigma\left(\frac{\partial^2 w}{\partial s^2} + \frac{1}{\rho'}\frac{\partial w}{\partial\nu}\right)\right\}, \quad H = D(1-\sigma)\frac{\partial}{\partial\nu}\left(\frac{\partial w}{\partial s}\right). \ldots\ldots\ldots\ldots(20)$$

These equations hold whenever the stress-couples are expressed by the formulæ (18).

In the problem of Article 90 we found for the potential energy of the plate, estimated per unit of area of the middle plane, the formula

$$\tfrac{1}{2}D\left[\left(\frac{1}{R_1} + \frac{1}{R_2}\right)^2 - 2(1-\sigma)\frac{1}{R_1R_2}\right],$$

or, in our present notation,

$$\tfrac{1}{2}D\left[(\kappa_1+\kappa_2)^2 - 2(1-\sigma)(\kappa_1\kappa_2 - \tau^2)\right]. \ldots\ldots\ldots\ldots\ldots(21)$$

We shall find that this formula also is correct, or approximately correct, in a wide class of problems.

THEORY OF MODERATELY THICK PLATES.

299. Method of determining the stress in a plate†.

We proceed to consider some particular solutions of the equations of equilibrium of an isotropic elastic solid body, subjected to surface tractions only, which are applicable to the problem of a plate deformed by given forces.

* Cf. Lord Rayleigh, *Theory of Sound*, vol. 1, § 216.

† The method was worked out briefly, and in a much more general fashion, by J. H. Michell, *London Math. Soc. Proc.*, vol. 31 (1900), p. 100.

These solutions will be obtained by means of the system of equations for the determination of the stress-components which were given in Article 92. It was there shown that, besides the equations

$$\frac{\partial X_x}{\partial x}+\frac{\partial X_y}{\partial y}+\frac{\partial X_z}{\partial z}=0,\quad \frac{\partial X_y}{\partial x}+\frac{\partial Y_y}{\partial y}+\frac{\partial Y_z}{\partial z}=0,\quad \frac{\partial X_z}{\partial x}+\frac{\partial Y_z}{\partial y}+\frac{\partial Z_z}{\partial z}=0, \quad \text{...(22)}$$

we have the two sets of equations

$$\nabla^2 X_x=-\frac{1}{1+\sigma}\frac{\partial^2\Theta}{\partial x^2},\quad \nabla^2 Y_y=-\frac{1}{1+\sigma}\frac{\partial^2\Theta}{\partial y^2},\quad \nabla^2 Z_z=-\frac{1}{1+\sigma}\frac{\partial^2\Theta}{\partial z^2}, \quad \text{......(23)}$$

and

$$\nabla^2 Y_z=-\frac{1}{1+\sigma}\frac{\partial^2\Theta}{\partial y\partial z},\quad \nabla^2 X_z=-\frac{1}{1+\sigma}\frac{\partial^2\Theta}{\partial z\partial x},\quad \nabla^2 X_y=-\frac{1}{1+\sigma}\frac{\partial^2\Theta}{\partial x\partial y}, \quad \text{...(24)}$$

where

$$\Theta=X_x+Y_y+Z_z. \quad \text{..........................(25)}$$

It was shown also that the function Θ is harmonic, so that $\nabla^2\Theta=0$, and that each of the stress-components satisfies the equation $\nabla^4 f=0$.

We shall suppose in the first place that the plate is held by forces applied at its edge only. Then the faces $z=\pm h$ are free from traction, or we have $X_z=Y_z=Z_z=0$ when $z=\pm h$. It follows from the third of equations (22) that $\partial Z_z/\partial z$ vanishes at $z=h$ and at $z=-h$. Hence Z_z satisfies the equation $\nabla^4 Z_z=0$ and the conditions $Z_z=0$, $\partial Z_z/\partial z=0$ at $z=\pm h$. If the plate had no boundaries besides the planes $z=\pm h$, the only possible value for Z_z would be zero. We shall take Z_z to vanish*. It then follows from the equations $\nabla^2\Theta=0$, $\nabla^2 Z_z=-(1+\sigma)^{-1}\partial^2\Theta/\partial z^2$, that Θ is of the form $\Theta_0+z\Theta_1$, where Θ_0 and Θ_1 are plane harmonic functions of x and y which are independent of z.

For the determination of X_z, Y_z we have the equations

$$\frac{\partial X_z}{\partial x}+\frac{\partial Y_z}{\partial y}=0,\quad \nabla^2 X_z=-\frac{1}{1+\sigma}\frac{\partial\Theta_1}{\partial x},\quad \nabla^2 Y_z=-\frac{1}{1+\sigma}\frac{\partial\Theta_1}{\partial y},$$

and the conditions that $X_z=Y_z=0$ at $z=\pm h$. A particular solution is given by the equations

$$X_z=\frac{1}{2}\frac{1}{1+\sigma}(h^2-z^2)\frac{\partial\Theta_1}{\partial x},\quad Y_z=\frac{1}{2}\frac{1}{1+\sigma}(h^2-z^2)\frac{\partial\Theta_1}{\partial y}. \quad \text{......(26)}$$

We shall take X_z and Y_z to have these forms. When X_z, Y_z, Z_z are known general formulæ can be obtained for X_x, Y_y, X_y.

If Θ_1 is a constant, X_z and Y_z vanish as well as Z_z, and the plate is then in a state of "plane stress." If Θ_1 depends upon x and y the plate is in a state of "generalized plane stress" (Article 94). We shall examine separately these two cases.

* J. H. Michell, *loc. cit.*, calls attention to the analogy of this procedure to the customary treatment of the condenser problem in Electrostatics.

300. Plane stress.

When X_z, Y_z, Z_z vanish throughout the plate there is a state of plane stress. We have already determined in Article 145 the most general forms for the remaining stress-components and the corresponding displacements. We found for Θ the expression

$$\Theta = \Theta_0 + \beta z, \qquad \text{.......(27)}$$

where Θ_0 is a plane harmonic function of x and y, and β is a constant. The stress-components X_x, Y_y, X_y are derived from a stress-function χ by the formulæ

$$X_x = \frac{\partial^2 \chi}{\partial y^2}, \quad Y_y = \frac{\partial^2 \chi}{\partial x^2}, \quad X_y = -\frac{\partial^2 \chi}{\partial x \partial y}, \qquad \text{.......(28)}$$

and χ has the form
$$\chi = \chi_0 + z\chi_1 - \frac{1}{2}\frac{\sigma}{1+\sigma} z^2 \Theta_0, \qquad \text{.......(29)}$$

where
$$\nabla_1^2 \chi_0 = \Theta_0, \quad \nabla_1^2 \chi_1 = \beta. \qquad \text{.......(30)}$$

If we introduce a pair of conjugate functions ξ, η of x and y which are such that

$$\frac{\partial \xi}{\partial x} = \frac{\partial \eta}{\partial y} = \Theta_0, \quad \frac{\partial \xi}{\partial y} = -\frac{\partial \eta}{\partial x}, \qquad \text{.......(31)}$$

the most general forms for χ_0 and χ_1 can be written

$$\chi_0 = \tfrac{1}{2} x\xi + f, \quad \chi_1 = \tfrac{1}{4}\beta(x^2 + y^2) + F, \qquad \text{.......(32)}$$

where f and F are plane harmonic functions. The displacement (u, v, w) is then expressed by the formulæ

$$\left.\begin{aligned} u &= \frac{1}{E}\left(\xi + \beta xz + \tfrac{1}{2}\sigma z^2 \frac{\partial \Theta_0}{\partial x}\right) - \frac{1+\sigma}{E}\frac{\partial}{\partial x}(\chi_0 + z\chi_1), \\ v &= \frac{1}{E}\left(\eta + \beta yz + \tfrac{1}{2}\sigma z^2 \frac{\partial \Theta_0}{\partial y}\right) - \frac{1+\sigma}{E}\frac{\partial}{\partial y}(\chi_0 + z\chi_1), \\ w &= -\frac{1}{E}\{\tfrac{1}{2}\beta(x^2 + y^2 + \sigma z^2) + \sigma z \Theta_0\} + \frac{1+\sigma}{E}\chi_1. \end{aligned}\right\} \qquad \text{.......(33)}$$

The solution represents two superposed stress-systems, one depending on Θ_0, χ_0, and the other on β, χ_1. These two systems are independent of each other.

301. Plate stretched by forces in its plane.

Taking the (Θ_0, χ_0) system, we have the displacement given by the equations

$$\left.\begin{aligned} u &= \frac{1}{E}\left(\xi + \tfrac{1}{2}\sigma z^2 \frac{\partial \Theta_0}{\partial x}\right) - \frac{1+\sigma}{E}\frac{\partial \chi_0}{\partial x}, \\ v &= \frac{1}{E}\left(\eta + \tfrac{1}{2}\sigma z^2 \frac{\partial \Theta_0}{\partial y}\right) - \frac{1+\sigma}{E}\frac{\partial \chi_0}{\partial y}, \\ w &= -\frac{\sigma}{E} z\Theta_0, \end{aligned}\right\} \qquad \text{.......(34)}$$

where χ_0 is of the form $\frac{1}{2}x\xi+f$, Θ_0 and f are plane harmonic functions, and ξ, η are determined by (31). The normal displacement of the middle plane vanishes, or the plate is not bent. The stress is expressed by the formulæ

$$\left.\begin{aligned} X_x &= \frac{\partial^2}{\partial y^2}\left(\chi_0 - \frac{1}{2}\frac{\sigma}{1+\sigma}z^2\Theta_0\right), \\ Y_y &= \frac{\partial^2}{\partial x^2}\left(\chi_0 - \frac{1}{2}\frac{\sigma}{1+\sigma}z^2\Theta_0\right), \\ X_y &= -\frac{\partial^2}{\partial x\,\partial y}\left(\chi_0 - \frac{1}{2}\frac{\sigma}{1+\sigma}z^2\Theta_0\right). \end{aligned}\right\}\quad\text{......(35)}$$

The stress-resultants T_1, T_2, S_1 are expressed by the equations

$$\left.\begin{aligned} T_1 &= \frac{\partial^2}{\partial y^2}\left(2h\chi_0 - \frac{1}{3}\frac{\sigma}{1+\sigma}h^3\Theta_0\right) \\ T_2 &= \frac{\partial^2}{\partial x^2}\left(2h\chi_0 - \frac{1}{3}\frac{\sigma}{1+\sigma}h^3\Theta_0\right), \\ S_1 &= -\frac{\partial^2}{\partial x\,\partial y}\left(2h\chi_0 - \frac{1}{3}\frac{\sigma}{1+\sigma}h^3\Theta_0\right). \end{aligned}\right\}\quad\text{......(36)}$$

The stress-resultants N_1, N_2, and the stress-couples G_1, G_2, H_1, vanish. The equations (11) and (12), in which X', Y', Z', L', M' vanish, are obviously satisfied by these forms.

When we transform the expressions for T_1, T_2, S_1 by means of the equations (4), we find that, at a point of the edge-line where the normal makes an angle θ with the axis of x, the tension and shearing-force T, S are given by the equations

$$T = \left(\cos^2\theta\frac{\partial^2}{\partial y^2} + \sin^2\theta\frac{\partial^2}{\partial x^2} - 2\sin\theta\cos\theta\frac{\partial^2}{\partial x\partial y}\right)\left(2h\chi_0 - \frac{1}{3}\frac{\sigma}{1+\sigma}h^3\Theta_0\right),$$

$$S = \left\{\sin\theta\cos\theta\left(\frac{\partial^2}{\partial x^2} - \frac{\partial^2}{\partial y^2}\right) - \cos 2\theta\frac{\partial^2}{\partial x\partial y}\right\}\left(2h\chi_0 - \frac{1}{3}\frac{\sigma}{1+\sigma}h^3\Theta_0\right).$$

When these equations are transformed by means of the formulæ (19) so as to eliminate the reference to fixed axes of x and y, they become

$$\left.\begin{aligned} T &= \left(\frac{\partial^2}{\partial s^2} + \frac{1}{\rho'}\frac{\partial}{\partial\nu}\right)\left(2h\chi_0 - \frac{1}{3}\frac{\sigma}{1+\sigma}h^3\Theta_0\right), \\ S &= -\frac{\partial}{\partial\nu}\left\{\frac{\partial}{\partial s}\left(2h\chi_0 - \frac{1}{3}\frac{\sigma}{1+\sigma}h^3\Theta_0\right)\right\}. \end{aligned}\right\}\quad\text{.........(37)}$$

These expressions are sufficiently general to represent the effects of any forces applied to the edge in the plane of the plate*. If the forces are applied by means of tractions specified in accordance with equations (35), the solution expressed by equations (34) is exact; but, if the applied tractions at the edge are distributed in any other way, without ceasing to be equivalent to

* The case of a circular plate was worked out in detail by Clebsch, *Elasticität*, § 42.

resultants of the types T, S, the solution represents the state of the plate with sufficient approximation at all points which are not close to the edge.

It may be observed that the stress-resultants and the potential energy per unit of area can be expressed in terms of the extension and shearing strain of the middle plane. If we write u, v for the values of u and v when $z=0$, and put

$$\epsilon_1=\frac{\partial \mathrm{u}}{\partial x},\quad \epsilon_2=\frac{\partial \mathrm{v}}{\partial y},\quad \varpi=\frac{\partial \mathrm{u}}{\partial y}+\frac{\partial \mathrm{v}}{\partial x},$$

we find
$$\epsilon_1=\frac{1}{E}\left(\frac{\partial^2\chi_0}{\partial y^2}-\sigma\frac{\partial^2\chi_0}{\partial x^2}\right),\quad \epsilon_2=\frac{1}{E}\left(\frac{\partial^2\chi_0}{\partial x^2}-\sigma\frac{\partial^2\chi_0}{\partial y^2}\right),\quad \epsilon_1+\epsilon_2=\frac{1-\sigma}{E}\Theta_0,$$

$$\varpi=-2\frac{1+\sigma}{E}\frac{\partial^2\chi_0}{\partial x\,\partial y},$$

and then we have

$$T_1=\frac{2Eh}{1-\sigma^2}(\epsilon_1+\sigma\epsilon_2)-\tfrac{1}{3}\frac{Eh^3\sigma}{1-\sigma^2}\frac{\partial^2}{\partial y^2}(\epsilon_1+\epsilon_2),$$

$$T_2=\frac{2Eh}{1-\sigma^2}(\epsilon_2+\sigma\epsilon_1)-\tfrac{1}{3}\frac{Eh^3\sigma}{1-\sigma^2}\frac{\partial^2}{\partial x^2}(\epsilon_1+\epsilon_2),$$

$$S_1=\frac{Eh}{1+\sigma}\varpi+\tfrac{1}{3}\frac{Eh^3\sigma}{1-\sigma^2}\frac{\partial^2}{\partial x\,\partial y}(\epsilon_1+\epsilon_2).$$

The potential energy per unit of area can be shown to be

$$\frac{Eh}{1-\sigma^2}\left[(\epsilon_1+\epsilon_2)^2-2(1-\sigma)(\epsilon_1\epsilon_2-\tfrac{1}{4}\varpi^2)\right]$$
$$+\tfrac{1}{3}\frac{Eh^3\sigma}{1-\sigma^2}\left[\epsilon_1\frac{\partial^2}{\partial x^2}(\epsilon_1+\epsilon_2)+\epsilon_2\frac{\partial^2}{\partial y^2}(\epsilon_1+\epsilon_2)+\varpi\frac{\partial^2}{\partial x\,\partial y}(\epsilon_1+\epsilon_2)\right]$$
$$+\tfrac{1}{20}\frac{\sigma^2}{1-\sigma}\frac{Eh^5}{1-\sigma^2}\left[\left\{\frac{\partial^2(\epsilon_1+\epsilon_2)}{\partial x^2}\right\}^2+\left\{\frac{\partial^2(\epsilon_1+\epsilon_2)}{\partial y^2}\right\}^2+2\left\{\frac{\partial^2(\epsilon_1+\epsilon_2)}{\partial x\,\partial y}\right\}^2\right].$$

Some special examples of the general theory will be useful to us presently.

(i) If we put $\Theta_0=0$, χ_0 is a plane harmonic function, and the state of the plate is one of plane *strain* involving no dilatation or rotation [cf. Article 14 (*d*)]. We have

$$u=-\frac{1+\sigma}{E}\frac{\partial\chi_0}{\partial x},\quad v=-\frac{1+\sigma}{E}\frac{\partial\chi_0}{\partial y},\quad w=0,$$

and
$$T_1=-T_2=2h\frac{\partial^2\chi_0}{\partial y^2},\quad S_1=-2h\frac{\partial^2\chi_0}{\partial x\,\partial y}.$$

(ii) If Θ_0 is constant we have $\xi=\Theta_0 x$, $\eta=\Theta_0 y$, and we may put $\chi_0=\tfrac{1}{4}\Theta_0(x^2+y^2)$, and then we have

$$u=\tfrac{1}{2}\frac{1-\sigma}{E}\Theta_0 x,\quad v=\tfrac{1}{2}\frac{1-\sigma}{E}\Theta_0 y,\quad w=-\frac{\sigma}{E}\Theta_0 z,$$

and
$$T_1=T_2=\Theta_0 h,\quad S_1=0.$$

This is the solution for uniform tension $\Theta_0 h$ all round the edge.

(iii) If $\Theta_0=ax$, where a is constant, we have $\xi=\tfrac{1}{2}a(x^2-y^2)$, $\eta=axy$, and we may put $\chi_0=\tfrac{1}{6}ax^3$, and then we have

$$u=\tfrac{1}{2}\frac{a}{E}(\sigma z^2-\sigma x^2-y^2),\quad v=\frac{a}{E}xy,\quad w=-\frac{\sigma a}{E}xz,$$

and
$$T_1=0,\quad T_2=2hax,\quad S_1=0.$$

A more general solution can be obtained by adding the displacement given in

(iv) By taking the function χ_0 in (i) to be of the second degree in x and y, we may obtain the most general solution in which the stress-components are independent of x and y, or the plate is stretched uniformly. The results may be expressed in terms of the quantities ϵ_1, ϵ_2, ϖ that define the stretching of the middle plane. We should find for the stress-components that do not vanish the expressions

$$X_x = E(\epsilon_1 + \sigma\epsilon_2)/(1-\sigma^2), \quad Y_y = E(\epsilon_2 + \sigma\epsilon_1)/(1-\sigma^2), \quad X_y = \tfrac{1}{2}E\varpi/(1+\sigma),$$

and for the displacement the expressions

$$u = \epsilon_1 x + \tfrac{1}{2}\varpi y, \quad v = \epsilon_2 y + \tfrac{1}{2}\varpi x, \quad w = -\sigma z(\epsilon_1 + \epsilon_2)/(1-\sigma).$$

302. Plate bent to a state of plane stress.

Omitting in equations (33) the terms that depend on Θ_0, χ_0, we have the displacement given by the equations

$$\left.\begin{aligned} u &= \frac{1}{E}\beta xz - \frac{1+\sigma}{E} z \frac{\partial \chi_1}{\partial x}, \\ v &= \frac{1}{E}\beta yz - \frac{1+\sigma}{E} z \frac{\partial \chi_1}{\partial y}, \\ w &= -\frac{\beta}{2E}(x^2+y^2+\sigma z^2) + \frac{1+\sigma}{E}\chi_1, \end{aligned}\right\} \quad \text{...............(38)}$$

where χ_1 has the form $\chi_1 = \frac{1}{4}\beta(x^2+y^2) + F$, and F is a plane harmonic function. The stress is expressed by the equations

$$X_x = z\frac{\partial^2 \chi_1}{\partial y^2}, \quad Y_y = z\frac{\partial^2 \chi_1}{\partial x^2}, \quad X_y = -z\frac{\partial^2 \chi_1}{\partial x \partial y}.$$

The stress-resultants vanish, and the stress-couples are given by the equations

$$G_1 = \tfrac{2}{3}h^3 \frac{\partial^2 \chi_1}{\partial y^2}, \quad G_2 = \tfrac{2}{3}h^3 \frac{\partial^2 \chi_1}{\partial x^2}, \quad H_1 = \tfrac{2}{3}h^3 \frac{\partial^2 \chi_1}{\partial x \partial y}. \quad \text{...........(39)}$$

The equations (11) and (12), in which X', Y', Z', L', M' vanish, are obviously satisfied by these forms.

The normal displacement w of the middle plane is given by the equation

$$\mathrm{w} = -\frac{\beta}{2E}(x^2+y^2) + \frac{1+\sigma}{E}\chi_1, \quad \text{....................(40)}$$

so that the curvature is expressed by the equations

$$\kappa_1 = -\frac{\beta}{E} + \frac{1+\sigma}{E}\frac{\partial^2 \chi_1}{\partial x^2}, \quad \kappa_2 = -\frac{\beta}{E} + \frac{1+\sigma}{E}\frac{\partial^2 \chi_1}{\partial y^2}, \quad \tau = \frac{1+\sigma}{E}\frac{\partial^2 \chi_1}{\partial x \partial y},$$

From these equations and the equation $\nabla_1^2 \chi_1 = \beta$, we find

$$\kappa_1 + \sigma\kappa_2 = -\frac{1-\sigma^2}{E}\frac{\partial^2 \chi_1}{\partial y^2}, \quad \kappa_2 + \sigma\kappa_1 = -\frac{1-\sigma^2}{E}\frac{\partial^2 \chi_1}{\partial x^2},$$

so that the formulæ (18) hold.

The stress-couples at the edge are expressible in the forms

$$G = \tfrac{2}{3}h^3\left(\frac{\partial^2 \chi_1}{\partial s^2} + \frac{1}{\rho'}\frac{\partial \chi_1}{\partial \nu}\right), \quad H = \tfrac{2}{3}h^3 \frac{\partial}{\partial \nu}\left(\frac{\partial \chi_1}{\partial s}\right), \quad \text{..............(41)}$$

and, if the edge is subjected to given forces, G and $\partial H/\partial s$ must have prescribed values at the edge. Since χ_1 satisfies the equation $\nabla_1^2\chi_1 = \beta$, the formulæ (41) for G and $\partial H/\partial s$ are not sufficiently general to permit of the satisfaction of such conditions. It follows that a plate free from any forces, except such as are applied at the edge and are statically equivalent to couples, will not be in a state of plane stress unless the couples can be expressed by the formulæ (41).

Some particular results are appended.

(i) When the plate is bent to a state of plane stress the sum of the principal curvatures of the surface into which the middle plane is bent is constant.

(ii) In the same case the potential energy per unit of area of the middle plane is given exactly by the formula (21).

(iii) A particular case will be found by taking the function F introduced in equations (32) to be of the second degree in x and y. Then χ_1 also is of the second degree in x and y, and we may take it to be homogeneous of this degree without altering the expressions for the stress-components. In this case w also is homogeneous of the second degree in x and y, and κ_1, κ_2, τ are constants. The value of χ_1 is

$$\chi_1 = -\tfrac{1}{2}\frac{E}{1-\sigma^2}\left[(\kappa_2+\sigma\kappa_1)\,x^2+(\kappa_1+\sigma\kappa_2)\,y^2-2\,(1-\sigma)\,\tau xy\right],$$

and the stress-components which do not vanish are given by the equations

$$X_x = -\frac{E}{1-\sigma^2}z\,(\kappa_1+\sigma\kappa_2),\quad Y_y = -\frac{E}{1-\sigma^2}z\,(\kappa_2+\sigma\kappa_1),\quad X_y = -\frac{E}{1+\sigma}z\tau.$$

(iv) This case includes that discussed in Article 90, and becomes, in fact, identical with it when the axes of x and y are chosen so that τ vanishes, that is to say so as to be parallel to the lines which become lines of curvature of the surface into which the middle plane is bent. Another special sub-case would be found by taking the plate to be rectangular, and the axes of x and y parallel to its edges, and supposing that κ_1 and κ_2 vanish, while τ is constant. We should then find

$$u = -\tau yz,\quad v = -\tau zx,\quad w = \tau xy.$$

The stress-resultants and the flexural couples G_1, G_2 vanish, and the torsional couples H_1 and H_2 are equal to $\pm D\,(1-\sigma)\,\tau$. The result is that a rectangular plate can be held in the form of an anticlastic surface $w = \tau xy$ by torsional couples of amount $D\,(1-\sigma)\,\tau$ per unit of length applied to its edges in proper senses, or by two pairs of forces directed normally to the plate and applied at its corners*. The two forces of a pair are applied in like senses at the ends of a diagonal, and those applied at the ends of the two diagonals have opposite senses. The magnitude of each force is $2D\,(1-\sigma)\,\tau$.

303. Generalized plane stress.

When Z_z vanishes everywhere, and X_z, Y_z vanish at $z = \pm h$, we take the values of X_z and Y_z to be given by equations (26) of Article 299. To determine X_x, Y_y, X_y we have the first two of equations (22) and (23), the third of equations (24), and equation (25), in which Z_z vanishes, X_z and Y_z are taken to be given by (26), and Θ has the form $\Theta_0 + z\Theta_1$, the functions

* H. Lamb, *London Math. Soc. Proc.*, vol. 21 (1891), p. 70.

Θ_0 and Θ_1 being plane harmonic functions of x, y and independent of z. The stress depending upon Θ_0 has been determined in Article 300, and we shall omit Θ_0. We have therefore the equations

$$\left.\begin{array}{c}\dfrac{\partial X_x}{\partial x}+\dfrac{\partial X_y}{\partial y}-\dfrac{z}{1+\sigma}\dfrac{\partial\Theta_1}{\partial x}=0,\quad \dfrac{\partial X_y}{\partial x}+\dfrac{\partial Y_y}{\partial y}-\dfrac{z}{1+\sigma}\dfrac{\partial\Theta_1}{\partial y}=0,\\ \nabla^2 X_x+\dfrac{z}{1+\sigma}\dfrac{\partial^2\Theta_1}{\partial x^2}=0,\quad \nabla^2 Y_y+\dfrac{z}{1+\sigma}\dfrac{\partial^2\Theta_1}{\partial y^2}=0,\quad \nabla^2 X_y+\dfrac{z}{1+\sigma}\dfrac{\partial^2\Theta_1}{\partial x\partial y}=0,\\ X_x+Y_y=z\Theta_1.\end{array}\right\} \quad \text{.........(42)}$$

From the first two of these equations we find

$$X_x=\frac{z}{1+\sigma}\Theta_1+\frac{\partial^2\chi'}{\partial y^2},\quad Y_y=\frac{z}{1+\sigma}\Theta_1+\frac{\partial^2\chi'}{\partial x^2},\quad X_y=-\frac{\partial^2\chi'}{\partial x\partial y},\quad \text{...(43)}$$

where χ' is a function of x, y, z; and the last equation of (42) gives

$$\nabla_1^2\chi'=-\frac{1-\sigma}{1+\sigma}z\Theta_1.$$

The remaining equations of (42) can now be transformed into the forms

$$\frac{\partial^2}{\partial y^2}\left(\frac{\partial^2\chi'}{\partial z^2}-\frac{2-\sigma}{1+\sigma}z\Theta_1\right)=0,\quad \frac{\partial^2}{\partial x^2}\left(\frac{\partial^2\chi'}{\partial z^2}-\frac{2-\sigma}{1+\sigma}z\Theta_1\right)=0,$$

$$\frac{\partial^2}{\partial x\partial y}\left(\frac{\partial^2\chi'}{\partial z^2}-\frac{2-\sigma}{1+\sigma}z\Theta_1\right)=0.$$

These equations show that the expression $\dfrac{\partial^2\chi'}{\partial z^2}-\dfrac{2-\sigma}{1+\sigma}z\Theta_1$ is a linear function of x and y, and we may take it to be zero without altering the values of X_x, Y_y, X_y. We therefore write

$$\chi'=z\chi_1'+\frac{2-\sigma}{6(1+\sigma)}z^3\Theta_1, \quad \text{........................(44)}$$

where

$$\nabla_1^2\chi_1'=-\frac{1-\sigma}{1+\sigma}\Theta_1. \quad \text{..........................(45)}$$

If we introduce two conjugate functions ξ_1, η_1 of x, y which are such that

$$\frac{\partial\xi_1}{\partial x}=\frac{\partial\eta_1}{\partial y}=\Theta_1,\quad \frac{\partial\xi_1}{\partial y}=-\frac{\partial\eta_1}{\partial x}, \quad \text{......................(46)}$$

we may express χ_1' in the form

$$\chi_1'=-\frac{1-\sigma}{2(1+\sigma)}x\xi_1+F_1, \quad \text{........................(47)}$$

where F_1 is a plane harmonic function. Thus the form of χ', and therewith also that of X_x, X_y, Y_y, is completely determined.

The displacement is determined by the equations of the types

$$\frac{\partial u}{\partial x}=\frac{1}{E}(X_x-\sigma Y_y-\sigma Z_z),\quad \frac{\partial w}{\partial y}+\frac{\partial v}{\partial z}=\frac{2(1+\sigma)}{E}Y_z,$$

in which Z_z vanishes, X_z and Y_z are given by (26), and X_x, Y_y, X_y by (43). The resulting forms for u, v, w are

$$\left.\begin{aligned} u &= -\frac{1}{E}\left[(1+\sigma)\,z\frac{\partial \chi_1'}{\partial x} + \tfrac{1}{6}(2-\sigma)\,z^3\frac{\partial \Theta_1}{\partial x}\right], \\ v &= -\frac{1}{E}\left[(1+\sigma)\,z\frac{\partial \chi_1'}{\partial y} + \tfrac{1}{6}(2-\sigma)\,z^3\frac{\partial \Theta_1}{\partial y}\right], \\ w &= \frac{1}{E}\left[(1+\sigma)\,\chi_1' + (h^2 - \tfrac{1}{2}\sigma z^2)\,\Theta_1\right]. \end{aligned}\right\} \quad \text{..........(48)}$$

304. Plate bent to a state of generalized plane stress.

The normal displacement w of the middle plane is given by the equation

$$\mathrm{w} = \frac{1}{E}\{h^2\Theta_1 + (1+\sigma)\,\chi_1'\}, \quad \text{..........(49)}$$

and, since $\nabla_1^2\Theta_1 = 0$, we have by (45)

$$\nabla_1^4\,\mathrm{w} = 0, \quad \text{..........(50)}$$

where ∇_1^4 denotes the operator $\partial^4/\partial x^4 + \partial^4/\partial y^4 + 2\partial^4/\partial x^2\partial y^2$, and then

$$\Theta_1 = -\frac{E}{1-\sigma}\nabla_1^2\mathrm{w}, \quad \chi_1' = \frac{E}{1+\sigma}\mathrm{w} + \frac{Eh^2}{1-\sigma^2}\nabla_1^2\mathrm{w}. \quad \text{..........(51)}$$

The stress-components are given by the equations

$$\left.\begin{aligned} X_x &= -\frac{Ez}{1-\sigma^2}\nabla_1^2\mathrm{w} + \frac{\partial^2}{\partial y^2}\left[\frac{E}{1+\sigma}z\mathrm{w} + \frac{E}{1-\sigma^2}\{h^2 z - \tfrac{1}{6}(2-\sigma)z^3\}\nabla_1^2\mathrm{w}\right], \\ Y_y &= -\frac{Ez}{1-\sigma^2}\nabla_1^2\mathrm{w} + \frac{\partial^2}{\partial x^2}\left[\frac{E}{1+\sigma}z\mathrm{w} + \frac{E}{1-\sigma^2}\{h^2 z - \tfrac{1}{6}(2-\sigma)z^3\}\nabla_1^2\mathrm{w}\right], \\ X_y &= -\frac{\partial^2}{\partial x\partial y}\left[\frac{E}{1+\sigma}z\mathrm{w} + \frac{E}{1-\sigma^2}\{h^2 z - \tfrac{1}{6}(2-\sigma)z^3\}\nabla_1^2\mathrm{w}\right], \\ X_z &= -\frac{1}{2}\frac{E(h^2-z^2)}{1-\sigma^2}\frac{\partial}{\partial x}\nabla_1^2\mathrm{w}, \quad Y_z = -\frac{1}{2}\frac{E(h^2-z^2)}{1-\sigma^2}\frac{\partial}{\partial y}\nabla_1^2\mathrm{w}, \quad Z_z = 0. \end{aligned}\right\} \quad \text{..........(52)}$$

The stress-resultants and stress-couples are given by the equations

$$\left.\begin{aligned} & T_1 = T_2 = S_1 = 0, \\ & N_1 = -D\frac{\partial}{\partial x}\nabla_1^2\mathrm{w}, \quad N_2 = -D\frac{\partial}{\partial y}\nabla_1^2\mathrm{w}, \\ & G_1 = -D\left(\frac{\partial^2\mathrm{w}}{\partial x^2} + \sigma\frac{\partial^2\mathrm{w}}{\partial y^2}\right) + \frac{8+\sigma}{10}Dh^2\frac{\partial^2}{\partial y^2}\nabla_1^2\mathrm{w}, \\ & G_2 = -D\left(\frac{\partial^2\mathrm{w}}{\partial y^2} + \sigma\frac{\partial^2\mathrm{w}}{\partial x^2}\right) + \frac{8+\sigma}{10}Dh^2\frac{\partial^2}{\partial x^2}\nabla_1^2\mathrm{w}, \\ & H_1 = D(1-\sigma)\frac{\partial^2\mathrm{w}}{\partial x\partial y} + \frac{8+\sigma}{10}Dh^2\frac{\partial^2}{\partial x\partial y}\nabla_1^2\mathrm{w}. \end{aligned}\right\} \quad \text{..........(53)}$$

Equations (11) and (12) in which X', Y', Z', L', M' vanish are obviously satisfied by these forms.

The stress-resultants and stress-couples belonging to any curve s of which the normal is ν can be expressed in the forms

$$\left.\begin{aligned} T &= S = 0, \quad N = -D\frac{\partial}{\partial\nu}\nabla_1^2 \mathrm{w}, \\ G &= -D\nabla_1^2\mathrm{w} + D(1-\sigma)\left(\frac{\partial^2}{\partial s^2} + \frac{1}{\rho'}\frac{\partial}{\partial\nu}\right)\left(\mathrm{w} + \frac{1}{10}\frac{8+\sigma}{1-\sigma}h^2\nabla_1^2\mathrm{w}\right), \\ H &= D(1-\sigma)\frac{\partial}{\partial\nu}\left\{\frac{\partial}{\partial s}\left(\mathrm{w} + \frac{1}{10}\frac{8+\sigma}{1-\sigma}h^2\nabla_1^2\mathrm{w}\right)\right\}, \end{aligned}\right\} \quad \ldots(54)$$

where ρ' denotes the radius of curvature of the curve. At a boundary to which given forces and couples are applied G and $N - \partial H/\partial s$ have given values. The solution is sufficiently general to admit of the satisfaction of such boundary-conditions. The solution expressed by (48) is exact if the applied tractions at the edges are distributed in accordance with (52), in which w satisfies (50); but, if they are distributed otherwise, without ceasing to be equivalent to resultants of the types N, G, H, the solution represents the state of the plate with sufficient approximation at all points which are not close to the edge.

The potential energy per unit of area can be shown to be

$$\begin{aligned} &\tfrac{1}{2}D\left[(\nabla_1^2\mathrm{w})^2 - 2(1-\sigma)\left\{\frac{\partial^2\mathrm{w}}{\partial x^2}\frac{\partial^2\mathrm{w}}{\partial y^2} - \left(\frac{\partial^2\mathrm{w}}{\partial x\partial y}\right)^2\right\}\right] \\ &+ \frac{8+\sigma}{10}Dh^2\left[\frac{\partial^2\mathrm{w}}{\partial x^2}\frac{\partial^2\nabla_1^2\mathrm{w}}{\partial x^2} + \frac{\partial^2\mathrm{w}}{\partial y^2}\frac{\partial^2\nabla_1^2\mathrm{w}}{\partial y^2} + 2\frac{\partial^2\mathrm{w}}{\partial x\partial y}\frac{\partial^2\nabla_1^2\mathrm{w}}{\partial x\partial y}\right] \\ &+ \tfrac{2}{5}\frac{Dh^2}{1-\sigma}\left[\left(\frac{\partial\nabla_1^2\mathrm{w}}{\partial x}\right)^2 + \left(\frac{\partial\nabla_1^2\mathrm{w}}{\partial y}\right)^2\right] \\ &- \frac{272+64\sigma+5\sigma^2}{420(1-\sigma)}Dh^4\left[\frac{\partial^2\nabla_1^2\mathrm{w}}{\partial x^2}\frac{\partial^2\nabla_1^2\mathrm{w}}{\partial y^2} - \left(\frac{\partial^2\nabla_1^2\mathrm{w}}{\partial x\partial y}\right)^2\right] \quad \ldots\ldots\ldots\ldots(55) \end{aligned}$$

The results here obtained include those found in Article 302 by putting $\Theta_1 = \beta$. Equations (53) show that the stress-couples are not expressed by the formulæ (18) unless the sum of the principal curvatures is a constant or a linear function of x and y. In like manner the formula (21) is not verified unless the sum of the principal curvatures is constant; but these formulæ yield approximate expressions for the stress-couples and the potential energy when h is small.

The theory which has been given in Article 301 and in this Article consists rather in the specification of forms of exact solutions of the equations of equilibrium than in the determination of complete solutions of these equations. The forms contain a number of unknown functions, and the complete solutions are to be obtained by adjusting these functions so as to satisfy certain differential equations such as (50) and certain boundary-conditions. These forms can represent the state of strain that would be produced in a plate of any shape by any forces applied to the edge, in so far as these forces are expressed adequately by a line-distribution of force, specified by components, T, S, $\mathrm{N} - \partial\mathrm{H}/\partial s$, and a line-distribution of flexural couple G.

305. Circular plate loaded at its centre*.

The problem of the circular plate supported or clamped at the edge and loaded at the centre may serve as an example of the theory just given. If a is the radius of the plate, and r denotes the distance of any point from the centre, we may take w to be a function of r only, and to be given by the equation

$$\left(\frac{\partial^2}{\partial r^2}+\frac{1}{r}\frac{\partial}{\partial r}\right)\mathrm{w}=\frac{W}{2\pi D}\log\frac{a}{r}+A, \qquad (56)$$

where W, A are constants, and then we have on any circle of radius r

$$N=\frac{W}{2\pi r}, \quad H=0,$$

and the resultant shearing force on the part of the plate within the circle is W. Hence W is the load at the centre of the plate. The complete primitive of (56) is

$$\mathrm{w}=\frac{W}{8\pi D}\left(r^2\log\frac{a}{r}+r^2\right)+\tfrac{1}{4}Ar^2+B+C\log r,$$

where B and C are constants of integration. If the plate is complete up to the centre, C must vanish, and we take therefore the solution

$$\mathrm{w}=\frac{W}{8\pi D}\left(r^2\log\frac{a}{r}+r^2\right)+\tfrac{1}{4}Ar^2+B.$$

The flexural couple G at any circle $r=a$ is given by the equation

$$G=-\frac{W}{4\pi}(1+\sigma)\log\frac{a}{r}+\frac{W}{8\pi}(1-\sigma)-\frac{W}{20\pi}(8+\sigma)\frac{h^2}{r^2}-\tfrac{1}{2}D(1+\sigma)A.$$

We may now determine the constants A and B. If the plate is supported at the edge, so that w and G vanish at $r=a$, we find

$$\mathrm{w}=\frac{W}{2\pi D}\left[\tfrac{1}{4}r^2\log\frac{a}{r}-\tfrac{1}{8}\frac{3+\sigma}{1+\sigma}(a^2-r^2)+\tfrac{1}{20}\frac{8+\sigma}{1+\sigma}\frac{h^2}{a^2}(a^2-r^2)\right], \qquad (57)$$

and the central deflexion, which is the value of $-\mathrm{w}$ at $r=0$, is

$$\frac{W}{2\pi D}\left(\tfrac{1}{8}\frac{3+\sigma}{1+\sigma}a^2-\tfrac{1}{20}\frac{8+\sigma}{1+\sigma}h^2\right).$$

If the plate is clamped at the edge, so that w and $\partial\mathrm{w}/\partial r$ vanish at $r=a$, we have

$$\mathrm{w}=\frac{W}{8\pi D}\left[r^2\log\frac{a}{r}-\tfrac{1}{2}(a^2-r^2)\right], \qquad (58)$$

and the central deflexion is $Wa^2/16\pi D$. If the plate is very thin the central deflexion is greater when it is supported at the edge than when it is clamped at the edge in the ratio $(3+\sigma):(1+\sigma)$, which is $13:5$ when $\sigma=\tfrac{1}{4}$.

306. Plate in a state of stress which is uniform, or varies uniformly, over its plane.

When the stress in a plate is the same at all points of any plane parallel to the faces of the plate the stress-components are independent of x and y, and the stress-equations of equilibrium become

$$\frac{\partial X_z}{\partial z}=0, \quad \frac{\partial Y_z}{\partial z}=0, \quad \frac{\partial Z_z}{\partial z}=0.$$

If the faces of the plate are free from traction it follows that X_z, Y_z, Z_z vanish, or the plate is in a state of plane stress. The most general state of stress, independent of x and y, which can be maintained in a cylindrical or prismatic body by tractions over its curved surface can be obtained by adding the solutions given in (iv) of Article 301 and (iii) of

* Results equivalent to those obtained here were given by Saint-Venant in the 'Annotated Clebsch,' *Note du* § 45.

Article 302. In these cases the stress is uniform over the cross-sections of the cylinder or prism.

When the stress-components are linear functions of x and y the stress varies uniformly over the cross-sections of the cylinder or prism. We may determine the most general possible states of stress in a prism when the ends are free from traction, there are no body forces, and the stress-components are linear functions of x and y. For this purpose we should express all the stress-components in such forms as

$$X_x = X_x' x + X_x'' y + X_x^{(0)},$$

where X_x', X_x'', $X_x^{(0)}$ are functions of z. When we introduce these forms into the various equations which the stress-components have to satisfy, the terms of these equations which contain x, or y, and the terms which are independent of x and y must separately satisfy the equations.

We take first the stress-equations of equilibrium. The equation

$$\frac{\partial X_x}{\partial x} + \frac{\partial X_y}{\partial y} + \frac{\partial X_z}{\partial z} = 0,$$

combined with the conditions that X_z vanishes at $z = \pm h$, gives us the equations

$$X_z' = 0, \quad X_z'' = 0, \quad \frac{\partial X_z^{(0)}}{\partial z} + X_x' + X_y'' = 0,$$

and in like manner we have the equations

$$Y_z' = 0, \quad Y_z'' = 0, \quad \frac{\partial Y_z^{(0)}}{\partial z} + X_y' + Y_y'' = 0.$$

It follows that X_z and Y_z are independent of x and y. The third of the stress-equations becomes therefore $\partial Z_z/\partial z = 0$, and, since Z_z vanishes at the faces of the plate ($z = \pm h$), it vanishes everywhere.

Again Θ is of the form $x\Theta' + y\Theta'' + \Theta^{(0)}$, where Θ', Θ'', $\Theta^{(0)}$ are functions of z, and, since Θ is an harmonic function, they must be linear functions of z. The equation $\nabla^2 X_z = -\dfrac{1}{1+\sigma}\dfrac{\partial^2 \Theta}{\partial x \partial z}$ takes the form $\partial^2 X_z/\partial z^2 = \text{constant}$, so that $\partial^3 X_z/\partial z^3 = 0$. Since X_z satisfies this equation and vanishes at $z = \pm h$, it must contain $z^2 - h^2$ as a factor, and since it is independent of x and y it must be of the form $A(z^2 - h^2)$, where A is constant. Like statements hold concerning Y_z.

It follows that, if a cylindrical body with its generators parallel to the axis of z is free from body forces and from traction on the plane ends, the most general type of stress which satisfies the condition that the stress-components are linear functions of x and y is included under the generalized plane stress discussed in Article 303 by taking Θ_0 and Θ_1 to be linear functions of x and y and restricting the auxiliary plane harmonic functions f and F_1 introduced in equations (32) and (47) to be of degree not higher than the third.

It may be shown that, in all the states of stress in a plate which are included in this category, the stress-components are expressible in terms of the quantities ϵ_1, ϵ_2, ϖ, which define the stretching of the middle plane, and κ_1, κ_2, τ, which define the curvature of the surface into which this plane is bent, by the formulæ

$$\left.\begin{aligned}
X_x &= \frac{E}{1-\sigma^2}\{\epsilon_1 + \sigma\epsilon_2 - (\kappa_1 + \sigma\kappa_2) z\},\\
Y_y &= \frac{E}{1-\sigma^2}\{\epsilon_2 + \sigma\epsilon_1 - (\kappa_2 + \sigma\kappa_1) z\},\\
X_y &= \frac{E}{1+\sigma}\{\tfrac{1}{2}\varpi - \tau z\},\\
X_z &= -\tfrac{1}{2}\frac{E(h^2 - z^2)}{1-\sigma^2}\frac{\partial}{\partial x}(\kappa_1 + \kappa_2),\\
Y_z &= -\tfrac{1}{2}\frac{E(h^2 - z^2)}{1-\sigma^2}\frac{\partial}{\partial y}(\kappa_1 + \kappa_2),\\
Z_z &= 0.
\end{aligned}\right\} \qquad \text{.........................(59)}$$

The stress-resultants and stress-couples are expressed by the formulæ

$$\left.\begin{aligned}&T_1=\frac{2Eh}{1-\sigma^2}(\epsilon_1+\sigma\epsilon_2),\quad T_2=\frac{2Eh}{1-\sigma^2}(\epsilon_2+\sigma\epsilon_1),\quad S_1=\frac{Eh}{1+\sigma}\varpi,\\&N_1=-D\frac{\partial}{\partial x}(\kappa_1+\kappa_2),\quad N_2=-D\frac{\partial}{\partial y}(\kappa_1+\kappa_2),\\&G_1=-D(\kappa_1+\sigma\kappa_2),\quad G_2=-D(\kappa_2+\sigma\kappa_1),\quad H_1=D(1-\sigma)\tau,\end{aligned}\right\}\quad \text{.........(60)}$$

and the potential energy per unit of area is

$$\begin{aligned}&\frac{Eh}{1-\sigma^2}[(\epsilon_1+\epsilon_2)^2-2(1-\sigma)(\epsilon_1\epsilon_2-\tfrac{1}{4}\varpi^2)]\\&+\tfrac{1}{2}D[(\kappa_1+\kappa_2)^2-2(1-\sigma)(\kappa_1\kappa_2-\tau^2)]\\&+\tfrac{2}{5}\frac{Dh^2}{1-\sigma}\left[\left\{\frac{\partial(\kappa_1+\kappa_2)}{\partial x}\right\}^2+\left\{\frac{\partial(\kappa_1+\kappa_2)}{\partial y}\right\}^2\right].\quad \text{........................(61)}\end{aligned}$$

307. Plate bent by pressure uniform over a face.

So far we have been discussing plates deformed by forces applied at the edges; we now consider plates bent by forces transverse to the initial position of the middle plane. The procedure will be similar to that explained in Article 299. We first find a particular solution of the equation satisfied by Z_z, adapted to satisfy the special conditions which hold at the faces $z=\pm h$, then find particular solutions of the equations satisfied by X_z and Y_z, also adapted to satisfy the special conditions which hold at the faces, and then deduce general formulæ for X_x, Y_y, X_y.

When the face $z=h$ is subjected to uniform pressure p, we have $\nabla^4 Z_z=0$ everywhere, $\partial Z_z/\partial z=0$ at $z=h$ and $z=-h$, $Z_z=-p$ at $z=h$, $Z_z=0$ at $z=-h$. A particular solution is

$$Z_z=\tfrac{1}{4}h^{-3}p(z+h)^2(z-2h)=\tfrac{1}{4}h^{-3}p(z^3-3h^2z-2h^3),\quad \text{......(62)}$$

and we take this to be the value of Z_z. To determine Θ we have the equations

$$\nabla^2\Theta=0,\quad \partial^2\Theta/\partial z^2=-\tfrac{3}{2}(1+\sigma)h^{-3}pz,$$

of which the most general solution has the form

$$\Theta=-\tfrac{1}{4}(1+\sigma)h^{-3}pz^3+\tfrac{3}{8}(1+\sigma)h^{-3}pz(x^2+y^2)+z\Theta_1+\Theta_0,$$

where Θ_1 and Θ_0 are plane harmonic functions. We may omit the terms $z\Theta_1$ and Θ_0 because the stress-systems that would be calculated from them have been found already. We take therefore for Θ the form

$$\Theta=-\tfrac{1}{4}(1+\sigma)h^{-3}pz^3+\tfrac{3}{8}(1+\sigma)h^{-3}pz(x^2+y^2).\quad \text{........(63)}$$

To determine X_z and Y_z we have the equations

$$\frac{\partial X_z}{\partial x}+\frac{\partial Y_z}{\partial y}+\frac{3p}{4h^3}(z^2-h^2)=0,\quad \nabla^2 X_z=-\frac{3px}{4h^3},\quad \nabla^2 Y_z=-\frac{3py}{4h^3},$$

and the conditions that X_z and Y_z vanish at $z=h$ and at $z=-h$. A particular solution is

$$X_z=\tfrac{3}{8}h^{-3}p(h^2-z^2)x,\quad Y_z=\tfrac{3}{8}h^{-3}p(h^2-z^2)y,\quad \text{...........(64)}$$

and, as in Article 299, we take X_z and Y_z to have these values.

To determine X_x, Y_y, X_y we have the equations

$$\left.\begin{array}{l}\dfrac{\partial X_x}{\partial x}+\dfrac{\partial X_y}{\partial y}=\dfrac{3pxz}{4h^3},\quad \dfrac{\partial X_y}{\partial x}+\dfrac{\partial Y_y}{\partial y}=\dfrac{3pyz}{4h^3},\\ \nabla^2 X_x=\nabla^2 Y_y=-\tfrac{3}{4}h^{-3}pz,\quad \nabla^2 X_y=0,\\ X_x+Y_y=\tfrac{1}{4}h^{-3}p\left[-(2+\sigma)z^3+3z\left\{\tfrac{1}{2}(1+\sigma)(x^2+y^2)+h^2\right\}+2h^3\right].\end{array}\right\}\quad(65)$$

To satisfy the first two of these equations we take X_x, Y_y, X_y to have the forms

$$X_x=\frac{3pz}{8h^3}(x^2+y^2)+\frac{\partial^2\chi}{\partial y^2},\quad Y_y=\frac{3pz}{8h^3}(x^2+y^2)+\frac{\partial^2\chi}{\partial x^2},\quad X_y=-\frac{\partial^2\chi}{\partial x\partial y},$$

where χ must satisfy the equation

$$\nabla_1^2\chi=-\frac{2+\sigma}{4}\frac{pz^3}{h^3}-\tfrac{3}{8}(1-\sigma)\frac{pz}{h^3}(x^2+y^2)+\tfrac{3}{4}\frac{pz}{h}+\tfrac{1}{2}p,$$

and then the remaining equations of (65) show that

$$\frac{\partial^2\chi}{\partial z^2}+\nabla_1^2\chi+\tfrac{9}{8}\frac{p}{h^3}z(x^2+y^2)$$

must be a linear function of x and y. As in previous Articles, this function may be taken to be zero without altering X_x, Y_y or X_y, and therefore χ must have the form

$$\chi=\frac{2+\sigma}{80}\frac{pz^5}{h^3}-\frac{2+\sigma}{16}\frac{pz^3}{h^3}(x^2+y^2)-\tfrac{1}{8}\frac{pz^3}{h}-\tfrac{1}{4}pz^2+z\chi_1''+\chi_0'',$$

where χ_1'' and χ_0'' are functions of x and y which satisfy the equations

$$\nabla_1^2\chi_1''=-\tfrac{3}{8}(1-\sigma)\frac{p}{h^3}(x^2+y^2)+\tfrac{3}{4}\frac{p}{h},\quad \nabla_1^2\chi_0''=\tfrac{1}{2}p;\quad\ldots\ldots\ldots(66)$$

and we may take for χ_1'', χ_0'' the particular solutions

$$\left.\begin{array}{l}\chi_1'=-\dfrac{3}{2^7}(1-\sigma)\dfrac{p}{h^3}(x^2+y^2)^2+\tfrac{3}{16}\dfrac{p}{h}(x^2+y^2),\\ \chi_0''=\tfrac{1}{8}p(x^2+y^2).\end{array}\right\}\quad\ldots\ldots\ldots\ldots(67)$$

More general integrals of the equations (66) need not be taken because the arbitrary plane harmonic functions that might be added to the solutions (67) give rise to stress-systems of the types already discussed.

The expressions which we have now found for X_x, Y_y, X_y are

$$\left.\begin{array}{l}X_x=\tfrac{1}{4}p+\tfrac{3}{8}p\dfrac{z}{h^3}(x^2+y^2+h^2)-\tfrac{3}{32}(1-\sigma)p\dfrac{z}{h^3}(x^2+3y^2)-\dfrac{2+\sigma}{8}p\dfrac{z^3}{h^3},\\ Y_y=\tfrac{1}{4}p+\tfrac{3}{8}p\dfrac{z}{h^3}(x^2+y^2+h^2)-\tfrac{3}{32}(1-\sigma)p\dfrac{z}{h^3}(3x^2+y^2)-\dfrac{2+\sigma}{8}p\dfrac{z^3}{h^3},\\ X_y=\tfrac{3}{16}(1-\sigma)p\dfrac{z}{h^3}xy.\end{array}\right\}\ldots(68)$$

The stress-components being given by (62), (64) and (68), the corresponding displacement is given by the formulæ

$$\left.\begin{aligned} u &= -\frac{1+\sigma}{E}\frac{px}{8h^3}\left[(2-\sigma)z^3 - 3h^2z - 2h^3 - \tfrac{3}{4}(1-\sigma)z(x^2+y^2)\right],\\ v &= -\frac{1+\sigma}{E}\frac{py}{8h^3}\left[(2-\sigma)z^3 - 3h^2z - 2h^3 - \tfrac{3}{4}(1-\sigma)z(x^2+y^2)\right],\\ w &= \frac{1+\sigma}{E}\frac{p}{16h^3}\left[(1+\sigma)z^4 - 6h^2z^2 - 8h^3z + 3(h^2-\sigma z^2)(x^2+y^2) - \tfrac{3}{8}(1-\sigma)(x^2+y^2)^2\right]. \end{aligned}\right\} \quad \text{.........(69)}$$

It is noteworthy that when the displacement is expressed by these formulæ the middle plane is slightly stretched. We have, in fact, when $z=0$,

$$\frac{\partial u}{\partial x} = \frac{\partial v}{\partial y} = \tfrac{1}{4}(1+\sigma)\frac{p}{E}, \quad \frac{\partial v}{\partial x} + \frac{\partial u}{\partial y} = 0.$$

The stress-resultants and stress-couples are given by the formulæ

$$\left.\begin{aligned} &T_1 = \tfrac{1}{2}ph, \quad T_2 = \tfrac{1}{2}ph, \quad S_1 = 0,\\ &N_1 = \tfrac{1}{2}px, \quad N_2 = \tfrac{1}{2}py,\\ &G_1 = \frac{p}{16}\{(3+\sigma)x^2 + (1+3\sigma)y^2\} + \frac{3-\sigma}{20}ph^2,\\ &G_2 = \frac{p}{16}\{(1+3\sigma)x^2 + (3+\sigma)y^2\} + \frac{3-\sigma}{20}ph^2,\\ &H_1 = -\tfrac{1}{8}(1-\sigma)pxy. \end{aligned}\right\} \quad \text{............(70)}$$

These forms obviously satisfy equations (11) and (12) in which X', Y', L', M' vanish and Z' is replaced by $-p$.

The middle plane is bent into the surface expressed by the equation

$$\mathrm{w} = -\tfrac{1}{64}\frac{p}{D}(x^2+y^2)\left(x^2+y^2-\frac{8h^2}{1-\sigma}\right); \quad \text{............(71)}$$

and we find
$$G_1 = -D(\kappa_1+\sigma\kappa_2) + \frac{8+\sigma+\sigma^2}{20(1-\sigma)}ph^2,$$
$$G_2 = -D(\kappa_2+\sigma\kappa_1) + \frac{8+\sigma+\sigma^2}{20(1-\sigma)}ph^2,$$
$$H_1 = D(1-\sigma)\tau.$$

The formulæ (18) are not exactly verified, but they are approximately correct when h is small.

308. Plate bent by pressure varying uniformly over a face.

Before proceeding with the discussion of particular illustrations of the solution obtained in Article 307 we extend the results to the case where the pressure on the face exposed to pressure is a linear function of x and y. It will be sufficient to take the case where p is replaced by $p_0 x$. By the process already employed we find for Z_z, Θ, X_z, Y_z the expressions

$$\left.\begin{aligned} Z_z &= \frac{p_0 x}{4h^3}(z^3 - 3h^2 z - 2h^3), \\ \Theta &= -(1+\sigma)\frac{p_0 x z^3}{4h^3} + \tfrac{3}{16}(1+\sigma)\frac{p_0 x z}{h^3}(x^2+y^2), \\ X_z &= \tfrac{3}{32}\frac{p_0}{h^3}(h^2-z^2)(3x^2+y^2) + \tfrac{1}{8}\frac{p_0}{h^3}(h^2-z^2)(2h^2-z^2), \\ Y_z &= \tfrac{3}{16}\frac{p_0}{h^3}(h^2-z^2)\,xy; \end{aligned}\right\} \quad \text{......(72)}$$

and thence we obtain, in the same way as before, the formulæ

$$\left.\begin{aligned} X_x &= \frac{p_0 x z}{16h^3}[12h^2 - (6+\sigma)z^2 + \tfrac{1}{2}(5+\sigma)x^2 + \tfrac{3}{2}(1+\sigma)y^2], \\ Y_y &= \frac{p_0 x}{16h^3}[8h^3 - (2+3\sigma)z^3 + \{\tfrac{1}{2}(1+5\sigma)x^2 + \tfrac{3}{2}(1+\sigma)y^2\}z], \\ X_y &= \frac{p_0 y z}{16h^3}[-(2-\sigma)z^2 + \tfrac{1}{2}(1-\sigma)(3x^2+y^2)]. \end{aligned}\right\} \quad \text{...(73)}$$

The displacement is then given by the formulæ

$$\left.\begin{aligned} u &= \frac{1+\sigma}{E}\frac{p_0}{4h^3}\Big[2zh^4 + z^2h^3 - \tfrac{1}{2}z^3h^2 + \frac{3-\sigma}{20}z^5 - h^3y^2 \\ &\qquad + \frac{1-\sigma}{32}z(5x^2+y^2)(x^2+y^2) + \tfrac{3}{2}zx^2h^2 - \frac{2-\sigma}{8}(3x^2+y^2)z^3\Big], \\ v &= \frac{1+\sigma}{E}\frac{p_0}{4h^3}\Big[2h^3xy + \frac{1-\sigma}{8}zxy(x^2+y^2) - \frac{2-\sigma}{4}xyz^3\Big], \\ w &= \frac{1+\sigma}{E}\frac{p_0}{4h^3}\Big[-\frac{1-\sigma}{32}x(x^2+y^2)^2 + \tfrac{1}{4}(x^3+3xy^2)h^2 \\ &\qquad - 2xzh^3 - \tfrac{3}{8}\sigma xz^2(x^2+y^2) - \tfrac{3}{2}xz^2h^2 + \frac{1+\sigma}{4}xz^4\Big]. \end{aligned}\right\} \quad \text{......(74)}$$

The middle plane is slightly stretched in a direction at right angles to that along which the pressure varies. We have, in fact, when $z=0$,

$$\frac{\partial u}{\partial x} = 0, \quad \frac{\partial v}{\partial y} = \tfrac{1}{2}(1+\sigma)\frac{p_0 x}{E}, \quad \frac{\partial v}{\partial x} + \frac{\partial u}{\partial y} = 0.$$

The stress-resultants and stress-couples are given by the formulæ

$$\left.\begin{aligned} &T_1 = 0, \quad T_2 = p_0 h x, \quad S_1 = 0, \\ &N_1 = \tfrac{1}{8}p_0(3x^2+y^2) + \tfrac{3}{10}p_0h^2, \quad N_2 = \tfrac{1}{4}p_0 xy, \\ &G_1 = \tfrac{1}{16}p_0[\tfrac{1}{3}(5+\sigma)x^3 + (1+\sigma)xy^2 + \tfrac{2}{5}(14-\sigma)h^2x], \\ &G_2 = \tfrac{1}{16}p_0[\tfrac{1}{3}(1+5\sigma)x^3 + (1+\sigma)xy^2 - \tfrac{2}{5}(2+3\sigma)h^2x], \\ &H_1 = \tfrac{1}{16}p_0[-\tfrac{1}{3}(1-\sigma)(3x^2y+y^3) + \tfrac{2}{5}(2-\sigma)h^2y]. \end{aligned}\right\} \quad \text{......(75)}$$

These forms obviously satisfy equations (11) and (12) in which X', Y', L', M' are put equal to zero and Z' is put equal to $-p_0 x$.

The middle plane is bent into the surface expressed by the equation

$$\text{w} = -\tfrac{1}{3}\frac{p_0}{D}x\left[\tfrac{1}{64}(x^2+y^2)^2 - \tfrac{1}{8}\frac{h^2}{1-\sigma}(x^2+3y^2)\right], \quad \ldots\ldots\ldots(76)$$

and we find

$$\left.\begin{aligned} G_1 &= -D(\kappa_1+\sigma\kappa_2) + \tfrac{1}{40}\frac{24-5\sigma+\sigma^2}{1-\sigma}p_0h^2x, \\ G_2 &= -D(\kappa_2+\sigma\kappa_1) + \tfrac{1}{40}\frac{8+9\sigma+3\sigma^2}{1-\sigma}p_0h^2x, \\ H_1 &= D(1-\sigma)\tau - \frac{8+\sigma}{40}p_0h^2y. \end{aligned}\right\}$$

The formulæ (18) are approximately correct when h is small.

309. Circular plate bent by uniform pressure and supported at the edge.

When a plate whose edge-line is a given curve is slightly bent by pressure, which is uniform, or varies uniformly, over one face, the stress-system is to be obtained by compounding with the solution obtained in Article 307 or 308 solutions of the types discussed in Articles 301 and 302 or 303, and adjusting the latter so that the boundary-conditions may be satisfied. We shall discuss the case of a clamped edge presently. When the edge is supported, the boundary-conditions which hold at the edge-line are

$$\text{w}=0, \quad G=0, \quad T=S=0. \quad \ldots\ldots\ldots\ldots\ldots\ldots(77)$$

Let the plate be subjected to uniform normal pressure p and supported at the edge, and let the edge-line be a circle $r=a$. The solution given in (71) yields the following values for w, G, T, S at $r=a$:

$$\text{w} = -\tfrac{1}{64}\frac{p}{D}a^2\left(a^2-\frac{8h^2}{1-\sigma}\right), \quad G=\frac{3+\sigma}{16}pa^2+\frac{3-\sigma}{20}ph^2, \quad T=\tfrac{1}{2}ph, \quad S=0.$$

The solution given in (ii) of Article 301 yields the values

$$\text{w}=0, \quad G=0, \quad T=\tfrac{1}{2}ph, \quad S=0$$

when Θ_0 is put equal to $\tfrac{1}{2}p$. The solution given in Article 302 yields zero values for T and S, and it may be adjusted to yield constant values for w and G at $r=a$ by putting $\chi_1=\tfrac{1}{4}\beta(x^2+y^2)+\gamma$, where γ is a constant. These values are

$$\text{w} = -\frac{1-\sigma}{4}\frac{\beta a^2}{E}+\frac{1+\sigma}{E}\gamma, \quad G=\tfrac{1}{3}h^3\beta.$$

If we put $\quad \beta=\dfrac{3p}{h^3}\left(\dfrac{3+\sigma}{16}a^2+\dfrac{3-\sigma}{20}h^2\right), \quad \gamma=\dfrac{3(1-\sigma)pa^2}{2h^3}\left(\dfrac{5+\sigma}{1+\sigma}\dfrac{a^2}{64}+\dfrac{8+\sigma+\sigma^2}{1-\sigma^2}\dfrac{h^2}{40}\right),$

the values of w and G at $r=a$, as given by the solutions in Article 302 and in Article 307, become identical.

We may now combine the three solutions so as to satisfy the conditions (77) at $r=a$. We find the following expressions for the components of displacement

$$\left.\begin{aligned} u &= \frac{px}{E}\left[\tfrac{1}{2}\sigma - \frac{3(1-\sigma)}{32}\frac{z}{h^3}\{(3+\sigma)a^2-(1+\sigma)r^2\} + \tfrac{3}{40}\frac{z}{h}(2+9\sigma-\sigma^2) - \tfrac{1}{8}\frac{z^3}{h^3}(2+\sigma-\sigma^2)\right], \\ v &= \frac{py}{E}\left[\tfrac{1}{2}\sigma - \frac{3(1-\sigma)}{32}\frac{z}{h^3}\{(3+\sigma)a^2-(1+\sigma)r^2\} + \tfrac{3}{40}\frac{z}{h}(2+9\sigma-\sigma^2) - \tfrac{1}{8}\frac{z^3}{h^3}(2+\sigma-\sigma^2)\right], \\ w &= \text{w} + \frac{pz}{E}\left[-\tfrac{1}{2}+\frac{3\sigma}{32}\frac{z}{h^3}\{(3+\sigma)a^2-2(1+\sigma)r^2\} - \tfrac{3}{40}\frac{z}{h}(5+2\sigma+\sigma^2) + \tfrac{1}{16}\frac{z^3}{h^3}(1+\sigma)^2\right], \end{aligned}\right\}$$

$$\ldots\ldots\ldots\ldots(78)$$

where

$$\text{w} = -\tfrac{1}{8}\frac{p}{D}(a^2-r^2)\left\{\tfrac{1}{8}\left(\frac{5+\sigma}{1+\sigma}a^2-r^2\right)+\tfrac{1}{5}\frac{8+\sigma+\sigma^2}{1-\sigma^2}h^2\right\}. \quad \ldots\ldots\ldots\ldots(79)$$

The stress-resultants and stress-couples at the edge vanish with the exception of N, which is equal to $\frac{1}{2}pa$.

The middle plane is bent into the surface expressed by the equation (79), and the right-hand member of this equation with its sign changed is the deflexion at any point. The comparison of this result with (57) of Article 305 shows that, when the plate is thin, the central deflexion due to uniformly distributed load is the same as for a load concentrated at the centre and equal to $\frac{1}{4}(5+\sigma)/(3+\sigma)$ of the total distributed load.

The middle plane is stretched uniformly, and the amount of the extension of any linear element of it is $\frac{1}{2}\sigma p/E$. This is half the amount by which the middle plane would be stretched if one face of the plate were supported on a smooth rigid plane and the other were subjected to the pressure p.

Linear filaments of the plate which are at right angles to its faces in the unstressed state do not remain straight or normal to the middle plane. The curved lines into which they are deformed are of the type expressed by the equation

$$U = U_0 + U_1 z + U_3 z^3,$$

where U is the radial displacement, and U_0, U_1, U_3 are given by the formulæ

$$U_0 = \frac{1}{2}\sigma\frac{pr}{E},$$

$$U_1 = -\frac{3pr}{Eh^3}\left[(3+\sigma)(1-\sigma)\frac{a^2}{32} - (1-\sigma^2)\frac{r^2}{32} - (2+9\sigma-\sigma^2)\frac{h^2}{40}\right],$$

$$U_3 = -\frac{pr}{Eh^3}\frac{2+\sigma-\sigma^2}{8}.$$

These lines are of the same form as those found in Article 95 for the deformed shapes of the initially vertical filaments of a narrow rectangular beam bent by a vertical load. The central tangents to these lines cut the surface into which the middle plane is bent at an angle

$$\tfrac{1}{2}\pi - \tfrac{3}{4}(1+\sigma)pr/Eh.$$

310. Plate bent by uniform pressure and clamped at the edge.

Let (u, v, w) be the displacement of any point of the middle plane. When the plate is clamped at the edge the conditions which must be satisfied at the edge-line are

$$\mathrm{u}=0, \quad \mathrm{v}=0, \quad \mathrm{w}=0, \quad \partial\mathrm{w}/\partial\nu=0, \quad \text{..................(80)}$$

ν denoting the direction of the normal to the edge-line. We seek to satisfy these conditions by a synthesis of the solutions in Articles 301, 303 and 307. We have

$$\mathrm{u} = \frac{1}{E}\left[\xi - (1+\sigma)\frac{\partial\chi_0}{\partial x} + \tfrac{1}{4}(1+\sigma)px\right],$$

$$\mathrm{v} = \frac{1}{E}\left[\eta - (1+\sigma)\frac{\partial\chi_0}{\partial y} + \tfrac{1}{4}(1+\sigma)py\right].$$

In these expressions ξ and η are conjugate functions of x and y which are related to a plane harmonic function Θ_0 by the equations

$$\frac{\partial\xi}{\partial x} = \frac{\partial\eta}{\partial y} = \Theta_0, \quad \frac{\partial\xi}{\partial y} = -\frac{\partial\eta}{\partial x},$$

and χ_0 is of the form $\frac{1}{2}x\xi + f$, where f is a plane harmonic function. The functions Θ_0 and f must be adjusted so that u and v vanish at the edge-line. One way of satisfying these conditions is to take Θ_0 to be constant. If we put

$$\Theta_0 - \tfrac{1}{2} = \frac{1+\sigma}{1-\sigma} p, \quad \xi = -\tfrac{1}{2}\frac{1+\sigma}{1-\sigma} px, \quad \eta = -\tfrac{1}{2}\frac{1+\sigma}{1-\sigma} py, \quad f = \tfrac{1}{8}\frac{1+\sigma}{1-\sigma} p(x^2-y^2),$$

we shall have

$$\chi_0 = -\tfrac{1}{8}\frac{1+\sigma}{1-\sigma} p(x^2+y^2);$$

and then u and v vanish for all values of x and y.

We may show that this is the only way of satisfying the conditions. For this purpose we put

$$U = \xi - (1+\sigma)\frac{\partial \chi_0}{\partial x}, \quad V = \eta - (1+\sigma)\frac{\partial \chi_0}{\partial y},$$

and then we have to show that there is only one way of choosing Θ_0, ξ, η, χ_0 which will make U and V take given values at a given boundary. This is the same thing as showing that if U and V vanish at the boundary they vanish everywhere. Since $\nabla_1^2 \chi_0 = \Theta_0$ we have

$$\frac{\partial \xi}{\partial x} = \frac{\partial \eta}{\partial y} = \frac{1}{1-\sigma}\left(\frac{\partial U}{\partial x} + \frac{\partial V}{\partial y}\right),$$

and we have also

$$\frac{\partial \xi}{\partial y} = -\frac{\partial \eta}{\partial x} = -\tfrac{1}{2}\left(\frac{\partial V}{\partial x} - \frac{\partial U}{\partial y}\right).$$

Since $\nabla_1^2 \xi = 0$, we have

$$\frac{1}{1-\sigma}\frac{\partial}{\partial x}\left(\frac{\partial U}{\partial x} + \frac{\partial V}{\partial y}\right) - \tfrac{1}{2}\frac{\partial}{\partial y}\left(\frac{\partial V}{\partial x} - \frac{\partial U}{\partial y}\right) = 0,$$

and we have also

$$\frac{1}{1-\sigma}\frac{\partial}{\partial y}\left(\frac{\partial U}{\partial x} + \frac{\partial V}{\partial y}\right) + \tfrac{1}{2}\frac{\partial}{\partial x}\left(\frac{\partial V}{\partial x} - \frac{\partial U}{\partial y}\right) = 0.$$

It follows that

$$\iint\left[U\left\{\frac{1}{1-\sigma}\frac{\partial}{\partial x}\left(\frac{\partial U}{\partial x} + \frac{\partial V}{\partial y}\right) - \tfrac{1}{2}\frac{\partial}{\partial y}\left(\frac{\partial V}{\partial x} - \frac{\partial U}{\partial y}\right)\right\} + V\left\{\frac{1}{1-\sigma}\frac{\partial}{\partial y}\left(\frac{\partial U}{\partial x} + \frac{\partial V}{\partial y}\right) + \tfrac{1}{2}\frac{\partial}{\partial x}\left(\frac{\partial V}{\partial x} - \frac{\partial U}{\partial y}\right)\right\}\right] dx\,dy = 0,$$

the integration being extended over any part of the middle plane. When it is extended over the area within the edge-line, and U and V vanish at the edge-line, the integral can be transformed into

$$-\iint\left[\frac{1}{1-\sigma}\left(\frac{\partial U}{\partial x} + \frac{\partial V}{\partial y}\right)^2 + \tfrac{1}{2}\left(\frac{\partial V}{\partial x} - \frac{\partial U}{\partial y}\right)^2\right] dx\,dy,$$

and this cannot vanish unless

$$\frac{\partial U}{\partial x} + \frac{\partial V}{\partial y} = 0, \text{ and } \frac{\partial V}{\partial x} - \frac{\partial U}{\partial y} = 0.$$

It follows that V and U would be conjugate functions of x and y which vanish at the edge-line, they would therefore vanish everywhere.

The form of w is given by the equation

$$\mathrm{w} = \frac{1}{E}\left[(1+\sigma)\chi_1' + h^2\Theta_1 - \frac{3}{2^7}\frac{1-\sigma^2}{h^3} p(x^2+y^2)^2 + \tfrac{3}{16}\frac{1+\sigma}{h} p(x^2+y^2)\right], \quad (81)$$

where Θ_1 is a plane harmonic function and $\nabla_1^2 \chi_1' = -\frac{1-\sigma}{1+\sigma}\Theta_1$. Any solution of the equation $D\nabla_1^4 \mathrm{w} = -p$ can be thrown into this form. To determine w we have the equation

$$D\nabla_1^4 \mathrm{w} = -p$$

and the boundary-conditions, viz.:

$$\mathrm{w} = 0 \text{ and } \partial \mathrm{w}/\partial \nu = 0$$

at the edge-line. There is only one value of w which satisfies these conditions. When w is known Θ_1 is given by the equation

$$\nabla_1^2 \mathrm{w} = \frac{1}{E}\left[-(1-\sigma)\Theta_1 - \tfrac{3}{8}\frac{1-\sigma^2}{h^3} p(x^2+y^2) + \tfrac{3}{4}\frac{1+\sigma}{h} p\right], \quad \text{...(82)}$$

and χ_1' is given by (81).

As an example we may take the case of a circular plate of radius a. The deflexion w is given by the equation

$$\mathrm{w} = -\tfrac{1}{64}\frac{p}{D}(a^2 - r^2)^2, \quad \text{.....................................(83)}$$

where r denotes distance from the centre. The central deflexion is one quarter of that which would be produced by the same total load concentrated at the centre (Article 305).

Another example is afforded by an elliptic plate* of which the boundary is given by the equation $x^2/a^2 + y^2/b^2 = 1$. It may be shown easily that

$$\mathrm{w} = -\tfrac{1}{8}\frac{p}{D}\left(1 - \frac{x^2}{a^2} - \frac{y^2}{b^2}\right)^2 \Big/ \left(\frac{3}{a^4} + \frac{3}{b^4} + \frac{2}{a^2 b^2}\right). \quad \text{......................(84)}$$

In the case of the circular plate equations (82) and (83) show that Θ_1 is constant, and it is therefore convenient to use the solution in the form given in Article 302 instead of Article 303. We have

$$\mathrm{w} = -\tfrac{1}{2}\frac{\beta}{E}r^2 + \frac{1+\sigma}{E}\chi_1 + \tfrac{3}{16}(1+\sigma)\frac{p}{Eh^3}\{h^2 r^2 - \tfrac{1}{8}(1-\sigma) r^4\},$$

where $\nabla_1^2 \chi_1 = \beta$. On comparing this form with (82) we see that

$$\chi_1 = \tfrac{1}{4}\beta r^2 - \frac{3}{2^7}(1-\sigma)\frac{pa^4}{h^3}, \quad \beta = -\tfrac{3}{16}\frac{p}{h^3}(1+\sigma)\left[a^2 - \frac{4h^2}{1-\sigma}\right].$$

The complete expressions for the components of displacement are then given by the equations

$$\left.\begin{aligned} u &= -\frac{pxz}{D}\left[\tfrac{1}{16}(a^2 - r^2) + \tfrac{1}{12}\frac{2-\sigma}{1-\sigma}z^2 - \tfrac{1}{2}\frac{h^2}{1-\sigma}\right], \\ v &= -\frac{pyz}{D}\left[\tfrac{1}{16}(a^2 - r^2) + \tfrac{1}{12}\frac{2-\sigma}{1-\sigma}z^2 - \tfrac{1}{2}\frac{h^2}{1-\sigma}\right], \\ w &= \mathrm{w} + \frac{pz}{D}\left[\tfrac{1}{24}\frac{1+\sigma}{1-\sigma}z^3 + \tfrac{1}{16}\frac{\sigma}{1-\sigma}za^2 - \tfrac{1}{8}\frac{\sigma}{1-\sigma}zr^2 - \tfrac{1}{4}\frac{zh^2}{(1-\sigma)^2} - \tfrac{1}{3}\frac{1-2\sigma}{(1-\sigma)^2}h^3\right], \end{aligned}\right\} \quad \text{......(85)}$$

where w is given by (83). In this case the middle plane is bent without extension. Linear elements of the plate which, in the unstressed state, are normal to the middle plane do not remain straight, nor do they cut at right angles the surface into which the middle plane is bent.

310 C. Additional deflexion due to the mode of fixing the edge.

In the above it is assumed that the edge is so fixed that no inclination of the tangent plane to the middle surface (at a point on the edge) to the initial middle plane is possible. Just as in Article 230, other modes of fixing are possible, and any other mode of fixing introduces an additional deflexion. We may exemplify this matter in the case of the circular plate bent by uniform pressure and clamped at the edge.

* The result was communicated to the Author by Prof. G. H. Bryan.

Let U denote the radial displacement at any point. The condition of clamping has been taken to be $\partial w/\partial r=0$ at $r=a$, but it might be taken to be $\partial U/\partial z=0$ at $z=0$, $r=a$. This condition would mean that the central tangents to linear filaments of the cylindrical bounding surface, which are initially normal to the middle plane, would remain normal to the initial position of the middle plane. We should then have to find w to satisfy $D\nabla_1^4 w=-p$, and to vanish at $r=a$, and adjust it so that we may also have $\partial U/\partial z=0$ at $z=0$, $r=a$. Now throughout the theory it has been assumed that the stress-component $\widehat{rz}$ is proportional to h^2-z^2 and is otherwise independent of z, and the only form for $\widehat{rz}$ at $r=a$ which is of this type, and yields the right resultant $\pi a^2 p$ for the whole plate, is given by the equation

$$(\widehat{rz})_{r=a}=\frac{3pa}{8h^3}(h^2-z^2),$$

as was found in equations (64). Further the stress-component $\widehat{rz}$ is connected with the displacement by the formula

$$\widehat{rz}=\frac{E}{2(1+\sigma)}\left(\frac{\partial U}{\partial z}+\frac{\partial w}{\partial r}\right).$$

Hence the condition we have now to express, viz.: that $\partial U/\partial z=0$ at $z=0$, $r=a$, is equivalent to the condition that, at $r=a$,

$$\frac{\partial w}{\partial r}=\frac{3(1+\sigma)pa}{4Eh}.$$

We should therefore have, instead of (83),

$$w=-\frac{p}{64D}\left[(a^2-r^2)^2+\frac{16}{1-\sigma}h^2(a^2-r^2)\right],$$

where the added term is the additional deflexion due to the mode of fixing.

311. Plate bent by uniformly varying pressure and clamped at the edge.

We seek to satisfy the conditions (80) at the edge-line by a synthesis of the solutions in Articles 301, 303 and 308. For u and v we have the forms

$$u=\frac{1}{E}\left[\xi-(1+\sigma)\frac{\partial\chi_0}{\partial x}-\tfrac{1}{4}(1+\sigma)p_0y^2\right],$$

$$v=\frac{1}{E}\left[\eta-(1+\sigma)\frac{\partial\chi_0}{\partial y}+\tfrac{1}{2}(1+\sigma)p_0xy\right],$$

in which the unknown functions must be chosen so that u and v vanish at the edge-line. We may show in the same way as in Article 310 that these conditions cannot be satisfied in more than one way. The unknown functions depend upon the shape of the edge-line.

When this line is a circle or an ellipse the conditions may be satisfied by assuming for ξ, η, Θ_0, χ_0 the forms

$$\xi=\gamma_1+\tfrac{1}{2}\alpha_1(x^2-y^2),\quad \eta=\alpha_1xy,\quad \Theta_0=\alpha_1x,$$

$$\chi_0=\tfrac{1}{4}\alpha_1x(x^2-y^2)+\tfrac{1}{3}\beta_1(x^3-3xy^2),$$

where α_1, β_1, γ_1 are constants. For a circle of radius a we should find

$$\alpha_1=-\frac{3p_0(1+\sigma)}{6-2\sigma},\quad \beta_1=\frac{p_0(3+5\sigma)}{4(6-2\sigma)},\quad \gamma_1=-\frac{a^2\sigma(1+\sigma)p_0}{6-2\sigma},$$

and thence

$$u=-\frac{\sigma(1+\sigma)}{6-2\sigma}\frac{p_0}{E}(a^2-r^2),\quad v=0.$$

For an ellipse given by the equation $x^2/a^2+y^2/b^2=1$ we should find

$$\alpha_1=-\frac{(1+\sigma)(a^2+2b^2)p_0}{2a^2(1-\sigma)+4b^2},\quad \beta_1=\frac{\{a^2(1+3\sigma)+2b^2(1+\sigma)\}p_0}{4\{2a^2(1-\sigma)+4b^2\}},\quad \gamma_1=-\frac{\sigma(1+\sigma)p_0a^2b^2}{2a^2(1-\sigma)+4b^2},$$

and thence
$$\mathrm{u}=\frac{1}{E}\frac{\sigma(1+\sigma)p_0a^2b^2}{2a^2(1-\sigma)+4b^2}\left(\frac{x^2}{a^2}+\frac{y^2}{b^2}-1\right),\quad \mathrm{v}=0.$$

In these cases the middle plane is slightly extended.

Again the form of w is given by the equation

$$\mathrm{w}=\frac{1}{E}[(1+\sigma)\chi_1'+h^2\Theta_1]-\tfrac{1}{3}\frac{p_0x}{D}\left[\tfrac{1}{64}(x^2+y^2)^2-\tfrac{1}{8}\frac{h^2}{1-\sigma}(x^2+3y^2)\right], \quad \text{...(86)}$$

so that w satisfies the equation

$$D\nabla_1^4\mathrm{w}=-p_0x$$

and the conditions

$$\mathrm{w}=0,\quad \partial\mathrm{w}/\partial\nu=0,$$

at the edge-line. These conditions determine w. When w is known, Θ_1 is given by the equation

$$\nabla_1^2\mathrm{w}=-\frac{1-\sigma}{E}\Theta_1-\frac{p_0x}{D}\left[\tfrac{1}{8}(x^2+y^2)-\tfrac{1}{2}\frac{h^2}{1-\sigma}\right], \quad \text{.........(87)}$$

and χ_1' is given by (86).

For the circle we have

$$\mathrm{w}=-\tfrac{1}{192}\frac{p_0x}{D}(a^2-r^2)^2; \quad \text{.....................................(88)}$$

and for the ellipse* we have

$$\mathrm{w}=-\tfrac{1}{24}\frac{p_0x}{D}\left(1-\frac{x^2}{a^2}-\frac{y^2}{b^2}\right)^2\Big/\left(\frac{5}{a^4}+\frac{1}{b^4}+\frac{2}{a^2b^2}\right). \quad \text{.....................(89)}$$

312. Plate bent by its own weight.

When the plane of the plate is horizontal, and the plate is bent by its own weight, the solution is to be obtained by superposing two stress-systems. In one of these stress-systems all the stress-components except Z_z vanish, and Z_z is $g\rho(z+h)$, the axis of z being drawn vertically upwards. The corresponding displacement is given by the equations

$$u=-\sigma g\rho(z+h)x/E,\quad v=-\sigma g\rho(z+h)y/E,\quad w=\tfrac{1}{2}g\rho\{z^2+2hz+\sigma(x^2+y^2)\}/E. \quad \text{.........(90)}$$

In the second stress-system there is pressure $2g\rho h$ on the face $z=h$ of the plate, and the solution is to be obtained from that in Article 307 by writing $2g\rho h$ for p. The surface into which the middle plane is bent is expressed by the equation

$$\mathrm{w}=\frac{g\rho\sigma}{2E}(x^2+y^2)-\tfrac{1}{32}\frac{g\rho h}{D}(x^2+y^2)\left(x^2+y^2-\frac{8h^2}{1-\sigma}\right), \quad \text{......(91)}$$

* The result was communicated to the Author by Prof. G. H. Bryan.

and the stress-couples are given by the equations

$$G_1 = -D(\kappa_1 + \sigma\kappa_2) + \frac{24 + 23\sigma + 3\sigma^2}{30(1-\sigma)} g\rho h^3,$$

$$G_2 = -D(\kappa_2 + \sigma\kappa_1) + \frac{24 + 23\sigma + 3\sigma^2}{30(1-\sigma)} g\rho h^3,$$

$$H_1 = D(1-\sigma)\tau.$$

The formulæ (18) are approximately correct when h is small.

To satisfy the boundary-conditions in a plate of any assigned shape, supported in any specified way, we must compound with the solution here indicated solutions of the types discussed in Articles 301 and 303, and adjust the latter solutions so as to satisfy these conditions.

312 C. Note on the theory of moderately thick plates.

The theory which has been explained in Articles 299—312 is of the same type as Saint-Venant's theory of the bending of a cantilever by terminal load (Chapter XV), and the extension (Chapter XVI) of that theory to include bending of a beam by uniform load, inasmuch as it proceeds from a particular assumption in regard to the nature of the stress-system, and, as a consequence, has to assume that the forces applied to the edge to maintain the conditions of "support" or "clamping" are distributed over the edge surface in a particular way. For example, at any place on the edge, the shearing stress of type X_z varies according to a parabolic law from one face to the other. It is, of course, unlikely that the forces actually applied to the edge of a plate should be distributed in this way, but this defect of the theory is not likely to be serious, the discrepancy between the calculated and actual displacements being of the nature of local perturbations. Among the consequences of the theory would be the existence of a deflexion analogous to what is called in the theory of beams the "additional deflexion due to shear." This is exemplified in Article 310 C.

The theory has here been developed, after Michell, from special assumptions in regard to the stress-components Z_z, X_z, Y_z, combined with the stress-equations of equilibrium, and with the equations which ensure the existence of a displacement properly connected with the stress-system. An entirely different method, applicable to circular plates of variable thickness, is given in a paper by G. D. Birkhoff, *Phil. Mag.* (Ser. 6), vol. 43 (1922), p. 953, and has been developed further by C. A. Garabedian, *Amer. Math. Soc. Trans.*, vol. 25 (1923), p. 343, and shown by him to lead to the results obtained for circular plates in Articles 309 and 310 above. He has also shown how the method can be extended so as to apply to the problem of a rectangular plate, bent by uniform pressure and supported at the edge, *Paris, C. R.*, t. 178 (1924), p. 619. The solution for a thick rectangular plate, bent by concentrated pressure at the centre of one face and supported at the edge, has been obtained by Mesnager, *Paris, C. R.*, t. 164 (1917), p. 721, by a method which is entirely different from that which has been developed above and from that adopted by Birkhoff and Garabedian.

APPROXIMATE THEORY OF THIN PLATES.

313. Bending of a thin plate by transverse forces.

There is an approximate theory of the bending of a thin plate by transverse forces* analogous to the theory of the bending and twisting of thin rods. Just as the theory of thin rods rests on approximate expressions for the flexural

* See Introduction, pp. 27—29.

and torsional couples in terms of the components of curvature and the twist, so the theory of thin plates rests on approximate expressions for the stress-couples in terms of the quantities that define the curvature of the bent middle surface. These expressions were found in equations (18) of Article 298 by a discussion of the special problem of the bending of a plate by couples applied to its edges, and the proposal to utilise them in other problems requires justification. This is provided to a certain extent by the remark that a number of special problems of the bending of plates by transverse forces have been solved in Articles 302—12, and in all of them the formulæ (18) connecting the stress-couples with the curvature of the bent middle surface are either exact, or else are approximately correct when the thickness of the plate is small compared with its other linear dimensions*. A general justification on the same lines as that of the corresponding theory for rods (Article 258) will be given in Article 329 of Chapter XXIV.

In a thin plane plate slightly bent by transverse forces the stress-couples are, according to this theory, expressed by the formulæ (18) in terms of quantities defining the curvature of the middle surface, and these quantities are connected with the transverse displacement of a point on this surface by the formulæ (17). In a plate so bent the appropriate equations of equilibrium are

$$\frac{\partial N_1}{\partial x} + \frac{\partial N_2}{\partial y} + Z' = 0, \quad \frac{\partial H_1}{\partial x} - \frac{\partial G_2}{\partial y} + N_2 = 0, \quad \frac{\partial G_1}{\partial x} - \frac{\partial H_1}{\partial y} - N_1 = 0.$$

By eliminating N_1 and N_2 from these we obtain the equation

$$\frac{\partial^2 G_1}{\partial x^2} + \frac{\partial^2 G_2}{\partial y^2} - 2\frac{\partial^2 H_1}{\partial x \partial y} + Z' = 0,$$

and by substituting from (17) and (18) in this equation we find the equation

$$D\nabla_1^4 \mathrm{w} = Z'. \qquad \text{.......................(92)}$$

The stress-couples G, H at the edge are given in accordance with (17) and (18) by the formulæ

$$G = -D\left\{\frac{\partial^2 \mathrm{w}}{\partial \nu^2} + \sigma\left(\frac{\partial^2 \mathrm{w}}{\partial s^2} + \frac{1}{\rho'}\frac{\partial \mathrm{w}}{\partial \nu}\right)\right\}, \quad H = D(1-\sigma)\frac{\partial}{\partial \nu}\left(\frac{\partial \mathrm{w}}{\partial s}\right).$$

To find an expression for the shearing force N in the direction of the normal to the plane of the plate we observe that

$$N = \cos\theta\left(\frac{\partial G_1}{\partial x} - \frac{\partial H_1}{\partial y}\right) + \sin\theta\left(\frac{\partial G_2}{\partial y} - \frac{\partial H_1}{\partial x}\right),$$

and then on substituting from (17) and (18) we find the formula

$$N = -D\frac{\partial}{\partial \nu}\nabla_1^2 \mathrm{w}. \qquad \text{.......................(93)}$$

To determine the normal displacement w of the middle plane we have the differential equation (92) and the boundary-conditions which hold at the

* A very elaborate investigation of exact solutions for various distributions of load has been given by J. Dougall, *Edinburgh Roy. Soc. Trans.*, vol. 41 (1904), and confirms the approximate theory.

edge of the plate. At a clamped edge w and $\partial w/\partial \nu$ vanish, at a supported edge w and G vanish, at an edge to which given forces are applied $N - \partial H/\partial s$ and G have given values.

The same differential equation and the same boundary-conditions would be obtained by the energy method by assuming the formula (21) for the potential energy estimated per unit of area of the middle plane*.

In all the solutions which we have found the differential equation (92) is correct whether the formulæ (18) and (21) are exactly or only approximately correct†. The solutions that would be obtained by the approximate method described in this Article differ from the exact solutions that would be obtained by the methods described in previous Articles only by very small amounts depending on the small corrections that ought to be made in the formulæ (18) for the stress-couples. In general the form of the bent plate is determined with sufficient approximation by the method of this Article.

There is a theory of the existence of solutions of equation (92), in which Z' is a given function of x and y, subject to special conditions at the edge of the plate. The case where the edge is clamped has been chiefly considered. For this theory reference may be made to J. Hadamard, *Paris, Mém....par divers savants*, t. 23, 1908, A. Korn, *Paris, Ann. Éc. norm.* (Sér. 3), t. 25, 1908, and G. Lauricella, *Acta math.*, t. 32, 1909.

With a view to estimating the strength of a plate to resist bending we may anticipate another result of the approximate theory of Chapter XXIV. It is there shown that, if the axis of x is along the tangent to that line of curvature for which the curvature of the middle surface is greatest, the tensile stress X_x is approximately equal to

$$\frac{3z}{2h^3} G_1,$$

where G_1 denotes the corresponding flexural couple, and the greatest tensile stress in the plate is accordingly equal to the numerical value of $\frac{3}{2} h^{-2} G$, where G is the greatest value of the flexural stress-couple.

It is customary to state‡ that the approximate theory is only valid so long as the transverse displacement is small compared with the thickness of the plate. This matter will be discussed further in Chapter XXIV A.

314. Illustrations of the approximate theory.

(*a*) *Circular plate loaded symmetrically*§.

When a circular plate of radius a supports a load Z' per unit of area which is a function of the distance r from the centre of the circle, equation (92) becomes

$$\frac{1}{r}\frac{\partial}{\partial r}\left[r\frac{\partial}{\partial r}\left\{\frac{1}{r}\frac{\partial}{\partial r}\left(r\frac{\partial w}{\partial r}\right)\right\}\right] = Z'/D,$$

the direction of the displacement w being the same as that of the load Z'. We shall record the results in a series of cases.

* The process of variation is worked out by Lord Rayleigh, *Theory of Sound*, § 215.

† A more general form which includes (92) in the special cases previously discussed is given by J. H. Michell, *loc. cit.*, p. 465.

‡ Cf. Kelvin and Tait, *Nat. Phil.*, Part II, § 632.

§ The general form of the solution and the special solutions (i)—(iv) were given by Poisson in his memoir of 1828. See Introduction, footnote 36. Solutions equivalent to those in (v) and (vi) were given by Saint-Venant in the 'Annotated Clebsch,' *Note du* § 45.

(i) When the total load W is distributed uniformly and the plate is supported at the edge

$$w=\frac{W}{64\pi a^2 D}(a^2-r^2)\left(\frac{5+\sigma}{1+\sigma}a^2-r^2\right)$$

(ii) When the total load W is distributed uniformly and the plate is clamped at the edge

$$w=\frac{W}{64\pi a^2 D}(a^2-r^2)^2.$$

(iii) When the load W is concentrated at the centre and the plate is supported at the edge

$$w=\frac{W}{8\pi D}\left[-r^2\log\frac{a}{r}+\frac{1}{2}\frac{3+\sigma}{1+\sigma}(a^2-r^2)\right].$$

(iv) When the load W is concentrated at the centre and the plate is clamped at the edge

$$w=\frac{W}{8\pi D}\left[-r^2\log\frac{a}{r}+\frac{1}{2}(a^2-r^2)\right].$$

(v) When the total load W is distributed uniformly round a circle of radius b and the plate is supported at the edge, w takes different forms according as $r>$ or $<b$. We find

$$w_{r<b}=\frac{W}{8\pi D}\left[-(r^2+b^2)\log\frac{a}{b}+(r^2-b^2)+\frac{(3+\sigma)a^2-(1-\sigma)b^2}{2(1+\sigma)a^2}(a^2-r^2)\right],$$

$$w_{r>b}=\frac{W}{8\pi D}\left[-(r^2+b^2)\log\frac{a}{r}+\frac{(3+\sigma)a^2-(1-\sigma)b^2}{2(1+\sigma)a^2}(a^2-r^2)\right].$$

(vi) When the total load W is distributed uniformly round a circle of radius b and the plate is clamped at the edge, we find

$$w_{r<b}=\frac{W}{8\pi D}\left[-(r^2+b^2)\log\frac{a}{b}+(r^2-b^2)+\frac{1}{2}\left(1+\frac{b^2}{a^2}\right)(a^2-r^2)\right],$$

$$w_{r>b}=\frac{W}{8\pi D}\left[-(r^2+b^2)\log\frac{a}{r}+\frac{1}{2}\left(1+\frac{b^2}{a^2}\right)(a^2-r^2)\right].$$

(b) *Application of the method of inversion*.*

The solutions given in (iii) and (iv) of (a), or in Article 305, show that, in the neighbourhood of a point where pressure P is applied, the displacement w in the direction of the pressure is of the form $(P/8\pi D)\,r^2\log r+\zeta$, where ζ is an analytic function of x and y which has no singularities at or near the point, and r denotes distance from the point.

Since w satisfies the equation $\nabla_1{}^4 w=0$ at all points at which there is no load we may apply the method of inversion explained in Article 154. Let O' be any point in the plane of the plate, P any point of the plate, P' the point inverse to P when O' is the centre of inversion, x', y' the coordinates of P', R' the distance of P' from O', w′ the function of x', y' into which w is transformed by the inversion. Then $R'^2 w'$ satisfies the equation $\nabla_1'^4(R'^2 w')=0$, where $\nabla_1'^4$ denotes the operator $\frac{\partial^4}{\partial x'^4}+\frac{\partial^4}{\partial y'^4}+2\frac{\partial^4}{\partial x'^2\partial y'^2}$.

It is clear that, if w and $\partial w/\partial\nu$ vanish at any bounding curve, $R'^2 w'$ and $\partial(R'^2 w')/\partial\nu'$ vanish at the transformed boundary, ν' denoting the direction of the normal to this boundary.

* J. H. Michell, *London Math. Soc. Proc.*, vol. 34 (1902), p. 223.

We apply this method to the problem of a circular plate clamped at the edge and loaded at one point O. Let O' be the inverse point of O with respect to the circle, C the centre of the circle, and a its radius, also let c be the distance of O from C. The solution for the plate clamped at the edge and supporting a load W at C is

$$\text{w}=\frac{W}{8\pi D}\left[-r^2\log\frac{a}{r}+\tfrac{1}{2}(a^2-r^2)\right],$$

where r denotes the distance of any point P from C. Now invert from O' with constant of inversion equal to a^4/c^2-a^2. The circle inverts into itself, C inverts into O, P inverts into P' so that, if $OP'=R$ and $O'P'=R'$, we have

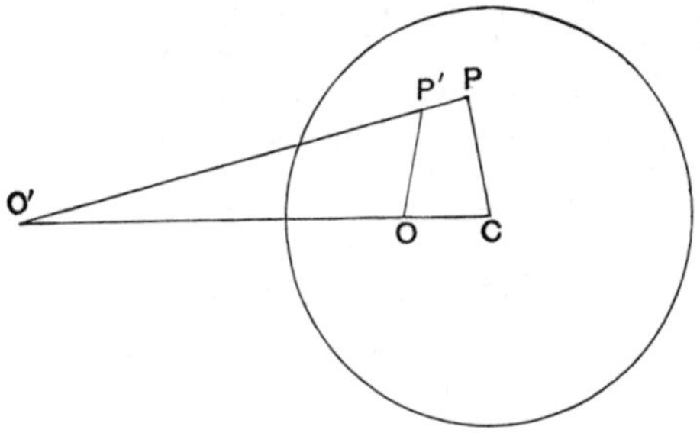

Fig. 70.

$$\frac{R}{r}=\frac{R'}{a^2/c}.$$

Hence $R'^2\text{w}'$ is

$$\frac{W}{8\pi D}R'^2\left[-\frac{a^4R^2}{c^2R'^2}\log\frac{cR'}{aR}+\tfrac{1}{2}\left(a^2-\frac{a^4R^2}{c^2R'^2}\right)\right],$$

or

$$\frac{Wa^4}{8\pi c^2 D}\left[-R^2\log\frac{cR'}{aR}+\tfrac{1}{2}\left(\frac{c^2}{a^2}R'^2-R^2\right)\right].$$

It follows that the displacement w of a circular plate of radius a clamped at the edge and supporting a load W' at a point O distant c from the centre is given by the equation

$$\text{w}=\frac{W'}{8\pi D}\left[-R^2\log\frac{cR'}{aR}+\tfrac{1}{2}\left(\frac{c^2}{a^2}R'^2-R^2\right)\right], \qquad\text{.....................(94)}$$

where R denotes the distance of any point of the plate from O, and R' denotes the distance of the same point from the point O', inverse to O with respect to the circle.

We may pass to a limit by increasing a indefinitely. Then the plate is clamped along a straight edge and is loaded at a point O. If O' is the optical image of O in the straight edge, the displacement in the direction of the load is given by the equation

$$\text{w}=\frac{W'}{8\pi D}\left[-R^2\log\frac{R'}{R}+\tfrac{1}{2}(R'^2-R^2)\right], \qquad\text{..........................(95)}$$

where R, R' denote the distances of any point of the plate from the points O and O'.

The contour lines in these two cases are drawn by Michell (*loc. cit.*).

(c) *Rectangular plate.*

(i) *Variable pressure. Two parallel edges supported.*

Let the edges of the plate be given by $x=0$, $x=2a$, $y=0$, $y=2b$, the two former being supported. Let the pressure Z' be expanded in a double trigonometric series* in the form

$$Z'=\Sigma\Sigma Z_{mn}\sin\frac{m\pi x}{2a}\sin\frac{n\pi y}{2b},$$

where m and n are integers. Then a particular solution of the equation (92) is

$$\text{w}=\frac{16}{\pi^4 D}\Sigma\Sigma Z_{mn}\frac{\sin(m\pi x/2a)\sin(n\pi y/2b)}{m^4/a^4+n^4/b^4+2m^2n^2/a^2b^2}.$$

This solution satisfies the boundary-conditions at the edges $x=0$ and $x=2a$, and, if all four edges are supported, it satisfies the boundary-conditions at the edges $y=0$ and $y=2b$ as well†.

* The method was initiated by Navier. See Todhunter and Pearson's *History*, vol. 1, p. 137.

† This case is further discussed by Saint-Venant in the 'Annotated Clebsch,' *Note du* § 73.

When the edges $y=0$ and $y=2b$ are not supported, we denote the above value of w by w_1, and seek to satisfy the conditions by assuming that $w=w_1+w_2$, where w_2 must satisfy the equation $\nabla_1^4 w_2=0$ at all points within the rectangle, the same conditions as w_1 at $x=0$ and $x=2a$, and such conditions as may be imposed on w_1+w_2 by the boundary-conditions at $y=0$ and $y=2b$. It is appropriate to assume for w_2 the form*

$$w_2=\Sigma Y_m \sin\frac{m\pi x}{2a},$$

where Y_m is a function of y but not of x. Then Y_m satisfies the equation

$$\frac{d^4 Y_m}{dy^4}-\frac{m^2\pi^2}{2a^2}\frac{d^2 Y_m}{dy^2}+\frac{m^4\pi^4}{16a^4}Y_m=0,$$

and the complete primitive is of the form

$$Y_m=A_m\cosh\frac{m\pi y}{2a}+B_m\sinh\frac{m\pi y}{2a}+y\left(A_m'\cosh\frac{m\pi y}{2a}+B_m'\sinh\frac{m\pi y}{2a}\right),$$

where A_m, B_m, A_m', B_m' are undetermined constants which can be adjusted to satisfy the boundary-conditions at $y=0$ and $y=2b$†. The special case where the edges $y=0$ and $y=2b$ are free includes the theory of a thin plank, bent by uniform load and supported at its ends (cf. Article 244 *supra*), and it also includes the theory of a rectangular plate bent by concentrated pressure at its centre and supported at two parallel edges—an apparatus by means of which it has been proposed to measure elastic constants‡.

(ii) *Uniform pressure. Supported edges.*

The important special problem of a rectangular plate, bent by uniform pressure applied to one face, and having its four edges supported, may be solved by a different method§. We shall take the edges of the plate to be given by $x=\pm a$ and $y=\pm b$, and denote the pressure applied to one face by p. Then the deflexion w is to be found to satisfy the equation||

$$D\nabla_1^4 w=p$$

at all points within the rectangle, and the conditions

$$w=0,\quad \nabla_1^2 w=0 \text{ at } x=\pm a,\quad y=\pm b.$$

We put

$$w=\frac{p}{8D}\{(a^2-x^2)(b^2-y^2)+\chi\},$$

then χ is a plane biharmonic function, which vanishes at the edges, and also satisfies the conditions

$$\nabla_1^2\chi=2(b^2-y^2) \text{ at } x=\pm a,\quad \nabla_1^2\chi=2(a^2-x^2) \text{ at } y=\pm b.$$

It is clear that χ must be an even function of x and of y.

The most general form of a plane biharmonic function is $xU+u$, where U and u are plane harmonic functions. An equally general form is $yV+v$, where V and v are plane harmonic functions, but this form is included in the other if U and V are conjugate

* This step was suggested by M. Lévy, *Paris, C. R.*, t. 129 (1899).

† A number of cases have been worked out by E. Estanave, 'Contribution à l'étude de l'équilibre élastique d'une plaque...' (*Thèse*), Paris, 1900.

‡ A. E. H. Tutton, *Phil. Trans. Roy. Soc.* (Ser. A), vol. 202 (1903).

§ H. Hencky, 'Der Spannungszustand in rechteckigen Platten' (*Diss.*) Darmstadt, published by R. Oldenbourg, München u. Berlin, 1913.

|| The sense of w is now taken to be that in which the pressure acts, or the face subjected to pressure to be $z=-h$.

functions. For problems connected with a rectangle, and vanishing values of the functions at the boundary, the natural forms to assume for even biharmonic functions are

$$X_n(x)\cos(n\pi y/2b) \text{ and } Y_n(y)\cos(n\pi x/2a),$$

where n is an uneven positive integer, and

$$X_n(x)=a\sinh\frac{n\pi a}{2b}\cosh\frac{n\pi x}{2b}-x\cosh\frac{n\pi a}{2b}\sinh\frac{n\pi x}{2b},$$

$$Y_n(y)=b\sinh\frac{n\pi b}{2a}\cosh\frac{n\pi y}{2a}-y\cosh\frac{n\pi b}{2a}\sinh\frac{n\pi y}{2a}.$$

We assume that χ can be expressed in the form

$$\chi=-\Sigma\left\{\frac{A_n}{n}a^3 Y_n(y)\cos\frac{n\pi x}{2a}+\frac{B_n}{n}b^3 X_n(x)\cos\frac{n\pi y}{2b}\right\},$$

where n is uneven, the A_n and B_n are constants to be determined, and the factors -1, n^{-1}, a^3, b^3 are suggested by a little experience of the analysis. Then we have

$$\nabla_1{}^2\chi=\Sigma\left(A_n\pi a^2\cosh\frac{n\pi b}{2a}\cosh\frac{n\pi y}{2a}\cos\frac{n\pi x}{2a}+B_n\pi b^2\cosh\frac{n\pi a}{2b}\cosh\frac{n\pi x}{2b}\cos\frac{n\pi y}{2b}\right).$$

Now we found in Article 221 (c) that, when $b>y>-b$,

$$b^2-y^2=32b^2\pi^{-3}\sum_{n=1}^{\infty}n^{-3}\sin(\tfrac{1}{2}n\pi)\cos(n\pi y/2b).$$

Hence we have

$$A_n=\frac{64}{\pi^4 n^3}\sin\frac{n\pi}{2}\operatorname{sech}^2\frac{n\pi b}{2a},\quad B_n=\frac{64}{\pi^4 n^3}\sin\frac{n\pi}{2}\operatorname{sech}^2\frac{n\pi a}{2b},$$

and we find that the deflexion w is expressed by the formula

$$\text{w}=\frac{p}{8D}\left[(a^2-x^2)(b^2-y^2)-\frac{64}{\pi^4}\sum_{n=1}^{\infty}\left\{\frac{a^3}{n^4}\sin\frac{n\pi}{2}\frac{Y_n(y)}{\cosh^2(n\pi b/2a)}\cos\frac{n\pi x}{2a}\right.\right.$$
$$\left.\left.+\frac{b^3}{n^4}\sin\frac{n\pi}{2}\frac{X_n(x)}{\cosh^2(n\pi a/2b)}\cos\frac{n\pi y}{2b}\right\}\right].$$

(iii) *Uniform pressure. Clamped edges.*

One of the most important of the special problems of Elasticity is that presented by a thin rectangular plate, bent by uniform pressure, and fixed at its edges so that no displacement or inclination is produced at the edges by the applied pressure.

With the notation of (ii) above, the analytical problem is to find a function w of x and y to satisfy the equation $D\nabla_1{}^4\text{w}=p$ within the rectangle bounded by $x=\pm a$, $y=\pm b$, and the special conditions

$$\text{w}=0,\quad \frac{\partial \text{w}}{\partial x}=0 \text{ at } x=\pm a;\quad \text{w}=0 \text{ and } \frac{\partial \text{w}}{\partial y}=0 \text{ at } y=\pm b.$$

No theoretically complete solution of this problem has been obtained, and recourse has been had, on the one hand, to experimental methods* of studying the problem, and, on the other hand, to methods of approximate numerical solution. Of these it is proper to notice first the method invented by W. Ritz†.

Ritz observed that the analytical problem is the same as that of determining w so as to render stationary the integral

$$\iint\left\{\tfrac{1}{2}D\left(\frac{\partial^2\text{w}}{\partial x^2}+\frac{\partial^2\text{w}}{\partial y^2}\right)^2-p\text{w}\right\}dx\,dy,$$

* Reference may be made to W. J. Crawford, *Edinburgh Roy. Soc. Proc.*, vol. 32 (1912), p. 348, and B. C. Laws, *London, Inst. Civil Engineers, Proc.*, 1922.

† *J. f. Math.* (*Crelle*), Bd. 135 (1909), p. 1, reprinted in *Ges. Werke Walther Ritz*, Paris, 1911, p. 192.

taken over the area of the rectangle, D and p being constants, and w and its normal derivative vanishing at the edges. He proposed to assume for w an expression of the form $\Sigma a_{mn} u_m(x) v_n(y)$, where $u_m(x)$ and $v_n(y)$ are functions which, with their normal derivatives, vanish at the appropriate edges, and the a_{mn} are constants. Suitable forms for the u's and v's are furnished by the normal functions of a doubly clamped bar*. The constants a_{mn} are to be determined by performing the integrations, retaining only a finite number of terms in the resulting double series, and rendering the function expressed by the finite series stationary by equating to zero its derivative with respect to any a_{mn}. In this way approximate values are obtained for these coefficients, and the approximation is improved by retaining a larger number of terms of the series. It will be observed that the series, when differentiated term by term, does not satisfy the differential equation for w, but proof was given that it must tend, as the number of terms increases indefinitely, to be an expression for a function which does satisfy this equation.

The method of Ritz has been worked out in detail for a square plate by C. G. Knott†, and also, as it appears, in a Paris thesis by M. Paschoud‡, and it has been applied to numerous problems of Elasticity by S. Timoschenko§, but for the special problem of the clamped rectangular plate, bent by uniform pressure, a simpler method of approximate numerical solution has been devised by H. Hencky (*loc. cit.*, p. 492 *supra*). To this we proceed.

As in (ii) above, we may put

$$\mathrm{w} = \frac{p}{8D}\{(a^2 - x^2)(b^2 - y^2) + \chi\},$$

where χ is a biharmonic function, even in both x and y, vanishing at $x = a$ and $y = b$, and satisfying the conditions

$$\frac{\partial \chi}{\partial x} = 2a(b^2 - y^2) \text{ at } x = a, \text{ and } \frac{\partial \chi}{\partial y} = 2b(a^2 - x^2) \text{ at } y = b,$$

and we may assume for χ the formula

$$\chi = -\frac{8}{\pi^2}\sum_{n=1}^{\infty}\left\{a^3\frac{A_n}{n^2}\operatorname{sech}^2\frac{n\pi b}{2a}\,Y_n(y)\cos\frac{n\pi x}{2a} + b^3\frac{B_n}{n^2}\operatorname{sech}^2\frac{n\pi a}{2b}\,X_n(x)\cos\frac{n\pi y}{2b}\right\},$$

where $X_n(x)$ and $Y_n(y)$ stand for the functions so denoted in (ii) above, and the summation refers to uneven integral values of n. Then the boundary-conditions yield two equations, which may be written

$$\frac{4a^2}{\pi}\sum_{m=1}^{\infty}\left\{\frac{A_m}{m}\operatorname{sech}^2\frac{m\pi b}{2a}\,Y_m(y)\sin\frac{m\pi}{2}\right\}$$
$$+\frac{8b^3}{\pi^2}\sum_{n=1}^{\infty}\left\{\frac{B_n}{n^2}\left(\tanh\frac{n\pi a}{2b} + \frac{n\pi a}{2b}\operatorname{sech}^2\frac{n\pi a}{2b}\right)\cos\frac{n\pi y}{2b}\right\} = 2a(b^2 - y^2)$$

and

$$\frac{4b^2}{\pi}\sum_{m=1}^{\infty}\left\{\frac{B_m}{m}\operatorname{sech}^2\frac{m\pi a}{2b}\,X_m(x)\sin\frac{m\pi}{2}\right\}$$
$$+\frac{8a^3}{\pi^2}\sum_{n=1}^{\infty}\left\{\frac{A_n}{n^2}\left(\tanh\frac{n\pi b}{2a} + \frac{n\pi b}{2a}\operatorname{sech}^2\frac{n\pi b}{2a}\right)\cos\frac{n\pi x}{2a}\right\} = 2b(a^2 - x^2),$$

* The problem has been discussed also by M. Mesnager, *Paris, C. R.*, t. 163 (1916), p. 661, who employed forms for u_m, v_n different from those used by Ritz. His numerical result for the central deflexion of a square plate does not agree with that found by the method of Ritz, and also by the method of Hencky, to be explained presently.

† *Edinburgh Roy. Soc. Proc.*, vol. 32 (1912), p. 390.

‡ See a memoir by Mesnager in *Paris, Ann. d. Ponts et Chaussées* (Sér. 9), t. 31 (1916), p. 319.

§ See, in particular, the papers cited on pp. 328 and 345 *supra* and also *Phil. Mag.* (Ser. 6), vol. 47 (1924), p. 1095.

where m, like n, is uneven, and the first equation holds in the interval $b>y>-b$, and the second holds in the interval $a>x>-a$.

Now we may assume that the function expressed by the first series in the first equation can be expanded in a series of cosines of uneven multiples of $\pi y/2b$, and that the coefficients may be determined, as in Article 221 (c), by multiplying by $\cos(n\pi y/2b)$, and integrating term by term with respect to y between the limits $-b$ and b, and we may make similar assumptions with regard to the first series in the second equation. Performing the integrations, and utilising the result of Art. 221 (c) in regard to the expansion of b^2-y^2, we find two equations which, after a little reduction, are found to be

$$\sum_{m=1}^{\infty} \sin\frac{m\pi}{2} \frac{n^4}{(n^2+m^2b^2/a^2)^2} A_m + \sin\frac{n\pi}{2} \frac{n\pi b}{16a} \frac{(n\pi a/b)+\sinh(n\pi a/b)}{\cosh^2(n\pi a/2b)} B_n = 1$$

and

$$\sin\frac{n\pi}{2} \frac{n\pi a^5}{16b^5} \frac{(n\pi b/a)+\sinh(n\pi b/a)}{\cosh^2(n\pi b/2a)} A_n + \sum_{m=1}^{\infty} \sin\frac{m\pi}{2} \frac{n^4}{(n^2b^2/a^2+m^2)^2} B_m = \frac{a^4}{b^4}.$$

Approximate numerical solutions of these equations can be obtained by assuming that all coefficients with suffixes greater than some fixed number can be neglected. Then it is soon found that increasing this number does not affect the coefficients with small suffixes. Hencky worked out some of the numerical details in the case of a square plate ($b=a$), and in that of a plate for which $b/a=1{\cdot}5$. The case where b is very great compared with a can, of course, be solved completely.

The most interesting quantities to calculate are the central deflexion, or the value of w at $x=0$, $y=0$, and the greatest flexural couple, or the numerical value of $D\dfrac{\partial^2 \text{w}}{\partial x^2}$ at $x=a$, $y=0$. The places of greatest weakness are the middle points of the long sides, and the maximum flexural couple is an index of the strength, or rather the weakness, of the plate. Some numerical values are given below.

A formula for w was given long ago by Grashof* in the form

$$\text{w} = \frac{p}{24D} \frac{(a^2-x^2)^2(b^2-y^2)^2}{a^4+b^4},$$

where the notation is that of this Article. The formula, though devoid of theoretical foundation, has often been treated with respect.

In the Table below, compiled partly from Hencky's results, will be found the values, answering to certain values of b/a, of the central deflexion, as a multiple of $pa^4/8D$, and the maximum flexural couple as a multiple of pa^2. According to Grashof's formula these multiples would be the same, and their values calculated from this formula are appended to the Table in the column marked G.

b/a	(central deflexion) $\div (pa^4/8D)$	(max. couple) $\div pa^2$	G
1	0·162†	0·205	0·167
1·5	0·281	0·306	0·278
2	0·329	0·33‡	0·314
∞	0·333	0·333	0·333

* *Theorie der Elasticität und Festigkeit*, Berlin, 1878.

† This figure is obtained independently of Hencky's arithmetic from the work in the papers by Knott and Paschoud already cited.

‡ It is difficult to get the figure in the third decimal place owing to slow convergence of the series.

It will be seen that Grashof's formula leads to a serious over-estimate of the strength of a plate which is at all nearly square. Another result which emerges is that the resistance to bending by uniform pressure of a clamped rectangular plate, whose length is more than twice its breadth, is practically the same as if its length were infinite.

(iv) *Some further researches.*

In Hencky's Dissertation the problems of a rectangular plate, supported or clamped at the edges, and subject to concentrated pressure at its centre, are also discussed.

It may be mentioned here that problems of equilibrium, similar to those considered above for circular, elliptic, and rectangular boundaries, but concerned with such forms as half an ellipse bounded by the transverse axis, have been discussed by B. Galerkin*, and the problems for a sector of a circle, by the same writer†.

(*d*) *Transverse vibrations of plates.*

The equation of vibration is obtained at once from (92) by substituting for Z' the expression $-2\rho h \dfrac{\partial^2 \mathrm{w}}{\partial t^2}$. We have

$$\frac{\partial^4 \mathrm{w}}{\partial x^4} + \frac{\partial^4 \mathrm{w}}{\partial y^4} + 2\frac{\partial^4 \mathrm{w}}{\partial x^2 \partial y^2} = -\frac{2\rho h}{D}\frac{\partial^2 \mathrm{w}}{\partial t^2}. \quad \text{.........................(96)}$$

When the plate vibrates in a normal mode w is of the form $\mathrm{W}\cos(pt+\epsilon)$, where W is a function of x and y which satisfies the equation

$$\frac{\partial^4 \mathrm{W}}{\partial x^4} + \frac{\partial^4 \mathrm{W}}{\partial y^4} + 2\frac{\partial^4 \mathrm{W}}{\partial x^2 \partial y^2} = \frac{3\rho(1-\sigma^2)p^2}{Eh^2}\mathrm{W};$$

and the possible values of p are to be determined by adapting the solution of this equation to satisfy the boundary-conditions. From the form of the coefficient of W in the right-hand member of this equation it appears that the frequencies are proportional to the thickness, and inversely proportional to the square of the linear dimension of the area within the edge-line.

The theory of those modes of transverse vibration of a circular plate in which the displacement is a function of distance from the centre was made out by Poisson‡, and the numerical determination of the frequencies of the graver modes of vibration was effected by him. In this case the boundary-conditions which he adopted become identical with Kirchhoff's boundary-conditions because the torsional couple H belonging to any circle concentric with the edge-line vanishes. The general theory of the transverse vibrations of a circular plate was obtained subsequently by Kirchhoff§, who gave a full numerical discussion of the results. The problem has also been discussed very fully by Lord Rayleigh||. The complete analytical solution of the problem of free vibrations of a square or rectangular plate has not yet been made out, but an approximate method of solution has been devised by W. Ritz¶. The case of elliptic plates has been considered by E. Mathieu** and A. Barthélémy††.

* *Messenger of Math.*, vol. 52 (1923), p. 99.

† *Paris, C. R.*, t. 178 (1924), p. 919.

‡ In the memoir of 1828 cited in the Introduction, footnote 36.

§ *J. f. Math.* (*Crelle*), Bd. 40 (1850), or *Ges. Abhandlungen*, p. 237, or *Vorlesungen über math. Physik, Mechanik*, Vorlesung 30.

|| *Theory of Sound*, vol. 1, Chapter x.

¶ *Ann. Phys.* (4te Folge), Bd. 28, 1909, p. 737, or *Ges. Werke Walther Ritz*, p. 265. See also Lord Rayleigh, *Phil. Mag.* (Ser. 6), vol. 22, 1911, p. 225, or *Scientific Papers*, vol. 6, p. 47.

** *J. de Math.* (*Liouville*), (Sér. 2), t. 14 (1869).

†† *Toulouse Mém. de l'Acad.*, t. 9 (1877).

The vibrations of a spinning disk have been discussed by H. Lamb and R. V. Southwell*, and further by R. V. Southwell†, who has also pointed out the consequences of the theory in regard to the design of high-speed disks‡.

(e) *Extensional vibrations of plates.*

We may in like manner investigate those vibrations of a plate which involve no transverse displacement of points of the middle plane, by taking the stress-resultants T_1, T_2, S_1 to be given by the approximate formulæ, [cf. (iv) of Article 301],

$$T_1=\frac{2Eh}{1-\sigma^2}\left(\frac{\partial u}{\partial x}+\sigma\frac{\partial v}{\partial y}\right),\quad T_2=\frac{2Eh}{1-\sigma^2}\left(\frac{\partial v}{\partial y}+\sigma\frac{\partial u}{\partial x}\right),\quad S_1=\frac{Eh}{1+\sigma}\left(\frac{\partial u}{\partial y}+\frac{\partial v}{\partial x}\right),$$

or the potential energy per unit of area of the middle plane to be given by the formula

$$\frac{Eh}{1-\sigma^2}\left[\left(\frac{\partial u}{\partial x}+\frac{\partial v}{\partial y}\right)^2-2(1-\sigma)\left\{\frac{\partial u}{\partial x}\frac{\partial v}{\partial y}-\tfrac{1}{4}\left(\frac{\partial u}{\partial y}+\frac{\partial v}{\partial x}\right)^2\right\}\right].$$

The equations of motion are

$$\frac{\partial T_1}{\partial x}+\frac{\partial S_1}{\partial y}=2\rho h\frac{\partial^2 u}{\partial t^2},\quad \frac{\partial S_1}{\partial x}+\frac{\partial T_2}{\partial y}=2\rho h\frac{\partial^2 v}{\partial t^2},$$

or

$$\left.\begin{aligned}\frac{\partial^2 u}{\partial x^2}+\tfrac{1}{2}(1-\sigma)\frac{\partial^2 u}{\partial y^2}+\tfrac{1}{2}(1+\sigma)\frac{\partial^2 v}{\partial x\,\partial y}&=\frac{\rho(1-\sigma^2)}{E}\frac{\partial^2 u}{\partial t^2},\\ \tfrac{1}{2}(1-\sigma)\frac{\partial^2 v}{\partial x^2}+\frac{\partial^2 v}{\partial y^2}+\tfrac{1}{2}(1+\sigma)\frac{\partial^2 u}{\partial x\,\partial y}&=\frac{\rho(1-\sigma^2)}{E}\frac{\partial^2 v}{\partial t^2}.\end{aligned}\right\}\quad\text{.................(97)}$$

At a free edge the stress-resultants denoted by T, S vanish. The form of the equations shows that there is a complete separation of modes of vibration involving transverse displacement, or flexure, from those involving displacement in the plane of the plate, or extension, and that the frequencies of the latter modes are independent of the thickness, while those of the former are proportional to the thickness§.

The equations of vibration (97) may be expressed very simply in terms of the areal dilatation Δ' and the rotation ϖ, these quantities being defined analytically by the equations

$$\Delta'=\frac{\partial u}{\partial x}+\frac{\partial v}{\partial y},\quad 2\varpi=\frac{\partial v}{\partial x}-\frac{\partial u}{\partial y}.\quad\text{............................(98)}$$

The equations take the forms

$$\frac{\partial\Delta'}{\partial x}-(1-\sigma)\frac{\partial\varpi}{\partial y}=\rho\frac{1-\sigma^2}{E}\frac{\partial^2 u}{\partial t^2},\qquad \frac{\partial\Delta'}{\partial y}+(1-\sigma)\frac{\partial\varpi}{\partial x}=\rho\frac{1-\sigma^2}{E}\frac{\partial^2 v}{\partial t^2}.\quad\text{.........(99)}$$

These forms can be transformed readily to any suitable curvilinear coordinates.

Consider more particularly the case of a plate with a circular edge-line. It is appropriate to use plane polar coordinates r, θ with origin at the centre of the circle. Let U, V be the projections of the displacement of a point on the middle plane upon the radius vector and a line at right angles to the radius vector. Then we have

$$u=U\cos\theta-V\sin\theta,\qquad v=U\sin\theta+V\cos\theta,\quad\text{.................(100)}$$

and

$$\Delta'=\frac{\partial U}{\partial r}+\frac{U}{r}+\frac{1}{r}\frac{\partial V}{\partial\theta},\qquad 2\varpi=\frac{\partial V}{\partial r}+\frac{V}{r}-\frac{1}{r}\frac{\partial U}{\partial\theta},\quad\text{.................(101)}$$

* *London Roy. Soc. Proc.* (Ser. A), vol. 99 (1921), p. 272.

† *London Roy. Soc. Proc.* (Ser. A), vol. 101 (1922), p. 133.

‡ *Brit. Assoc. Rep.* 1921, p. 341.

§ Equations equivalent to (97) were obtained by Poisson and Cauchy, see Introduction, footnotes 36 and 124. Poisson investigated also the symmetrical radial vibrations of a circular plate, obtaining a frequency equation equivalent to (107), and evaluating the frequencies of the graver modes of this type.

and the stress-resultants belonging to any circle $r=\text{const.}$ are T, S, where

$$T=\frac{2Eh}{1-\sigma^2}\left[\frac{\partial U}{\partial r}+\sigma\left(\frac{U}{r}+\frac{1}{r}\frac{\partial V}{\partial \theta}\right)\right],\quad S=\frac{Eh}{1+\sigma}\left[\frac{\partial V}{\partial r}-\frac{V}{r}+\frac{1}{r}\frac{\partial U}{\partial \theta}\right]. \quad \text{......(102)}$$

The equations of vibration give

$$\nabla_1{}^2\Delta'=\frac{\rho(1-\sigma^2)}{E}\frac{\partial^2\Delta'}{\partial t^2},\quad \nabla_1{}^2\varpi=\frac{2\rho(1+\sigma)}{E}\frac{\partial^2\varpi}{\partial t^2}. \quad \text{......(103)}$$

We put

$$U=U_n\cos n\theta\cos pt,\quad V=V_n\sin n\theta\cos pt, \quad \text{......(104)}$$

where U_n and V_n are functions of r, and we write

$$\kappa^2=\rho(1-\sigma^2)p^2/E,\quad \kappa'^2=2\rho(1+\sigma)p^2/E. \quad \text{......(105)}$$

Then Δ' is of the form $A'J_n(\kappa r)\cos n\theta\cos pt$, and ϖ is of the form $B'J_n(\kappa' r)\sin n\theta\cos pt$, where A' and B' are constants, and J_n denotes Bessel's function of order n. The forms of U and V are given by the equations

$$U=\left[A\frac{dJ_n(\kappa r)}{dr}+nB\frac{J_n(\kappa' r)}{r}\right]\cos n\theta\cos pt,\quad V=-\left[nA\frac{J_n(\kappa r)}{r}+B\frac{dJ_n(\kappa' r)}{dr}\right]\sin n\theta\cos pt, \quad \text{......(106)}$$

and with these forms we have

$$\Delta'=-A\kappa^2J_n(\kappa r)\cos n\theta\cos pt,\quad 2\varpi=B\kappa'^2J_n(\kappa' r)\sin n\theta\cos pt.$$

We can have free vibrations in which V vanishes and U is independent of θ; the frequency equation is

$$\frac{dJ_1(\kappa a)}{da}+\frac{\sigma}{a}J_1(\kappa a)=0, \quad \text{......(107)}$$

a being the radius of the edge-line. We can also have free vibrations in which U vanishes and V is independent of θ; the frequency equation is

$$\frac{dJ_1(\kappa' a)}{da}=\frac{J_1(\kappa' a)}{a}. \quad \text{......(108)}$$

These two modes of symmetrical vibration appear to be the homologues of certain modes of vibration of a complete thin spherical shell (cf. Article 335 *infra*). The mode in which U vanishes and V is independent of θ is the homologue of the modes in which there is no displacement parallel to the radius of the sphere. The mode in which V vanishes and U is independent of θ seems to be the homologue of the quicker modes of symmetrical vibration of a sphere in which there is no rotation about the radius of the sphere.

In the remaining modes of extensional vibration of the plate the motion is compounded of two: one characterized by the absence of areal dilatation, and the other by the absence of rotation about the normal to the plane of the plate. The frequency equation is to be formed by eliminating the ratio $A:B$ between the equations

$$\left.\begin{aligned}-A\left[\frac{1-\sigma}{a}\frac{dJ_n(\kappa a)}{da}+\left(\kappa^2-\frac{1-\sigma}{a^2}n^2\right)J_n(\kappa a)\right]+nB(1-\sigma)\left[\frac{1}{a}\frac{dJ_n(\kappa' a)}{da}-\frac{1}{a^2}J_n(\kappa' a)\right]&=0,\\ -2nA\left[\frac{1}{a}\frac{dJ_n(\kappa a)}{da}-\frac{1}{a^2}J_n(\kappa a)\right]+B\left[\frac{2}{a}\frac{dJ_n(\kappa' a)}{da}+\left(\kappa'^2-\frac{2n^2}{a^2}\right)J_n(\kappa' a)\right]&=0.\end{aligned}\right\} \quad \text{......(109)}$$

These modes of vibration seem not to be of sufficient physical importance to make it worth while to attempt to calculate the roots numerically.

CHAPTER XXIII

INEXTENSIONAL DEFORMATION OF CURVED PLATES OR SHELLS

315. A CURVED plate or shell may be described geometrically by means of its middle surface, its edge-line, and its thickness. We shall take the thickness to be constant and denote it by $2h$, so that any normal to the middle surface is cut by the faces in two points distant h from the middle surface on opposite sides of it. We shall suppose that the edge of the plate cuts the middle surface at right angles; the curve of intersection is the edge-line. The case in which the plate or shell is open, so that there is an edge, is much more important than the case of a closed shell, because an open shell, or a plane plate with an edge, can be bent into an appreciably different shape without producing in it strains which are too large to be dealt with by the mathematical theory of Elasticity.

The like possibility of large changes of shape accompanied by very small strains was recognized in Chapter XVIII as an essential feature of the behaviour of a thin rod; but there is an important difference between the theory of rods and that of plates arising from a certain geometrical restriction. The extension of any linear element of the middle surface of a strained plate or shell, like the extension of the central-line of a strained rod, must be small. In the case of a rod this condition does not restrict in any way the shape of the strained central-line; and this shape may be determined, as in Chapters XIX and XXI, by taking the central-line to be unextended. But, in the case of the shell, the condition that no line on the middle surface is altered in length restricts the strained middle surface to a certain family of surfaces, viz. those which are applicable upon the unstrained middle surface*. In the particular case of a plane plate, the strained middle surface must, if the displacement is inextensional, be a developable surface. Since the middle surface can undergo but a slight extension, the strained middle surface can differ but slightly from one of the surfaces applicable upon the unstrained middle surface; in other words, it must be derivable from such a surface by a displacement which is everywhere small.

316. Change of curvature in inextensional deformation.

We begin with the case in which the middle surface is deformed without extension by a displacement which is everywhere small. Let the equations of the lines of curvature of the unstrained surface be expressed in the forms

* For the literature of the theory of surfaces applicable one on another we may refer to the Article by A. Voss, 'Abbildung und Abwickelung zweier Flächen auf einander' in *Ency. d. math. Wiss.*, III. D 6*a*.

$\alpha=$ const. and $\beta=$ const., where α and β are functions of position on the surface, and let R_1, R_2 denote the principal radii of curvature of the surface at a point, R_1 being the radius of curvature of that section drawn through the normal at the point which contains the tangent at the point to a curve of the family β (along which α is variable). When the shell is strained without extension of the middle surface, the curves $\alpha=$ const. and $\beta=$ const. become two families of curves drawn on the strained middle surface, which cut at right angles, but are not in general lines of curvature of the deformed surface. The curvature of this surface can be determined by its principal radii of curvature, and by the angles at which its lines of curvature cut the curves α and β. Let $\frac{1}{R_1}+\delta\frac{1}{R_1}$ and $\frac{1}{R_2}+\delta\frac{1}{R_2}$ be the new principal curvatures at any point. Since the surface is bent without stretching, the measure of curvature is unaltered*, or we have

$$\left(\frac{1}{R_1}+\delta\frac{1}{R_1}\right)\left(\frac{1}{R_2}+\delta\frac{1}{R_2}\right)=\frac{1}{R_1R_2},$$

or, correctly to the first order in $\delta\frac{1}{R_1}$ and $\delta\frac{1}{R_2}$,

$$\frac{1}{R_2}\,\delta\frac{1}{R_1}+\frac{1}{R_1}\,\delta\frac{1}{R_2}=0. \qquad\qquad (1)$$

Again let ψ be the angle at which the line of curvature associated with the principal curvature $\frac{1}{R_1}+\delta\frac{1}{R_1}$ cuts the curve $\beta=$ const. on the deformed surface, and let R_1', R_2' be the radii of curvature of normal sections of this surface drawn through the tangents to the curves $\beta=$ const. and $\alpha=$ const. In general ψ must be small, and R_1', R_2' can differ but little from R_1, R_2. The indicatrix of the surface, referred to axes of x and y which coincide with these tangents, is given by the equation

$$\frac{x^2}{R_1'}+\frac{y^2}{R_2'}+xy\tan 2\psi\left(\frac{1}{R_1'}-\frac{1}{R_2'}\right)=\text{const.}$$

Referred to axes of ξ and η which coincide with the tangents to the lines of curvature, the equation of the indicatrix is

$$\xi^2\left(\frac{1}{R_1}+\delta\frac{1}{R_1}\right)+\eta^2\left(\frac{1}{R_2}+\delta\frac{1}{R_2}\right)=\text{const.},$$

and therefore we have

$$\left.\begin{aligned}&\frac{1}{R_1'}+\frac{1}{R_2'}=\frac{1}{R_1}+\frac{1}{R_2}+\delta\frac{1}{R_1}+\delta\frac{1}{R_2},\\&\frac{1}{R_1'R_2'}-\tfrac{1}{4}\tan^2 2\psi\left(\frac{1}{R_1'}-\frac{1}{R_2'}\right)^2=\left(\frac{1}{R_1}+\delta\frac{1}{R_1}\right)\left(\frac{1}{R_2}+\delta\frac{1}{R_2}\right)=\frac{1}{R_1R_2}.\end{aligned}\right\}\quad\ldots(2)$$

* The theorem is due to Gauss, 'Disquisitiones generales circa superficies curvas,' *Göttingen Comm. Rec.*, t. 6 (1828), or *Werke*, Bd. 4, p. 217. Cf. Salmon, *Geometry of three dimensions*, 4th edition, p. 355.

The bending of the surface is determined by the three quantities κ_1, κ_2, τ defined by the equations

$$\kappa_1 = \frac{1}{R_1'} - \frac{1}{R_1}, \quad \kappa_2 = \frac{1}{R_2'} - \frac{1}{R_2}, \quad \tau = \tfrac{1}{2}\tan 2\psi\left(\frac{1}{R_1'} - \frac{1}{R_2'}\right). \quad \text{......(3)}$$

The curvature $1/R'$ of the normal section drawn through that tangent line of the strained middle surface which makes an angle ω with the curve $\beta = \text{const.}$ is given by the equation

$$\frac{1}{R'} = \frac{\cos^2\omega}{R_1'} + \frac{\sin^2\omega}{R_2'} + 2\tau \sin\omega\cos\omega,$$

and the curvature $1/R$ of the corresponding normal section of the unstrained middle surface is given by the equation

$$\frac{1}{R} = \frac{\cos^2\omega}{R_1} + \frac{\sin^2\omega}{R_2},$$

so that the change of curvature in this normal section is given by the equation

$$\frac{1}{R'} - \frac{1}{R} = \kappa_1\cos^2\omega + \kappa_2\sin^2\omega + 2\tau\sin\omega\cos\omega. \quad \text{............(4)}$$

We shall refer to κ_1, κ_2, τ as the *changes of curvature*.

In general, if $R_1 \neq R_2$, equations (2) give, correctly to the first order,

$$\delta\frac{1}{R_1} = \kappa_1, \quad \delta\frac{1}{R_2} = \kappa_2, \quad \frac{\kappa_1}{R_2} + \frac{\kappa_2}{R_1} = 0.$$

For example, in the case of a cylinder, or any developable surface, if the lines $\beta = \text{const.}$ are the generators, κ_1 vanishes, and $\tan 2\psi = -2\tau R_2$.

The case of a sphere is somewhat exceptional because of the indeterminateness of the lines of curvature. In this case, putting $R_1 = R_2$, we find from (1)

$$\delta\frac{1}{R_1} = -\delta\frac{1}{R_2} = \delta\frac{1}{R} \text{ say;}$$

and then we have, correctly to the first order,

$$\kappa_1 + \kappa_2 = 0, \quad \tan 2\psi = 2\tau/(\kappa_1 - \kappa_2) = \tau/\kappa_1,$$

and, correctly to the second order,

$$\left(\delta\frac{1}{R}\right)^2 = -\kappa_1\kappa_2 + \tau^2 = \kappa_1^2 + \tau^2,$$

but κ_1 and κ_2 are not equal to $\delta\frac{1}{R_1}$ and $\delta\frac{1}{R_2}$ unless $\tau = 0$, and ψ is not small unless τ is small compared with κ_1.

The result that, in the case of a cylinder slightly deformed without extension, $\kappa_1 = 0$, or there is no change of curvature in normal sections containing the generators, has been noted by Lord Rayleigh as "the principle upon which metal is corrugated." He has also applied the result expressed here as $\kappa_1/R_2 + \kappa_2/R_1 = 0$ to the explanation of the behaviour of Bourdon's gauge*.

* *London Roy. Soc. Proc.*, vol. 45 (1889), p. 105, or *Scientific Papers*, vol. 3, p. 217. Additional references to papers dealing with Bourdon's gauge are given by Th. v. Kármán in *Ency. d. math. Wiss.*, Bd. IV., Art. 27, p. 355.

317. Typical flexural strain.

We imagine a state of strain in the shell which is such that, while no line on the middle surface is altered in length, the linear elements initially normal to the unstrained middle surface remain straight, become normal to the strained middle surface, and suffer no extension or contraction. We express the components of strain in this state with reference to axes of x, y, z, which are directed along the tangents to the curves β and α at a point P_1 on the strained middle surface and the normal to this surface at P_1. Let P be the point of the unstrained middle surface of which P_1 is the displaced position, and let δs be an element of arc of a curve s, drawn on the unstrained surface, and issuing from P; also let R be the radius of curvature of the normal section of this surface drawn through the tangent to s at P. The normals to the middle surface at points of s meet a surface parallel to the middle surface, and at a small distance z from it, in a corresponding curve, and the length of the corresponding element of arc of this curve is approximately equal to $\{(R-z)/R\}\,\delta s$*. When the surface is bent so that R is changed into R', and z and δs are unaltered, this length becomes $\{(R'-z)/R'\}\,\delta s$ approximately. Hence the extension† of the element in question is

$$\left(\frac{R'-z}{R'}-\frac{R-z}{R}\right)\Big/\frac{R-z}{R},\ \text{or, approximately,}\ -z\left(\frac{1}{R'}-\frac{1}{R}\right).$$

Let the tangent to s at P cut the curve β at P at an angle ω. The direction of the corresponding curve on the parallel surface is nearly the same; and the extension of the element of arc of this curve can be expressed as

$$e_{xx}\cos^2\omega+e_{yy}\sin^2\omega+e_{xy}\sin\omega\cos\omega.$$

Equating the two expressions for this extension, and using (4), we find

$$e_{xx}\cos^2\omega+e_{yy}\sin^2\omega+e_{xy}\sin\omega\cos\omega=-z\,(\kappa_1\cos^2\omega+\kappa_2\sin^2\omega+2\tau\sin\omega\cos\omega),$$

and therefore $$e_{xx}=-z\kappa_1,\quad e_{yy}=-z\kappa_2,\quad e_{xy}=-2z\tau.$$

In the imagined state of strain e_{zx}, e_{yz}, e_{zz} vanish. With this strain we may compound any strain by which the linear elements initially normal to the unstrained middle surface become extended, or curved, or inclined to the strained middle surface. The most important case is that in which there is no traction on any surface parallel to the middle surface. In this case the stress-components denoted by X_z, Y_z, Z_z vanish, and the strain-components e_{zx}, e_{yz}, e_{zz} are given by the equations

$$e_{zx}=0,\quad e_{yz}=0,\quad e_{zz}=-\{\sigma/(1-\sigma)\}\,(e_{xx}+e_{yy}),$$

where σ is Poisson's ratio for the material, supposed isotropic. In this state of strain the linear elements initially normal to the unstrained middle surface

* Near a point on the middle surface the equation of this surface can be taken to be $2\zeta=\xi^2/R_1+\eta^2/R_2$, and the coordinates of the point in which the normal at (ξ', η') meets the parallel surface can be shown, by forming the equations of the normal, to be approximately $\xi'(1-z/R_1)$ and $\eta'(1-z/R_2)$. Putting $\xi'=\delta s\,.\cos\omega$, $\eta'=\delta s\,.\sin\omega$, and neglecting z^2/R_1^2 and z^2/R_2^2, we obtain the result stated in the text.

† Cf. Lord Rayleigh, *Theory of Sound*, 2nd edition, p. 411.

remain straight, become normal to the strained middle surface, and suffer a certain extension specified by the value of e_{zz} written above. It is clear that this extension can have very little effect* in modifying the expressions for e_{xx}, e_{yy}, e_{xy}, and we may therefore take as approximate expressions for the strain-components

$$e_{xx} = -z\kappa_1,\ e_{yy} = -z\kappa_2,\ e_{zz} = \frac{\sigma}{1-\sigma} z(\kappa_1+\kappa_2),\ e_{xy} = -2\tau z,\ e_{zx} = e_{yz} = 0. \ \ldots(5)$$

This state of strain may be described as the *typical flexural strain*.

The corresponding stress-components are

$$X_x = -\frac{E}{1-\sigma^2} z(\kappa_1+\sigma\kappa_2),\quad Y_y = -\frac{E}{1-\sigma^2} z(\kappa_2+\sigma\kappa_1),$$

$$X_y = -\frac{E}{1+\sigma} z\tau,\quad X_z = Y_z = Z_z = 0,$$

where E is Young's modulus for the material. The strain-energy-function takes the form

$$\tfrac{1}{2}\frac{Ez^2}{1-\sigma^2}[(\kappa_1+\kappa_2)^2 - 2(1-\sigma)(\kappa_1\kappa_2-\tau^2)].$$

The *potential energy of bending*, estimated per unit of area of the middle surface, is obtained by integrating this expression with respect to z between the limits $-h$ and h, the thickness of the shell being $2h$. The result can be written

$$\tfrac{1}{2}D[(\kappa_1+\kappa_2)^2 - 2(1-\sigma)(\kappa_1\kappa_2-\tau^2)], \ \ldots\ldots\ldots\ldots\ldots(6)$$

where D is the "flexural rigidity" $\frac{2}{3}Eh^3/(1-\sigma^2)$. In the case of a cylinder, or any developable surface, this expression becomes $\frac{1}{2}D\{\kappa_2^2 + 2(1-\sigma)\tau^2\}$. In the case of a sphere it becomes $\frac{4}{3}\mu h^3(\kappa_1^2+\tau^2)$, or $\frac{4}{3}\mu h^3\left(\delta\frac{1}{R}\right)^2$, where μ is the rigidity of the material†.

318. Method of calculating the changes of curvature.

The conditions which must be satisfied by the displacement in order that the middle surface may suffer no extension may be found by a straightforward method. Let $A\delta\alpha$ be the element of arc of a curve $\beta = \text{const.}$ between two curves α and $\alpha+\delta\alpha$, $B\delta\beta$ the element of arc of a curve $\alpha = \text{const.}$ between two curves β and $\beta+\delta\beta$; also let x', y', z' be the coordinates of a point on the strained middle surface referred to any suitable axes. We form expressions for x', y', z' in terms of the coordinates of the point before strain and of any suitable components of displacement. Since curves on the middle surface retain

* It will be seen in the more complete investigation of Article 327 below that such effects are not entirely negligible.

† These are the expressions used by Lord Rayleigh, *Theory of Sound*, 2nd edition, Chapter X A.

their lengths, and cut at the same angles after strain as before strain, we must have

$$\frac{1}{A}\left[\left(\frac{\partial x'}{\partial \alpha}\right)^2+\left(\frac{\partial y'}{\partial \alpha}\right)^2+\left(\frac{\partial z'}{\partial \alpha}\right)^2\right]^{\frac{1}{2}}=1,\quad \frac{1}{B}\left[\left(\frac{\partial x'}{\partial \beta}\right)^2+\left(\frac{\partial y'}{\partial \beta}\right)^2+\left(\frac{\partial z'}{\partial \beta}\right)^2\right]^{\frac{1}{2}}=1,$$

$$\frac{\partial x'}{\partial \alpha}\frac{\partial x'}{\partial \beta}+\frac{\partial y'}{\partial \alpha}\frac{\partial y'}{\partial \beta}+\frac{\partial z'}{\partial \alpha}\frac{\partial z'}{\partial \beta}=0.$$

These equations give us three partial differential equations connecting the components of displacement.

The changes of curvature also may be calculated by a fairly straightforward method. The direction-cosines l, m, n of the normal drawn in a specified sense to the strained middle surface can be expressed in such forms as

$$l=\pm\frac{1}{AB}\left(\frac{\partial y'}{\partial \alpha}\frac{\partial z'}{\partial \beta}-\frac{\partial z'}{\partial \alpha}\frac{\partial y'}{\partial \beta}\right),$$

and the ambiguous sign can always be determined. The equations of the normal are

$$\frac{x-x'}{l}=\frac{y-y'}{m}=\frac{z-z'}{n};$$

and, if (x, y, z) is a centre of principal curvature, we have

$$x=x'+l\rho',\quad y=y'+m\rho',\quad z=z'+n\rho',$$

where ρ' is the corresponding principal radius of curvature; ρ' is estimated as positive when the normal (l, m, n) is drawn from (x', y', z') towards (x, y, z). If $(\alpha+\delta\alpha, \beta+\delta\beta)$ is a point on the surface near to (x', y', z') on that line of curvature through (x', y', z') for which the radius of curvature is ρ', the quantities x, y, z, ρ' are unaltered, to the first order in $\delta\alpha, \delta\beta$, by changing α into $\alpha+\delta\alpha$ and β into $\beta+\delta\beta$. The quantity we have already called $\tan\psi$ is one of the two values of the ratio $B\delta\beta/A\delta\alpha$. Hence $\tan\psi$ and ρ' are determined by the equations

$$\frac{\partial x'}{\partial \alpha}\delta\alpha+\frac{\partial x'}{\partial \beta}\delta\beta+\rho'\left(\frac{\partial l}{\partial \alpha}\delta\alpha+\frac{\partial l}{\partial \beta}\delta\beta\right)=0,$$

$$\frac{\partial y'}{\partial \alpha}\delta\alpha+\frac{\partial y'}{\partial \beta}\delta\beta+\rho'\left(\frac{\partial m}{\partial \alpha}\delta\alpha+\frac{\partial m}{\partial \beta}\delta\beta\right)=0,$$

$$\frac{\partial z'}{\partial \alpha}\delta\alpha+\frac{\partial z'}{\partial \beta}\delta\beta+\rho'\left(\frac{\partial n}{\partial \alpha}\delta\alpha+\frac{\partial n}{\partial \beta}\delta\beta\right)=0.$$

These three equations are really equivalent to only two, for it follows from the mode of formation of the expressions for l, m, n, and from the equation $l^2+m^2+n^2=1$, that, when we multiply the left-hand members by l, m, n and add the results, the sum vanishes identically. By eliminating the ratio $\delta\alpha/\delta\beta$ from two of these equations we form an equation for ρ', and the values of $1/\rho'$ are $\frac{1}{R_1}+\delta\frac{1}{R_1}$ and $\frac{1}{R_2}+\delta\frac{1}{R_2}$; by eliminating ρ' from two of the equations we form an equation for $\delta\beta/\delta\alpha$, which determines $\tan\psi$.

We shall exemplify these methods in the cases of cylindrical and spherical shells. In more difficult cases, or when there is extension as well as change of curvature, it is advisable to use a more powerful method. One such method will be given later; others have been given by H. Lamb* and Lord Rayleigh†. The results for cylindrical and spherical shells may, of course, be obtained by the general methods; but these cases are so important that it seems to be worth while to show how they may be investigated by an analysis which presents no difficulties beyond the manipulation of some rather long expressions. The results in these cases were obtained by Lord Rayleigh‡.

319. Inextensional deformation of a cylindrical shell.

(a) *Formulæ for the displacement.*

When the middle surface is a circular cylinder of radius a, we take the quantities α and β at any point to be respectively the distance along the generator drawn through the point, measured from a fixed circular section, and the angle between the axial plane containing the point and a fixed axial plane; and we write x and ϕ in place of α and β. We resolve the displacement of the point into components: u along the generator, v along the tangent to the circular section, w along the normal to the surface drawn inwards. The coordinates x', y', z' of the corresponding point on the strained middle surface are given by the equations

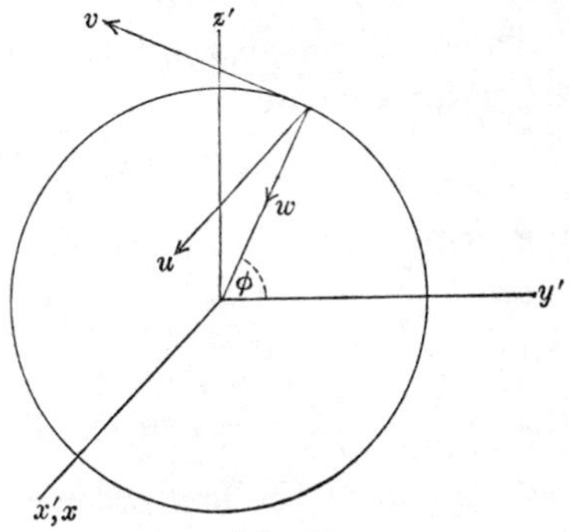

Fig. 71.

$$x' = x + u, \quad y' = (a - w)\cos\phi - v\sin\phi,$$
$$z' = (a - w)\sin\phi + v\cos\phi.$$

The conditions that the displacement may be inextensional are

$$\left\{\left(\frac{\partial x'}{\partial x}\right)^2 + \left(\frac{\partial y'}{\partial x}\right)^2 + \left(\frac{\partial z'}{\partial x}\right)^2\right\}^{\frac{1}{2}} = 1, \quad \frac{1}{a}\left\{\left(\frac{\partial x'}{\partial \phi}\right)^2 + \left(\frac{\partial y'}{\partial \phi}\right)^2 + \left(\frac{\partial z'}{\partial \phi}\right)^2\right\}^{\frac{1}{2}} = 1$$
$$\frac{\partial x'}{\partial x}\frac{\partial x'}{\partial \phi} + \frac{\partial y'}{\partial x}\frac{\partial y'}{\partial \phi} + \frac{\partial z'}{\partial x}\frac{\partial z'}{\partial \phi} = 0.$$

On writing down the equations

$$\frac{\partial x'}{\partial x} = 1 + \frac{\partial u}{\partial x}, \quad \frac{\partial y'}{\partial x} = -\frac{\partial w}{\partial x}\cos\phi - \frac{\partial v}{\partial x}\sin\phi, \quad \frac{\partial z'}{\partial x} = -\frac{\partial w}{\partial x}\sin\phi + \frac{\partial v}{\partial x}\cos\phi,$$
$$\frac{\partial x'}{\partial \phi} = \frac{\partial u}{\partial \phi}, \quad \frac{\partial y'}{\partial \phi} = -\left(\frac{\partial w}{\partial \phi} + v\right)\cos\phi - \left(a - w + \frac{\partial v}{\partial \phi}\right)\sin\phi,$$
$$\frac{\partial z'}{\partial \phi} = \left(a - w + \frac{\partial v}{\partial \phi}\right)\cos\phi - \left(\frac{\partial w}{\partial \phi} + v\right)\sin\phi,$$

* *London Math. Soc. Proc.*, vol. 21 (1891), p. 119.

† *Theory of Sound*, 2nd edition, vol. 1, Chapter X A.

‡ *London Math. Soc. Proc.*, vol. 13 (1882), or *Scientific Papers*, vol. 1, p. 551, and the paper cited on p. 501 *supra*. See also *Theory of Sound*, 2nd edition, vol. 1, Chapter X A.

we see that these conditions are, to the first order in u, v, w,

$$\frac{\partial u}{\partial x}=0, \quad w=\frac{\partial v}{\partial \phi}, \quad \frac{\partial v}{\partial x}+\frac{1}{a}\frac{\partial u}{\partial \phi}=0. \qquad \text{.................(7)}$$

These equations show that u is independent of x, and v and w are linear functions of x.

If the edge-line consists of two circles $x=$ const., u, v, w must be periodic in ϕ with period 2π, and the most general possible forms are

$$\left.\begin{aligned} u&=-\Sigma \frac{a}{n} B_n \sin(n\phi+\beta_n), \quad v=\Sigma\left[A_n \cos(n\phi+\alpha_n)+B_n x\cos(n\phi+\beta_n)\right], \\ w&=-\Sigma\, n\left[A_n \sin(n\phi+\alpha_n)+B_n x \sin(n\phi+\beta_n)\right], \end{aligned}\right\} \qquad \text{.........(8)}$$

where A_n, B_n, α_n, β_n are constants, and the summations refer to different integral values of n.

(b) *Changes of curvature.*

The direction-cosines l, m, n of the normal to the strained middle surface drawn inwards are

$$l=\frac{1}{a}\left(\frac{\partial y'}{\partial x}\frac{\partial z'}{\partial \phi}-\frac{\partial z'}{\partial x}\frac{\partial y'}{\partial \phi}\right), \ldots.$$

We write down the values of $\partial x'/\partial x, \ldots$, simplified by using (7), in the forms

$$\frac{\partial x'}{\partial x}=1, \quad \frac{\partial y'}{\partial x}=\frac{1}{a}\frac{\partial u}{\partial \phi}\sin\phi-\frac{\partial w}{\partial x}\cos\phi, \quad \frac{\partial z'}{\partial x}=-\frac{1}{a}\frac{\partial u}{\partial \phi}\cos\phi-\frac{\partial w}{\partial x}\sin\phi,$$

$$\frac{\partial x'}{\partial \phi}=\frac{\partial u}{\partial \phi}, \quad \frac{\partial y'}{\partial \phi}=-a\sin\phi-\left(v+\frac{\partial w}{\partial \phi}\right)\cos\phi, \quad \frac{\partial z'}{\partial \phi}=a\cos\phi-\left(v+\frac{\partial w}{\partial \phi}\right)\sin\phi,$$

and we find, to the first order in u, v, w,

$$l=-\frac{\partial w}{\partial x}, \quad m=-\cos\phi+\frac{1}{a}\left(v+\frac{\partial w}{\partial \phi}\right)\sin\phi, \quad n=-\sin\phi-\frac{1}{a}\left(v+\frac{\partial w}{\partial \phi}\right)\cos\phi.$$

The principal radii of curvature and the directions of the lines of curvature are given by the equations

$$\frac{1}{\rho'^2}\left(\frac{\partial x'}{\partial x}\frac{\partial y'}{\partial \phi}-\frac{\partial y'}{\partial x}\frac{\partial x'}{\partial \phi}\right)+\frac{1}{\rho'}\left(\frac{\partial x'}{\partial x}\frac{\partial m}{\partial \phi}+\frac{\partial l}{\partial x}\frac{\partial y'}{\partial \phi}-\frac{\partial m}{\partial x}\frac{\partial x'}{\partial \phi}-\frac{\partial y'}{\partial x}\frac{\partial l}{\partial \phi}\right)$$
$$+\frac{\partial l}{\partial x}\frac{\partial m}{\partial \phi}-\frac{\partial m}{\partial x}\frac{\partial l}{\partial \phi}=0,$$

and
$$(\delta x)^2\left(\frac{\partial x'}{\partial x}\frac{\partial m}{\partial x}-\frac{\partial y'}{\partial x}\frac{\partial l}{\partial x}\right)+(\delta\phi)^2\left(\frac{\partial x'}{\partial \phi}\frac{\partial m}{\partial \phi}-\frac{\partial y'}{\partial \phi}\frac{\partial l}{\partial \phi}\right)$$
$$+\delta x\,\delta\phi\left(\frac{\partial x'}{\partial x}\frac{\partial m}{\partial \phi}+\frac{\partial m}{\partial x}\frac{\partial x'}{\partial \phi}-\frac{\partial y'}{\partial x}\frac{\partial l}{\partial \phi}-\frac{\partial l}{\partial x}\frac{\partial y'}{\partial \phi}\right)=0.$$

For the purpose of calculating the coefficients in these equations we write down the values of $\partial l/\partial x, \ldots$, simplifying them slightly by means of (7) and by the observation that v and w are linear functions of x. We have

$$\frac{\partial l}{\partial x}=0, \qquad \frac{\partial m}{\partial x}=\frac{\sin\phi}{a}\frac{\partial}{\partial x}\left(v+\frac{\partial w}{\partial \phi}\right),$$

$$\frac{\partial l}{\partial \phi}=-\frac{\partial^2 w}{\partial x\partial \phi}, \quad \frac{\partial m}{\partial \phi}=\sin\phi\left\{1+\frac{1}{a}\left(\frac{\partial^2 w}{\partial \phi^2}+w\right)\right\}+\frac{\cos\phi}{a}\left(v+\frac{\partial w}{\partial \phi}\right).$$

We know beforehand that, when terms of the second order in u, v, w are neglected, one value of $1/\rho'$ is zero and the other is $1/a + \kappa_2$; also the value of $a\delta\phi/\delta x$ is $\tan\psi$, and $\tan 2\psi = -2a\tau$. We can now write down the above equations for ρ' and $\delta x/\delta\phi$ in the forms (correct to the first order in u, v, w)

$$\left(\frac{1}{a}+\kappa_2\right)\left[-a\sin\phi-\left(v+\frac{\partial w}{\partial\phi}\right)\cos\phi\right] + \left[\sin\phi+\frac{1}{a}\left(v+\frac{\partial w}{\partial\phi}\right)\cos\phi+\frac{1}{a}\left(\frac{\partial^2 w}{\partial\phi^2}+w\right)\sin\phi\right]=0,$$

and
$$\frac{1}{a}\frac{\partial}{\partial x}\left(v+\frac{\partial w}{\partial\phi}\right)\sin\phi+\frac{1}{a^2}\tan^2\psi\left(\frac{\partial u}{\partial\phi}-a\frac{\partial^2 w}{\partial x\partial\phi}\right)\sin\phi + \frac{1}{a}\tan\psi\left[\sin\phi+\frac{1}{a}\left(v+\frac{\partial w}{\partial\phi}\right)\cos\phi+\frac{1}{a}\left(\frac{\partial^2 w}{\partial\phi^2}+w\right)\sin\phi\right]=0.$$

The former of these gives, to the first order in u, v, w,

$$\kappa_2=\frac{1}{a^2}\left(\frac{\partial^2 w}{\partial\phi^2}+w\right), \qquad \text{.........................(9)}$$

and the latter gives, to the same order,

$$\tan 2\psi=-2\frac{\partial}{\partial x}\left(v+\frac{\partial w}{\partial\phi}\right),$$

or
$$\tau=\frac{1}{a}\frac{\partial}{\partial x}\left(v+\frac{\partial w}{\partial\phi}\right). \qquad \text{.........................(10)}$$

With the values of u, v, w given in (8) these results become

$$\left.\begin{aligned}\kappa_2&=\Sigma\frac{n^3-n}{a^2}\left[A_n\sin(n\phi+\alpha_n)+B_n x\sin(n\phi+\beta_n)\right],\\ \tau&=-\Sigma\frac{n^2-1}{a}B_n\cos(n\phi+\beta_n).\end{aligned}\right\} \qquad \text{......(11)}$$

320. Inextensional deformation of a spherical shell.

(a) *Formulæ for the displacement.*

When the middle surface is a sphere of radius a we take the coordinates α and β to be ordinary spherical polar coordinates, and write θ, ϕ for α, β. The displacement is specified by components u along the tangent to the meridian in the direction of increase of θ, v along the tangent to the parallel in the direction of increase of ϕ, w along the normal to the surface drawn inwards. The Cartesian coordinates of a point on the strained middle surface are given by the equations

$$x'=(a-w)\sin\theta\cos\phi + u\cos\theta\cos\phi - v\sin\phi,$$

$$y'=(a-w)\sin\theta\sin\phi + u\cos\theta\sin\phi + v\cos\phi,$$

$$z'=(a-w)\cos\theta - u\sin\theta.$$

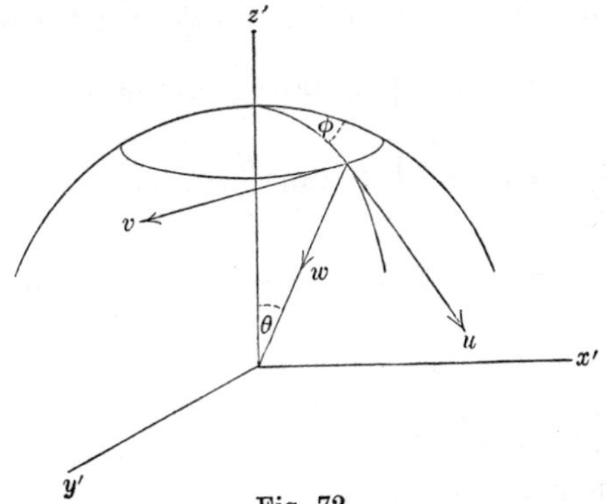

Fig. 72.

The conditions that the displacement may be inextensional are

$$\frac{1}{a}\left[\left(\frac{\partial x'}{\partial\theta}\right)^2+\left(\frac{\partial y'}{\partial\theta}\right)^2+\left(\frac{\partial z'}{\partial\theta}\right)^2\right]^{\frac{1}{2}}=1,\quad \frac{1}{a\sin\theta}\left[\left(\frac{\partial x'}{\partial\phi}\right)^2+\left(\frac{\partial y'}{\partial\phi}\right)^2+\left(\frac{\partial z'}{\partial\phi}\right)^2\right]^{\frac{1}{2}}=1,$$

$$\frac{\partial x'}{\partial\theta}\frac{\partial x'}{\partial\phi}+\frac{\partial y'}{\partial\theta}\frac{\partial y'}{\partial\phi}+\frac{\partial z'}{\partial\theta}\frac{\partial z'}{\partial\phi}=0.$$

We write down the equations

$$\frac{\partial x'}{\partial\theta}=\left[\left(a-w+\frac{\partial u}{\partial\theta}\right)\cos\theta-\left(\frac{\partial w}{\partial\theta}+u\right)\sin\theta\right]\cos\phi-\frac{\partial v}{\partial\theta}\sin\phi,$$

$$\frac{\partial y'}{\partial\theta}=\left[\left(a-w+\frac{\partial u}{\partial\theta}\right)\cos\theta-\left(\frac{\partial w}{\partial\theta}+u\right)\sin\theta\right]\sin\phi+\frac{\partial v}{\partial\theta}\cos\phi,$$

$$\frac{\partial z'}{\partial\theta}=-\left(a-w+\frac{\partial u}{\partial\theta}\right)\sin\theta-\left(\frac{\partial w}{\partial\theta}+u\right)\cos\theta,$$

and

$$\frac{\partial x'}{\partial\phi}=-\left[(a-w)\sin\theta+u\cos\theta+\frac{\partial v}{\partial\phi}\right]\sin\phi+\left[\frac{\partial u}{\partial\phi}\cos\theta-v-\frac{\partial w}{\partial\phi}\sin\theta\right]\cos\phi,$$

$$\frac{\partial y'}{\partial\phi}=\left[(a-w)\sin\theta+u\cos\theta+\frac{\partial v}{\partial\phi}\right]\cos\phi+\left[\frac{\partial u}{\partial\phi}\cos\theta-v-\frac{\partial w}{\partial\phi}\sin\theta\right]\sin\phi,$$

$$\frac{\partial z'}{\partial\phi}=-\frac{\partial u}{\partial\phi}\sin\theta-\frac{\partial w}{\partial\phi}\cos\theta.$$

The conditions that the displacement may be inextensional are, to the first order in u, v, w,

$$w=\frac{\partial u}{\partial\theta},\quad w\sin\theta=u\cos\theta+\frac{\partial v}{\partial\phi},$$

$$\sin\theta\frac{\partial v}{\partial\theta}+\cos\theta\left(\frac{\partial u}{\partial\phi}\cos\theta-v-\frac{\partial w}{\partial\phi}\sin\theta\right)+\sin\theta\left(\frac{\partial u}{\partial\phi}\sin\theta+\frac{\partial w}{\partial\phi}\cos\theta\right)=0,$$

or, as they may be written,

$$w=\frac{\partial u}{\partial\theta},\quad \sin\theta\frac{\partial}{\partial\theta}\frac{u}{\sin\theta}=\frac{\partial}{\partial\phi}\frac{v}{\sin\theta},\quad \frac{\partial}{\partial\phi}\frac{u}{\sin\theta}+\sin\theta\frac{\partial}{\partial\theta}\frac{v}{\sin\theta}=0.\quad\text{...(12)}$$

The last two of these equations show that $u/\sin\theta$ and $v/\sin\theta$ are conjugate functions of $\log(\tan\frac{1}{2}\theta)$ and ϕ.

If the edge-line consists of two circles of latitude, u, v, w must be periodic in ϕ with period 2π, and the most general possible forms for them are

$$\left.\begin{aligned}u&=\sin\theta\,\Sigma\left[A_n\tan^n\frac{\theta}{2}\cos(n\phi+\alpha_n)+B_n\cot^n\frac{\theta}{2}\cos(n\phi+\beta_n)\right],\\ v&=\sin\theta\,\Sigma\left[A_n\tan^n\frac{\theta}{2}\sin(n\phi+\alpha_n)-B_n\cot^n\frac{\theta}{2}\sin(n\phi+\beta_n)\right],\\ w&=\Sigma\left[(n+\cos\theta)A_n\tan^n\frac{\theta}{2}\cos(n\phi+\alpha_n)\right.\\ &\qquad\left.-(n-\cos\theta)B_n\cot^n\frac{\theta}{2}\cos(n\phi+\beta_n)\right],\end{aligned}\right\}\quad\text{...(13)}$$

where A_n, B_n, α_n, β_n are constants, and the summations refer to different integral values of n.

If in the formulæ (13) we put $n=0$, we find displacements of the type

$$u=A_0\sin\theta\cos\alpha,\quad v=A_0\sin\theta\sin\alpha,\quad w=A_0\cos\theta\cos\alpha,$$

the terms in B being of the same type. The components of this displacement in the directions of x', y', z' are

$$-A_0\sin\alpha\sin\theta\sin\phi,\quad A_0\sin\alpha\sin\theta\cos\phi,\quad -A_0\cos\alpha,$$

and this displacement is compounded of a translation $-A_0\cos\alpha$ in the direction of the axis of z' and a rotation $A_0 a^{-1}\sin\alpha$ about this axis.

If in the formulæ (13) we put $n=1$, we find displacements of the types

$$u=A_1(1-\cos\theta)\cos(\phi+\alpha),\quad v=A_1(1-\cos\theta)\sin(\phi+\alpha),\quad w=A_1\sin\theta\cos(\phi+\alpha),$$

and

$$u=B_1(1+\cos\theta)\cos(\phi+\beta),\quad v=-B_1(1+\cos\theta)\sin(\phi+\beta),\quad w=-B_1\sin\theta\cos(\phi+\beta).$$

The former is equivalent to a translation $(-A_1\cos\alpha,\ A_1\sin\alpha,\ 0)$ and a rotation $A_1 a^{-1}(\sin\alpha,\cos\alpha,0)$; and the latter is equivalent to a translation $(B_1\cos\beta,\ -B_1\sin\beta,\ 0)$ and a rotation $B_1 a^{-1}(\sin\beta,\cos\beta,0)$.

It appears from what has just been said that all the displacements obtained from (13) by putting $n=0$ or 1 are possible in a rigid body, and the terms for which n has these values may be omitted from the summations. Similar results can be proved in the case of cylindrical shells.

If the edge-line consists of one circle of latitude, and the pole $\theta=0$ is included, we must omit from (13) the terms in $\cot^n\frac{1}{2}\theta$, $(n>1)$, for these terms become infinite at the pole. If the sphere is complete the terms in $\tan^n\frac{1}{2}\theta$, $(n>1)$, must be omitted also; that is to say no inextensional displacements are possible in a complete spherical shell except such as are possible in a rigid body*.

(b) *Changes of curvature.*

We form next expressions for the direction-cosines l, m, n of the normal to the deformed surface, by means of such formulæ as

$$l=\frac{1}{a^2\sin\theta}\left(\frac{\partial y'}{\partial\phi}\frac{\partial z'}{\partial\theta}-\frac{\partial z'}{\partial\phi}\frac{\partial y'}{\partial\theta}\right);$$

and for this purpose we first write down the expressions for $\partial x'/\partial\theta,\dots$ simplified by means of equations (12). We have

$$\frac{\partial x'}{\partial\theta}=a\cos\theta\cos\phi-\left(\frac{\partial w}{\partial\theta}+u\right)\sin\theta\cos\phi-\frac{\partial v}{\partial\theta}\sin\phi,$$

$$\frac{\partial y'}{\partial\theta}=a\cos\theta\sin\phi-\left(\frac{\partial w}{\partial\theta}+u\right)\sin\theta\sin\phi+\frac{\partial v}{\partial\theta}\cos\phi,$$

$$\frac{\partial z'}{\partial\theta}=-a\sin\theta-\left(\frac{\partial w}{\partial\theta}+u\right)\cos\theta,$$

and

$$\frac{\partial x'}{\partial\phi}=-a\sin\theta\sin\phi+\left(\frac{\partial u}{\partial\phi}\cos\theta-v-\frac{\partial w}{\partial\phi}\sin\theta\right)\cos\phi,$$

$$\frac{\partial y'}{\partial\phi}=a\sin\theta\cos\phi+\left(\frac{\partial u}{\partial\phi}\cos\theta-v-\frac{\partial w}{\partial\phi}\sin\theta\right)\sin\phi,$$

$$\frac{\partial z'}{\partial\phi}=-\frac{\partial u}{\partial\phi}\sin\theta-\frac{\partial w}{\partial\phi}\cos\theta.$$

* This result is in accordance with the theorem that a closed surface cannot be bent without stretching. This theorem is due to J. H. Jellett, *Dublin Roy. Irish Acad. Trans.*, vol. 22 (1855).

Hence we have, to the first order in u, v, w,

$$l = -\sin\theta\cos\phi - \frac{1}{a}\left(\frac{\partial w}{\partial\theta} + u\right)\cos\theta\cos\phi + \frac{1}{a}\left(v + \frac{1}{\sin\theta}\frac{\partial w}{\partial\phi}\right)\sin\phi,$$

$$m = -\sin\theta\sin\phi - \frac{1}{a}\left(\frac{\partial w}{\partial\theta} + u\right)\cos\theta\sin\phi - \frac{1}{a}\left(v + \frac{1}{\sin\theta}\frac{\partial w}{\partial\phi}\right)\cos\phi,$$

$$n = -\cos\theta + \frac{1}{a}\left(\frac{\partial w}{\partial\theta} + u\right)\sin\theta.$$

Exactly as in the case of the cylinder, the principal curvatures and the directions of the lines of curvature are determined by the compatible equations

$$\frac{\partial x'}{\partial\theta}\delta\theta + \frac{\partial x'}{\partial\phi}\delta\phi + \rho'\left(\frac{\partial l}{\partial\theta}\delta\theta + \frac{\partial l}{\partial\phi}\delta\phi\right) = 0,$$

$$\cdots\cdots\cdots$$

and we therefore write down the following equations, in which we put for shortness $X = \frac{1}{a}\left(\frac{\partial w}{\partial\theta} + u\right)$, $Y = \frac{1}{a}\left(v + \frac{1}{\sin\theta}\frac{\partial w}{\partial\phi}\right)$,

$$\frac{\partial l}{\partial\theta} = -\left(1 + \frac{\partial X}{\partial\theta}\right)\cos\theta\cos\phi + X\sin\theta\cos\phi + \frac{\partial Y}{\partial\theta}\sin\phi,$$

$$\frac{\partial m}{\partial\theta} = -\left(1 + \frac{\partial X}{\partial\theta}\right)\cos\theta\sin\phi + X\sin\theta\sin\phi - \frac{\partial Y}{\partial\theta}\cos\phi,$$

$$\frac{\partial n}{\partial\theta} = \left(1 + \frac{\partial X}{\partial\theta}\right)\sin\theta + X\cos\theta,$$

and

$$\frac{\partial l}{\partial\phi} = \left(\sin\theta + X\cos\theta + \frac{\partial Y}{\partial\phi}\right)\sin\phi - \left(\frac{\partial X}{\partial\phi}\cos\theta - Y\right)\cos\phi,$$

$$\frac{\partial m}{\partial\phi} = -\left(\sin\theta + X\cos\theta + \frac{\partial Y}{\partial\phi}\right)\cos\phi - \left(\frac{\partial X}{\partial\phi}\cos\theta - Y\right)\sin\phi,$$

$$\frac{\partial n}{\partial\phi} = \sin\theta\frac{\partial X}{\partial\phi}.$$

Our procedure in this case must be a little different from that adopted in the case of the cylinder because, to the first order, the sum and product of the principal curvatures are unaltered by the strain. We therefore begin by finding the equation for $\tan\psi$, or $\sin\theta\delta\phi/\delta\theta$. This equation may be written

$$\left(\frac{\partial x'}{\partial\theta} + \frac{\tan\psi}{\sin\theta}\frac{\partial x'}{\partial\phi}\right)\left(\frac{\partial m}{\partial\theta} + \frac{\tan\psi}{\sin\theta}\frac{\partial m}{\partial\phi}\right) = \left(\frac{\partial y'}{\partial\theta} + \frac{\tan\psi}{\sin\theta}\frac{\partial y'}{\partial\phi}\right)\left(\frac{\partial l}{\partial\theta} + \frac{\tan\psi}{\sin\theta}\frac{\partial l}{\partial\phi}\right),$$

and, by direct substitution of the values written above for $\partial x'/\partial\theta, \ldots$, it is found to be

$$\left(\frac{\partial v}{\partial\theta} - a\frac{\partial Y}{\partial\theta}\right)\cos\theta + \frac{\tan\psi}{\sin\theta}\,a\left(\sin\theta\frac{\partial X}{\partial\theta} - X\cos\theta - \frac{\partial Y}{\partial\phi}\right)\cos\theta$$
$$+\frac{\tan^2\psi}{\sin^2\theta}\left\{a\left(\frac{\partial X}{\partial\phi}\cos\theta - Y\right) - \left(\frac{\partial u}{\partial\phi}\cos\theta - v - \frac{\partial w}{\partial\phi}\sin\theta\right)\right\}\sin\theta = 0.$$

Now we have

$$\frac{\partial v}{\partial \theta} - a\frac{\partial Y}{\partial \theta} = -\frac{\partial}{\partial \theta}\left(\frac{1}{\sin\theta}\frac{\partial w}{\partial \phi}\right),$$

$$a\left(\frac{\partial X}{\partial \phi}\cos\theta - Y\right) - \left(\frac{\partial u}{\partial \phi}\cos\theta - v - \frac{\partial w}{\partial \phi}\sin\theta\right) = \sin\theta\cos\theta\frac{\partial}{\partial \theta}\left(\frac{1}{\sin\theta}\frac{\partial w}{\partial \phi}\right),$$

$$a\left(\sin\theta\frac{\partial X}{\partial \theta} - X\cos\theta - \frac{\partial Y}{\partial \phi}\right) = \sin\theta\left(\frac{\partial^2 w}{\partial \theta^2} + \frac{\partial u}{\partial \theta}\right) - \cos\theta\left(\frac{\partial w}{\partial \theta} + u\right) - \frac{\partial v}{\partial \phi} - \frac{1}{\sin\theta}\frac{\partial^2 w}{\partial \phi^2}$$

$$= \sin\theta\left[\left(\frac{\partial^2 w}{\partial \theta^2} + w\right) - \left(\frac{1}{\sin^2\theta}\frac{\partial^2 w}{\partial \phi^2} + \cot\theta\frac{\partial w}{\partial \theta} + w\right)\right],$$

where, in the last line, use has been made of the equations (12). But, since $w = \partial u/\partial\theta$, and u satisfies the equation obtained by eliminating v from the second and third of (12), viz.:

$$\frac{\partial^2 u}{\partial \phi^2} + \sin^2\theta\frac{\partial^2 u}{\partial \theta^2} - \sin\theta\cos\theta\frac{\partial u}{\partial \theta} + u = 0,$$

it follows that

$$\frac{1}{\sin^2\theta}\frac{\partial^2 w}{\partial \phi^2} + \cot\theta\frac{\partial w}{\partial \theta} + w = \frac{1}{\sin^2\theta}\frac{\partial}{\partial \theta}\left(-\sin^2\theta\frac{\partial^2 u}{\partial \theta^2} + \sin\theta\cos\theta\frac{\partial u}{\partial \theta} - u\right) + \cot\theta\frac{\partial w}{\partial \theta} + w$$

$$= -\frac{\partial^2 w}{\partial \theta^2} - w.$$

Hence the equation for $\tan\psi$ becomes

$$\tan 2\psi = \frac{\partial}{\partial \theta}\left(\frac{1}{\sin\theta}\frac{\partial w}{\partial \phi}\right) \Big/ \left(\frac{\partial^2 w}{\partial \theta^2} + w\right).$$

One of the equations for determining ρ' is

$$\frac{\partial z'}{\partial \theta}\delta\theta + \frac{\partial z'}{\partial \phi}\delta\phi + \rho'\left(\frac{\partial n}{\partial \theta}\delta\theta + \frac{\partial n}{\partial \phi}\delta\phi\right) = 0,$$

or

$$\frac{a}{\rho'} = \frac{\left(1 + \dfrac{\partial X}{\partial \theta}\right)\sin\theta + X\cos\theta + \dfrac{\partial X}{\partial \phi}\tan\psi}{\sin\theta + X\cos\theta + \dfrac{1}{a}\left(\dfrac{\partial u}{\partial \phi} + \cot\theta\dfrac{\partial w}{\partial \phi}\right)\tan\psi}$$

$$= 1 + \frac{\partial X}{\partial \theta} + \frac{\tan\psi}{\sin\theta}\left\{\frac{\partial X}{\partial \phi} - \frac{1}{a}\left(\frac{\partial u}{\partial \phi} + \cot\theta\frac{\partial w}{\partial \phi}\right)\right\}$$

$$= 1 + \frac{1}{a}\left(\frac{\partial^2 w}{\partial \theta^2} + w\right) + \frac{\tan\psi}{a}\frac{\partial}{\partial \theta}\left(\frac{1}{\sin\theta}\frac{\partial w}{\partial \phi}\right)$$

$$= 1 + \frac{1}{a}\left(\frac{\partial^2 w}{\partial \theta^2} + w\right)\sec 2\psi.$$

But, using the notation of Article 316, we have

$$\frac{1}{\rho'} - \frac{1}{a} = \kappa_1\cos^2\psi + \kappa_2\sin^2\psi + \tau\sin 2\psi$$

$$= \kappa_1(\cos 2\psi + \sin 2\psi\tan 2\psi)$$

$$= \kappa_1\sec 2\psi.$$

It follows that

$$\kappa_1 = \frac{1}{a^2}\left(\frac{\partial^2 w}{\partial \theta^2} + w\right), \quad \tau = \frac{1}{a^2}\frac{\partial}{\partial \theta}\left(\frac{1}{\sin\theta}\frac{\partial w}{\partial \phi}\right). \quad \text{............(14)}$$

With the values of u, v, w given in (13) we now find

$$\left.\begin{aligned} \kappa_1 = -\kappa_2 = \Sigma \frac{n^3 - n}{a^2 \sin^2\theta}\left[A_n \tan^n \frac{\theta}{2}\cos(n\phi + \alpha_n) - B_n \cot^n \frac{\theta}{2}\cos(n\phi + \beta_n)\right], \\ \tau = -\Sigma \frac{n^3 - n}{a^2 \sin^2\theta}\left[A_n \tan^n \frac{\theta}{2}\sin(n\phi + \alpha_n) + B_n \cot^n \frac{\theta}{2}\sin(n\phi + \beta_n)\right]. \end{aligned}\right\} \quad \text{.........(15)}$$

321. Inextensional vibrations.

If we assume that the state of strain in a vibrating shell is that which has been described in Article 317 as the typical flexural strain, we may calculate the frequency of vibration by forming expressions for the kinetic and potential energies*. We illustrate this method in the cases of cylindrical and spherical shells.

(i) *Cylindrical shells.*

The kinetic energy, estimated per unit of area of the middle surface, is

$$\rho h \left[\left(\frac{\partial u}{\partial t}\right)^2 + \left(\frac{\partial v}{\partial t}\right)^2 + \left(\frac{\partial w}{\partial t}\right)^2\right],$$

where ρ is the density of the material, and u, v, w are given by (8), in which the coefficients A_n, B_n are to be regarded as functions of t. The kinetic energy T of the vibrating shell is obtained by integrating this expression over the area of the middle surface. If the ends of the shell are given by $x = \pm l$, we find

$$T = 2\pi\rho a l h \Sigma \left[(1 + n^2)\left(\frac{dA_n}{dt}\right)^2 + \left\{\frac{a^2}{n^2} + \tfrac{1}{3}(1 + n^2) l^2\right\}\left(\frac{dB_n}{dt}\right)^2\right] \text{....(16)}$$

The potential energy of bending, estimated per unit of area of the middle surface, is

$$\tfrac{1}{2} D [\kappa_2^2 + 2(1 - \sigma)\tau^2],$$

where κ_2 and τ are given by (11). The potential energy V of the vibrating shell is obtained by integrating this expression over the area of the middle surface. We find

$$V = D\pi l \Sigma \frac{(n^2 - 1)^2}{a^3}[n^2 A_n^2 + \{\tfrac{1}{3} n^2 l^2 + 2(1 - \sigma) a^2\} B_n^2]. \quad \text{......(17)}$$

The coefficients A_n, B_n in the expressions (8) for the displacement may be regarded as generalized coordinates, and the expressions for T and V show that they are "principal coordinates," so that the various modes of vibration specified by different A's or B's are executed independently of each other.

* The theory of inextensional vibrations is due to Lord Rayleigh, *London Math. Soc. Proc.*, vol. 13 (1881), or *Scientific Papers*, vol. 1, p. 551, and *London Roy. Soc. Proc.*, vol. 45 (1889), p. 105, or *Scientific Papers*, vol. 3, p. 217. See also *Theory of Sound*, second edition, vol. 1, Chapter X A. A discussion of the conditions for the existence of practically inextensional modes of vibration will be given in Chapter XXIV *infra*.

The vibrations in which all the B's and all but one of the A's vanish are two-dimensional and take place in planes at right angles to the axis of the cylinder. The type is expressed by the equations

$$u = 0, \quad v = A_n \cos n\phi, \quad w = -nA_n \sin n\phi,$$

in which A_n is proportional to a simple harmonic function of the time with a period $2\pi/p$, and p is given by the equation

$$p^2 = \frac{D}{2\rho h a^4} \frac{n^2(n^2-1)^2}{n^2+1} = \frac{Eh^2}{3\rho(1-\sigma^2)a^4} \frac{n^2(n^2-1)^2}{n^2+1}. \quad \text{.........(18)}$$

The vibrations in which all the A's and all but one of the B's vanish are three-dimensional. The type is expressed by the equations

$$u = -\frac{a}{n} B_n \sin n\phi, \quad v = xB_n \cos n\phi, \quad w = -nxB_n \sin n\phi,$$

and the frequency $p/2\pi$ is given by the equation

$$p^2 = \frac{Eh^2}{3\rho(1-\sigma^2)a^4} \frac{n^2(n^2-1)^2}{n^2+1} \frac{1+6(1-\sigma)a^2/n^2l^2}{1+3a^2/n^2(n^2+1)l^2}. \quad \text{.........(19)}$$

If either n or l/a is at all large the two values of p belonging to the same value of n are nearly equal.

(ii) *Spherical shell.*

We shall suppose the middle surface to be bounded by a circle of latitude $\theta = \alpha$, and that the pole $\theta = 0$ is included. Then in (13) and (15) the coefficients B_n vanish. The kinetic energy T is given by the equation

$$T = \pi\rho a^2 h \Sigma \left[\left(\frac{dA_n}{dt}\right)^2 \int_0^\alpha \sin\theta \{2\sin^2\theta + (\cos\theta + n)^2\} \tan^{2n}\frac{\theta}{2}\, d\theta\right] \text{....(20)}$$

The potential energy of bending, estimated per unit of area of the middle surface, is $\frac{4}{3}\mu h^3 (\kappa_1^2 + \tau^2)$, where κ_1 and τ are given by (15) with the B's omitted. Hence the potential energy V of the vibrating shell is given by the equation

$$V = \tfrac{8}{3}\pi\mu \frac{h^3}{a^2} \Sigma \left[n^2(n^2-1)^2 A_n^2 \int_0^\alpha \tan^{2n}\frac{\theta}{2} \frac{d\theta}{\sin^3\theta}\right]. \quad \text{.........(21)}$$

The coefficients A_n in the expressions for the components of displacement can be regarded as "principal coordinates"* and the frequency can be written down.

In a principal mode the type of vibration is expressed by the equations

$$u = A_n \sin\theta \tan^n\frac{\theta}{2} \cos n\phi, \quad v = A_n \sin\theta \tan^n\frac{\theta}{2} \sin n\phi,$$

$$w = A_n(n + \cos\theta)\tan^n\frac{\theta}{2} \cos n\phi,$$

* When the edge-line consists of two circles of latitude, so that the coefficients B occur as well as the coefficients A, the A's and B's are not principal coordinates, for terms containing such products as $(dA_n/dt).(dB_n/dt)$ occur in the expression for T. See Lord Rayleigh, *Theory of Sound*, second edition, vol. 1, Chapter X A.

in which A_n is proportional to a simple harmonic function of the time. The frequency $p_n/2\pi$ is given by the equation

$$p_n^2 = \tfrac{8}{3}\frac{\mu}{\rho}\frac{h^2}{a^4} n^2 (n^2-1)^2$$
$$\times \left(\int_0^\alpha \tan^{2n}\frac{\theta}{2}\frac{d\theta}{\sin^3\theta}\right) \Big/ \left(\int_0^\alpha \sin\theta\{2\sin^2\theta + (\cos\theta+n)^2\}\tan^{2n}\frac{\theta}{2}\,d\theta\right)$$

In this expression n may be any integer greater than unity.

The integrations can always be performed. We have

$$\int_0^\alpha \tan^{2n}\frac{\theta}{2}\frac{d\theta}{\sin^3\theta} = \tfrac{1}{8}\left[\frac{\tan^{2n-2}\frac{\alpha}{2}}{n-1} + 2\frac{\tan^{2n}\frac{\alpha}{2}}{n} + \frac{\tan^{2n+2}\frac{\alpha}{2}}{n+1}\right],$$

$$\int_0^\alpha \sin\theta\{2\sin^2\theta + (\cos\theta+n)^2\}\tan^{2n}\frac{\theta}{2}\,d\theta = \int_{1+\cos\alpha}^{2} \frac{(2-x)^n}{x^n}\left[(n-1)^2 + 2(n+1)x - x^2\right]dx,$$

and the second of these can be evaluated for any integral value of n. In the case of a hemisphere ($\alpha = \frac{1}{2}\pi$) Lord Rayleigh (*loc. cit.*) finds the frequencies p_2, p_3, p_4 for $n=2, 3, 4$ to be given by

$$p_2 = \frac{h}{a^2}\sqrt{\left(\frac{2}{3}\frac{\mu}{\rho}\right)}(5{\cdot}240),\quad p_3 = \frac{h}{a^2}\sqrt{\left(\frac{2}{3}\frac{\mu}{\rho}\right)}(14{\cdot}726),\quad p_4 = \frac{h}{a^2}\sqrt{\left(\frac{2}{3}\frac{\mu}{\rho}\right)}(28{\cdot}462).$$

In the case of a saucer of 120° ($\alpha = \frac{1}{3}\pi$) he finds

$$p_2 = \frac{h}{a^2}\sqrt{\left(\frac{2}{3}\frac{\mu}{\rho}\right)}(7{\cdot}9947),\quad p_3 = \frac{h}{a^2}\sqrt{\left(\frac{2}{3}\frac{\mu}{\rho}\right)}(20{\cdot}911)$$

In the case of a very small aperture in a nearly complete sphere ($\alpha = \pi$ nearly) the frequency calculated from the above formula* is given approximately by

$$p_n^2 = \frac{h^2}{a^4}\frac{8}{3}\frac{\mu}{\rho}\frac{n^2(n^2-1)}{(\pi-\alpha)^4}.$$

* Cf. H. Lamb, *loc. cit.*, p. 505.

CHAPTER XXIV

GENERAL THEORY OF THIN PLATES AND SHELLS

322. Formulæ relating to the curvature of surfaces.

For the investigations in the last Chapter the elements of the theory of the curvature of surfaces are adequate. For the purpose of developing a more general method of treatment of the problem of curved plates or shells we shall require some further results of this theory. It seems best to begin by obtaining these results.

Let α, β denote any two parameters by means of which the position of a point on a surface can be expressed, so that the equations $\alpha = \text{const.}$, $\beta = \text{const.}$, represent families of curves traced on the surface. Let χ be the angle between the tangents of these curves at any point; χ is in general a function of α and β. The linear element ds of any curve traced on the surface is given by the formula

$$(ds)^2 = A^2 (d\alpha)^2 + B^2 (d\beta)^2 + 2AB \cos \chi \, d\alpha \, d\beta, \qquad \text{...............(1)}$$

where A and B are, in general, functions of α, β. Let a right-handed system of moving axes of x, y, z be constructed so that the origin is at a point (α, β) of the surface, the axis of z is the normal to the surface at the origin, drawn in a chosen sense, the axis of x is the tangent to the curve $\beta = \text{const.}$ which passes through the origin, drawn in the sense of increase of α, and the axis of y is tangential to the surface, and at right angles to the axis of x*. When the origin of this triad of axes moves over the surface the directions of the axes change. If t represents the time, the components of velocity of the origin are

$$A\frac{d\alpha}{dt} + B\frac{d\beta}{dt}\cos\chi, \quad B\frac{d\beta}{dt}\sin\chi, \quad 0,$$

parallel to the instantaneous positions of the axes of x, y, z. The components of the angular velocity of the system of axes, referred to these same directions, can be expressed in the forms

$$p_1\frac{d\alpha}{dt} + p_2\frac{d\beta}{dt}, \quad q_1\frac{d\alpha}{dt} + q_2\frac{d\beta}{dt}, \quad r_1\frac{d\alpha}{dt} + r_2\frac{d\beta}{dt},$$

in which the quantities $p_1, \ldots$ are functions of α and β.

The quantities $p_1, \ldots$ are connected with each other and with A, B, χ by the systems of equations (2) and (3) below. These results may be obtained as follows:

* When the curves $\alpha = \text{const.}$ and $\beta = \text{const.}$ cut at right angles we suppose that the parameters α and β, and the positive sense of the normal to the surface, are so chosen that the directions in which α and β increase and this normal are the directions of a right-handed system of axes.

Let x, y, z denote the coordinates of a fixed point referred to the moving axes. Then x, y, z are functions of a and β, and the conditions that the point remains fixed while the axes move are the three equations

$$\frac{\partial x}{\partial a}\frac{da}{dt}+\frac{\partial x}{\partial \beta}\frac{d\beta}{dt}-y\left(r_1\frac{da}{dt}+r_2\frac{d\beta}{dt}\right)+z\left(q_1\frac{da}{dt}+q_2\frac{d\beta}{dt}\right)+A\frac{da}{dt}+B\frac{d\beta}{dt}\cos\chi=0,$$

$$\frac{\partial y}{\partial a}\frac{da}{dt}+\frac{\partial y}{\partial \beta}\frac{d\beta}{dt}-z\left(p_1\frac{da}{dt}+p_2\frac{d\beta}{dt}\right)+x\left(r_1\frac{da}{dt}+r_2\frac{d\beta}{dt}\right)+B\frac{d\beta}{dt}\sin\chi=0,$$

$$\frac{\partial z}{\partial a}\frac{da}{dt}+\frac{\partial z}{\partial \beta}\frac{d\beta}{dt}-x\left(q_1\frac{da}{dt}+q_2\frac{d\beta}{dt}\right)+y\left(p_1\frac{da}{dt}+p_2\frac{d\beta}{dt}\right)=0.$$

Since these hold for all values of da/dt and $d\beta/dt$, we have the six equations

$$\frac{\partial x}{\partial a}=-A+r_1y-q_1z,\qquad \frac{\partial y}{\partial a}=p_1z-r_1x,\qquad \frac{\partial z}{\partial a}=q_1x-p_1y,$$

$$\frac{\partial x}{\partial \beta}=-B\cos\chi+r_2y-q_2z,\quad \frac{\partial y}{\partial \beta}=-B\sin\chi+p_2z-r_2x,\quad \frac{\partial z}{\partial \beta}=q_2x-p_2y.$$

The conditions of compatibility of these equations are three equations of the form $\frac{\partial}{\partial\beta}\left(\frac{\partial x}{\partial a}\right)=\frac{\partial}{\partial a}\left(\frac{\partial x}{\partial \beta}\right)$; and, in forming the differential coefficients, we may use the above expressions for $\partial x/\partial a$, ... The results must hold for all values of x, y, z.

The process just sketched leads to the equations*

$$\left.\begin{aligned}\frac{\partial p_1}{\partial\beta}-\frac{\partial p_2}{\partial\alpha}&=q_1r_2-q_2r_1,\\ \frac{\partial q_1}{\partial\beta}-\frac{\partial q_2}{\partial\alpha}&=r_1p_2-r_2p_1,\\ \frac{\partial r_1}{\partial\beta}-\frac{\partial r_2}{\partial\alpha}&=p_1q_2-p_2q_1,\end{aligned}\right\}\quad\text{......................(2)}$$

and

$$\left.\begin{aligned}r_1&=-\frac{\partial\chi}{\partial\alpha}-\frac{1}{B\sin\chi}\left(\frac{\partial A}{\partial\beta}-\cos\chi\frac{\partial B}{\partial\alpha}\right),\\ r_2&=\frac{1}{A\sin\chi}\left(\frac{\partial B}{\partial\alpha}-\cos\chi\frac{\partial A}{\partial\beta}\right),\\ \frac{q_2}{B}+\frac{p_1}{A}\sin\chi&=\frac{q_1}{A}\cos\chi.\end{aligned}\right\}\quad\text{...............(3)}$$

To express the curvature of the surface we form the equations of the normal at $(\alpha+\delta\alpha,\ \beta+\delta\beta)$ referred to the axes of x, y, z at (α, β). The direction-cosines of the normal are, with sufficient approximation, $(q_1\delta\alpha+q_2\delta\beta)$, $-(p_1\delta\alpha+p_2\delta\beta)$, 1, and the equations are

$$\frac{x-(A\delta\alpha+B\delta\beta\cos\chi)}{(q_1\delta\alpha+q_2\delta\beta)}=\frac{y-B\delta\beta\sin\chi}{-(p_1\delta\alpha+p_2\delta\beta)}=z.$$

It follows that the lines of curvature are given by the differential equation

$$Ap_1(d\alpha)^2+B(p_2\cos\chi+q_2\sin\chi)(d\beta)^2+\{Ap_2+B(p_1\cos\chi+q_1\sin\chi)\}\,d\alpha d\beta=0,$$

.........(4)

* The sets of equations (2) and (3) were obtained by D. Codazzi, *Paris, Mém...par divers savants*, t. 27 (1882).

and that the principal radii of curvature are the roots of the equation

$$R^2(p_1q_2-p_2q_1)-R\{Ap_2-B(p_1\cos\chi+q_1\sin\chi)\}+AB\sin\chi=0. \quad\ldots(5)$$

From these results the equation of the indicatrix of the surface is easily found to be

$$-\frac{q_1}{A}x^2+\left(\frac{p_2}{B\sin\chi}-\frac{p_1}{A}\cot\chi\right)y^2+2\frac{p_1}{A}xy=\text{const.} \quad\ldots\ldots\ldots(6)$$

The measure of curvature is given by (5) and the third of (2) in the form

$$\frac{1}{AB\sin\chi}\left(\frac{\partial r_1}{\partial\beta}-\frac{\partial r_2}{\partial\alpha}\right).$$

323. Simplified formulæ relating to the curvature of surfaces.

When the curves $\alpha=$ const. and $\beta=$ const. are lines of curvature on the surface the formulæ are simplified very much. In this case the axes of x and y are the principal tangents at a point, the axis of z being the normal at the point. We have

$$\chi=\tfrac{1}{2}\pi,\quad p_1=0,\quad q_2=0, \quad\ldots\ldots\ldots\ldots\ldots\ldots\ldots\ldots(7)$$

and the roots of equation (5) are $-A/q_1$ and B/p_2. We shall write

$$\frac{1}{R_1}=-\frac{q_1}{A},\quad \frac{1}{R_2}=\frac{p_2}{B}, \quad\ldots\ldots\ldots\ldots\ldots\ldots\ldots\ldots(8)$$

so that R_1, R_2 are the radii of curvature of normal sections of the surface drawn through those tangent lines which are axes of x, y at any point. We have also

$$\left.\begin{aligned} r_1&=-\frac{1}{B}\frac{\partial A}{\partial\beta},\quad r_2=\frac{1}{A}\frac{\partial B}{\partial\alpha},\\ \frac{AB}{R_1R_2}&=-\frac{\partial}{\partial\alpha}\left(\frac{1}{A}\frac{\partial B}{\partial\alpha}\right)-\frac{\partial}{\partial\beta}\left(\frac{1}{B}\frac{\partial A}{\partial\beta}\right),\end{aligned}\right\} \quad\ldots\ldots\ldots\ldots(9)$$

and

$$\frac{\partial}{\partial\alpha}\left(\frac{B}{R_2}\right)=\frac{1}{R_1}\frac{\partial B}{\partial\alpha},\quad \frac{\partial}{\partial\beta}\left(\frac{A}{R_1}\right)=\frac{1}{R_2}\frac{\partial A}{\partial\beta}. \quad\ldots\ldots\ldots\ldots(10)$$

324. Extension and curvature of the middle surface of a plate or shell.

In general we shall regard the middle surface in the unstressed state as a curved surface, and take the curves $\alpha=$ const. and $\beta=$ const. to be the lines of curvature. In the case of a plane plate α and β may be ordinary Cartesian coordinates, or they may be curvilinear orthogonal coordinates. In the case of a sphere α and β could be taken to be ordinary spherical polar coordinates. Equations (7)—(10) hold in the unstressed state. When the plate is deformed the curves that were lines of curvature become two families of curves, traced on the strained middle surface, which cut each other at an angle that may differ slightly from a right angle. We denote the angle by χ and its cosine by ϖ, and we denote by ϵ_1 and ϵ_2 the extensions of linear elements which, in the unstressed state, lie along the curves $\beta=$ const. and

$\alpha = \text{const.}$ The quantities α and β may be regarded as parameters which determine a point of the strained middle surface, and the formula for the linear element is

$$(ds)^2 = A^2(1+\epsilon_1)^2(d\alpha)^2 + B^2(1+\epsilon_2)^2(d\beta)^2 + 2AB(1+\epsilon_1)(1+\epsilon_2)\varpi\, d\alpha\, d\beta.$$

As in Article 322, we may construct a system of moving orthogonal axes of x, y, z with the origin on the strained middle surface, the axis of z along the normal at the origin to this surface, and the axis of x along the tangent at the origin to a curve $\beta = \text{const.}$ The components of velocity of the origin parallel to the instantaneous positions of the axes of x and y are

$$A(1+\epsilon_1)\frac{d\alpha}{dt} + B(1+\epsilon_2)\varpi\frac{d\beta}{dt}, \quad B(1+\epsilon_2)\sin\chi\frac{d\beta}{dt}.$$

The components of angular velocity of the triad of axes referred to these same directions will be denoted by

$$p_1'\frac{d\alpha}{dt} + p_2'\frac{d\beta}{dt}, \quad q_1'\frac{d\alpha}{dt} + q_2'\frac{d\beta}{dt}, \quad r_1'\frac{d\alpha}{dt} + r_2'\frac{d\beta}{dt}.$$

Then in equations (2) and (3) we must replace A by $A(1+\epsilon_1)$, B by $B(1+\epsilon_2)$, $p_1, p_2, \ldots r_2$ by $p_1', p_2', \ldots r_2'$. The directions of the lines of curvature of the strained middle surface, the values of the sum and product of the principal curvatures, and the equation of the indicatrix are found by making similar changes in the formulæ (4)—(6).

If we retain first powers only of ϵ_1, ϵ_2, ϖ, equations (3) give

$$\left.\begin{aligned} r_1' &= -\frac{1}{B}\frac{\partial A}{\partial \beta} + \frac{\partial \varpi}{\partial \alpha} + \frac{\varpi}{B}\frac{\partial B}{\partial \alpha} + \frac{\epsilon_2}{B}\frac{\partial A}{\partial \beta} - \frac{A}{B}\frac{\partial \epsilon_1}{\partial \beta},\\ r_2' &= \frac{1}{A}\frac{\partial B}{\partial \alpha} - \frac{\varpi}{A}\frac{\partial A}{\partial \beta} - \frac{\epsilon_1}{A}\frac{\partial B}{\partial \alpha} + \frac{B}{A}\frac{\partial \epsilon_2}{\partial \alpha},\\ \frac{q_2'}{B} + \frac{p_1'}{A} &= \varpi\frac{q_1'}{A} + \epsilon_1\frac{p_1'}{A} + \epsilon_2\frac{q_2'}{B}. \end{aligned}\right\} \quad \ldots\ldots\ldots\ldots(11)$$

The indicatrix of the strained middle surface is given, to the same order of approximation, by the formula

$$-\frac{q_1'}{A}(1-\epsilon_1)x^2 + \left\{\frac{p_2'}{B}(1-\epsilon_2) - \frac{p_1'}{A}\varpi\right\}y^2 + 2\frac{p_1'}{A}(1-\epsilon_1)xy = \text{const.}$$

If R_1', R_2' denote the radii of curvature of normal sections of the strained middle surface drawn through the axes of x and y at any point, and ψ the angle which one of the lines of curvature of this surface drawn through the point makes with the axis of x at the point, we have, to the same order,

$$\left.\begin{aligned} &\frac{1}{R_1'} = -\frac{q_1'}{A}(1-\epsilon_1), \quad \frac{1}{R_2'} = \frac{p_2'}{B}(1-\epsilon_2) - \frac{p_1'}{A}\varpi,\\ &\tan 2\psi = -\frac{2p_1'}{A}(1-\epsilon_1)\Big/\left[\frac{q_1'}{A}(1-\epsilon_1) + \frac{p_2'}{B}(1-\epsilon_2) - \frac{p_1'}{A}\varpi\right]. \end{aligned}\right\} \ldots(12)$$

It is clear from these formulæ that, when the extension is known, the state of the strained middle surface as regards curvature is defined by the quantities

$$-q_1'/A,\quad p_2'/B,\quad p_1'/A.$$

We shall write $$-\frac{q_1'}{A}-\frac{1}{R_1}=\kappa_1,\quad \frac{p_2'}{B}-\frac{1}{R_2}=\kappa_2,\quad \frac{p_1'}{A}=\tau \quad\text{..............(13)}$$

and shall refer to κ_1, κ_2, τ as the "changes of curvature." In the particular cases of a plane plate which becomes slightly bent, and a shell which undergoes a small inextensional displacement, these quantities become identical with those which were denoted by the same letters in Chapters XXII and XXIII.

The measure of curvature is given by the formula

$$\frac{1-\epsilon_1-\epsilon_2}{AB}\left(\frac{\partial r_1'}{\partial \beta}-\frac{\partial r_2'}{\partial \alpha}\right),$$

where r_1', r_2' are given by the first two of (11). When there is no extension the values of r_1', r_2' for the deformed surface are identical with those of r_1, r_2 for the unstrained surface, and the measure of curvature is unaltered by the strain (Gauss's theorem). The sum of the principal curvatures, being equal to $1/R_1'+1/R_2'$, can be found from the formulæ (12).

325. Method of calculating the extension and the changes of curvature.

To calculate $\epsilon_1, \ldots p_1', \ldots$ in terms of the coordinates of a point on the strained middle surface, or of the displacement of a point on the unstrained middle surface, we introduce a scheme of nine direction-cosines expressing the directions of the moving axes of x, y, z at any point relative to fixed axes of x, y, z. Let the scheme be

	x	y	z
x	l_1	m_1	n_1
y	l_2	m_2	n_2
z	l_3	m_3	n_3

. ...(14)

If now x, y, z denote the coordinates of a point on the strained middle surface, the direction-cosines l_1, m_1, n_1 of the tangent to the curve $\beta=$ const. which passes through the point are given by the equations

$$A(1+\epsilon_1)\,l_1=\frac{\partial \mathrm{x}}{\partial \alpha},\quad A(1+\epsilon_1)\,m_1=\frac{\partial \mathrm{y}}{\partial \alpha},\quad A(1+\epsilon_1)\,n_1=\frac{\partial \mathrm{z}}{\partial \alpha}\text{....(15)}$$

The direction-cosines of the tangent to the curve $\alpha=$ const. which passes through the point are $l_2\sin\chi+l_1\cos\chi, \ldots$, and therefore, when ϖ^2 and $\varpi\epsilon_2$ are neglected, l_2, m_2, n_2 are given by the equations

$$B\{(1+\epsilon_2)\,l_2+\varpi l_1\}=\frac{\partial \mathrm{x}}{\partial \beta},\quad B\{(1+\epsilon_2)\,m_2+\varpi m_1\}=\frac{\partial \mathrm{y}}{\partial \beta},$$

$$B\{(1+\epsilon_2)\,n_2+\varpi n_1\}=\frac{\partial \mathrm{z}}{\partial \beta}.\quad\text{....................(16)}$$

The direction-cosines l_3, m_3, n_3 of the normal to the strained middle surface are given by the equations

$$l_3 = m_1 n_2 - m_2 n_1, \quad m_3 = n_1 l_2 - n_2 l_1, \quad n_3 = l_1 m_2 - l_2 m_1. \qquad \text{......(17)}$$

From equations (15) and (16) we find, correctly to the first order in ϵ_1, ϵ_2, ϖ,

$$\left.\begin{aligned} 1 + 2\epsilon_1 &= \frac{1}{A^2}\left\{\left(\frac{\partial \mathrm{x}}{\partial \alpha}\right)^2 + \left(\frac{\partial \mathrm{y}}{\partial \alpha}\right)^2 + \left(\frac{\partial \mathrm{z}}{\partial \alpha}\right)^2\right\}, \\ 1 + 2\epsilon_2 &= \frac{1}{B^2}\left\{\left(\frac{\partial \mathrm{x}}{\partial \beta}\right)^2 + \left(\frac{\partial \mathrm{y}}{\partial \beta}\right)^2 + \left(\frac{\partial \mathrm{z}}{\partial \beta}\right)^2\right\}, \\ \varpi &= \frac{1}{AB}\left\{\frac{\partial \mathrm{x}}{\partial \alpha}\frac{\partial \mathrm{x}}{\partial \beta} + \frac{\partial \mathrm{y}}{\partial \alpha}\frac{\partial \mathrm{y}}{\partial \beta} + \frac{\partial \mathrm{z}}{\partial \alpha}\frac{\partial \mathrm{z}}{\partial \beta}\right\}. \end{aligned}\right\} \qquad \text{............(18)}$$

Again, since the line whose direction-cosines referred to the moving axes are l_1, l_2, l_3, that is the axis of x, is fixed relatively to the fixed axes, the ordinary formulæ connected with moving axes give us three equations of the type

$$\frac{\partial l_1}{\partial \alpha}\frac{d\alpha}{dt} + \frac{\partial l_1}{\partial \beta}\frac{d\beta}{dt} - l_2\left(r_1'\frac{d\alpha}{dt} + r_2'\frac{d\beta}{dt}\right) + l_3\left(q_1'\frac{d\alpha}{dt} + q_2'\frac{d\beta}{dt}\right) = 0;$$

and, by expressing the fixity of the axes of y and z, we obtain two other such sets of equations. From these we find the formulæ

$$\left.\begin{aligned} p_1' &= l_3\frac{\partial l_2}{\partial \alpha} + m_3\frac{\partial m_2}{\partial \alpha} + n_3\frac{\partial n_2}{\partial \alpha}, \quad & p_2' &= l_3\frac{\partial l_2}{\partial \beta} + m_3\frac{\partial m_2}{\partial \beta} + n_3\frac{\partial n_2}{\partial \beta}, \\ q_1' &= l_1\frac{\partial l_3}{\partial \alpha} + m_1\frac{\partial m_3}{\partial \alpha} + n_1\frac{\partial n_3}{\partial \alpha}, \quad & q_2' &= l_1\frac{\partial l_3}{\partial \beta} + m_1\frac{\partial m_3}{\partial \beta} + n_1\frac{\partial n_3}{\partial \beta}, \\ r_1' &= l_2\frac{\partial l_1}{\partial \alpha} + m_2\frac{\partial m_1}{\partial \alpha} + n_2\frac{\partial n_1}{\partial \alpha}, \quad & r_2' &= l_2\frac{\partial l_1}{\partial \beta} + m_2\frac{\partial m_1}{\partial \beta} + n_2\frac{\partial n_1}{\partial \beta}. \end{aligned}\right\} \quad \text{...(19)}$$

The formulæ (18) enable us to calculate ϵ_1, ϵ_2, ϖ, and the formulæ (19) give us the means of calculating p_1', ...

326. Formulæ relating to small displacements.

Let u, v, w denote the components of displacement of any point on the unstrained middle surface referred to the tangents at the point to the curves β = const. and α = const. and the normal at the point to the surface. We wish to calculate the extension and the changes of curvature in terms of u, v, w and their differential coefficients with respect to α and β.

(a) *The extension.*

According to the formulæ (18) we require expressions for $\partial \mathrm{x}/\partial \alpha$, ... where x, y, z are the coordinates of a point on the strained middle surface referred to fixed axes. We shall choose as these fixed axes the lines of reference for u, v, w at a particular point on the unstrained middle surface, and obtain the required expressions by an application of the method of moving axes.

Let $P(\alpha, \beta)$ be the chosen point on the unstrained middle surface, $P'(\alpha+\delta\alpha, \beta+\delta\beta)$ a neighbouring point on this surface. The lines of reference for u, v, w are a triad of moving axes, and the position of these axes when the origin is at P' is to be obtained from the position when the origin is at P by a small translation and a small rotation. The components of the translation, referred to the axes at P, are $A\delta\alpha$, $B\delta\beta$, 0. The components of the rotation, referred to the same axes, are given by the results in Article 323 in the forms

$$\frac{B\delta\beta}{R_2}, \qquad -\frac{A\delta\alpha}{R_1}, \qquad -\frac{\partial A}{\partial\beta}\frac{\delta\alpha}{B}+\frac{\partial B}{\partial\alpha}\frac{\delta\beta}{A}.$$

When P is displaced to P_1 and P' to P_1', the x, y, z of P_1 are the same as the u, v, w of P; the x, y, z of P_1' are

$$\mathrm{x}+(\partial \mathrm{x}/\partial\alpha)\,\delta\alpha+(\partial \mathrm{x}/\partial\beta)\,\delta\beta, \ldots,$$

and the u, v, w of P' are

$$u+(\partial u/\partial\alpha)\,\delta\alpha+(\partial u/\partial\beta)\,\delta\beta, \ldots.$$

These quantities are connected by the ordinary formulæ relating to moving axes, viz.:

$$\frac{\partial \mathrm{x}}{\partial\alpha}\delta\alpha+\frac{\partial \mathrm{x}}{\partial\beta}\delta\beta=A\delta\alpha+\left(\frac{\partial u}{\partial\alpha}\delta\alpha+\frac{\partial u}{\partial\beta}\delta\beta\right)-v\left(-\frac{\partial A}{\partial\beta}\frac{\delta\alpha}{B}+\frac{\partial B}{\partial\alpha}\frac{\delta\beta}{A}\right)+w\left(-\frac{A\delta\alpha}{R_1}\right),$$

$$\frac{\partial \mathrm{y}}{\partial\alpha}\delta\alpha+\frac{\partial \mathrm{y}}{\partial\beta}\delta\beta=B\delta\beta+\left(\frac{\partial v}{\partial\alpha}\delta\alpha+\frac{\partial v}{\partial\beta}\delta\beta\right)-w\frac{B\delta\beta}{R_2}+u\left(-\frac{\partial A}{\partial\beta}\frac{\delta\alpha}{B}+\frac{\partial B}{\partial\alpha}\frac{\delta\beta}{A}\right),$$

$$\frac{\partial \mathrm{z}}{\partial\alpha}\delta\alpha+\frac{\partial \mathrm{z}}{\partial\beta}\delta\beta=\left(\frac{\partial w}{\partial\alpha}\delta\alpha+\frac{\partial w}{\partial\beta}\delta\beta\right)-u\left(-\frac{A\delta\alpha}{R_1}\right)+v\frac{B\delta\beta}{R_2};$$

and in these formulæ we may equate coefficients of $\delta\alpha$ and $\delta\beta$.

The above process leads to the following expressions for $\partial\mathrm{x}/\partial\alpha, \ldots$:

$$\left.\begin{aligned}\frac{\partial \mathrm{x}}{\partial\alpha}&=A+\frac{\partial u}{\partial\alpha}+\frac{v}{B}\frac{\partial A}{\partial\beta}-\frac{Aw}{R_1}, & \frac{\partial \mathrm{y}}{\partial\alpha}&=\frac{\partial v}{\partial\alpha}-\frac{u}{B}\frac{\partial A}{\partial\beta}, & \frac{\partial \mathrm{z}}{\partial\alpha}&=\frac{\partial w}{\partial\alpha}+\frac{Au}{R_1},\\ \frac{\partial \mathrm{x}}{\partial\beta}&=\frac{\partial u}{\partial\beta}-\frac{v}{A}\frac{\partial B}{\partial\alpha}, & \frac{\partial \mathrm{y}}{\partial\beta}&=B+\frac{\partial v}{\partial\beta}+\frac{u}{A}\frac{\partial B}{\partial\alpha}-\frac{Bw}{R_2}, & \frac{\partial \mathrm{z}}{\partial\beta}&=\frac{\partial w}{\partial\beta}+\frac{Bv}{R_2}.\end{aligned}\right\} \quad \ldots(20)$$

When products of u, v, w and their differential coefficients are neglected the formulæ (18) and (20) give

$$\left.\begin{aligned}\epsilon_1&=\frac{1}{A}\frac{\partial u}{\partial\alpha}+\frac{v}{AB}\frac{\partial A}{\partial\beta}-\frac{w}{R_1}, \qquad \epsilon_2=\frac{1}{B}\frac{\partial v}{\partial\beta}+\frac{u}{AB}\frac{\partial B}{\partial\alpha}-\frac{w}{R_2},\\ \varpi&=\frac{1}{A}\frac{\partial v}{\partial\alpha}+\frac{1}{B}\frac{\partial u}{\partial\beta}-\frac{u}{AB}\frac{\partial A}{\partial\beta}-\frac{v}{AB}\frac{\partial B}{\partial\alpha}.\end{aligned}\right\} \quad \ldots\ldots(21)$$

These formulæ determine the *extension.*

When the displacement is inextensional u, v, w satisfy the system of partial differential equations obtained from (21) by equating the right-hand members to zero. As we saw in particular cases, in Articles 319 and 320, the assumption that the displacement is inextensional is almost enough to determine the forms of u, v, w as functions of α and β.

(*b*) *The changes of curvature.*

According to the formulæ (19) we require expressions for the direction-cosines $l_1, \ldots$ of the moving axes referred to the fixed axes; we require also expressions for $\partial l_1/\partial\alpha, \ldots$. We shall choose our fixed axes as before to be the lines of reference for u, v, w at one point P of the unstrained middle surface.

By (15), (16), (17), (20), (21) we can write down expressions for the values of $l_1, \dots$ at the corresponding point P_1 of the strained middle surface in the forms

$$\left.\begin{aligned} &l_1=1, \quad m_1=\frac{1}{A}\frac{\partial v}{\partial \alpha}-\frac{u}{AB}\frac{\partial A}{\partial \beta}, \quad n_1=\frac{1}{A}\frac{\partial w}{\partial \alpha}+\frac{u}{R_1},\\ &l_2=-\frac{1}{A}\frac{\partial v}{\partial \alpha}+\frac{u}{AB}\frac{\partial A}{\partial \beta}, \quad m_2=1, \quad n_2=\frac{1}{B}\frac{\partial w}{\partial \beta}+\frac{v}{R_2},\\ &l_3=-\frac{1}{A}\frac{\partial w}{\partial \alpha}-\frac{u}{R_1}, \quad m_3=-\frac{1}{B}\frac{\partial w}{\partial \beta}-\frac{v}{R_2}, \quad n_3=1. \end{aligned}\right\} \quad \dots\dots\dots(22)$$

These are not the general expressions for $l_1, \dots$ at any point. They are expressions for the direction-cosines of the moving axes at a point on the strained middle surface, referred to the lines of reference for u, v, w at the *corresponding point* of the unstrained middle surface. For these latter direction-cosines we may introduce the orthogonal scheme

	u	v	w
x	L_1	M_1	N_1
y	L_2	M_2	N_2
z	L_3	M_3	N_3

Then we have the values

$$\left.\begin{aligned} &L_1=1, \quad M_1=\frac{1}{A}\frac{\partial v}{\partial \alpha}-\frac{u}{AB}\frac{\partial A}{\partial \beta}, \quad N_1=\frac{1}{A}\frac{\partial w}{\partial \alpha}+\frac{u}{R_1},\\ &L_2=-\frac{1}{A}\frac{\partial v}{\partial \alpha}+\frac{u}{AB}\frac{\partial A}{\partial \beta}, \quad M_2=1, \quad N_2=\frac{1}{B}\frac{\partial w}{\partial \beta}+\frac{v}{R_2},\\ &L_3=-\frac{1}{A}\frac{\partial w}{\partial \alpha}-\frac{u}{R_1}, \quad M_3=-\frac{1}{B}\frac{\partial w}{\partial \beta}-\frac{v}{R_2}, \quad N_3=1; \end{aligned}\right\} \quad \dots\dots(23)$$

and these hold for all points. We apply the method of moving axes to deduce expressions for $\partial l_1/\partial \alpha, \dots$; and then we form the expressions for $p_1', \dots$ in accordance with (19).

The direction-cosines of the axes of x, y, z at a neighbouring point P_1', referred to the lines of reference for u, v, w at P', would be denoted by $L_1+(\partial L_1/\partial a)\,\delta a+(\partial L_1/\partial \beta)\,\delta\beta, \dots$; the direction-cosines of the axes of x, y, z at P_1', referred to the fixed axes, which are the lines of reference for u, v, w at P, would be denoted by $l_1+(\partial l_1/\partial a)\,\delta a+(\partial l_1/\partial \beta)\,\delta\beta, \dots$. Since the components of the rotation of the lines of reference for u, v, w are

$$\frac{B\delta\beta}{R_2}, \qquad -\frac{A\delta a}{R_1}, \qquad -\frac{\partial A}{\partial \beta}\frac{\delta a}{B}+\frac{\partial B}{\partial a}\frac{\delta\beta}{A},$$

we have the ordinary formulæ connected with moving axes in the forms

$$\frac{\partial l_1}{\partial a}\delta a+\frac{\partial l_1}{\partial \beta}\delta\beta=\left(\frac{\partial L_1}{\partial a}\delta a+\frac{\partial L_1}{\partial \beta}\delta\beta\right)-M_1\left(-\frac{\partial A}{\partial \beta}\frac{\delta a}{B}+\frac{\partial B}{\partial a}\frac{\delta\beta}{A}\right)+N_1\left(-\frac{A\delta a}{R_1}\right),$$

$$\frac{\partial m_1}{\partial a}\delta a+\frac{\partial m_1}{\partial \beta}\delta\beta=\left(\frac{\partial M_1}{\partial a}\delta a+\frac{\partial M_1}{\partial \beta}\delta\beta\right)-N_1\frac{B\delta\beta}{R_2}+L_1\left(-\frac{\partial A}{\partial \beta}\frac{\delta a}{B}+\frac{\partial B}{\partial a}\frac{\delta\beta}{A}\right),$$

$$\frac{\partial n_1}{\partial a}\delta a+\frac{\partial n_1}{\partial \beta}\delta\beta=\left(\frac{\partial N_1}{\partial a}\delta a+\frac{\partial N_1}{\partial \beta}\delta\beta\right)-L_1\left(-\frac{A\delta a}{R_1}\right)+M_1\frac{B\delta\beta}{R_2},$$

with similar formulæ in which the suffix 1 attached to l, m, n and L, M, N is replaced successively by 2 and 3. On substituting for $L_1, \dots$ the values given in (23), we find

$$\frac{\partial l_1}{\partial \alpha}=\frac{1}{AB}\frac{\partial A}{\partial \beta}\left(\frac{\partial v}{\partial \alpha}-\frac{u}{B}\frac{\partial A}{\partial \beta}\right)-\frac{1}{R_1}\left(\frac{\partial w}{\partial \alpha}+\frac{Au}{R_1}\right),$$

$$\frac{\partial l_1}{\partial \beta}=-\frac{1}{A^2}\frac{\partial B}{\partial \alpha}\left(\frac{\partial v}{\partial \alpha}-\frac{u}{B}\frac{\partial A}{\partial \beta}\right),$$

$$\frac{\partial m_1}{\partial \alpha}=\frac{\partial}{\partial \alpha}\left(\frac{1}{A}\frac{\partial v}{\partial \alpha}-\frac{u}{AB}\frac{\partial A}{\partial \beta}\right)-\frac{1}{B}\frac{\partial A}{\partial \beta},$$

$$\frac{\partial m_1}{\partial \beta}=\frac{\partial}{\partial \beta}\left(\frac{1}{A}\frac{\partial v}{\partial \alpha}-\frac{u}{AB}\frac{\partial A}{\partial \beta}\right)-\frac{B}{R_2}\left(\frac{1}{A}\frac{\partial w}{\partial \alpha}+\frac{u}{R_1}\right)=\frac{1}{A}\frac{\partial B}{\partial \alpha},$$

$$\frac{\partial n_1}{\partial \alpha}=\frac{\partial}{\partial \alpha}\left(\frac{1}{A}\frac{\partial w}{\partial \alpha}+\frac{u}{R_1}\right)+\frac{A}{R_1},$$

$$\frac{\partial n_1}{\partial \beta}=\frac{\partial}{\partial \beta}\left(\frac{1}{A}\frac{\partial w}{\partial \alpha}+\frac{u}{R_1}\right)+\frac{B}{R_2}\left(\frac{1}{A}\frac{\partial v}{\partial \alpha}-\frac{u}{AB}\frac{\partial A}{\partial \beta}\right),$$

and

$$\frac{\partial l_2}{\partial \alpha}=\frac{\partial}{\partial \alpha}\left(-\frac{1}{A}\frac{\partial v}{\partial \alpha}+\frac{u}{AB}\frac{\partial A}{\partial \beta}\right)+\frac{1}{B}\frac{\partial A}{\partial \beta}-\frac{A}{R_1}\left(\frac{1}{B}\frac{\partial w}{\partial \beta}+\frac{v}{R_2}\right),$$

$$\frac{\partial l_2}{\partial \beta}=\frac{\partial}{\partial \beta}\left(-\frac{1}{A}\frac{\partial v}{\partial \alpha}+\frac{u}{AB}\frac{\partial A}{\partial \beta}\right)-\frac{1}{A}\frac{\partial B}{\partial \alpha},$$

$$\frac{\partial m_2}{\partial \alpha}=\frac{1}{AB}\frac{\partial A}{\partial \beta}\left(\frac{\partial v}{\partial \alpha}-\frac{u}{B}\frac{\partial A}{\partial \beta}\right),$$

$$\frac{\partial m_2}{\partial \beta}=-\frac{1}{R_2}\left(\frac{\partial w}{\partial \beta}+\frac{Bv}{R_2}\right)-\frac{1}{A^2}\frac{\partial B}{\partial \alpha}\left(\frac{\partial v}{\partial \alpha}-\frac{u}{B}\frac{\partial A}{\partial \beta}\right),$$

$$\frac{\partial n_2}{\partial \alpha}=\frac{\partial}{\partial \alpha}\left(\frac{1}{B}\frac{\partial w}{\partial \beta}+\frac{v}{R_2}\right)-\frac{1}{R_1}\left(\frac{\partial v}{\partial \alpha}-\frac{u}{B}\frac{\partial A}{\partial \beta}\right),$$

$$\frac{\partial n_2}{\partial \beta}=\frac{\partial}{\partial \beta}\left(\frac{1}{B}\frac{\partial w}{\partial \beta}+\frac{v}{R_2}\right)+\frac{B}{R_2}.$$

In calculating $p_1', \dots$ from the formulæ (19), we write for $l_1, \dots$ the values given in (22), and for $\partial l_1/\partial \alpha, \dots$ the values just found, and we observe that, since the scheme (14) is orthogonal, two of the formulæ (19) can be written

$$q_1'=-\left(l_3\frac{\partial l_1}{\partial \alpha}+m_3\frac{\partial m_1}{\partial \alpha}+n_3\frac{\partial n_1}{\partial \alpha}\right),\qquad q_2'=-\left(l_3\frac{\partial l_1}{\partial \beta}+m_3\frac{\partial m_1}{\partial \beta}+n_3\frac{\partial n_1}{\partial \beta}\right).$$

The process just described leads to the formulæ

$$\left.\begin{aligned}
p_1' &= \frac{\partial}{\partial \alpha}\left(\frac{1}{B}\frac{\partial w}{\partial \beta}+\frac{v}{R_2}\right)-\frac{1}{B}\frac{\partial A}{\partial \beta}\left(\frac{1}{A}\frac{\partial w}{\partial \alpha}+\frac{u}{R_1}\right)-\frac{1}{R_1}\left(\frac{\partial v}{\partial \alpha}-\frac{u}{B}\frac{\partial A}{\partial \beta}\right),\\
q_1' &= -\frac{A}{R_1}-\frac{\partial}{\partial \alpha}\left(\frac{1}{A}\frac{\partial w}{\partial \alpha}+\frac{u}{R_1}\right)-\frac{1}{B}\frac{\partial A}{\partial \beta}\left(\frac{1}{B}\frac{\partial w}{\partial \beta}+\frac{v}{R_2}\right),\\
r_1' &= -\frac{1}{B}\frac{\partial A}{\partial \beta}+\frac{\partial}{\partial \alpha}\left(\frac{1}{A}\frac{\partial v}{\partial \alpha}-\frac{u}{AB}\frac{\partial A}{\partial \beta}\right)+\frac{A}{R_1}\left(\frac{1}{B}\frac{\partial w}{\partial \beta}+\frac{v}{R_2}\right),
\end{aligned}\right\} \quad (24)$$

and

$$\left.\begin{aligned}
p_2' &= \frac{B}{R_2}+\frac{\partial}{\partial \beta}\left(\frac{1}{B}\frac{\partial w}{\partial \beta}+\frac{v}{R_2}\right)+\frac{1}{A}\frac{\partial B}{\partial \alpha}\left(\frac{1}{A}\frac{\partial w}{\partial \alpha}+\frac{u}{R_1}\right),\\
q_2' &= -\frac{\partial}{\partial \beta}\left(\frac{1}{A}\frac{\partial w}{\partial \alpha}+\frac{u}{R_1}\right)+\frac{1}{A}\frac{\partial B}{\partial \alpha}\left(\frac{1}{B}\frac{\partial w}{\partial \beta}+\frac{v}{R_2}\right)-\frac{B}{AR_2}\left(\frac{\partial v}{\partial \alpha}-\frac{u}{B}\frac{\partial A}{\partial \beta}\right),\\
r_2' &= \frac{1}{A}\frac{\partial B}{\partial \alpha}+\frac{\partial}{\partial \beta}\left(\frac{1}{A}\frac{\partial v}{\partial \alpha}-\frac{u}{AB}\frac{\partial A}{\partial \beta}\right)-\frac{B}{R_2}\left(\frac{1}{A}\frac{\partial w}{\partial \alpha}+\frac{u}{R_1}\right).
\end{aligned}\right\} \quad (25)$$

We can now write down the formulæ for the *changes of curvature* in the forms

$$\left.\begin{aligned}\kappa_1 &= \frac{1}{A}\frac{\partial}{\partial \alpha}\left(\frac{1}{A}\frac{\partial w}{\partial \alpha}+\frac{u}{R_1}\right)+\frac{1}{AB}\frac{\partial A}{\partial \beta}\left(\frac{1}{B}\frac{\partial w}{\partial \beta}+\frac{v}{R_2}\right),\\ \kappa_2 &= \frac{1}{B}\frac{\partial}{\partial \beta}\left(\frac{1}{B}\frac{\partial w}{\partial \beta}+\frac{v}{R_2}\right)+\frac{1}{AB}\frac{\partial B}{\partial \alpha}\left(\frac{1}{A}\frac{\partial w}{\partial \alpha}+\frac{u}{R_1}\right),\\ \tau &= \frac{1}{A}\frac{\partial}{\partial \alpha}\left(\frac{1}{B}\frac{\partial w}{\partial \beta}+\frac{v}{R_2}\right)-\frac{1}{A^2B}\frac{\partial A}{\partial \beta}\frac{\partial w}{\partial \alpha}-\frac{1}{AR_1}\frac{\partial v}{\partial \alpha}.\end{aligned}\right\} \quad \text{.........(26)}$$

The above formulæ admit of various verifications:

(i) In the case of a plane plate, when α and β are Cartesian coordinates, we have

$$\kappa_1=\frac{\partial^2 w}{\partial \alpha^2},\quad \kappa_2=\frac{\partial^2 w}{\partial \beta^2},\quad \tau=\frac{\partial^2 w}{\partial \alpha \partial \beta}.$$

These results agree with the formulæ in Article 298.

(ii) In the cases of cylindrical and spherical shells, the conditions that the displacement may be inextensional can be found as particular cases of the formulæ (21), and the expressions for the changes of curvature, found by simplifying (26) in accordance with these conditions, agree with those obtained in Articles 319 and 320.

(iii) Let a sphere be slightly deformed by purely normal displacement, in such a way that the radius becomes $a+bP_n(\cos\theta)$, where b is small, P_n denotes Legendre's nth coefficient, and θ is the co-latitude. The sum and product of the principal curvatures of the deformed surface can be shown, by means of the formulæ of this Article and those of Article 324, to be

$$\frac{2}{a}+\frac{b}{a^2}(n-1)(n+2)P_n(\cos\theta) \quad\text{and}\quad \frac{1}{a^2}+\frac{b}{a^3}(n-1)(n+2)P_n(\cos\theta),$$

correctly to the first order in b. These are known results.

(iv) For any surface, when ϵ_1, ϵ_2, ϖ are given by (21), and p_1', ... are given by (24) and (25), equations (11) are satisfied identically, squares and products of u, v, w and their differential coefficients being, of course, omitted.

327. Nature of the strain in a bent plate or shell.

To investigate the state of strain in a bent plate or shell we suppose that the middle surface is actually deformed, with but slight extension of any linear element, so that it becomes a surface differing but slightly from some one or other of the surfaces which are applicable upon the unstrained middle surface. We regard the strained middle surface as given; and we imagine a state of the plate in which the linear elements that are initially normal to the unstrained middle surface remain straight, become normal to the strained middle surface, and suffer no extension. Let P be any point on the unstrained middle surface, and let P be displaced to P_1 on the strained middle surface. Let x, y, z be the coordinates of P_1 referred to the fixed axes. The points P and P_1 have the same α and β. Let Q be any point on the normal at P to the unstrained middle surface, and let z be the distance of Q from P, reckoned as positive in the sense already chosen for the normal to the surface. When the plate is displaced as described above, Q comes to the point Q_1 of which the coordinates are

$$\mathrm{x}+l_3 z,\quad \mathrm{y}+m_3 z,\quad \mathrm{z}+n_3 z,$$

where, as in Article 325, l_3, m_3, n_3 are the direction-cosines of the normal to the strained middle surface.

The actual state of the plate, when it is deformed so that the middle surface has the assigned form, can be obtained from this imagined state by imposing an additional displacement upon the points Q_1. Let ξ, η, ζ denote the components of this additional displacement, referred to axes of x, y, z with origin at P_1 which are drawn as specified in Article 324. Then the coordinates of the final position of Q are

$$\mathrm{x} + l_1\xi + l_2\eta + l_3(z+\zeta), \quad \mathrm{y} + m_1\xi + m_2\eta + m_3(z+\zeta),$$
$$\mathrm{z} + n_1\xi + n_2\eta + n_3(z+\zeta). \quad \ldots(27)$$

In these expressions $l_1, \ldots$ are the direction-cosines so denoted in Article 325, x, y, z, $l_1, \ldots n_3$ are functions of α and β, and ξ, η, ζ are functions of α, β, z.

We consider the changes which must be made in these expressions when, instead of the points P, Q, we take neighbouring points P', Q', so that Q' is on the normal to the unstrained middle surface at P', and the distance $P'Q'$ is $z+\delta z$, where δz is small. Let P be (α, β) and P' $(\alpha+\delta\alpha, \beta+\delta\beta)$, where $\delta\alpha$ and $\delta\beta$ are small; and let r denote the distance QQ', and l, m, n the direction-cosines of the line QQ', referred to the tangents at P to the curves $\beta=$ const. and $\alpha=$ const. which pass through P and the normal to the unstrained middle surface at P. The quantities α, β, z may be regarded as the parameters of a triply orthogonal family of surfaces. The surfaces $z=$ const. are parallel to the middle surface; and the surfaces $\alpha=$ const. and $\beta=$ const. are developable surfaces, the generators of which are the normals to the unstrained middle surface drawn at points on its several lines of curvature. The linear element QQ' or r is expressed in terms of these parameters by the formula

$$\left[\left\{A\left(1-\frac{z}{R_1}\right)\delta\alpha\right\}^2 + \left\{B\left(1-\frac{z}{R_2}\right)\delta\beta\right\}^2 + (\delta z)^2\right]^{\frac{1}{2}},$$

and the projections of this element on the tangents to the curves $\beta=$ const., $\alpha=$ const., drawn on the middle surface, and on the normal to this surface are lr, mr, nr. Hence we have the formulæ

$$\delta\alpha = \frac{l\mathrm{r}}{A(1-z/R_1)}, \quad \delta\beta = \frac{m\mathrm{r}}{B(1-z/R_2)}, \quad \delta z = n\mathrm{r}. \quad \ldots\ldots\ldots(28)$$

In calculating the coordinates of the final position of Q' we have in (27) to replace

$$\mathrm{x} \text{ by } \mathrm{x} + \frac{\partial \mathrm{x}}{\partial\alpha}\delta\alpha + \frac{\partial \mathrm{x}}{\partial\beta}\delta\beta, \ldots,$$
$$l_1 \text{ by } l_1 + l_2(r_1'\delta\alpha + r_2'\delta\beta) - l_3(q_1'\delta\alpha + q_2'\delta\beta),$$
$$l_2 \text{ by } l_2 + l_3(p_1'\delta\alpha + p_2'\delta\beta) - l_1(r_1'\delta\alpha + r_2'\delta\beta),$$
$$l_3 \text{ by } l_3 + l_1(q_1'\delta\alpha + q_2'\delta\beta) - l_2(p_1'\delta\alpha + p_2'\delta\beta),$$
$$\ldots,$$
$$\xi \text{ by } \xi + \frac{\partial\xi}{\partial\alpha}\delta\alpha + \frac{\partial\xi}{\partial\beta}\delta\beta + \frac{\partial\xi}{\partial z}\delta z, \ldots,$$
$$z \text{ by } z + \delta z.$$

We use also the formulæ (15) and (16) for $\partial x/\partial\alpha, \ldots$ and the formulæ (28) for $\delta\alpha, \delta\beta, \delta z$.

Let r_1 denote the distance between the final positions of Q and Q'. We express r_1 as a homogeneous quadratic function of l, m, n, and deduce expressions for the components of strain by means of the formula

$$r_1^2 = r^2[(l^2+m^2+n^2) + 2(e_{xx}l^2 + e_{yy}m^2 + e_{zz}n^2 + e_{yz}mn + e_{zx}nl + e_{xy}lm)].$$

Now the difference of the x-coordinates of the final positions of Q and Q' is

$$\begin{aligned} &l_1(1+\epsilon_1)\frac{lr}{1-z/R_1} + \{l_1\varpi + l_2(1+\epsilon_2)\}\frac{mr}{1-z/R_2} \\ &+\xi\left\{(l_2r_1'-l_3q_1')\frac{lr}{A(1-z/R_1)} + (l_2r_2'-l_3q_2')\frac{mr}{B(1-z/R_2)}\right\} \\ &+\eta\left\{(l_3p_1'-l_1r_1')\frac{lr}{A(1-z/R_1)} + (l_3p_2'-l_1r_2')\frac{mr}{B(1-z/R_2)}\right\} \\ &+(z+\zeta)\left\{(l_1q_1'-l_2p_1')\frac{lr}{A(1-z/R_1)} + (l_1q_2'-l_2p_2')\frac{mr}{B(1-z/R_2)}\right\} \\ &+l_1\left\{\frac{\partial\xi}{\partial\alpha}\frac{lr}{A(1-z/R_1)} + \frac{\partial\xi}{\partial\beta}\frac{mr}{B(1-z/R_2)} + \frac{\partial\xi}{\partial z}nr\right\} \\ &+l_2\left\{\frac{\partial\eta}{\partial\alpha}\frac{lr}{A(1-z/R_1)} + \frac{\partial\eta}{\partial\beta}\frac{mr}{B(1-z/R_2)} + \frac{\partial\eta}{\partial z}nr\right\} \\ &+l_3\left\{\frac{\partial\zeta}{\partial\alpha}\frac{lr}{A(1-z/R_1)} + \frac{\partial\zeta}{\partial\beta}\frac{mr}{B(1-z/R_2)} + \left(1+\frac{\partial\zeta}{\partial z}\right)nr\right\}. \end{aligned}$$

The differences of the y- and z-coordinates can be written down by substituting m_1, m_2, m_3 and n_1, n_2, n_3 successively for l_1, l_2, l_3. Since the scheme (14) is orthogonal, we find the value of r_1^2 in the form

$$\begin{aligned} r_1^2 = r^2&\left[l + \frac{l}{1-z/R_1}\left\{\frac{z}{R_1} + \epsilon_1 - \frac{r_1'}{A}\eta + \frac{q_1'}{A}(z+\zeta) + \frac{1}{A}\frac{\partial\xi}{\partial\alpha}\right\}\right. \\ &\left.\quad + \frac{m}{1-z/R_2}\left\{\varpi - \frac{r_2'}{B}\eta + \frac{q_2'}{B}(z+\zeta) + \frac{1}{B}\frac{\partial\xi}{\partial\beta}\right\} + n\frac{\partial\xi}{\partial z}\right]^2 \\ + r^2&\left[\frac{l}{1-z/R_1}\left\{-\frac{p_1'}{A}(z+\zeta) + \frac{r_1'}{A}\xi + \frac{1}{A}\frac{\partial\eta}{\partial\alpha}\right\} + m\right. \\ &\left.\quad + \frac{m}{1-z/R_2}\left\{\frac{z}{R_2} + \epsilon_2 - \frac{p_2'}{B}(z+\zeta) + \frac{r_2'}{B}\xi + \frac{1}{B}\frac{\partial\eta}{\partial\beta}\right\} + n\frac{\partial\eta}{\partial z}\right]^2 \\ + r^2&\left[\frac{l}{1-z/R_1}\left\{-\frac{q_1'}{A}\xi + \frac{p_1'}{A}\eta + \frac{1}{A}\frac{\partial\zeta}{\partial\alpha}\right\} + \frac{m}{1-z/R_2}\left\{-\frac{q_2'}{B}\xi + \frac{p_2'}{B}\eta + \frac{1}{B}\frac{\partial\zeta}{\partial\beta}\right\}\right. \\ &\left.\quad + n\left(1+\frac{\partial\zeta}{\partial z}\right)\right]^2 \quad\ldots\ldots\ldots\ldots(29) \end{aligned}$$

In deducing expressions for the components of strain we observe that, in order that the strains may be small, it is clearly necessary that the quantities

$$\frac{z}{1-z/R_1}\left(\frac{q_1'}{A}+\frac{1}{R_1}\right),\quad \frac{z}{1-z/R_2}\left(-\frac{p_2'}{B}+\frac{1}{R_2}\right),\quad \frac{z}{1-z/R_2}\frac{q_2'}{B} - \frac{z}{1-z/R_1}\frac{p_1'}{A}$$

should be small. The third of equations (11) in Article 324 shows that $p_1'/A + q_2'/B$ is a small quantity, and we see therefore that, in the notation of (13) in Article 324, the quantities $z\kappa_1$, $z\kappa_2$, $z\tau$ must be small.

The expressions for the components of strain which we obtain from (29) are

$$\left.\begin{aligned}
e_{xx} &= \frac{1}{1-z/R_1}\left\{\epsilon_1 - z\kappa_1 + \frac{1}{A}\left(\frac{\partial\xi}{\partial\alpha} - r_1'\eta + q_1'\zeta\right)\right\},\\
e_{yy} &= \frac{1}{1-z/R_2}\left\{\epsilon_2 - z\kappa_2 + \frac{1}{B}\left(\frac{\partial\eta}{\partial\beta} - p_2'\zeta + r_2'\xi\right)\right\},\\
e_{xy} &= \frac{\varpi}{1-z/R_2} - \tau z\left(\frac{1}{1-z/R_1} + \frac{1}{1-z/R_2}\right) + \frac{z}{1-z/R_2}\left(\frac{q_2'}{B} + \frac{p_1'}{A}\right)\\
&\quad + \frac{1}{1-z/R_1}\frac{1}{A}\left(\frac{\partial\eta}{\partial\alpha} - p_1'\zeta + r_1'\xi\right) + \frac{1}{1-z/R_2}\frac{1}{B}\left(\frac{\partial\xi}{\partial\beta} - r_2'\eta + q_2'\zeta\right),\\
e_{zz} &= \frac{\partial\zeta}{\partial z},\\
e_{zx} &= \frac{\partial\xi}{\partial z} + \frac{1}{1-z/R_1}\frac{1}{A}\left(\frac{\partial\zeta}{\partial\alpha} - q_1'\xi + p_1'\eta\right),\\
e_{yz} &= \frac{\partial\eta}{\partial z} + \frac{1}{1-z/R_2}\frac{1}{B}\left(\frac{\partial\zeta}{\partial\beta} - q_2'\xi + p_2'\eta\right).
\end{aligned}\right\} \quad \ldots(30)$$

In these expressions ξ, η, ζ are functions of α, β, z which vanish with z for all relevant values of α, β.

We observe that the values found in Article 317 for e_{xx}, e_{yy}, e_{xy} would be obtained from the above by omitting ϵ_1, ϵ_2, ϖ and ξ, η, ζ, and replacing $1-z/R_1$ and $1-z/R_2$ by unity.

328. Specification of stress in a bent plate or shell.

The stress-resultants and stress-couples in a curved plate or shell, or in a plane plate which is appreciably bent, may be defined in a similar way to that adopted in Article 294 for a plane plate slightly deformed. Let s denote any curve drawn on the strained middle surface, ν the normal to this curve drawn in a chosen sense on the tangent plane of the surface at a point P_1, and let the sense of description of s be such that the directions of the normal ν, the tangent to s, and the normal to the surface at P_1, in the sense already chosen as positive, are parallel to the axes of a right-handed system. We draw a normal section of the strained middle surface through the tangent to s at P_1, and mark out on it a small area by the normal to the surface at P_1 and the normal to the (plane) curve of section at a neighbouring point P_1'. The tractions exerted across this area, by the portion of the plate on that side of s towards which ν is drawn, upon the remaining portion, are reduced to a force at P_1 and a couple. The average components of this force and couple per unit of length of P_1P_1' are found by dividing the measures of the components by the measure of this length. The limits of these averages are the stress-resultants and stress-couples belonging to the curve s at the point P_1. We denote them, as in Article 294, by T, S, N, H, G. For the expression of them we take temporary axes of x', y', z along the normal ν, the tangent to s, and the normal to the strained middle surface at P_1, and denote by $X'_{x'}, \ldots$ the stress-components referred to these axes. Then, taking R' to be the radius of curvature of the normal section of the surface drawn through the tangent to s at P_1, we have the formulæ

$$T=\int_{-h}^{h} X'_{x'}\left(1-\frac{z}{R'}\right) dz, \quad S=\int_{-h}^{h} X'_{y'}\left(1-\frac{z}{R'}\right) dz, \quad N=\int_{-h}^{h} X'_{z}\left(1-\frac{z}{R'}\right) dz,$$

$$H=\int_{-h}^{h} -zX'_{y'}\left(1-\frac{z}{R'}\right) dz, \quad G=\int_{-h}^{h} zX'_{x'}\left(1-\frac{z}{R'}\right) dz.$$

When we refer to the axes of x, y, z specified in Article 324, and denote the stress-resultants and stress-couples belonging to curves which are normal to the axes of x and y respectively by attaching a suffix 1 or 2 to $T, \ldots$, we obtain the formulæ

$$\left.\begin{aligned} T_1&=\int_{-h}^{h} X_x\left(1-\frac{z}{R_2'}\right) dz, \quad S_1=\int_{-h}^{h} X_y\left(1-\frac{z}{R_2'}\right) dz, \quad N_1=\int_{-h}^{h} X_z\left(1-\frac{z}{R_2'}\right) dz,\\ H_1&=\int_{-h}^{h} -zX_y\left(1-\frac{z}{R_2'}\right) dz, \quad G_1=\int_{-h}^{h} zX_x\left(1-\frac{z}{R_2'}\right) dz,\end{aligned}\right\} \quad (31)$$

and

$$\left.\begin{aligned} T_2&=\int_{-h}^{h} Y_y\left(1-\frac{z}{R_1'}\right) dz, \quad S_2=\int_{-h}^{h} -X_y\left(1-\frac{z}{R_1'}\right) dz, \quad N_2=\int_{-h}^{h} Y_z\left(1-\frac{z}{R_1'}\right) dz,\\ H_2&=\int_{-h}^{h} zX_y\left(1-\frac{z}{R_1'}\right) dz, \quad G_2=\int_{-h}^{h} zY_y\left(1-\frac{z}{R_1'}\right) dz,\end{aligned}\right\} \quad (32)$$

in which R_1' and R_2' denote, as in Article 324, the radii of curvature of normal sections of the strained middle surface drawn through the axes of x and y.

We observe that the relations $S_1+S_2=0$ and $H_1+H_2=0$, which hold in the case of a plane plate slightly deformed, do not hold when the strained middle surface is appreciably curved. The relations between the T, S, N, G, H for an assigned direction of ν and those for the two special directions x and y, which we found in Article 295 for a plane plate slightly deformed, are also disturbed by the presence of an appreciable curvature.

329. Approximate formulæ for the strain, the stress-resultants and the stress-couples.

We can deduce from (30) of Article 327 approximate expressions for the components of strain by arguments precisely similar to those employed in Articles 257 and 259. Since ξ, η, ζ vanish with z for all values of α and β, and $\partial\xi/\partial z, \ldots$ must be small quantities of the order of admissible strains, ξ, η, ζ and their differential coefficients with respect to α and β may, for a first approximation, be omitted. Further, for a first approximation, we may omit the products of z/R_1 or z/R_2 and any component of strain. In particular, since $q_2'/B + p_1'/A$ is of the order ϵ_1/R_1, we omit the product of this quantity and z; and, for the same reason, we replace such terms as $\frac{\epsilon_1}{1-z/R_1}$ and $\frac{z\kappa_1}{1-z/R_1}$ by ϵ_1 and $z\kappa_1$. By these processes we obtain the approximate formulæ*

$$e_{xx} = \epsilon_1 - z\kappa_1,\quad e_{yy} = \epsilon_2 - z\kappa_2,\quad e_{xy} = \varpi - 2z\tau,\quad e_{zx} = \frac{\partial \xi}{\partial z},\quad e_{yz} = \frac{\partial \eta}{\partial z},\quad e_{zz} = \frac{\partial \zeta}{\partial z} \quad \text{....(33)}$$

In these ξ, η, ζ may, for a first approximation, be regarded as independent of α and β. In case the middle surface is unextended, or the extensional strains ϵ_1, ϵ_2, ϖ are small compared with the flexural strains $z\kappa_1$, $z\kappa_2$, $z\tau$, these expressions may be simplified further by the omission of ϵ_1, ϵ_2, ϖ.

The approximate formulæ (33) for the strain-components, as well as the more exact formulæ (30), contain the unknown displacements ξ, η, ζ, and it is necessary to obtain values for these quantities, or at any rate for their differential coefficients with respect to z, which shall be at least approximately correct.

We begin with the case of a plane plate, and take α, β to be Cartesian rectangular coordinates, so that A and B are equal to unity, and $1/R_1$ and $1/R_2$ vanish. In the formulæ (33) ξ, η, ζ are approximately independent of α, β. We consider a slender cylindrical or prismatic portion of the plate such as would fit into a fine hole drilled transversely through it. We may take the cross-section of this prism to be so small that within it ϵ_1, ϵ_2, ϖ and κ_1, κ_2, τ may be treated as constants. Then the strain-components, as expressed by (33), are the same at all points in a cross-section of the slender prism. If there are no body forces and no tractions on the faces of the plate, we know from Article 306 that the stress in the slender prism, in which the strains are uniform over any cross-section, is plane stress. Hence, to this order of approximation X_z, Y_z, Z_z vanish, and we have

$$\frac{\partial \xi}{\partial z} = 0,\quad \frac{\partial \eta}{\partial z} = 0,\quad \frac{\partial \zeta}{\partial z} = -\frac{\sigma}{1-\sigma}\{\epsilon_1 + \epsilon_2 - z(\kappa_1 + \kappa_2)\}. \quad \text{.........(34)}$$

The remaining stress-components are then given by the equations

$$X_x = \frac{E}{1-\sigma^2}\{\epsilon_1 + \sigma\epsilon_2 - z(\kappa_1 + \sigma\kappa_2)\},\quad Y_y = \frac{E}{1-\sigma^2}\{\epsilon_2 + \sigma\epsilon_1 - z(\kappa_2 + \sigma\kappa_1)\},$$

$$X_y = \frac{E}{2(1+\sigma)}(\varpi - 2\tau z). \quad \text{...(35)}$$

From these results we may deduce approximate formulæ for the stress-resultants and stress-couples. For this purpose we omit from the formulæ (31)

* Equivalent formulæ in the case of a plane plate were given by Kirchhoff, *Vorlesungen über math. Physik, Mechanik*, Vorlesung 30.

and (32) the factors $(1 - z/R_2')$ and $(1 - z/R_1')$. We should obtain zero values for N_1, N_2, while T_1, ... and G_1, ... would be given by the formulæ

$$T_1 = \frac{2Eh}{1-\sigma^2}(\epsilon_1 + \sigma\epsilon_2), \quad T_2 = \frac{2Eh}{1-\sigma^2}(\epsilon_2 + \sigma\epsilon_1), \quad -S_2 = S_1 = \frac{Eh}{1+\sigma}\varpi, \quad \text{...(36)}$$

and

$$G_1 = -D(\kappa_1 + \sigma\kappa_2), \quad G_2 = -D(\kappa_2 + \sigma\kappa_1), \quad -H_2 = H_1 = D(1-\sigma)\tau. \quad \text{...(37)}$$

To the same order of approximation the strain-energy per unit of area is given by the formula

$$\{Eh/(1-\sigma^2)\}\left[(\epsilon_1+\epsilon_2)^2 - 2(1-\sigma)(\epsilon_1\epsilon_2 - \tfrac{1}{4}\varpi^2)\right] + \tfrac{1}{3}D\left[(\kappa_1+\kappa_2)^2 - 2(1-\sigma)(\kappa_1\kappa_2 - \tau^2)\right]. \quad \text{...(38)}$$

To get a closer approximation in the case of a plane plate we may regard the strain in the slender prism as varying uniformly over the cross-sections. Then we know from Article 306 that X_z and Y_z do not vanish, but the third of (34) and the formulæ (35) still hold, and therefore also (36) and (37) are still approximately correct, while N_1 and N_2 are given according to the result of Article 306 by the formulæ

$$N_1 = -D\frac{\partial}{\partial x}(\kappa_1 + \kappa_2), \quad N_2 = -D\frac{\partial}{\partial y}(\kappa_1 + \kappa_2).$$

These values for N_1, N_2 could be found also from (12) of Article 296 by omitting the couples L', M' and substituting for G_1, G_2, H_1 from (37).

From this discussion of the case of a plane plate we may conclude that the approximate expressions (33) and (34) for the components of strain are adequate for the purpose of determining the stress-couples; but, except in cases where the extension of the middle plane is an important feature of the deformation, they are inadequate for determining the stress-resultants of types N_1, N_2. The formulæ (37) for the stress-couples are the same as those which we used in Articles 313, 314. The results obtained in Articles 307, 308, 312 seem to warrant the conclusion that the expressions (37) for the stress-couples are sufficient approximations in practically important cases whether the plate is free from the action of body forces and of tractions on its faces or not.

The justification of the approximate theory of the bending of thin plane plates, described in Article 313, has now been given. It may be added that, in the cases to which the theory applies, the extensional strains are small compared with the flexural strains, and then a comparison of equations (35) and (37) shows that the most important of the stress-components are given by the equations

$$X_x = \frac{3z}{2h^3}G_1, \quad Y_y = \frac{3z}{2h^3}G_2, \quad X_y = -\frac{3z}{2h^3}H_1.$$

The numerically greatest tension in the plate is the value of X_x at the place where, for a suitably chosen axis of x, the value of z is h, or $-h$, and G_1 has its greatest value. This happens at a face of the plate, at a point whose projection on the middle plane is the point where the greatest principal curvature of the bent middle surface occurs, and the corresponding direction of the axis of x is the tangent to that line of curvature which has the greatest curvature. The greatest tension is $3G/2h^2$, where G is the corresponding flexural couple.

In the case of a curved plate or shell we may, for a first approximation, use the formulæ (33) and the theorem of Article 306 in the same way as for a plane plate. Thus equations (34) and (35) are still approximately correct. We may obtain from them the terms of lowest order in the expressions for the stress-resultants of the type T, S and the stress-couples. On substituting in the formulæ (31) and (32), we find, to the first order in h,

$$T_1 = \frac{2Eh}{1-\sigma^2}(\epsilon_1 + \sigma\epsilon_2), \quad T_2 = \frac{2Eh}{1-\sigma^2}(\epsilon_2 + \sigma\epsilon_1), \quad -S_2 = S_1 = \frac{Eh}{1+\sigma}\varpi, \ldots(36\ bis)$$

and, to the third order in h,

$$\left.\begin{aligned} G_1 &= -D\left\{\kappa_1 + \sigma\kappa_2 + \frac{1}{R_2'}(\epsilon_1 + \sigma\epsilon_2)\right\}, \quad G_2 = -D\left\{\kappa_2 + \sigma\kappa_1 + \frac{1}{R_1'}(\epsilon_2 + \sigma\epsilon_1)\right\}, \\ H_1 &= D(1-\sigma)\left(\tau + \frac{1}{2}\frac{\varpi}{R_2'}\right), \quad H_2 = -D(1-\sigma)\left(\tau + \frac{1}{2}\frac{\varpi}{R_1'}\right). \end{aligned}\right\} \ldots(39)$$

This first approximation includes two extreme cases. In the first the extensional strains ϵ_1, ϵ_2, ϖ are small compared with the flexural strains $z\kappa_1$, $z\kappa_2$, $z\tau$. The stress-couples are then given by the formulæ

$$G_1 = -D(\kappa_1 + \sigma\kappa_2), \quad G_2 = -D(\kappa_2 + \sigma\kappa_1), \quad -H_2 = H_1 = D(1-\sigma)\tau, \ldots(37\ bis)$$

and the strain-energy per unit of area is given by the formula which we found by means of a certain assumption in Article 317, viz.:

$$\tfrac{1}{2}D[(\kappa_1 + \kappa_2)^2 - 2(1-\sigma)(\kappa_1\kappa_2 - \tau^2)],$$

but the stress-resultants are not sufficiently determined.

In the second extreme case the flexural strains $z\kappa_1$, $z\kappa_2$, $z\tau$ are small compared with the extensional strains ϵ_1, ϵ_2, ϖ. Then the stress-resultants of type T, S are given by the formulæ (36), and the stress-resultants of type N and the stress-couples are unimportant. The strain-energy per unit of area is given by the formula

$$\{Eh/(1-\sigma^2)\}[(\epsilon_1 + \epsilon_2)^2 - 2(1-\sigma)(\epsilon_1\epsilon_2 - \tfrac{1}{4}\varpi^2)]. \ldots\ldots\ldots\ldots(40)$$

When the extensional strains are comparable with the flexural strains, so that, for example, ϖ is of the order $h\tau$, the stress-resultants of type T, S are given with sufficient approximation by (36), and the stress-couples are given with sufficient approximation by (37), while the strain-energy per unit of area is given by (38).

From this analysis of the various possible cases it appears that, whenever the stress-couples G_1, G_2, H_1, H_2 need be calculated at all, they may be calculated from the formulæ (37) instead of (39).

When the extensional strains are large compared with the flexural strains, approximate equations of equilibrium can be formed by the method of variation described in Article 115, by taking the strain-energy per unit of area to be given by the formula (40). In the same case approximate equations of vibration can be formed by using this expression (40) for the strain-energy and the expression $\rho h\left[\left(\frac{\partial u}{\partial t}\right)^2+\left(\frac{\partial v}{\partial t}\right)^2+\left(\frac{\partial w}{\partial t}\right)^2\right]$ for the kinetic energy per unit of area.

The strain-energy per unit of area is not, in general, expressed correctly to the third order in h by (38). The complete expression would contain additional terms. In general the complete expression for the strain-energy must be formed before equations of equilibrium and vibration can be obtained by the variational method*. We shall use a different method of forming the equations.

The approximate expression (38) for the strain-energy suggests, as the correct form, a function expansible in rising powers of h, and having for coefficients of the various powers of h expressions determined by the displacement of the middle surface only. Lord Rayleigh† has called attention to the fact that, when there are tractions on the faces of the shell, no such form is possible, and has illustrated the matter by the two-dimensional displacement of a cylindrical tube subjected to surface pressure. In this problem the first approximation, given by (40), is undisturbed by the surface pressures.

330. Second approximation in the case of a curved plate or shell.

In the case of an appreciably curved middle surface we can make some progress with a second approximation provided that the displacement is small. Such an approximation is unnecessary unless the extensional strains ϵ_1, ϵ_2, ϖ are small compared with the flexural strains $z\kappa_1$, $z\kappa_2$, $z\tau$. We shall suppose that this is the case. In calculating the strains e_{xx}, ... from (30) instead of (33) we observe that the term $\epsilon_1(1-z/R_1)^{-1}$ may still be replaced by ϵ_1, and that the term $-z\kappa_1(1-z/R_1)^{-1}$ may be replaced by $-z\kappa_1-z^2\kappa_1/R_1$. The values of ξ, η, ζ which were given by the first approximation are

$$\xi=0,\quad \eta=0,\quad \zeta=-\frac{\sigma}{1-\sigma}\{(\epsilon_1+\epsilon_2)z-\tfrac{1}{2}(\kappa_1+\kappa_2)z^2\},$$

and these values may be substituted in the first three of (30). Further, in the terms of (30) that contain ξ, η, ζ we may replace p_1', ... by the corresponding quantities relating to the unstrained shell, that is to say we may put $p_1'=q_2'=0$, $p_2'/B=1/R_2$, $-q_1'/A=1/R_1$. We reject all terms of the types $\epsilon_1 z/R_1$, $\epsilon_1\kappa_1 z$, $\kappa_1^2 z^2$. We thus obtain the equations

$$\left.\begin{aligned} e_{xx}&=\epsilon_1-z\kappa_1-z^2\frac{\kappa_1}{R_1}-\frac{1}{2}\frac{\sigma}{1-\sigma}z^2\frac{\kappa_1+\kappa_2}{R_1},\\ e_{yy}&=\epsilon_2-z\kappa_2-z^2\frac{\kappa_2}{R_2}-\frac{1}{2}\frac{\sigma}{1-\sigma}z^2\frac{\kappa_1+\kappa_2}{R_2},\\ e_{xy}&=\varpi-2\tau z-\tau z^2(1/R_1+1/R_2).\end{aligned}\right\}\quad\text{.......................(41)}$$

From the formula for e_{xy} we can calculate S_1 and S_2 by means of (31) and (32) of Article 328, and in this calculation we may replace $1/R_1'$ and $1/R_2'$ by $1/R_1$ and $1/R_2$. We find

$$\left.\begin{aligned} S_1&=\frac{Eh}{1+\sigma}\varpi+D(1-\sigma)\frac{\tau}{R_2}-\tfrac{1}{2}D(1-\sigma)\tau\left(\frac{1}{R_1}+\frac{1}{R_2}\right),\\ S_2&=-\frac{Eh}{1+\sigma}\varpi-D(1-\sigma)\frac{\tau}{R_1}+\tfrac{1}{2}D(1-\sigma)\tau\left(\frac{1}{R_1}+\frac{1}{R_2}\right).\end{aligned}\right\}\quad\text{...........(42)}$$

* A. B. Basset, *Phil. Trans. Roy. Soc.* (Ser. A), vol. 181 (1890).

† *London Math. Soc. Proc.*, vol. 20 (1889), p. 372, or *Scientific Papers*, vol. 3, p. 280.

In calculating a second approximation to T_1 and T_2 we may not assume that Z_z vanishes. As in the case of the plane plate, we take the shell to be free from the action of body forces and of tractions on its faces. We observe that the axes of x, y, z specified in Article 323 are parallel to the normals to three surfaces of a triply orthogonal family. This is the family considered in Article 327, and the parameters of the surfaces are α, β, z. We write temporarily γ in place of z, and use the notation of Articles 19 and 58. The values of h_1, h_2, h_3 are given by the equations

$$\frac{1}{h_1}=A\left(1-\frac{\gamma}{R_1}\right), \quad \frac{1}{h_2}=B\left(1-\frac{\gamma}{R_2}\right), \quad \frac{1}{h_3}=1.$$

We write down an equation of the type of (19) in Article 58 by resolving along the normal to the surface γ. This equation is

$$\frac{1}{AB}\left(1-\frac{\gamma}{R_1}\right)^{-1}\left(1-\frac{\gamma}{R_2}\right)^{-1}\left[\frac{\partial}{\partial\alpha}\left\{B\left(1-\frac{\gamma}{R_2}\right)\widehat{\gamma\alpha}\right\}+\frac{\partial}{\partial\beta}\left\{A\left(1-\frac{\gamma}{R_1}\right)\widehat{\gamma\beta}\right\}\right.$$
$$\left.+\frac{\partial}{\partial\gamma}\left\{AB\left(1-\frac{\gamma}{R_1}\right)\left(1-\frac{\gamma}{R_2}\right)\widehat{\gamma\gamma}\right\}\right]$$
$$-\frac{\widehat{\alpha\alpha}}{A}\left(1-\frac{\gamma}{R_1}\right)^{-1}\frac{\partial}{\partial\gamma}\left\{A\left(1-\frac{\gamma}{R_1}\right)\right\}-\frac{\widehat{\beta\beta}}{B}\left(1-\frac{\gamma}{R_2}\right)^{-1}\frac{\partial}{\partial\gamma}\left\{B\left(1-\frac{\gamma}{R_2}\right)\right\}=0.$$

Returning to our previous notation, we write this equation

$$\frac{\partial}{\partial\alpha}\left\{B\left(1-\frac{z}{R_2}\right)X_z\right\}+\frac{\partial}{\partial\beta}\left\{A\left(1-\frac{z}{R_1}\right)Y_z\right\}+\frac{\partial}{\partial z}\left\{AB\left(1-\frac{z}{R_1}\right)\left(1-\frac{z}{R_2}\right)Z_z\right\}$$
$$+\frac{AB}{R_1}\left(1-\frac{z}{R_2}\right)X_x+\frac{AB}{R_2}\left(1-\frac{z}{R_1}\right)Y_y=0.$$

To obtain an approximation to Z_z, we substitute in this equation for $X_x, \ldots$ the values given by the first approximation, and integrate with respect to z. We determine the constant of integration so that Z_z may vanish at $z=h$ and $z=-h$. We must omit the terms containing X_z and Y_z and use the approximate values given in (35) for X_x and Y_y. Further we may omit the factors $1-z/R_1$ and $1-z/R_2$ and such terms as $\epsilon_1 z/R_1$. We thus find the formula

$$Z_z=-\frac{1}{2}\frac{E}{1-\sigma^2}(h^2-z^2)\left(\frac{\kappa_1+\sigma\kappa_2}{R_1}+\frac{\kappa_2+\sigma\kappa_1}{R_2}\right). \quad \text{.....................(43)}$$

Now we have

$$X_x=\frac{E}{1-\sigma^2}(e_{xx}+\sigma e_{yy})+\frac{\sigma}{1-\sigma}Z_z, \quad Y_y=\frac{E}{1-\sigma^2}(e_{yy}+\sigma e_{xx})+\frac{\sigma}{1-\sigma}Z_z,$$

and hence, by means of the formulæ for e_{xx}, e_{yy}, Z_z, we calculate approximate values for T_1, T_2 in the forms*

$$\left.\begin{aligned} T_1&=\frac{2Eh}{1-\sigma^2}(\epsilon_1+\sigma\epsilon_2)+D\left[\kappa_1\left(\frac{1}{R_2}-\frac{1}{R_1}\right)-\frac{1}{2}\frac{\sigma}{1-\sigma}(\kappa_1+\kappa_2)\left(\frac{1}{R_1}+\frac{\sigma}{R_2}\right)\right.\\ &\qquad\left.-\frac{\sigma}{1-\sigma}\left(\frac{\kappa_1+\sigma\kappa_2}{R_1}+\frac{\kappa_2+\sigma\kappa_1}{R_2}\right)\right],\\ T_2&=\frac{2Eh}{1-\sigma^2}(\epsilon_2+\sigma\epsilon_1)+D\left[\kappa_2\left(\frac{1}{R_1}-\frac{1}{R_2}\right)-\frac{1}{2}\frac{\sigma}{1-\sigma}(\kappa_1+\kappa_2)\left(\frac{1}{R_2}+\frac{\sigma}{R_1}\right)\right.\\ &\qquad\left.-\frac{\sigma}{1-\sigma}\left(\frac{\kappa_1+\sigma\kappa_2}{R_1}+\frac{\kappa_2+\sigma\kappa_1}{R_2}\right)\right].\end{aligned}\right\} \quad \text{...(44)}$$

The formulæ for the stress-couples are not affected by the second approximation, so far at any rate as terms of the order $D\kappa_1$ are concerned.

* The approximate forms of S_1, S_2, T_1, T_2 obtained in this Article agree substantially with those found by a different process by A. B. Basset, *loc. cit.*, p. 532, in the cases of cylindrical and spherical shells to which he restricts his discussion. His forms contain some additional terms which are of the order here neglected.

331. Equations of equilibrium.

The equations of equilibrium are formed by equating to zero the resultant and resultant moment of all the forces applied to a portion of the plate or shell. We consider a portion bounded by the faces and by the surfaces formed by the aggregates of the normals drawn to the strained middle surface at points of a curvilinear quadrilateral, which is made up of two neighbouring arcs of each of the families of curves α and β. Since the extension of the middle surface is small, we may neglect the extensions of the sides of the quadrilateral, and we may regard it as a curvilinear rectangle. We denote the bounding curves of the curvilinear rectangle by α, $\alpha+\delta\alpha$, β, $\beta+\delta\beta$, and resolve the stress-resultants on the sides in the directions of the fixed axes of x, y, z which coincide with the tangents to β and α at their point of intersection and the normal to the strained middle surface at this point (Fig. 73).

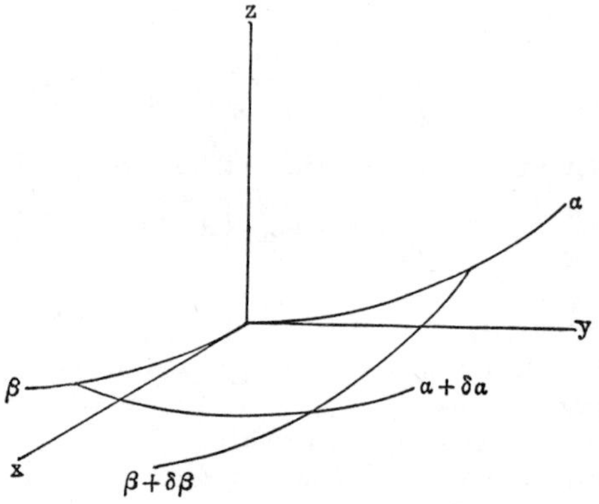

Fig. 73.

Fig. 74 shows the directions and senses of the stress-resultants on the edges of the curvilinear rectangle, those across the edges $\alpha+\delta\alpha$ and $\beta+\delta\beta$ being distinguished by accents. The axes of the stress-couples H_1, G_1 have the same directions as T_1, S_1; those of H_2, G_2 have the same directions as T_2, S_2.

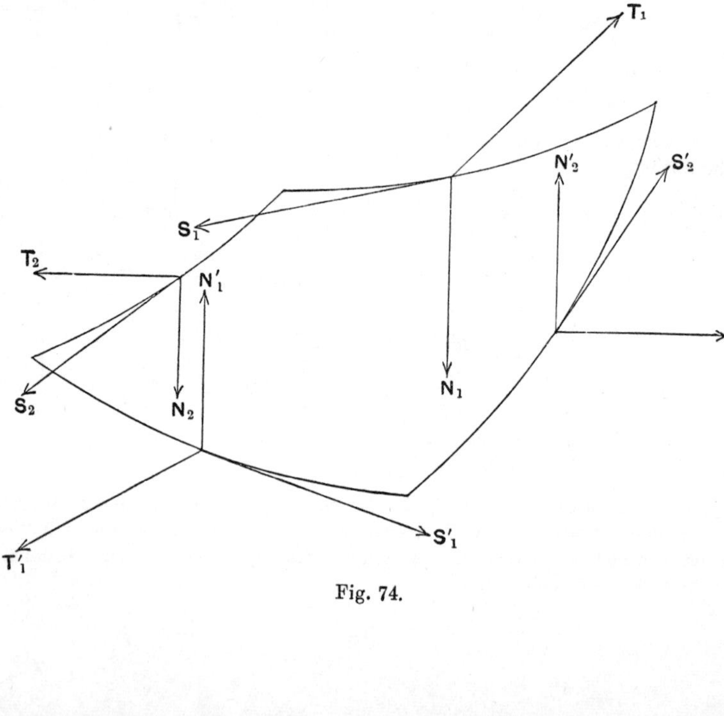

Fig. 74.

The stress-resultants on the side α of the rectangle yield a force having components

$$-T_1 B\delta\beta, \quad -S_1 B\delta\beta, \quad -N_1 B\delta\beta$$

parallel to the axes of x, y, z. The corresponding component forces for the side $\alpha+\delta\alpha$ are to be obtained by applying the usual formulæ relating to moving axes; for the quantities T_1, S_1, N_1 are the components of a vector referred to moving axes of x, y, z, which are defined by the tangent to the curve $\beta=$ const. which passes through any point and the normal to the strained middle surface at the point. In resolving the forces acting across the side $\alpha+\delta\alpha$ parallel to the fixed axes, we have to allow for a change of α into $\alpha+\delta\alpha$, and for the small rotation $(p_1'\delta\alpha, q_1'\delta\alpha, r_1'\delta\alpha)$. Hence the components parallel to the axes of x, y, z of the force acting across the side $\alpha+\delta\alpha$ are respectively

$$T_1 B\delta\beta + \delta\alpha\frac{\partial}{\partial\alpha}(T_1 B\delta\beta) - S_1 B\delta\beta\,.\,r_1'\delta\alpha + N_1 B\delta\beta\,.\,q_1'\delta\alpha,$$

$$S_1 B\delta\beta + \delta\alpha\frac{\partial}{\partial\alpha}(S_1 B\delta\beta) - N_1 B\delta\beta\,.\,p_1'\delta\alpha + T_1 B\delta\beta\,.\,r_1'\delta\alpha,$$

$$N_1 B\delta\beta + \delta\alpha\frac{\partial}{\partial\alpha}(N_1 B\delta\beta) - T_1 B\delta\beta\,.\,q_1'\delta\alpha + S_1 B\delta\beta\,.\,p_1'\delta\alpha.$$

In like manner we write down the forces acting across the sides β and $\beta+\delta\beta$. For β we have

$$S_2 A\delta\alpha, \quad -T_2 A\delta\alpha, \quad -N_2 A\delta\alpha;$$

and for $\beta+\delta\beta$ we have

$$-S_2 A\delta\alpha - \delta\beta\frac{\partial}{\partial\beta}(S_2 A\delta\alpha) - T_2 A\delta\alpha\,.\,r_2'\delta\beta + N_2 A\delta\alpha\,.\,q_2'\delta\beta,$$

$$T_2 A\delta\alpha + \delta\beta\frac{\partial}{\partial\beta}(T_2 A\delta\alpha) - N_2 A\delta\alpha\,.\,p_2'\delta\beta - S_2 A\delta\alpha\,.\,r_2'\delta\beta,$$

$$N_2 A\delta\alpha + \delta\beta\frac{\partial}{\partial\beta}(N_2 A\delta\alpha) + S_2 A\delta\alpha\,.\,q_2'\delta\beta + T_2 A\delta\alpha\,.\,p_2'\delta\beta.$$

Let X', Y', Z' and L', M', 0 denote, as in Article 296, the components, parallel to the axes of x, y, z, of the force- and couple-resultant of the externally applied forces estimated per unit of area of the middle surface. Since the area within the rectangle can be taken to be $AB\delta\alpha\delta\beta$, we can write down, three of the equations of equilibrium in the forms

$$\left.\begin{aligned}
&\frac{\partial(T_1 B)}{\partial\alpha} - \frac{\partial(S_2 A)}{\partial\beta} - (r_1' S_1 B + r_2' T_2 A) + (q_1' N_1 B + q_2' N_2 A) + ABX' = 0,\\
&\frac{\partial(S_1 B)}{\partial\alpha} + \frac{\partial(T_2 A)}{\partial\beta} - (p_1' N_1 B + p_2' N_2 A) + (r_1' T_1 B - r_2' S_2 A) + ABY' = 0,\\
&\frac{\partial(N_1 B)}{\partial\alpha} + \frac{\partial(N_2 A)}{\partial\beta} - (q_1' T_1 B - q_2' S_2 A) + (p_1' S_1 B + p_2' T_2 A) + ABZ' = 0.
\end{aligned}\right\}\quad(45)$$

Again the moments of the forces and the couples acting across the sides of the rectangle can be written down. For the side α we have the component couples

$$-H_1 B\delta\beta, \quad -G_1 B\delta\beta, \quad 0,$$

and for the side $\alpha + \delta\alpha$ we have the component couples

$$H_1 B\delta\beta + \delta\alpha \frac{\partial}{\partial\alpha}(H_1 B\delta\beta) - G_1 B\delta\beta \,.\, r_1'\delta\alpha,$$

$$G_1 B\delta\beta + \delta\alpha \frac{\partial}{\partial\alpha}(G_1 B\delta\beta) + H_1 B\delta\beta \,.\, r_1'\delta\alpha,$$

$$-H_1 B\delta\beta \,.\, q_1'\delta\alpha + G_1 B\delta\beta \,.\, p_1'\delta\alpha;$$

for the side β we have the component couples

$$G_2 A\delta\alpha, \quad -H_2 A\delta\alpha, \quad 0,$$

and for the side $\beta + \delta\beta$ we have the component couples

$$-G_2 A\delta\alpha - \delta\beta \frac{\partial}{\partial\beta}(G_2 A\delta\alpha) - H_2 A\delta\alpha \,.\, r_2'\delta\beta,$$

$$H_2 A\delta\alpha + \delta\beta \frac{\partial}{\partial\beta}(H_2 A\delta\alpha) - G_2 A\delta\alpha \,.\, r_2'\delta\beta,$$

$$G_2 A\delta\alpha \,.\, q_2'\delta\beta + H_2 A\delta\alpha \,.\, p_2'\delta\beta.$$

Further the moments about the axes of the forces acting across the sides $\alpha + \delta\alpha$ and $\beta + \delta\beta$ can be taken to be

$$B\delta\beta \,.\, N_2 A\delta\alpha, \quad -A\delta\alpha \,.\, N_1 B\delta\beta, \quad A\delta\alpha \,.\, S_1 B\delta\beta + B\delta\beta \,.\, S_2 A\delta\alpha.$$

The equations of moments can therefore be written in the forms

$$\left.\begin{aligned} &\frac{\partial(H_1 B)}{\partial\alpha} - \frac{\partial(G_2 A)}{\partial\beta} - (G_1 B r_1' + H_2 A r_2') + (N_2 + L')AB = 0, \\ &\frac{\partial(G_1 B)}{\partial\alpha} + \frac{\partial(H_2 A)}{\partial\beta} + (H_1 B r_1' - G_2 A r_2') - (N_1 - M')AB = 0, \\ &G_1 B p_1' + G_2 A q_2' - (H_1 B q_1' - H_2 A p_2') + (S_1 + S_2)AB = 0. \end{aligned}\right\} \quad \ldots(46)$$

Equations (45) and (46) are the equations of equilibrium.

332. Boundary-conditions.

The system of stress-resultants and stress-couples belonging to a curve s drawn on the middle surface can be modified after the fashion explained in Article 297, but account must be taken of the curvature of the surface. Regarding the curve s as a polygon of a large number of sides, we replace the couple $H\delta s$ acting on the side δs by two forces, each of amount H, acting at the ends of this side in opposite senses in lines parallel to the normal to the surface at one extremity of δs; and we do the like with the couples acting on the contiguous sides. If $P'PP''$ is a short arc of s, and the arcs $P'P$ and PP'' are each equal to δs, these operations leave us with a force of a certain magnitude, direction and sense at the typical point P. The forces at P and

P'', arising from the couple on the arc PP'', are each equal to H, and their lines of action are parallel to the normal at P, the force at P being in the negative sense of this normal. The forces at P' and P arising from the couple on the arc $P'P$ are each equal to $H - \delta H$, and their lines of action are parallel to the normal at P', the force at P being in the positive sense of this normal. Now let $R_1^{(1)}$, $R_2^{(1)}$ be the principal radii of curvature of the strained middle surface at P, so that the equation of this surface referred to axes of ξ, η, z which coincide with the principal tangents at P and the normal is approximately

$$z - \tfrac{1}{2}\{\xi^2/R_1^{(1)} + \eta^2/R_2^{(1)}\} = 0.$$

Also let ϕ be the angle which the tangent at P to $P'PP''$ makes with the axis of ξ. The point P' has coordinates $-\delta s \cos\phi$, $-\delta s \sin\phi$, 0, and the direction-cosines of the normal at P' are, with sufficient approximation, $\delta s \cos\phi/R_1^{(1)}$, $\delta s \sin\phi/R_2^{(1)}$, 1. The force at P arising from the couple on $P'P$ has components $H\delta s\cos\phi/R_1^{(1)}$, $H\delta s\sin\phi/R_2^{(1)}$, $H-\delta H$ parallel to the axes of ξ, η, z. Hence the force at P arising from the couples on $P'P$ and PP'' has components parallel to the normal to s drawn on the surface, the tangent to s and the normal to the surface, which are

$$H\delta s \sin\phi\cos\phi\,(1/R_1^{(1)} - 1/R_2^{(1)}), \quad H\delta s/R', \quad -\delta H,$$

where R', $= [\cos^2\phi/R_1^{(1)} + \sin^2\phi/R_2^{(1)}]^{-1}$, is the radius of curvature of the normal section having the same tangent line as the curve s. Hence the stress-resultants T, S, N and stress-couples H, G can be replaced by stress-resultants

$$T + \tfrac{1}{2}H\sin 2\phi\,\{1/R_1^{(1)} - 1/R_2^{(1)}\}, \quad S + H/R', \quad N - \partial H/\partial s, \quad \ldots(47)$$

and a flexural couple G.

The boundary-conditions at an edge to which forces are applied, or at a free edge, can now be written down in the manner explained in Article 297. The formulæ (47) are simplified in case the plate or shell is but little bent, for then the radii of curvature and the position of the edge-line relative to the lines of curvature may be determined from the unstrained, instead of the strained, middle surface. They are simplified still more in case the edge is a line of curvature*, for then H does not contribute to T.

332 A. Buckling of a rectangular plate under edge thrust.

The theory of the equilibrium of thin shells will be applied to particular cases in Chapter XXIV A. Special problems for plane plates have already been discussed in Chapter XXII and the theory will be developed further in Chapter XXIV A. As exemplifying the application of the equations of Article 331 we shall consider here the question of the stability of a plane rectangular plate under edge thrust parallel to its plane. The problem will be treated by the method used in Article 267 A *supra*.

If the thrusts are not too great, the plate simply contracts in its plane in the manner indicated in Article 301. We take the centre of the rectangle as origin, and lines parallel

* The result that, in this case, H contributes to S as well as to N was noted by A. B. Basset, *loc. cit.*, p. 532. See also the paper by H. Lamb cited on p. 505.

to the edges as axes of x and y, and take the edges in the unstrained state to be given by the equations $x=\pm a$, $y=\pm b$. Let P_1 and P_2 be the values of the thrusts along these pairs of edges respectively. Then in the simply contracted state $T_1=-P_1$ and $T_2=-P_2$ everywhere and the remaining stress-resultants and the stress-couples vanish.

We now suppose that P_1 and P_2 are such that a very small transverse displacement w can be maintained by them in the plate so contracted. Using x and y in place of α, β, we have $A=B=1$, and $1/R_1=1/R_2=0$, and the formulæ of Article 326 give

$$p_1'=-q_2'=\tau=\frac{\partial^2 w}{\partial x\,\partial y},\quad q_1'=-\frac{\partial^2 w}{\partial x^2}=-\kappa_1,\quad p_2'=\frac{\partial^2 w}{\partial y^2}=\kappa_2,\quad r_1'=r_2'=0.$$

Equations (46) of Article 331 with the formulæ (37) of Article 329 give

$$D(1-\sigma)\frac{\partial^3 w}{\partial x^2\,\partial y}+D\left(\frac{\partial^3 w}{\partial y^3}+\sigma\frac{\partial^3 w}{\partial x^2\,\partial y}\right)+N_2=0,$$

$$-D\left(\frac{\partial^3 w}{\partial x^3}+\sigma\frac{\partial^3 w}{\partial x\,\partial y^2}\right)-D(1-\sigma)\frac{\partial^3 w}{\partial x\,\partial y^2}-N_1=0,$$

$$S_1+S_2=0,$$

where quantities of the second order in w are omitted. The third of these equations and the first two of equations (45) of Article 331 are satisfied by putting

$$T_1=-P_1,\quad T_2=-P_2,\quad S_1=S_2=0,$$

and boundary-conditions relating to the stress-resultants of types T and S are also satisfied. The third of equations (45) becomes, on omission of terms of the second order in w,

$$D\left(\frac{\partial^4 w}{\partial x^4}+\frac{\partial^4 w}{\partial y^4}+2\frac{\partial^4 w}{\partial x^2\,\partial y^2}\right)+P_1\frac{\partial^2 w}{\partial x^2}+P_2\frac{\partial^2 w}{\partial y^2}=0.$$

If the plate is "supported" at the edges, we must have $w=0$ and $\kappa_1+\sigma\kappa_2=0$ at $x=\pm a$, and $w=0$ and $\kappa_2+\sigma\kappa_1=0$ at $x=\pm b$. The solution is of the form

$$w=W\sin\frac{m\pi(x+a)}{2a}\sin\frac{n\pi(y+b)}{2b},$$

where m and n are integers and W is constant, provided

$$\tfrac{1}{4}D\pi^2\left(\frac{m^2}{a^2}+\frac{n^2}{b^2}\right)^2=P_1\frac{m^2}{a^2}+P_2\frac{n^2}{b^2}.$$

When the thrusts satisfy this condition the equilibrium is critical*. Exactly as in the problem of the strut (Article 264 *supra*) the simply contracted state of equilibrium of the plate is unstable if P_1 or P_2 exceed the smallest values consistent with this equation. For example, if P_1 and P_2 are equal their common value may not exceed $\tfrac{1}{4}D\pi^2\left(\frac{1}{a^2}+\frac{1}{b^2}\right)$.

Exactly as in Article 267 A we might have obtained a slightly more correct form of the condition by taking account of the contraction of the middle surface, but the correction would be of no practical importance.

For further investigations concerning the stability of thin plates reference may be made to papers by R. V. Southwell and S. W. Skan, *London Roy. Soc. Proc.* (Ser. A), vol. 105 (1924), p. 582, and W. R. Dean in the same *Proceedings*, vol. 106 (1924), p. 268.

333. Theory of the vibrations of thin shells.

The equations of vibration are to be formed by substituting for the external forces and couples X', Y', Z' and L', M' which occur in equations (45) and (46) of Article 331 the expressions for the reversed kinetic reactions and their moments. If we neglect "rotatory inertia" the values to be substituted for

* The result is due to G. H. Bryan, *London Math. Soc. Proc.*, vol. 22, 1891, p. 54.

L', M' are zero. When we use the components u, v, w of displacement defined in Article 326, the expressions to be substituted for (X', Y', Z') are $-2\rho h\,(\partial^2 u/\partial t^2, \partial^2 v/\partial t^2, \partial^2 w/\partial t^2)$.

In forming the equations we omit all products of u, v, w and their differential coefficients; and, since the stress-resultants and stress-couples are linear functions of these quantities, we may simplify the equations by replacing $p_1', \ldots$ by their values in the unstrained state, that is to say, by the values given for $p_1, \ldots$ in Article 323.

The equations (46) of Article 331 become

$$\left.\begin{aligned}
&\frac{1}{AB}\left\{\frac{\partial(H_1 B)}{\partial\alpha} - \frac{\partial(G_2 A)}{\partial\beta} + G_1\frac{\partial A}{\partial\beta} - H_2\frac{\partial B}{\partial\alpha}\right\} + N_2 = 0,\\
&\frac{1}{AB}\left\{\frac{\partial(G_1 B)}{\partial\alpha} + \frac{\partial(H_2 A)}{\partial\beta} - H_1\frac{\partial A}{\partial\beta} - G_2\frac{\partial B}{\partial\alpha}\right\} - N_1 = 0,\\
&\frac{H_1}{R_1} + \frac{H_2}{R_2} + S_1 + S_2 = 0;
\end{aligned}\right\} \quad \ldots\ldots(48)$$

and the equations (45) become

$$\left.\begin{aligned}
&\frac{1}{AB}\left\{\frac{\partial(T_1 B)}{\partial\alpha} - \frac{\partial(S_2 A)}{\partial\beta} + S_1\frac{\partial A}{\partial\beta} - T_2\frac{\partial B}{\partial\alpha}\right\} - \frac{N_1}{R_1} = 2\rho h\frac{\partial^2 u}{\partial t^2},\\
&\frac{1}{AB}\left\{\frac{\partial(S_1 B)}{\partial\alpha} + \frac{\partial(T_2 A)}{\partial\beta} - T_1\frac{\partial A}{\partial\beta} - S_2\frac{\partial B}{\partial\alpha}\right\} - \frac{N_2}{R_2} = 2\rho h\frac{\partial^2 v}{\partial t^2},\\
&\frac{1}{AB}\left\{\frac{\partial(N_1 B)}{\partial\alpha} + \frac{\partial(N_2 A)}{\partial\beta}\right\} + \frac{T_1}{R_1} + \frac{T_2}{R_2} = 2\rho h\frac{\partial^2 w}{\partial t^2}.
\end{aligned}\right\} \quad \ldots(49)$$

The equations (49), some of the quantities in which are connected by the relations (48), are the equations of vibration.

These equations are to be transformed into a system of partial differential equations for the determination of u, v, w, by expressing the various quantities involved in them in terms of u, v, w and their differential coefficients. This transformation may be effected by means of the theory given in preceding Articles of this Chapter. Equations (37) of Article 329 express G_1, G_2, H_1, H_2 in terms of κ_1, κ_2, τ, and equations (26) of Article 326 express κ_1, κ_2, τ in terms of u, v, w. By the first two of equations (48) therefore we have N_1, N_2 expressed in terms of u, v, w. Equations (36) of Article 329 give a first approximation to S_1, S_2, T_1, T_2 in terms of ϵ_1, ϵ_2, ϖ, and equations (21) of Article 326 express ϵ_1, ϵ_2, ϖ in terms of u, v, w. A closer approximation to S_1, S_2, T_1, T_2 is given in equations (42) and (44) of Article 330; and they are there expressed in terms of κ_1, κ_2, τ as well as ϵ_1, ϵ_2, ϖ; so that they can still be expressed in terms of u, v, w. When these approximate values are substituted in the third of equations (48) it becomes an identity. When N_1, N_2, S_1, S_2, T_1, T_2 are expressed in terms of u, v, w, the desired transformation is effected.

The *theory of the vibrations of a plane plate*, already treated provisionally in Article 314 (*d*) and (*e*), is included in this theory. In all the equations we have to take $1/R_1$ and $1/R_2$ to be zero. The equations (48) and (49) fall into two sets. One set contains $\partial^2 u/\partial t^2$, $\partial^2 v/\partial t^2$ and the stress-resultants of the type T, S; the other set contains $\partial^2 w/\partial t^2$, the stress-resultants of type N, and the stress-couples. Now, in this case, the stress-resultants of type T, S are expressible in terms of ϵ_1, ϵ_2, ϖ by the formulæ (36) of Article 329, and ϵ_1, ϵ_2, ϖ are expressible in terms of u, v by the formulæ

$$\epsilon_1 = \frac{\partial u}{\partial \alpha}, \quad \epsilon_2 = \frac{\partial v}{\partial \beta}, \quad \varpi = \frac{\partial v}{\partial \alpha} + \frac{\partial u}{\partial \beta},$$

α and β being ordinary Cartesian coordinates. Hence one of the two sets of equations into which (48) and (49) fall becomes identical with the equations of extensional vibration given in Article 314 (*e*). Further, the stress-couples are expressible in terms of κ_1, κ_2, τ by the formulæ (37) of Article 329 and κ_1, κ_2, τ are expressible in terms of w by the formulæ

$$\kappa_1 = \frac{\partial^2 w}{\partial \alpha^2}, \quad \kappa_2 = \frac{\partial^2 w}{\partial \beta^2}, \quad \tau = \frac{\partial^2 w}{\partial \alpha \partial \beta},$$

while N_1 and N_2 are expressible in terms of the stress-couples by the equations

$$N_1 = \frac{\partial G_1}{\partial \alpha} + \frac{\partial H_2}{\partial \beta}, \quad N_2 = \frac{\partial G_2}{\partial \beta} - \frac{\partial H_1}{\partial \alpha}.$$

The second of the two sets of equations into which (48) and (49) fall is equivalent to the equation of transverse vibration given in Article 314 (*d*).

In applying the results of Articles 329 and 330 to vibrations we make a certain assumption. A similar assumption is, as we noted in Article 277, made habitually in the theory of the vibrations of thin rods. We assume in fact that the state of strain within a thin plate or shell, when vibrating, is of a type which has been determined by using the equations of equilibrium. For example, in the case of a plane plate vibrating transversely, we assume that the internal strain in a small portion of the plate is very nearly the same as that which would be produced in the portion if it were held in equilibrium, with the middle plane bent to the same curvature. Consider a little more closely the state of a cylindrical or prismatic portion of a plane plate, such as would fit into a fine hole drilled transversely through it. We are assuming that, when the plate vibrates, any such prismatic portion is practically adjusted to equilibrium at each instant during a period. This being so, the most important components of strain in the portion, when the plate vibrates transversely, are given by

$$e_{xx} = -z\kappa_1, \quad e_{yy} = -z\kappa_2, \quad e_{xy} = -2z\tau, \quad e_{zz} = \{\sigma/(1-\sigma)\} z(\kappa_1 + \kappa_2),$$

and, when it vibrates in its plane, they are given by

$$e_{xx} = \epsilon_1, \quad e_{yy} = \epsilon_2, \quad e_{xy} = \varpi, \quad e_{zz} = -\{\sigma/(1-\sigma)\}(\epsilon_1 + \epsilon_2);$$

in both cases e_{zz} is adjusted so that the stress-component Z_z vanishes. It is clear that the assumption is justified if the periods of vibration of the plate are long compared with the periods of those modes of free vibration of the prismatic portion which would involve strain of such types as are assumed. Now the period of any mode of transverse vibration of the plate is directly proportional to the square of some linear dimension of the area contained within the edge-line and inversely proportional to the thickness, and the period of any mode of extensional vibration is directly proportional to some linear dimension of the area contained within the edge-line and independent of the thickness, while the period of any mode of free vibration of the prismatic portion, involving strains of such types as those assumed, is proportional to the linear dimensions of the portion, or, at an outside estimate, to the thickness of the plate. There is nothing in this argument peculiar to a plane plate; and we may conclude that it is legitimate to assume that, when a plate or shell is vibrating, the state of strain in any small portion is practically the same, at any instant, as it would be if the plate or shell were held in equilibrium, with its middle surface stretched and bent as it is at the instant. We see also that we ought to make the reservation that the argument by which the assumption is justified diminishes in cogency as the frequency of the mode of vibration increases*.

The most important result obtained by means of this assumption is the approximate determination of the stress-component Z_z. When there is equilibrium and the plate is plane, $Z_z=0$ to a second approximation; when there is equilibrium and the middle surface is curved, Z_z vanishes to a first approximation, and by the second approximation we express it as proportional to (h^2-z^2) and to a function which is linear in the principal curvatures and the changes of curvature. The results in regard to Z_z as a function of h and z can be illustrated by a discussion, based on the general equations of vibration of elastic solid bodies, of the vibrations of an infinite plate of finite thickness. Such a discussion has been given by Lord Rayleigh†; and from his results it can be shown that, in this case, there are classes of vibrations in which Z_z vanishes throughout the plate, and that, in the remaining classes, the expression for Z_z can be expanded in rising powers of h and z, and the expansion contains no terms of degree lower than the fourth.

When the middle surface is curved the components of displacement u, v, w must satisfy the differential equations (49) transformed as explained above, and they must also satisfy the boundary-conditions at the edge of the shell. At a free edge the flexural couple and the three linear combinations of the stress-resultants and the torsional couple expressed in (47) of Article 332 must vanish. The order of the system of equations is, in general, sufficiently high to admit of the satisfaction of such conditions; but the actual solution has not been effected in any particular case.

A method of approximate treatment of the problem depends upon the observation that the expressions for the stress-couples, and therefore also for

* The argument is clearly applicable with some modifications of detail to the theory of the vibrations of thin rods.

† *London Math. Soc. Proc.*, vol. 20 (1889), p. 225, or *Scientific Papers*, vol. 3, p. 249.

N_1, N_2, contain as a factor D or $\frac{2}{3}Eh^3/(1-\sigma^2)$ while the expressions for the remaining stress-resultants contain two terms, one proportional to h, and the other to h^3. Both members of each of the equations (49) can be divided by h; and then those terms of them which depend upon ϵ_1, ϵ_2, ϖ are independent of h, and the remaining terms contain h^2 as a factor. We should expect to get an approximately correct solution by omitting the terms in h^2. When this is done two of the boundary-conditions at a free edge, viz.: those of the type $G=0$, $N-\partial H/\partial s=0$, disappear; and the system of equations is of a sufficiently high order to admit of the satisfaction of the remaining boundary-conditions. Since h has disappeared from the equations and conditions, the frequency is independent of the thickness. The extension of the middle surface is the most important feature of the deformation, but it is necessarily accompanied by bending. The theory of such *extensional vibrations* may be obtained very simply by the energy method, as was noted in Article 329.

The extensional modes of vibration of a thin shell are analogous to the extensional vibrations of a thin plane plate, to which reference has already been made in this Article and in (*e*) of Article 314. The consideration of the case of a slightly curved middle surface shows at once that an open shell must also possess modes of vibration analogous to the transverse vibrations of a plane plate, and having frequencies which are much less than those of the extensional vibrations. The existence of such modes of vibration may be established by the following argument:

A superior limit for the frequency of the gravest tone can be found by assuming any convenient type of vibration; for, in any vibrating system, the frequency obtained by assuming the type cannot be less than the least frequency of natural vibration*. If we assume as the type of vibration one in which no line on the middle surface is altered in length, we may calculate the frequency by means of the formulæ for the kinetic energy and the potential energy of bending, as in Article 321. Since the kinetic energy contains h as a factor, and the potential energy h^3, the frequency is proportional to h. The frequency of such *inextensional vibrations* of a shell of given form can be lowered indefinitely in comparison with that of any mode of extensional vibration by diminishing h. It follows that the gravest mode of vibration cannot, in general, be of extensional type†.

If we assume that the vibration is of strictly inextensional type the forms of the components of displacement as functions of α, β are, as we saw in Articles 319, 320, and 326, very narrowly restricted. If displacements which satisfy the conditions of no extension are substituted in the expressions for

* Lord Rayleigh, *Theory of Sound*, vol. 1, § 89.

† The case of a closed sheet, such as a thin spherical shell, is an obvious exception, for there can be no inextensional displacement. A shell of given small thickness, completely closed except for a small aperture, is also exceptional when the aperture is small enough.

the stress-resultants and stress-couples, the equations of motion and the boundary-conditions cannot, in general, be satisfied.* It is clear, therefore, that the vibrations must involve some extension. To constrain the shell to vibrate in an inextensional mode forces would have to be applied at its edges and over its faces. When these forces are not applied, the displacement must differ from any which satisfies the conditions of no extension. But, in any of the graver modes of vibration, the difference must be slight; for, otherwise, the mode of vibration would be practically an extensional one, and the frequency could not be nearly small enough. From the form of the equations of vibration we may conclude that the requisite extension must be very small over the greater part of the surface; but near the edge it must be of sufficient importance to secure the satisfaction of the boundary-conditions†.

334. Vibrations of a thin cylindrical shell.

It is convenient to illustrate the theory by discussing in some detail the vibrations of a cylindrical shell. As in Article 319 we shall take a to be the radius of the shell, and write x for α and ϕ for β, and we shall suppose the edge-line to consist of two circles $x=l$ and $x=-l$. According to the results of Article 326, the extension and the changes of curvature are given by the equations

$$\epsilon_1=\frac{\partial u}{\partial x},\qquad \epsilon_2=\frac{1}{a}\left(\frac{\partial v}{\partial \phi}-w\right),\qquad \varpi=\frac{\partial v}{\partial x}+\frac{1}{a}\frac{\partial u}{\partial \phi},$$

$$\kappa_1=\frac{\partial^2 w}{\partial x^2},\qquad \kappa_2=\frac{1}{a^2}\left(\frac{\partial^2 w}{\partial \phi^2}+\frac{\partial v}{\partial \phi}\right),\qquad \tau=\frac{1}{a}\frac{\partial}{\partial x}\left(\frac{\partial w}{\partial \phi}+v\right).$$

The displacement being periodic in ϕ with period 2π, and the shell being supposed to vibrate in a normal mode with frequency $p/2\pi$, we shall take u, v, w to be proportional to sines, or cosines, of multiples of ϕ, and to a simple harmonic function of t with period $2\pi/p$. The equations of vibration then become a system of linear equations with constant coefficients for the determination of u, v, w as functions of x. We shall presently form these equations; but, before doing so, we consider the order of the system. The expressions for ϵ_1, ϵ_2, ϖ contain first differential coefficients only; that for κ_1 contains a second differential coefficient. Hence G_1 and G_2 contain second differential coefficients, and N_1 contains a third differential coefficient. The third equation of (49) contains $\partial^4 w/\partial x^4$ in a term which is omitted when we form the

* In the particular cases of spherical and cylindrical shells the failure of the inextensional displacement to satisfy the equations of motion and the boundary-conditions can be definitely proved. The case of cylindrical shells is dealt with in Article 334 (d).

† The difficulty arising from the fact that inextensional displacements do not admit of the satisfaction of the boundary-conditions is that to which I called attention in my paper of 1888 (see Introduction, footnote 133). The explanation that the extension, proved to be necessary, may be practically confined to a narrow region near the edge, and yet may be sufficiently important at the edge to secure the satisfaction of the boundary-conditions, was given simultaneously by A. B. Bassett and H. Lamb in the papers cited on pp. 532 and 505. These authors illustrated the possibility of this explanation by means of the solution of certain statical problems.

equations of extensional vibration. Thus the complete equations of vibration will be of a much higher order than the equations of extensional vibration. It will be seen presently that the former are a system of the 8th order, and the latter a system of the 4th order. The reduction of the order of the system which occurs when the equations of extensional vibration are taken instead of the complete equations is of fundamental importance. It does not depend at all on the cylindrical form of the middle surface.

(a) *General equations.*

In accordance with what has been said above, we take

$$u=U\sin n\phi\cos(pt+\epsilon),\quad v=V\cos n\phi\cos(pt+\epsilon),\quad w=W\sin n\phi\cos(pt+\epsilon),\ \ldots(50)$$

where U, V, W are functions of x. Then we have

$$\epsilon_1=\frac{dU}{dx}\sin n\phi\cos(pt+\epsilon),\quad \epsilon_2=-\frac{W+nV}{a}\sin n\phi\cos(pt+\epsilon),$$

$$\varpi=\left(\frac{dV}{dx}+n\frac{U}{a}\right)\cos n\phi\cos(pt+\epsilon),$$

$$\kappa_1=\frac{d^2W}{dx^2}\sin n\phi\cos(pt+\epsilon),\quad \kappa_2=-\frac{nV+n^2W}{a^2}\sin n\phi\cos(pt+\epsilon),$$

$$\tau=\frac{1}{a}\frac{d}{dx}(V+nW)\cos n\phi\cos(pt+\epsilon).$$

Also
$$G_1=-D\sin n\phi\cos(pt+\epsilon)\left(\frac{d^2W}{dx^2}-\sigma\frac{nV+n^2W}{a^2}\right),$$

$$G_2=-D\sin n\phi\cos(pt+\epsilon)\left(\sigma\frac{d^2W}{dx^2}-\frac{nV+n^2W}{a^2}\right),$$

$$H_1=D\cos n\phi\cos(pt+\epsilon)\frac{(1-\sigma)}{a}\left(n\frac{dW}{dx}+\frac{dV}{dx}\right)=-H_2.$$

The first two of equations (48) become

$$N_1=\frac{\partial G_1}{\partial x}+\frac{1}{a}\frac{\partial H_2}{\partial\phi},\quad N_2=\frac{1}{a}\frac{\partial G_2}{\partial\phi}-\frac{\partial H_1}{\partial x},$$

and we have

$$N_1=-D\sin n\phi\cos(pt+\epsilon)\left\{\frac{d^3W}{dx^3}-\frac{1}{a^2}\left(n^2\frac{dW}{dx}+n\frac{dV}{dx}\right)\right\},$$

$$N_2=-D\cos n\phi\cos(pt+\epsilon)\left\{\frac{n}{a}\frac{d^2W}{dx^2}-\frac{n^3}{a^3}W+\frac{1-\sigma}{a}\frac{d^2V}{dx^2}-\frac{n^2}{a^3}V\right\}.$$

We have also

$$T_1=D\left[\frac{3}{h^2}(\epsilon_1+\sigma\epsilon_2)+\frac{2-2\sigma-3\sigma^2}{2(1-\sigma)}\frac{\kappa_1}{a}-\frac{2\sigma+\sigma^2}{2(1-\sigma)}\frac{\kappa_2}{a}\right],$$

$$T_2=D\left[\frac{3}{h^2}(\epsilon_2+\sigma\epsilon_1)-\frac{\sigma+2\sigma^2}{2(1-\sigma)}\frac{\kappa_1}{a}-\frac{2+\sigma}{2(1-\sigma)}\frac{\kappa_2}{a}\right],$$

$$S_1=\tfrac{1}{2}D(1-\sigma)\left[\frac{3}{h^2}\varpi+\frac{\tau}{a}\right],\quad S_2=\tfrac{1}{2}D(1-\sigma)\left[-\frac{3}{h^2}\varpi+\frac{\tau}{a}\right],$$

where ϵ_1, κ_1, ... have the values given above. The equations of vibration are

$$\frac{\partial T_1}{\partial x}-\frac{1}{a}\frac{\partial S_2}{\partial\phi}+2\rho hp^2u=0,\quad \frac{\partial S_1}{\partial x}+\frac{1}{a}\frac{\partial T_2}{\partial\phi}-\frac{N_2}{a}+2\rho hp^2v=0,\quad \frac{\partial N_1}{\partial x}+\frac{1}{a}\frac{\partial N_2}{\partial\phi}+\frac{T_2}{a}+2\rho hp^2w=0,$$

or, in terms of U, V, W,

$$\frac{3D}{h^3}\left[\frac{d}{dx}\left(\frac{dU}{dx}-\sigma\,\frac{W+nV}{a}\right)-\frac{1-\sigma}{2}\,\frac{n}{a}\left(\frac{dV}{dx}+\frac{nU}{a}\right)\right]+2\rho p^2 U$$

$$+\frac{D}{h}\left[\frac{2-2\sigma-3\sigma^2}{2(1-\sigma)a}\,\frac{d^3W}{dx^3}+\frac{1+2\sigma^2}{2(1-\sigma)}\,\frac{n}{a^3}\,\frac{d}{dx}(V+nW)\right]=0, \quad \text{.........................(51)}$$

$$\frac{3D}{h^3}\left[\frac{n}{a}\left(\sigma\,\frac{dU}{dx}-\frac{W+nV}{a}\right)+\tfrac{1}{2}(1-\sigma)\,\frac{d}{dx}\left(\frac{dV}{dx}+\frac{nU}{a}\right)\right]+2\rho p^2 V$$

$$+\frac{D}{h}\left[-\frac{\sigma+2\sigma^2}{2(1-\sigma)}\,\frac{n}{a^2}\,\frac{d^2W}{dx^2}+\frac{2+\sigma}{2(1-\sigma)}\,\frac{n^2}{a^4}(V+nW)+\tfrac{1}{2}\,\frac{(1-\sigma)}{a^2}\,\frac{d^2}{dx^2}(V+nW)\right.$$

$$\left.+\frac{n}{a^2}\,\frac{d^2W}{dx^2}-\frac{n^3}{a^4}W+\frac{1-\sigma}{a^2}\,\frac{d^2V}{dx^2}-\frac{n^2}{a^4}V\right]=0, \quad \text{.....................(52)}$$

$$\frac{3D}{h^3}\left[\frac{\sigma}{a}\,\frac{dU}{dx}-\frac{W+nV}{a^2}\right]+2\rho p^2 W$$

$$-\frac{D}{h}\left[\frac{d^4W}{dx^4}-\frac{2n^2}{a^2}\,\frac{d^2W}{dx^2}+\frac{n^4}{a^4}W-(2-\sigma)\,\frac{n}{a^2}\,\frac{d^2V}{dx^2}+\frac{n^3}{a^4}V\right.$$

$$\left.+\frac{\sigma+2\sigma^2}{2(1-\sigma)a^2}\,\frac{d^2W}{dx^2}-\frac{2+\sigma}{2(1-\sigma)}\,\frac{n}{a^4}(nV+W)\right]=0. \quad \text{.....................(53)}$$

The boundary-conditions at $x=l$ and $x=-l$ are

$$T_1=0,\quad S_1+\frac{H_1}{a}=0,\quad N_1-\frac{1}{a}\,\frac{\partial H_1}{\partial\phi}=0,\quad G_1=0,$$

and all the left-hand members can be expressed as linear functions of U, V, W and their differential coefficients with respect to x.

The system of equations for the determination of u, v, w as functions of x has now been expressed as a linear system of the 8th order with constant coefficients. These coefficients contain the unknown constant p^2 as well as the known constants h and n; and n, being the number of wave-lengths to the circumference, can be chosen at pleasure. If we disregard the fact that h is small compared with a or l, we can solve the equations by assuming that, apart from the simple harmonic factors depending upon ϕ and t, the quantities u, v, w are of the form ξe^{mx}, ηe^{mx}, ζe^{mx}, where ξ, η, ζ, m are constants. The constant m is a root of a determinantal equation of the 8th degree, which is really of the 4th degree in m^2, for it contains no terms of any uneven degree. The coefficients in this equation depend upon p^2. When m satisfies this equation the ratios $\xi:\eta:\zeta$ are determined, in terms of m and p^2, by any two of the three equations of motion. Thus, apart from ϕ and t factors, the solution is of the form

$$u=\sum_{r=1}^{4}(\xi_r e^{m_r x}+\xi_r' e^{-m_r x}),\quad v=\sum_{r=1}^{4}(\eta_r e^{m_r x}+\eta_r' e^{-m_r x}),\quad w=\sum_{r=1}^{4}(\zeta_r e^{m_r x}+\zeta_r' e^{-m_r x}),$$

in which the constants ξ_r, ξ_r' are arbitrary, but the constants η_r, ... are expressed as multiples of them. The boundary-conditions at $x=l$ and $x=-l$ give eight homogeneous linear equations connecting the ξ, ξ'; and the elimination of the ξ, ξ' from these equations leads to an equation to determine p^2. This is the frequency equation.

(b) *Extensional vibrations.*

The equations of extensional vibration are obtained by omitting the terms in equations (51)—(53) which have the coefficient D/h. The determinantal equation for m^2 becomes a quadratic. The boundary-conditions at $x=\pm l$ become $T_1=0$, $S_1=0$, or

$$\frac{dU}{dx}-\sigma\frac{W+nV}{a}=0, \quad \frac{dV}{dx}+\frac{nU}{a}=0.$$

Since h does not occur in the differential equations or the boundary-conditions, the frequencies are independent of h.

In the case of *symmetrical vibrations*, in which u, v, w are independent of ϕ, we take

$$u=U\cos(pt+\epsilon), \quad v=V\cos(pt+\epsilon), \quad w=W\cos(pt+\epsilon),$$

and we find the equations

$$\frac{E}{1-\sigma^2}\left(\frac{d^2U}{dx^2}-\frac{\sigma}{a}\frac{dW}{dx}\right)+\rho p^2U=0, \quad \frac{E}{2(1+\sigma)}\frac{d^2V}{dx^2}+\rho p^2V=0,$$

$$\frac{E}{1-\sigma^2}\left(\frac{\sigma}{a}\frac{dU}{dx}-\frac{1}{a^2}W\right)+\rho p^2W=0.$$

The boundary-conditions at $x=\pm l$ are

$$\frac{dU}{dx}-\sigma\frac{W}{a}=0, \quad \frac{dV}{dx}=0.$$

There are two classes of symmetrical vibrations. In the first class U and W vanish, so that the displacement is tangential to the circular sections of the cylinder. In this class of vibrations we have

$$V=\eta\cos\frac{n\pi x}{l}, \quad p^2=\frac{E}{2\rho(1+\sigma)}\frac{n^2\pi^2}{l^2},$$

where n is an integer. These vibrations are analogous to the torsional vibrations of a solid cylinder considered in Article 200. In the second class V vanishes, so that the displacement takes place in planes through the axis, and we find

$$U=\xi\cos\frac{n\pi x}{l}, \quad W=\zeta\sin\frac{n\pi x}{l},$$

where ξ and ζ are connected by the equations

$$\left[p^2-\frac{E}{\rho(1-\sigma^2)}\frac{n^2\pi^2}{l^2}\right]\xi-\frac{E\sigma}{\rho(1-\sigma^2)}\frac{n\pi}{la}\zeta=0,$$

$$\left[p^2-\frac{E}{\rho(1-\sigma^2)}\frac{1}{a^2}\right]\zeta-\frac{E\sigma}{\rho(1-\sigma^2)}\frac{n\pi}{la}\xi=0.$$

The equation for p^2 is

$$p^4-p^2\frac{E}{\rho(1-\sigma^2)}\left(\frac{1}{a^2}+\frac{n^2\pi^2}{l^2}\right)+\frac{E^2n^2\pi^2}{\rho^2(1-\sigma^2)a^2l^2}=0.$$

If the length is great compared with the diameter, so that a/l is small, the two types of vibration are (i) almost purely radial, with a frequency $\{E/\rho(1-\sigma^2)\}^{\frac{1}{2}}/2\pi a$, and (ii) almost purely longitudinal, with a frequency $n(E/\rho)^{\frac{1}{2}}/2l$. The latter are of the same kind as the extensional vibrations of a thin rod (Article 278).

A more detailed investigation of the extensional vibrations of cylindrical shells with edges will be found in my paper cited in the Introduction, footnote 133. For a shell of infinite length the radial vibrations have been discussed by A. B. Basset, *London Math. Soc. Proc.*, vol. 21 (1891), p. 53, and the various modes of vibration have been investigated very fully by Lord Rayleigh, *London, Roy. Soc. Proc.*, vol. 45 (1889), p. 443, or *Scientific Papers*, vol. 3, p. 244. See also *Theory of Sound*, 2nd edition, vol. 1, Chapter X A.

(c) *Inextensional vibrations**.

The displacement in a principal mode of vibration is either two-dimensional and given by the formulæ

$$u=0,\quad v=A_n\cos(p_n t+\epsilon_n)\cos(n\phi+a_n),\quad w=-nA_n\cos(p_n t+\epsilon_n)\sin(n\phi+a_n),$$

where
$$p_n^2=\frac{D}{2\rho ha^4}\,\frac{n^2(n^2-1)^2}{n^2+1};$$

or else the displacement is three-dimensional and given by the formulæ

$$u=-\frac{a}{n}B_n\cos(p_n't+\epsilon_n')\sin(n\phi+\beta_n),\quad v=xB_n\cos(p_n't+\epsilon_n')\cos(n\phi+\beta_n),$$
$$w=-nxB_n\cos(p_n't+\epsilon_n')\sin(n\phi+\beta_n),$$

where
$$p_n'^2=\frac{D}{2\rho ha^4}\,\frac{n^2(n^2-1)^2}{n^2+1}\,\frac{1+6(1-\sigma)a^2/n^2l^2}{1+3a^2/n^2(n^2+1)l^2}.$$

All the values of p and p' are proportional to h.

(d) *Inexactness of the inextensional displacement.*

To verify the failure of the assumed inextensional displacement to satisfy the equations of motion, it is sufficient to calculate T_2 from the equations of motion, and compare the result with the second of the formulæ (44). Taking the two-dimensional vibration specified by A_n, we have the equation

$$\frac{T_2}{a}=-\frac{\partial N_1}{\partial x}-\frac{1}{a}\frac{\partial N_2}{\partial\phi}-2\rho hp_n^2w$$
$$=-\frac{Dn^3(n^2-1)}{a^4}\left(1-\frac{n^2-1}{n^2+1}\right)A_n\sin(n\phi+a_n)\cos(p_nt+\epsilon_n)$$
$$=-\frac{2Dn^3(n^2-1)}{(n^2+1)a^4}A_n\sin(n\phi+a_n)\cos(p_nt+\epsilon_n);$$

but we have also

$$T_2=-\frac{2+\sigma}{2(1-\sigma)}\frac{D\kappa_2}{a}$$
$$=-\frac{2+\sigma}{2(1-\sigma)}\frac{Dn(n^2-1)}{a^3}A_n\sin(n\phi+a_n)\cos(p_nt+\epsilon_n).$$

The two values of T_2 are different, and the equations of motion are not satisfied by the assumed displacement. It is clear that a correction of the displacement involving but slight extension would enable us to satisfy the differential equations.

Two of the boundary-conditions are $G_1=0$, $N_1-a^{-1}\partial H_1/\partial\phi=0$. When the vibration is two-dimensional, G_1 is independent of x, and cannot vanish at any particular value of x unless $A_n=0$. When the vibration is three-dimensional, N_1 and H_1 are independent of x, and $N_1-a^{-1}\partial H_1/\partial\phi$ cannot vanish at any particular value of x unless $B_n=0$. Thus the boundary-conditions cannot be satisfied by the assumed displacement. The correction of the displacement required to satisfy the boundary-conditions would appear to be more important than that required to satisfy the differential equations.

(e) *Nature of the correction to be applied to the inextensional displacement.*

It is clear that the existence of practically inextensional vibrations is connected with the fact that, when the vibrations are taken to be extensional, the order of the system of equations of vibration is reduced from eight to four. In the determinantal equation indicated in (a) of this Article the terms which contain m^8 and m^6 have h^2 as a factor, and thus two of the values

* See Chapter XXIII, Articles 319 and 321.

of m^2 are large of the order $1/h$. The way in which the solutions which depend on the large values of m would enable us to satisfy the boundary-conditions may be illustrated by the solution of the following statical problem*:

A portion of a circular cylinder bounded by two generators and two circular sections is held bent into a surface of revolution by forces applied along the bounding generators, the circular edges being free, in such a way that the displacement v tangential to the circular sections is proportional to the angular coordinate ϕ; it is required to find the displacement.

We are to have $v = c\phi$, where c is constant, while u and w are independent of ϕ. Hence

$$\epsilon_1 = \frac{\partial u}{\partial x}, \quad \epsilon_2 = \frac{c-w}{a}, \quad \varpi = 0, \quad \kappa_1 = \frac{\partial^2 w}{\partial x^2}, \quad \kappa_2 = \frac{c}{a^2}, \quad \tau = 0.$$

The stress-resultants S_1, S_2 and the stress-couples H_1, H_2 vanish, and we have

$$G_1 = -D\left(\frac{\partial^2 w}{\partial x^2} + \frac{\sigma c}{a^2}\right), \quad G_2 = -D\left(\frac{c}{a^2} + \sigma\frac{\partial^2 w}{\partial x^2}\right), \quad N_1 = -D\frac{\partial^3 w}{\partial x^3}, \quad N_2 = 0.$$

The equations of equilibrium are

$$\frac{\partial T_1}{\partial x} = 0, \quad \frac{\partial T_2}{\partial \phi} = 0, \quad -D\frac{\partial^4 w}{\partial x^4} + \frac{T_2}{a} = 0,$$

and the boundary-conditions at $x = \pm l$ are

$$T_1 = 0, \quad N_1 = 0, \quad G_1 = 0.$$

We seek to satisfy these equations and conditions approximately by the assumption that the extensional strains ϵ_1, ϵ_2 are of the same order as the flexural strains $h\kappa_1$, $h\kappa_2$. When this is the case T_1 and T_2 are given with sufficient approximation by the formulæ

$$T_1 = (3D/h^2)(\epsilon_1 + \sigma\epsilon_2), \quad T_2 = (3D/h^2)(\epsilon_2 + \sigma\epsilon_1).$$

To satisfy the equation $\partial T_1/\partial x = 0$ and the condition $T_1 = 0$ at $x = \pm l$ we must put $T_1 = 0$, or $\epsilon_1 = -\sigma\epsilon_2$, and then we have $T_2 = 3D(1-\sigma^2)\epsilon_2/h^2$. The equations of equilibrium are now reduced to the equation

$$-\frac{\partial^4 w}{\partial x^4} + \frac{3(1-\sigma^2)}{a^2 h^2}(c - w) = 0,$$

while the boundary-conditions at $x = \pm l$ become

$$-\frac{\partial^2 w}{\partial x^2} + \frac{\sigma c}{a^2} = 0, \quad \frac{\partial^3 w}{\partial x^3} = 0.$$

If we take $c - w$ to be a sum of terms of the form ζe^{mx}, then m^2 is large of the order $1/h$; and the solution is found to be

$$w = c + C_1 \cosh(qx/a)\cos(qx/a) + C_2 \sinh(qx/a)\sin(qx/a),$$

* This is the problem solved for this purpose by H. Lamb, *loc. cit.*, p. 505. The same point in the theory was illustrated by A. B. Basset, *loc. cit.*, p. 533, by means of a different statical problem.

where $q^2 = (a/2h)\sqrt{\{3(1-\sigma^2)\}}$,

and
$$C_1 = -\frac{\sigma c}{q^2}\frac{\sinh(ql/a)\cos(ql/a) - \cosh(ql/a)\sin(ql/a)}{\sinh(2ql/a) + \sin(2ql/a)},$$
$$C_2 = -\frac{\sigma c}{q^2}\frac{\sinh(ql/a)\cos(ql/a) + \cosh(ql/a)\sin(ql/a)}{\sinh(2ql/a) + \sin(2ql/a)}.$$

The form of the solution shows that near the boundaries ϵ_1, ϵ_2, $h\kappa_1$, $h\kappa_2$ are all of the same order of magnitude, but that, at a distance from the boundaries which is at all large compared with $(ah)^{\frac{1}{2}}$, ϵ_1 and ϵ_2 become small in comparison with $h\kappa_2$.

It may be shown that, in this statical problem, the potential energy due to extension is actually of the order $\sqrt{(h/a)}$ of the potential energy due to bending*. In the case of vibrations we may infer that the extensional strain, which is necessary in order to secure the satisfaction of the boundary-conditions, is practically confined to so narrow a region near the edge that its effect in altering the total amount of the potential energy, and therefore the periods of vibration, is negligible.

335. Vibrations of a thin spherical shell.

The case in which the middle surface is a complete spherical surface, and the shell is thin, has been investigated by H. Lamb† by means of the general equations of vibration of elastic solids. All the modes of vibration are extensional, and they fall into two classes, analogous to those of a solid sphere investigated in Article 194, and characterized respectively by the absence of a radial component of the displacement and by the absence of a radial component of the rotation. In any mode of either class the displacement is expressible in terms of spherical surface harmonics of a single integral degree. In the case of vibrations of the first class the frequency $p/2\pi$ is connected with the degree n of the harmonics by the equation

$$p^2a^2\rho/\mu = (n-1)(n+2), \quad \text{.......................(54)}$$

where a is the radius of the sphere. In the case of vibrations of the second class the frequency is connected with the degree of the harmonics by the equation

$$\frac{p^4a^4\rho^2}{\mu^2} - \frac{p^2a^2\rho}{\mu}\left[(n^2+n+4)\frac{1+\sigma}{1-\sigma} + (n^2+n-2)\right] + 4(n^2+n-2)\left(\frac{1+\sigma}{1-\sigma}\right) = 0.$$
$$\text{....................(55)}$$

If n exceeds unity there are two modes of vibration of the second class, and the gravest tone belongs to the slower of those two modes of vibration of this class for which $n = 2$. Its frequency $p/2\pi$ is given by

$$p = \sqrt{(\mu/\rho)}\, a^{-1}(1{\cdot}176),$$

* For further details in regard to this problem the reader is referred to the paper by H. Lamb already cited.

† *London Math. Soc. Proc.*, vol. 14 (1883), p. 50.

if Poisson's ratio for the material is taken to be $\frac{1}{4}$. The frequencies of all these modes are independent of the thickness.

In the limiting case of a plane plate the modes of vibration fall into two main classes, one inextensional, with displacement normal to the plane of the plate, and the other extensional, with displacement parallel to the plane of the plate. See Articles 314 (*d*) and (*e*) and 333. The case of an infinite plate of finite thickness has been discussed by Lord Rayleigh*, starting from the general equations of vibration of elastic solids, and using methods akin to those described in Article 214 *supra*. There is a class of extensional vibrations involving displacement parallel to the plane of the plate; and the modes of this class fall into two sub-classes, in one of which there is no displacement of the middle plane. The other of these two sub-classes appears to be the analogue of the tangential vibrations of a complete thin spherical shell. There is a second class of extensional vibrations involving a component of displacement normal to the plane of the plate as well as a tangential component, and, when the plate is thin, the normal component is small compared with the tangential component. The normal component of displacement vanishes at the middle plane, and the normal component of the rotation vanishes everywhere; so that the vibrations of this class are analogous to the vibrations of the second class of a complete thin spherical shell. There is also a class of flexural vibrations involving a displacement normal to the plane of the plate, and a tangential component of displacement which is small compared with the normal component when the plate is thin. The tangential component vanishes at the middle plane, so that the displacement is approximately inextensional. In these vibrations the linear elements which are initially normal to the middle plane remain straight and normal to the middle plane throughout the motion, and the frequency is approximately proportional to the thickness. There are no inextensional vibrations of a complete thin spherical shell.

The case of an open spherical shell or bowl stands between these extreme cases. When the aperture is very small, or the spherical surface is nearly complete, the vibrations must approximate to those of a complete spherical shell. When the angular radius of the aperture, measured from the included pole, is small, and the radius of the sphere is large, the vibrations must approximate to those of a plane plate. In intermediate cases there must be vibrations of practically inextensional type and also vibrations of extensional type.

Purely inextensional vibrations of a thin spherical shell, of which the edge-line is a circle, have been discussed in detail by Lord Rayleigh† by the methods

* *London Math. Soc. Proc.*, vol. 20 (1889), p. 225, or *Scientific Papers*, vol. 3, p. 249.

† *London Math. Soc. Proc.*, vol. 13 (1881), or *Scientific Papers*, vol. 1, p. 551. See also *Theory of Sound*, 2nd edition, vol. 1, Chapter X A.

described in Article 321 *supra*. In the case of a hemispherical shell the frequency $p/2\pi$ of the gravest tone is given by

$$p = \sqrt{(\mu/\rho)}\,(h/a^2)\,(4{\cdot}279).$$

When the angular radius α of the aperture is nearly equal to π, or the spherical surface is nearly complete, the frequency $p/2\pi$ of the gravest mode of inextensional vibration is given by $p = \sqrt{(\mu/\rho)}\,\{h/a^2(\pi-\alpha)^2\}\,(5{\cdot}657)$. By supposing $\pi - \alpha$ to diminish sufficiently, while h remains constant, we can make the frequency of the gravest inextensional mode as great as we please in comparison with the frequency of the gravest (extensional) mode of vibration of the complete spherical shell. Thus the general argument by which we establish the existence of practically inextensional modes breaks down in the case of a nearly complete spherical shell with a small aperture.

When the general equations of vibration are formed by the method illustrated above in the case of the cylindrical shell, the components of displacement being taken to be proportional to sines or cosines of multiples of the longitude ϕ, and also to a simple harmonic function of t, they are a system of linear equations of the 8th order for the determination of the components of displacement as functions of the co-latitude θ. The boundary-conditions at the free edge require the vanishing, at a particular value of θ, of four linear combinations of the components of displacement and certain of their differential coefficients with respect to θ. The order of the system of equations is high enough to admit of the satisfaction of such conditions; and the solution of the system of equations, subject to these conditions, would lead, if it could be effected, to the determination of the types of vibration and the frequencies.

The extensional vibrations can be investigated by the method illustrated above in the case of the cylindrical shell. The system of equations is of the fourth order, and there are two boundary-conditions*. In any mode of vibration the motion is compounded of two motions, one involving no radial component of displacement, and the other no radial component of rotation. Each motion is expressible in terms of a single spherical surface harmonic, but the degrees of the harmonics are not in general integers. The degree α of the harmonic by which the motion with no radial component of displacement is specified is connected with the frequency by equation (54), in which α is written for n; and the degree β of the harmonic by which the motion with no radial component of rotation is specified is connected with the frequency by equation (55), in which β is written for n. The two degrees α and β are connected by a transcendental equation, which is the frequency equation. The vibrations do not generally fall into classes in the same way as those of a complete shell; but, as the open shell approaches completeness, its modes of extensional vibration tend to pass over into those of the complete shell.

* The equations were formed and solved by E. Mathieu, *J. de l'École polytechnique*, t. 51 (1883). The extensional vibrations of spherical shells are also discussed in the paper by the present writer cited in the Introduction, footnote 133.

The existence of modes of vibration which are practically inextensional is clearly bound up with the fact that, when the vibrations are assumed to be extensional, the order of the system of differential equations of vibration is reduced from 8 to 4. As in the case of the cylindrical shell, it may be shown that the vibrations cannot be strictly inextensional, and that the correction of the displacement required to satisfy the boundary-conditions is more important than that required to satisfy the differential equations. We may conclude that, near the free edge, the extensional strains are comparable with the flexural strains, but that the extension is practically confined to a narrow region near the edge.

If we trace in imagination the gradual changes in the system of vibrations as the surface becomes more and more curved*, beginning with the case of a plane plate, and ending with that of a complete spherical shell, one class of vibrations, the practically inextensional class, appears to be totally lost. The reason of this would seem to lie in the rapid rise of frequency of all the modes of this class when the aperture in the surface is much diminished.

The theoretical problem of the vibrations of a spherical shell acquires great practical interest from the fact that an open spherical shell is the best representative of a bell which admits of analytical treatment. It may be taken as established that the vibrations of practical importance are inextensional, and the essential features of the theory of them have, as we have seen, been made out. The tones and modes of vibration of bells have been investigated experimentally by Lord Rayleigh†. He found that the nominal pitch of a bell, as specified by English founders, is not that of its gravest tone, but that of the tone which stands fifth in order of increasing frequency; in this mode of vibration there are eight nodal meridians.

* The process is suggested by H. Lamb in the paper cited on p. 505.

† *Phil. Mag.* (Ser. 5), vol. 29 (1890), p. 1, or *Scientific Papers*, vol. 3, p. 318, or *Theory of Sound*, 2nd edition, vol. 1, Chapter X.

CHAPTER XXIVA

EQUILIBRIUM OF THIN PLATES AND SHELLS

335 C. Large deformations of plates and shells.

The theory of thin plates and shells was developed primarily for the purpose of giving an account of the vibrations of such bodies, and was afterwards applied to statical questions. The displacements associated with vibrations are always extremely small. The ordinary approximate theory of the bending of plates under pressure was founded upon an extension, to more general cases, of results, which were obtained from certain exact or approximate solutions of the equations of equilibrium of elastic solid bodies*. In such solutions it is always understood that, apart from a displacement which would be possible in a rigid body, the displacement of any particle is very small in comparison with the linear dimensions of the body. It thus came to be assumed that the theory is inapplicable, unless the transverse displacement of the bent plate is a very small fraction of its thickness. The theories of Kirchhoff and Clebsch, and the theory of Chapter XXIV, were devised to take account of the possibility that the displacement of the middle surface may be of any order of magnitude, provided that the plate or shell is not overstrained. This condition shows at once that, if the displacement is not very small, the strained middle surface must be, either exactly or very nearly, a surface applicable upon the unstrained middle surface. In the particular case of a plane plate, the initially plane middle surface must, after strain, be either a developable surface, or derivable from such a surface by a displacement which is everywhere small. In a large thin plate, such as a sheet of metal a metre square and a millimetre thick, the displacement may be comparable with the thickness, and need not be small compared with the length or breadth. In dealing with displacements which are not necessarily small in comparison with the thickness, we have to distinguish cases where the ratio of some displacement to the facial linear dimensions need not be small, from cases where it must be. All the necessary equations for the discussion of both classes of cases have been obtained in Chapter XXIV. We shall now illustrate the former class of cases by an example of some historical interest, and then proceed to the consideration of the other class.

335 D. Plate bent to cylindrical form.

We suppose that an initially plane rectangular plate is bent without extension into the form of a circular cylinder with two edges as generators, and seek the forces that must be applied to it to hold it in this form.

Let x, y be rectangular cartesian coordinates specifying the position of a point on the unstrained middle surface, $x = \pm a$ the equations of the edges

* Reference is here made to the theories of Poisson and Kelvin and Tait.

which become generators of the cylinder, $y = \pm b$ the equations of the edges which become arcs of circles, $2h$ the thickness of the plate, R the radius of the cylinder. The same quantities x, y can be used as curvilinear coordinates specifying the position of a point on the cylinder of radius R. We shall put x for α and y for β in the relevant formulæ of Chapter XXIV. Then $A = 1$ and $B = 1$, and the formulæ of Article 324 become

$$p_1' = 0, \quad q_1' = -\frac{1}{R}, \quad r_1' = 0, \quad p_2' = 0, \quad q_2' = 0, \quad r_2' = 0,$$

with

$$\epsilon_1 = 0, \quad \epsilon_2 = 0, \quad \varpi = 0, \quad \kappa_1 = \frac{1}{R}, \quad \kappa_2 = 0, \quad \tau = 0.$$

The stress-resultants of types T, S and the stress-couples are given by equations (36) and (37) of Article 329, so that we have

$$T_1 = T_2 = S_1 = S_2 = 0, \quad G_1 = -\frac{D}{R}, \quad G_2 = -\sigma\frac{D}{R}, \quad H_1 = H_2 = 0.$$

The first two of equations (46) of Article 331 can be satisfied by putting

$$N_1 = N_2 = 0, \quad L' = M' = 0,$$

and the third of these equations is satisfied identically. Equations (45) of the same Article then require

$$X' = Y' = Z' = 0.$$

The boundary-conditions of Article 332 show that couples of magnitude D/R must be applied to the straight edges $x = \pm a$, and couples of magnitude $-\sigma D/R$ must be applied to the circular edges $y = \pm b$.

The greatest extension of any linear filament is the value of $-z\kappa_1$ at $z = -h$, or it is h/R; and it is therefore necessary that R should be so great compared with h that the quotient h/R is small of the order of admissible (elastic) strains.

It appears that, if the thickness is small enough, or the radius of curvature great enough, the plate can be held bent into the cylindrical form by couples applied at its edges only, and that the couples applied to the edges that become arcs of circles have to those applied to the edges that remain straight the ratio $\sigma : 1$. The relation of the couples to the curvature is exactly the same as in the case where the curvature is very small (Article 90).

It seems almost obvious that, if suitable forces are applied at the straight edges only, the other edges becoming free, the cylindrical form can be, at least very nearly, maintained. We shall therefore seek to satisfy the conditions of the problem by assuming that the middle surface can be derived from the cylindrical surface by a small displacement.

Let this displacement be resolved into components u along the tangent to a circle $y = \text{const.}$, v along the generator $x = \text{const.}$, and w along the normal to the cylinder drawn inwards. A little experience shows that it is advisable to assume that u is of the form ϵx, where ϵ is a small constant, and that v and w are independent of x. In the formulæ of Article 326 we have to put

$$R_1 = R, \quad A = B = 1.$$

Then we find

$$\epsilon_1 = \epsilon - \frac{w}{R}, \quad \epsilon_2 = \frac{dv}{dy}, \quad \varpi = 0,$$

$$p_1' = 0, \quad q_1' = -\frac{1}{R} - \frac{\epsilon}{R}, \quad r_1' = \frac{1}{R}\frac{dw}{dy}, \quad p_2' = \frac{d^2w}{dy^2}, \quad q_2' = 0, \quad r_2' = 0.$$

The stress-resultants of types T, S are given by the formulæ

$$T_1 = \frac{3D}{h^2}\left(\epsilon - \frac{w}{R} + \sigma\frac{dv}{dy}\right), \quad T_2 = \frac{3D}{h^2}\left(\frac{dv}{dy} + \sigma\epsilon - \frac{\sigma w}{R}\right), \quad -S_2 = S_1 = 0.$$

The quantities called κ_1, κ_2, τ are the differences of the values of the rotation elements $-q_1'/A$, p_2'/B, p_1'/A in the strained and unstrained states, so that we have

$$\kappa_1 = \frac{1+\epsilon}{R}, \quad \kappa_2 = \frac{d^2w}{dy^2}, \quad \tau = 0,$$

and the stress-couples are given by the formulæ

$$G_1 = -D\left(\frac{1+\epsilon}{R} + \sigma\frac{d^2w}{dy^2}\right), \quad G_2 = -D\left(\sigma\frac{1+\epsilon}{R} + \frac{d^2w}{dy^2}\right), \quad -H_2 = H_1 = 0.$$

Equations (46) of Article 331 give, on omission of terms of the second order in the displacement,

$$D\left(\frac{d^3w}{dy^3} + \frac{1}{R^2}\frac{dw}{dy}\right) + N_2 = 0, \quad N_1 = 0,$$

and the equations (45) of the same Article give in the same way

$$\frac{dT_2}{dy} = 0, \quad \frac{dN_2}{dy} + \frac{T_1}{R} = 0.$$

The boundary-conditions at $y = \pm b$ are

$$T_2 = 0, \quad N_2 = 0, \quad G_2 = 0.$$

To satisfy these equations and conditions it is first necessary that T_2 should vanish everywhere, so that

$$\frac{dv}{dy} = \sigma\left(\frac{w}{R} - \epsilon\right),$$

and then the formula for T_1 becomes

$$T_1 = -\frac{3D}{h^2}(1-\sigma^2)\left(\frac{w}{R} - \epsilon\right).$$

Substitution of this formula for T_1 in the equation connecting N_2 and T_1, followed by elimination of N_2 from the resulting equation and the equation connecting N_2 and w, then yields the equation

$$\frac{d^4w}{dy^4} + \frac{1}{R^2}\frac{d^2w}{dy^2} + \frac{3(1-\sigma^2)}{h^2R}\left(\frac{w}{R} - \epsilon\right) = 0.$$

The relevant solutions of this equation, being even functions of y, are of the form $w = \epsilon R + C_1 \cosh qy \cos q'y + C_2 \sinh qy \sin q'y$, where $\pm (q + \iota q')$ and $\pm (q - \iota q')$ are the complex roots of the quartic equation

$$m^4 h^2 R^2 + m^2 h^2 + 3(1 - \sigma^2) = 0.$$

Since h/R is very small, these roots are large in absolute value, and q and q' are given with sufficient approximation by putting

$$q = q' = \frac{\{3(1-\sigma)^2\}^{\frac{1}{4}}}{(2hR)^{\frac{1}{2}}}.$$

The boundary-condition $N_2 = 0$ at $y = \pm b$ is satisfied, to the same order of approximation, by making $d^3 W/dy^3$ vanish at $y = b$, so that

$$C_1 (\cosh qb \sin qb + \sinh qb \cos qb) + C_2 (\cosh qb \sin qb - \sinh qb \cos qb) = 0.$$

The boundary-condition $G_2 = 0$ at $y = \pm b$ is then satisfied, with sufficient approximation, by putting

$$Rq^2 \{C_1 (-2 \sinh qb \sin qb) + C_2 (2 \cosh qb \cos qb)\} + \sigma = 0.$$

Thus the constants C_1, C_2 are determined.

The constant ϵ may then be determined so that w may vanish at $y = \pm b$. It will be found that

$$\epsilon = -\frac{\sigma}{2R^2 q^2} \frac{\sinh 2qb - \sin 2qb}{\sinh 2qb + \sin 2qb},$$

so that ϵ is small of order h/R at least, and w is small of order h at least. Then u and v are small of the same order as w.

If R is of the same order as b, qb is large of the order $\sqrt{(b/h)}$. The principal extension of the middle surface $(w/R - \epsilon)$ is small of the order h/R near the edges $y = \pm b$, and diminishes rapidly as the distance from the edge increases, according to the law

$$\frac{2\sigma}{\sqrt{\{3(1-\sigma^2)\}}} \frac{h}{R} e^{-qd} \cos\left(qd + \frac{\pi}{4}\right),$$

where d denotes distance from the edge. The other principal extension is the product of this and σ. It thus appears that the extension of the middle surface is everywhere small of the order of admissible strains, extremely small except near the edges, but there rising in importance in such a way as to secure the satisfaction of the boundary-conditions $G_2 = 0$ and $N_2 = 0$.

We thus meet with a second example of an "edge-effect" similar to that which occurred in the solution of a statical problem in Article 334 (*e*).

The cases where b is small or great compared with R can be discussed in the same way. The former approximates to the case of a bar, bent to an appreciable curvature, the latter is the case of a plate bent to a small curvature. The case where hR is comparable with b^2 is that where qb is moderate, so that e^{-qb} is small, and is included in the foregoing discussion for qb large. This case is that of the "flexure of a broad very thin band (such as a watch-spring) bent into a circle of radius comparable with a third proportional to its thickness and breadth"—a problem to which Kelvin and Tait* drew attention, and which was afterwards solved, as above, by H. Lamb†.

335 E. Large thin plate subjected to pressure.

Proceeding now to discuss the magnitude of the transverse displacement in a plate, we consider a large thin plate, fixed at its edges and subjected to pressure on one face. As the thickness diminishes, and the transverse displacement increases, the flexural rigidity diminishes rapidly, the extensional strain, arising from the stretching of the initially plane middle surface, increases, and the importance of the tensile stress-resultants of type T, S increases in comparison with that of the shearing stress-resultants of type N. In extreme cases it may even happen that N_1 and N_2 are negligible in comparison with T_1, T_2, S_1, S_2, and that the extensional strains of type ϵ_1 are comparable with the flexural strains of type $h\kappa_1$. In such cases it will not be sufficient to estimate the extensional strains by the simplified formulæ of Article 326, but recourse must be had to the more exact formulæ of Article 325.

We take the unstrained middle plane to be the plane of x, y, and specify the displacement of a point on it by components u, v, w, where w is the transverse displacement in the direction of the axis of z. Then in the formulæ of Article 325 we have to put $x+u$, $y+v$, w for x, y, z. It is generally sufficient to omit quantities of the second order in differential coefficients of u, v, but it may be necessary to retain them in the case of w. Writing x for α and y for β, and putting $A=B=1$, we find

$$\epsilon_1=\frac{\partial u}{\partial x}+\frac{1}{2}\left(\frac{\partial w}{\partial x}\right)^2,\quad \epsilon_2=\frac{\partial v}{\partial y}+\frac{1}{2}\left(\frac{\partial w}{\partial y}\right)^2,\quad \varpi=\frac{\partial v}{\partial x}+\frac{\partial u}{\partial y}+\frac{\partial w}{\partial x}\frac{\partial w}{\partial y}.$$

The curvature of the deformed middle surface is expressed with sufficient approximation by the formulæ of Article 326, so that we have

$$\kappa_1=\frac{\partial^2 w}{\partial x^2},\quad \kappa_2=\frac{\partial^2 w}{\partial y^2},\quad \tau=\frac{\partial^2 w}{\partial x\partial y},$$

and, in the same way, the rotation elements p_1', ... are given, with sufficient approximation, by the formulæ

$$p_1'=\frac{\partial^2 w}{\partial x\partial y},\quad q_1'=-\frac{\partial^2 w}{\partial x^2},\quad r_1'=0,\quad p_2'=\frac{\partial^2 w}{\partial y^2},\quad q_2'=-\frac{\partial^2 w}{\partial x\partial y},\quad r_2'=0.$$

The stress-resultants of type T, S are given by the formulæ

$$T_1=\frac{3D}{h^2}(\epsilon_1+\sigma\epsilon_2),\quad T_2=\frac{3D}{h^2}(\epsilon_2+\sigma\epsilon_1),\quad -S_2=S_1=\frac{3D}{2h^2}(1-\sigma)\varpi,$$

and the stress-couples by the formulæ

$$G_1=-D(\kappa_1+\sigma\kappa_2),\quad G_2=-D(\kappa_2+\sigma\kappa_1),\quad -H_2=H_1=D(1-\sigma)\tau.$$

* *Nat. Phil.*, Part II, § 717.

† *Manchester, Lit. and Phil. Soc., Mem. and Proc.* (Ser. 4), vol. 3 (1890), p. 216, and *Phil. Mag.* Ser. 5), vol. 31 (1891), p. 182.

We suppose the plate to be subjected to pressure p on the face $z=-h$. Then equations (46) of Article 331 give

$$N_1=\frac{\partial G_1}{\partial x}+\frac{\partial H_2}{\partial y},\quad N_2=-\frac{\partial H_1}{\partial x}+\frac{\partial G_2}{\partial y},$$

and equations (45) of the same Article become

$$\frac{\partial T_1}{\partial x}-\frac{\partial S_2}{\partial y}-N_1\frac{\partial^2 w}{\partial x^2}-N_2\frac{\partial^2 w}{\partial x\partial y}=0,$$

$$\frac{\partial S_1}{\partial x}+\frac{\partial T_2}{\partial y}-N_1\frac{\partial^2 w}{\partial x\partial y}-N_2\frac{\partial^2 w}{\partial y^2}=0,$$

$$\frac{\partial N_1}{\partial x}+\frac{\partial N_2}{\partial y}+T_1\frac{\partial^2 w}{\partial x^2}-S_2\frac{\partial^2 w}{\partial x\partial y}+S_1\frac{\partial^2 w}{\partial x\partial y}+T_2\frac{\partial^2 w}{\partial y^2}+p=0,$$

and it will generally be sufficient to omit the terms in N_1, N_2 from the first two of these. Then these two equations become

$$\frac{\partial T_1}{\partial x}+\frac{\partial S_1}{\partial y}=0,\quad \frac{\partial S_1}{\partial x}+\frac{\partial T_2}{\partial y}=0,$$

showing that T_1, T_2, S_1 can be expressed in terms of a function U by the formulæ

$$T_1=\frac{\partial^2 U}{\partial y^2},\quad T_2=\frac{\partial^2 U}{\partial x^2},\quad S_1=-\frac{\partial^2 U}{\partial x\partial y},$$

just as in the theory of plane stress. The remaining equation of equilibrium becomes

$$-D\nabla_1^4 w+\frac{\partial^2 U}{\partial y^2}\frac{\partial^2 w}{\partial x^2}+\frac{\partial^2 U}{\partial x^2}\frac{\partial^2 w}{\partial y^2}-2\frac{\partial^2 U}{\partial x\partial y}\frac{\partial^2 w}{\partial x\partial y}+p=0.$$

On expressing T_1, T_2, S_1 in terms of differential coefficients of u, v, w, and eliminating u and v by means of the identity

$$\frac{\partial^2}{\partial y^2}\frac{\partial u}{\partial x}+\frac{\partial^2}{\partial x^2}\frac{\partial v}{\partial y}=\frac{\partial^2}{\partial x\partial y}\left(\frac{\partial v}{\partial x}+\frac{\partial u}{\partial y}\right),$$

we obtain the equation

$$\nabla_1^4 U+3(1-\sigma^2)\frac{D}{h^2}\left\{\frac{\partial^2 w}{\partial x^2}\frac{\partial^2 w}{\partial y^2}-\left(\frac{\partial^2 w}{\partial x\partial y}\right)^2\right\}=0.$$

We have thus two non-linear partial differential equations to determine w and U as functions of x and y.

The theory is effectively due to A. Föppl*, and the difficulty of solving the non-linear equations has been noted by Th. v. Kármán†, as one of two difficulties which beset the application of the theory of plates to technical questions, the other being that, at a fixed edge, the analytical conditions assumed to apply to "supported" or "clamped" edges are never fulfilled exactly. Approximate methods of dealing with the differential equations, in the cases of circular and rectangular plates, have been devised by H. Hencky‡. We shall not pursue the matter here in this way, but illustrate the theory by the comparatively simple example of a very long strip fixed at its edges.

* *Vorlesungen ü. technische Mechanik*, Bd. 5, Leipzig, 1907, § 24.

† *Ency. d. math. Wiss.*, Bd. IV. 2, II, Leipzig, 1910, § 8.

‡ *Zeitschr. f. Math. u. Phys.*, Bd. 63 (1914), p. 311, and *Zeitschr. f. angewandte Math. u. Mechanik*, Bd. 1 (1921), p. 81. The case of the circular plate has also been discussed, with some other examples, by J. Prescott, *Phil. Mag.* (Ser. 6), vol. 43 (1922), p. 97.

335 F. Long strip. Supported edges.

We shall treat the strip as of infinite length, and take its edges to be given by the equations $x = \pm a$. We shall take the pressure p to be constant.

The component displacement v vanishes, and u and w are independent of y. The relevant equations are

$$T_1 = \frac{3D}{h^2}\left\{\frac{du}{dx} + \frac{1}{2}\left(\frac{dw}{dx}\right)^2\right\}, \quad T_2 = \frac{3D}{h^2}\,\sigma\left\{\frac{du}{dx} + \frac{1}{2}\left(\frac{dw}{dx}\right)^2\right\}, \quad -S_2 = S_1 = 0,$$

$$G_1 = -D\frac{d^2w}{dx^2}, \quad G_2 = -\sigma D\frac{d^2w}{dx^2}, \quad -H_2 = H_1 = 0,$$

$$N_1 = -D\frac{d^3w}{dx^3}, \quad N_2 = 0,$$

$$\frac{dT_1}{dx} - N_1\frac{d^2w}{dx^2} = 0, \quad \frac{dN_1}{dx} + T_1\frac{d^2w}{dx^2} + p = 0.$$

The boundary-conditions to be satisfied at the edges $x = \pm a$ are

$$u = 0, \quad w = 0, \quad G_1 = 0.$$

The system of differential equations to be solved reduces to the pair

$$\frac{dT_1}{dx} + D\frac{d^2w}{dx^2}\frac{d^3w}{dx^3} = 0, \quad D\frac{d^4w}{dx^4} - T_1\frac{d^2w}{dx^2} - p = 0.$$

The first can be integrated in the form

$$T_1 = a_1 - \tfrac{1}{2}D\left(\frac{d^2w}{dx^2}\right)^2,$$

where a_1 is constant, and the second becomes

$$D\frac{d^4w}{dx^4} - \left\{a_1 - \tfrac{1}{2}D\left(\frac{d^2w}{dx^2}\right)^2\right\}\frac{d^2w}{dx^2} - p = 0.$$

We seek an approximate solution on the supposition that the term

$$-\tfrac{1}{2}D\left(\frac{d^2w}{dx^2}\right)^2$$

may be omitted. Then, putting

$$a_1 = Dm^2,$$

and observing that w must be an even function of x, we find that w must be of the form

$$w = A + B\cosh mx - \frac{1}{2}\frac{p}{Dm^2}x^2,$$

where A and B are constants. Introducing the conditions that w and d^2w/dx^2 vanish at $x = a$, we obtain the formula

$$w = \frac{p}{Dm^2}\left\{\tfrac{1}{2}(a^2 - x^2) - \frac{1}{m^2}\left(1 - \frac{\cosh mx}{\cosh ma}\right)\right\},$$

which reduces approximately, when m is very small, to the formula given by the ordinary approximate theory, viz.

$$w = \frac{p}{24D}(5a^2 - x^2)(a^2 - x^2).$$

The remaining boundary-condition, $u = 0$ at $x = \pm a$, leads to an equation connecting ma with (pa^4/Eh^4). By equating the expression for T_1 in terms of differential coefficients of u and w to a_1 or Dm^2, integrating both sides of the resulting equation with respect to x between the limits 0 and a, and observing that u must vanish with x, we obtain the equation

$$m^2 a = \frac{3}{2h^2}\int_0^a \left(\frac{dw}{dx}\right)^2 dx,$$

giving

$$m^8 a^8 \cosh^2 ma =$$
$$\frac{27}{8}(1-\sigma^2)^2\left(\frac{pa^4}{Eh^4}\right)^2\left\{\left(\frac{1}{3}m^2a^2 - 2\right)\cosh^2 ma + \frac{5}{2}\frac{\sinh ma \cosh ma}{ma} - \frac{1}{2}\right\}$$

From this equation it is found that, when ma is small,

$$\frac{pa^4}{Eh^4} \to \frac{2}{3}(1-\sigma^2)^{-1}\sqrt{\left(\frac{210}{17}\right)}\, ma;$$

as ma increases pa^4/Eh^4 also increases, and, when ma is great,

$$\frac{pa^4}{Eh^4} \to \frac{2}{3}\sqrt{2}\,.\,(1-\sigma^2)^{-1} m^3 a^3.$$

The results were obtained on the supposition that $\frac{1}{2}D(d^2w/dx^2)^2$ could be neglected in comparison with a_1, or Dm^2. The maximum value of the neglected term occurs at $x = 0$, and the ratio of this maximum to Dm^2 is, for any given value of ma,

$$\frac{9(1-\sigma^2)^2}{8}\left(\frac{pa^4}{Eh^4}\right)^2\left(\frac{\cosh ma - 1}{m^3a^3\cosh ma}\right)^2\frac{h^2}{a^2},$$

which is always small of order $(h/a)^2$. Thus the omission of the neglected term is justified.

The resistance of the plate to pressure is seen to depend upon the quantity (pa^4/Eh^4), but the constituent ratios h/a and p/E, which enter into this expression, may not be given arbitrarily, since they must be subject to the condition which secures that the plate is not overstrained. This condition may be expressed in the statement that the maximum value of the extension e_{xx}, or $\epsilon_1 - z\kappa_1$, must be numerically less than some small number depending upon the material. We denote this number by ϵ. The extensional strain ϵ_1 is $T_1h^2/3D$, or $\frac{1}{3}m^2h^2$, and the maximum value of the flexural strain $-\kappa_1 z$ occurs at $x = 0$, $z = h$, where it is $\frac{3}{2}(1-\sigma^2)\dfrac{pa^4}{Eh^4}\dfrac{1}{m^2a^2}\left(1 - \dfrac{1}{\cosh ma}\right)\dfrac{h^2}{a^2}$. Thus we have the relation of inequality

$$\frac{1}{3}\frac{h^2}{a^2}m^2a^2\left[1 + \frac{9}{2}(1-\sigma^2)\frac{pa^4}{Eh^4}\frac{1}{m^4a^4}\left(1 - \frac{1}{\cosh ma}\right)\right] < \epsilon.$$

The second term in the square brackets is the ratio of the flexural to the extensional strain of the middle surface. The meaning of the relation of inequality may be expressed graphically by regarding the ratios h/a and p/E as coordinates of a point in a plane, and plotting the curve obtained from this relation by replacing the sign $<$ by the sign $=$. When ma is very small, the flexural strain is great compared with the extensional strain, and

$$\frac{h}{a} \to \left(\frac{17}{210}\right)^{\frac{1}{4}} \left(\frac{2\epsilon}{ma}\right)^{\frac{1}{2}},$$

also

$$\frac{p}{E} \to \frac{4}{3}\frac{1}{1-\sigma^2}\left(\frac{17}{210}\right)^{\frac{1}{2}}\frac{2\epsilon^2}{ma},$$

so that the curve nearly coincides with the parabola

$$\frac{p}{E} = \frac{4}{3}\frac{\epsilon}{1-\sigma^2}\left(\frac{h}{a}\right)^2.$$

As ma increases, the curve lies above this parabola. When ma becomes very great, the flexural strain is small compared with the extensional strain, and

$$\frac{h}{a} \to \frac{(3\epsilon)^{\frac{1}{2}}}{ma}, \quad \frac{p}{E} \to \frac{6\sqrt{2}}{1-\sigma^2}\frac{\epsilon^2}{ma},$$

so that the curve touches at the origin the straight line

$$\frac{p}{E} = \frac{2\sqrt{6}}{1-\sigma^2}\epsilon^{\frac{3}{2}}\frac{h}{a}.$$

A point situated below the curve, and in that quadrant of the plane in which h/a and p/E are positive, corresponds to simultaneous values of h/a and p/E for which the plate will not be overstrained. The curve may be described as the "curve of safety." The values of h/a must, of course, be rather small, of order 0·05 or less, or the body under discussion could hardly be called a "plate," and the theory of thin plates would not apply to it. The values of p/E must also be small, of order ϵ or less, but this condition is included in the condition that the representative point $(h/a, p/E)$ must lie below the curve of safety.

Let w_0' denote the central deflexion, the value of w at $x=0$, that would be given by the ordinary approximate theory, and let w_0 denote the value given by the present more exact theory. We have

$$\frac{w_0'}{h} = \frac{5}{16}(1-\sigma^2)\frac{pa^4}{Eh^4},$$

and

$$\frac{w_0}{h} = \frac{3}{4}(1-\sigma^2)\frac{(m^2a^2-2)\cosh ma + 2}{m^4a^4\cosh ma}\frac{pa^4}{Eh^4}.$$

When ma is very small, these tend to equality. As ma increases, w_0/h is less than w_0'/h, and both increase. When ma is very great,

$$w_0/h \to \tfrac{1}{2}\sqrt{2}\,ma,$$

but, of course, it does not really increase indefinitely, being kept down by the condition of safety. Taking account of this condition, we find that, as $ma \to \infty$,

$$w_0/h \to \surd(6\epsilon) . (a/2h).$$

Without overstrain w_0/h can be a quite considerable number (such as 20 or 30) in a large thin plate.

The appended short Table, in the calculation of which σ has been taken to be $\frac{1}{4}$, shows how the values of w_0/h and w_0'/h increase for moderate fractional values of ma.

ma	0·1	0·2	0·3	0·4	0·5
w_0/h	0·0732	0·1464	0·2196	0·2928	0·3659
w_0'/h	0·0735	0·1488	0·2277	0·3119	0·4032

From this Table it appears that the ordinary approximate theory gives a fair approximation up to about $ma = 0·3$. The corresponding value of pa^4/Eh^4 is about 0·7771.

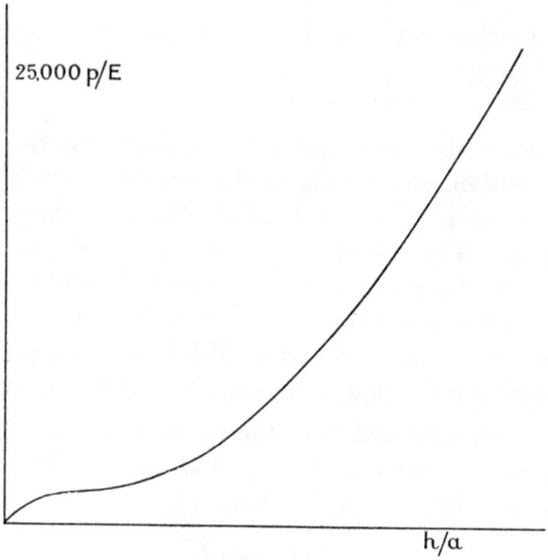

Fig. 75.

The following Table gives some related values of ma and pa^4/Eh^4, and the corresponding values on the curve of safety of h/a and $10^7 \times p/E$, the values of σ and ϵ being taken to be $\frac{1}{4}$ and 0·0005. Fig. 75 shows the form of the curve of safety, the values of p/E being magnified 25,000 times in comparison with those of h/a. The inflexion in the figure indicates the transition from states in which the resistance is mainly flexural to states in which it is mainly tensile.

ma	pa^4/Eh^4	h/a	$10^7 \times p/E$
0·1	0·249	0·0528	19·6
0·16	0·404	0·0411	12·0
0·2	0·508	0·0370	9·54
0·3	0·777	0·0300	6·27
0·4	1·065	0·0257	4·67
0·5	1·38	0·0228	3·73
1	3·51	0·0155	2·05
1·5	7·17	0·0123	1·62
2	13·10	0·0103	1·47
2·5	22·2	0·00893	1·41
3	34·8	0·00795	1·395
4	74·7	0·00656	1·37
5	139	0·00558	1·35
6	233	0·00487	1·31
16	4164	0·00215	0·889

335 G. Long strip. Clamped edges.

When the edges $x=\pm a$ are clamped, we have $\partial w/\partial x=0$ at $x=\pm a$ instead of $G_1=0$. Then, with the same notation,

$$w=\frac{p}{Dm^2}\left\{\tfrac{1}{2}(a^2-x^2)-a^2\,\frac{\cosh ma-\cosh mx}{ma\sinh ma}\right\},$$

reducing approximately, when ma is small, to the formula

$$w=\frac{p}{24D}(a^2-x^2)^2,$$

that would be given by the ordinary approximate theory.

In this case the condition that $u=0$ at $x=\pm a$ gives the equation

$$m^8a^8\sinh^2 ma=\frac{27}{8}(1-\sigma^2)^2\left(\frac{pa^4}{Eh^4}\right)^2\{(\tfrac{1}{3}m^2a^2+2)\sinh^2 ma-\tfrac{3}{2}ma\sinh ma\cosh ma-\tfrac{1}{2}m^2a^2\}.$$

When ma is small

$$\frac{pa^4}{Eh^4}\to\sqrt{(140)}\,(1-\sigma^2)^{-1}\,ma,$$

as ma increases, pa^4/Eh^4 increases, and, when ma is great,

$$\frac{pa^4}{Eh^4}\to\frac{2\sqrt{2}}{3}(1-\sigma^2)^{-1}m^3a^3.$$

The condition that the plate is not overstrained is

$$\frac{1}{3}\frac{h^2}{a^2}m^2a^2\left[1+\frac{9}{2}(1-\sigma^2)\frac{pa^4}{Eh^4}\frac{1}{m^4a^4}\left(\frac{ma\cosh ma}{\sinh ma}-1\right)\right]<\epsilon,$$

where the second term in the square brackets is the ratio of the flexural strain at the edges to the extensional strain of the middle surface; and the equation of the curve of safety is obtained by replacing the sign $<$ by the sign $=$. When ma is very small,

$$\frac{h}{a}\to(140)^{-\frac{1}{4}}\left(\frac{2\epsilon}{ma}\right)^{\frac{1}{2}},$$

and

$$\frac{p}{E}\to 2\,(140)^{-\frac{1}{2}}(1-\sigma^2)^{-1}\frac{2\epsilon^2}{ma},$$

so that the curve nearly coincides with the parabola

$$\frac{p}{E}=\frac{2\epsilon}{1-\sigma^2}\left(\frac{h}{a}\right)^2.$$

When ma is very great,

$$\frac{h}{a} \to \left(\frac{3\epsilon}{1+3\sqrt{2}}\right)^{\frac{1}{2}} \frac{1}{ma},$$

and

$$\frac{p}{E} \to \frac{6\sqrt{2}}{19+6\sqrt{2}} \frac{\epsilon^2}{1-\sigma^2} \frac{1}{ma},$$

so that the curve touches at the origin the straight line

$$\frac{p}{E} = \frac{2\sqrt{6}}{(1+3\sqrt{2})^{\frac{3}{2}}} \frac{\epsilon^{\frac{3}{2}}}{1-\sigma^2} \frac{h}{a}.$$

The results are obtained on the supposition that $\frac{1}{2}D(d^2w/dx^2)^2$ can be neglected in comparison with Dm^2. The maximum value of the neglected term occurs at $x = \pm a$, and the ratio of this maximum to Dm^2 is, for any given value of ma,

$$\frac{9}{8}(1-\sigma^2)^2 \left(\frac{pa^4}{Eh^4}\right)^2 \left(\frac{ma \cosh ma - \sinh ma}{m^3a^3 \sinh ma}\right)^2 \frac{h^2}{a^2}.$$

For very small values of ma this is small of the order $35\left(\frac{h}{a}\right)^2$, for moderate values of ma it is small of the order $(h/a)^2$, and for great values of ma it tends to m^2h^2, so that, if the plate is not overstrained, it tends to $3\epsilon/(1+3\sqrt{2})$. Thus it is always small, and the supposition is justified.

It is noteworthy that the ratio of the flexural to the extensional strain is large of order $(1/ma)$ when ma is small, just as in the case of supported edges, but, when ma is great, the ratio tends to a finite limit $3\sqrt{2} : 1$ in the present case, and to zero in the case of supported edges.

The ordinary approximate theory now gives a fair approximation up to about $ma=0{\cdot}7$, for which, with $\sigma=\frac{1}{4}$ and the previous notation (w_0' and w_0 for the central deflexions, as given by the approximate and more exact theories), it is found that $w_0'/h=0{\cdot}1263$ and $w_0/h=0{\cdot}1203$. The corresponding value of pa^4/Eh^4 is $2{\cdot}156$. It appears that the ordinary theory gives a better approximation in the case of clamped, than in that of supported, edges, and that the transverse deflexion need not be a very small fraction of the thickness. The condition that the plate is not overstrained is, as before, that the representative point $(h/a, p/E)$ lies below the curve of safety. The general form of this curve is like that found for supported edges, but not exactly the same.

EQUILIBRIUM OF THIN SHELLS

336. Small displacement.

Passing now to the theory of the equilibrium of thin shells, subjected to external forces, we shall suppose that the displacement is everywhere small. The equations of equilibrium (45) and (46) of Article 331 are a set of six equations connecting the six stress-resultants $T_1, \ldots$ and the four stress-couples $G_1, \ldots$ with the displacement (u, v, w); for the six quantities of type p_1', which occur in these equations, have been connected with u, v, w by equations (24) and (25) of Article 326. If the first approximations to the stress-resultants and stress-couples are regarded as sufficient, four of the six stress-resultants and all the stress-couples are expressed in terms of the quantities $\epsilon_1, \epsilon_2, \varpi$ and κ_1, κ_2, τ by equations (36) and (37) of Article 329; and these quantities are expressed in terms of u, v, w by equations (21) and (26) of Article 326. We have therefore a set of six differential equations to determine the five quantities N_1, N_2, u, v, w. Apart from the apparent redundancy of the set of differential equations, the method consists in simplifying the equations by omitting all terms which are of order higher than the first in N_1, N_2, u, v, w, and then solving the differential equations as if they were exact and not merely approximate.

The excess of the number of equations above the number of quantities to be determined would constitute a serious difficulty if the equations were exact; but the difficulty disappears when the approximate character of the equations is taken into account. The apparently redundant equation is the 3rd of equations (46) of Article 331. Now the expressions for the stress-couples G_1, ... are of the first order in u, v, w, and the expressions for p_1', ... in terms of u, v, w contain terms which are of the first order in u, v, w, and some of them also contain terms independent of u, v, w, but p_1' and q_2' contain no such terms. When terms of order higher than the first in u, v, w are omitted, the 3rd of equations (46) of Article 331 takes the form

$$\frac{H_1}{R_1}+\frac{H_2}{R_2}+S_1+S_2=0,$$

and this equation cannot in general be reconciled with equations (36) and (37) of Article 329. When the more exact equations (42) of Article 330 are employed to express S_1, S_2 in terms of u, v, w it becomes an identity. On the other hand, when H_1 and H_2 may be neglected it is satisfied identically by the simpler expressions given in (36) of Article 329. In either case there are sufficient equations to determine the unknown quantities in terms of the variables α, β, by which the position of a point on the middle surface is specified; and they are a system of differential equations of a sufficiently high order to admit of the satisfaction of arbitrary boundary-conditions of stress or displacement at the edge of the shell.

337. The middle surface a surface of revolution.

The case where the middle surface is a surface of revolution, including technically important problems relating to cylindrical, spherical, and conical shells, will chiefly occupy us. We choose as the variable β the angle, which the axial plane, passing through a point of the unstrained middle surface, makes with a fixed axial plane. This will be denoted by ϕ. The corresponding B is the distance of the point from the axis of revolution, and it is independent of ϕ, but is, in general, a function of the other variable α. The quantity A and the principal curvatures ($1/R_1$ and $1/R_2$) of the unstrained middle surface are also functions of α and independent of ϕ. When, as we shall generally assume, the edge of the shell consists of two circles of latitude ($\alpha=$ const.), the forces acting upon the shell must either be independent of ϕ or periodic functions of ϕ with period 2π, and we may suppose them expanded in Fourier's series of sines and cosines of integral multiples of ϕ. The components of displacement and the stress-resultants and stress-couples may be supposed to be expanded in similar series. Whenever the thickness $2h$ is independent of ϕ, we may treat separately the terms of these series which contain sines or cosines of $n\phi$, n being zero or any positive integer. To avoid the constant repetition of $\sin n\phi$ or $\cos n\phi$ it is convenient to introduce a new notation. In doing this we shall take occasion to avoid also the constant repetition of the quantity $2Eh/(1-\sigma^2)$. We shall write

$$\left.\begin{aligned}
&u = U\cos(n\phi+\epsilon),\quad v = V\sin(n\phi+\epsilon),\quad w = W\cos(n\phi+\epsilon),\\
&T_1 = \frac{2Eh}{1-\sigma^2}t_1\cos(n\phi+\epsilon),\quad T_2 = \frac{2Eh}{1-\sigma^2}t_2\cos(n\phi+\epsilon),\\
&S_1 = \frac{2Eh}{1-\sigma^2}s_1\sin(n\phi+\epsilon),\quad S_2 = \frac{2Eh}{1-\sigma^2}s_2\sin(n\phi+\epsilon),\\
&N_1 = \frac{2Eh}{1-\sigma^2}n_1\cos(n\phi+\epsilon),\quad N_2 = \frac{2Eh}{1-\sigma^2}n_2\sin(n\phi+\epsilon),\\
&G_1 = \frac{2Eh}{1-\sigma^2}g_1\cos(n\phi+\epsilon),\quad G_2 = \frac{2Eh}{1-\sigma^2}g_2\cos(n\phi+\epsilon),\\
&H_1 = \frac{2Eh}{1-\sigma^2}h_1\sin(n\phi+\epsilon) = -H_2.
\end{aligned}\right\}\quad \text{...(1)}$$

The equations show that no other arrangements of sine and cosine are permissible.

The equations connecting $U, \ldots$ with $t_1, \ldots$ are

$$\left.\begin{aligned}
&t_1 = \frac{1}{A}\frac{dU}{d\alpha} - \frac{W}{R_1} + \sigma\left(\frac{U}{AB}\frac{dB}{d\alpha} + \frac{nV}{B} - \frac{W}{R_2}\right),\\
&t_2 = \sigma\left(\frac{1}{A}\frac{dU}{d\alpha} - \frac{W}{R_1}\right) + \frac{U}{AB}\frac{dB}{d\alpha} + \frac{nV}{B} - \frac{W}{R_2},\\
&g_1 = -\tfrac{1}{3}h^2\left\{\frac{1}{A}\frac{d}{d\alpha}\left(\frac{1}{A}\frac{dW}{d\alpha} + \frac{U}{R_1}\right) + \sigma\left(\frac{nV}{BR_2} - \frac{n^2W}{B^2}\right) + \frac{\sigma}{AB}\frac{dB}{d\alpha}\left(\frac{1}{A}\frac{dW}{d\alpha} + \frac{U}{R_1}\right)\right\},\\
&g_2 = -\tfrac{1}{3}h^2\left\{\frac{\sigma}{A}\frac{d}{d\alpha}\left(\frac{1}{A}\frac{dW}{d\alpha} + \frac{U}{R_1}\right) + \frac{nV}{BR_2} - \frac{n^2W}{B^2} + \frac{1}{AB}\frac{dB}{d\alpha}\left(\frac{1}{A}\frac{dW}{d\alpha} + \frac{U}{R_1}\right)\right\},\\
&h_1 = \tfrac{1}{3}h^2(1-\sigma)\left\{\frac{1}{A}\frac{d}{d\alpha}\left(\frac{V}{R_2} - \frac{nW}{B}\right) - \frac{1}{AR_1}\frac{dV}{d\alpha}\right\},
\end{aligned}\right\}$$

$$\text{...............(2)}$$

together with an additional equation involving s_1 or s_2 or both. For a first approximation we have

$$s_1 = -s_2 = \tfrac{1}{2}(1-\sigma)\left(\frac{1}{A}\frac{dV}{d\alpha} - \frac{nU}{B} - \frac{V}{AB}\frac{dB}{d\alpha}\right), \quad \text{...........(3)}$$

but we know that this approximation is not always sufficient.

In such problems as that of a shell strained by uniform pressure applied to one face, or rotating about its axis of figure, we have to take $n=0$. In such a problem as that of a cylindrical tube with a horizontal axis strained by its own weight, we have to take $n=1$. We shall refer to problems of this latter kind as problems of "lateral forces."

The half-thickness h will be taken to be independent of both α and ϕ.

We shall assume that the external couples, denoted by L' and M' in equations (46) of Article 331, vanish. Then the equations of equilibrium become

$$\left.\begin{aligned}
&\frac{d}{d\alpha}(t_1 B) - ns_2 A - t_2\frac{dB}{d\alpha} + AB\left(\frac{1-\sigma^2}{2Eh}X'' - \frac{n_1}{R_1}\right) = 0,\\
&\frac{d}{d\alpha}(s_1 B) - nt_2 A - s_2\frac{dB}{d\alpha} + AB\left(\frac{1-\sigma^2}{2Eh}Y'' - \frac{n_2}{R_2}\right) = 0,\\
&\frac{d}{d\alpha}(n_1 B) + nn_2 A + AB\left(\frac{1-\sigma^2}{2Eh}Z'' + \frac{t_1}{R_1} + \frac{t_2}{R_2}\right) = 0,\\
&\frac{d}{d\alpha}(h_1 B) + ng_2 A + h_1\frac{dB}{d\alpha} + ABn_2 = 0,\\
&\frac{d}{d\alpha}(g_1 B) - nh_1 A - g_2\frac{dB}{d\alpha} - ABn_1 = 0,\\
&\qquad h_1\left(\frac{1}{R_1} - \frac{1}{R_2}\right) + s_1 + s_2 = 0.
\end{aligned}\right\} \quad \ldots\ldots(4)$$

In obtaining these equations X', Y', Z' have been taken to be equal to

$$X''\cos(n\phi+\epsilon),\quad Y''\sin(n\phi+\epsilon),\quad Z''\cos(n\phi+\epsilon).$$

Unless $n=0$ or 1 external forces of these types are not very important, but forces applied at the edges may be.

338. Torsion.

When $n=0$, the equations fall into two sets: one in which V vanishes, and the other in which U and W vanish. For the latter a general solution, the same for all surfaces of revolution, can be obtained. We take X' and Z' to vanish, and we note that t_1, t_2, g_1, g_2, n_1 all vanish.

In this case we can obtain a sufficient approximation by omitting h_1, n_2 and adopting equations (3). We find

$$s_1 B^2 + \frac{1-\sigma^2}{2Eh}\int AB^2 Y'\,d\alpha = \text{const.}, \quad \ldots\ldots\ldots\ldots\ldots\ldots(5)$$

and

$$\frac{V}{B} = \frac{2}{1-\sigma}\int\frac{s_1 A}{B}\,d\alpha + \text{const.} \quad \ldots\ldots\ldots\ldots\ldots\ldots(6)$$

If $Y'=0$ the solution represents torsion of the shell by forces of type S_1 applied along the edges. If Y' is not zero, the solution serves to eliminate Y' from the equations, whenever Y' is independent of ϕ.

We proceed to the discussion of other solutions in the special cases of cylindrical, spherical, and conical shells.

CYLINDRICAL SHELL

339. Symmetrical conditions.

(a) *Extensional solution.*

Let the middle surface be a right circular cylinder of radius a, and let the distance, measured along the axis, of a point of this surface from a specified circular section be denoted by x. We may take $\alpha = x$. Then we have

$$A = 1, \quad B = a, \quad \frac{1}{R_1} = 0, \quad \frac{1}{R_2} = \frac{1}{a}, \quad \frac{dB}{d\alpha} = 0. \quad \text{..............(7)}$$

It is clear that, when the boundary-conditions are suitable, we can obtain solutions, which are sufficiently exact for practical purposes, by omitting g_1, g_2, h_1, as being small of the order $(h^2/a)(t_1, t_2, s_1)$, and adopting equations (3). We shall describe such solutions as "extensional." Equations (4) show that in working out these solutions we may put n_1 and n_2 equal to zero.

When all the conditions are symmetrical about the axis, so that $n = 0$, and we are not dealing with torsion, we put $V = 0$. We also put $\epsilon = 0$. Equations (3) then show that $s_1 = s_2 = 0$. Equations (4) then give

$$\frac{dt_1}{dx} + \frac{1-\sigma^2}{2Eh} X' = 0, \quad t_2 = -a\frac{1-\sigma^2}{2Eh} Z'. \quad \text{................(8)}$$

The first of these gives

$$t_1 + \frac{1-\sigma^2}{2Eh}\int_0^x X'\,dx = \text{const.} = a_1 \text{ say.} \quad \text{................(9)}$$

The second of equations (8) combined with the second of equations (2) then gives

$$W = a\sigma\frac{dU}{dx} + a^2\frac{1-\sigma^2}{2Eh} Z'; \quad \text{......................(10)}$$

and equation (9) combined with the first of equations (2) gives, on substituting from (10),

$$\frac{dU}{dx} = \frac{a_1}{1-\sigma^2} - \frac{1}{2Eh}\int_0^x X'\,dx - \frac{\sigma a}{2Eh} Z',$$

so that $$U = a_2 + \frac{a_1 x}{1-\sigma^2} - \frac{1}{2Eh}\int_0^x\left\{\int_0^x X'\,dx\right\}dx - \frac{\sigma a}{2Eh}\int_0^x Z'\,dx, \quad \text{...(11)}$$

where a_2 is an arbitrary constant.

It appears that by means of the extensional solution we can eliminate the external forces, but we cannot in general satisfy the boundary-conditions at the edges. For example, we could not solve the problem of a tube strained by external pressure and plugged at the ends. In such problems the stress-resultant of type N_1 cannot vanish.

(*b*) *Edge-effect.*

Putting n and V zero we see from the fifth of equations (2) that h_1 vanishes. Then, whether we use equations (3) or the more complete equations (42) of Article 330, we may conclude that s_1, s_2 vanish. We have seen that the extensional solution and the solution for torsion permit us to satisfy the equations (4) containing external forces, and we may now simplify the system of equations by omitting X', Y', Z'.

The equations (4) become, on omitting those which are satisfied identically,

$$\frac{dt_1}{dx}=0, \quad n_2=0, \quad \frac{dn_1}{dx}+\frac{t_2}{a}=0, \quad \frac{dg_1}{dx}-n_1=0, \quad \text{.........(12)}$$

and the relevant equations of (2) become

$$t_1=\frac{dU}{dx}-\sigma\frac{W}{a}, \quad t_2=\sigma\frac{dU}{dx}-\frac{W}{a}, \quad g_1=-\tfrac{1}{3}h^2\frac{d^2W}{dx^2}. \quad \text{.........(13)}$$

The first of equations (12) gives $t_1=\text{const.}$ If we retained this constant we should merely reproduce the results of the extensional solution, so far as these depend upon the arbitrary constant a_1. For our present purpose it is sufficient to put

$$t_1=0, \quad \text{..................................(14)}$$

and consequently

$$\frac{dU}{dx}=\sigma\frac{W}{a}, \quad \text{..............................(15)}$$

and

$$t_2=-(1-\sigma^2)\frac{W}{a}. \quad \text{..........................(16)}$$

On eliminating n_1 between the 3rd and 4th of equations (12) and substituting for g_1 and t_2 from (13) and (16), we find the equation

$$-\tfrac{1}{3}h^2\frac{d^4W}{dx^4}-(1-\sigma^2)\frac{W}{a^2}=0, \quad \text{...................(17)}$$

the complete primitive of which can be written

$$W=e^{qx/a}(A_1\cos qx/a+B_1\sin qx/a)+e^{-qx/a}(A_2\cos qx/a+B_2\sin qx/a), \quad \text{...(18)}$$

where A_1, B_1, A_2, B_2 are arbitrary constants, and

$$q=(a/2h)^{\frac{1}{2}}\{3(1-\sigma^2)\}^{\frac{1}{4}}. \quad \text{.....................(19)}$$

It will be observed that this quantity is the same as that which was denoted by q in the special problem discussed in Article 334 (*e*).

The integration of equation (15) introduces an additional arbitrary constant. If we retained this constant we should merely reproduce the results of the extensional solution, so far as these depend upon the arbitrary constant a_2. For our present purpose it is sufficient to put

$$U=\frac{\sigma}{2q}\left[e^{qx/a}\{(A_1-B_1)\cos qx/a+(A_1+B_1)\sin qx/a\}\right.$$
$$\left.-e^{-qx/a}\{(A_2+B_2)\cos qx/a-(A_2-B_2)\sin qx/a\}\right]. \quad \text{......(20)}$$

The results here obtained indicate a state of stress existing in the parts of the shell that are near the edges, and such that the stress-resultants and stress-couples diminish to very small values at a distance from the edges comparable with a mean proportional between the thickness and the diameter. We describe this special state as the "edge-effect."

The "edge-effect" here considered is of a quite different character from those which have been encountered in Articles 334 (*e*) and 335 D. There the extensional strains were in general small compared with the flexural strains, but rose in importance near to free edges so as to secure the satisfaction of the boundary-conditions. Here the flexural strains are in general small compared with the extensional strains but rise in importance in the neighbourhood of fixed edges so as to secure the satisfaction of conditions of fixity.

It will be observed that the combination of the solution in Article 338 with the two solutions in this Article permits us to assign to the values of t_1, s_1, n_1 and g_1 at the two edges any values, which are consistent with the conditions of rigid body equilibrium expressed by equations (5) and (9).

340. Tube under pressure.

To illustrate the satisfaction of boundary-conditions, restricting the *displacement*, we shall work out the problem of a thin cylindrical tube, subject to uniform external pressure of amount p_0 per unit of area, the ends being kept fixed, and the deformed generators being tangential to their initial directions at the ends. We shall take the cylinder to be of length l and measure x from one end. The boundary-conditions are

$$U=0, \quad W=0, \quad \frac{dW}{dx}=0 \text{ at } x=0 \text{ and at } x=l. \qquad \text{.................(21)}$$

In this problem $X'=0$ and $Z'=p_0$. The complete expressions for U and W are

$$U=a_2+a_1\frac{x}{1-\sigma^2}-\frac{\sigma a x}{2Eh}p_0+\frac{\sigma}{2q}\left[e^{qx/a}\{(A_1-B_1)\cos qx/a+(A_1+B_1)\sin qx/a\}\right.$$
$$\left.-e^{-qx/a}\{(A_2+B_2)\cos qx/a-(A_2-B_2)\sin qx/a\}\right],$$

$$W=a_1\frac{\sigma a}{1-\sigma^2}-\frac{\sigma^2a^2}{2Eh}p_0+\frac{1-\sigma^2}{2Eh}a^2p_0$$
$$+e^{qx/a}(A_1\cos qx/a+B_1\sin qx/a)+e^{-qx/a}(A_2\cos qx/a+B_2\sin qx/a).$$

The boundary-conditions at the end $x=0$ give

$$\left.\begin{aligned} &a_2+\frac{\sigma}{2q}\{(A_1-B_1)-(A_2+B_2)\}=0,\\ &a_1\frac{\sigma a}{1-\sigma^2}+\frac{1-2\sigma^2}{2Eh}a^2p_0+A_1+A_2=0,\\ &A_1+B_1-A_2+B_2=0.\end{aligned}\right\} \qquad \text{.......................(22)}$$

The condition $dW/dx=0$ at $x=l$ gives, on writing z for ql/a,

$$e^z\{(A_1+B_1)\cos z-(A_1-B_1)\sin z\}+e^{-z}\{-(A_2-B_2)\cos z-(A_2+B_2)\sin z\}=0,$$

which can be written

$$(A_1+A_2)(\sinh z\cos z-\cosh z\sin z)+(A_1-A_2)(\cosh z\cos z-\sinh z\sin z)$$
$$+(B_1+B_2)(\cosh z\cos z+\sinh z\sin z)+(B_1-B_2)(\sinh z\cos z+\cosh z\sin z)=0.$$

On substituting from the 3rd equation of (22) this becomes

$$(B_1-B_2)(\sinh z\cos z+\cosh z\sin z)+(A_1+A_2)(\sinh z\cos z-\cosh z\sin z)$$
$$+2(B_1+B_2)\sinh z\sin z=0. \qquad \text{......(23)}$$

Now the equation $W=0$ at $x=l$, combined with the 2nd and 3rd equations of (22), gives

$$-(A_1+A_2)+(A_1+A_2)\cosh z\cos z+(B_1+B_2)(\cosh z\sin z-\sinh z\cos z)$$
$$+(B_1-B_2)\sinh z\sin z=0,$$

and by means of this equation and (23) we may express the ratios of B_1-B_2 and B_1+B_2 to (A_1+A_2). We find

$$\frac{A_1+A_2}{\sinh z+\sin z}=\frac{B_1+B_2}{\cosh z-\cos z}=\frac{B_1-B_2}{-(\sinh z-\sin z)}. \quad\text{.................(24)}$$

Again the equation $U=0$ at $x=l$ gives

$$\frac{\sigma}{2q}\{(A_1+A_2)(\cosh z\sin z+\sinh z\cos z)+(A_1-A_2)(\cosh z\cos z+\sinh z\sin z)$$
$$+(B_1+B_2)(\sinh z\sin z-\cosh z\cos z)+(B_1-B_2)(\cosh z\sin z-\sinh z\cos z)\}$$
$$+\alpha_2+\alpha_1\frac{l}{1-\sigma^2}-\frac{\sigma a l}{2Eh}p_0=0.$$

On substituting from the 3rd of equations (22) and equation (24) this reduces to

$$\frac{\sigma}{q}(B_1+B_2)+\alpha_2+\alpha_1\frac{l}{1-\sigma^2}-\frac{\sigma a l}{2Eh}p_0=0. \quad\text{.......................(25)}$$

Now the 1st and 3rd of (22) give

$$\alpha_2=\frac{\sigma}{q}(B_1+B_2); \quad\text{.......................................(26)}$$

and hence, using the 2nd of (22) and (24), we have

$$\left(\frac{l}{\sigma a}\frac{\sinh z+\sin z}{\cosh z-\cos z}-\frac{2\sigma}{q}\right)(B_1+B_2)=-\frac{1-\sigma^2}{\sigma}\frac{al}{2Eh}p_0. \quad\text{..................(27)}$$

All the constants are now determined; none of them becomes large through the largeness of q, but α_2 becomes small.

To exemplify the diminution of the edge-effect with increasing distance from an edge, we may calculate the variable part of W. It may be shown to be

$$\frac{B_1+B_2}{\cosh ql/a-\cos ql/a}\left\{\cosh\frac{q(l-x)}{a}\sin\frac{qx}{a}+\sinh\frac{q(l-x)}{a}\cos\frac{qx}{a}\right.$$
$$\left.+\cosh\frac{qx}{a}\sin\frac{q(l-x)}{a}+\sinh\frac{qx}{a}\cos\frac{q(l-x)}{a}\right\}.$$

When x is near zero the most important term is approximately $(B_1+B_2)e^{-qx/a}$, and when x is near l it is approximately $(B_1+B_2)e^{-q(l-x)/a}$.

341. Stability of a tube under external pressure.

Before proceeding with the integration of the equations of Article 337 for a cylindrical shell, under conditions answering to values of n, which exceed zero, we shall turn aside to discuss the technically important problem of the conditions of collapse of a thin cylindrical tube, subject to external pressure p_0. To simplify the problem as much as possible we shall assume that the conditions, which hold at the ends of the tube, are such that the state of the tube, when the pressure is too small to produce collapse, is expressed with sufficient approximation by the extensional solution of Article 339 (a), and in this solution we shall further take X' and α_1 to vanish. Thus this state is given by the equations

$$T_1=S_1=S_2=N_1=N_2=0,\quad G_1=G_2=H_1=H_2=0,$$

and

$$T_2=-ap_0. \quad\text{............................(28)}$$

It may be observed that these results can be deduced easily from those of Article 100 by taking r_0-r_1 to be small and adjusting e so that $\widehat{zz}=0$.

We have now to suppose that a small additional displacement (u', v', w') is superposed upon the displacement answering to this state. Let $T_1', \ldots G_1', \ldots$ be the stress-resultants and stress-couples calculated from this displacement. Then the stress-resultant of type T_2 is $-ap_0 + T_2'$. In forming the equations of equilibrium, we must omit all quantities of the second order in u', v', w', but we must not omit the products of p_0 and quantities which are of the first order in u', v', w'. In particular we must replace A and B by $A(1+\epsilon_1)$, $B(1+\epsilon_2)$ in any terms that contain p_0. In regard to the calculation of S_1' and S_2' we shall use the equation

$$S_1' + S_2' = H_1'/a,$$

and replace equations (3) by the equation

$$S_1' - S_2' = \frac{2Eh}{1+\sigma}\left(\frac{\partial v'}{\partial x} + \frac{1}{a}\frac{\partial u'}{\partial \phi}\right).$$

This procedure is equivalent to adopting equations (42) of Article 330. For the calculation of the remaining stress-resultants and the stress-couples it sufficient to use the equations (36) and (37) of Article 329.

One of the equations of equilibrium is used for the calculation of S_1', S_2'. Two others give

$$N_1' a = a\frac{\partial G_1'}{\partial x} - \frac{\partial H_1'}{\partial \phi}, \quad N_2' a = -a\frac{\partial H_1'}{\partial x} + \frac{\partial G_2'}{\partial \phi}.$$

On substituting from these in the remaining equations we find the set of three equations

$$\left.\begin{aligned}
&\frac{\partial T_1'}{\partial x} - \frac{1}{a}\frac{\partial S_2'}{\partial \phi} + p_0 r_2' = 0,\\
&\frac{\partial S_1'}{\partial x} + \frac{1}{a}\frac{\partial T_2'}{\partial \phi} + \frac{1}{a}\frac{\partial H_1'}{\partial x} - \frac{1}{a^2}\frac{\partial G_2'}{\partial \phi} = 0,\\
&\frac{\partial^2 G_1'}{\partial x^2} - \frac{2}{a}\frac{\partial^2 H_1'}{\partial x \partial \phi} + \frac{1}{a^2}\frac{\partial^2 G_2'}{\partial \phi^2} - p_2'(1+\epsilon_1)p_0 + \frac{T_2'}{a} + (1+\epsilon_1)(1+\epsilon_2)p_0 = 0.
\end{aligned}\right\} \ldots (29)$$

In these equations we are to put

$$T_1' = \frac{2Eh}{1-\sigma^2}\left\{\frac{\partial u'}{\partial x} + \frac{\sigma}{a}\left(\frac{\partial v'}{\partial \phi} - w'\right)\right\}, \quad T_2' = \frac{2Eh}{1-\sigma^2}\left\{\sigma\frac{\partial u'}{\partial x} + \frac{1}{a}\left(\frac{\partial v'}{\partial \phi} - w'\right)\right\},$$

$$S_1' = \frac{Eh}{1+\sigma}\left\{\frac{\partial v'}{\partial x} + \frac{1}{a}\frac{\partial u'}{\partial \phi} + \frac{h^2}{3a^2}\left(\frac{\partial^2 w'}{\partial x \partial \phi} + \frac{\partial v'}{\partial x}\right)\right\},$$

$$S_2' = -\frac{Eh}{1+\sigma}\left\{\frac{\partial v'}{\partial x} + \frac{1}{a}\frac{\partial u'}{\partial \phi} - \frac{h^2}{3a^2}\left(\frac{\partial^2 w'}{\partial x \partial \phi} + \frac{\partial v'}{\partial x}\right)\right\},$$

$$G_1' = -\frac{2}{3}\frac{Eh^3}{1-\sigma^2}\left\{\frac{\partial^2 w'}{\partial x^2} + \frac{\sigma}{a^2}\left(\frac{\partial^2 w'}{\partial \phi^2} + \frac{\partial v'}{\partial \phi}\right)\right\},$$

$$G_2' = -\frac{2}{3}\frac{Eh^3}{1-\sigma^2}\left\{\sigma\frac{\partial^2 w'}{\partial x^2} + \frac{1}{a^2}\left(\frac{\partial^2 w'}{\partial \phi^2} + \frac{\partial v'}{\partial \phi}\right)\right\}$$

$$H_1' = \frac{2}{3}\frac{Eh^3}{1+\sigma}\frac{1}{a}\left(\frac{\partial^2 w'}{\partial x \partial \phi} + \frac{\partial v'}{\partial x}\right),$$

and we are also to put

$$p_2' = 1 + \frac{1}{a}\left(\frac{\partial^2 w'}{\partial \phi^2} + \frac{\partial v'}{\partial \phi}\right), \quad r_2' = \frac{\partial^2 v'}{\partial x \partial \phi} - \frac{\partial w'}{\partial x}, \quad \epsilon_1 = \frac{\partial u'}{\partial x}, \quad \epsilon_2 = \frac{1}{a}\left(\frac{\partial v'}{\partial \phi} - w'\right).$$

We assume as expressions for the components of displacement the forms

$$u' = U \cos mx \sin n\phi, \quad v' = V \sin mx \cos n\phi, \quad w' = W \sin mx \sin n\phi, \ldots(30)$$

and write

$$p_0 = \frac{2Eh}{1-\sigma^2}\frac{\Psi}{a}. \quad \ldots\ldots\ldots\ldots\ldots\ldots(31)$$

Equations (29) become, on omitting terms of order higher than the first in U, V, W,

$$\left(m^2 + \frac{1-\sigma}{2}\frac{n^2}{a^2}\right)U + \left(\frac{1+\sigma}{2} + \Psi - \frac{1-\sigma}{2}\frac{h^2}{3a^2}\right)\frac{mn}{a}V$$
$$+ \left(\sigma + \Psi - \frac{1-\sigma}{2}\frac{h^2}{3a^2}n^2\right)\frac{m}{a}W = 0,$$

$$\frac{1+\sigma}{2}\frac{mn}{a}U + \left(\frac{1-\sigma}{2}m^2 + \frac{n^2}{a^2} + \frac{1-\sigma}{2}\frac{h^2}{a^2}m^2 + \frac{h^2}{3a^4}\right)V$$
$$+ \left(\frac{n}{a^2} + \frac{3-\sigma}{2}\frac{h^2}{3a^2}m^2 n + \frac{h^2}{3a^4}n^3\right)W = 0,$$

$$\frac{\sigma m}{a}U + \left(\frac{n}{a^2} + \frac{2-\sigma}{3}\frac{h^2}{a^2}m^2 n + \frac{h^2}{3a^4}n^3\right)V$$
$$+ \left(\frac{1}{a^2} - \frac{n^2-1}{a^2}\Psi + \frac{h^2}{3}m^4 + \frac{2h^2}{3}\frac{m^2n^2}{a^2} + \frac{h^2}{3a^4}n^4\right)W = 0.$$

The elimination of U, V, W from these equations leads to a determinantal equation determining Ψ in terms of a, h, m, n. This equation may be simplified by observing that Ψ must be small of the order $(a/h)(p_0/E)$, and we may therefore approximate by omitting terms of the orders Ψ^2 or Ψh^2. We may also omit terms containing h^4. Further, m must be of the order $\frac{1}{l}$, where l is the length of the tube, and we may omit terms which contain $h^2 m$. The determinantal equation is then

$$\begin{vmatrix} m^2 + \frac{1-\sigma}{2}\frac{n^2}{a^2}, & \left(\frac{1+\sigma}{2} + \Psi\right)\frac{mn}{a}, & (\sigma+\Psi)\frac{m}{a} \\ \frac{1+\sigma}{2}\frac{mn}{a}, & \frac{1-\sigma}{2}m^2 + \frac{n^2}{a^2} + \frac{h^2}{3a^4}n^2, & \frac{n}{a^2} + \frac{h^2}{3a^4}n^3 \\ \frac{\sigma m}{a}, & \frac{n}{a^2} + \frac{h^2}{3a^4}n^3, & \frac{1}{a^2} - \frac{n^2-1}{a^2}\Psi + \frac{h^2 n^4}{3a^4} \end{vmatrix} = 0,$$

and, when we evaluate the determinant, omitting terms of the orders indicated, we find

$$\frac{1-\sigma}{2a^2}\left[-\Psi\left\{(n^2-1)\left(\frac{n^2}{a^2} + m^2\right)^2 + \sigma m^4\right\} + \left\{(1-\sigma^2)m^4 + \frac{h^2}{3a^6}n^4(n^2-1)^2\right\}\right] = 0,$$

or approximately

$$\Psi = \frac{h^2}{3a^2}(n^2-1) + (1-\sigma^2)\frac{m^4 a^4}{n^4(n^2-1)}.$$

The condition that the tube may be unstable in respect of a small displacement of the type specified by m and n is therefore

$$p_0 = \frac{2Eh}{a}\left\{\frac{(n^2-1)h^2}{3(1-\sigma^2)a^2} + \frac{m^4a^4}{n^4(n^2-1)}\right\}. \qquad (32)$$

The forms (30) would admit of the satisfaction of boundary-conditions of the type $T_1 = 0$, $v = 0$, $w = 0$, at the ends $x = 0$ and $x = l$ of the tube, if m is an integral multiple of π/l. Also the pressure required to produce collapse, given by (32), increases as m increases. With these boundary-conditions the least pressure, for which collapse is possible, is given by putting $m = \pi/l$.

When the tube is very long equation (32) becomes

$$p_0 = (n^2-1)\frac{D}{a^3},$$

so that a very long tube cannot collapse unless the pressure exceeds $3D/a^3$; and, when this value is but slightly exceeded, it collapses by flattening the section to an elliptic form ($n = 2$).

But, for a shorter tube, collapse into a form given by $n = 3$ may occur for a smaller value of p_0 than collapse into a form given by $n = 2$. The condition that this should happen is

$$m^4a^4\left\{\frac{1}{2^4(2^2-1)} - \frac{1}{3^4(3^2-1)}\right\} > \frac{h^2}{3(1-\sigma^2)a^2}\{(3^2-1)-(2^2-1)\},$$

or

$$m^4a^4 > \frac{432}{5}\frac{h^2}{(1-\sigma^2)a^2}.$$

When this condition is satisfied the tube collapses so that its section becomes a three-lobed curve of the form given by the equation $r = a + b\cos 3\phi$, where b/a is small. This statement holds provided m is not too great; but, as m increases or l diminishes, a value will be arrived at, which is such that the value of p_0 given by $n = 4$ is smaller than the value given by $n = 3$. Then the tube collapses so that its section becomes a four-lobed curve. If m becomes large the validity of the approximations which led to (32) becomes doubtful.

It follows from the nature of the quantity called Z' that, when there is internal pressure p_1 as well as external pressure p_0, the left-hand member of equation (32) should be $p_0 - p_1$.

The result that, for a very long tube, the pressure required to produce collapse is $3D/a^3$ or $\{2E/(1-\sigma^2)\}(h/a)^3$, was obtained by G. H. Bryan*. The analogous result for a ring is given in Article 275 *supra*. The fact that tubes sometimes collapse so that the section becomes elliptic, sometimes so that it becomes a three-lobed curve, and so on, had been observed long before by W. Fairbairn†, but it remained without explanation until the problem was attacked by R. V. Southwell‡. The problem was discussed by Southwell in

* *Cambridge, Phil. Soc. Proc.*, vol. 6 (1888), p. 287.

† *Phil. Trans. Roy. Soc.*, vol. 148 (1859), p. 389.

‡ *Phil. Trans. Roy. Soc.* (Ser. A), vol. 213 (1913), p. 187.

this memoir as an example of the application of his theory of elastic stability, and the solution, including the result expressed in equation (32), was there obtained by him without using the theory of thin shells. In another paper*, written later although published earlier, the same writer obtained the results by a method (based on the theory of thin shells) which has been followed to some extent in this Article. The reader, who wishes for further information on the experimental as well as the theoretical aspect of the subject, may refer to a valuable Report by G. Cook in *Brit. Assoc. Rep.*, 1913, and to papers by Cook and Southwell in *Phil. Mag.* (Ser. 6), vol. 28 (1914) and vol. 29 (1915).

It should be noted that the theoretical solution has been obtained by assuming rather exceptional terminal conditions. The application of it to the problem of the stability of a boiler flue, which is strengthened to resist collapse by "collapse rings" placed at intervals along the length of the flue, is discussed by Southwell in the papers cited, also by Cook in *Brit. Assoc. Rep.*, 1923, p. 345.

342. Lateral forces.

(*a*) *Extensional solution.*

We return to the integration of the equations (4) for a cylindrical shell in the case where $n=1$, and begin with an extensional solution in which g_1, g_2, h_1, n_1, n_2 are omitted, and s_1 and s_2 are given by (3). The relevant equations included in (4) are

$$\left.\begin{aligned} \frac{dt_1}{dx}+\frac{s_1}{a}+\frac{1-\sigma^2}{2Eh}X''=0,\\ \frac{ds_1}{dx}-\frac{t_2}{a}+\frac{1-\sigma^2}{2Eh}Y''=0,\\ \frac{t_2}{a}+\frac{1-\sigma^2}{2Eh}Z''=0,\end{aligned}\right\} \qquad\qquad (33)$$

while equations (2) and (3) give

$$\left.\begin{aligned} t_1=\frac{dU}{dx}+\sigma\frac{V-W}{a},\\ t_2=\sigma\frac{dU}{dx}+\frac{V-W}{a},\\ s_1=\tfrac{1}{2}(1-\sigma)\left(\frac{dV}{dx}-\frac{U}{a}\right).\end{aligned}\right\} \qquad\qquad (34)$$

The 2nd and 3rd of equations (33) give

$$\frac{ds_1}{dx}+\frac{1-\sigma^2}{2Eh}(Y''+Z'')=0,$$

from which we get

$$s_1=a_1-\frac{1-\sigma^2}{2Eh}\int_0^x(Y''+Z'')\,dx=0, \qquad\qquad (35)$$

where a_1 is a constant of integration. The 1st of equations (33) then gives

$$t_1=a_2-\frac{a_1}{a}x-\frac{1-\sigma^2}{2Eh}\int_0^x X''\,dx+\frac{1-\sigma^2}{2Eh}\int_0^x\left\{\int_0^x(Y''+Z'')\,dx\right\}dx=0, \ldots(36)$$

* *Phil. Mag.* (Ser. 6), vol. 25 (1913), p. 687.

where a_2 is a constant of integration. Thus s_1, t_1, t_2 are known, for t_2 is given by the 3rd of equations (33). The 1st and 2nd of equations (34) give

$$\frac{dU}{dx}=\frac{t_1-\sigma t_2}{1-\sigma^2},$$

so that

$$U=a_3+\int_0^x \frac{t_1-\sigma t_2}{1-\sigma^2}\,dx, \qquad \text{..........(37)}$$

where a_3 is a constant of integration. Thus U is known. The 3rd of equations (34) gives

$$\frac{dV}{dx}=\frac{U}{a}+\frac{2s_1}{1-\sigma},$$

so that

$$V=a_4+\int_0^x\left(\frac{U}{a}+\frac{2s_1}{1-\sigma}\right)dx, \qquad \text{..........(38)}$$

where a_4 is a constant of integration. The 1st and 2nd of equations (34) then give

$$W=V-a\frac{t_2-\sigma t_1}{1-\sigma^2}, \qquad \text{..........(39)}$$

in which V is known, so that W is determined. The extensional solution involves four arbitrary constants, and answers to the two solutions given in Article 338 and 339 (a) for the case where $n=0$. It enables us to eliminate the external forces from the equations of equilibrium.

(b) *Edge-effect.*

In investigating the edge-effect we shall omit X'', Y'', Z'', and take s_1 and s_2 to be given by the equations

$$\left.\begin{aligned} s_1+s_2&=\frac{h_1}{a},\\ s_1-s_2&=(1-\sigma)\left(\frac{dV}{dx}-\frac{U}{a}\right),\end{aligned}\right\} \qquad \text{..........(40)}$$

the 1st of which is one of the equations of equilibrium. This procedure is equivalent to adopting equations (42) of Article 330. The remaining five of the equations of equilibrium become

$$\left.\begin{aligned} \frac{dt_1}{dx}-\frac{s_2}{a}&=0,\\ \frac{ds_1}{dx}-\frac{t_2}{a}-\frac{n_2}{a}&=0,\\ \frac{dn_1}{dx}+\frac{n_2}{a}+\frac{t_2}{a}&=0,\\ \frac{dh_1}{dx}+\frac{g_2}{a}+n_2&=0,\\ \frac{dg_1}{dx}-\frac{h_1}{a}-n_1&=0.\end{aligned}\right\} \qquad \text{..........(41)}$$

The 2nd and 3rd of these equations give $s_1 + n_1 = \text{const.}$ If we retain this constant, we shall only reproduce the results of the extensional solution, in so far as they depend upon α_1. We shall therefore take

$$s_1 + n_1 = 0. \qquad \text{.............................(42)}$$

When we substitute for n_1 from this equation in the 5th of equations (41), multiply the left-hand member of the equation so obtained by $1/a$, substitute $-s_2$ for $s_1 - h_1/a$, and subtract from the left-hand member of the 1st equation of (41), we find that $t_1 - g_1/a = \text{const.}$ If we retain this constant, we shall only reproduce the results of the extensional solution, in so far as they depend upon α_2. We shall therefore take

$$t_1 - \frac{g_1}{a} = 0. \qquad \text{.............................(43)}$$

In the 1st of equations (41) substitute $s_1 - h_1/a$ for $-s_2$, and from the 2nd and 4th of equations (41) eliminate n_2. We obtain the two equations

$$\left.\begin{aligned} &\frac{dt_1}{dx} + \frac{1}{a}\left(s_1 - \frac{h_1}{a}\right) = 0, \\ &\frac{d}{dx}\left(s_1 + \frac{h_1}{a}\right) - \frac{1}{a}\left(t_2 - \frac{g_2}{a}\right) = 0. \end{aligned}\right\} \qquad \text{....................(44)}$$

Equation (42) gives n_1 when s_1 is known, one of the equations of (41) can be used to find n_2 when the other quantities are known, and there remain three equations, which can be taken to be (43) and (44).

Equations (2) are in this case

$$\left.\begin{aligned} &t_1 = \frac{dU}{dx} + \sigma\frac{V-W}{a}, \quad t_2 = \sigma\frac{dU}{dx} + \frac{V-W}{a}, \quad g_1 = -\frac{h^2}{3}\left(\frac{d^2W}{dx^2} + \sigma\frac{V-W}{a^2}\right), \\ &g_2 = -\frac{h^2}{3}\left(\sigma\frac{d^2W}{dx^2} + \frac{V-W}{a^2}\right), \quad h_1 = \frac{h^2}{3}(1-\sigma)\frac{d}{dx}\left(\frac{V-W}{a}\right). \end{aligned}\right\} \qquad \text{..............(45)}$$

In these equations and equations (40) we shall put

$$\eta = \frac{V-W}{a^2}, \quad \zeta = \frac{dW}{dx} - \frac{U}{a},$$

and find

$$\left.\begin{aligned} &t_1 = a\left(\frac{d^2W}{dx^2} + \sigma\eta\right) - a\frac{d\zeta}{dx}, \quad t_2 = a\left(\sigma\frac{d^2W}{dx^2} + \eta\right) - \sigma a\frac{d\zeta}{dx}, \\ &s_1 - s_2 = (1-\sigma)\left(a^2\frac{d\eta}{dx} + \zeta\right), \quad s_1 + s_2 = \frac{h^2}{3}(1-\sigma)\frac{d\eta}{dx}, \\ &g_1 = -\frac{h^2}{3}\left(\frac{d^2W}{dx^2} + \sigma\eta\right), \quad g_2 = -\frac{h^2}{3}\left(\sigma\frac{d^2W}{dx^2} + \eta\right), \quad h_1 = \frac{h^2}{3}(1-\sigma)\,a\frac{d\eta}{dx}. \end{aligned}\right\} \qquad (46)$$

Now equation (43) combined with the 1st and 5th of equations (46) gives

$$t_1 = -\left\{\frac{h^2}{3a}\Big/\left(1 + \frac{h^2}{3a^2}\right)\right\}\frac{d\zeta}{dx}, \qquad \text{......................(47)}$$

and the elimination of s_2 and η from the 3rd, 4th and 7th of equations (46) gives

$$h_1 = \left\{\frac{2h^2}{3a}\Big/\left(1+\frac{h^2}{3a^2}\right)\right\} s_1 - \left\{\frac{h^2}{3a}\Big/\left(1+\frac{h^2}{3a^2}\right)\right\}(1-\sigma)\,\zeta. \quad \text{......(48)}$$

On introducing these values of t_1 and h_1 into the 1st of equations (44), we find the equation

$$\frac{h^2}{3}\left(\frac{d^2\zeta}{dx^2} - \frac{1-\sigma}{a^2}\zeta\right) = \left(1 - \frac{h^2}{3a^2}\right) s_1. \quad \text{..................(49)}$$

Again, from the 1st and 2nd of equations (46) we obtain the equation

$$t_2 - \sigma t_1 = (1-\sigma^2)\, a\eta,$$

and, on combining this with the 7th equation of (46), we get

$$\frac{h^2}{3}\left(\frac{dt_2}{dx} - \sigma\frac{dt_1}{dx}\right) = (1+\sigma)\, h_1,$$

or by (48)

$$\left(1+\frac{h^2}{3a^2}\right)\left(\frac{dt_2}{dx} - \sigma\frac{dt_1}{dx}\right) = \frac{1+\sigma}{a}\{2s_1 - (1-\sigma)\,\zeta\}. \quad \text{...........(50)}$$

Now the 2nd and 6th of equations (46) give

$$t_2 - \frac{g_2}{a} = \left(1+\frac{h^2}{3a^2}\right) t_2 + \sigma\frac{h^2}{3a}\frac{d\zeta}{dx},$$

so that by the 2nd equation of (44)

$$\left(1+\frac{h^2}{3a^2}\right) t_2 = -\sigma\frac{h^2}{3a}\frac{d\zeta}{dx} + a\frac{d}{dx}\left(s_1 + \frac{h_1}{a}\right), \quad \text{..............(51)}$$

or by (48)

$$\left(1+\frac{h^2}{3a^2}\right) t_2 = -\sigma\frac{h^2}{3a}\frac{d\zeta}{dx} + a\frac{d}{dx}\left\{\frac{1+\dfrac{h^2}{a^2}}{1+\dfrac{h^2}{3a^2}}\, s_1 - \frac{\dfrac{h^2}{3a^2}}{1+\dfrac{h^2}{3a^2}}(1-\sigma)\,\zeta\right\}.$$

On substituting from this equation and equation (47) in equation (50) we find the equation

$$a\left(1+\frac{h^2}{a^2}\right)\frac{d^2 s_1}{dx^2} - \frac{h^2}{3a^2}(1-\sigma)\frac{d^2\zeta}{dx^2} = \frac{1+\sigma}{a}\{2s_1 - (1-\sigma)\,\zeta\}\left(1+\frac{h^2}{3a^2}\right),$$

or by (49)

$$\left(1+\frac{h^2}{a^2}\right)\frac{d^2 s_1}{dx^2} - \left\{2(1+\sigma)\left(1+\frac{h^2}{3a^2}\right) + (1-\sigma)\left(1-\frac{h^2}{3a^2}\right)\right\}\frac{s_1}{a^2}$$

$$= -\left\{(1-\sigma^2)\left(1+\frac{h^2}{3a^2}\right) - (1-\sigma)^2\frac{h^2}{3a^2}\right\}\frac{\zeta}{a^2}. \quad \text{.........(52)}$$

The integration of equations (49) and (52) presents no difficulty. The primitives are of the forms

$$\zeta = A_1 e^{m_1 x} + A_2 e^{m_2 x} + A_3 e^{m_3 x} + A_4 e^{m_4 x},$$

$$s_1 = B_1 e^{m_1 x} + B_2 e^{m_2 x} + B_3 e^{m_3 x} + B_4 e^{m_4 x},$$

where

$$B_r\left(1-\frac{h^2}{3a^2}\right) = \frac{h^2}{3}\left(m_r^2 - \frac{1-\sigma}{a^2}\right) A_r, \qquad (r = 1, 2, 3, 4),$$

and the four values of m_r approximate to the complex fourth roots of

$$-3(1-\sigma^2)/h^2a^2.$$

When ζ and s_1 are known all the stress-resultants and stress-couples are known, and η also is known, without any additional integration, but such integration is required in order to determine the displacement w. Thus two additional arbitrary constants will be introduced. They may, however, be omitted as they can only reproduce the results of the extensional solution, in so far as these depend upon the constants a_3, a_4, and the displacement determined by these constants is a rigid-body displacement.

Apart from the constants a_3, a_4, which do not affect the stress-resultants or stress-couples, the solution obtained by combining the extensional solution and the edge-effect, contains six arbitrary constants a_1, a_2, A_1, A_2, A_3, A_4. These are sufficient to secure that T_1, S_1+H_1/a, $N_1-a^{-1}\partial H_1/\partial\phi$, G_1 shall have any values at the edges which they can have, these values being necessarily restricted by the conditions of rigid-body equilibrium, expressed by the two equations $n_1+s_1=\text{const.}$ and $t_1-g_1/a=\text{const.}$ The way in which H_1 enters into the expressions for the quantities, which can be given at the edges, has been explained in Article 332.

An example which repays detailed investigation is afforded by a long cylindrical tube, held so that at one end $x=0$ its axis is horizontal, and bent by a load concentrated at the other end $x=l$, the load being applied by forces of the types N_1, S_1 proportional to $\cos\phi$ and $\sin\phi$, where ϕ vanishes in the vertical plane passing through the axis. It can be proved that, apart from a local perturbation, the curvature of the axis is precisely that given by the ordinary theory of flexure (Chapter XV). The local perturbation is the edge-effect near the loaded end, and the stress answering to it diminishes, as the distance from the loaded end increases, nearly according to the exponential law $e^{-q(l-x)/a}$, where q is the quantity so denoted in Article 339 (*b*).

343. General unsymmetrical conditions.

When the conditions correspond with values of n which exceed unity two novel circumstances arise. One of them is concerned with the isolation of the edge-effect. In previous solutions this isolation was brought about by equating to zero the arbitrary constants which occur in two of the integrals of the equations of equilibrium, these integrals expressing conditions of rigid-body equilibrium. When $n>1$ all the conditions of rigid-body equilibrium are satisfied identically, and recourse must be had to a new method.

The other novel circumstance is the geometrical possibility of purely inextensional displacement. When $n=0$, or 1, the only possible inextensional displacements are rigid-body displacements, and arbitrary constants expressing such displacements have duly made their appearance in previous solutions. They do not affect the stress-resultants or the stress-couples. When $n>1$, the place of such rigid-body displacements is taken by purely inextensional displacements, which affect the values of the stress-couples, but not those of the stress-resultants, in so far as these can be expressed by equations (2) and (3).

(*a*) *Extensional solution.*

We consider first the extensional solution. As before, we are to omit g_1, g_2, n_1, n_2, h_1, and take equations (3) as giving a sufficient approximation to s_1, s_2. The relevant equations are

$$\frac{dt_1}{dx}+n\frac{s_1}{a}+\frac{1-\sigma^2}{2Eh}X''=0,\quad \frac{ds_1}{dx}-n\frac{t_2}{a}+\frac{1-\sigma^2}{2Eh}Y''=0,\quad \frac{t_2}{a}+\frac{1-\sigma^2}{2Eh}Z''=0$$

with

$$t_1=\frac{dU}{dx}+\sigma\frac{nV-W}{a},\quad t_2=\sigma\frac{dU}{dx}+\frac{nV-W}{a},\quad s_1=\frac{1-\sigma}{2}\left(\frac{dV}{dx}-\frac{nU}{a}\right).$$

The 2nd and 3rd equations of the former set give

$$\frac{ds_1}{dx}+\frac{1-\sigma^2}{2Eh}(Y''+nZ'')=0,$$

and from this we obtain the equation

$$s_1=a_1-\frac{1-\sigma^2}{2Eh}\int_{x_0}^{x}(Y''+nZ'')\,dx,$$

where a_1 is an arbitrary constant, and x_0 an appropriate fixed value of x, e.g. the value at one edge. Thus s_1 is known and the 1st equation of the same set gives

$$t_1=a_2-\int_{x_0}^{x}\left(n\frac{s_1}{a}+\frac{1-\sigma^2}{2Eh}X''\right)dx,$$

where a_2 is an arbitrary constant. Further t_2 is given by the 3rd equation of the same set, and thus t_1, t_2, s_1 are known. Then U is to be found from the equation

$$\frac{dU}{dx}=\frac{t_1-\sigma t_2}{1-\sigma^2}.$$

which gives

$$U=A_n+\int_{x_0}^{x}\frac{t_1-\sigma t_2}{1-\sigma^2}\,dx,$$

where A_n is an arbitrary constant. Thus U is known, and V is to be found from the equation

$$\frac{dV}{dx}=\frac{nU}{a}+\frac{2s_1}{1-\sigma},$$

which gives

$$V=B_n+\frac{nx}{a}A_n+\frac{n}{a}\int_{x_0}^{x}\left\{\int_{x_0}^{x}\frac{t_1-\sigma t_2}{1-\sigma^2}\,dx\right\}dx+\int_{x_0}^{x}\frac{2s_1}{1-\sigma}\,dx,$$

where B_n is an arbitrary constant. Thus V is known and W is given by the equation

$$W=nV-\frac{t_2-\sigma t_1}{(1-\sigma^2)\,a}.$$

The terms of W which contain A_n and B_n are $nB_n+n^2x\,A_n/a$, and the terms of U, V, W which contain A_n and B_n express the most general inextensional displacement answering to the assumed value of n.

(*b*) *Approximately inextensional solution.*

The inextensional displacement does not contribute to the stress-resultants of type T, S, if these are calculated by means of equations (2) and (3), but it contributes to the stress-couples, and thence to the stress-resultants of type N. If we find the stress-couples in terms of A_n, B_n, deduce the values of n_1, n_2 from the 4th and 5th of equations (4) and substitute in the 2nd and 3rd of equations (4), we shall find that these equations are not satisfied. We therefore remove the terms containing A_n, B_n from the extensional solution, and regard them as the basis of a new solution, in which the displacement is actually or approximately inextensional. It will appear, and may as well be assumed, that the displacement is only approximately inextensional, and is actually of the type considered in Article 330, in which the flexural strains are large compared with the extensional strains.

We write down the results of Article 330 in the form appropriate to a cylindrical shell, viz.

$$\left.\begin{aligned}
t_1&=\frac{dU}{dx}+\sigma\frac{nV-W}{a}+\frac{h^2}{3a}\left\{\frac{2-2\sigma-3\sigma^2}{2(1-\sigma)}\frac{d^2W}{dx^2}-\frac{\sigma(2+\sigma)}{2(1-\sigma)}\frac{nV-n^2W}{a^2}\right\},\\
t_2&=\sigma\frac{dU}{dx}+\frac{nV-W}{a}-\frac{h^2}{3a}\left\{\frac{\sigma(1+2\sigma)}{2(1-\sigma)}\frac{d^2W}{dx^2}+\frac{2+\sigma}{2(1-\sigma)}\frac{nV-n^2W}{a^2}\right\},\\
s_1&=\tfrac{1}{2}(1-\sigma)\left\{\left(\frac{dV}{dx}-\frac{nU}{a}\right)+\frac{h^2}{3a^2}\left(\frac{dV}{dx}-n\frac{dW}{dx}\right)\right\},\\
s_2&=-\tfrac{1}{2}(1-\sigma)\left\{\left(\frac{dV}{dx}-\frac{nU}{a}\right)-\frac{h^2}{3a^2}\left(\frac{dV}{dx}-n\frac{dW}{dx}\right)\right\},
\end{aligned}\right\}\quad\ldots(53)$$

and assume that U, V, W are of the forms

$$U=A_n+h^2U',\quad V=nA_n\frac{x}{a}+B_n+h^2V',\quad W=n^2A_n\frac{x}{a}+nB_n+h^2W',$$

where U', V', W' are to be determined. In $t_1, \ldots$ we shall not retain terms containing any power of h above the second, and in like manner we shall take as sufficient approximations to g_1, g_2, h_1 the formulæ

$$g_1=\frac{h^2}{3a^2}\sigma\left\{n^2(n^2-1)A_n\frac{x}{a}+n(n^2-1)B_n\right\},\quad g_2=\frac{h^2}{3a^2}\left\{n^2(n^2-1)A_n\frac{x}{a}+n(n^2-1)B_n\right\},$$

$$h_1=-(1-\sigma)\frac{h^2}{3a^2}n(n^2-1)A_n.$$

Then the 4th and 5th of equations (4) give

$$n_1=\frac{dg_1}{dx}-n\frac{h_1}{a}=\frac{h^2}{3a^3}n^2(n^2-1)A_n,$$

$$n_2=-\frac{dh_1}{dx}-n\frac{g_2}{a}=-\frac{h^2}{3a^3}\left\{n^3(n^2-1)A_n\frac{x}{a}+n^2(n^2-1)B_n\right\}.$$

The 6th of equations (4) is satisfied identically, and the 1st, 2nd and 3rd of these equations can be written

$$\frac{dt_1}{dx}-\frac{ns_2}{a}=0,\quad \frac{ds_1}{dx}-\frac{nt_2}{a}-\frac{n_2}{a}=0,\quad t_2+nn_2=0,$$

where external forces are omitted, as the displacement answering to them is part of the extensional solution.

In these equations we substitute for n_2, and introduce the forms for t_1, t_2, s_1, s_2 expressed by (53), at the same time replacing $U, \ldots$ by $A_n+h^2U', \ldots$, and neglecting powers of h above the second. The terms of $t_1, \ldots$ which contain $U', \ldots$ may be written $h^2t_1', \ldots$, where

$$t_1'=\frac{dU'}{dx}+\sigma\frac{nV'-W'}{a},\quad t_2'=\sigma\frac{dU'}{dx}+\frac{nV'-W'}{a},\quad s_1'=\tfrac{1}{2}(1-\sigma)\left(\frac{dV'}{dx}-n\frac{U'}{a}\right),$$

and then

$$t_1=h^2\left[t_1'+\frac{\sigma(2+\sigma)}{6(1-\sigma)a^3}\left\{n^2(n^2-1)A_n\frac{x}{a}+n(n^2-1)B_n\right\}\right],$$

$$t_2=h^2\left[t_2'+\frac{2+\sigma}{6(1-\sigma)a^3}\left\{n^2(n^2-1)A_n\frac{x}{a}+n(n^2-1)B_n\right\}\right],$$

$$s_1=h^2\left\{s_1'-\frac{1-\sigma}{6a^3}n(n^2-1)A_n\right\},\quad s_2=h^2\left\{-s_1'-\frac{1-\sigma}{6a^3}n(n^2-1)A_n\right\}.$$

The equations satisfied by t_1', t_2', s_1' are then

$$\frac{dt_1'}{dx}+\frac{ns_1'}{a}+\frac{(1+2\sigma^2)\,n^2(n^2-1)}{6(1-\sigma)\,a^4}A_n=0,$$

$$\frac{ds_1'}{dx}-\frac{nt_2'}{a}-\frac{\sigma}{2(1-\sigma)\,a^4}\left\{n^3(n^2-1)\,A_n\frac{x}{a}+n^2(n^2-1)\,B_n\right\}=0,$$

$$t_2'+\frac{2+\sigma}{6(1-\sigma)\,a^3}\left\{n^2(n^2-1)\,A_n\frac{x}{a}+n(n^2-1)\,B_n\right\}-\frac{1}{3a^3}\left\{n^4(n^2-1)\,A_n\frac{x}{a}+n^3(n^2-1)\,B_n\right\}=0.$$

The process of solving these equations, so as to express t_1', t_2', s_1' in terms of A_n, B_n, is the same as the process by which, in the extensional solution, t_1, t_2, s_1 were expressed in terms of X'', Y'', Z'', except that now no constants of integration answering to α_1, α_2 are to be added. When t_1', t_2', s_1' are found the process of finding U', V', W' is the same as the process by which, in the extensional solution, U, V, W were obtained from t_1, t_2, s_1 except that now no constants of integration answering to A_n, B_n are to be added.

(c) *Edge-effect.*

To determine the edge-effect we have the equations of equilibrium

$$\frac{dt_1}{dx}-\frac{n}{a}s_2=0,\quad \frac{ds_1}{dx}-\frac{n}{a}t_2-\frac{n_2}{a}=0,\quad \frac{dn_1}{dx}+\frac{n}{a}n_2+\frac{t_2}{a}=0,$$

$$n_1=\frac{dg_1}{dx}-\frac{n}{a}h_1,\quad n_2=-\frac{dh_1}{dx}-\frac{n}{a}g_2,\quad s_1+s_2=\frac{h_1}{a},$$

with

$$t_1=\frac{dU}{dx}+\sigma\frac{nV-W}{a},\quad t_2=\sigma\frac{dU}{dx}+\frac{nV-W}{a},\quad s_1-s_2=(1-\sigma)\left(\frac{dV}{dx}-\frac{n}{a}U\right),$$

$$g_1=-\frac{h^2}{3}\left(\frac{d^2W}{dx^2}+\sigma\frac{nV-n^2W}{a^2}\right),\ g_2=-\frac{h^2}{3}\left(\sigma\frac{d^2W}{dx^2}+\frac{nV-n^2W}{a^2}\right),\ h_1=(1-\sigma)\frac{h^2}{3a}\left(\frac{dV}{dx}-n\frac{dW}{dx}\right).$$

We eliminate n_1, n_2 from the equations of equilibrium, obtaining the equations

$$\frac{dt_1}{dx}-\frac{n}{a}s_2=0,\quad \frac{d}{dx}\left(s_1+\frac{h_1}{a}\right)-\frac{n}{a}\left(t_2-\frac{g_2}{a}\right)=0,\quad \frac{d^2g_1}{dx^2}-\frac{2n}{a}\frac{dh_1}{dx}-\frac{n^2}{a^2}g_2+\frac{t_2}{a}=0,$$

and then express these equations in terms of U, V, W. The resulting equations are

$$\frac{d^2U}{dx^2}-\frac{1-\sigma}{2}\frac{n^2}{a^2}U+\left(\frac{1+\sigma}{2}\frac{n}{a}-\frac{1-\sigma}{2}\frac{nh^2}{3a^3}\right)\frac{dV}{dx}+\left(-\frac{\sigma}{a}+\frac{1-\sigma}{2}\frac{n^2h^2}{3a^3}\right)\frac{dW}{dx}=0,$$

$$-\frac{1+\sigma}{2}\frac{n}{a}\frac{dU}{dx}+\frac{1-\sigma}{2}\left(1+\frac{h^2}{a^2}\right)\frac{d^2V}{dx^2}-\frac{n^2}{a^2}\left(1+\frac{h^2}{3a^2}\right)V-\frac{3-\sigma}{6}\frac{nh^2}{a^2}\frac{d^2W}{dx^2}+\frac{n}{a^2}\left(1+\frac{n^2h^2}{3a^2}\right)W=0,$$

$$\frac{\sigma}{a}\frac{dU}{dx}-(2-\sigma)\frac{nh^2}{3a^2}\frac{d^2V}{dx^2}+\frac{n}{a^2}\left(1+\frac{n^2h^2}{3a^2}\right)V-\frac{h^2}{3}\frac{d^4W}{dx^4}+2\frac{n^2h^2}{3a^2}\frac{d^2W}{dx^2}-\frac{1}{a^2}\left(1+\frac{n^4h^2}{3a^2}\right)W=0.$$

To solve them we assume that U, V, W are proportional to e^{mx} and then we have an equation for m in the form

$$a_1(b_2c_3-b_3c_2)+a_2(b_3c_1-b_1c_3)+a_3(b_1c_2-b_2c_1)=0,$$

where

$$a_1=m^2-\frac{1-\sigma}{2}\frac{n^2}{a^2},\quad b_1=\left(\frac{1+\sigma}{2}-\frac{1-\sigma}{2}\frac{h^2}{3a^2}\right)\frac{mn}{a},\quad c_1=\left(-\sigma+\frac{1-\sigma}{2}n^2\frac{h^2}{3a^2}\right)\frac{m}{a},$$

$$a_2=-\frac{1+\sigma}{2}\frac{mn}{a},\quad b_2=\frac{1-\sigma}{2}\left(1+\frac{h^2}{a^2}\right)m^2-\left(1+\frac{h^2}{3a^2}\right)\frac{n^2}{a^2},$$

$$c_2=-\frac{3-\sigma}{2}\frac{h^2}{3a^2}m^2n+\left(1+\frac{n^2h^2}{3a^2}\right)\frac{n}{a^2},$$

$$a_3=\frac{\sigma m}{a},\quad b_3=-(2-\sigma)\frac{h^2}{3a^2}m^2n+\left(1+\frac{n^2h^2}{3a^2}\right)\frac{n}{a^2},$$

$$c_3=-\frac{h^2}{3}m^4+2\frac{h^2}{3a^2}m^2n^2-\frac{1}{a^2}\left(1+\frac{n^4h^2}{3a^2}\right).$$

This equation is in general of the 8th degree, but when h is small compared with a it can be shown to have four roots near to zero and four which are large of the order $1/\sqrt{(ah)}$. To see this we simplify the constituents $b_1, \ldots$ by replacing any such factor as $1+h^2/a^2$ by unity. When this is done, we find that the simplified form of $b_2c_3-b_3c_2$ contains no term independent of m or linear in m, and the term of it which contains m^2 is

$$\left\{-\frac{1-\sigma}{2}\frac{1}{a^2}-\frac{2h^2}{3a^2}\frac{n^4}{a^2}+\frac{7-3\sigma}{2}\frac{h^2}{3a^2}\frac{n^2}{a^2}\right\}m^2,$$

and this can be simplified to $-\frac{1}{2}(1-\sigma)\,m^2/a^2$. When this is done and the left-hand member of the equation is multiplied out, and the coefficient of each power of m simplified by retaining only the lowest power of h which occurs in that coefficient, it is found to take the form

$$-\frac{1-\sigma}{2}\frac{h^2}{3}m^8+2(1-\sigma)\frac{h^2}{3a^2}n^2m^6-\frac{1-\sigma}{2}\frac{1-\sigma^2}{a^2}m^4=0,$$

which has four zero roots and four large roots, which approximate to the four values of $\{-3(1-\sigma^2)\}^{1/4}/\sqrt{(ah)}$. Closer approximations to the large roots can be found, if desired, by retaining the original values of $b_1, \ldots$.

Denoting the large roots by m_1, m_2, m_3, m_4, we have solutions of the differential equations for U, V, W in the forms

$$U=A_1e^{m_1x}+A_2e^{m_2x}+A_3e^{m_3x}+A_4e^{m_4x},\qquad V=B_1e^{m_1x}+\ldots,\qquad W=C_1e^{m_1x}+\ldots,$$

in which the coefficients C may be regarded as arbitrary, and the coefficients A and B may be determined in terms of them by the differential equations. These solutions represent the edge-effect.

It will be observed that the stress, or displacement, answering to the edge-effect diminishes, with increasing distance from the edge, in the same way as in the problems of symmetrical and lateral forces. Further it will be observed that the extensional solution, the approximately inextensional solution, and the solution for the edge-effect contain eight arbitrary constants, and so make it possible to satisfy any conditions of stress or displacement at the edges.

SPHERICAL SHELL

344. Extensional solution.

When the middle surface is a sphere of radius a we take α to be the colatitude θ measured from a fixed pole. Then we have

$$\alpha=\theta,\quad A=a,\quad B=a\sin\theta,\quad \frac{1}{R_1}=\frac{1}{R_2}=\frac{1}{a},\quad \frac{dB}{d\alpha}=a\cos\theta.$$

For an extensional solution answering to any value of n we omit g_1, g_2, h_1 and determine s_1 and s_2 by equations (3). The 6th of equations (4) is satisfied identically, and the 4th and 5th of these equations show that, to the order of approximation involved in the neglect of g_1, g_2, h_1, the quantities n_1, n_2 are also negligible. The first three of equations (4) become

$$\left.\begin{aligned}&\frac{d}{d\theta}(t_1\sin\theta)+ns_1-t_2\cos\theta+a\sin\theta\frac{1-\sigma^2}{2Eh}X''=0,\\&\frac{d}{d\theta}(s_1\sin\theta)-nt_2+s_1\cos\theta+a\sin\theta\frac{1-\sigma^2}{2Eh}Y''=0,\\&t_1+t_2+a\frac{1-\sigma^2}{2Eh}Z''=0,\end{aligned}\right\}\quad\ldots\ldots(54)$$

and equations (2) and (3) give

$$\left.\begin{aligned} t_1 &= \frac{1}{a}\frac{dU}{d\theta} + \sigma\left(\frac{U}{a}\cot\theta + \frac{nV}{a\sin\theta}\right) - (1+\sigma)\frac{W}{a}, \\ t_2 &= \frac{\sigma}{a}\frac{dU}{d\theta} + \left(\frac{U}{a}\cot\theta + \frac{nV}{a\sin\theta}\right) - (1+\sigma)\frac{W}{a}, \\ s_1 &= \tfrac{1}{2}(1-\sigma)\left(\frac{1}{a}\frac{dV}{d\theta} - \frac{V}{a}\cot\theta - \frac{nU}{a\sin\theta}\right). \end{aligned}\right\} \quad \text{.........(55)}$$

The third of equations (54) combined with the 1st and 2nd of equations (55) gives

$$2\frac{W}{a} = \frac{1}{a}\left(\frac{dU}{d\theta} + U\cot\theta + \frac{nV}{\sin\theta}\right) + a\frac{1-\sigma}{2Eh}Z'', \quad \text{...........(56)}$$

and, on eliminating W by means of this equation, the 1st and 2nd of equations (55) become

$$\left.\begin{aligned} t_1 &= \tfrac{1}{2}(1-\sigma)\left\{\frac{1}{a}\frac{dU}{d\theta} - \frac{U\cos\theta + nV}{a\sin\theta} - \frac{1+\sigma}{2Eh}aZ''\right\}, \\ t_2 &= \tfrac{1}{2}(1-\sigma)\left\{-\frac{1}{a}\frac{dU}{d\theta} + \frac{U\cos\theta + nV}{a\sin\theta} - \frac{1+\sigma}{2Eh}aZ''\right\}. \end{aligned}\right\} \quad \text{......(57)}$$

On substituting from equations (57) and the 3rd of equations (55), the 1st and 2nd of equations (54) become

$$\frac{d}{d\theta}\left\{\sin\theta\left(\frac{dU}{d\theta} - \frac{U\cos\theta + nV}{\sin\theta}\right)\right\} + n\left(\frac{dV}{d\theta} - \frac{V\cos\theta + nU}{\sin\theta}\right)$$

$$+\cos\theta\left(\frac{dU}{d\theta} - \frac{U\cos\theta + nV}{\sin\theta}\right)$$

$$+a^2\frac{1+\sigma}{Eh}\left\{X''\sin\theta - \frac{1}{2}\frac{d}{d\theta}(Z''\sin\theta) + \tfrac{1}{2}Z''\cos\theta\right\} = 0,$$

$$\frac{d}{d\theta}\left\{\sin\theta\left(\frac{dV}{d\theta} - \frac{V\cos\theta + nU}{\sin\theta}\right)\right\} + n\left(\frac{dU}{d\theta} - \frac{U\cos\theta + nV}{\sin\theta}\right)$$

$$+\cos\theta\left(\frac{dV}{d\theta} - \frac{V\cos\theta + nU}{\sin\theta}\right) + a^2\frac{1+\sigma}{Eh}\{Y''\sin\theta + \tfrac{1}{2}nZ''\} = 0,$$

which may be written

$$\frac{d^2U}{d\theta^2} + \cot\theta\frac{dU}{d\theta} + \left(1 - \cot^2\theta - \frac{n^2}{\sin^2\theta}\right)U - 2n\frac{\cos\theta}{\sin^2\theta}V = -a^2\frac{1+\sigma}{Eh}\left(X'' - \frac{1}{2}\frac{dZ''}{d\theta}\right),$$

$$\frac{d^2V}{d\theta^2} + \cot\theta\frac{dV}{d\theta} + \left(1 - \cot^2\theta - \frac{n^2}{\sin^2\theta}\right)V - 2n\frac{\cos\theta}{\sin^2\theta}U = -a^2\frac{1+\sigma}{Eh}\left(Y'' + \frac{n}{2\sin\theta}Z''\right).$$

When $n = 0$ the second of these equations can only lead to the solution of Article 338. To solve the first of them for U we observe that a particular integral of the homogeneous equation obtained by equating the left-hand member to zero is $U = \sin\theta$. On putting

$$U = U_0\sin\theta,$$

we find the equation

$$\frac{d^2 U_0}{d\theta^2} + 3\cot\theta \frac{dU_0}{d\theta} = -a^2 \frac{1+\sigma}{Eh}\left(X'' - \frac{1}{2}\frac{dZ''}{d\theta}\right)\operatorname{cosec}\theta,$$

from which

$$\frac{dU_0}{d\theta} = a_1 \operatorname{cosec}^3\theta - a^2\frac{1+\sigma}{Eh}\operatorname{cosec}^3\theta\int_{\theta_0}^{\theta}\sin^2\theta\left(X'' - \frac{1}{2}\frac{dZ''}{d\theta}\right)d\theta,$$

where a_1 is a constant of integration, and θ_0 is any particular value of θ, e.g. the value at one edge of the shell. Hence we obtain the complete primitive of the equation for U in the form

$$U = b_1\sin\theta - \tfrac{1}{2}a_1(\cot\theta - \sin\theta\log_e\tan\tfrac{1}{2}\theta)$$
$$- a^2\frac{1+\sigma}{Eh}\sin\theta\int_{\theta_0}^{\theta}\operatorname{cosec}^3\theta\left\{\int_{\theta_0}^{\theta}\sin^2\theta\left(X'' - \frac{1}{2}\frac{dZ''}{d\theta}\right)d\theta\right\}d\theta. \quad \text{....(58)}$$

When $n > 0$ we put

$$\xi = U + V, \quad \eta = U - V;$$

the equations for U and V give

$$\frac{d^2\xi}{d\theta^2} + \cot\theta\frac{d\xi}{d\theta} + \left(1 - \cot^2\theta - \frac{n^2}{\sin^2\theta}\right)\xi - 2n\frac{\cos\theta}{\sin^2\theta}\xi$$
$$= -a^2\frac{1+\sigma}{Eh}\left(X'' - \frac{1}{2}\frac{dZ''}{d\theta} + Y'' + \frac{n}{2\sin\theta}Z''\right),$$

$$\frac{d^2\eta}{d\theta^2} + \cot\theta\frac{d\eta}{d\theta} + \left(1 - \cot^2\theta - \frac{n^2}{\sin^2\theta}\right)\eta + 2n\frac{\cos\theta}{\sin^2\theta}\eta$$
$$= -a^2\frac{1+\sigma}{Eh}\left(X'' - \frac{1}{2}\frac{dZ''}{d\theta} - Y'' - \frac{n}{2\sin\theta}Z''\right).$$

When $n = 1$ particular integrals of the homogeneous equations obtained by equating the left-hand members of these equations to zero are $\xi = 1 - \cos\theta$, $\eta = 1 + \cos\theta$. We find as before

$$\left.\begin{aligned}
\xi &= b_1(1-\cos\theta) + \tfrac{1}{4}a_1\left\{(1-\cos\theta)\log_e\tan\tfrac{1}{2}\theta - \frac{2-\cos\theta}{1-\cos\theta}\right\} \\
&\quad - a^2\frac{1+\sigma}{Eh}(1-\cos\theta)\int_{\theta_0}^{\theta}\frac{1}{(1-\cos\theta)^2\sin\theta} \\
&\quad \times\left\{\int_{\theta_0}^{\theta}(1-\cos\theta)\sin\theta\left(X'' - \frac{1}{2}\frac{dZ''}{d\theta} + Y'' + \frac{1}{2\sin\theta}Z''\right)d\theta\right\}d\theta, \\
\eta &= b_2(1+\cos\theta) + \tfrac{1}{4}a_2\left\{(1+\cos\theta)\log_e\tan\tfrac{1}{2}\theta + \frac{2+\cos\theta}{1+\cos\theta}\right\} \\
&\quad - a^2\frac{1+\sigma}{Eh}(1+\cos\theta)\int_{\theta_0}^{\theta}\frac{1}{(1+\cos\theta)^2\sin\theta} \\
&\quad \times\left\{\int_{\theta_0}^{\theta}(1+\cos\theta)\sin\theta\left(X'' - \frac{1}{2}\frac{dZ''}{d\theta} - Y'' - \frac{1}{2\sin\theta}Z''\right)d\theta\right\}d\theta.
\end{aligned}\right\}$$

.........(59)

When $n>1$, particular integrals of the equations, obtained from the equations determining ξ and η by equating their right-hand members to zero, are $\xi=\sin\theta\tan^n\frac{1}{2}\theta$ and $\eta=\sin\theta\cot^n\frac{1}{2}\theta$. The complete primitives of the equations for ξ and η are

$$\left.\begin{aligned}\xi &= b_1\sin\theta\tan^n\tfrac{1}{2}\theta+a_1\sin\theta\cot^n\tfrac{1}{2}\theta\left(\frac{2}{n}+\frac{1}{n+1}\cot^2\tfrac{1}{2}\theta+\frac{1}{n-1}\tan^2\tfrac{1}{2}\theta\right)\\ &\quad -a^2\frac{1+\sigma}{Eh}\sin\theta\tan^n\tfrac{1}{2}\theta\int_{\theta_0}^{\theta}\operatorname{cosec}^3\theta\cot^{2n}\tfrac{1}{2}\theta\\ &\quad\times\left\{\int_{\theta_0}^{\theta}\sin^2\theta\tan^n\tfrac{1}{2}\theta\left(X''+Y''-\frac{1}{2}\frac{dZ''}{d\theta}+\frac{n}{2\sin\theta}Z''\right)d\theta\right\}d\theta,\\ \eta &= b_2\sin\theta\cot^n\tfrac{1}{2}\theta+a_2\sin\theta\tan^n\tfrac{1}{2}\theta\left(\frac{2}{n}+\frac{1}{n+1}\tan^2\tfrac{1}{2}\theta+\frac{1}{n-1}\cot^2\tfrac{1}{2}\theta\right)\\ &\quad -a^2\frac{1+\sigma}{Eh}\sin\theta\cot^n\tfrac{1}{2}\theta\int_{\theta_0}^{\theta}\operatorname{cosec}^3\theta\tan^{2n}\tfrac{1}{2}\theta\\ &\quad\times\left\{\int_{\theta_0}^{\theta}\sin^2\theta\cot^n\tfrac{1}{2}\theta\left(X''-Y''-\frac{1}{2}\frac{dZ''}{d\theta}-\frac{n}{2\sin\theta}Z''\right)d\theta\right\}d\theta.\end{aligned}\right\}\quad\text{.........(60)}$$

In each case W is given by (56) when U and V are known.

The method of integration here explained permits of the elimination of the external forces in all cases*. It may be noted that, when $n=0$ and there are no external forces, equations (54) and (55) give either

$$U=0,\quad t_1=t_2=0,\quad s_1\sin^2\theta=\text{const.},\quad\text{..................(61)}$$

or

$$V=0,\quad s_1=0,\quad t_2=-t_1,\quad t_1\sin^2\theta=\text{const.}\quad\text{...........(62)}$$

Further when $n=1$ and there are no external forces equations (54) give

$$\left.\begin{aligned}t_1\sin\theta\cos\theta-s_1\sin\theta&=\text{const.}\\ s_1\sin\theta\cos\theta-t_1\sin\theta&=\text{const.}\end{aligned}\right\}\quad\text{.....................(63)}$$

We observe that, when $n=0$ or 1, the solution contains terms which represent a rigid-body displacement; but, when $n>1$, the corresponding terms represent an inextensional displacement, exactly as in Article 343. The terms containing b_1 and b_2 in equations (60) should therefore be removed, and made the basis of an approximately inextensional solution. This solution can be found for any value of n.

345. Edge-effect. Symmetrical conditions.

In a spherical shell the sixth of the equations of equilibrium (4) is satisfied identically by adopting equations (3), and there is no necessity to have recourse to the second approximation for s_1 and s_2. So we take these to be expressed by (3). When the conditions are symmetrical, so that $n=0$, we either have $U=0$, and then we have the solution for torsion, or else we have

* The method will be found in a paper by the writer in *London Math. Soc. Proc.*, vol. 20 (1889), p. 89.

$V=0$, and then s_1, s_2, h_1 all vanish. We may suppose the external forces to be eliminated by means of the extensional solution, and then the relevant equations become

$$\left.\begin{aligned} \frac{d}{d\theta}(t_1 \sin\theta) - t_2\cos\theta - n_1\sin\theta &= 0,\\ n_2 &= 0,\\ \frac{d}{d\theta}(n_1\sin\theta) + (t_1+t_2)\sin\theta &= 0,\\ \frac{d}{d\theta}(g_1\sin\theta) - g_2\cos\theta - n_1 a\sin\theta &= 0, \end{aligned}\right\} \quad \text{..............(64)}$$

with

$$\left.\begin{aligned} t_1 &= \frac{1}{a}\left\{\frac{dU}{d\theta} + \sigma U\cot\theta - (1+\sigma)W\right\},\\ t_2 &= \frac{1}{a}\left\{\sigma\frac{dU}{d\theta} + U\cot\theta - (1+\sigma)W\right\},\\ g_1 &= -\frac{h^2}{3a^2}\left\{\frac{d^2W}{d\theta^2} + \frac{dU}{d\theta} + \sigma\cot\theta\left(\frac{dW}{d\theta}+U\right)\right\},\\ g_2 &= -\frac{h^2}{3a^2}\left\{\sigma\left(\frac{d^2W}{d\theta^2}+\frac{dU}{d\theta}\right) + \cot\theta\left(\frac{dW}{d\theta}+U\right)\right\}. \end{aligned}\right\} \quad \text{.........(65)}$$

From the 1st and 3rd of equations (64) we eliminate t_2, obtaining the equation $\frac{d}{d\theta}(t_1\sin^2\theta + n_1\sin\theta\cos\theta) = 0$, so that we have

$$t_1\sin^2\theta + n_1\sin\theta\cos\theta = \text{const.}$$

If we retain this constant we shall merely reproduce results included in those obtained in the extensional solution. We therefore write

$$t_1 = -n_1\cot\theta. \quad \text{..............................(66)}$$

Then the 1st of equations (64) becomes

$$t_2 = -\frac{dn_1}{d\theta} \quad \text{..................................(67)}$$

Now put
$$\frac{dW}{d\theta} + U = \xi.$$

Then the 3rd and 4th of equations (65) give

$$g_1 = -\frac{h^2}{3a^2}\left(\frac{d\xi}{d\theta} + \sigma\xi\cot\theta\right), \quad g_2 = -\frac{h^2}{3a^2}\left(\sigma\frac{d\xi}{d\theta} + \xi\cot\theta\right),$$

and the 4th of equations (64) becomes

$$\frac{h^2}{3a^3}\left\{\frac{d}{d\theta}\left(\frac{d\xi}{d\theta}+\sigma\xi\cot\theta\right) + (1-\sigma)\cot\theta\left(\frac{d\xi}{d\theta} - \xi\cot\theta\right)\right\} + n_1 = 0,$$

or
$$\frac{h^2}{3a^2}\left[\frac{d^2\xi}{d\theta^2} + \cot\theta\frac{d\xi}{d\theta} - (\cot^2\theta+\sigma)\xi\right] = -n_1. \quad \text{...........(68)}$$

Again the 1st and 2nd of equations (65) give

$$\frac{d}{d\theta}\frac{a(t_2-\sigma t_1)}{1-\sigma^2}=\frac{d}{d\theta}(U\cot\theta-W)=\frac{d}{d\theta}(U\cot\theta)+U-\xi$$

$$=\cot\theta\left(\frac{dU}{d\theta}-U\cot\theta\right)-\xi=\cot\theta\frac{a(t_1-t_2)}{1-\sigma}-\xi,$$

and from (66) and (67) this becomes

$$\frac{d^2n_1}{d\theta^2}-\sigma\frac{d}{d\theta}(n_1\cot\theta)-(1+\sigma)\cot\theta\left(n_1\cot\theta-\frac{dn_1}{d\theta}\right)=\frac{1-\sigma^2}{a}\xi,$$

or

$$\frac{d^2n_1}{d\theta^2}+\cot\theta\frac{dn_1}{d\theta}-(\cot^2\theta-\sigma)n_1=\frac{1-\sigma^2}{a}\xi. \quad\text{...........(69)}$$

To solve the equations (68) and (69) introduce two constant multipliers α and β, and form the equation

$$\left(\frac{d^2}{d\theta^2}+\cot\theta\frac{d}{d\theta}-\cot^2\theta\right)\left(\alpha n_1+\beta\frac{\xi}{a}\right)+\sigma\left(\alpha n_1-\beta\frac{\xi}{a}\right)+\frac{3a^2}{h^2}\beta n_1-(1-\sigma^2)\alpha\frac{\xi}{a}=0.$$

This will take the form

$$\left(\frac{d^2}{d\theta^2}+\cot\theta\frac{d}{d\theta}+k+1-\operatorname{cosec}^2\theta\right)\left(\alpha n_1+\beta\frac{\xi}{a}\right)=0, \quad\text{.........(70)}$$

if α, β, k are made to satisfy the equations

$$\sigma\alpha+\frac{3a^2}{h^2}\beta=k\alpha, \quad \sigma\beta+(1-\sigma^2)\alpha=-k\beta,$$

which require

$$k^2-\sigma^2+\frac{3(1-\sigma^2)a^2}{h^2}=0. \quad\text{.......................(71)}$$

When k is found from this equation the ratio $\alpha:\beta$ is given by the equation

$$(\sigma+k)\beta=-(1-\sigma^2)\alpha. \quad\text{.......................(72)}$$

If we put $\cos\theta=\mu$ equation (70) can be written

$$\left\{(1-\mu^2)\frac{d^2}{d\mu^2}-2\mu\frac{d}{d\mu}+\nu(\nu+1)-\frac{1}{1-\mu^2}\right\}\left(\alpha n_1+\beta\frac{\xi}{a}\right)=0, \quad\text{...(73)}$$

where $\nu(\nu+1)=1+k$, so that

$$(\nu^2+\nu-1)^2-\sigma^2+\frac{3(1-\sigma^2)a^2}{h^2}=0, \quad\text{.................(74)}$$

and equation (73) is the equation satisfied by generalized spherical harmonics of order ν (not an integer). In fact, if ν were an integer one of the solutions of (73) would be $\sqrt{(1-\mu^2)}\frac{dP_\nu(\mu)}{d\mu}$, $P_\nu(\mu)$ denoting Legendre's νth coefficient. In the present case there are apparently four values of ν, but two of them are irrelevant being obtained from the other two by changing ν into $-(\nu+1)$. Thus there are effectively two values say ν_1 and ν_2, both large of the order

$\{3(1-\sigma^2)\}^{\frac{1}{4}}(1\pm i)\sqrt{(a/2h)}$. The integrals of equations (68) and (69) are therefore expressed by equations of the form

$$\left.\begin{aligned} n_1 - \frac{1-\sigma^2}{\nu_1(\nu_1+1)+\sigma-1}\frac{\xi}{a} &= A_1 P_{\nu_1}{}^1(\mu) + B_1 Q_{\nu_1}{}^1(\mu), \\ n_1 - \frac{1-\sigma^2}{\nu_2(\nu_2+1)+\sigma-1}\frac{\xi}{a} &= A_2 P_{\nu_2}{}^1(\mu) + B_2 Q_{\nu_2}{}^1(\mu), \end{aligned}\right\}\quad\ldots\ldots\ldots(75)$$

where A_1, B_1, A_2, B_2 are arbitrary constants, and $P_\nu{}^1(\mu)$, $Q_\nu{}^1(\mu)$ are two independent integrals of the equation

$$\frac{d}{d\mu}\left\{(1-\mu^2)\frac{dy}{d\mu}\right\} + \nu(\nu+1)y - \frac{y}{1-\mu^2} = 0.$$

The orders ν_1, ν_2 of the generalized spherical harmonics being complex, the constants A_1, ... are also complex, and they can be adjusted so that n_1 and ξ are real. The theory of the functions and expressions for them as hypergeometric series are given by E. W. Hobson*, who has also obtained (pp. 486, 487 of the paper cited) expressions for them adapted to rapid approximate calculation when ν is large. On omission of numerical factors, which are here irrelevant, these expressions are

$$\begin{aligned} P_\nu{}^1(\cos\theta) = {}& \frac{\cos\{(\nu+\frac{1}{2})\theta+\frac{1}{4}\pi\}}{(2\sin\theta)^{\frac{1}{2}}} + \frac{1^2-4}{2(2\nu+3)}\frac{\cos\{(\nu+\frac{3}{2})\theta-\frac{1}{4}\pi\}}{(2\sin\theta)^{\frac{3}{2}}} \\ & + \frac{(1^2-4)(3^2-4)}{2.4(2\nu+3)(2\nu+5)}\frac{\cos\{(\nu+\frac{5}{2})\theta-\frac{3}{4}\pi\}}{(2\sin\theta)^{\frac{5}{2}}} + \ldots, \end{aligned}$$

$$\begin{aligned} Q_\nu{}^1(\cos\theta) = {}& \frac{\cos\{(\nu+\frac{1}{2})\theta+\frac{3}{4}\pi\}}{(2\sin\theta)^{\frac{1}{2}}} - \frac{1^2-4}{2(2\nu+3)}\frac{\cos\{(\nu+\frac{3}{2})\theta+\frac{5}{4}\pi\}}{(2\sin\theta)^{\frac{3}{2}}} \\ & + \frac{(1^2-4)(3^2-4)}{2.4(2\nu+3)(2\nu+5)}\frac{\cos\{(\nu+\frac{5}{2})\theta+\frac{7}{4}\pi\}}{(2\sin\theta)^{\frac{5}{2}}} - \ldots. \end{aligned}$$

When ν is complex of the form $p+iq$, these series involve real exponentials of the form $e^{q\theta}$ and $e^{-q\theta}$, and thus we can see that the edge-effect diminishes with increasing distance from an edge according to the exponential law, in much the same way as we found in the case of a cylindrical shell in Article 340.

The problem of a spherical shell under symmetrical forces has been the subject of numerous researches. The effective step in the solution, the formation of equations (68) and (69), with the recognition of the possibility of solving the resulting equation (70) in terms of series having exponential factors, was taken by H. Reissner†. The recognition of the equations as of a type solvable by hypergeometric series, and the extension of the method to conical and annular shells under symmetrical forces, will be found in papers by E. Meissner‡. The method is worked out in full detail for a spherical shell under symmetrical forces by L. Bolle§. The connexion of the functions involved with spherical harmonics does not seem to have been noticed.

* *Phil. Trans. Roy. Soc.*, vol. 187 (1897), p. 443.

† "Spannungen in Kugelschalen (Kuppeln)," *Müller-Breslau-Festschrift*, Leipzig, 1912, p. 181.

‡ *Physikalische Zeitschrift*, 1913, p. 343, and *Vierteljahrsschrift d. Naturforschenden Ges. in Zürich*, 1915, p. 23.

§ "Festigkeitsberechnung von Kugelschalen" (Diss.), Zurich, 1916.

We may now regard n_1 and ξ as known, then equations (66) and (67) give t_1 and t_2; and, ξ being $dW/d\theta + U$, the 3rd and 4th of equations (65) give g_1 and g_2, while n_2 vanishes. Thus all the stress-resultants and stress-couples are known. Further, since

$$\frac{dU}{d\theta} - U\cot\theta = \frac{a}{1-\sigma}(t_1 - t_2) = \frac{a}{1-\sigma}\left(\frac{dn_1}{d\theta} - n_1\cot\theta\right),$$

we have
$$U = \frac{an_1}{1-\sigma} + b_1\sin\theta,$$

where b_1 is a constant of integration, which may, however, be put equal to zero, as the same term occurs in the extensional solution. Then the equation

$$U\cot\theta - W = \frac{a(t_2 - \sigma t_1)}{1-\sigma^2}$$

gives W. In order to satisfy given boundary-conditions of force or displacement at the edges it is generally necessary to combine an extensional solution with the edge-effect.

The equations determining the edge-effect in a spherical shell have not been integrated, except in the case where $n=0$. It may be observed here that, when $n=1$, the equations of equilibrium possess two integrals answering to equations (63), and these can be shown to be

$$n_1\sin^2\theta - t_1\sin\theta\cos\theta + s_1\sin\theta = \text{const.},$$

$$\left(t_1 - \frac{g_1}{a}\right)\sin\theta - \left(s_1 + \frac{h_1}{a}\right)\cos\theta = \text{const.}$$

In order to determine the edge-effect in the case where $n=1$ we should begin by equating to zero the constants in the right-hand members of these equations.

CONICAL SHELL

346. Extensional solution. Symmetrical conditions.

When the middle surface is a right circular cone of angle 2γ, we take α to be the distance r of a point on the surface from the vertex of the cone, and then we have

$$\alpha = r,\quad A = 1,\quad B = r\sin\gamma,\quad \frac{1}{R_1} = 0,\quad \frac{1}{R_2} = \frac{1}{r\tan\gamma},\quad \frac{dB}{d\alpha} = \sin\gamma.$$

When $n = 0$, the extensional solutions include the solution for torsion, which may be recorded here in the form

$$\left.\begin{aligned} s_1 &= \frac{a_1}{r^2} - \frac{1-\sigma^2}{2Ehr^2}\int_{r_0}^{r} r^2 Y'\,dr, \\ V &= b_1 r + \frac{2r}{1-\sigma}\int_{r_0}^{r}\frac{s_1}{r}\,dr, \end{aligned}\right\} \qquad\qquad (76)$$

and a solution in which V and s_1 vanish. In equations (76) a_1 and b_1 are constants of integration, and r_0 a suitably chosen fixed value of r.

For the extensional solution in which V and s_1 vanish we have the equations

$$\left.\begin{aligned}\frac{d}{dr}(t_1 r) - t_2 + \frac{1-\sigma^2}{2Eh} rX'' = 0,\\ \frac{t_2}{r\tan\gamma} + \frac{1-\sigma^2}{2Eh} Z'' = 0,\end{aligned}\right\} \quad \text{.....................(77)}$$

with

$$\left.\begin{aligned}t_1 = \frac{dU}{dr} + \sigma\left(\frac{U}{r} - \frac{W}{r\tan\gamma}\right),\\ t_2 = \sigma\frac{dU}{dr} + \left(\frac{U}{r} - \frac{W}{r\tan\gamma}\right).\end{aligned}\right\} \quad \text{.....................(78)}$$

From equations (77) we find

$$\left.\begin{aligned}t_1 &= \frac{a_2}{r} - \frac{1-\sigma^2}{2Ehr}\int_{r_0}^{r} r(X'' + Z''\tan\gamma)\,dr,\\ t_2 &= -\frac{1-\sigma^2}{2Eh} rZ''\tan\gamma,\end{aligned}\right\} \quad \text{..............(79)}$$

where a_2 is a constant of integration. Thus t_1 and t_2 are known. From equations (78) we then find

$$\left.\begin{aligned}U &= b_2 + \int_{r_0}^{r}\frac{t_1 - \sigma t_2}{1-\sigma^2}\,dr,\\ W &= U\tan\gamma - r\tan\gamma\frac{t_2 - \sigma t_1}{1-\sigma^2},\end{aligned}\right\} \quad \text{.................(80)}$$

where b_2 is a constant of integration. Thus U and W are known.

347. Edge-effect. Symmetrical conditions.

As in previous examples we take s_1, s_2 and h_1 to vanish, and omit external forces. We have the equations

$$\left.\begin{aligned}\frac{d}{dr}(t_1 r) - t_2 = 0,\\ n_2 = 0,\\ \frac{d}{dr}(n_1 r) + \frac{t_2}{\tan\gamma} = 0,\\ \frac{d}{dr}(g_1 r) - g_2 - n_1 r = 0.\end{aligned}\right\} \quad \text{......................(81)}$$

From the 1st and 3rd of equations (81) we obtain the equation

$$t_1 r + n_1 r\tan\gamma = \text{const.},$$

and, as before, we equate the constant in the right-hand member to zero, thus obtaining the equation

$$n_1 = -t_1\cot\gamma. \quad \text{..............................(82)}$$

Then there remain two equations, viz.

$$\left.\begin{aligned} t_2 &= \frac{d}{dr}(t_1 r), \\ g_2 &= \frac{d}{dr}(g_1 r) + t_1 r \cot\gamma. \end{aligned}\right\} \qquad \text{.......................(83)}$$

Again, we have the equations

$$\left.\begin{aligned} t_1 &= \frac{dU}{dr} + \sigma\left(\frac{U}{r} - \frac{W}{r\tan\gamma}\right), \\ t_2 &= \sigma\frac{dU}{dr} + \left(\frac{U}{r} - \frac{W}{r\tan\gamma}\right), \\ g_1 &= -\frac{h^2}{3}\left(\frac{d^2W}{dr^2} + \frac{\sigma}{r}\frac{dW}{dr}\right), \\ g_2 &= -\frac{h^2}{3}\left(\sigma\frac{d^2W}{dr^2} + \frac{1}{r}\frac{dW}{dr}\right). \end{aligned}\right\} \qquad \text{.....................(84)}$$

In these we write ξ for dW/dr. The 2nd of equations (83) becomes, on substituting for g_1, g_2 from the 3rd and 4th of equations (84) and using (82),

$$\frac{h^2}{3}\left\{\frac{d}{dr}\left(r\frac{d\xi}{dr} + \sigma\xi\right) - \left(\sigma\frac{d\xi}{dr} + \frac{\xi}{r}\right)\right\} + n_1 r = 0,$$

or

$$\frac{h^2}{3}\left(\frac{d^2\xi}{dr^2} + \frac{1}{r}\frac{d\xi}{dr} - \frac{\xi}{r^2}\right) + n_1 = 0. \qquad \text{.....................(85)}$$

Now the 1st and 2nd of equations (84) give

$$U = W\cot\gamma + r\frac{t_2 - \sigma t_1}{1-\sigma^2},$$

$$\frac{dU}{dr} = \frac{t_1 - \sigma t_2}{1-\sigma^2}.$$

We eliminate U from these equations, thus obtaining the equation

$$(1-\sigma^2)\,\xi\cot\gamma + \frac{d}{dr}\{r(t_2 - \sigma t_1)\} - (t_1 - \sigma t_2) = 0,$$

which becomes, on substituting for t_2 from the 1st of equations (83) and for t_1 from (82),

$$\frac{d}{dr}\left\{r\frac{d}{dr}(n_1 r)\right\} - n_1 - (1-\sigma^2)\,\xi\cot^2\gamma = 0,$$

or

$$\frac{d^2 n_1}{dr^2} + \frac{3}{r}\frac{dn_1}{dr} - \frac{1-\sigma^2}{r^2\tan^2\gamma}\,\xi = 0. \qquad \text{.....................(86)}$$

On putting

$$n_1 r = \eta, \quad r = \tfrac{1}{2}x^2, \qquad \text{.........................(87)}$$

equations (85) and (86) become

$$\left.\begin{aligned} &\frac{d^2\xi}{dx^2} + \frac{1}{x}\frac{d\xi}{dx} - \frac{4}{x^2}\xi + \frac{6}{h^2}\eta = 0, \\ &\frac{d^2\eta}{dx^2} + \frac{1}{x}\frac{d\eta}{dx} - \frac{4}{x^2}\eta - \frac{2(1-\sigma^2)}{\tan^2\gamma}\,\xi = 0. \end{aligned}\right\} \qquad \text{...............(88)}$$

To solve these equations put

$$-\frac{2(1-\sigma^2)}{\tan^2\gamma}\xi = k^2\eta, \quad \frac{6}{h^2}\eta = k^2\xi,$$

so that

$$k^4 = -\frac{12(1-\sigma^2)}{h^2\tan^2\gamma}, \quad \text{.......................}(89)$$

then the integrals of the equations are Bessel's functions of kx of order 2. There are four complex values of k, but two of them are irrelevant, as the Bessel's functions are not altered by changing the sign of k. The two relevant values of k are

$$(1 \pm i)\{3(1-\sigma^2)\}^{\frac{1}{4}}/(h\tan\gamma)^{\frac{1}{2}}, \text{ or say } (1 \pm i)m^{\frac{1}{2}},$$

where

$$m = \{3(1-\sigma^2)\}^{\frac{1}{2}}/h\tan\gamma. \quad \text{.......................}(90)$$

The integrals of the equations (88) are then

$$\left.\begin{aligned}\xi &= A_1J_2\{(1+i)(2mr)^{\frac{1}{2}}\} + B_1Y_2\{(1+i)(2mr)^{\frac{1}{2}}\} \\ &\quad + A_2J_2\{(1-i)(2mr)^{\frac{1}{2}}\} + B_2Y_2\{(1-i)(2mr)^{\frac{1}{2}}\}, \\ \eta &= \frac{1-\sigma^2}{m\tan^2\gamma}\, i\,[A_1J_2\{(1+i)(2mr)^{\frac{1}{2}}\} + B_1Y_2\{(1+i)(2mr)^{\frac{1}{2}}\}] \\ &\quad - \frac{1-\sigma^2}{m\tan^2\gamma}\, i\,[A_2J_2\{(1-i)(2mr)^{\frac{1}{2}}\} + B_2Y_2\{(1-i)(2mr)^{\frac{1}{2}}\}].\end{aligned}\right\} \text{...(91)}$$

In equations (91) the constants A_1, B_1, ... are complex and may be adjusted so that the values of ξ and η are real. By means of the semi-convergent expansions of the Bessel's functions we can see that the edge-effect diminishes with increasing distance from an edge in much the same way as it has been found to do in previous examples.

The integration of the equations for a conical shell under symmetrical forces is due to E. Meissner*, who has also pointed out that for a shell of variable thickness, proportional to distance from the vertex of the cone, the integration can be effected without introducing any transcendental functions. A detailed investigation for the case of uniform thickness and for a number of laws of variable thickness has been given by F. Dubois†.

When ξ and η are known, dW/dr and n_1 are known, and by equation (82) and the 1st of equations (83) t_1 and t_2 are known. Also g_1 and g_2 are known, and thus all the stress-resultants and stress-couples are known. To determine the displacement an additional integration is required, in order to find W from the known value of ξ, or dW/dr. When W is known, U is known from the equation giving $t_2 - \sigma t_1$. In effecting the integration for W no constant need be added, as an additive constant in the expression for W occurs also in the extensional solution.

* *loc. cit. ante*, p. 589.

† "Über die Festigkeit der Kegelschale" (Diss.), Zürich, 1917.

348. Extensional solution. Lateral forces.

In a conical shell, when $n=1$ and g_1, g_2, h_1 are neglected, equations (4) become

$$\left.\begin{aligned}\frac{d}{dr}(t_1 r)\sin\gamma+s_1-t_2\sin\gamma+\frac{1-\sigma^2}{2Eh}rX''\sin\gamma=0,\\ \frac{d}{dr}(s_1 r)\sin\gamma-t_2+s_1\sin\gamma+\frac{1-\sigma^2}{2Eh}rY''\sin\gamma=0,\\ t_2+\frac{1-\sigma^2}{2Eh}rZ''\tan\gamma=0.\end{aligned}\right\}\quad\text{.........(92)}$$

On multiplying the 1st of equations (92) by $\sin\gamma$, the 2nd by -1, and the 3rd by $-\cos^2\gamma$, and adding, we obtain the equation

$$\frac{d}{dr}(t_1 r)\sin^2\gamma-\frac{d}{dr}(s_1 r)\sin\gamma+\frac{1-\sigma^2}{2Eh}r(X''\sin\gamma-Y''-Z''\cos\gamma)\sin\gamma=0,$$

which can be integrated in the form

$$t_1 r\sin\gamma-s_1 r=a_1-\frac{1-\sigma^2}{2Eh}\int_{r_0}^{r} r(X''\sin\gamma-Y''-Z''\cos\gamma)\,dr.\quad\text{......(93)}$$

The elimination of t_2 between the 1st and 2nd of equations (92) gives

$$\frac{d}{dr}(t_1 r)\sin\gamma-\frac{d}{dr}(s_1 r)\sin^2\gamma+s_1\cos^2\gamma+\frac{1-\sigma^2}{2Eh}r(X''-Y''\sin\gamma)\sin\gamma=0,$$

and the elimination of $t_1 r$ between this equation and (93) gives

$$\left\{\frac{d}{dr}(s_1 r)+s_1\right\}\cos^2\gamma+\frac{1-\sigma^2}{2Eh}r(Y''\cos^2\gamma+Z''\cos\gamma)=0,$$

which can be integrated in the form

$$s_1 r^2\cos\gamma=a_2-\frac{1-\sigma^2}{2Eh}\int_{r_0}^{r} r^2(Y''\cos\gamma+Z'')\,dr.\quad\text{............(94)}$$

From equations (93) and (94) t_1 and s_1 are known, and t_2 is known from the 3rd of equations (92).

Now equations (2) and (3) give

$$\left.\begin{aligned}t_1&=\frac{dU}{dr}+\sigma\left(\frac{U}{r}+\frac{V}{r\sin\gamma}-\frac{W}{r\tan\gamma}\right),\\ t_2&=\sigma\frac{dU}{dr}+\left(\frac{U}{r}+\frac{V}{r\sin\gamma}-\frac{W}{r\tan\gamma}\right),\\ s_1&=\tfrac{1}{2}(1-\sigma)\left(\frac{dV}{dr}-\frac{V}{r}-\frac{U}{r\sin\gamma}\right).\end{aligned}\right\}\quad\text{...............(95)}$$

From these we find

$$\frac{dU}{dr}=\frac{t_1-\sigma t_2}{1-\sigma^2},$$

whence

$$U=b_1+\int_{r_0}^{r}\frac{t_1-\sigma t_2}{1-\sigma^2}\,dr;\quad\text{........................(96)}$$

and we also find

$$r\frac{d}{dr}\left(\frac{V}{r}\right)=\frac{U}{r\sin\gamma}+\frac{2s_1}{1-\sigma},$$

whence, U and s_1 being known, we find

$$V=b_2 r+r\int_{r_0}^{r}\left\{\frac{U}{r^2\sin\gamma}+\frac{2s_1}{(1-\sigma)\,r}\right\}dr. \quad\text{..............(97)}$$

Thus U and V are known and W is given by the equation

$$W=U\tan\gamma+V\sec\gamma-\frac{t_2-\sigma t_1}{1-\sigma^2}\,r\tan\gamma. \quad\text{..............(98)}$$

349. Edge-effect. Lateral forces.

In a conical shell, when g_1, g_2, h_1 are not neglected, equations (3) do not give a sufficient approximation to s_1 and s_2, for these are necessarily connected by the 6th of equations (4), which becomes

$$s_1+s_2=\frac{h_1}{r\tan\gamma}.$$

We shall proceed, exactly as in the problem of a cylindrical shell, to take s_1 and s_2 to satisfy this equation, while s_1-s_2 is the same as if equations (3) held. This procedure is equivalent to adopting, as far as s_1 and s_2 are concerned, the second approximation given in Article 330.

As the problem is rather intricate it may be desirable to sketch the method in advance. We first write down the relevant equations of the set (4), and obtain two integrals of them. One of these integrals will be found to express n_1 in terms of t_1 and s_1, the other will not involve n_1 or n_2. We shall then obtain a set of three equations connecting $t_1, t_2, s_1, g_1, g_2, h_1$. This part of the work will be marked (*a*). We shall then proceed in a second part, marked (*b*), to express the quantities $t_1, \ldots$ in terms of two quantities, one of which is $U/r-\tan\gamma\,(dW/dr-W/r)$, while the other is $t_1-g_1/(r\tan\gamma)$. In a third part of the work, marked (*c*), we shall obtain two linear differential equations connecting these two quantities. Here a certain approximation will be allowed. In a fourth part, marked (*d*), we shall show how to integrate the equations in a form suitable for expressing the edge-effect.

(*a*) *Integrals of the equations of equilibrium.*

When $n=1$ the equations of equilibrium of the conical shell become

$$\left.\begin{aligned}
&\frac{d}{dr}(t_1 r)\sin\gamma-s_2-t_2\sin\gamma=0,\\
&\frac{d}{dr}(s_1 r)\sin\gamma-t_2-s_2\sin\gamma-n_2\cos\gamma=0,\\
&\frac{d}{dr}(n_1 r)\sin\gamma+n_2+t_2\cos\gamma=0,\\
&\frac{d}{dr}(h_1 r)\sin\gamma+g_2+h_1\sin\gamma+n_2 r\sin\gamma=0,\\
&\frac{d}{dr}(g_1 r)\sin\gamma-h_1-g_2\sin\gamma-n_1 r\sin\gamma=0,\\
&-h_1\cos\gamma+(s_1+s_2)\,r\sin\gamma=0.
\end{aligned}\right\}\quad\text{......................(99)}$$

We multiply the left-hand members of the 1st, 2nd, and 3rd of these equations in order by $\sin\gamma$, -1, and $-\cos\gamma$, and add, obtaining the equation

$$\frac{d}{dr}(t_1 r)\sin^2\gamma - \frac{d}{dr}(s_1 r)\sin\gamma - \frac{d}{dr}(n_1 r)\sin\gamma\cos\gamma = 0,$$

which is immediately integrable. As in previous examples no constant of integration need be introduced, and we may write the integral in the form

$$n_1\cos\gamma = t_1\sin\gamma - s_1. \qquad (100)$$

We eliminate t_2 from the 1st and 2nd of equations (99), obtaining the equation

$$\frac{d}{dr}(t_1 r)\sin\gamma - \frac{d}{dr}(s_1 r)\sin^2\gamma - s_2\cos^2\gamma + n_2\sin\gamma\cos\gamma = 0.$$

We eliminate g_2 from the 4th and 5th of equations (99), obtaining the equation

$$\frac{d}{dr}(g_1 r)\sin\gamma + \frac{d}{dr}(h_1 r)\sin^2\gamma - h_1\cos^2\gamma + n_2 r\sin^2\gamma - n_1 r\sin\gamma = 0.$$

From these two equations we eliminate n_2, obtaining the equation

$$r\frac{d}{dr}(t_1 r)\sin^2\gamma - \frac{d}{dr}(g_1 r)\sin\gamma\cos\gamma - r\frac{d}{dr}(s_1 r)\sin^3\gamma - rs_2\sin\gamma\cos^2\gamma$$
$$-\frac{d}{dr}(h_1 r)\sin^2\gamma\cos\gamma + h_1\cos^3\gamma + n_1 r\sin\gamma\cos\gamma = 0.$$

In this equation we substitute for n_1 from equation (100), and for rs_2 from the 6th of equations (99), obtaining the equation

$$r\frac{d}{dr}(t_1 r)\sin^2\gamma - \frac{d}{dr}(g_1 r)\sin\gamma\cos\gamma - r\frac{d}{dr}(s_1 r)\sin^3\gamma + (rs_1\sin\gamma - h_1\cos\gamma)\cos^2\gamma$$
$$-\frac{d}{dr}(h_1 r)\sin^2\gamma\cos\gamma + h_1\cos^3\gamma + r\sin\gamma\,(t_1\sin\gamma - s_1) = 0,$$

or

$$\frac{d}{dr}(t_1 r^2)\sin^2\gamma - \frac{d}{dr}(g_1 r)\sin\gamma\cos\gamma - \frac{d}{dr}(s_1 r^2)\sin^3\gamma - \frac{d}{dr}(h_1 r)\sin^2\gamma\cos\gamma = 0,$$

which is immediately integrable. Here again no constant of integration need be introduced, and we may write the integral in the form

$$t_1 - \frac{g_1}{r\tan\gamma} - \sin\gamma\left(s_1 + \frac{h_1}{r\tan\gamma}\right) = 0. \qquad (101)$$

Now the 1st of equations (99) gives

$$\frac{d}{dr}(t_1 r) + \frac{1}{\sin\gamma}\left(s_1 - \frac{h_1}{r\tan\gamma}\right) = t_2. \qquad (102)$$

The 5th of equations (99) becomes, on substituting from (100) for n_1,

$$g_2 = \frac{d}{dr}(g_1 r) - t_1 r\tan\gamma + \left(s_1 - \frac{h_1}{r\tan\gamma}\right) r\sec\gamma,$$

and, by eliminating $s_1 - h_1/(r\tan\gamma)$ between this equation and (102), we obtain the equation

$$t_2 - \frac{g_2}{r\tan\gamma} = \frac{1}{r}\frac{d}{dr}\left\{r^2\left(t_1 - \frac{g_1}{r\tan\gamma}\right)\right\}. \qquad (103)$$

The set of six equations (99) may now be replaced by equation (100), giving n_1, the 3rd of equations (99), giving n_2, the 6th of equations (99), giving s_2, and the equations (101), (102), and (103), which do not contain n_1, n_2, or s_2.

(*b*) *Introduction of the displacement.*

The set of equations connecting $t_1, \ldots$ with the displacement is

$$\left.\begin{aligned}
t_1 &= \frac{dU}{dr} + \sigma\left(\frac{U}{r} + \frac{V - W\cos\gamma}{r\sin\gamma}\right),\\
t_2 &= \sigma\,\frac{dU}{dr} + \frac{U}{r} + \frac{V - W\cos\gamma}{r\sin\gamma},\\
s_1 - s_2 &= (1-\sigma)\left(\frac{dV}{dr} - \frac{V}{r} - \frac{U}{r\sin\gamma}\right),\\
g_1 &= -\frac{h^2}{3}\left\{\frac{d^2W}{dr^2} + \sigma\left(\frac{V\cos\gamma - W}{r^2\sin^2\gamma} + \frac{1}{r}\frac{dW}{dr}\right)\right\},\\
g_2 &= -\frac{h^2}{3}\left\{\sigma\,\frac{d^2W}{dr^2} + \frac{V\cos\gamma - W}{r^2\sin^2\gamma} + \frac{1}{r}\frac{dW}{dr}\right\},\\
h_1 &= \frac{h^2}{3}(1-\sigma)\frac{d}{dr}\left(\frac{V\cos\gamma - W}{r\sin\gamma}\right),
\end{aligned}\right\} \quad \text{.............. (104)}$$

and with these we have to associate the 6th of equations (99).

In these equations we put

$$\left.\begin{aligned}
\frac{U}{r} - \tan\gamma\left(\frac{dW}{dr} - \frac{W}{r}\right) &= \xi,\\
\frac{V\cos\gamma - W}{r\sin^2\gamma} + \frac{dW}{dr} &= \eta.
\end{aligned}\right\} \quad \text{.............................. (105)}$$

Then we have

$$U = r\xi + \left(r\frac{dW}{dr} - W\right)\tan\gamma,$$

$$V = \frac{\sin^2\gamma}{\cos\gamma}\left(r\eta - r\frac{dW}{dr}\right) + W\sec\gamma,$$

and these equations give

$$\begin{aligned}
\frac{U}{r} + \frac{V - W\cos\gamma}{r\sin\gamma} &= \xi + \left(\frac{dW}{dr} - \frac{W}{r}\right)\tan\gamma + \tan\gamma\left(\eta - \frac{dW}{dr}\right) + \frac{W}{r\sin\gamma\cos\gamma} - \frac{W}{r\tan\gamma}\\
&= \xi + \eta\tan\gamma,
\end{aligned}$$

and

$$\begin{aligned}
\frac{dV}{dr} - \frac{V}{r} - \frac{U}{r\sin\gamma} &= \frac{\sin^2\gamma}{\cos\gamma}\left(r\frac{d\eta}{dr} - r\frac{d^2W}{dr^2}\right) + r\frac{d}{dr}\left(\frac{W}{r}\right)\sec\gamma - \frac{\xi}{\sin\gamma} - \left(\frac{dW}{dr} - \frac{W}{r}\right)\sec\gamma\\
&= \frac{\sin^2\gamma}{\cos\gamma}\,r\left(\frac{d\eta}{dr} - \frac{d^2W}{dr^2}\right) - \frac{\xi}{\sin\gamma},
\end{aligned}$$

with

$$\frac{dU}{dr} = \frac{d}{dr}(r\xi) + r\frac{d^2W}{dr^2}\tan\gamma.$$

and

$$\frac{d}{dr}\left(\frac{V\cos\gamma - W}{r\sin\gamma}\right) = \sin\gamma\left(\frac{d\eta}{dr} - \frac{d^2W}{dr^2}\right).$$

Hence equations (104) become

$$\left.\begin{aligned}
t_1 &= \tan\gamma\left(r\frac{d^2W}{dr^2} + \sigma\eta\right) + \frac{d}{dr}(r\xi) + \sigma\xi,\\
t_2 &= \tan\gamma\left(\sigma r\frac{d^2W}{dr^2} + \eta\right) + \sigma\frac{d}{dr}(r\xi) + \xi,\\
s_1 - s_2 &= (1-\sigma)\left\{-\frac{\xi}{\sin\gamma} + \frac{\sin^2\gamma}{\cos\gamma}\,r\left(\frac{d\eta}{dr} - \frac{d^2W}{dr^2}\right)\right\},\\
g_1 &= -\frac{h^2}{3}\left(\frac{d^2W}{dr^2} + \frac{\sigma\eta}{r}\right),\\
g_2 &= -\frac{h^2}{3}\left(\sigma\frac{d^2W}{dr^2} + \frac{\eta}{r}\right),\\
h_1 &= \frac{h^2}{3}(1-\sigma)\sin\gamma\left(\frac{d\eta}{dr} - \frac{d^2W}{dr^2}\right),
\end{aligned}\right\} \quad \text{............ (106)}$$

and we have the additional equation, the 6th of (99), in the form

$$s_1+s_2=\frac{h_1}{r\tan\gamma}.$$

Now the 1st and 4th of equations (106) yield a single relation between t_1, g_1 and ξ, and this relation can be put in the form

$$t_1\left(1+\frac{h^2}{3r^2\tan^2\gamma}\right)=\left(t_1-\frac{g_1}{r\tan\gamma}\right)+\frac{h^2}{3r^2\tan^2\gamma}\left\{\frac{d}{dr}(r\xi)+\sigma\xi\right\}. \quad\text{......(107)}$$

The same relation may also be used to express g_1 in terms of $\{t_1-g_1/(r\tan\gamma)\}$ and ξ. In the same way from the 2nd and 5th of equations (106) we can obtain the equation

$$t_2\left(1+\frac{h^2}{3r^2\tan^2\gamma}\right)=\left(t_2-\frac{g_2}{r\tan\gamma}\right)+\frac{h^2}{3r^2\tan^2\gamma}\left\{\sigma\frac{d}{dr}(r\xi)+\xi\right\}, \quad\text{......(108)}$$

and use this relation to express g_2 in terms of $\{t_2-g_2/(r\tan\gamma)\}$ and ξ. Then, since $\{t_2-g_2/(r\tan\gamma)\}$ is connected with $\{t_1-g_1/(r\tan\gamma)\}$ by (103), we have t_1, t_2, g_1, g_2 expressed in terms of $\{t_1-g_1/(r\tan\gamma)\}$ and ξ.

Again the 3rd and 6th of equations (106) with the 6th of equations (99) yield a single relation between s_1, h_1 and ξ, and this relation can be put in the form

$$s_1\left(1+\frac{h^2}{r^2\tan^2\gamma}\right)=\left(s_1+\frac{h_1}{r\tan\gamma}\right)\left(1+\frac{h^2}{3r^2\tan^2\gamma}\right)-(1-\sigma)\frac{h^2}{3}\frac{\xi\cos^2\gamma}{r^2\sin^3\gamma}, \quad\text{...(109)}$$

and thus by (101) s_1 is expressed in terms of $\{t_1-g_1/(r\tan\gamma)\}$ and ξ. The same relation avails to express h_1 also in terms of the same two quantities.

(c) *Formation of two linear differential equations.*

It remains to obtain two equations for the determination of ξ and $\{t_1-g_1/(r\tan\gamma)\}$. One of these can be obtained directly from the equations already found. For the other we have recourse again to equations (106). We write the 1st and 2nd of equations (106) in the forms

$$\frac{t_2-\sigma t_1}{1-\sigma^2}=\eta\tan\gamma+\xi,$$

$$\frac{t_1-\sigma t_2}{1-\sigma^2}=r\frac{d^2W}{dr^2}\tan\gamma+\frac{d}{dr}(r\xi),$$

and eliminate η and W from these equations and the equation

$$\frac{2s_1}{1-\sigma}+\frac{\xi}{\sin\gamma}=\left(1+\frac{h^2}{3r^2\tan^2\gamma}\right)r\frac{\sin^2\gamma}{\cos\gamma}\left(\frac{d\eta}{dr}-\frac{d^2W}{dr^2}\right).$$

We thus obtain the equation

$$\left(1+\frac{h^2}{3r^2\tan^2\gamma}\right)r\sin\gamma\left\{\frac{d}{dr}(t_2-\sigma t_1)-\frac{t_1-\sigma t_2}{r}+\frac{\xi}{r}(1-\sigma^2)\right\}=2s_1(1+\sigma)+\frac{1-\sigma^2}{\sin\gamma}\xi. \quad\text{.........(110)}$$

In proceeding now to form the two equations for determining ξ and $\{t_1-g_1/(r\tan\gamma)\}$ we shall permit ourselves a certain approximation, depending upon the circumstance that h/r is small. In equations (107)—(110) there are terms which contain factors of the form $\{\alpha+(h^2/r^2)\beta\}$, and other terms which do not contain such factors. In any term, containing a factor of this form, an approximation may be made by omitting $(h^2/r^2)\beta$ as small in comparison with α. We shall not alter any expression which does not contain such a factor. For example we shall not alter the expression

$$\frac{h^2}{3r^2\tan^2\gamma}\left\{\frac{d}{dr}(r\xi)+\sigma\xi\right\},$$

which occurs in the right-hand member of equation (107). According to this plan we have, as approximate equivalents of equations (107)—(109), the three equations

$$\left.\begin{aligned} t_1 &= \left(t_1 - \frac{g_1}{r\tan\gamma}\right) + \frac{h^2}{3r^2\tan^2\gamma}\left\{\frac{d}{dr}(r\xi)+\sigma\xi\right\},\\ t_2 &= \left(t_2 - \frac{g_2}{r\tan\gamma}\right) + \frac{h^2}{3r^2\tan^2\gamma}\left\{\sigma\frac{d}{dr}(r\xi)+\xi\right\},\\ s_1 &= \left(s_1 + \frac{h_1}{r\tan\gamma}\right) - (1-\sigma)\frac{h^2}{3}\frac{\xi\cos^2\gamma}{r^2\sin^3\gamma}, \end{aligned}\right\} \quad \text{.................(111)}$$

and these give to the same order of approximation,

$$\left.\begin{aligned} g_1 &= \frac{h^2}{3r\tan\gamma}\left\{\frac{d}{dr}(r\xi)+\sigma\xi\right\},\\ g_2 &= \frac{h^2}{3r\tan\gamma}\left\{\sigma\frac{d}{dr}(r\xi)+\xi\right\},\\ h_1 &= (1-\sigma)\frac{h^2\xi\cos\gamma}{3r\sin^2\gamma}. \end{aligned}\right\} \quad \text{.........................(112)}$$

Now write

$$L = t_1 - \frac{g_1}{r\tan\gamma}, \quad \text{...................................(113)}$$

and express t_1, t_2 in terms of L and ξ by means of the 1st and 2nd of equations (111) and equation (103). We find

$$\left.\begin{aligned} t_1 &= L + \frac{h^2}{3r^2\tan^2\gamma}\left\{\frac{d}{dr}(r\xi)+\sigma\xi\right\},\\ t_2 &= \frac{1}{r}\frac{d}{dr}(Lr^2) + \frac{h^2}{3r^2\tan^2\gamma}\left\{\sigma\frac{d}{dr}(r\xi)+\xi\right\}. \end{aligned}\right\} \quad \text{..................(114)}$$

Also by the 3rd of equations (111), combined with equation (101) and the 3rd of equations (112), we have

$$s_1 - \frac{h_1}{r\tan\gamma} = \frac{L}{\sin\gamma} - \tfrac{2}{3}(1-\sigma)\frac{h^2\xi\cos^2\gamma}{r^2\sin^3\gamma}. \quad \text{....................(115)}$$

Now substitute from (114) and (115) in (102). We obtain the equation

$$\frac{h^2}{3\tan^2\gamma}\frac{d}{dr}\left[\frac{1}{r}\left\{\frac{d}{dr}(r\xi)+\sigma\xi\right\}\right] - \tfrac{2}{3}(1-\sigma)\frac{h^2\xi\cos^2\gamma}{r^2\sin^4\gamma} - \frac{h^2}{3r^2\tan^2\gamma}\left\{\sigma\frac{d}{dr}(r\xi)+\xi\right\} = L\left(1-\frac{1}{\sin^2\gamma}\right)$$

or

$$\frac{h^2}{3}\left[\frac{d^2\xi}{dr^2} + \frac{1}{r}\frac{d\xi}{dr} - \left\{2(1+\sigma)+2\frac{1-\sigma}{\sin^2\gamma}\right\}\frac{\xi}{r^2}\right] = -L. \quad \text{...............(116)}$$

This is the first of the required equations. It has, as premised, been formed without using equation (110).

We next form an approximate equivalent of equation (110) according to the plan adopted for forming equations (111). It is

$$\frac{dt_2}{dr} - \frac{t_1}{r} - \sigma\left(\frac{dt_1}{dr} - \frac{t_2}{r}\right) - \frac{2s_1(1+\sigma)}{r\sin\gamma} = \frac{1-\sigma^2}{r}\xi\left(\frac{1}{\sin^2\gamma}-1\right). \quad \text{.........(117)}$$

In this equation we substitute for t_1 and t_2 from equations (114), and for s_1 from the 3rd of equations (111), and in this last eliminate $\{s_1 + h_1/(r\tan\gamma)\}$ by means of (101). We thus obtain the equation

$$\begin{aligned} &\frac{d}{dr}\left(r\frac{dL}{dr}+2L\right) - \frac{L}{r} + 2\sigma\frac{L}{r} - \frac{2(1+\sigma)}{r\sin^2\gamma}L\\ &+ \frac{h^2}{3\tan^2\gamma}\left[\frac{d}{dr}\left(\frac{\sigma}{r}\frac{d\xi}{dr}+\frac{1+\sigma}{r^2}\xi\right) - \left(\frac{1}{r^2}\frac{d\xi}{dr}+\frac{1+\sigma}{r^3}\xi\right) - \sigma\frac{d}{dr}\left(\frac{1}{r}\frac{d\xi}{dr}+\frac{1+\sigma}{r^2}\xi\right)\right.\\ &\left.+\sigma\left(\frac{\sigma}{r^2}\frac{d\xi}{dr}+\frac{1+\sigma}{r^3}\xi\right) + \frac{2(1-\sigma^2)}{r^3\sin^2\gamma}\xi\right] = \frac{1-\sigma^2}{r\tan^2\gamma}\xi. \quad \text{......(118)} \end{aligned}$$

The coefficient of $\frac{1}{3}h^2 \cot^2 \gamma$ in the left-hand member of this equation is

$$\{\xi(1-\sigma^2)/r^3\}(-3+2\operatorname{cosec}^2\gamma),$$

and the equation becomes

$$\frac{d^2(Lr)}{dr^2}+\frac{1}{r}\frac{d(Lr)}{dr}-\left\{2(1-\sigma)+2\frac{1+\sigma}{\sin^2\gamma}\right\}\frac{L}{r}=\frac{1-\sigma^2}{r\tan^2\gamma}\,\xi\left\{1-\frac{h^2(2-3\sin^2\gamma)}{3r^2\sin^2\gamma}\right\},$$

or, by our method of approximation,

$$\frac{d^2(Lr)}{dr^2}+\frac{1}{r}\frac{d(Lr)}{dr}-\left\{2(1-\sigma)+2\frac{1+\sigma}{\sin^2\gamma}\right\}\frac{L}{r}=\frac{1-\sigma^2}{r\tan^2\gamma}\,\xi. \quad\text{.........(119)}$$

This is the second of the required equations.

(*d*) *Method of solution of the equations.*

We shall now transform equations (116) and (119) by putting

$$Lr=h\zeta,\quad r=\tfrac{1}{2}hx^2. \quad\text{.........(120)}$$

The equations become

$$\left.\begin{aligned}\frac{d^2\xi}{dx^2}+\frac{1}{x}\frac{d\xi}{dx}-8\left(1+\sigma+\frac{1-\sigma}{\sin^2\gamma}\right)\frac{\xi}{x^2}&=-6\zeta,\\ \frac{d^2\zeta}{dx^2}+\frac{1}{x}\frac{d\zeta}{dx}-8\left(1-\sigma+\frac{1+\sigma}{\sin^2\gamma}\right)\frac{\zeta}{x^2}&=\frac{2(1-\sigma^2)}{\tan^2\gamma}\,\xi.\end{aligned}\right\} \quad\text{.........(121)}$$

Between these equations we eliminate ζ, obtaining for ξ the linear differential equation of the fourth order

$$\frac{d^4\xi}{dx^4}+\frac{2}{x}\frac{d^3\xi}{dx^3}-(1+a_1+a_2)\frac{1}{x^2}\frac{d^2\xi}{dx^2}+(1+3a_1-a_2)\frac{1}{x^3}\frac{d\xi}{dx}+\left\{\frac{12(1-\sigma^2)}{\tan^2\gamma}-(4a_1-a_1a_2)\frac{1}{x^4}\right\}\xi=0, \quad\text{.........(122)}$$

where for brevity we have written

$$a_1=8\{1+\sigma+(1-\sigma)\operatorname{cosec}^2\gamma\},\quad a_2=8\{1-\sigma+(1+\sigma)\operatorname{cosec}^2\gamma\}. \quad\text{.........(123)}$$

If ξ were found from equation (122), ζ or Lr/h would be known from the 1st of equations (121), and then, as we have seen, all the stress-resultants and stress-couples would be known. To determine the displacement a further integration would be necessary, because the expressions (106) for $t_1, \ldots$ contain W only in the form d^2W/dr^2.

Although the solution of (122) cannot be expressed in terms of known functions, the theory of linear differential equations avails for the determination of an approximate solution, with an arbitrarily small margin of error, suitable for the expression of the edge-effect. The equation has no singularities for finite values of x other than $x=0$. As $x=\sqrt{(2r/h)}$, we require a solution which shall be valid for large values of x. Now the equation possesses four independent integrals of the type described as "normal integrals*." To determine them we first assume for ξ an expression of the form

$$\xi=e^{mx}X, \quad\text{.........(124)}$$

obtaining for X the equation

$$\begin{aligned}&\frac{d^4X}{dx^4}+\left(4m+\frac{2}{x}\right)\frac{d^3X}{dx^3}+\left(6m^2+\frac{6m}{x}-\frac{1+a_1+a_2}{x^2}\right)\frac{d^2X}{dx^2}\\&+\left(4m^3+\frac{6m^2}{x}-2m\frac{1+a_1+a_2}{x^2}+\frac{1+3a_1-a_2}{x^3}\right)\frac{dX}{dx}\\&+\left\{m^4+\frac{2m^3}{x}-m^2\frac{1+a_1+a_2}{x^2}+m\frac{1+3a_1-a_2}{x^3}+\frac{12(1-\sigma^2)}{\tan^2\gamma}+\frac{a_1a_2-4a_1}{x^4}\right\}X=0,\end{aligned} \quad\text{.........(125)}$$

* Reference may be made to A. R. Forsyth, *Theory of Differential Equations*, vol. 4 (Cambridge, 1902), ch. 7. The series involved in the expressions for normal integrals may diverge, and become "asymptotic expansions," valid, in spite of divergence, for the purpose of approximate calculation.

and then we transform this equation by putting

$$x=\frac{1}{z}, \qquad \text{.........(126)}$$

obtaining the equation

$$z^8\frac{d^4X}{dz^4}+\{12z^7-(4m+2z)z^6\}\frac{d^3X}{dz^3}+[36z^6-6(4m+2z)z^5+\{6m^2+6mz-(1+a_1+a_2)z^2\}z^4]\frac{d^2X}{dz^2}$$
$$+[24z^5-6(4m+2z)z^4+2\{6m^2+6mz-(1+a_1+a_2)z^2\}z^3$$
$$-\{4m^3+6m^2z-2m(1+a_1+a_2)z^2+(1+3a_1-a_2)z^3\}z^2]\frac{dX}{dz}$$
$$+\Big\{m^4+\frac{12(1-\sigma^2)}{\tan^2\gamma}+2m^3z-m^2(1+a_1+a_2)z^2+m(1+3a_1-a_2)z^3$$
$$+(a_1a_2-4a_1)z^4\Big\}X=0. \qquad \text{......(127)}$$

We seek a solution of this equation in series in the form

$$X=z^s(c_0+c_1z+c_2z^2+c_3z^3+\ldots), \qquad \text{.........(128)}$$

and find that such a solution is formally possible if, and only if,

$$m^4+\frac{12(1-\sigma^2)}{\tan^2\gamma}=0, \qquad \text{.........(129)}$$

and

$$s=\tfrac{1}{2}.$$

There is no difficulty in obtaining as many of the coefficients c_1, c_2, ... as we wish. The coefficient c_0 is arbitrary. Since there are four complex values of m, which satisfy (129), there are four independent solutions of this kind, and they suffice to determine the edge-effect. It is known that, in general, the series such as that in the right-hand member of (128) are not convergent, but avail for the approximate numerical calculation of the functions such as X. In this property they resemble the well-known "semi-convergent expansions" of Bessel's functions, these expansions being, in fact, particular examples of asymptotic expansions of integrals, which are analogous to normal integrals, of linear differential equations.

350. Extensional solution. Unsymmetrical conditions.

In a conical shell, under conditions answering to values of n which exceed unity, we can have an extensional solution. For this we neglect g_1, g_2, h_1, n_1, n_2 and use equations (3) to express s_1, s_2. The relevant equations among equations (4) become

$$\left.\begin{aligned}\frac{d}{dr}(t_1r)\sin\gamma+ns_1-t_2\sin\gamma+\frac{1-\sigma^2}{2Eh}r\sin\gamma X''=0,\\ \frac{d}{dr}(s_1r)\sin\gamma-nt_2+s_1\sin\gamma+\frac{1-\sigma^2}{2Eh}r\sin\gamma Y''=0,\\ t_2\cos\gamma+\frac{1-\sigma^2}{2Eh}r\sin\gamma Z''=0.\end{aligned}\right\} \qquad \text{......(130)}$$

On eliminating t_2 between the 2nd and 3rd of equations (130), we obtain the equation

$$\frac{d}{dr}(s_1r^2)+\frac{1-\sigma^2}{2Eh}r^2(Y''+nZ''\sec\gamma)=0,$$

which can be integrated in the form

$$s_1r^2=a_1-\frac{1-\sigma^2}{2Eh}\int_{r_0}^{r}r^2(Y''+nZ''\sec\gamma)\,dr, \qquad \text{.........(131)}$$

where r_0 is an appropriate fixed value of r, and a_1 is a constant of integration. Thus s_1 is known. By substituting for t_2 from the 3rd of equations (130) the 1st of these equations becomes

$$\frac{d}{dr}(t_1 r)\sin\gamma + ns_1 + \frac{1-\sigma^2}{2Eh} r\,(X'' + Z''\tan\gamma)\sin\gamma = 0,$$

which can be integrated in the form

$$t_1 r = a_2 - \int_{r_0}^{r}\left\{\frac{n}{\sin\gamma}s_1 + \frac{1-\sigma^2}{2Eh} r\,(X'' + Z''\tan\gamma)\right\} dr = 0, \quad \text{...(132)}$$

where a_2 is a constant of integration. Thus t_1, s_1, t_2 are known.

To determine the displacement we have the equations

$$\left.\begin{aligned} t_1 &= \frac{dU}{r} + \sigma\left(\frac{U}{r} + \frac{nV}{r\sin\gamma} - \frac{W}{r\tan\gamma}\right), \\ t_2 &= \sigma\frac{dU}{dr} + \left(\frac{U}{r} + \frac{nV}{r\sin\gamma} - \frac{W}{r\tan\gamma}\right), \\ s_1 &= \tfrac{1}{2}(1-\sigma)\left(\frac{dV}{dr} - \frac{V}{r} - \frac{nU}{r\sin\gamma}\right). \end{aligned}\right\} \quad \text{...(133)}$$

The first two of these equations give

$$\frac{dU}{dr} = \frac{t_1 - \sigma t_2}{1-\sigma^2},$$

which can be integrated in the form

$$U = A_n + \int_{r_0}^{r}\frac{t_1 - \sigma t_2}{1-\sigma^2} dr, \quad \text{...(134)}$$

where A_n is a constant of integration. The 3rd of equations (133) gives

$$\frac{d}{dr}\left(\frac{V}{r}\right) = \frac{nU}{r^2\sin\gamma} + \frac{2s_1}{(1-\sigma)r},$$

which can be integrated in the form

$$V = -\frac{nA_n}{\sin\gamma} + B_n r + \frac{n}{\sin\gamma} r\int_{r_0}^{r}\frac{1}{r^2}\left\{\int_{r_0}^{r}\frac{t_1-\sigma t_2}{1-\sigma^2}dr\right\}dr + \frac{2}{1-\sigma} r\int_{r_0}^{r}\frac{s_1}{r}dr, \quad \text{...(135)}$$

where B_n is a constant of integration. Now that U and V are known W is determined by the equation

$$W = U\tan\gamma + nV\sec\gamma - \frac{t_2 - \sigma t_1}{1-\sigma^2} r\tan\gamma, \quad \text{...(136)}$$

where the terms of W which contain A_n and B_n are

$$A_n\left(\tan\gamma - \frac{n^2}{\sin\gamma\cos\gamma}\right) + nB_n r\sec\gamma.$$

351. Approximately inextensional solution.

The terms containing A_n, B_n represent an inextensional displacement. We have thus determined, as functions of r, ϕ, the general expressions for the inextensional displacement of a conical shell in the forms*

$$\left.\begin{aligned} u &= A_n\cos(n\phi+\epsilon), \quad v = \left(-\frac{nA_n}{\sin\gamma}+B_nr\right)\sin(n\phi+\epsilon), \\ w &= \left\{A_n\left(\tan\gamma-\frac{n^2}{\sin\gamma\cos\gamma}\right)+nB_nr\sec\gamma\right\}\cos(n\phi+\epsilon). \end{aligned}\right\} \quad \ldots(137)$$

Just as in the case of the cylindrical shell, investigated in Article 343, the terms containing A_n and B_n ought to be removed from the extensional solution, and made the basis of an approximately inextensional solution. In this solution the displacement is expressed by the formulæ

$$\left.\begin{aligned} U &= A_n + h^2U', \quad V = -\frac{nA_n}{\sin\gamma}+B_nr+h^2V', \\ W &= A_n\left(\tan\gamma-\frac{n^2}{\sin\gamma\cos\gamma}\right)+nB_nr\sec\gamma+h^2W', \end{aligned}\right\} \quad \ldots\ldots(138)$$

where U', V', W' are functions of r as yet undetermined. The quantities g_1, g_2, h_1 are given by the equations

$$g_1 = -\tfrac{1}{3}h^2\left\{\frac{d^2W}{dr^2}+\sigma\left(\frac{nV\cos\gamma-n^2W}{r^2\sin^2\gamma}+\frac{1}{r}\frac{dW}{dr}\right)\right\},$$

$$g_2 = -\tfrac{1}{3}h^2\left\{\sigma\frac{d^2W}{dr^2}+\left(\frac{nV\cos\gamma-n^2W}{r^2\sin^2\gamma}+\frac{1}{r}\frac{dW}{dr}\right)\right\},$$

$$h_1 = \tfrac{1}{3}h^2(1-\sigma)\frac{d}{dr}\left(\frac{V\cos\gamma-nW}{r\sin\gamma}\right),$$

and they are expressed with sufficient approximation by omitting U', V', W' in equations (138). Thus we get

$$\left.\begin{aligned} g_1 &= -\frac{h^2}{3}\sigma\left\{\frac{n^2(n^2-1)}{\sin^3\gamma\cos\gamma}\frac{A_n}{r^2}-\frac{n(n^2-1)}{\sin^2\gamma\cos\gamma}\frac{B_n}{r}\right\}, \\ g_2 &= -\frac{h^2}{3}\left\{\frac{n^2(n^2-1)}{\sin^3\gamma\cos\gamma}\frac{A_n}{r^2}-\frac{n(n^2-1)}{\sin^2\gamma\cos\gamma}\frac{B_n}{r}\right\}, \\ h_1 &= -\frac{h^2}{3}(1-\sigma)\frac{n(n^2-1)}{\sin^2\gamma\cos\gamma}\frac{A_n}{r^2}. \end{aligned}\right\} \quad \ldots\ldots\ldots(139)$$

The quantities n_1, n_2 are given by the 4th and 5th of equations (4) in the forms

$$n_2r\sin\gamma = -\frac{d}{dr}(h_1r)\sin\gamma - ng_2 - h_1\sin\gamma,$$

$$n_1r\sin\gamma = -\frac{d}{dr}(g_1r)\sin\gamma - nh_1 - g_2\sin\gamma,$$

* Cf. Lord Rayleigh, *London Math. Soc. Proc.*, vol. 13 (1882), p. 4, or *Scientific Papers*, vol. 1, p. 551.

which become on using (139)

$$\left.\begin{aligned} n_2 &= \frac{h^2}{3}\left\{\frac{n^3(n^2-1)}{\sin^4\gamma\cos\gamma}\frac{A_n}{r^3} - \frac{n^2(n^2-1)}{\sin^3\gamma\cos\gamma}\frac{B_n}{r^2}\right\}, \\ n_1 r\sin\gamma &= \frac{h^2}{3}\left\{\frac{2n^2(n^2-1)}{\sin^2\gamma\cos\gamma}\frac{A_n}{r^2} - \frac{n(n^2-1)}{\sin\gamma\cos\gamma}\frac{B_n}{r}\right\}. \end{aligned}\right\} \quad\text{.........(140)}$$

The solution which we seek is independent of externally applied forces, as the effects to which these give rise can be found from the extensional solution, so we omit X'', Y'', Z'' from the first three of equations (4). On substituting for n_1, n_2 from equations (140), these three equations become

$$\left.\begin{aligned} &\frac{d}{dr}(t_1 r)\sin\gamma - ns_2 - t_2\sin\gamma = 0, \\ &\frac{d}{dr}(s_1 r)\sin\gamma - nt_2 - s_2\sin\gamma - \frac{h^2}{3}\left\{\frac{n^3(n^2-1)}{\sin^4\gamma}\frac{A_n}{r^3} - \frac{n^2(n^2-1)}{\sin^3\gamma}\frac{B_n}{r^2}\right\} = 0, \\ &t_2\cos\gamma + \frac{h^2}{3}\left\{\frac{n^2(n^2-1)}{\sin^2\gamma\cos\gamma}\left(\frac{n^2}{\sin^2\gamma} - 4\right)\frac{A_n}{r^3} - \frac{n(n^2-1)}{\sin\gamma\cos\gamma}\left(\frac{n^2}{\sin^2\gamma} - 1\right)\frac{B_n}{r^2}\right\} = 0. \end{aligned}\right\}$$

............(141)

In these we are to calculate t_1, t_2, s_1, s_2 from the formulæ found in Article 330. In the case of a conical shell these formulæ give

$$t_1 = \frac{dU}{dr} + \sigma\left(\frac{U}{r} + \frac{nV - W\cos\gamma}{r\sin\gamma}\right)$$
$$+ \frac{h^2}{3r\tan\gamma}\left\{\frac{2-2\sigma-3\sigma^2}{2(1-\sigma)}\frac{d^2W}{dr^2} - \frac{\sigma(2+\sigma)}{2(1-\sigma)}\left(\frac{nV\cos\gamma - n^2W}{r^2\sin^2\gamma} + \frac{1}{r}\frac{dW}{dr}\right)\right\},$$

$$t_2 = \sigma\frac{dU}{dr} + \left(\frac{U}{r} + \frac{nV - W\cos\gamma}{r\sin\gamma}\right)$$
$$- \frac{h^2}{3r\tan\gamma}\left\{\frac{\sigma(1+2\sigma)}{2(1-\sigma)}\frac{d^2W}{dr^2} + \frac{2+\sigma}{2(1-\sigma)}\left(\frac{nV\cos\gamma - n^2W}{r^2\sin^2\gamma} + \frac{1}{r}\frac{dW}{dr}\right)\right\},$$

$$s_1 = \tfrac{1}{2}(1-\sigma)\left\{\left(\frac{dV}{dr} - \frac{V}{r} - \frac{nU}{r\sin\gamma}\right) + \frac{h^2}{3r\tan\gamma}\frac{d}{dr}\left(\frac{V\cos\gamma - nW}{r\sin\gamma}\right)\right\},$$

$$s_2 = -\tfrac{1}{2}(1-\sigma)\left\{\left(\frac{dV}{dr} - \frac{V}{r} - \frac{nU}{r\sin\gamma}\right) - \frac{h^2}{3r\tan\gamma}\frac{d}{dr}\left(\frac{V\cos\gamma - nW}{r\sin\gamma}\right)\right\}.$$

Now we write for brevity

$$\left.\begin{aligned} t_1' &= \frac{dU'}{dr} + \sigma\left(\frac{U'}{r} + \frac{nV' - W'\cos\gamma}{r\sin\gamma}\right), \\ t_2' &= \sigma\frac{dU'}{dr} + \left(\frac{U'}{r} + \frac{nV' - W'\cos\gamma}{r\sin\gamma}\right), \\ s_1' &= \tfrac{1}{2}(1-\sigma)\left(\frac{dV'}{dr} - \frac{V'}{r} - \frac{nU'}{r\sin\gamma}\right). \end{aligned}\right\} \quad\text{............(142)}$$

Then we find

$$\left.\begin{aligned}
t_1 &= h^2\left[t_1' - \frac{\sigma(2+\sigma)}{6(1-\sigma)}\left\{\frac{n^2(n^2-1)}{\sin^4\gamma}\frac{A_n}{r^3} - \frac{n(n^2-1)}{\sin^3\gamma}\frac{B_n}{r^2}\right\}\right],\\
t_2 &= h^2\left[t_2' - \frac{2+\sigma}{6(1-\sigma)}\left\{\frac{n^2(n^2-1)}{\sin^4\gamma}\frac{A_n}{r^3} - \frac{n(n^2-1)}{\sin^3\gamma}\frac{B_n}{r^2}\right\}\right],\\
s_1 &= h^2\left\{s_1' - \frac{1-\sigma}{6}\frac{n(n^2-1)}{\sin^3\gamma}\frac{A_n}{r^3}\right\},\\
s_2 &= h^2\left\{-s_1' - \frac{1-\sigma}{6}\frac{n(n^2-1)}{\sin^3\gamma}\frac{A_n}{r^3}\right\},
\end{aligned}\right\} \quad \ldots(143)$$

and equations (141) become

$$\left.\begin{aligned}
&\frac{d}{dr}(t_1'r)\sin\gamma + ns_1' - t_2'\sin\gamma + \frac{1+\sigma+\sigma^2}{2(1-\sigma)}\frac{n^2(n^2-1)}{\sin^3\gamma}\frac{A_n}{r^3}\\
&\qquad\qquad - \frac{2+3\sigma+\sigma^2}{6(1-\sigma)}\frac{n(n^2-1)}{\sin^2\gamma}\frac{B_n}{r^2} = 0,\\
&\frac{d}{dr}(s_1'r)\sin\gamma - nt_2' + s_1'\sin\gamma + \frac{1-\sigma}{2}\frac{n(n^2-1)}{\sin^2\gamma}\frac{A_n}{r^3}\\
&\qquad\qquad + \frac{\sigma}{2(1-\sigma)}\left\{\frac{n^3(n^2-1)}{\sin^4\gamma}\frac{A_n}{r^3} - \frac{n^2(n^2-1)}{\sin^3\gamma}\frac{B_n}{r^2}\right\} = 0,\\
&t_2'\cos\gamma + \left\{\frac{n^2}{3\sin^2\gamma} - \frac{4}{3} - \frac{2+\sigma}{6(1-\sigma)}\cot^2\gamma\right\}\frac{n^2(n^2-1)}{\sin^2\gamma\cos\gamma}\frac{A_n}{r^3}\\
&\qquad\qquad - \left\{\frac{n^2}{3\sin^2\gamma} - \frac{1}{3} - \frac{2+\sigma}{6(1-\sigma)}\cot^2\gamma\right\}\frac{n(n^2-1)}{\sin\gamma\cos\gamma}\frac{B_n}{r^2} = 0.
\end{aligned}\right\} \quad (144)$$

The 3rd of equations (144) gives t_2', and the 1st and 2nd of these equations are to be solved for s_1' and t_1' in just the same way as the 1st and 2nd of equations (130) were solved for s_1 and t_1, with the difference that now no constants of integration, answering to a_1 and a_2, are to be introduced. Then t_1', t_2', s_1' are known, and equations (142) are to be solved for U', V', W' in the same way as equations (133) were solved for U, V, W, with the difference that now no constants of integration, answering to A_n and B_n, are to be introduced.

The solution for the edge-effect, to which we proceed, will contain four additional arbitrary constants, which with a_1, a_2, A_n, B_n can be adjusted so that T_1, G_1, $S_1 + H_1/(r\tan\gamma)$, $N_1 - r^{-1}\cot\gamma\,(\partial H_1/\partial\phi)$ may have given values at the two edges.

352. Edge-effect. Unsymmetrical conditions.

The process of determining the edge-effect in a conical shell, for any integral value of n, is the process of solving a certain system of differential equations; not obtaining the most general solution of those equations, but obtaining a solution of a particular form, analogous to the form that was found in the case of lateral forces. The equations of the system fall into two sets. One set arises from the equations of equilibrium, which become

$$\left.\begin{aligned}
&\frac{d}{dr}(t_1 r)\sin\gamma - ns_2 - t_2\sin\gamma = 0,\\
&\frac{d}{dr}(s_1 r)\sin\gamma - nt_2 - s_2\sin\gamma - n_2\cos\gamma = 0,\\
&\frac{d}{dr}(n_1 r)\sin\gamma + nn_2 + t_2\cos\gamma = 0,\\
&\frac{d}{dr}(h_1 r)\sin\gamma + ng_2 + h_1\sin\gamma + n_2 r\sin\gamma = 0,\\
&\frac{d}{dr}(g_1 r)\sin\gamma - nh_1 - g_2\sin\gamma - n_1 r\sin\gamma = 0,\\
&-h_1\cos\gamma + (s_1+s_2)\, r\sin\gamma = 0.
\end{aligned}\right\} \quad \text{......(145)}$$

The other set arises from the equations expressing the stress-resultants and stress-couples in terms of the displacement. The equations of this set are

$$\left.\begin{aligned}
t_1 &= \frac{dU}{dr} + \sigma\left(\frac{U}{r} + \frac{nV - W\cos\gamma}{r\sin\gamma}\right),\\
t_2 &= \sigma\frac{dU}{dr} + \left(\frac{U}{r} + \frac{nV - W\cos\gamma}{r\sin\gamma}\right),\\
s_1 - s_2 &= (1-\sigma)\left(\frac{dV}{dr} - \frac{V}{r} - \frac{nU}{r\sin\gamma}\right),\\
g_1 &= -\frac{h^2}{3}\left\{\frac{d^2W}{dr^2} + \sigma\left(\frac{nV\cos\gamma - n^2W}{r^2\sin^2\gamma} + \frac{1}{r}\frac{dW}{dr}\right)\right\},\\
g_2 &= -\frac{h^2}{3}\left\{\sigma\frac{d^2W}{dr^2} + \left(\frac{nV\cos\gamma - n^2W}{r^2\sin^2\gamma} + \frac{1}{r}\frac{dW}{dr}\right)\right\},\\
h_1 &= \frac{h^2}{3}(1-\sigma)\frac{d}{dr}\left(\frac{V\cos\gamma - nW}{r\sin\gamma}\right).
\end{aligned}\right\} \quad \text{...(146)}$$

It will be observed that the 6th of equations (145) and the 3rd of equations (146) are equivalent to the formulæ for S_1, S_2 in Article 330.

We shall simplify the equations (146) a little by introducing instead of U, V, W the quantities ξ, η, ζ defined by the equations

$$\xi = \frac{U}{r}, \quad \eta = \frac{V\cos\gamma - nW}{r\sin\gamma}, \quad \zeta = \frac{W}{r}. \quad \text{...............(147)}$$

Then the solution is effected in three stages. The first stage, marked (*a*), consists in eliminating n_1, n_2, s_2 by means of the 4th, 5th, and 6th of equations (145), so as to obtain three equations containing t_1, t_2, s_1, g_1, g_2, h_1, and transforming these, by means of (146) and (147), into three equations for determining ξ, η, ζ. The second stage, marked (*b*), consists in assuming for ξ, η, ζ such forms as $e^{mx}X$, where

$$\frac{x^2}{2} = \frac{r}{h},$$

and obtaining the equations which the quantities of the type X must satisfy. The third stage, marked (c), consists in assuming the quantities of the type X to be expressible in the form

$$z^a(c_0 + c_1 z + c_2 z^2 + \ldots),$$

where $z = x^{-1}$, and determining the coefficients $m, a, c_0, c_1, \ldots$, in so far as these are not arbitrary.

(a) *Formation of the equations.*

In the first three of equations (145) we substitute for s_2, n_1, n_2 from the last three, obtaining the equations

$$\left.\begin{aligned}
&\frac{d}{dr}(t_1 r) + \frac{n}{\sin\gamma}\left(s_1 - \frac{h_1}{r\tan\gamma}\right) - t_2 = 0,\\
&\left\{\frac{d}{dr}(s_1 r) + s_1\right\}\sin\gamma + \frac{\cos\gamma}{r}\frac{d}{dr}(h_1 r) - n\left(t_2 - \frac{g_2}{r\tan\gamma}\right) = 0,\\
&\frac{d^2}{dr^2}(g_1 r)\sin\gamma - \frac{2n}{r}\frac{d}{dr}(h_1 r) - \frac{dg_2}{dr}\sin\gamma - \frac{n^2 g_2}{r\sin\gamma} + t_2\cos\gamma = 0.
\end{aligned}\right\} \quad \ldots\ldots\ldots(148)$$

We eliminate U, V, W from equations (146) by using equations (147), obtaining the equations

$$\left.\begin{aligned}
t_1 &= \frac{d}{dr}(r\xi) + \sigma\left(\xi + n\eta\sec\gamma + \frac{n^2 - \cos^2\gamma}{\sin\gamma\cos\gamma}\zeta\right),\\
t_2 &= \sigma\frac{d}{dr}(r\xi) + \left(\xi + n\eta\sec\gamma + \frac{n^2 - \cos^2\gamma}{\sin\gamma\cos\gamma}\zeta\right),\\
s_1 &= \frac{1-\sigma}{2}\left\{-\frac{n}{\sin\gamma}\xi + \left(r\tan\gamma + \frac{h^2}{3r\tan\gamma}\right)\frac{d\eta}{dr} + nr\frac{d\zeta}{dr}\sec\gamma\right\},\\
g_1 &= -\frac{h^2}{3}\left[\frac{d^2}{dr^2}(r\zeta) + \sigma\left\{\frac{n\eta}{r\sin\gamma} + \frac{1}{r}\frac{d}{dr}(r\zeta)\right\}\right],\\
g_2 &= -\frac{h^2}{3}\left[\sigma\frac{d^2}{dr^2}(r\zeta) + \left\{\frac{n\eta}{r\sin\gamma} + \frac{1}{r}\frac{d}{dr}(r\zeta)\right\}\right],\\
h_1 &= \frac{h^2}{3}(1-\sigma)\frac{d\eta}{dr}.
\end{aligned}\right\} \quad \ldots\ldots(149)$$

Then we put

$$r = \rho h, \quad \ldots\ldots\ldots\ldots(150)$$

and substitute from (149) in (148) obtaining three equations from which h is explicitly absent. The condition that h is small is now replaced by the condition that a solution is required for large values of ρ. A little simplification is effected by putting

$$\xi_1 = \xi\rho, \qquad \eta_1 = \eta\rho, \qquad \zeta_1 = \zeta\rho. \quad \ldots\ldots\ldots\ldots(151)$$

Then the three equations become

$$\left(\rho\frac{d^2\xi_1}{d\rho^2} + \frac{d\xi_1}{d\rho} - \frac{\xi_1}{\rho}\right)\sin\gamma - \frac{n^2(1-\sigma)}{2\sin\gamma}\frac{\xi_1}{\rho} + \sigma n\tan\gamma\frac{d\eta_1}{d\rho} + n\frac{1-\sigma}{2}\tan\gamma\left(\frac{d\eta_1}{d\rho} - \frac{\eta_1}{\rho}\right)$$

$$-n\frac{1-\sigma}{6\tan\gamma}\frac{1}{\rho^2}\left(\frac{d\eta_1}{d\rho} - \frac{\eta_1}{\rho}\right) - n\tan\gamma\frac{\eta_1}{\rho} + \left(n^2\frac{1+\sigma}{2\cos\gamma} - \sigma\cos\gamma\right)\frac{d\zeta_1}{d\rho} - n^2\left(\frac{3-\sigma}{2\cos\gamma} - \cos\gamma\right)\frac{\zeta_1}{\rho} = 0,$$

$$\ldots\ldots\ldots(152)$$

$$-n\frac{1+\sigma}{2}\frac{d\xi_1}{d\rho}-n\frac{3-\sigma}{2}\frac{\xi_1}{\rho}+\frac{1-\sigma}{2}\frac{\sin^2\gamma}{\cos\gamma}\left(\rho\frac{d^2\eta_1}{d\rho^2}+\frac{d\eta_1}{d\rho}-\frac{\eta_1}{\rho}\right)+\frac{1-\sigma}{2}\cos\gamma\left(\frac{1}{\rho}\frac{d^2\eta_1}{d\rho^2}-\frac{1}{\rho^2}\frac{d\eta_1}{d\rho}+\frac{\eta_1}{\rho^3}\right)$$

$$-\frac{n^2}{\cos\gamma}\frac{\eta_1}{\rho}-\frac{n^2\cos\gamma}{3\sin^2\gamma}\frac{\eta_1}{\rho^3}+\frac{1-\sigma}{2}n\tan\gamma\left(\rho\frac{d^2\zeta_1}{d\rho^2}+\frac{d\zeta_1}{d\rho}-\frac{\zeta_1}{\rho}\right)-\frac{\sigma n}{3\tan\gamma}\frac{1}{\rho}\frac{d^2\zeta_1}{d\rho^2}-\frac{n}{3\tan\gamma}\frac{1}{\rho^2}\frac{d\zeta_1}{d\rho}$$

$$-n\frac{n^2-\cos^2\gamma}{\sin\gamma\cos\gamma}\frac{\zeta_1}{\rho}=0, \qquad \text{......(153)}$$

and

$$\sigma\cos\gamma\frac{d\xi_1}{d\rho}+\frac{\xi_1}{\rho}\cos\gamma-n\frac{2-\sigma}{3}\frac{1}{\rho}\frac{d^2\eta_1}{d\rho^2}+\frac{n}{\rho^2}\frac{d\eta_1}{d\rho}+n\frac{\eta_1}{\rho}+\left(\frac{n^3}{3\sin^2\gamma}-\frac{4n}{3}\right)\frac{\eta_1}{\rho^3}$$

$$-\frac{\sin\gamma}{3}\left(\rho\frac{d^4\zeta_1}{d\rho^4}+2\frac{d^3\zeta_1}{d\rho^3}-\frac{1}{\rho}\frac{d^2\zeta_1}{d\rho^2}+\frac{1}{\rho^2}\frac{d\zeta_1}{d\rho}\right)+\frac{\sigma n^2}{3\sin\gamma}\frac{1}{\rho}\frac{d^2\zeta_1}{d\rho^2}+\frac{n^2}{3\sin\gamma}\frac{1}{\rho^2}\frac{d\zeta_1}{d\rho}+\frac{n^2-\cos^2\gamma}{\sin\gamma}\frac{\zeta_1}{\rho}=0. \qquad \text{.........(154)}$$

(b) *Preparation for solution.*

In the three equations (152), (153), (154) we change the independent variable by putting

$$\rho=\tfrac{1}{2}x^2. \qquad \text{..(155)}$$

It will prove convenient presently to have $x\xi_1$ as a dependent variable instead of ξ_1, so we put

$$\xi_2=x\xi_1, \qquad \text{..(156)}$$

and write the three equations in the forms

$$\frac{\sin\gamma}{2}\left(\frac{d^2\xi_2}{dx^2}-\frac{1}{x}\frac{d\xi_2}{dx}-\frac{3}{x^2}\xi_2\right)-n^2\frac{1-\sigma}{\sin\gamma}\frac{\xi_2}{x^2}+n\frac{1+\sigma}{2}\frac{d\eta_1}{dx}\tan\gamma-n(3-\sigma)\frac{\eta_1}{x}\tan\gamma$$

$$-2n\frac{1-\sigma}{3\tan\gamma}\left(\frac{1}{x^4}\frac{d\eta_1}{dx}-\frac{2}{x^5}\eta_1\right)+\left(n^2\frac{1+\sigma}{2\cos\gamma}-\sigma\cos\gamma\right)\frac{d\zeta_1}{dx}-\left(n^2\frac{3-\sigma}{\cos\gamma}-2\cos\gamma\right)\frac{\zeta_1}{x}=0, \qquad \text{.........(157)}$$

$$-n\frac{1+\sigma}{2}\frac{1}{x^2}\frac{d\xi_2}{dx}-n\frac{5-3\sigma}{2}\frac{\xi_2}{x^3}+\frac{1-\sigma}{4}\frac{\sin^2\gamma}{\cos\gamma}\left(\frac{d^2\eta_1}{dx^2}+\frac{1}{x}\frac{d\eta_1}{dx}-\frac{4}{x^2}\eta_1\right)$$

$$+(1-\sigma)\cos\gamma\left(\frac{1}{x^4}\frac{d^2\eta_1}{dx^2}-\frac{3}{x^5}\frac{d\eta_1}{dx}+\frac{4}{x^6}\eta_1\right)-\frac{2n^2}{\cos\gamma}\frac{\eta_1}{x^2}-\frac{8n^3\cos\gamma}{3\sin^2\gamma}\frac{\eta_1}{x^6}$$

$$+\frac{1-\sigma}{4}n\tan\gamma\left(\frac{d^2\zeta_1}{dx^2}+\frac{1}{x}\frac{d\zeta_1}{dx}-\frac{4}{x^2}\zeta_1\right)-\frac{2\sigma n}{3\tan\gamma}\left(\frac{1}{x^4}\frac{d^2\zeta_1}{dx^2}-\frac{1}{x^5}\frac{d\zeta_1}{dx}\right)$$

$$-\frac{4n}{3\tan\gamma}\frac{1}{x^5}\frac{d\zeta_1}{dx}-2n\frac{n^2-\cos^2\gamma}{\sin\gamma\cos\gamma}\frac{\zeta_1}{x^2}=0, \qquad \text{......(158)}$$

and

$$\sigma\frac{d\xi_2}{dx}\cos\gamma+\frac{2-\sigma}{x}\xi_2\cos\gamma-2n\frac{2-\sigma}{3}\frac{1}{x^2}\frac{d^2\eta_1}{dx^2}+2n\frac{8-\sigma}{3}\frac{1}{x^3}\frac{d\eta_1}{dx}+\left(\frac{8n^3}{3\sin^2\gamma}-\frac{32}{3}n\right)\frac{\eta_1}{x^4}+2n\eta_1$$

$$-\frac{\sin\gamma}{6}\left(\frac{d^4\zeta_1}{dx^4}-\frac{2}{x}\frac{d^3\zeta_1}{dx^3}-\frac{1}{x^2}\frac{d^2\zeta_1}{dx^2}+\frac{9}{x^3}\frac{d\zeta_1}{dx}\right)+\frac{2\sigma n^2}{3\sin\gamma}\left(\frac{1}{x^2}\frac{d^2\zeta_1}{dx^2}-\frac{1}{x^3}\frac{d\zeta_1}{dx}\right)$$

$$+\frac{4n^2}{3\sin\gamma}\frac{1}{x^3}\frac{d\zeta_1}{dx}+2\frac{n^2-\cos^2\gamma}{\sin\gamma}\zeta_1=0. \qquad \text{......(159)}$$

Equations (157), (158), (159) are three linear differential equations for the determination of ξ_2, η_1, ζ_1 as functions of x, and we seek solutions of a certain type answering to the normal integrals of a single linear differential equation. The first step is to put

$$\xi_2 = Xe^{mx}, \quad \eta_1 = Ye^{mx}, \quad \zeta_1 = Ze^{mx}, \quad \text{......(160)}$$

where m is at present undetermined. Then X, Y, Z satisfy the three equations

$$\frac{\sin\gamma}{2}\left\{\left(\frac{d^2X}{dx^2} + 2m\frac{dX}{dx} + m^2X\right) - \frac{1}{x}\left(\frac{dX}{dx} + mX\right) - \frac{3}{x^2}X\right\} - n^2\frac{1-\sigma}{\sin\gamma}\frac{X}{x^2}$$
$$+ n\frac{1+\sigma}{2}\tan\gamma\left(\frac{dY}{dx} + mY\right) - n(3-\sigma)\tan\gamma\frac{Y}{x} - 2n\frac{1-\sigma}{3\tan\gamma}\left\{\frac{1}{x^4}\left(\frac{dY}{dx} + mY\right) - \frac{2}{x^5}Y\right\}$$
$$+ \left(n^2\frac{1+\sigma}{2\cos\gamma} - \sigma\cos\gamma\right)\left(\frac{dZ}{dx} + mZ\right) - \left(n^2\frac{3-\sigma}{\cos\gamma} - 2\cos\gamma\right)\frac{Z}{x} = 0, \quad \text{......(161)}$$

$$-n\frac{1+\sigma}{2}\frac{1}{x^2}\left(\frac{dX}{dx} + mX\right) - n\frac{5-3\sigma}{2}\frac{X}{x^3}$$
$$+ \frac{1-\sigma}{4}\frac{\sin^2\gamma}{\cos\gamma}\left\{\left(\frac{d^2Y}{dx^2} + 2m\frac{dY}{dx} + m^2Y\right) + \frac{1}{x}\left(\frac{dY}{dx} + mY\right) - \frac{4}{x^2}Y\right\}$$
$$+ (1-\sigma)\cos\gamma\left\{\frac{1}{x^4}\left(\frac{d^2Y}{dx^2} + 2m\frac{dY}{dx} + m^2Y\right) - \frac{3}{x^5}\left(\frac{dY}{dx} + mY\right) + \frac{4}{x^6}Y\right\}$$
$$- \frac{2n^2}{\cos\gamma}\frac{Y}{x^2} - \frac{8n^3\cos\gamma}{3\sin^2\gamma}\frac{Y}{x^6}$$
$$+ \frac{1-\sigma}{4}n\tan\gamma\left\{\left(\frac{d^2Z}{dx^2} + 2m\frac{dZ}{dx} + m^2Z\right) + \frac{1}{x}\left(\frac{dZ}{dx} + mZ\right) - \frac{4}{x^2}Z\right\}$$
$$- \frac{2\sigma n}{3\tan\gamma}\left\{\frac{1}{x^4}\left(\frac{d^2Z}{dx^2} + 2m\frac{dZ}{dx} + m^2Z\right) - \frac{1}{x^5}\left(\frac{dZ}{dx} + mZ\right)\right\} - \frac{4n}{3\tan\gamma}\frac{1}{x^5}\left(\frac{dZ}{dx} + mZ\right)$$
$$- 2n\frac{n^2 - \cos^2\gamma}{\sin\gamma\cos\gamma}\frac{1}{x^2}Z = 0, \quad \text{......(162)}$$

and

$$\sigma\cos\gamma\left(\frac{dX}{dx} + mX\right) + (2-\sigma)\frac{\cos\gamma}{x}X - 2n\frac{2-\sigma}{3}\frac{1}{x^2}\left(\frac{d^2Y}{dx^2} + 2m\frac{dY}{dx} + m^2Y\right)$$
$$+ 2n\frac{8-\sigma}{3}\frac{1}{x^3}\left(\frac{dY}{dx} + mY\right) + \left(\frac{8n^3}{3\sin^2\gamma} - \frac{32}{3}n\right)\frac{Y}{x^4} + 2nY$$
$$- \frac{\sin\gamma}{6}\left\{\left(\frac{d^4Z}{dx^4} + 4m\frac{d^3Z}{dx^3} + 6m^2\frac{d^2Z}{dx^2} + 4m^3\frac{dZ}{dx} + m^4Z\right)\right.$$
$$\left. - \frac{2}{x}\left(\frac{d^3Z}{dx^3} + 3m\frac{d^2Z}{dx^2} + 3m^2\frac{dZ}{dx} + m^3Z\right) - \frac{1}{x^2}\left(\frac{d^2Z}{dx^2} + 2m\frac{dZ}{dx} + m^2Z\right) + \frac{9}{x^3}\left(\frac{dZ}{dx} + mZ\right)\right\}$$
$$+ \frac{2\sigma n^2}{3\sin\gamma}\left\{\frac{1}{x^2}\left(\frac{d^2Z}{dx^2} + 2m\frac{dZ}{dx} + m^2Z\right) - \frac{1}{x^3}\left(\frac{dZ}{dx} + mZ\right)\right\} + \frac{4n^2}{3\sin\gamma}\frac{1}{x^3}\left(\frac{dZ}{dx} + mZ\right)$$
$$+ 2\frac{n^2 - \cos^2\gamma}{\sin\gamma}Z = 0. \quad \text{......(163)}$$

(c) *Solution of the equations.*

We wish tc obtain solutions of these equations in series proceeding by powers of x^{-1}. We write

$$z = \frac{1}{x}, \quad \text{......(164)}$$

and assume for X, Y, Z expressions of the form

$$X = z^a(a_0 + a_1z + a_2z^2 + \dots), \quad Y = z^b(b_0 + b_1z + b_2z^2 + \dots), \quad Z = z^c(c_0 + c_1z + c_2z^2 + \dots).$$

Then we have, for example,

$$\frac{dZ}{dx} = -z^2 \frac{dZ}{dz} = -z^{c+1}\{c_0 c + c_1(c+1)z + c_2(c+2)z^2 + \ldots\},$$

$$\frac{d^2Z}{dx^2} = -z^2 \frac{d}{dz}\left(\frac{dZ}{dx}\right) = z^{c+2}\{c_0 c(c+1) + c_1(c+1)(c+2)z + c_2(c+2)(c+3)z^2 + \ldots\},$$

and so on. We substitute the serial expressions for X, dX/dx, ... d^4Z/dx^4 in the left-hand members of equations (161), (162), (163), and equate to zero the coefficients of the various powers of z, beginning with the lowest. We thus obtain sufficient equations to determine m, the exponents a, b, c, and the coefficients $a_0, a_1, \ldots, b_0, b_1, \ldots, c_1, c_2, \ldots$ in terms of c_0, which remains arbitrary. It will appear that there are four values of m, and so there are four solutions of this type. If this process is carried out it will very soon appear that $a = b = c = -\frac{1}{2}$. So it is simpler to assume the forms

$$X = z^{-\frac{1}{2}}(a_0 + a_1 z + a_2 z^2 + \ldots),\quad Y = z^{-\frac{1}{2}}(b_0 + b_1 z + b_2 z^2 + \ldots),\quad Z = z^{-\frac{1}{2}}(c_0 + c_1 z + c_2 z^2 + \ldots). \qquad \ldots\ldots\ldots(165)$$

Then we have, for example,

$$\frac{dZ}{dx} = \tfrac{1}{2} z^{\frac{1}{2}}(c_0 - c_1 z - 3c_2 z^2 - 5c_3 z^3 - \ldots),$$

$$\frac{d^2Z}{dx^2} = \tfrac{1}{4} z^{\frac{3}{2}}(-c_0 + 3c_1 z + 3.5c_2 z^2 + 5.7c_3 z^3 + \ldots),$$

$$\frac{d^3Z}{dx^3} = \tfrac{1}{8} z^{\frac{5}{2}}(3c_0 - 3.5c_1 z - 3.5.7c_2 z^2 - 5.7.9c_3 z^3 + \ldots),$$

$$\frac{d^4Z}{dx^4} = \tfrac{1}{16} z^{\frac{7}{2}}(-3.5c_0 + 3.5.7c_1 z + 3.5.7.9c_2 z^2 + 5.7.9.11c_3 z^3 + \ldots).$$

The terms of lowest degree in the three equations are the terms containing $z^{-\frac{1}{2}}$. Equating their coefficients to zero, we obtain the equations

$$\left.\begin{aligned} \frac{\sin\gamma}{2} m^2 a_0 + n\frac{1+\sigma}{2}\tan\gamma\, m b_0 + \left(n^2 \frac{1+\sigma}{2\cos\gamma} - \sigma\cos\gamma\right) m c_0 = 0,\\ \frac{1-\sigma}{4}\frac{\sin^2\gamma}{\cos\gamma} m^2 b_0 + \frac{1-\sigma}{4} n \tan\gamma\, m^2 c_0 = 0,\\ \sigma\cos\gamma\, m a_0 + 2nb_0 + \left(-\frac{\sin\gamma}{6} m^4 + 2\frac{n^2 - \cos^2\gamma}{\sin\gamma}\right) c_0 = 0, \end{aligned}\right\} \quad \ldots\ldots(166)$$

yielding the results

$$a_0 = \frac{2\sigma}{m\tan\gamma} c_0, \qquad b_0 = -\frac{n}{\sin\gamma} c_0, \qquad \ldots\ldots\ldots\ldots\ldots(167)$$

and

$$m^4 + 12(1-\sigma^2)\cot^2\gamma = 0. \qquad \ldots\ldots\ldots\ldots\ldots(168)$$

The four complex values of m given by (168) are the same as occurred in the problem of the conical shell, strained by lateral forces, which was discussed in Article 349. The present solution applies to the case of lateral forces ($n=1$), as well as to conditions answering to greater values of n.

When m satisfies equation (168), and the left-hand members of equations (166) are multiplied in order by $2\sigma m \sin\gamma$, $4(2+\sigma)n$, and $-m^2\sin\gamma\tan\gamma$, and added, the coefficients of a_0, b_0, c_0 are all zero. This remark is important because the same thing would happen if we formed the equations like (166), containing no coefficients a_κ, b_κ, c_κ, of suffix greater than κ, by equating to zero the coefficients of $z^{\kappa-\frac{1}{2}}$ in equations (161), (162), (163), and multiplied their left-hand members in order by the same three expressions $2\sigma m \sin\gamma, \ldots$, then we should find that a_κ, b_κ, c_κ would all disappear from the equation so formed. It is therefore convenient to form a new equation from equations (161), (162), (163) by multiplying the left-hand members of these equations in order by $2\sigma m \sin\gamma$, $4(2+\sigma)n$, and $-m^2 \sin\gamma \tan\gamma$ and adding. We thus obtain the equation

$$\sigma m \sin^2\gamma \left\{\left(\frac{d^2X}{dx^2}+2m\frac{dX}{dx}+m^2X\right)-\frac{1}{x}\left(\frac{dX}{dx}+mX\right)-\frac{3}{x^2}X\right\}-2mn^2\sigma(1-\sigma)\frac{X}{x^2}$$

$$-2n^2(2+\sigma)\left\{\frac{1+\sigma}{x^2}\left(\frac{dX}{dx}+mX\right)+\frac{5-3\sigma}{x^3}X\right\}-m^2\sin^2\gamma\left\{\sigma\left(\frac{dX}{dx}+mX\right)+(2-\sigma)\frac{X}{x}\right\}$$

$$+2\sigma m\sin\gamma\left[n\frac{1+\sigma}{2}\tan\gamma\left(\frac{dY}{dx}+mY\right)-n(3-\sigma)\tan\gamma\frac{Y}{x}\right.$$

$$\left.-2n\frac{1-\sigma}{3\tan\gamma}\left\{\frac{1}{x^4}\left(\frac{dY}{dx}+mY\right)-\frac{2}{x^5}Y\right\}\right]$$

$$+4(2+\sigma)n\left[\frac{1-\sigma}{4}\frac{\sin^2\gamma}{\cos\gamma}\left\{\left(\frac{d^2Y}{dx^2}+2m\frac{dY}{dx}+m^2Y\right)+\frac{1}{x}\left(\frac{dY}{dx}+mY\right)-\frac{4}{x^2}Y\right\}-\frac{2n^2}{\cos\gamma}\frac{Y}{x^2}\right.$$

$$\left.+(1-\sigma)\cos\gamma\left\{\frac{1}{x^4}\left(\frac{d^2Y}{dx^2}+2m\frac{dY}{dx}+m^2Y\right)-\frac{3}{x^5}\left(\frac{dY}{dx}+mY\right)+\frac{4}{x^6}Y\right\}-\frac{8n^3\cos\gamma}{3\sin^2\gamma}\frac{Y}{x^6}\right]$$

$$-m^2\sin\gamma\tan\gamma\left[-2n\frac{2-\sigma}{3}\frac{1}{x^2}\left(\frac{d^2Y}{dx^2}+2m\frac{dY}{dx}+m^2Y\right)+2n\frac{8-\sigma}{3}\frac{1}{x^3}\left(\frac{dY}{dx}+mY\right)\right.$$

$$\left.+\left(\frac{8n^3}{3\sin^2\gamma}-\frac{32n}{3}\right)\frac{Y}{x^4}+2nY\right]$$

$$+2\sigma m\sin\gamma\left[\left(n^2\frac{1+\sigma}{2\cos\gamma}-\sigma\cos\gamma\right)\left(\frac{dZ}{dx}+mZ\right)-\left(n^2\frac{3-\sigma}{\cos\gamma}-2\cos\gamma\right)\frac{Z}{x}\right]$$

$$+4(2+\sigma)n\left[\frac{1-\sigma}{4}n\tan\gamma\left\{\left(\frac{d^2Z}{dx^2}+2m\frac{dZ}{dx}+m^2Z\right)+\frac{1}{x}\left(\frac{dZ}{dx}+mZ\right)-\frac{4}{x^2}Z\right\}\right.$$

$$-2n\frac{n^2-\cos^2\gamma}{\sin\gamma\cos\gamma}\frac{Z}{x^2}-\frac{2\sigma n}{3\tan\gamma}\left\{\frac{1}{x^4}\left(\frac{d^2Z}{dx^2}+2m\frac{dZ}{dx}+m^2Z\right)-\frac{1}{x^5}\left(\frac{dZ}{dx}+mZ\right)\right\}$$

$$\left.-\frac{4n}{3\tan\gamma}\frac{1}{x^5}\left(\frac{dZ}{dx}+mZ\right)\right]$$

$$-m^2\sin\gamma\tan\gamma\left[-\frac{\sin\gamma}{6}\left\{\left(\frac{d^4Z}{dx^4}+4m\frac{d^3Z}{dx^3}+6m^2\frac{d^2Z}{dx}+4m^3\frac{dZ}{dx}+m^4Z\right)\right.\right.$$

$$\left.-\frac{2}{x}\left(\frac{d^3Z}{dx^3}+3m\frac{d^2Z}{dx^2}+3m^2\frac{dZ}{dx}+m^3Z\right)-\frac{1}{x^2}\left(\frac{d^2Z}{dx^2}+2m\frac{dZ}{dx}+m^2Z\right)+\frac{9}{x^3}\left(\frac{dZ}{dx}+mZ\right)\right\}$$

$$+\frac{2\sigma n^2}{3\sin\gamma}\left\{\frac{1}{x^2}\left(\frac{d^2Z}{dx^2}+2m\frac{dZ}{dx}+m^2Z\right)-\frac{1}{x^3}\left(\frac{dZ}{dx}+mZ\right)\right\}+\frac{4n^2}{3\sin\gamma}\frac{1}{x^3}\left(\frac{dZ}{dx}+mZ\right)$$

$$\left.+2\frac{n^2-\cos^2\gamma}{\sin\gamma}Z\right]=0. \quad \text{.........(169)}$$

In future we shall use equation (169) instead of equation (163). If from equations (161), (162), (169) we select the terms containing $z^{\kappa-\frac{1}{2}}$, and equate them to zero, the first two will contain a_κ, b_κ, c_κ, but the third will not contain any a's, b's or c's with suffixes higher than $\kappa-1$. For example, taking $\kappa=1$, equation (169) will yield a new equation connecting a_0, b_0, c_0, with which we shall deal presently, and equations (161) and (162) will yield two equations containing a_1, b_1, c_1. Again, taking $\kappa=2$, equation (169) will yield a new equation containing a_1, b_1, c_1, and equations (161) and (162) will yield two equations containing a_2, b_2, c_2. Thus the equations, by which a_κ, b_κ, c_κ are to be determined, are obtained by equating to zero the coefficients of $z^{\kappa-\frac{1}{2}}$ in (161) and (162), and the coefficient of $z^{\kappa+\frac{1}{2}}$ in (169).

In particular by equating to zero the coefficient of $z^{\frac{1}{2}}$ in equation (169) we obtain the equation

$$-\tfrac{1}{2}\sigma m^2 \sin^2\gamma \,.\, a_0 - m^2\sin^2\gamma\,(2-\sigma)\,a_0 + \tfrac{1}{2}\sigma\,(1+\sigma)\,mn\,\frac{\sin^2\gamma}{\cos\gamma}\,b_0 - 2\sigma\,(3-\sigma)\,mn\,\frac{\sin^2\gamma}{\cos\gamma}\,b_0$$
$$+2\,(2+\sigma)\,(1-\sigma)\,mn\,\frac{\sin^2\gamma}{\cos\gamma}\,b_0 + \tfrac{1}{2}\sigma m\sin\gamma\left(n^2\,\frac{1+\sigma}{\cos\gamma} - 2\sigma\cos\gamma\right)c_0$$
$$-2\sigma m\sin\gamma\left(n^2\,\frac{3-\sigma}{\cos\gamma} - 2\cos\gamma\right)c_0 + 2mn^2\,(2+\sigma)\,(1-\sigma)\tan\gamma\,.\,c_0 = 0.$$

On substituting for a_0 and b_0 from equations (167) this equation becomes an identity.

It may by observed that, if we had not assumed the exponents a, b, c to be equal to $-\frac{1}{2}$, but had left them undetermined, it would still have been necessary that the coefficient of z^{c+1} in an equation formed in the same way as (169) should vanish identically, and this condition would have led to the determination of a, b, and c.

We now equate to zero the coefficients of $z^{\frac{1}{2}}$ in equations (161) and (162), obtaining the equations

$$\frac{\sin\gamma}{2}\,m^2 a_1 + \frac{1+\sigma}{2}\,n\tan\gamma\,(mb_1 + \tfrac{1}{2}b_0) - n\,(3-\sigma)\tan\gamma\,.\,b_0 + \left(n^2\,\frac{1+\sigma}{2\cos\gamma} - \sigma\cos\gamma\right)(mc_1 + \tfrac{1}{2}c_0)$$
$$-\left(n^2\,\frac{3-\sigma}{\cos\gamma} - 2\cos\gamma\right)c_0 = 0,$$

and

$$\frac{1-\sigma}{4}\,\frac{\sin^2\gamma}{\cos\gamma}\,(m^2 b_1 + 2mb_0) + \frac{1-\sigma}{4}\,n\tan\gamma\,(m^2 c_1 + 2mc_0) = 0,$$

which, combined with (167), yield

$$a_1 = \frac{2\sigma}{m\tan\gamma}\,c_1 - \frac{4-\sigma}{m^2\tan\gamma}\,c_0,\quad b_1 = -\frac{n}{\sin\gamma}\,c_1. \quad \text{.................(170)}$$

We also equate to zero the coefficient of $z^{\frac{3}{2}}$ in equation (169), obtaining the equation

$$-\sigma m\sin^2\gamma\left(2ma_1 + \frac{15}{4}\,a_0\right) - 2n^2\,(2+\sigma)\,(1+\sigma)\,ma_0 - 2n^2\,\sigma\,(1-\sigma)\,ma_0$$
$$-m^2\sin^2\gamma\,\{-\tfrac{1}{2}\sigma a_1 + (2-\sigma)\,a_1\}$$
$$-\tfrac{1}{2}\sigma\,(1+\sigma)\,mn\,\frac{\sin^2\gamma}{\cos\gamma}\,b_1 - 2\sigma\,(3-\sigma)\,mn\,\frac{\sin^2\gamma}{\cos\gamma}\,b_1 - (2+\sigma)\,(1-\sigma)\,n\,\frac{\sin^2\gamma}{\cos\gamma}\,\frac{15}{4}\,b_0$$
$$-\frac{8n^3\,(2+\sigma)}{\cos\gamma}\,b_0 + 2n\,\frac{2-\sigma}{3}\,m^4\,\frac{\sin^2\gamma}{\cos\gamma}\,b_0$$
$$-\sigma m\sin\gamma\left(n^2\,\frac{1+\sigma}{2\cos\gamma} - \sigma\cos\gamma\right)c_1 - 2\sigma m\sin\gamma\left(n^2\,\frac{3-\sigma}{\cos\gamma} - 2\cos\gamma\right)$$
$$-(2+\sigma)\,(1-\sigma)\,n^2\tan\gamma\,\frac{15}{4}\,c_0 - 8\,(2+\sigma)\,n^2\,\frac{n^2-\cos^2\gamma}{\sin\gamma\cos\gamma}\,c_0 - m^4\,\frac{\sin^3\gamma}{3\cos\gamma}\left(2mc_1 + \frac{11}{4}\,c_0\right)$$
$$-\frac{2\sigma n^2}{3}\,m^4\tan\gamma\,.\,c_0 = 0,$$

and, on substituting from (167) and (170), this equation can be expressed as a relation between c_1 and c_0, which yields, after some reduction involving the use of (168),

$$c_1 = -\left(\frac{4n^2}{\sin^2\gamma} + \frac{19}{8}\right)\frac{c_0}{m}. \quad \text{.................................(171)}$$

From this value of c_1 we find instead of (170)

$$a_1 = -\left(\frac{8n^2\sigma}{\sin^2\gamma} + 4 + \frac{15}{4}\,\sigma\right)\frac{c_0}{m^2\tan\gamma},\quad b_1 = \left(\frac{4n^3}{\sin^3\gamma} + \frac{19n}{8\sin\gamma}\right)\frac{c_0}{m}. \quad \text{......(172)}$$

It is clear that we can proceed in this way to determine as many coefficients as we please. The equations determining a_2, b_2, c_2, for example, will be found, after some reduction, to be

$$\left.\begin{aligned} b_2 \sin\gamma + nc_2 &= -\frac{4n(2+\sigma)}{m^2\tan^2\gamma}c_0, \\ ma_2\sin\gamma - 2\sigma c_2\cos\gamma &= \left\{4(6+\sigma)n^2\frac{\cos\gamma}{\sin^2\gamma} + \frac{12+19\sigma}{8}\cos\gamma\right\}\frac{c_0}{m^2}, \\ c_2 &= \left(8\frac{n^4}{\sin^4\gamma} + \frac{19n^2}{4\sin^2\gamma} - \frac{47}{128}\right)\frac{c_0}{m^2}. \end{aligned}\right\} \quad \text{......(173)}$$

The process clearly becomes very troublesome as the suffixes increase, but the coefficients already obtained are all that are likely to be useful in any special problem. If either n or $\operatorname{cosec}\gamma$ is large, the solution can only be applied to shells in which (h/r) is everywhere very small. With this reservation we may regard the problem of a conical shell, deformed by given forces, as completely solved.

NOTES

NOTE A

Terminology and notation.

QUESTIONS of notation, and of the most appropriate nomenclature, for elasticity have been much discussed. Reference may be made to the writings of W. J. M. Rankine[1], to Lord Kelvin's account of Rankine's nomenclature[2], to K. Pearson's[3] efforts after consistency and uniformity, to pronouncements on the subject by H. Lamb[4] and W. Voigt[5]. The following tables show some of the more important notations for strain-components and stress-components.

Strain-components.

Text[6]	Kelvin and Tait[7]	Kirchhoff[8]	Saint-Venant[9]	Pearson[3]	v. Kármán[10]
e_{xx}, e_{yy}, e_{zz}	e, f, g	x_x, y_y, z_z	$\delta_x, \delta_y, \delta_z$	s_x, s_y, s_z	$\epsilon_x, \epsilon_y, \epsilon_z$
e_{yz}, e_{zx}, e_{xy}	a, b, c	y_z, z_x, x_y	g_{yz}, g_{zx}, g_{xy}	$\sigma_{yz}, \sigma_{zx}, \sigma_{xy}$	$\gamma_{yz}, \gamma_{zx}, \gamma_{xy}$

Stress-components.

Text[11] and Kirchhoff[8]	Kelvin and Tait[7]	Lamé[12]	Saint-Venant[9]	Pearson[3]	v. Kármán[10]
X_x, Y_y, Z_z	P, Q, R	N_1, N_2, N_3	t_{xx}, t_{yy}, t_{zz}	$\widehat{xx}, \widehat{yy}, \widehat{zz}$	$\sigma_x, \sigma_y, \sigma_z$
Y_z, Z_x, X_y	S, T, U	T_1, T_2, T_3	t_{yz}, t_{zx}, t_{xy}	$\widehat{yz}, \widehat{zx}, \widehat{xy}$	$\tau_{yz}, \tau_{zx}, \tau_{xy}$

1 *Cambridge and Dublin Math. J.*, vol. 6 (1851), p. 47, or *Miscellaneous Scientific Papers*, p. 67; also *Phil. Trans. Roy. Soc.*, vol. 146 (1856), or *Miscellaneous Scientific Papers*, p. 119. In the first of these memoirs the word "strain" was appropriated to express relative displacement, and in the second the word "stress" was appropriated to express internal actions between the parts of a body. The memoir of 1856 also contains Rankine's nomenclature for elastic constants of æolotropic solid bodies.

2 *Baltimore Lectures on Molecular Dynamics*, Cambridge, 1904.

3 Todhunter and Pearson's *History*, vol. 1, Note B.

4 *London Math. Soc. Proc.*, vol. 21 (1891), p. 73.

5 *Rapports présentés au Congrès International de Physique*, t. 1, Paris, 1900.

6 For the definitions see Article 8.

7 *Natural Philosophy*, Part 2.

8 *Vorlesungen über math. Physik, Mechanik.*

9 *Théorie de l'élasticité des corps solides de Clebsch*, Paris, 1883, frequently referred to as the "Annotated Clebsch."

10 Th. v. Kármán gives this notation, as frequent in technical literature, in the Article "Festigkeitsprobleme in Maschinenbau," *Ency. d. math. Wiss.*, Bd. IV, Art. 27.

11 For the definitions see Article 47.

12 *Leçons sur la théorie mathématique de l'élasticité des corps solides.*

Kelvin and Tait's notation for strain-components and stress-components has been adopted by Lord Rayleigh and J. H. Michell, among others, and it was used in the first edition of this book. Kirchhoff's notation for stress-components has met with very general acceptance, but there seems to be no equally suggestive and convenient notation for strain-components. The notation X_ν, Y_ν, Z_ν for the components of traction across a plane, the normal to which is in the direction ν, is supported by Voigt[5].

The word "shear" has been used in the sense attached to it in the text by Kelvin and Tait. Rankine[13] proposed to use it for what has here been called "tangential traction." The word "traction" has been used in the sense attached to it in the text by Kelvin and Tait. Pearson[3] uses "traction" in the sense here attached to "tension." The strains which have here been called "extension" and "shearing strain" have been called by him "stretch" and "slide." It appears to be desirable to maintain a distinction between "simple shear," or "pure shear," and "shearing strain," and also between "tangential traction" and "shearing stress."

The "stress equations" of equilibrium or motion (Article 54) are called by Pearson[3] "body-stress-equations," and the equations of equilibrium or motion in terms of displacements (Article 91) are called by him "body-shift-equations." The terms "Young's modulus," "rigidity," "modulus of compression" (Articles 69, 73) are adopted from Kelvin and Tait[7]; these quantities are called by Pearson[3] the "stretch modulus," the "slide-modulus," and the "dilatation-modulus." The number here called "Poisson's ratio" is called by Pearson[3] the "stretch-squeeze ratio."

For isotropic solids Lamé[12] introduced the two constants λ and μ of Article 69; μ is the rigidity and $\lambda+\frac{2}{3}\mu$ is the modulus of compression. Kelvin and Tait and Lord Rayleigh have used the letter n to denote the rigidity. Saint-Venant[9] used the letter G. Many writers, including Clebsch and Kelvin and Tait, have used the letter E, as it is used in this book, to denote Young's modulus: in Lord Rayleigh's *Theory of Sound* the letter q is used. Poisson's ratio, here denoted by σ, has been denoted so by Kelvin and Tait, Clebsch and Lord Rayleigh have denoted it by μ, Saint-Venant and Pearson by η. In many of the writings of Italian elasticians the constants $(\lambda+2\mu)/\rho$ and μ/ρ are used, and denoted by Ω^2 and ω^2; Ω and ω are the velocities of irrotational and equivoluminal waves. Kirchhoff[8] used two constants which he denoted by K and θ; K is the rigidity, and θ is the number $\sigma/(1-2\sigma)$, where σ is Poisson's ratio. Kelvin and Tait[7] used two constants m, n connected with Lamé's λ and μ by the equations $m=\lambda+\mu$, $n=\mu$. According to v. Kármán[10] in recent German technical literature Young's modulus is denoted by E, the reciprocal of Poisson's ratio by m, and the rigidity by G.

In the case of æolotropic solids there are comparatively few competing notations. Pearson[3] has suggested the following notation for the elastic constants which we have denoted after Voigt[5] by $c_{11}, \ldots$:—

$$c_{11}=|\,xxxx\,|,\ c_{12}=|\,xxyy\,|,\ \ldots\ c_{44}=|\,yzyz\,|,\ \ldots.$$

The rule is that any suffix 1, 2 or 3 is to be replaced by xx, yy or zz, and any suffix 4, 5 or 6 is to be replaced by yz, zx or xy. The first two letters in any symbol refer to a component of stress, as X_x, and the last two letters to a component of strain, as e_{xx}. The letters in either of these pairs can be interchanged without altering the meaning of the symbol. The conditions $(c_{sr}=c_{rs})$, expressing that there is a strain-energy-function, are represented by the statement that the two pairs of letters in a symbol are interchangeable. Cauchy's relations (Article 66) amount to the statement that the order of the letters is indifferent.

[13] *Applied Mechanics.*

The constants by which the strain is expressed in terms of the stress, denoted in Articles 72 and 73 by $C_{11}/\Pi, \ldots$, are denoted by Voigt[5] by $s_{11}, \ldots$, and this usage has been followed by Liebisch[14]. Voigt[5] has proposed the name "modulus" for these coefficients, but this proposal seems to run counter to the usage implied in such phrases as "Young's modulus." Names for the coefficients $c_{11}, \ldots$ and $C_{11}/\Pi, \ldots$ were proposed by Rankine[1], and accounts of his terminology will be found in Lord Kelvin's *Baltimore Lectures* and in Todhunter and Pearson's *History*, vol. 2.

NOTE B

The notion of stress.

One way of introducing the notion of stress into an abstract conceptual scheme of Rational Mechanics is to accept it as a fundamental notion derived from experience. The notion is simply that of mutual action between two bodies in contact, or between two parts of the same body separated by an imagined surface; and the physical reality of such modes of action is, in this view, admitted as part of the conceptual scheme. It is perhaps in this meaning that we are to understand the dictum of Kelvin and Tait[15] that "force is a direct object of sense." This was the method followed by Euler[16] in his formulation of the principles of Hydrostatics and Hydrodynamics, and by Cauchy[17] in his earliest writings on Elasticity. When this method is followed, a distinction is established between the two types of forces which we have called "body forces" and "surface tractions," the former being conceived as due to direct action at a distance, and the latter to contact action.

Natural Philosophers have not, as a rule, been willing to accept distance actions and contact actions as equally fundamental. It has been held generally that a more complete analysis would reveal an underlying identity between the two modes of action. Sometimes it has been sought to replace action at a distance by stress in a medium; at other times to represent actions generally recognized as contact actions by means of central forces acting directly at a distance[18]. As an example of the former procedure, we may cite Maxwell's stress-system equivalent to electrostatic attractions and repulsions[19]. The alternative procedure is exemplified in many of the early discussions of Elasticity, and an account will be given presently of Cauchy's use of it to determine the stress-strain relations in a crystalline material[20]. Any such reduction of contact actions to distance actions tends to obliterate the distinction between surface tractions and body forces, and it has been customary to maintain the distinction by means of an hypothesis concerning the molecular structure of bodies. In such theories as Cauchy's the apparent contact actions are traced to distance actions between "molecules," and these actions are supposed not to extend beyond a certain region surrounding a "molecule," known as the "region of molecular activity." The body forces, on the other hand, are traced to distance actions which are sensible at sensible distances. Thus a second way of introducing the notion of stress is to base it upon an hypothesis concerning intermolecular forces.

14 *Physikalische Krystallographie*, Leipzig, 1891.

15 *Nat. Phil.*, Part 1, p. 220.

16 *Berlin Hist. de l'Acad.*, t. 11 (1755).

17 *Exercices de mathématique*, t. 2 (1827), p. 42. Cauchy's work dates from 1822, see Introduction, footnote 32.

18 The fluctuation of scientific opinion in this matter has been sketched by Maxwell in a lecture on "Action at a distance," *Scientific Papers*, vol. 2, p. 311.

19 *Electricity and Magnetism*, 2nd edition (Oxford, 1881), vol. 1, Part 1, Chapter V. Cf. Article 53 (vi) *supra*.

20 "De la pression ou tension dans un système de points matériels," *Exercices de mathématique*, t. 3. (1828), p. 213.

A third way is found in an application of the theory of energy. Let us suppose that a strain-energy-function exists, and that the equations of equilibrium or vibration of a solid body are investigated by the method of Article 115, and let the energy of that portion of the body which is contained within any closed surface S be increased by increasing the displacement. Part of the increment of this energy is expressed as a surface integral of the form

$$\iint\left[\left\{\frac{\partial W}{\partial e_{xx}}\cos(x,\nu)+\frac{\partial W}{\partial e_{xy}}\cos(y,\nu)+\frac{\partial W}{\partial e_{zx}}\cos(z,\nu)\right\}\delta u+\ldots+\ldots\right]dS.$$

Now in the formulation of Mechanics by means of the theory of energy, "forces" intervene as the coefficients of increments of the displacement in the expression for the increment of the energy. The above expression at once suggests the existence of forces which act at the surface bounding any portion of the body, and are to be estimated as so much per unit of area of the surface. In this view the notion of stress becomes a secondary or derived notion, the fundamental notions being energy, the distinction of various kinds of energy, and the localization of energy in a body. This method appears to be restricted at present to cases in which a strain-energy-function exists.

The first and third of these methods are more appropriate than the second to a theory of the kind sometimes called "macroscopic" or large-scale, such as the theory of Elasticity for the most part is. In the second method, on the other hand, a "structure" theory, molecular, or atomic, or sub-atomic, is presupposed. To be adequate for the purposes of the theory of Elasticity, a structure theory of solid bodies ought to provide a foundation for the notion of stress, it ought to lead to Hooke's law, and it ought to lead, as another consequence, to the existence of a strain-energy-function. Further it ought to include the possibility that the relations between elastic constants, which have been called "Cauchy's relations," may not hold. These are four tests.

Most of the structure theories that have been employed in the Mechanics of solid bodies represent the molecules, or it may be the atoms, or it may be some other elementary constituents of bodies, as simple centres of force, endowed with the property of mass. Such elements are supposed to exert forces, one upon another, the force between any two elements P and P' being directed along the line joining them, and the force exerted by P on P' being equal and opposite to that exerted by P' on P. It is usual to suppose that the forces between structure elements vanish when the distances between such elements exceed a certain distance, usually described as the "radius of the sphere of molecular activity." This is not strictly necessary. It would be sufficient to assume that they diminish so rapidly with increasing distance as to become negligible at distances which are small compared with the smallest that can be measured by ordinary apparatus.

Definition of stress in a system of particles.

Any structure theory of the kind just described provides a foundation for the notion of stress. This notion is introduced as follows: Let a plane p pass through a point O within the region occupied by the body, or system of structure elements, and let the normal to p, drawn in a specified sense, be denoted by ν. Let P, P' denote two structure elements, situated on the two sides of p, and such that the line PP', in the sense from P to P', makes an acute angle with the direction ν. Let C denote a curve of area S drawn on p so as to contain the point O. The linear dimensions of C are supposed to be such that the forces between structure elements, whose distances apart are of the order of these linear dimensions, are negligible; but they are also supposed to be small compared with distances that can be measured by ordinary apparatus. The lines of action of some of the forces between structure elements such as P and P' cross p within C. The force-resultant F of all such forces, considered as acting upon the elements such as P, can be defined to be the *traction* across S of that part of the body, towards which ν is drawn, upon the other part; and the quotient F/S is the *traction per unit area* across the plane p at the point O. Tractions so defined have identical properties with those introduced in Chapter II, and lead in the same way to the definition of components of stress.

Cauchy's theory. Lattice of simple point-elements.

Structure theories, which have in common the notions already explained, differ from one another in the additional assumptions that are made as to the masses of the different structure elements, as to the law of force between these elements, and as to the arrangement of these elements. In the simplest of them it is assumed that all the masses are equal, that the force is a function of the distance only, and that the elements form a *homogeneous assemblage*. This means that, if A, B, C are any three points of the assemblage, there is a point D in the assemblage so situated that CD is equal and parallel to AB, and has the same sense as AB. Another way of describing the arrangement is to say that the structure elements occupy the points of a *lattice*. A lattice is defined as a set of points such that, if the coordinates of one of them are x_0, y_0, z_0, the coordinates of the others are expressed by the formulæ

$$x_0+n_1a_1+n_2a_2+n_3a_3,\quad y_0+n_1b_1+n_2b_2+n_3b_3,\quad z_0+n_1c_1+n_2c_2+n_3c_3,$$

where $a_1, a_2, \ldots, c_3$ are fixed constants, and n_1, n_2, n_3 may be any integral numbers positive or negative.

This theory—the simplest of all those structure theories in which the elements are attracting or repelling particles—is that which was developed by Cauchy and Poisson to account for the elastic properties of crystalline solids. The application to isotropic solids is made by supposing that in them the crystallization is confused, so that no part, at all large compared with molecular dimensions, forms a single homogeneous assemblage. It seems to be desirable to work out the theory so far as to show how it leads to Hooke's law, to a strain-energy-function, and to Cauchy's relations. In the development of the theory its founders replaced certain summations by integrations, and this step afterwards provoked criticism, which suggested that Cauchy's result might not be a necessary consequence of the theory, but might depend upon this doubtful step. It will appear that the step is unnecessary, and that Cauchy's result cannot be evaded in this way.

Formulæ for the components of initial stress.

We shall now take the system to be of the simple type that has just been described, and form expressions for the components of stress in accordance with the definition of stress in a system of particles. The plane p will be taken to be parallel to the plane $x=0$ of a coordinate system, and the sense of the normal to it that of x increasing, so that the x of P' is greater than the x of P. The distance between P and P' will be denoted by r, the force between them, estimated as an attraction, by $\phi(r)$, and the direction cosines of the line from P to P' by λ, μ, ν. Then λ is positive. The force-resultant F of all the forces between pairs of elements such as P and P' can be resolved into components parallel to the axes, and equal to $\Sigma_0\{\lambda\phi(r)\}$, $\Sigma_0\{\mu\phi(r)\}$, $\Sigma_0\{\nu\phi(r)\}$, where the symbol Σ_0 denotes a certain summation. This summation is to be taken over all pairs of elements, the lines joining which cross the plane p within the curve C, of area S, surrounding the point O. If PP' is a line fulfilling these conditions, there are multitudes of other lines, of the same length and direction as PP', which also fulfil them. The summation is effected by first counting these lines, and then summing for all the relevant values of r and λ, μ, ν. Relevant values of λ, μ, ν are those determining the directions of lines joining one lattice point to another, with the restriction that λ is positive. This restriction will be removed presently. Relevant values of r are such as can be distances between lattice points, and are smaller than the linear dimensions of C. To count the number of the lines that have the same r, λ, μ, ν, we observe that it is the number of lattice points whose distance from some point within C, measured in the direction (λ, μ, ν), does not exceed r; and this is the number of lattice points P' in the volume of a cylinder, whose height is $r\lambda$, and whose base is the part of the plane p within the curve C. This again is the quotient of the mass within the cylinder divided by the mass at any lattice point P'; or it is expressed by $(\rho\lambda rS)/m$, where m is the mass of a structure element, and ρ is the density of the body at O. The components of the traction across p at O can therefore be expressed as

$$(\rho/m)\,S\,.\,\Sigma_1\{\lambda^2 r\phi(r)\},\ (\rho/m)\,S\,.\,\Sigma_1\{\lambda\mu r\phi(r)\},\ (\rho/m)\,S\,.\,\Sigma_1\{\lambda\nu r\phi(r)\},$$

where the symbol Σ_1 indicates summation over all the relevant values of r and λ, μ, ν. Here λ is necessarily positive, but this restriction can be removed. Any lattice point bisects the distance between two others, so that with any possible r and λ, μ, ν there is associated an equal r with the signs of λ, μ, ν reversed. Thus we may express the component tractions in the forms

$$(\rho/2m)\,S\,.\,\Sigma\{\lambda^2 r\phi(r)\},\ (\rho/2m)\,S\,.\,\Sigma\{\lambda\mu r\phi(r)\},\ (\rho/2m)\,S\,.\,\Sigma\{\lambda\nu r\phi(r)\},$$

where the symbol Σ indicates summation over *all* relevant values of r and λ, μ, ν (λ positive or negative).

It follows that the components of stress at the point O are given by such formulæ as

$$X_x=(\rho/2m)\,\Sigma\{\lambda^2 r\phi(r)\},\quad Y_x=(\rho/2m)\,\Sigma\{\lambda\mu r\phi(r)\}.$$

If the body is not in a state of stress these six quantities vanish. If it is in a state of initial stress, these six quantities are the components of that stress. We shall denote them by $X_x^{(0)}$, $Y_x^{(0)}$, ...

Changes due to strain.

We have now to investigate the changes that are made in the above expressions when the body undergoes a small strain, accompanied by a small rotation. It may be assumed that, in a region of dimensions comparable with those of C, the strain (expressed by components $e_{xx}, \dots e_{xy}$) is homogeneous, and the rotation (expressed by components ϖ_x, ϖ_y, ϖ_z) is uniform. Then the effect of the strain is to transform the lattice into a slightly different lattice. Any r, associated with a particular λ, μ, ν, becomes $r(1+e)$, where

$$e=e_{xx}\lambda^2+e_{yy}\mu^2+e_{zz}\nu^2+e_{yz}\mu\nu+e_{zx}\nu\lambda+e_{xy}\lambda\mu,$$

and any $r\lambda$ becomes $r\lambda+\delta(r\lambda)$, where

$$\delta(r\lambda)=e_{xx}r\lambda+(\tfrac{1}{2}e_{xy}-\varpi_z)\,r\mu+(\tfrac{1}{2}e_{zx}+\varpi_y)\,r\nu,$$

with similar formulæ for $\delta(r\mu)$ and $\delta(r\nu)$. Further ρ becomes

$$\rho(1-e_{xx}-e_{yy}-e_{zz}).$$

Hence X_x becomes $X_x^{(0)}+\delta X_x$, where

$$\delta X_x=-(e_{xx}+e_{yy}+e_{zz})\,X_x^{(0)}+2e_{xx}X_x^{(0)}+(e_{xy}-2\varpi_z)\,Y_x^{(0)}+(e_{zx}+2\varpi_y)\,Z_x^{(0)}$$
$$+(\rho/2m)\,\Sigma[\lambda^2 r\{r\phi'(r)-\phi(r)\}(e_{xx}\lambda^2+e_{yy}\mu^2+e_{zz}\nu^2+e_{yz}\mu\nu+e_{zx}\nu\lambda+e_{xy}\lambda\mu)],$$

and in like manner Y_x becomes $Y_x^{(0)}+\delta Y_x$, where

$$\delta Y_x=-(e_{xx}+e_{yy}+e_{zz})\,Y_x^{(0)}+(\tfrac{1}{2}e_{xy}+\varpi_z)\,X_x^{(0)}+(\tfrac{1}{2}e_{xy}-\varpi_z)\,Y_y^{(0)}$$
$$+(\tfrac{1}{2}e_{zx}+\varpi_y)\,Y_z^{(0)}+(\tfrac{1}{2}e_{yz}-\varpi_x)\,Z_x^{(0)}+(e_{xx}+e_{yy})\,X_y^{(0)}+(\rho/2m)\,\Sigma[\lambda\mu r\{r\phi'(r)$$
$$-\phi(r)\}(e_{xx}\lambda^2+e_{yy}\mu^2+\dots+e_{xy}\lambda\mu)].$$

These expressions are equivalent to Cauchy's results stated in Art. 75.

When there is no initial stress, these formulæ show that the components of stress are linear functions of the components of strain, thus verifying Hooke's law; and they show that the stress-strain relations have such forms as

$$X_x = c_{11} e_{xx} + c_{12} e_{yy} + c_{13} e_{zz} + c_{14} e_{yz} + c_{15} e_{zx} + c_{16} e_{xy},$$
$$X_y = c_{61} e_{xx} + c_{62} e_{yy} + c_{63} e_{zz} + c_{64} e_{yz} + c_{65} e_{zx} + c_{66} e_{xy},$$

where

$$c_{11} = (\rho/2m) \Sigma [\lambda^4 r \{r\phi'(r) - \phi(r)\}],$$
$$c_{12} = (\rho/2m) \Sigma [\lambda^2 \mu^2 r \{r\phi'(r) - \phi(r)\}],$$
$$\ldots\ldots$$

There are 15 of these coefficients, 15 being the number of homogeneous products of the fourth degree of the three quantities λ, μ, ν; so that we have, not only the relations of the type $c_{rs} = c_{sr}$, required for the existence of a strain-energy-function, but also, in addition, the three relations of each of the types $c_{12} = c_{66}$ and $c_{14} = c_{56}$, which are Cauchy's relations.

It appears that Cauchy's relations are an inevitable consequence of the assumed structure theory, and do not depend upon replacing summations by integrations.

Lattice of multiple point-elements.

The simplest structure theory having failed, it becomes necessary to devise something more complex. This was recognized by Poisson[21], who proposed to regard the molecules of a crystal as little rigid bodies, capable of rotation as well as of translatory displacement. The suggestion was, after a long time, worked out in detail by Voigt[22]. A little later Lord Kelvin announced the result that Cauchy's relations could be avoided by imagining a crystal to consist of two interpenetrating homogeneous assemblages[23] of point-elements of the kind considered above. A more general construction of this kind has been devised by M. Born[24], who proposed to regard each structure element of a crystal as a set of attracting and repelling particles, the particles of all the sets being similarly arranged relatively to each other, and the sets being similarly situated and oriented with respect to a lattice. Born showed how this construction could be adapted to accord with current views of the nature of atoms as aggregates of electric charges. His theory is developed with the object of accounting for thermal and other properties of solid bodies as well as their elastic properties.

In what follows we shall set before ourselves the more modest aim of showing that an extremely simple construction of the kind devised by Born is adequate as a foundation for the notion of stress in the theory of Elasticity. With this aim in view we can permit ourselves certain simplifications which would be out of place in a more general discussion of the atomic theory of solid bodies.

We propose to take, as representing structure elements of a crystal, pairs of associated point-elements. Each structure element is to consist of two constituent particles, which we call M and N. In the unstressed state these are to be arranged so that all the M's form a homogeneous assemblage, or are at the points of a lattice, and all the N's form a congruent homogeneous assemblage, or are at the points of another lattice, which could be

[21] S. D. Poisson, *Paris, Mém. de l'Acad.*, t. 18 (1842).

[22] W. Voigt, *Göttingen Abh.* 1887, and *Lehrbuch d. Kristallphysik*, Leipzig u. Berlin, 1910, VII Kap. II Abschn.

[23] Sir W. Thomson, *Edinburgh Roy. Soc. Proc.*, vol. 16 (1890), reprinted in *Math. and Phys. Papers*, vol. 3, p. 395. See also Appendix *J* to Lord Kelvin's *Baltimore Lectures* Cambridge, 1904.

[24] M. Born, *Dynamik d. Kristallgitter*, Leipzig u. Berlin, 1915. A second edition with a new title, *Atomtheorie d. festen Zustandes*, appeared in 1923 as a part of *Ency. d. math. Wiss.*, Bd. v, and was also published separately at Leipzig and Berlin.

obtained from the M-lattice by a translatory displacement. The components of this displacement parallel to fixed axes of x, y, z are denoted by a, b, c, so that, for example, a is the excess of the x-coordinate of any N above the x-coordinate of the associated M. If (M, N) is one associated pair, and (M', N') another, the distances MM' and NN' are equal. They will be denoted by r. The distances MN, MN', $M'N$ will be denoted by q, r', r''. The particles M are assumed to act upon each other with attractive or repulsive forces, as the P's did in the simple structure theory, and the force between M and M', estimated as an attraction, is denoted by $\phi(r)$. In like manner the particles N are assumed to act upon each other, and the force between N and N', estimated as an attraction, is assumed to be the same as the force between M and M', viz.: $\phi(r)$. The M's are also assumed to act upon the N's. The force between M and the associated N is denoted by $F(q)$, the force between M and N' is denoted by $\chi(r')$, and the force between M' and N by $\chi(r'')$, all being estimated as attractions. The functions ϕ, F, χ may be the same, or different, or the same with differences of sign only. The direction cosines of MM' and NN', in the sense from M to M', will be denoted by λ, μ, ν; the direction cosines of MN', in the sense from M to N', will be denoted by λ', μ', ν': the direction cosines of NM', in the sense from N to M', will be denoted by λ'', μ'', ν''. As regards the masses of the particles, the simplifying assumption is made that they are all equal. The mass of any one particle will be denoted by m.

We shall proceed in the same way as in the simple structure theory, first finding expressions for the component tractions across a plane, deducing formulæ for the initial stress, evaluating the changes due to strain and rotation, thence verifying Hooke's law, proving the existence of the strain-energy-function, and showing that Cauchy's relations are not necessarily true. There is, however, a new circumstance in the new theory, one which did not require attention in the previous theory, viz.: the condition that each particle in any structure element must be in equilibrium under the forces exerted upon it by other particles. In the previous theory this condition was satisfied identically, because with any two particles P and P' there was associated a third P'', such that P bisects $P'P''$. In the present more complex structure this is not the case. It will be most appropriate to introduce this condition of equilibrium of particles after obtaining formulæ for the initial stress.

In other expositions of the theory it has been usual to obtain the results from an energy function, but it seems to be desirable to determine the form of the stress-strain relations directly from the definition of stress in a system of particles.

Formulæ for the initial stress.

As before we consider the traction across the part of a plane x=const. that is within the curve C. There will be five types of lines joining particles, viz.: those specified by MM', NN', MN', NM', and MN, and we can write down each of the component tractions in the form of five sums. Thus the x-component is

$$\Sigma_0\{\lambda\,\phi(r)\}+\Sigma_0\{\lambda\,\phi(r)\}+\Sigma_0\{\lambda'\,\chi(r')\}+\Sigma_0\{\lambda''\,\chi(r'')\}+\Sigma_0\{(a/q)\,F(q)\},$$

the y-component is

$$\Sigma_0\{\mu\,\phi(r)\}+\Sigma_0\{\mu\,\phi(r)\}+\Sigma_0\{\mu'\,\chi(r')\}+\Sigma_0\{\mu''\,\chi(r'')\}+\Sigma_0\{(b/q)\,F(q)\},$$

and the z-component is

$$\Sigma_0\{\nu\,\phi(r)\}+\Sigma_0\{\nu\,\phi(r)\}+\Sigma_0\{\nu'\,\chi(r')\}+\Sigma_0\{\nu''\,\chi(r'')\}+\Sigma_0\{(c/q)\,F(q)\}.$$

The summations symbolized by Σ_0 are to be taken over all the pairs of particles whose joining lines cut the plane within C, and are such that λ, λ', λ'' are all positive. It is also convenient to assume temporarily that a is positive. This assumption may be regarded as being, not a restriction of generality, but a definition discriminating between M and N. It will be removed presently.

The summations are effected by first counting the lines that have the same defining quantities, such as λ, μ, ν, r, and then summing for all the relevant values of these quantities.

The number of lines of type MM' is the number of lattice points M' in a cylinder, of height λr, standing on the part of the plane that is within C; and this is the quotient of the sum of the masses at all these points divided by the mass at one of them, or it is $\frac{1}{2}(\rho S\lambda r)/m$, where the factor $\frac{1}{2}$ makes its appearance because the mass within the cylinder is the sum of the masses, not merely of all the M's in it, but also of all the N's in it. In the same way we can count the lines of the other types. The results are that the x- and y-components of the traction are expressed by the formulæ

$$(\rho/m)\,S\,[\Sigma_1\{\lambda^2 r\,\phi(r)\}+\tfrac{1}{2}\Sigma_1\{\lambda'^2 r'\,\chi(r')\}+\tfrac{1}{2}\Sigma_1\{\lambda''^2 r''\,\chi(r'')\}+\tfrac{1}{2}(a^2/q)\,F(q)],$$

$$(\rho/m)\,S\,[\Sigma_1\{\lambda\mu\, r\,\phi(r)\}+\tfrac{1}{2}\Sigma_1\{\lambda'\mu'\, r'\,\chi(r')\}+\tfrac{1}{2}\Sigma_1\{\lambda''\mu''\, r''\,\chi(r'')\}+\tfrac{1}{2}(ab/q)\,F(q)],$$

where the summations symbolized by Σ_1 refer to the relevant values of such quantities as λ, μ, ν, and r, and it is still understood that the quantities λ, λ', λ'' are positive.

The assemblage of the M's (and that of the N's) is like that of the P's in the previous theory, and thus the restriction to positive λ can be removed by multiplying by $\frac{1}{2}$, and taking the summation to refer to all directions along which points in the same lattice are met with. To see how the quantities λ', μ', ν', r' are affected by reversing the signs of λ', μ', ν', we observe that, if (M, N) and (M', N') are two structure elements, and M'' is a point of the M-lattice such that M bisects $M'M''$, then there is also a point N'' of the N-lattice such that N bisects $N'N''$, and then MN'' is equal and parallel, but opposite in sense, to NM', and NM'' is equal and parallel, but opposite in sense, to MN'. Thus the effect of reversing λ', μ', ν' is to change them into a possible λ'', μ'', ν'', and to change the r' belonging to them into the corresponding r''. We may therefore remove the restrictions that λ' and λ'' are positive by condensing the terms containing r' and r'' into a single term (in r'), allowing λ', μ', ν' to take all their possible values in the two combined lattices, and multiplying by $\frac{1}{2}$.

As regards the sign of a, if M is on the nearer side and N on the further side of the plane, so that a is positive, the component tractions arising from $F(q)$ are

$$(a/q)\,F(q)\times(\rho/2m)\,S\times a,\quad (b/q)\,F(q)\times(\rho/2m)\,S\times b,\quad (c/q)\,F(q)\times(\rho/2m)\,S\times c.$$

But, if M is on the further side and N on the nearer side, so that a is negative, they are

$$(-a/q)\,F(q)\times(\rho/2m)\,S\times(-a),\quad (-b/q)\,F(q)\times(\rho/2m)\,S\times(-b),$$

$$(-c/q)\,F(q)\times(\rho/2m)\,S\times(-c).$$

Thus the form of the terms contributed by $F(q)$ to the tractions across the part of the plane within C is independent of the sign of a.

We may accordingly write down the expressions for the components of initial stress in such forms as

$$X_x^{(0)}=(\rho/2m)\,[\Sigma\{\lambda^2 r\,\phi(r)\}+\Sigma\{\lambda'^2 r'\,\chi(r')\}+(a^2/q)\,F(q)],$$

$$Y_x^{(0)}=(\rho/2m)\,[\Sigma\{\lambda\mu\, r\,\phi(r)\}+\Sigma\{\lambda'\mu'\, r'\,\chi(r')\}+(ab/q)\,F(q)],$$

where the summations symbolized by Σ refer to all relevant pairs of particles. When there is no initial stress these expressions vanish, and in what follows this will be assumed to be the case.

Equilibrium of a particle.

We consider a particle, M say. The conditions that it may be in equilibrium in the initial state are

$$\Sigma\{\lambda'\,\chi(r')\}+(a/q)\,F(q)=0,\quad \Sigma\{\mu'\,\chi(r')\}+(b/q)\,F(q)=0,\quad \Sigma\{\nu'\,\chi(r')\}+(c/q)\,F(q)=0.$$

In the same way we may write down the conditions of equilibrium of a particle N in the forms

$$\Sigma\{\lambda''\chi(r'')\}-(a/q)F(q)=0,\quad \Sigma\{\mu''\chi(r'')\}-(b/q)F(q)=0,\quad \Sigma\{\nu''\chi(r'')\}-(c/q)F(q)=0,$$

but these are not new equations, because all the possible values of λ'', μ'', ν'', r'' are possible values of $-\lambda'$, $-\mu'$, $-\nu'$, r', and conversely. We have thus three equations in addition to those expressing the vanishing of the initial stress.

Changes due to strain.

We have now to find the changes that are made in the various quantities when the body undergoes a small strain, accompanied by a small rotation. Just as in the previous theory the strain may be regarded as homogeneous, and the rotation as uniform, throughout the portion of the body over which the summations extend.

To specify the strain and rotation of the body it is convenient to think of the centres of mass of the structure elements, that is the middle points of the lines of type MN, as forming a lattice. If the middle point of MN is denoted by P, the coordinates of any P in the unstressed state are given by such expressions as

$$x_0+n_1a_1+n_2a_2+n_3a_3,\quad y_0+n_1b_1+n_2b_2+n_3b_3,\quad z_0+n_1c_1+n_2c_2+n_3c_3,$$

where x_0, y_0, z_0 are constants which are not altered by the strain or rotation, the nine constants $a_1, a_2, \ldots, c_3$ specify the lattice, and n_1, n_2, n_3 are integers specifying the point P of the lattice. The coordinates of the M associated with P are obtained from those of P by adding $-\frac{1}{2}a$, $-\frac{1}{2}b$, $-\frac{1}{2}c$, and the coordinates of the N associated with the same P are obtained from those of P by adding $\frac{1}{2}a$, $\frac{1}{2}b$, $\frac{1}{2}c$. The coordinates of M' are obtained from those of M by substituting n_1', n_2', n_3' for n_1, n_2, n_3, and the coordinates of N' are obtained from those of N by the same substitution. The effect of the strain and rotation is to replace the lattice specified by $a_1, a_2, \ldots, c_3$ by a lattice specified by slightly different constants $a_1+\delta a_1, \ldots$, and further to change a, b, c into $a+\delta a$, $b+\delta b$, $c+\delta c$. So far as the geometry of the system is concerned, δa, δb, δc are unrestricted, except by the condition that they must be small, but it will appear that they are determined by the conditions of equilibrium of a particle. The quantities $\delta a_1, \ldots$ are given in terms of the components of strain and rotation by the formulæ

$$\left.\begin{aligned}\delta a_k&=e_{xx}a_k+(\tfrac{1}{2}e_{xy}-\varpi_z)\,b_k+(\tfrac{1}{2}e_{zx}+\varpi_y)\,c_k,\\ \delta b_k&=(\tfrac{1}{2}e_{xy}+\varpi_z)\,a_k+e_{yy}b_k+(\tfrac{1}{2}e_{yz}-\varpi_x)\,c_k,\\ \delta c_k&=(\tfrac{1}{2}e_{zx}-\varpi_y)\,a_k+(\tfrac{1}{2}e_{yz}+\varpi_x)\,b_k+e_{zz}c_k.\end{aligned}\right\}\quad (k=1,2,3)$$

The quantity λr is the excess of the x-coordinate of M' above that of M, and we can therefore write down the equation

$$\delta(\lambda r)=e_{xx}\lambda r+(\tfrac{1}{2}e_{xy}-\varpi_z)\,\mu r+(\tfrac{1}{2}e_{zx}+\varpi_y)\,\nu r,$$

giving the change produced in λr by the strain and rotation. The quantity $\lambda' r'$ is the excess of the x-coordinate of N' above that of M, or it is $\lambda r+a$, and we can therefore write down the equation

$$\delta(\lambda' r')=e_{xx}(\lambda' r'-a)+(\tfrac{1}{2}e_{xy}-\varpi_z)(\mu' r'-b)+(\tfrac{1}{2}e_{zx}+\varpi_y)(\nu' r'-c)+\delta a,$$

giving the change produced in $\lambda' r'$ by the strain and rotation. Similar formulæ can be written down for $\delta(\mu r)$, $\delta(\nu r)$, $\delta(\mu' r')$, $\delta(\nu' r')$. From the equations

$$r^2=(\lambda r)^2+(\mu r)^2+(\nu r)^2,\quad r'^2=(\lambda' r')^2+(\mu' r')^2+(\nu' r')^2$$

we then find

$$\begin{aligned}\delta r&=er,\\ \delta r'&=e'r'+\lambda'\{\delta a-e_{xx}a-(\tfrac{1}{2}e_{xy}-\varpi_z)\,b-(\tfrac{1}{2}e_{zx}+\varpi_y)\,c\}\\ &\quad+\mu'\{\delta b-(\tfrac{1}{2}e_{xy}+\varpi_z)\,a-e_{yy}b-(\tfrac{1}{2}e_{yz}-\varpi_x)\,c\}\\ &\quad+\nu'\{\delta c-(\tfrac{1}{2}e_{zx}-\varpi_y)\,a-(\tfrac{1}{2}e_{yz}+\varpi_x)\,b-e_{zz}c\},\end{aligned}$$

where

$$e = e_{xx}\lambda^2 + e_{yy}\mu^2 + e_{zz}\nu^2 + e_{yz}\mu\nu + e_{zx}\nu\lambda + e_{xy}\lambda\mu,$$

$$e' = e_{xx}\lambda'^2 + e_{yy}\mu'^2 + e_{zz}\nu'^2 + e_{yz}\mu'\nu' + e_{zx}\nu'\lambda' + e_{xy}\lambda'\mu'.$$

We also have

$$q\,\delta q = a\,\delta a + b\,\delta b + c\,\delta c.$$

Thus the changes in all the quantities that occur have been expressed. It is however convenient to modify those of the above formulæ which contain δa, δb, δc by writing

$$\delta_1 a = \delta a + \varpi_z b - \varpi_y c, \quad \delta_1 b = \delta b + \varpi_x c - \varpi_z a, \quad \delta_1 c = \delta c + \varpi_y a - \varpi_x b.$$

Then we have

$$\delta(\lambda' r') = e_{xx}(\lambda' r' - a) + \tfrac{1}{2}e_{xy}(\mu' r' - b) + \tfrac{1}{2}e_{zx}(\nu' r' - c) - \varpi_z \mu' r' + \varpi_y \nu' r' + \delta_1 a,$$

$$\delta r' = e' r' + \lambda'(\delta_1 a - e_{xx} a - \tfrac{1}{2}e_{xy} b - \tfrac{1}{2}e_{zx} c) + \mu'(\delta_1 b - \tfrac{1}{2}e_{xy} a - e_{yy} b - \tfrac{1}{2}e_{yz} c)$$
$$+ \nu'(\delta_1 c - \tfrac{1}{2}e_{zx} a - \tfrac{1}{2}e_{yz} b - e_{zz} c),$$

$$q\,\delta q = a\,\delta_1 a + b\,\delta_1 b + c\,\delta_1 c.$$

Equations of equilibrium of a particle in the strained state.

We consider the changes due to strain and rotation in the left-hand members of the equations of equilibrium of a particle, that is to say in the expressions of the type

$$\Sigma\{\lambda' \chi(r')\} + (a/q) F(q).$$

In order that the particle may be in equilibrium in the strained state we must have three equations of the type

$$\Sigma\left[\frac{\chi(r')}{r'}\delta(\lambda' r') + \lambda' r' \frac{d}{dr'}\left\{\frac{\chi(r')}{r'}\right\}\delta r'\right] + \frac{F(q)}{q}(\delta_1 a - \varpi_z b + \varpi_y c) + a\frac{d}{dq}\left\{\frac{F(q)}{q}\right\}\delta q = 0.$$

The coefficient of ϖ_y in the left-hand member is

$$\Sigma\{\nu' \chi(r')\} + (c/q) F(q),$$

which vanishes by one of the equations of equilibrium in the initial state. In like manner the coefficient of ϖ_z vanishes. Thus the equation becomes linear and homogeneous in $e_{xx}, e_{yy}, \dots, e_{xy}, \delta_1 a, \delta_1 b, \delta_1 c$. Two similar equations are obtained in the same way, and thus we have three equations to determine $\delta_1 a, \delta_1 b, \delta_1 c$ in terms of $e_{xx}, e_{yy}, \dots, e_{xy}$. These three equations could be solved so as to express $\delta_1 a, \delta_1 b, \delta_1 c$ as linear functions of $e_{xx}, \dots, e_{xy}$, and the results could be written

$$\delta_1 a = a_1 e_{xx} + a_2 e_{yy} + \dots + a_6 e_{xy}, \quad \delta_1 b = \beta_1 e_{xx} + \dots + \beta_6 e_{xy}, \quad \delta_1 c = \gamma_1 e_{xx} + \dots + \gamma_6 e_{xy}.$$

When these expressions for $\delta_1 a, \dots$ are introduced into the set of three equations, these equations become identities, holding for all values of the ratios $e_{xx} : e_{yy} : \dots : e_{xy}$. It is therefore most convenient to obtain a set of 18 equations to determine the 18 constants $a_1, \dots, \gamma_6$ by equating to zero the coefficients of $e_{xx}, \dots, e_{xy}$ in each of the three identities. This comes to the same thing as replacing $\delta_1 a, \dots$ by $a_1 e_{xx} + \dots, \dots$ in each of the three equations of the type

$$\Sigma\left[\frac{\chi(r')}{r'}\{\delta(\lambda' r') + \mu' r' \varpi_z - \nu' r' \varpi_y\} + \lambda' r' \frac{d}{dr'}\left\{\frac{\chi(r')}{r'}\right\}\delta r'\right] + \frac{F(q)}{q}\delta_1 a + a\frac{d}{dq}\left\{\frac{F(q)}{q}\right\}\delta q = 0,$$

and equating the coefficients of $e_{xx}, \dots$ separately to zero. These equations are, of course, linear and homogeneous in $e_{xx}, \dots, e_{xy}, \delta_1 a, \delta_1 b, \delta_1 c$, and free from $\varpi_x, \varpi_y, \varpi_z$. It may be noted that the first expression under the sign of summation in the equation just written gives rise to terms

$$e_{xx}\Sigma\{\lambda' \chi(r')\} + \tfrac{1}{2}e_{xy}\Sigma\{\mu' \chi(r')\} + \tfrac{1}{2}e_{zx}\Sigma\{\nu' \chi(r')\},$$

and these can be replaced by

$$-q^{-1}F(q)(e_{xx}a + \tfrac{1}{2}e_{xy}b + \tfrac{1}{2}e_{zx}c).$$

Then by means of an abbreviated notation the 18 equations can be compressed into a small compass. We shall write

$$(l,\ m,\ n)=\Sigma\,[\lambda'^{l}\mu'^{m}\nu'^{n}\{r'\chi'(r')-\chi(r')\}],$$
$$\{l,\ m,\ n\}=\Sigma\,[\lambda'^{l}\mu'^{m}\nu'^{n}\{\chi'(r')-r'^{-1}\chi(r')\}],$$
$$T=q^{-2}\{F'(q)-q^{-1}F(q)\},$$
$$d_1=a,\quad d_2=b,\quad d_3=c,$$
$$a_{r,s}=\theta\,[\Sigma\,\{r'^{-1}\chi(r')\}+q^{-1}F(q)]+d_r d_s T+\{l,\ m,\ n\},$$

where $\theta=1$ or 0 according as r and s are the same or different, and l, m, n are given by the rule that $d_r d_s$, the coefficient of T, is the same as $d_1{}^l d_2{}^m d_3{}^n$, e.g., for $r=s=1$, $d_r d_s=d_1{}^2$, and $l=2$, $m=0$, $n=0$. Then the equations are of two types. The first type is

$$(l,\ m,\ n)+d_r d_s^2\,T-a_{r,s}d_s+a_{1,r}a_s+a_{2,r}\beta_s+a_{3,r}\gamma_s=0,$$

where r and s separately can take any of the values 1, 2, 3, and (l, m, n) is determined by the rule $d_r d_s^2=d_1{}^l d_2{}^m d_3{}^n$. The second type is

$$(l,\ m,\ n)+d_r d_{s+1} d_{s+2}\,T-\tfrac{1}{2}\,(a_{r,s+1}d_{s+2}+a_{r,s+2}d_{s+1})+a_{1,r}a_{3+s}+a_{2,r}\beta_{3+s}+a_{3,r}\gamma_{3+s}=0,$$

where again r and s separately can take any of the values 1, 2, 3, and now if $s+1$ or $s+2$ in a suffix of d or a is greater than 3 it is to be replaced by its excess above 3. Here again (l, m, n) is determined by the rule $d_r d_{s+1} d_{s+2}=d_1{}^l d_2{}^m d_3{}^n$. It may be noted that

$$a_{r,s}=a_{s,r}.$$

Strain-energy-function.

We consider the changes due to strain and rotation in the right-hand members of the equations expressing the initial stress, that is to say in such expressions as

$$(\rho/2m)\,[\Sigma\,\{\lambda^2 r\,\phi(r)\}+\Sigma\,\{\lambda'^2 r'\,\chi(r')\}+a^2 q^{-1}F(q)],$$

which, it will be remembered, vanish in the initial state. We need not attend to the change in ρ, because, for example, the contribution of $\delta\rho$ to the right-hand member of the above equation is $(\delta\rho/\rho)X_x^{(0)}$, which vanishes. We get at once expressions for the stress components in such forms as

$$X_x=\frac{\rho}{2m}\,\Sigma\left[2\lambda\,\phi(r)\,\delta(\lambda r)+\lambda^2 r^2\,\frac{d}{dr}\left\{\frac{\phi(r)}{r}\right\}\delta r+2\lambda'\,\chi(r')\,\delta(\lambda' r')+\lambda'^2 r'^2\,\frac{d}{dr'}\left\{\frac{\chi(r')}{r'}\right\}\delta r'\right]$$
$$+\frac{\rho}{2m}\left[2a\,\frac{F(q)}{q}\,(\delta_1 a-b\varpi_z+c\varpi_y)+a^2\,\frac{d}{dq}\left\{\frac{F(q)}{q}\right\}\delta q\right],$$

$$Y_x=\frac{\rho}{2m}\,\Sigma\left[\phi(r)\,\{\lambda\,\delta(\mu r)+\mu\,\delta(\lambda r)\}+\lambda\mu r^2\,\frac{d}{dr}\left\{\frac{\phi(r)}{r}\right\}\delta r\right.$$
$$\left.+\chi'(r')\,\{\lambda'\,\delta(\mu' r')+\mu'\,\delta(\lambda' r')\}+\lambda'\mu' r'^2\,\frac{d}{dr'}\left\{\frac{\chi(r')}{r'}\right\}\delta r'\right]$$
$$+\frac{\rho}{2m}\left[\frac{F(q)}{q}\,\{a\,(\delta_1 b-c\varpi_x+a\varpi_z)+b\,(\delta_1 a-b\varpi_z+c\varpi_y)\}+ab\,\frac{d}{dq}\left\{\frac{F(q)}{q}\right\}\delta q\right],$$

and in these we have to substitute the values previously found for $\delta(\lambda r), \ldots, \delta q$. It is verified immediately that ϖ_x, ϖ_y, ϖ_z disappear from these expressions, so that the stress components $X_x, \ldots$ are linear functions of the strain components $e_{xx}, \ldots$, or we have Hooke's law.

It is convenient to evaluate first the contributions to $X_x, \ldots$ of the variation δr, which is er, and of the term $e'r'$ in $\delta r'$. Denoting these contributions by $X_x^{(1)}, \ldots$, we can write them down at once in such forms as

$$X_x^{(1)}=(\rho/2m)\,\Sigma\,[\lambda^4 r\,\{r\,\phi'(r)-\phi(r)\}+\lambda'^4 r'\,\{r'\chi'(r')-\chi(r')\}],$$

and can observe that they are entirely similar to the expressions for the stress components in the previous theory. If $X_x^{(1)}, \dots$ were complete expressions for the stress components, we should have, not only a strain-energy-function, but also inevitably Cauchy's relations.

Let the remaining terms in the expressions for the stress components be denoted by $X_x^{(2)}, \dots$, so that, for example,

$$X_x = X_x^{(1)} + X_x^{(2)}.$$

Then it is not difficult to write down the coefficient of any strain component in any of the expressions such as $X_x^{(2)}$. We proceed to verify the conditions for the existence of the strain-energy-function. These are relations of the four types

$$\frac{\partial X_x^{(2)}}{\partial e_{yy}} = \frac{\partial Y_y^{(2)}}{\partial e_{xx}}, \quad \frac{\partial X_x^{(2)}}{\partial e_{xy}} = \frac{\partial Y_x^{(2)}}{\partial e_{xx}}, \quad \frac{\partial X_x^{(2)}}{\partial e_{yz}} = \frac{\partial Y_z^{(2)}}{\partial e_{xx}}, \quad \frac{\partial Y_x^{(2)}}{\partial e_{yz}} = \frac{\partial Y_z^{(2)}}{\partial e_{xy}}.$$

It will be sufficient to verify one of these, and we choose the second, the method for the others being precisely similar. We have

$$\begin{aligned}\frac{\partial X_x^{(2)}}{\partial e_{xy}} = \frac{\rho}{2m} \Sigma \Big[& 2\lambda \phi(r) \tfrac{1}{2}\mu r + 2\lambda' \chi(r') \{\tfrac{1}{2}(\mu' r' - b) + \alpha_6\} \\ & + \lambda'^2 r'^2 \frac{d}{dr'}\left\{\frac{\chi(r')}{r'}\right\} (-\tfrac{1}{2} b\lambda' - \tfrac{1}{2} a\mu' + \lambda'\alpha_6 + \mu'\beta_6 + \nu'\gamma_6) \Big] \\ & + \frac{\rho}{2m}\left[2a \frac{F(q)}{q} \alpha_6 + a^2 \frac{d}{dq}\left\{\frac{F(q)}{q}\right\}\left(\frac{a}{q}\alpha_6 + \frac{b}{q}\beta_6 + \frac{c}{q}\gamma_6\right)\right],\end{aligned}$$

$$\begin{aligned}\frac{\partial Y_x^{(2)}}{\partial e_{xx}} = \frac{\rho}{2m} \Sigma \Big[& \phi(r)\mu\lambda r + \chi(r') \{\lambda'\beta_1 + \mu'(\lambda' r' - a) + \mu'\alpha_1\} \\ & + \lambda'\mu' r'^2 \frac{d}{dr'}\left\{\frac{\chi(r')}{r'}\right\} (-a\lambda' + \lambda'\alpha_1 + \mu'\beta_1 + \nu'\gamma_1) \Big] \\ & + \frac{\rho}{2m}\left[\frac{F(q)}{q}(a\beta_1 + b\alpha_1) + ab \frac{d}{dq}\left\{\frac{F(q)}{q}\right\}\left(\frac{a}{q}\alpha_1 + \frac{b}{q}\beta_1 + \frac{c}{q}\gamma_1\right)\right].\end{aligned}$$

In these such terms as $\Sigma\{\lambda'\chi(r')\}$ may be replaced by such terms as $-aq^{-1}F(q)$. When this is done some terms cancel identically, and some sets of terms vanish in virtue of the equations such as $X_x^{(0)}=0$, which express the vanishing of the initial stress. Retaining all the terms that do not disappear in this way, and using notation already introduced, we find

$$\begin{aligned}\frac{2m}{\rho}\left(\frac{\partial X_x^{(2)}}{\partial e_{xy}} - \frac{\partial Y_x^{(2)}}{\partial e_{xx}}\right) = & -\tfrac{1}{2} d_2 (3, 0, 0) + \tfrac{1}{2} d_1 (2, 1, 0) \\ & + \alpha_6 \{(3, 0, 0) + d_1^3 T\} + \beta_6 \{(2, 1, 0) + d_1^2 d_2 T\} + \gamma_6 \{(2, 0, 1) + d_1^2 d_3 T\} \\ & - \alpha_1 \{(2, 1, 0) + d_1^2 d_2 T\} - \beta_1 \{(1, 2, 0) + d_1 d_2^2 T\} \\ & - \gamma_1 \{(1, 1, 1) + d_1 d_2 d_3 T\}.\end{aligned}$$

The three last lines are

$$\begin{aligned}& \alpha_6 (d_1 a_{1,1} - a_{1,1}\alpha_1 - a_{1,2}\beta_1 - a_{1.3}\gamma_1) + \beta_6 (d_1 a_{1,2} - a_{1,2}\alpha_1 - a_{2,2}\beta_1 - a_{3,2}\gamma_1) \\ & \quad + \gamma_6 (d_1 a_{3,1} - a_{3,1}\alpha_1 - a_{3,2}\beta_1 - a_{3,3}\gamma_1) - \alpha_1 (\tfrac{1}{2} d_1 a_{1,2} + \tfrac{1}{2} d_2 a_{1,1} - a_{1,1}\alpha_6 - a_{1,2}\beta_6 - a_{1,3}\gamma_6) \\ & \quad - \beta_1 (\tfrac{1}{2} d_1 a_{2,2} + \tfrac{1}{2} d_2 a_{2,1} - a_{2,1}\alpha_6 - a_{2,2}\beta_6 - a_{2,3}\gamma_6) \\ & \quad - \gamma_1 (\tfrac{1}{2} d_1 a_{2,3} + \tfrac{1}{2} d_2 a_{3,1} - a_{3,1}\alpha_6 - a_{3,2}\beta_6 - a_{3,3}\gamma_6).\end{aligned}$$

The terms that are quadratic in the coefficients α, β, γ cancel, and the linear terms come to

$$d_1 (a_{1,1}\alpha_6 + a_{2,1}\beta_6 + a_{3,1}\gamma_6) - \tfrac{1}{2} d_1 (a_{1,2}\alpha_1 + a_{2,2}\beta_1 + a_{3,2}\gamma_1) - \tfrac{1}{2} d_2 (a_{1,1}\alpha_1 + a_{1,2}\beta_1 + a_{1,3}\gamma_1)$$

or

$$\begin{aligned}& -d_1 \{(2, 1, 0) + d_1^2 d_2 T - \tfrac{1}{2} d_1 a_{1,2} - \tfrac{1}{2} d_2 a_{1,1}\} + \tfrac{1}{2} d_1 \{(2, 1, 0) + d_1^2 d_2 T - d_1 a_{1,2}\} \\ & \qquad + \tfrac{1}{2} d_2 \{(3, 0, 0) + d_1^3 T - d_1 a_{1,1}\},\end{aligned}$$

which is

$$-\tfrac{1}{2} d_1 (2, 1, 0) + \tfrac{1}{2} d_2 (3, 0, 0).$$

Thus the relation in question is verified.

It was, of course, really obvious that there must be a strain-energy-function, quadratic in the strain components, as soon as it was proved that the stress components are linear functions of the strain components. For in a system of attracting and repelling particles, when the force between two particles is a function of the distance between them, there must be a potential energy function, which depends on these distances only.

Failure of Cauchy's relations.

If Cauchy's relations were true we should have three additional relations of each of the types

$$\frac{\partial X_x^{(2)}}{\partial e_{yy}} = \frac{\partial Y_x^{(2)}}{\partial e_{xy}}, \quad \frac{\partial X_x^{(2)}}{\partial e_{yz}} = \frac{\partial Y_x^{(2)}}{\partial e_{zx}}.$$

It will be sufficient to consider the first only. We have

$$\frac{\partial X_x^{(2)}}{\partial e_{yy}} = \frac{\rho}{2m} \Sigma \left[2\lambda' \chi(r') \alpha_2 + \lambda'^2 r'^2 \frac{d}{dr'} \left\{ \frac{\chi(r')}{r'} \right\} (-\mu' b + \lambda' \alpha_2 + \mu' \beta_2 + \nu' \gamma_2) \right]$$
$$+ \frac{\rho}{2m} \left[2a \frac{F(q)}{q} \alpha_2 + a^2 \frac{d}{dq} \left\{ \frac{F(q)}{q} \right\} \left(\frac{a}{q} \alpha_2 + \frac{b}{q} \beta_2 + \frac{c}{q} \gamma_2 \right) \right]$$

$$\frac{\partial Y_x^{(2)}}{\partial e_{xy}} = \frac{\rho}{2m} \Sigma \left[r\phi(r) \tfrac{1}{2}(\lambda^2 + \mu^2) + \chi'(r') \{\lambda' \tfrac{1}{2}(\lambda' r' - a) + \mu' \tfrac{1}{2}(\mu' r' - b) + \lambda' \beta_6 + \mu' \alpha_6\} \right.$$
$$\left. + \lambda' \mu' r'^2 \frac{d}{dr'} \left\{ \frac{\chi(r')}{r'} \right\} (-\tfrac{1}{2}\lambda' b - \tfrac{1}{2}\mu' a + \lambda' \alpha_6 + \mu' \beta_6 + \nu' \gamma_6) \right]$$
$$+ \frac{\rho}{2m} \left[\frac{F(q)}{q} (a\beta_6 + b\alpha_6) + ab \frac{d}{dq} \left\{ \frac{F(q)}{q} \right\} \left(\frac{a}{q} \alpha_6 + \frac{b}{q} \beta_6 + \frac{c}{q} \gamma_6 \right) \right].$$

As before, certain terms cancel in virtue of the equations of equilibrium of a particle in the initial state, and certain sets of terms vanish through the vanishing of the initial stress. Retaining all the other terms, we find

$$\frac{2m}{\rho} \left(\frac{\partial X_x^{(2)}}{\partial e_{yy}} - \frac{\partial Y_x^{(2)}}{\partial e_{xy}} \right) = -\tfrac{1}{2} d_2 (2, 1, 0) + \tfrac{1}{2} d_1 (1, 2, 0)$$
$$+ \alpha_2 \{(3, 0, 0) + d_1^3 T\} + \beta_2 \{(2, 1, 0) + d_1^2 d_2 T\} + \gamma_2 \{(2, 0, 1) + d_1^2 d_3 T\}$$
$$- \alpha_6 \{(2, 1, 0) + d_1^2 d_2 T\} - \beta_6 \{(1, 2, 0) + d_1 d_2^2 T\}$$
$$- \gamma_6 \{(1, 1, 1) + d_1 d_2 d_3 T\}.$$

The last three lines are the same as

$$\alpha_2 (d_1 a_{1,1} - a_{1,1} \alpha_1 - a_{1,2} \beta_1 - a_{1,3} \gamma_1) + \beta_2 (d_1 a_{1,2} - a_{1,2} \alpha_1 - a_{2,2} \beta_1 - a_{3,2} \gamma_1)$$
$$+ \gamma_2 (d_1 a_{1,3} - a_{1,3} \alpha_1 - a_{2,3} \beta_1 - a_{3,3} \gamma_1) - \alpha_6 (\tfrac{1}{2} d_1 a_{1,2} + \tfrac{1}{2} d_2 a_{1,1} - a_{1,1} \alpha_6 - a_{1,2} \beta_6 - a_{1,3} \gamma_6)$$
$$- \beta_6 (\tfrac{1}{2} d_1 a_{2,2} + \tfrac{1}{2} d_2 a_{1,2} - a_{1,2} \alpha_6 - a_{2,2} \beta_6 - a_{3,2} \gamma_6)$$
$$- \gamma_6 (\tfrac{1}{2} d_1 a_{2,3} + \tfrac{1}{2} d_2 a_{3,1} - a_{1,3} \alpha_6 - a_{2,3} \beta_6 - a_{3,3} \gamma_6).$$

The terms which are quadratic in the coefficients α, β, γ do not now cancel, and the linear terms come to

$$-d_1 \{(1, 2, 0) + d_1 d_2^2 T - d_2 a_{1,2}\} + \tfrac{1}{2} d_1 \{(1, 2, 0) + d_1 d_2^2 T - \tfrac{1}{2} d_1 a_{2,2} - \tfrac{1}{2} d_2 a_{1,2}\}$$
$$+ \tfrac{1}{2} d_2 \{(2, 1, 0) + d_1^2 d_2 T - \tfrac{1}{2} d_1 a_{1,2} - \tfrac{1}{2} d_2 a_{1,1}\}.$$

or

$$-\tfrac{1}{2} d_1 (1, 2, 0) + \tfrac{1}{2} d_2 (2, 1, 0) - \tfrac{1}{4} (d_1^2 a_{2,2} + d_2^2 a_{1,1} - 2 d_1 d_2 a_{1,2}).$$

There is therefore no necessity for the expression to vanish, and its vanishing would imply some particular configuration of the lattices, or some particular specification of the forces between the particles.

It has thus been proved that Cauchy's relations are not a necessary consequence of the structure theory, which represents a crystal by a lattice of pairs of point-elements, and it may be concluded that it would not be a necessary consequence of any structure theory of the more general type devised by Born.

NOTE C

Applications of the method of moving axes.

The theory of moving axes may be based on the result obtained in Article 35. Let a figure of invariable form rotate about an axis of which the direction cosines, referred to fixed axes, are l, m, n, and let it turn through an angle $\delta\theta$ in time δt. At the beginning of this interval of time let any point belonging to the figure be at the point of which the coordinates, referred to the fixed axes, are x, y, z; then at the end of the interval the same point of the figure will have moved to the point of which the coordinates are

$$x+(mz-ny)\sin\delta\theta-\{x-l(lx+my+nz)\}(1-\cos\delta\theta), \dots.$$

Hence the components of velocity of the moving point at the instant when it passes through the point (x, y, z) are

$$-yn\frac{d\theta}{dt}+zm\frac{d\theta}{dt}, \qquad -zl\frac{d\theta}{dt}+xn\frac{d\theta}{dt}, \qquad -xm\frac{d\theta}{dt}+yl\frac{d\theta}{dt}.$$

We may localize a vector of magnitude $d\theta/dt$ in the axis (l, m, n), and specify it by components $\omega_x, \omega_y, \omega_z$, so that $\omega_x=l\,d\theta/dt, \dots$. This vector is the angular velocity of the figure. The components of the velocity of the moving point which is passing through the point (x, y, z) at the instant t are then

$$-y\omega_z+z\omega_y, \qquad -z\omega_x+x\omega_z, \qquad -x\omega_y+y\omega_x.$$

Let a triad of orthogonal axes of (x', y', z'), having its origin at the origin of the fixed axes of (x, y, z), and such that they can be derived from the axes of (x, y, z) by a rotation, rotate with the figure; and let the directions of the moving axes at the instant t be specified by the scheme of nine direction cosines.

	x	y	z
x'	l_1	m_1	n_1
y'	l_2	m_2	n_2
z'	l_3	m_3	n_3

Let $\theta_1, \theta_2, \theta_3$ denote the components of the angular velocity of the rotating figure parallel to the axes of x', y', z', so that

$$\omega_x=l_1\theta_1+l_2\theta_2+l_3\theta_3, \dots,$$

and let a point (x', y', z') move so as to be invariably connected with the figure. The coordinates of this point referred to the fixed axes are, at the instant t, $l_1x'+l_2y'+l_3z', \dots$, and we may equate two expressions for the components of velocity of the point. We thus obtain three equations of the type

$$\frac{d}{dt}(l_1x'+l_2y'+l_3z')=-(m_1x'+m_2y'+m_3z')(n_1\theta_1+n_2\theta_2+n_3\theta_3)$$
$$+(n_1x'+n_2y'+n_3z')(m_1\theta_1+m_2\theta_2+m_3\theta_3).$$

Since the axes of (x', y', z') can be derived from those of (x, y, z) by a rotation, we have such equations as

$$m_1n_2-m_2n_1=l_3.$$

The above equations hold for all values of x', y', z', and therefore, x', y', z' being independent of the time, we have the nine equations

$$\left.\begin{aligned}
\frac{dl_1}{dt} &= l_2\theta_3 - l_3\theta_2, & \frac{dl_2}{dt} &= l_3\theta_1 - l_1\theta_3, & \frac{dl_3}{dt} &= l_1\theta_2 - l_2\theta_1,\\
\frac{dm_1}{dt} &= m_2\theta_3 - m_3\theta_2, & \frac{dm_2}{dt} &= m_3\theta_1 - m_1\theta_3, & \frac{dm_3}{dt} &= m_1\theta_2 - m_2\theta_1,\\
\frac{dn_1}{dt} &= n_2\theta_3 - n_3\theta_2, & \frac{dn_2}{dt} &= n_3\theta_1 - n_1\theta_3, & \frac{dn_3}{dt} &= n_1\theta_2 - n_2\theta_1.
\end{aligned}\right\} \quad \text{.........(1)}$$

Now let u, v, w be the projections on the fixed axes of any vector, u', v', w' the projections of the same vector on the moving axes at time t. We have such equations as

$$\frac{du}{dt} = \frac{d}{dt}(l_1u' + l_2v' + l_3w')$$

$$= l_1\left(\frac{du'}{dt} - v'\theta_3 + w'\theta_2\right) + l_2\left(\frac{dv'}{dt} - w'\theta_1 + u'\theta_3\right) + l_3\left(\frac{dw'}{dt} - u'\theta_2 + v'\theta_1\right). \quad \text{.........(2)}$$

Hence the projections on the moving axes of that vector whose projections on the fixed axes are

$$\frac{du}{dt},\ \frac{dv}{dt},\ \frac{dw}{dt}$$

are
$$\frac{du'}{dt} - v'\theta_3 + w'\theta_2,\ \frac{dv'}{dt} - w'\theta_1 + u'\theta_3,\ \frac{dw'}{dt} - u'\theta_2 + v'\theta_1. \quad \text{..................(3)}$$

We may abandon the condition that the origin of the moving axes coincides with that of the fixed axes. The formulæ (1) are unaltered, and the formulæ (2) also are unaltered unless u, v, w are the coordinates of a point. Let x_0, y_0, z_0 be the coordinates of the origin of the moving axes referred to the fixed axes, x, y, z and x', y' z' those of any moving point referred respectively to the fixed axes and the moving axes. We have such formulæ as

$$x = x_0 + l_1x' + l_2y' + l_3z',$$

and therefore

$$\frac{dx}{dt} = \frac{dx_0}{dt} + l_1\left(\frac{dx'}{dt} - y'\theta_3 + z'\theta_2\right) + l_2\left(\frac{dy'}{dt} - z'\theta_1 + x'\theta_3\right) + l_3\left(\frac{dz'}{dt} - x'\theta_2 + y'\theta_1\right).$$

Let u_0', v_0', w_0' be the projections of the velocity of the origin of (x', y', z') on the instantaneous positions of the moving axes, then we have

$$\frac{dx_0}{dt} = l_1u_0' + l_2v_0' + l_3w_0'.$$

Hence the projections of the velocity of any moving point upon the instantaneous positions of the moving axes are

$$u_0' + \frac{dx'}{dt} - y'\theta_3 + z'\theta_2,\quad v_0' + \frac{dy'}{dt} - z'\theta_1 + x'\theta_3,\quad w_0' + \frac{dz'}{dt} - x'\theta_2 + y'\theta_1. \quad \text{......(4)}$$

These formulæ can be utilized for the calculation of differential coefficients. Let α, β, γ, ... be any parameters, and let a triad of orthogonal axes of x', y', z' be associated with any system of values of the parameters, so that, when the parameters are given, the position of the origin of this triad and the directions of the axes are known. Let the position of a point relative to the variable axes be supposed to be known; the coordinates x', y', z' of the point are then known functions of α, β, γ, ... Let x, y, z be the coordinates of the point referred to fixed axes. Then x, y, z also are functions of α, β, γ, ..., and we wish to calculate the values of $\partial x/\partial\alpha$, ... When α, β, γ, ... are altered the origin of the variable axes undergoes a displacement and the axes undergo a rotation, and we may regard this displacement and rotation as being effected continuously with certain velocities. Thus we have a velocity of the origin and an angular velocity of the triad of axes. This velocity and angular velocity being denoted, as before, by their components u_0', v_0', w_0' and θ_1, θ_2, θ_3, referred to the instantaneous positions of the variable axes, the quantities u_0', ..., θ_1, ... are linear functions of $d\alpha/dt$, $d\beta/dt$, ..., and the coefficients of $d\alpha/dt$, ... in these functions are known functions of α, β, γ, ... Thus we have such equations as

$$\frac{\partial x}{\partial\alpha}\frac{d\alpha}{dt}+\frac{\partial x}{\partial\beta}\frac{d\beta}{dt}+\ldots=l_1\left\{u_0'+\left(\frac{\partial x'}{\partial\alpha}\frac{d\alpha}{dt}+\frac{\partial x'}{\partial\beta}\frac{d\beta}{dt}+\ldots\right)-y'\theta_3+z'\theta_2\right\}$$
$$+l_2\left\{v_0'+\left(\frac{\partial y'}{\partial\alpha}\frac{d\alpha}{dt}+\frac{\partial y'}{\partial\beta}\frac{d\beta}{dt}+\ldots\right)-z'\theta_1+x'\theta_3\right\}$$
$$+l_3\left\{w_0'+\left(\frac{\partial z'}{\partial\alpha}\frac{d\alpha}{dt}+\frac{\partial z'}{\partial\beta}\frac{d\beta}{dt}+\ldots\right)-x'\theta_2+y'\theta_1\right\}.$$

We may equate the coefficients of $d\alpha/dt$, $d\beta/dt$, ... on the two sides of these equations, the quantities u_0', ..., θ_1, ... being expressed as linear functions of $d\alpha/dt$, ...

In like manner, if u, v, w and u', v', w' denote the projections of any vector on the fixed and variable axes, equations (2) give us formulæ for calculating $\partial u/\partial\alpha$, ... In applications of the method it is generally most convenient to take the fixed axes to coincide with the positions of the variable axes that are determined by particular values α, β, γ, ... of the parameters, then in equations (2) we may put $l_1=m_2=n_3=1$ and $l_2=\ldots=0$. When this is done the values of $\partial u/\partial\alpha$, ... belonging to these particular values of α, ... are given by formulæ of the type

$$\frac{\partial u}{\partial\alpha}\frac{d\alpha}{dt}+\frac{\partial u}{\partial\beta}\frac{d\beta}{dt}+\frac{\partial u}{\partial\gamma}\frac{d\gamma}{dt}+\ldots=\left(\frac{\partial u'}{\partial\alpha}\frac{d\alpha}{dt}+\frac{\partial u'}{\partial\beta}\frac{d\beta}{dt}+\frac{\partial u'}{\partial\gamma}\frac{d\gamma}{dt}+\ldots\right)-v'\theta_3+w'\theta_2. \quad \ldots(5)$$

The above process has been used repeatedly in Chapters XVIII, XXI, XXIV. As a further illustration we take some questions concerning curvilinear orthogonal coordinates. The coordinates being α, β, γ, the expression for the linear element being

$$\{(d\alpha/h_1)^2+(d\beta/h_2)^2+(d\gamma/h_3)^2\}^{\frac{1}{2}},$$

and the variable axes being the normals to the surfaces, we have

$$u_0'=\frac{1}{h_1}\frac{d\alpha}{dt},\quad v_0'=\frac{1}{h_2}\frac{d\beta}{dt},\quad w_0'=\frac{1}{h_3}\frac{d\gamma}{dt}.$$

To determine the values of θ_1, θ_2, θ_3 we have recourse to Dupin's theorem cited in Article 19. It follows from this theorem that the tangents drawn on a surface γ, at points of its intersection with a surface β, to the curves in which the surface is cut by two neighbouring

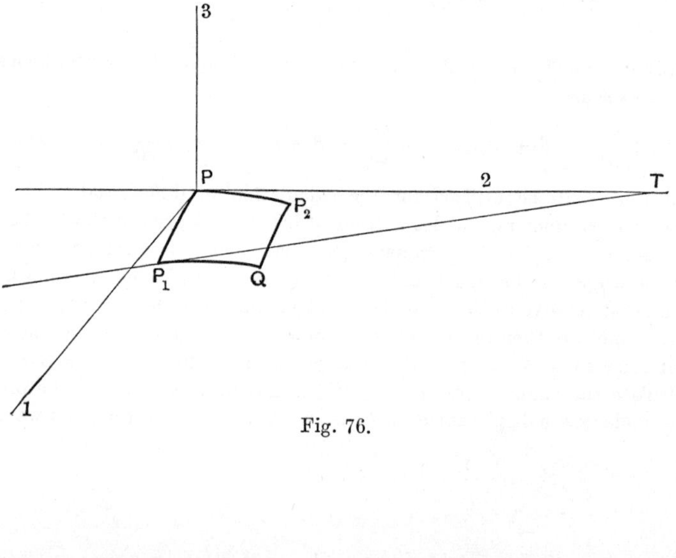

Fig. 76.

surfaces of the family α, say α and $\alpha+\delta\alpha$, ultimately intersect when $\delta\alpha$ is diminished indefinitely, and the point of ultimate intersection T is a centre of principal curvature of the surface β. In Fig. 76 the point P is (α, β, γ), P_1 is $(\alpha+\delta\alpha, \beta, \gamma)$, P_2 is $(\alpha, \beta+\delta\beta, \gamma)$, Q is $(\alpha+\delta\alpha, \beta+\delta\beta, \gamma)$. The length of the arc PP_1 can be taken to be $\delta\alpha/h_1$, and the excess of the length P_2Q above PP_1 is, to the second order, $\delta\beta\,\frac{\partial}{\partial\beta}\left(\frac{\delta\alpha}{h_1}\right)$. We may regard the tangents to PP_2 at P and P_1Q at P_1 as intersecting in T, and take the length of PP_2 to be $\delta\beta/h_2$. Then the angle PTP_1 is $-h_2\frac{\partial}{\partial\beta}\left(\frac{1}{h_1}\right)\delta\alpha$. Hence the coefficient of $d\alpha/dt$ in θ_3 is $-h_2\frac{\partial}{\partial\beta}\left(\frac{1}{h_1}\right)$. In like manner the coefficient of $d\beta/dt$ in θ_3 is $h_1\frac{\partial}{\partial\alpha}\left(\frac{1}{h_2}\right)$. We can now write down the formulæ

$$\left.\begin{aligned}\theta_1&=h_2\frac{\partial}{\partial\beta}\left(\frac{1}{h_3}\right)\frac{d\gamma}{dt}-h_3\frac{\partial}{\partial\gamma}\left(\frac{1}{h_2}\right)\frac{d\beta}{dt},\\ \theta_2&=h_3\frac{\partial}{\partial\gamma}\left(\frac{1}{h_1}\right)\frac{d\alpha}{dt}-h_1\frac{\partial}{\partial\alpha}\left(\frac{1}{h_3}\right)\frac{d\gamma}{dt},\\ \theta_3&=h_1\frac{\partial}{\partial\alpha}\left(\frac{1}{h_2}\right)\frac{d\beta}{dt}-h_2\frac{\partial}{\partial\beta}\left(\frac{1}{h_1}\right)\frac{d\alpha}{dt}.\end{aligned}\right\}\quad\text{.....(6)}$$

The above argument shows that the principal curvatures of the surface γ, belonging to its lines of intersection with surfaces α and β, are respectively

$$-h_2h_3\frac{\partial}{\partial\gamma}\left(\frac{1}{h_2}\right)\text{ and }h_1h_3\frac{\partial}{\partial\gamma}\left(\frac{1}{h_1}\right).$$

We have similar formulæ for the principal curvatures of the surfaces α and β.

Let L, M, N be the direction cosines of a fixed line referred to the normals of the surfaces at a particular point (α, β, γ), and let L', M', N' be the direction cosines of the same line referred to the variable axes at any point. Then L', M', N' are functions of α, β, γ, but L, M, N are independent of α, β, γ. We may use the formulæ (5), and in them we may replace u, v, w by L, M, N and u', v', w' by L', M', N'. We find

$$\frac{\partial L'}{\partial\alpha}=-M'h_2\frac{\partial}{\partial\beta}\left(\frac{1}{h_1}\right)-N'h_3\frac{\partial}{\partial\gamma}\left(\frac{1}{h_1}\right),\quad\frac{\partial L'}{\partial\beta}=M'h_1\frac{\partial}{\partial\alpha}\left(\frac{1}{h_2}\right),\quad\frac{\partial L'}{\partial\gamma}=N'h_1\frac{\partial}{\partial\alpha}\left(\frac{1}{h_3}\right),$$

$$\frac{\partial M'}{\partial\alpha}=L'h_2\frac{\partial}{\partial\beta}\left(\frac{1}{h_1}\right),\quad\frac{\partial M'}{\partial\beta}=-N'h_3\frac{\partial}{\partial\gamma}\left(\frac{1}{h_2}\right)-L'h_1\frac{\partial}{\partial\alpha}\left(\frac{1}{h_2}\right),\quad\frac{\partial M'}{\partial\gamma}=N'h_2\frac{\partial}{\partial\beta}\left(\frac{1}{h_3}\right),$$

$$\frac{\partial N'}{\partial\alpha}=L'h_3\frac{\partial}{\partial\gamma}\left(\frac{1}{h_1}\right),\quad\frac{\partial N'}{\partial\beta}=M'h_3\frac{\partial}{\partial\gamma}\left(\frac{1}{h_2}\right),\quad\frac{\partial N'}{\partial\gamma}=-L'h_1\frac{\partial}{\partial\alpha}\left(\frac{1}{h_3}\right)-M'h_2\frac{\partial}{\partial\beta}\left(\frac{1}{h_3}\right).$$

These formulæ were used in Article 58.

To investigate expressions for the *components of strain* and *rotation*[25] we take (u', v', w') to be the displacement $(u_\alpha, u_\beta, u_\gamma)$, and (u, v, w) to be the displacement referred to fixed axes of x, y, z which coincide with the normals to the surfaces α, β, γ at the point (α, β, γ). Then we have, for example, at (α, β, γ)

$$\frac{\partial u}{\partial x}=h_1\frac{\partial u}{\partial\alpha},\quad\frac{\partial u}{\partial y}=h_2\frac{\partial u}{\partial\beta},\quad\frac{\partial u}{\partial z}=h_3\frac{\partial u}{\partial\gamma}.$$

Now using the formulæ (5) and (6) we have

$$\frac{\partial u}{\partial\alpha}\frac{d\alpha}{dt}+\frac{\partial u}{\partial\beta}\frac{d\beta}{dt}+\frac{\partial u}{\partial\gamma}\frac{d\gamma}{dt}=\frac{\partial u_\alpha}{\partial\alpha}\frac{d\alpha}{dt}+\frac{\partial u_\alpha}{\partial\beta}\frac{d\beta}{dt}+\frac{\partial u_\alpha}{\partial\gamma}\frac{d\gamma}{dt}$$
$$-u_\beta\left\{h_1\frac{\partial}{\partial\alpha}\left(\frac{1}{h_2}\right)\frac{d\beta}{dt}-h_2\frac{\partial}{\partial\beta}\left(\frac{1}{h_1}\right)\frac{d\alpha}{dt}\right\}+u_\gamma\left\{h_3\frac{\partial}{\partial\gamma}\left(\frac{1}{h_1}\right)\frac{d\alpha}{dt}-h_1\frac{\partial}{\partial\alpha}\left(\frac{1}{h_3}\right)\frac{d\gamma}{dt}\right\},$$

......

[25] Cf. R. R. Webb, *Messenger of Math.*, vol. 11 (1882), p. 146.

and from these we have

$$\frac{\partial u}{\partial x}=h_1\left\{\frac{\partial u_\alpha}{\partial \alpha}+h_2u_\beta\frac{\partial}{\partial\beta}\left(\frac{1}{h_1}\right)+h_3u_\gamma\frac{\partial}{\partial\gamma}\left(\frac{1}{h_1}\right)\right\},$$

$$\frac{\partial u}{\partial y}=h_2\left\{\frac{\partial u_\alpha}{\partial \beta}-h_1u_\beta\frac{\partial}{\partial\alpha}\left(\frac{1}{h_2}\right)\right\},\qquad \frac{\partial u}{\partial z}=h_3\left\{\frac{\partial u_\alpha}{\partial \gamma}-h_1u_\gamma\frac{\partial}{\partial\alpha}\left(\frac{1}{h_3}\right)\right\}.$$

......

The formulæ (36) of Article 20 and (38) of Article 21 can now be written down.

To investigate the *stress-equations*[25] we take the same system of fixed axes, and consider the resultants of the tractions on the faces of a curvilinear parallelepiped bounded by surfaces α, $\alpha+\delta\alpha$, β, $\beta+\delta\beta$, γ, $\gamma+\delta\gamma$. (Cf. Fig. 3 in Article 21.) We may take the areas of the faces α, β, γ to be Δ_1, Δ_2, Δ_3, where

$$\Delta_1=\delta\beta\,\delta\gamma/h_2h_3,\quad \Delta_2=\delta\gamma\,\delta\alpha/h_3h_1,\quad \Delta_3=\delta\alpha\,\delta\beta/h_1h_2.$$

The tractions per unit of area across the surface α can be expressed by X_α, Y_α, Z_α or by $\widehat{\alpha\alpha}$, $\widehat{\alpha\beta}$, $\widehat{\gamma\alpha}$, and the resultant tractions across the face Δ_1 can be expressed as $X_\alpha\Delta_1$, $Y_\alpha\Delta_1$, $Z_\alpha\Delta_1$ or as $\widehat{\alpha\alpha}\Delta_1$, $\widehat{\alpha\beta}\Delta_1$, $\widehat{\gamma\alpha}\Delta_1$. In the formulæ (5) $X_\alpha\Delta_1$, $Y_\alpha\Delta_1$, $Z_\alpha\Delta_1$ can take the places of u, v, w, and $\widehat{\alpha\alpha}\Delta_1$, $\widehat{\alpha\beta}\Delta_1$, $\widehat{\gamma\alpha}\Delta_1$ the places u', v', w'. Similarly $X_\beta\Delta_2$, $Y_\beta\Delta_2$, $Z_\beta\Delta_2$ can take the places of u, v, w, and $\widehat{\alpha\beta}\Delta_2$, $\widehat{\beta\beta}\Delta_2$, $\widehat{\beta\gamma}\Delta_2$ those of u', v', w', and so on. Now the equations of motion can be expressed in such forms as

$$\delta\alpha\frac{\partial}{\partial\alpha}(X_\alpha\Delta_1)+\delta\beta\frac{\partial}{\partial\beta}(X_\beta\Delta_2)+\delta\gamma\frac{\partial}{\partial\gamma}(X_\gamma\Delta_3)+\rho F_\alpha\frac{\delta\alpha\,\delta\beta\,\delta\gamma}{h_1h_2h_3}=\rho f_\alpha\frac{\delta\alpha\,\delta\beta\,\delta\gamma}{h_1h_2h_3},$$

where the notation is the same as in Article 58. We have the equations

$$\frac{\partial}{\partial\alpha}(X_\alpha\Delta_1)\frac{d\alpha}{dt}+\frac{\partial}{\partial\beta}(X_\alpha\Delta_1)\frac{d\beta}{dt}+\frac{\partial}{\partial\gamma}(X_\alpha\Delta_1)\frac{d\gamma}{dt}$$

$$=\frac{\partial}{\partial\alpha}(\widehat{\alpha\alpha}\Delta_1)\frac{d\alpha}{dt}+\frac{\partial}{\partial\beta}(\widehat{\alpha\alpha}\Delta_1)\frac{d\beta}{dt}+\frac{\partial}{\partial\gamma}(\widehat{\alpha\alpha}\Delta_1)\frac{d\gamma}{dt}-\widehat{\alpha\beta}\Delta_1\theta_3+\widehat{\gamma\alpha}\Delta_1\theta_2,$$

$$\frac{\partial}{\partial\alpha}(X_\beta\Delta_2)\frac{d\alpha}{dt}+\frac{\partial}{\partial\beta}(X_\beta\Delta_2)\frac{d\beta}{dt}+\frac{\partial}{\partial\gamma}(X_\beta\Delta_2)\frac{d\gamma}{dt}$$

$$=\frac{\partial}{\partial\alpha}(\widehat{\alpha\beta}\Delta_2)\frac{d\alpha}{dt}+\frac{\partial}{\partial\beta}(\widehat{\alpha\beta}\Delta_2)\frac{d\beta}{dt}+\frac{\partial}{\partial\gamma}(\widehat{\alpha\beta}\Delta_2)\frac{d\gamma}{dt}-\widehat{\beta\beta}\Delta_2\theta_3+\widehat{\beta\gamma}\Delta_2\theta_2,$$

$$\frac{\partial}{\partial\alpha}(X_\gamma\Delta_3)\frac{d\alpha}{dt}+\frac{\partial}{\partial\beta}(X_\gamma\Delta_3)\frac{d\beta}{dt}+\frac{\partial}{\partial\gamma}(X_\gamma\Delta_3)\frac{d\gamma}{dt}$$

$$=\frac{\partial}{\partial\alpha}(\widehat{\gamma\alpha}\Delta_3)\frac{d\alpha}{dt}+\frac{\partial}{\partial\beta}(\widehat{\gamma\alpha}\Delta_3)\frac{d\beta}{dt}+\frac{\partial}{\partial\gamma}(\widehat{\gamma\alpha}\Delta_3)\frac{d\gamma}{dt}-\widehat{\beta\gamma}\Delta_3\theta_3+\widehat{\gamma\gamma}\Delta_3\theta_2,$$

where θ_2, θ_3 are given by (6). Equation (19) in Article 58 can be written down at once.

INDEX OF AUTHORS CITED

[*The numbers refer to pages*]

INDEX OF MATTERS TREATED

[*The numbers refer to pages*]

CATALOG OF DOVER BOOKS

BOOKS EXPLAINING SCIENCE AND MATHEMATICS

THE COMMON SENSE OF THE EXACT SCIENCES, W. K. Clifford. Introduction by James Newman, edited by Karl Pearson. For 70 years this has been a guide to classical scientific and mathematical thought. Explains with unusual clarity basic concepts, such as extension of meaning of symbols, characteristics of surface boundaries, properties of plane figures, vectors, Cartesian method of determining position, etc. Long preface by Bertrand Russell. Bibliography of Clifford. Corrected, 130 diagrams redrawn. 249pp. 5⅜ x 8.
T61 Paperbound **$1.60**

SCIENCE THEORY AND MAN, Erwin Schrödinger. This is a complete and unabridged reissue of SCIENCE AND THE HUMAN TEMPERAMENT plus an additional essay: "What is an Elementary Particle?" Nobel Laureate Schrödinger discusses such topics as nature of scientific method, the nature of science, chance and determinism, science and society, conceptual models for physical entities, elementary particles and wave mechanics. Presentation is popular and may be followed by most people with little or no scientific training. "Fine practical preparation for a time when laws of nature, human institutions . . . are undergoing a critical examination without parallel," Waldemar Kaempffert, N. Y. TIMES. 192pp. 5⅜ x 8.
T428 Paperbound **$1.35**

PIONEERS OF SCIENCE, O. Lodge. Eminent scientist-expositor's authoritative, yet elementary survey of great scientific theories. Concentrating on individuals—Copernicus, Brahe, Kepler, Galileo, Descartes, Newton, Laplace, Herschel, Lord Kelvin, and other scientists—the author presents their discoveries in historical order adding biographical material on each man and full, specific explanations of their achievements. The clear and complete treatment of the post-Newtonian astronomers is a feature seldom found in other books on the subject. Index. 120 illustrations. xv + 404pp. 5⅜ x 8.
T716 Paperbound **$1.50**

THE EVOLUTION OF SCIENTIFIC THOUGHT FROM NEWTON TO EINSTEIN, A. d'Abro. Einstein's special and general theories of relativity, with their historical implications, are analyzed in non-technical terms. Excellent accounts of the contributions of Newton, Riemann, Weyl, Planck, Eddington, Maxwell, Lorentz and others are treated in terms of space and time, equations of electromagnetics, finiteness of the universe, methodology of science. 21 diagrams. 482pp. 5⅜ x 8.
T2 Paperound **$2.00**

THE RISE OF THE NEW PHYSICS, A. d'Abro. A half-million word exposition, formerly titled THE DECLINE OF MECHANISM, for readers not versed in higher mathematics. The only thorough explanation, in everyday language, of the central core of modern mathematical physical theory, treating both classical and modern theoretical physics, and presenting in terms almost anyone can understand the equivalent of 5 years of study of mathematical physics. Scientifically impeccable coverage of mathematical-physical thought from the Newtonian system up through the electronic theories of Dirac and Heisenberg and Fermi's statistics. Combines both history and exposition; provides a broad yet unified and detailed view, with constant comparison of classical and modern views on phenomena and theories. "A must for anyone doing serious study in the physical sciences," JOURNAL OF THE FRANKLIN INSTITUTE. "Extraordinary faculty . . . to explain ideas and theories of theoretical physics in the language of daily life," ISIS. First part of set covers philosophy of science, drawing upon the practice of Newton, Maxwell, Poincaré, Einstein, others, discussing modes of thought, experiment, interpretations of causality, etc. In the second part, 100 pages explain grammar and vocabulary of mathematics, with discussions of functions, groups, series, Fourier series, etc. The remainder is devoted to concrete, detailed coverage of both classical and quantum physics, explaining such topics as analytic mechanics, Hamilton's principle, wave theory of light, electromagnetic waves, groups of transformations, thermodynamics, phase rule, Brownian movement, kinetics, special relativity, Planck's original quantum theory, Bohr's atom, Zeeman effect, Broglie's wave mechanics, Heisenberg's uncertainty, Eigen-values, matrices, scores of other important topics. Discoveries and theories are covered for such men as Alembert, Born, Cantor, Debye, Euler, Foucault, Galois, Gauss, Hadamard, Kelvin, Kepler, Laplace, Maxwell, Pauli, Rayleigh, Volterra, Weyl, Young, more than 180 others. Indexed. 97 illustrations. ix + 982pp. 5⅜ x 8.
T3 Volume 1, Paperbound **$2.00**
T4 Volume 2, Paperbound **$2.00**

CONCERNING THE NATURE OF THINGS, Sir William Bragg. Christmas lectures delivered at the Royal Society by Nobel laureate. Why a spinning ball travels in a curved track; how uranium is transmuted to lead, etc. Partial contents: atoms, gases, liquids, crystals, metals, etc. No scientific background needed; wonderful for intelligent child. 32pp. of photos, 57 figures. xii + 232pp. 5⅜ x 8.
T31 Paperbound **$1.35**

THE UNIVERSE OF LIGHT, Sir William Bragg. No scientific training needed to read Nobel Prize winner's expansion of his Royal Institute Christmas Lectures. Insight into nature of light, methods and philosophy of science. Explains lenses, reflection, color, resonance, polarization, x-rays, the spectrum, Newton's work with prisms, Huygens' with polarization, Crookes' with cathode ray, etc. Leads into clear statement of 2 major historical theories of light, corpuscle and wave. Dozens of experiments you can do. 199 illus., including 2 full-page color plates. 293pp. 5⅜ x 8.
S538 Paperbound **$1.85**

Relativity, quantum theory, nuclear physics

THE PRINCIPLE OF RELATIVITY, A. Einstein, H. Lorentz, M. Minkowski, H. Weyl. These are the 11 basic papers that founded the general and special theories of relativity, all translated into English. Two papers by Lorentz on the Michelson experiment, electromagnetic phenomena. Minkowski's SPACE & TIME, and Weyl's GRAVITATION & ELECTRICITY. 7 epoch-making papers by Einstein: ELECTROMAGNETICS OF MOVING BODIES, INFLUENCE OF GRAVITATION IN PROPAGATION OF LIGHT, COSMOLOGICAL CONSIDERATIONS, GENERAL THEORY, and 3 others. 7 diagrams. Special notes by A. Sommerfeld. 224pp. 5⅜ x 8.
S81 Paperbound **$1.75**

SPACE TIME MATTER, Hermann Weyl. "The standard treatise on the general theory of relativity," (Nature), written by a world-renowned scientist, provides a deep clear discussion of the logical coherence of the general theory, with introduction to all the mathematical tools needed: Maxwell, analytical geometry, non-Euclidean geometry, tensor calculus, etc. Basis is classical space-time, before absorption of relativity. Partial contents: Euclidean space, mathematical form, metrical continuum, relativity of time and space, general theory. 15 diagrams. Bibliography. New preface for this edition. xviii + 330pp. 5⅜ x 8.
S267 Paperbound **$1.85**

PRINCIPLES OF QUANTUM MECHANICS, W. V. Houston. Enables student with working knowledge of elementary mathematical physics to develop facility in use of quantum mechanics, understand published work in field. Formulates quantum mechanics in terms of Schroedinger's wave mechanics. Studies evidence for quantum theory, for inadequacy of classical mechanics, 2 postulates of quantum mechanics; numerous important, fruitful applications of quantum mechanics in spectroscopy, collision problems, electrons in solids; other topics. "One of the most rewarding features . . . is the interlacing of problems with text," Amer. J. of Physics. Corrected edition. 21 illus. Index. 296pp. 5⅜ x 8. S524 Paperbound **$1.85**

PHYSICAL PRINCIPLES OF THE QUANTUM THEORY, Werner Heisenberg. A Nobel laureate discusses quantum theory; Heisenberg's own work, Compton, Schroedinger, Wilson, Einstein, many others. Written for physicists, chemists who are not specialists in quantum theory, only elementary formulae are considered in the text; there is a mathematical appendix for specialists. Profound without sacrifice of clarity. Translated by C. Eckart, F. Hoyt. 18 figures. 192pp. 5⅜ x 8. S113 Paperbound **$1.25**

SELECTED PAPERS ON QUANTUM ELECTRODYNAMICS, edited by **J. Schwinger.** Facsimiles of papers which established quantum electrodynamics, from initial successes through today's position as part of the larger theory of elementary particles. First book publication in any language of these collected papers of Bethe, Bloch, Dirac, Dyson, Fermi, Feynman, Heisenberg, Kusch, Lamb, Oppenheimer, Pauli, Schwinger, Tomonoga, Weisskopf, Wigner, etc. 34 papers in all, 29 in English, 1 in French, 3 in German, 1 in Italian. Preface and historical commentary by the editor. xvii + 423pp. 6⅛ x 9¼. S444 Paperbound **$2.45**

THE FUNDAMENTAL PRINCIPLES OF QUANTUM MECHANICS, WITH ELEMENTARY APPLICATIONS, E. C. Kemble. An inductive presentation, for the graduate student or specialist in some other branch of physics. Assumes some acquaintance with advanced math; apparatus necessary beyond differential equations and advanced calculus is developed as needed. Although a general exposition of principles, hundreds of individual problems are fully treated, with applications of theory being interwoven with development of the mathematical structure. The author is the Professor of Physics at Harvard Univ. "This excellent book would be of great value to every student . . . a rigorous and detailed mathematical discussion of all of the principal quantum-mechanical methods . . . has succeeded in keeping his presentations clear and understandable," Dr. Linus Pauling, J. of the American Chemical Society. Appendices: calculus of variations, math. notes, etc. Indexes. 611pp. 5⅜ x 8.
S472 Paperbound **$2.95**

ATOMIC SPECTRA AND ATOMIC STRUCTURE, G. Herzberg. Excellent general survey for chemists, physicists specializing in other fields. Partial contents: simplest line spectra and elements of atomic theory, building-up principle and periodic system of elements, hyperfine structure of spectral lines, some experiments and applications. Bibilography. 80 figures. Index. xii + 257pp. 5⅜ x 8. S115 Paperbound **$1.95**

THE THEORY AND THE PROPERTIES OF METALS AND ALLOYS, N. F. Mott, H. Jones. Quantum methods used to develop mathematical models which show interrelationship of basic chemical phenomena with crystal structure, magnetic susceptibility, electrical, optical properties. Examines thermal properties of crystal lattice, electron motion in applied field, cohesion, electrical resistance, noble metals, para-, dia-, and ferromagnetism, etc. "Exposition . . . clear . . . mathematical treatment . . . simple," Nature. 138 figures. Bibliography. Index. xiii + 320pp. 5⅜ x 8. S456 Paperbound **$1.85**

FOUNDATIONS OF NUCLEAR PHYSICS, edited by **R. T. Beyer.** 13 of the most important papers on nuclear physics reproduced in facsimile in the original languages of their authors: the papers most often cited in footnotes, bibliographies. Anderson, Curie, Joliot, Chadwick, Fermi, Lawrence, Cockcroft, Hahn, Yukawa. UNPARALLELED BIBLIOGRAPHY. 122 double-columned pages, over 4,000 articles, books classified. 57 figures. 288pp. 6⅛ x 9¼.
S19 Paperbound **$1.75**

MESON PHYSICS, R. E. Marshak. Traces the basic theory, and explicity presents results of experiments with particular emphasis on theoretical significance. Phenomena involving mesons as virtual transitions are avoided, eliminating some of the least satisfactory predictions of meson theory. Includes production and study of π mesons at nonrelativistic nucleon energies, contrasts between π and μ mesons, phenomena associated with nuclear interaction of π mesons, etc. Presents early evidence for new classes of particles and indicates theoretical difficulties created by discovery of heavy mesons and hyperons. Name and subject indices. Unabridged reprint. viii + 378pp. 5⅜ x 8. S500 Paperbound **$1.95**

See also: **STRANGE STORY OF THE QUANTUM, B. Hoffmann; FROM EUCLID TO EDDINGTON, E. Whittaker; MATTER AND LIGHT, THE NEW PHYSICS, L. de Broglie; THE EVOLUTION OF SCIENTIFIC THOUGHT FROM NEWTON TO EINSTEIN, A. d'Abro; THE RISE OF THE NEW PHYSICS, A. d'Abro; THE THEORY OF GROUPS AND QUANTUM MECHANICS, H. Weyl; SUBSTANCE AND FUNCTION, & EINSTEIN'S THEORY OF RELATIVITY, E. Cassirer; FUNDAMENTAL FORMULAS OF PHYSICS, D. H. Menzel.**

Hydrodynamics

HYDRODYNAMICS, H. Dryden, F. Murnaghan, Harry Bateman. Published by the National Research Council in 1932 this enormous volume offers a complete coverage of classical hydrodynamics. Encyclopedic in quality. Partial contents: physics of fluids, motion, turbulent flow, compressible fluids, motion in 1, 2, 3 dimensions; viscous fluids rotating, laminar motion, resistance of motion through viscous fluid, eddy viscosity, hydraulic flow in channels of various shapes, discharge of gases, flow past obstacles, etc. Bibliography of over 2,900 items. Indexes. 23 figures. 634pp. 5⅜ x 8. S303 Paperbound **$2.75**

A TREATISE ON HYDRODYNAMICS, A. B. Basset. Favorite text on hydrodynamics for 2 generations of physicists, hydrodynamical engineers, oceanographers, ship designers, etc. Clear enough for the beginning student, and thorough source for graduate students and engineers on the work of d'Alembert, Euler, Laplace, Lagrange, Poisson, Green, Clebsch, Stokes, Cauchy, Helmholtz, J. J. Thomson, Love, Hicks, Greenhill, Besant, Lamb, etc. Great amount of documentation on entire theory of classical hydrodynamics. Vol I: theory of motion of frictionless liquids, vortex, and cyclic irrotational motion, etc. 132 exercises. Bibliography. 3 Appendixes. xii + 264pp. Vol II: motion in viscous liquids, harmonic analysis, theory of tides, etc. 112 exercises. Bibliography. 4 Appendixes. xv + 328pp. Two volume set. 5⅜ x 8.
S724 Vol I Paperbound **$1.75**
S725 Vol II Paperbound **$1.75**
The set **$3.50**

HYDRODYNAMICS, Horace Lamb. Internationally famous complete coverage of standard reference work on dynamics of liquids & gases. Fundamental theorems, equations, methods, solutions, background, for classical hydrodynamics. Chapters include Equations of Motion, Integration of Equations in Special Gases, Irrotational Motion, Motion of Liquid in 2 Dimensions, Motion of Solids through Liquid-Dynamical Theory, Vortex Motion, Tidal Waves, Surface Waves, Waves of Expansion, Viscosity, Rotating Masses of liquids. Excellently planned, arranged; clear, lucid presentation. 6th enlarged, revised edition. Index. Over 900 footnotes, mostly bibliographical. 119 figures. xv + 738pp. 6⅛ x 9¼. S256 Paperbound **$2.95**

See also: **FUNDAMENTAL FORMULAS OF PHYSICS, D. H. Menzel; THEORY OF FLIGHT, R. von Mises; FUNDAMENTALS OF HYDRO- AND AEROMECHANICS, L. Prandtl and O. G. Tietjens; APPLIED HYDRO- AND AEROMECHANICS, L. Prandtl and O. G. Tietjens; HYDRAULICS AND ITS APPLICATIONS, A. H. Gibson; FLUID MECHANICS FOR HYDRAULIC ENGINEERS, H. Rouse.**

Acoustics, optics, electromagnetics

ON THE SENSATIONS OF TONE, Hermann Helmholtz. This is an unmatched coordination of such fields as acoustical physics, physiology, experiment, history of music. It covers the entire gamut of musical tone. Partial contents: relation of musical science to acoustics, physical vs. physiological acoustics, composition of vibration, resonance, analysis of tones by sympathetic resonance, beats, chords, tonality, consonant chords, discords, progression of parts, etc. 33 appendixes discuss various aspects of sound, physics, acoustics, music, etc. Translated by A. J. Ellis. New introduction by Prof. Henry Margenau of Yale. 68 figures. 43 musical passages analyzed. Over 100 tables. Index. xix + 576pp. 6⅛ x 9¼.
S114 Paperbound **$2.95**

THE THEORY OF SOUND, Lord Rayleigh. Most vibrating systems likely to be encountered in practice can be tackled successfully by the methods set forth by the great Nobel laureate, Lord Rayleigh. Complete coverage of experimental, mathematical aspects of sound theory. Partial contents: Harmonic motions, vibrating systems in general, lateral vibrations of bars, curved plates or shells, applications of Laplace's functions to acoustical problems, fluid friction, plane vortex-sheet, vibrations of solid bodies, etc. This is the first inexpensive edition of this great reference and study work. Bibliography. Historical introduction by R. B. Lindsay. Total of 1040pp. 97 figures. 5⅜ x 8.
S292, S293, Two volume set, paperbound, **$4.00**

THE DYNAMICAL THEORY OF SOUND, H. Lamb. Comprehensive mathematical treatment of the physical aspects of sound, covering the theory of vibrations, the general theory of sound, and the equations of motion of strings, bars, membranes, pipes, and resonators. Includes chapters on plane, spherical, and simple harmonic waves, and the Helmholtz Theory of Audition. Complete and self-contained development for student and specialist; all fundamental differential equations solved completely. Specific mathematical details for such important phenomena as harmonics, normal modes, forced vibrations of strings, theory of reed pipes, etc. Index. Bibliography. 86 diagrams. viii + 307pp. 5⅜ x 8. S655 Paperbound **$1.50**

WAVE PROPAGATION IN PERIODIC STRUCTURES, L. Brillouin. A general method and application to different problems: pure physics, such as scattering of X-rays of crystals, thermal vibration in crystal lattices, electronic motion in metals; and also problems of electrical engineering. Partial contents: elastic waves in 1-dimensional lattices of point masses. Propagation of waves along 1-dimensional lattices. Energy flow. 2 dimensional, 3 dimensional lattices. Mathieu's equation. Matrices and propagation of waves along an electric line. Continuous electric lines. 131 illustrations. Bibliography. Index. xii + 253pp. 5⅜ x 8.
S34 Paperbound **$1.85**

THEORY OF VIBRATIONS, N. W. McLachlan. Based on an exceptionally successful graduate course given at Brown University, this discusses linear systems having 1 degree of freedom, forced vibrations of simple linear systems, vibration of flexible strings, transverse vibrations of bars and tubes, transverse vibration of circular plate, sound waves of finite amplitude, etc. Index. 99 diagrams. 160pp. 5⅜ x 8. S190 Paperbound **$1.35**

LOUD SPEAKERS: THEORY, PERFORMANCE, TESTING AND DESIGN, N. W. McLachlan. Most comprehensive coverage of theory, practice of loud speaker design, testing; classic reference, study manual in field. First 12 chapters deal with theory, for readers mainly concerned with math. aspects; last 7 chapters will interest reader concerned with testing, design. Partial contents: principles of sound propagation, fluid pressure on vibrators, theory of moving-coil principle, transients, driving mechanisms, response curves, design of horn type moving coil speakers, electrostatic speakers, much more. Appendix. Bibliography. Index. 165 illustrations, charts. 411pp. 5⅜ x 8. S588 Paperbound **$2.25**

MICROWAVE TRANSMISSION, J. S. Slater. First text dealing exclusively with microwaves, brings together points of view of field, circuit theory, for graduate student in physics, electrical engineering, microwave technician. Offers valuable point of view not in most later studies. Uses Maxwell's equations to study electromagnetic field, important in this area. Partial contents: infinite line with distributed parameters, impedance of terminated line, plane waves, reflections, wave guides, coaxial line, composite transmission lines, impedance matching, etc. Introduction. Index. 76 illus. 319pp. 5⅜ x 8.
S564 Paperbound **$1.50**

THE ANALYSIS OF SENSATIONS, Ernst Mach. Great study of physiology, psychology of perception, shows Mach's ability to see material freshly, his "incorruptible skepticism and independence." (Einstein). Relation of problems of psychological perception to classical physics, supposed dualism of physical and mental, principle of continuity, evolution of senses, will as organic manifestation, scores of experiments, observations in optics, acoustics, music, graphics, etc. New introduction by T. S. Szasz, M. D. 58 illus. 300-item bibliography. Index. 404pp. 5⅜ x 8. S525 Paperbound **$1.75**

APPLIED OPTICS AND OPTICAL DESIGN, A. E. Conrady. With publication of vol. 2, standard work for designers in optics is now complete for first time. Only work of its kind in English; only detailed work for practical designer and self-taught. Requires, for bulk of work, no math above trig. Step-by-step exposition, from fundamental concepts of geometrical, physical optics, to systematic study, design, of almost all types of optical systems. Vol. 1: all ordinary ray-tracing methods; primary aberrations; necessary higher aberration for design of telescopes, low-power microscopes, photographic equipment. Vol. 2: (Completed from author's notes by R. Kingslake, Dir. Optical Design, Eastman Kodak.) Special attention to high-power microscope, anastigmatic photographic objectives. "An indispensable work," J., Optical Soc. of Amer. "As a practical guide this book has no rival," Transactions, Optical Soc. Index. Bibliography. 193 diagrams. 852pp. 6⅛ x 9¼. Vol. 1 T611 Paperbound **$2.95**
Vol. 2 T612 Paperbound **$2.95**

THE THEORY OF OPTICS, Paul Drude. One of finest fundamental texts in physical optics, classic offers thorough coverage, complete mathematical treatment of basic ideas. Includes fullest treatment of application of thermodynamics to optics; sine law in formation of images, transparent crystals, magnetically active substances, velocity of light, apertures, effects depending upon them, polarization, optical instruments, etc. Introduction by A. A. Michelson. Index. 110 illus. 567pp. 5⅜ x 8. S532 Paperbound **$2.45**

OPTICKS, Sir Isaac Newton. In its discussions of light, reflection, color, refraction, theories of wave and corpuscular theories of light, this work is packed with scores of insights and discoveries. In its precise and practical discussion of construction of optical apparatus, contemporary understandings of phenomena it is truly fascinating to modern physicists, astronomers, mathematicians. Foreword by Albert Einstein. Preface by I. B. Cohen of Harvard University. 7 pages of portraits, facsimile pages, letters, etc. cxvi + 414pp. 5⅜ x 8. S205 Paperbound **$2.00**

OPTICS AND OPTICAL INSTRUMENTS: AN INTRODUCTION WITH SPECIAL REFERENCE TO PRACTICAL APPLICATIONS, B. K. Johnson. An invaluable guide to basic practical applications of optical principles, which shows how to set up inexpensive working models of each of the four main types of optical instruments—telescopes, microscopes, photographic lenses, optical projecting systems. Explains in detail the most important experiments for determining their accuracy, resolving power, angular field of view, amounts of aberration, all other necessary facts about the instruments. Formerly "Practical Optics." Index. 234 diagrams. Appendix. 224pp. 5⅜ x 8. S642 Paperbound **$1.65**

PRINCIPLES OF PHYSICAL OPTICS, Ernst Mach. This classical examination of the propagation of light, color, polarization, etc. offers an historical and philosophical treatment that has never been surpassed for breadth and easy readability. Contents: Rectilinear propagation of light. Reflection, refraction. Early knowledge of vision. Dioptrics. Composition of light. Theory of color and dispersion. Periodicity. Theory of interference. Polarization. Mathematical representation of properties of light. Propagation of waves, etc. 279 illustrations, 10 portraits. Appendix. Indexes. 324pp. 5⅜ x 8. S178 Paperbound **$1.75**

FUNDAMENTALS OF ELECTRICITY AND MAGNETISM, L. B. Loeb. For students of physics, chemistry, or engineering who want an introduction to electricity and magnetism on a higher level and in more detail than general elementary physics texts provide. Only elementary differential and integral calculus is assumed. Physical laws developed logically, from magnetism to electric currents, Ohm's law, electrolysis, and on to static electricity, induction, etc. Covers an unusual amount of material; one third of book on modern material: solution of wave equation, photoelectric and thermionic effects, etc. Complete statement of the various electrical systems of units and interrelations. 2 Indexes. 75 pages of problems with answers stated. Over 300 figures and diagrams. xix +669pp. 5⅜ x 8. S745 Paperbound **$2.75**

THE ELECTROMAGNETIC FIELD, Max Mason & Warren Weaver. Used constantly by graduate engineers. Vector methods exclusively: detailed treatment of electrostatics, expansion methods, with tables converting any quantity into absolute electromagnetic, absolute electrostatic, practical units. Discrete charges, ponderable bodies, Maxwell field equations, etc. Introduction. Indexes. 416pp. 5⅜ x 8. S185 Paperbound **$2.00**

ELECTRICAL THEORY ON THE GIORGI SYSTEM, P. Cornelius. A new clarification of the fundamental concepts of electricity and magnetism, advocating the convenient m.k.s. system of units that is steadily gaining followers in the sciences. Illustrating the use and effectiveness of his terminology with numerous applications to concrete technical problems, the author here expounds the famous Giorgi system of electrical physics. His lucid presentation and well-reasoned, cogent argument for the universal adoption of this system form one of the finest pieces of scientific exposition in recent years. 28 figures. Index. Conversion tables for translating earlier data into modern units. Translated from 3rd Dutch edition by L. J. Jolley. x + 187pp. 5½ x 8¾. S909 Clothbound **$6.00**

THEORY OF ELECTRONS AND ITS APPLICATION TO THE PHENOMENA OF LIGHT AND RADIANT HEAT, H. Lorentz. Lectures delivered at Columbia University by Nobel laureate Lorentz. Unabridged, they form a historical coverage of the theory of free electrons, motion, absorption of heat, Zeeman effect, propagation of light in molecular bodies, inverse Zeeman effect, optical phenomena in moving bodies, etc. 109 pages of notes explain the more advanced sections. Index. 9 figures. 352pp. 5⅜ x 8. S173 Paperbound **$1.85**

TREATISE ON ELECTRICITY AND MAGNETISM, James Clerk Maxwell. For more than 80 years a seemingly inexhaustible source of leads for physicists, mathematicians, engineers. Total of 1082pp. on such topics as Measurement of Quantities, Electrostatics, Elementary Mathematical Theory of Electricity, Electrical Work and Energy in a System of Conductors, General Theorems, Theory of Electrical Images, Electrolysis, Conduction, Polarization, Dielectrics, Resistance, etc. "The greatest mathematical physicist since Newton," Sir James Jeans. 3rd edition. 107 figures, 21 plates. 1082pp. 5⅜ x 8. S636-7, 2 volume set, paperbound **$4.00**

See also: **FUNDAMENTAL FORMULAS OF PHYSICS, D. H. Menzel; MATHEMATICAL ANALYSIS OF ELECTRICAL & OPTICAL WAVE MOTION, H. Bateman.**

Mechanics, dynamics, thermodynamics, elasticity

MECHANICS VIA THE CALCULUS, P. W. Norris, W. S. Legge. Covers almost everything, from linear motion to vector analysis: equations determining motion, linear methods, compounding of simple harmonic motions, Newton's laws of motion, Hooke's law, the simple pendulum, motion of a particle in 1 plane, centers of gravity, virtual work, friction, kinetic energy of rotating bodies, equilibrium of strings, hydrostatics, sheering stresses, elasticity, etc. 550 problems. 3rd revised edition. xii + 367pp. 6 x 9. S207 Clothbound **$3.95**

A TREATISE ON DYNAMICS OF A PARTICLE, E. J. Routh. Elementary text on dynamics for beginning mathematics or physics student. Unusually detailed treatment from elementary definitions to motion in 3 dimensions, emphasizing concrete aspects. Much unique material important in recent applications. Covers impulsive forces, rectilinear and constrained motion in 2 dimensions, harmonic and parabolic motion, degrees of freedom, closed orbits, the conical pendulum, the principle of least action, Jacobi's method, and much more. Index. 559 problems, many fully worked out, incorporated into text. xiii + 418pp. 5⅜ x 8.
S696 Paperbound **$2.25**

DYNAMICS OF A SYSTEM OF RIGID BODIES (Elementary Section), E. J. Routh. Revised 7th edition of this standard reference. This volume covers the dynamical principles of the subject, and its more elementary applications: finding moments of inertia by integration, foci of inertia, d'Alembert's principle, impulsive forces, motion in 2 and 3 dimensions, Lagrange's equations, relative indicatrix, Euler's theorem, large tautochronous motions, etc. Index. 55 figures. Scores of problems. xv + 443pp. 5⅜ x 8. S664 Paperbound **$2.35**

DYNAMICS OF A SYSTEM OF RIGID BODIES (Advanced Section), E. J. Routh. Revised 6th edition of a classic reference aid. Much of its material remains unique. Partial contents: moving axes, relative motion, oscillations about equilibrium, motion. Motion of a body under no forces, any forces. Nature of motion given by linear equations and conditions of stability. Free, forced vibrations, constants of integration, calculus of finite differences, variations, precession and nutation, motion of the moon, motion of string, chain, membranes. 64 figures. 498pp. 5⅜ x 8. S229 Paperbound **$2.35**

DYNAMICAL THEORY OF GASES, James Jeans. Divided into mathematical and physical chapters for the convenience of those not expert in mathematics, this volume discusses the mathematical theory of gas in a steady state, thermodynamics, Boltzmann and Maxwell, kinetic theory, quantum theory, exponentials, etc. 4th enlarged edition, with new material on quantum theory, quantum dynamics, etc. Indexes. 28 figures. 444pp. 6⅛ x 9¼.
S136 Paperbound **$2.45**

FOUNDATIONS OF POTENTIAL THEORY, O. D. Kellogg. Based on courses given at Harvard this is suitable for both advanced and beginning mathematicians. Proofs are rigorous, and much material not generally avialable elsewhere is included. Partial contents: forces of gravity, fields of force, divergence theorem, properties of Newtonian potentials at points of free space, potentials as solutions of Laplace's equations, harmonic functions, electrostatics, electric images, logarithmic potential, etc. One of Grundlehren Series. ix + 384pp. 5⅜ x 8.
S144 Paperbound **$1.98**

THERMODYNAMICS, Enrico Fermi. Unabridged reproduction of 1937 edition. Elementary in treatment; remarkable for clarity, organization. Requires no knowledge of advanced math beyond calculus, only familiarity with fundamentals of thermometry, calorimetry. Partial Contents: Thermodynamic systems; First & Second laws of thermodynamics; Entropy; Thermodynamic potentials: phase rule, reversible electric cell; Gaseous reactions: van't Hoff reaction box, principle of LeChatelier; Thermodynamics of dilute solutions: osmotic & vapor pressures, boiling & freezing points; Entropy constant. Index. 25 problems. 24 illustrations. x + 160pp. 5⅜ x 8. S361 Paperbound **$1.75**

THE THERMODYNAMICS OF ELECTRICAL PHENOMENA IN METALS and A CONDENSED COLLECTION OF THERMODYNAMIC FORMULAS, P. W. Bridgman. Major work by the Nobel Prizewinner: stimulating conceptual introduction to aspects of the electron theory of metals, giving an intuitive understanding of fundamental relationships concealed by the formal systems of Onsager and others. Elementary mathematical formulations show clearly the fundamental thermodynamical relationships of the electric field, and a complete phenomenological theory of metals is created. This is the work in which Bridgman announced his famous "thermomotive force" and his distinction between "driving" and "working" electromotive force. We have added in this Dover edition the author's long unavailable tables of thermodynamic formulas, extremely valuable for the speed of reference they allow. Two works bound as one. Index. 33 figures. Bibliography. xviii + 256pp. 5⅜ x 8. S723 Paperbound **$1.65**

REFLECTIONS ON THE MOTIVE POWER OF FIRE, by Sadi Carnot, and other papers on the 2nd law of thermodynamics by E. Clapeyron and R. Clausius. Carnot's "Reflections" laid the groundwork of modern thermodynamics. Its non-technical, mostly verbal statements examine the relations between heat and the work done by heat in engines, establishing conditions for the economical working of these engines. The papers by Clapeyron and Clausius here reprinted added further refinements to Carnot's work, and led to its final acceptance by physicists. Selections from posthumous manuscripts of Carnot are also included. All papers in English. New introduction by E. Mendoza. 12 illustrations. xxii + 152pp. 5⅜ x 8.
S661 Paperbound **$1.50**

TREATISE ON THERMODYNAMICS, Max Planck. Based on Planck's original papers this offers a uniform point of view for the entire field and has been used as an introduction for students who have studied elementary chemistry, physics, and calculus. Rejecting the earlier approaches of Helmholtz and Maxwell, the author makes no assumptions regarding the nature of heat, but begins with a few empirical facts, and from these deduces new physical and chemical laws. 3rd English edition of this standard text by a Nobel laureate. xvi + 297pp. 5⅜ x 8. S219 Paperbound **$1.75**